Solutions Manual

Don Lavigne
Austin Community College

Intermediate Algebra
for College Students

Sixth Edition

Allen R. ANGEL

PEARSON
Prentice
Hall

Editor-in-Chief: Chris Hoag
Senior Acquisitions Editor: Paul Murphy
Editorial Assistant: Kerri-Ann O'Donnell
Assistant Managing Editor: John Matthews
Production Editor: Donna Crilly
Supplement Cover Manager: Paul Gourhan
Supplement Cover Designer: Joanne Alexandris
Manufacturing Buyer: Ilene Kahn

© 2004 by Pearson Education, Inc.
Pearson Education, Inc.
Upper Saddle River, NJ 07458

Printed in the United States of America

10 9 8 7 6 5 4 3 2 1

ISBN 0-13-140068-1

Pearson Education Ltd., *London*
Pearson Education Australia Pty. Ltd., *Sydney*
Pearson Education Singapore, Pte. Ltd.
Pearson Education North Asia Ltd., *Hong Kong*
Pearson Education Canada, Inc., *Toronto*
Pearson Educación de Mexico, S.A. de C.V.
Pearson Education—Japan, *Tokyo*
Pearson Education Malaysia, Pte. Ltd.
Pearson Education, *Upper Saddle River, New Jersey*

Table of Contents

Chapter 1

Exercise Set 1.1

1–9.   Answers will vary.

11. Answers will vary.

13. Do all the homework and preview the new material to be covered in class.

15. (1) Carefully write down any formulas or ideas that you need to remember.

    (2) Look over the entire exam quickly to get an idea of its length and to make sure that no pages are missing. You will need to pace yourself to make sure that you complete the entire exam. Be prepared to spend more time on problems worth more points.

    (3) Read the test directions carefully.

    (4) Read each problem carefully. Answer each question completely and make sure you have answered the specific question asked.

    (5) Starting with number 1, work each question in order. If you come across a problem that you are not sure of, do not spend too much time on it. Continue working the problems that you understand. After completing all other questions, come back to finish those questions you are not sure of. Do not spend too much time on any one question.

    (6) Attempt each problem. You may be able to earn at least partial credit.

    (7) Work carefully and write clearly so that your instructor can read your work. Also, it is easy to make mistakes when your writing is unclear.

    (8) Check your work and your answers if you have time.

    (9) Do not be concerned if others finish the test before you. Do not be disturbed if you are the last to finish. Use all your extra time to check your work.

17. The more you put into the course, the more you will get out of it.

19. Answers will vary.

Exercise Set 1.2

1. A variable is a letter used to represent various numbers.

3. A set is a collection of objects.

5. The null or empty set is a set that contains no elements.

7. The five inequality symbols are:
   $>$, is greater than
   $\geq$, is greater than or equal to
   $<$, is less than
   $\leq$, is less than or equal to
   $\neq$, is not equal to

9. $\{3, 4, 5, 6\}$

11. Every integer is also a rational number because it can be written with a denominator of 1.

13. True; the set of whole numbers contains the set of natural numbers.

15. True; this is how the real numbers are defined.

17. True; every integer can be written as a fraction with a denominator of 1.

19. True; this is how the rational and irrational numbers are defined.

21. True; there are no integers between π and 4.

23. $3 < 4$

25. $-3 < 0$

27. $-1 > -1.01$

29. $-5 < -3$

31. $-14.98 > -14.99$

33. $1.1 < 1.9$

35. $-\pi > -4$

37. $-\dfrac{7}{8} > -\dfrac{8}{9}$

39. $A = \{0\}$

41. $C = \{18, 20\}$

43. $E = \{0,1,2\}$

45. $H = \{0,7,14,21,28,\ldots\}$

47. $J = \{1,2,3,4,\ldots\}$, or $J = N$

49. a. 4 is a natural number.

b. 4 and 0 are whole numbers.

c. -3, 4 and 0 are integers.

d. $-3, 4, \dfrac{1}{2}, \dfrac{5}{9}, 0, -1.23$ and $\dfrac{99}{100}$ are rational numbers.

e. $\sqrt{2}$ and $\sqrt{8}$ are irrational numbers.

f. $-3, 4, \dfrac{1}{2}, \dfrac{5}{9}, 0, \sqrt{2}, \sqrt{8}, -1.23$ and $\dfrac{99}{100}$ are real numbers.

51. $A \cup B = \{1,2,3,4,5,6,7,8\}$
$A \cap B = \{2,4\}$

53. $A \cup B = \{-3,-2,-1,0,1,2\}$
$A \cap B = \{-1,0\}$

55. $A \cup B = \{2,4,6,8,10\}$
$A \cap B = \{\ \}$ or $\varnothing$

57. $A \cup B = \{0,5,10,15,20,25,30\}$
$A \cap B = \{\ \}$ or $\varnothing$

59. $A \cup B = \{-1,0,1,e,i,\pi\}$
$A \cap B = \{-1,0,1\}$

61. The set of natural numbers.

63. The set of whole number multiples of three.

65. The set of odd integers.

67. a. Set A is the set of all x such that x is a natural number less than 8.

b. $A = \{1,2,3,4,5,,6,7\}$

69. $\{x | x \geq 0\}$

71. $\{z | z \leq 3\}$

73. $\{p | -4 \leq p < 3\}$

75. $\{q | q > -2 \text{ and } q \in N\}$

77. $\{r | r \leq \pi \text{ and } r \in W\}$

79. $\{x | x \geq 2\}$

81. $\{x | x < 5 \text{ and } x \in I\}$ or $\{x | x \leq 4 \text{ and } x \in I\}$

83. $\{x | -3 < x \leq 5\}$

85. $\{x | -2.5 \leq x < 4.2\}$

87. $\{x | -3 \leq x \leq 1 \text{ and } x \in I\}$

89. Yes; the set of natural numbers is a subset of the set of whole numbers

91. Yes; the set of integers is a subset of the set of rational numbers.

93. No; the set of rational numbers is not a subset of the set of irrational numbers.

95. Yes; the set of irrational numbers is a subset of the set of real numbers.

97. Answers may vary.
Possible answer: $\left\{\dfrac{3}{2}, \dfrac{4}{3}, \dfrac{5}{4}, \dfrac{6}{5}, \dfrac{7}{6}\right\}$

99. Answers may vary.
Possible answer: $A = \{2,4,5,6,9\}$,
$B = \{4,5,8,9\}$
Therefore, $A \cup B = \{2,4,5,6,8,9\}$ and
$A \cap B = \{4,5,9\}$

101. a. The set of brands that are in either category is: {Old Navy, The Gap, Tommy Hilfiger, Abercrombie & Fitch, Express/The Limited, Nike, Adidas, Polo/Ralph Lauren, FUBU}

b. Part (a) represents the union because it asks for the brands in either category.

c. The set of brands that are in both categories is: {Tommy Hilfiger}

   d.   Part (c) represents the intersection because it asks for the brands that are common to both categories.

103. a. $A = \{$Alex, James$\}$, $B = \{$Alex, James, George, Connor$\}$, $C = \{$Alex, Stephen$\}$, $D = \{$Alex, George, Connor$\}$

   b. $\{$Alex$\}$

   c.   Only Alex met all the requirements to receive the Wolf Badge.

105. a. $A = \{1, 3, 4, 5, 6, 7\}$

   b. $B = \{2, 3, 4, 6, 8\}$

   c. $A \cup B = \{1, 2, 3, 4, 5, 6, 7, 8\}$

   d. $A \cap B = \{3, 4, 6\}$

107. a. $\{x | x > 1\}$ includes fractions and decimal numbers which the other set does not contain.

   b. $\{2, 3, 4, 5, \ldots\}$

   c.   No, since it is not possible to list all real numbers greater than 1 in roster form.

109. a. $\dfrac{1}{9} = 0.111\ldots$ so $\dfrac{1}{9} = 0.\overline{1}$

       $\dfrac{2}{9} = 0.222\ldots$ so $\dfrac{2}{9} = 0.\overline{2}$

       $\dfrac{3}{9} = 0.333\ldots$ so $\dfrac{3}{9} = 0.\overline{3}$

   b. $\dfrac{4}{9} = 0.444\ldots$ so $\dfrac{4}{9} = 0.\overline{4}$

       $\dfrac{5}{9} = 0.555\ldots$ so $\dfrac{5}{9} = 0.\overline{5}$

       $\dfrac{6}{9} = 0.666\ldots$ so $\dfrac{6}{9}$ or $\dfrac{2}{3} = 0.\overline{6}$

   c.   Based on (a) and (b), we deduce that $0.\overline{9} = \dfrac{9}{9} = 1$.

Exercise Set 1.3

  1.   Additive inverses or opposites are two numbers that sum to 0.

  3.   No, the absolute value of every real number is not always a positive number because $|0|$ is not positive.

5.   Since a and $-a$ are the same distance from 0 on a number line, $|a| = |-a|$, is true for all real numbers, R.

7.   Since $|a| = \begin{cases} a, & a \geq 0 \\ -a, & a \leq 0 \end{cases}$, then $|a| = -a$ only when $a \leq 0$.

9.   Since $|5| = 5$ and $|-5| = 5$, the desired values for a are 5 and -5.

15. $-\dfrac{a}{b}$ or $\dfrac{-a}{b}$

17. a. $a + b = b + a$

19.   In general, $a + (b \cdot c) \neq (a + b) \cdot (a + c)$. To see this, consider $2 + (3 \cdot 4)$ and $(2 + 3) \cdot (2 + 4)$. The left side is $2 + (3 \cdot 4) = 2 + 12 = 14$ and the right side is $(2 + 3) \cdot (2 + 4) = 5 \cdot 6 = 30$.

21. $|5| = 5$

23. $|-7| = 7$

25. $\left| -\dfrac{7}{8} \right| = \dfrac{7}{8}$

27. $|0| = 0$

29. $-|-7| = -7$

31. $-\left| \dfrac{5}{9} \right| = -\dfrac{5}{9}$

33. $|-7| = 7$
      $|7| = 7$
      $|-7| = |7|$

35. $|-5| = 5$
      $-5 = -5$
      $|-5| > -5$

37. $|-\pi| = \pi \approx 3.14$
      $-3 = -3$
      $|-\pi| > -3$

39. $|-7| = 7$
      $-|3| = -3$
      $|-7| > -|3|$

41. $-(-3) = 3$
$-|-3| = -3$
$-(-3) > -|-3|$

43. $|19| = 19$
$|-25| = 25$
$|19| < |-25|$

45. $-|5|, -2, -1, |-3|, 4,$

47. $-32, -|4|, 4, |-7|, 15$

49. $-|2.9|, -2.4, -2.1, -2, |-2.8|$

51. $-2, \dfrac{1}{3}, \left|-\dfrac{1}{2}\right|, \left|\dfrac{3}{5}\right|, \left|-\dfrac{3}{4}\right|$

53. $7 + (-6) = 1$

55. $-11 + 10 = -1$

57. $-9 - (-5) = -9 + 5 = -4$

59. $-14.21 - (-13.22) = -14.21 + 13.22 = -0.99$

61. $-\dfrac{5}{12} - \left(-\dfrac{7}{8}\right) = -\dfrac{5}{12} + \dfrac{7}{8}$
$= -\dfrac{10}{24} + \dfrac{21}{24}$
$= \dfrac{-10 + 21}{24}$
$= \dfrac{11}{24}$

63. $9 - (-2.31) + (-4.39) = 9 + 2.31 - 4.39$
$= 6.92$

65. $8.9 - |8.5| - |17.6| = 8.9 - 8.5 - 17.6$
$= 0.4 - 17.6$
$= -17.2$

67. $|5 - 12| - |3| = |-7| - |3|$
$= 7 - 3$
$= 4$

69. $-|-3| - |7| + (6 + |-2|) = -|-3| - |7| + (6 + 2)$
$= -|-3| - |7| + 8$
$= -3 - 7 + 8$
$= -10 + 8$
$= -2$

71. $\left(\dfrac{3}{5} + \dfrac{3}{4}\right) - \dfrac{1}{2} = \left(\dfrac{12}{20} + \dfrac{15}{20}\right) - \dfrac{1}{2}$
$= \left(\dfrac{12 + 15}{20}\right) - \dfrac{1}{2}$
$= \dfrac{27}{20} - \dfrac{1}{2}$
$= \dfrac{27}{20} - \dfrac{10}{20}$
$= \dfrac{27 - 10}{20}$
$= \dfrac{17}{20}$

73. $-5 \cdot 7 = -35$

75. $-4\left(-\dfrac{5}{16}\right) = \left(-\dfrac{4}{1}\right)\left(-\dfrac{5}{16}\right)$
$= -\dfrac{4}{1} \cdot \dfrac{5}{16}$
$= \dfrac{(-4)(-5)}{(1)(16)}$
$= \dfrac{20}{16}$
$= \dfrac{5}{4}$

77. $(-1)(-2)(-1)(2)(-3) = 2(-1)(2)(-3)$
$= -2(2)(-3)$
$= -4(-3)$
$= 12$

79. $(-1.1)(3.4)(8.3)(-7.6)$
$= -3.74(8.3)(-7.6)$
$= -31.042(-7.6)$
$= 235.9192$

81. $-55 \div (-11) = \dfrac{-55}{-11}$
$= 5$

83. $-\dfrac{5}{9} \div \dfrac{-5}{9} = \dfrac{-5}{9} \cdot \dfrac{9}{-5}$
$= \dfrac{-45}{-45}$
$= 1$

85.
$$\left(-\frac{3}{4}\right) \div \left|-8\right| = \frac{-3}{4} \div 8$$
$$= \frac{-3}{4} \cdot \frac{1}{8}$$
$$= \frac{-3 \cdot 1}{4 \cdot 8}$$
$$= \frac{-3}{32}$$

87.
$$\left|-\frac{5}{6}\right| \div \left|\frac{-1}{2}\right| = \frac{5}{6} \div \frac{1}{2}$$
$$= \frac{5}{6} \cdot \frac{2}{1}$$
$$= \frac{5 \cdot 2}{6 \cdot 1}$$
$$= \frac{10}{6}$$
$$= \frac{5}{3}$$

89.
$$10 - 14 = 10 + (-14)$$
$$= -4$$

91.
$$-56 \div 7 = \frac{-56}{7}$$
$$= -8$$

93.
$$3\left(-\frac{2}{3}\right)\left(-\frac{5}{2}\right) = -\frac{6}{3}\left(-\frac{5}{2}\right)$$
$$= \frac{30}{6}$$
$$= 5$$

95.
$$(-3.2)(4.9)(-2.73) = (-15.68)(-2.73)$$
$$= 42.8064$$

97.
$$-16.4 - (-9.6) - 14.8 = -16.4 + 9.6 - 14.8$$
$$= -6.8 - 14.8$$
$$= -21.6$$

99.
$$-\left|8\right| \cdot \left|\frac{-1}{2}\right| = -(8)\left(\frac{1}{2}\right)$$
$$= -4$$

101.
$$\left|-\frac{9}{4}\right| \div \left|-\frac{4}{9}\right| = \frac{9}{4} \div \frac{4}{9}$$
$$= \frac{9}{4} \cdot \frac{9}{4}$$
$$= \frac{9 \cdot 9}{4 \cdot 4}$$
$$= \frac{81}{16}$$

103.
$$5 - \left|-7\right| + 3 - \left|-2\right| = 5 - 7 + 3 - 2$$
$$= -2 + 3 - 2$$
$$= 1 - 2$$
$$= -1$$

105.
$$\left(-\frac{3}{5} - \frac{4}{9}\right) - \left(-\frac{2}{3}\right) = \left(-\frac{3}{5} - \frac{4}{9}\right) + \frac{2}{3}$$
$$= \left(-\frac{27}{45} - \frac{20}{45}\right) + \frac{2}{3}$$
$$= \left(\frac{-27 - 20}{45}\right) + \frac{2}{3}$$
$$= -\frac{47}{45} + \frac{2}{3}$$
$$= -\frac{47}{45} + \frac{30}{45}$$
$$= \frac{-47 + 30}{45}$$
$$= \frac{-17}{45} \text{ or } -\frac{17}{45}$$

107.
$$(25 - \left|32\right|)(-6 - 5) = (25 - 32)(-6 - 5)$$
$$= (-7)(-11)$$
$$= 77$$

109. $c + d = d + c$; Commutative property of addition

111. $b \cdot 0 = 0$; Multiplicative property of zero

113. $(x + 3) + 6 = x + (3 + 6)$; Associative property of addition

115. $x = 1 \cdot x$; Identity property of multiplication

117. $5(xy) = (5x)y$; Associative property of multiplication

119. $4(x + y + 2) = 4x + 4y + 8$; Distributive property

121. $5 + 0 = 5$; Identity property of addition

123. $3 + (-3) = 0$; Inverse property of addition

125. $x \cdot \dfrac{1}{x} = 1$; Inverse property of multiplication

127. $-(-x) = x$; Double negative property

129. -6 is the additive inverse

$\dfrac{1}{6}$ is the multiplicative inverse

131. $\dfrac{22}{7}$ is the additive inverse

$-\dfrac{7}{22}$ is the multiplicative inverse

133. The change in temperature is $140° - 40° = 100°\,\text{F}$

135. Final depth is $-358.9 + 210.7 = -148.2$ ft or 148.2 ft below the starting point.

137. a. $47,600 - 60,000 = -12,400$
The author will owe $12,400 to the publisher.

    b. $87,500 - 60,000 = 27,500$
The author will receive $27,500 from the publisher.

139. a. refund

    b. $4(3000) = 12,000$
$12,000 - 10,125 = 1875$

141. Answers will vary.

143. **a.** $\begin{aligned} \text{N.M.} - \text{Conn.} &= \$3944 - (-\$2840) \\ &= \$3944 + \$2840 \\ &= \$6784 \end{aligned}$

    b. $\begin{aligned} \text{Okla.} - \text{Mich.} &= \$1866 - (-\$1042) \\ &= \$1866 + \$1042 \\ &= \$2908 \end{aligned}$

    c. $\begin{aligned} \text{Va.} - \text{N.J.} &= \$3069 - (-\$2342) \\ &= \$3069 + \$2342 \\ &= \$5411 \end{aligned}$

    d. $\begin{aligned} \text{Texas} - \text{Calif.} &= (-\$189) - (-\$685) \\ &= (-\$189) + \$685 \\ &= \$496 \end{aligned}$

145. $1 - 2 + 3 - 4 + 5 - 6 + \ldots + 99 - 100$
Group in pairs:
$= (1-2) + (3-4) + (5-6) + \ldots + (99-100)$
Simplify all 50 pairs
$= -1 + (-1) + (-1) + \ldots + (-1)$
$= -1(50)$
$= -50$

147. $\dfrac{(1)|-2|(-3)|4|(-5)}{|-1|(-2)|-3|(4)|-5|} = \dfrac{(1)\cdot(2)\cdot(-3)\cdot(4)\cdot(-5)}{(1)\cdot(-2)\cdot(3)\cdot(4)\cdot(5)}$

$\qquad\qquad = \dfrac{120}{-120}$

$\qquad\qquad = -1$

149. True; the set of real numbers contains the irrational numbers.

151. a. 3, 4, –2, and 0 are integers.

b. 3, 4, -2, $\dfrac{5}{6}$, and 0 are rational numbers.

c. $\sqrt{3}$ is an irrational number.

d. 3, 4, -2, $\dfrac{5}{6}$, $\sqrt{3}$, and 0 are real numbers.

153. $\{x|-4 < x \le 6\}$

Exercise Set 1.4

1. a. In the expression a^n, a is called the base.

b. In the expression a^n, n is called the exponent.

3. a. In the expression $\sqrt[n]{a}$, n is called the index.

b. In the expression $\sqrt[n]{a}$, a is called the radicand.

5. The principal square root of a positive number radicand is the positive number whose square equals the radicand.

7. A negative number raised to an odd power is a negative number.

9. Answers will vary.

11. b. $16 \div 2^2 + 6 \cdot 4 - 24 \div 6$
$= 16 \div 4 + 6 \cdot 4 - 24 \div 6$
$= 4 + 24 - 4$
$= 28 - 4$
$= 24$

13. $3^2 = 3 \cdot 3 = 9$

15. $-3^2 = -(3)(3) = -9$

17. $(-3)^2 = (-3)(-3) = 9$

19. $-\left(\dfrac{3}{5}\right)^4 = -\left(\dfrac{3}{5}\right)\left(\dfrac{3}{5}\right)\left(\dfrac{3}{5}\right)\left(\dfrac{3}{5}\right) = -\dfrac{81}{625}$

21. $-\left(-\dfrac{5}{6}\right)^2 = -\left(-\dfrac{5}{6}\right)\left(-\dfrac{5}{6}\right) = -\dfrac{25}{36}$

23. $-\sqrt{36} = -(6) = -6$ since $6 \cdot 6 = 36$.

25. $\sqrt[3]{-27} = -3$ since $(-3)(-3)(-3) = -27$

27. $\sqrt[3]{0.001} = 0.1$ since $(0.1)(0.1)(0.1) = 0.001$

29. $(0.35)^4 \approx 0.015$

31. $\left(\dfrac{5}{7}\right)^7 \approx 0.095$

33. $(6.721)^{5.9} \approx 76,183.335$

35. $\sqrt[3]{5} \approx 1.710$

37. $\sqrt[5]{362.65} \approx 3.250$

39. $-\sqrt[3]{\dfrac{20}{53}} \approx -0.723$

41. a. x^2 becomes $3^2 = 3 \cdot 3 = 9$

b. $-x^2$ becomes $-3^2 = -3 \cdot 3 = -9$

43. a. x^2 becomes $1^2 = 1 \cdot 1 = 1$

b. $-x^2$ becomes $-1^2 = -1 \cdot 1 = -1$

45. a. x^2 becomes $(-1)^2 = (-1)(-1) = 1$

b. $-x^2$ becomes $-(-1)^2 = -(-1)(-1) = -1$

47. a. x^2 becomes $\left(\dfrac{1}{3}\right)^2 = \left(\dfrac{1}{3}\right)\left(\dfrac{1}{3}\right) = \dfrac{1}{9}$

b. $-x^2$ becomes $-\left(\dfrac{1}{3}\right)^2 = -\left(\dfrac{1}{3}\right)\left(\dfrac{1}{3}\right) = -\dfrac{1}{9}$

49. a. x^3 becomes $3^3 = 3 \cdot 3 \cdot 3 = 27$

b. $-x^3$ becomes $-3^3 = -(3 \cdot 3 \cdot 3) = -27$

51. a. x^3 becomes $(-3)^3 = (-3)(-3)(-3) = -27$

b. $-x^3$ becomes
$-(-3)^3 = -(-3)(-3)(-3) = 27$

53. a. x^3 becomes $(-2)^3 = (-2)(-2)(-2) = -8$

    b. $-x^3$ becomes $-(-2)^3 = -(-2)(-2)(-2) = 8$

55. a. x^3 becomes $\left(\frac{2}{3}\right)^3 = \left(\frac{2}{3}\right)\left(\frac{2}{3}\right)\left(\frac{2}{3}\right) = \frac{8}{27}$

    b. $-x^3$ becomes $-\left(\frac{2}{3}\right)^3 = -\left(\frac{2}{3}\right)\left(\frac{2}{3}\right)\left(\frac{2}{3}\right) = -\frac{8}{27}$

57. $3^2 + 2^3 - 2^2 - 3^3 = 9 + 8 - 4 - 27$
$$= 17 - 31$$
$$= -14$$

59. $-2^2 - 2^3 + 1^{10} + (-2)^3 = -4 - 8 + 1 + (-8)$
$$= -4 - 8 + 1 - 8$$
$$= -12 + 1 - 8$$
$$= -11 - 8$$
$$= -19$$

61. $(1.5)^2 - (3.9)^2 + (-2.1)^3 = 2.25 - 15.21 - 9.261$
$$= -12.96 - 9.261$$
$$= -22.221$$

63. $\left(-\frac{1}{2}\right)^4 - \left(\frac{1}{2}\right)^2 + \left(-\frac{1}{2}\right)^3 = \frac{1}{16} - \frac{1}{4} - \frac{1}{8}$
$$= \frac{2}{32} - \frac{8}{32} - \frac{4}{32}$$
$$= -\frac{10}{32}$$
$$= -\frac{5}{16}$$

65. $2 + 5 \cdot 8 = 2 + 40$
$$= 42$$

67. $18 - 6 \div 6 + 5 = 18 - 1 + 5 = 17 + 5 = 22$

69. $\frac{3}{4} \div \frac{1}{2} - 2 + 2 \div 4 = \frac{3}{2} - 2 + 2 \div 4$
$$= \frac{3}{2} - 2 + \frac{1}{2}$$
$$= 0$$

71. $\frac{1}{2} \cdot \frac{2}{3} \div \frac{3}{4} - \frac{1}{6} \cdot \left(-\frac{1}{3}\right) = \frac{1}{3} \div \frac{3}{4} - \frac{1}{6} \cdot \left(-\frac{1}{3}\right)$
$$= \frac{1}{3} \cdot \frac{4}{3} - \frac{1}{6} \cdot \left(-\frac{1}{3}\right)$$
$$= \frac{4}{9} - \left(-\frac{1}{18}\right)$$
$$= \frac{8}{18} + \left(\frac{1}{18}\right)$$
$$= \frac{9}{18}$$
$$= \frac{1}{2}$$

73. $-3 + 7 \div \left[\left(3 + 2^2\right) - \left(2^4 - 3^2 + 1\right)\right]$
$$-3 + 7 \div \left[(3 + 4) - (16 - 9 + 1)\right]$$
$$-3 + 7 \div \left[(7) - (8)\right]$$
$$-3 + 7 \div (-1)$$
$$-3 + (-7)$$
$$-10$$

75. $5\left(\sqrt[3]{27} + \sqrt[4]{16}\right) \div \frac{\sqrt{100}}{2} = 5(3 + 2) \div \frac{\sqrt{100}}{2}$
$$= 5(5) \div \frac{10}{2}$$
$$= 25 \div 5$$
$$= 5$$

77. $\{[(12 - 15) - 3] - 2\}^2 = \{[(-3) - 3] - 2\}^2$
$$= [(-6) - 2]^2$$
$$= (-8)^2$$
$$= 64$$

79. $4\left[5(13 - 3) \div (25 \div 5)^2\right]^2 = 4\left[5(10) \div (5)^2\right]^2$
$$= 4[50 \div 25]^2$$
$$= 4[2]^2$$
$$= 4 \cdot 4$$
$$= 16$$

81.
$$\frac{4-(2+3)^2-6}{4(3-2)-3^2} = \frac{4-(5)^2-6}{4(1)-3^2}$$
$$= \frac{4-25-6}{4(1)-9}$$
$$= \frac{4-25-6}{4-9}$$
$$= \frac{-21-6}{-5}$$
$$= \frac{-27}{-5}$$
$$= \frac{27}{5}$$

83.
$$\frac{8+4\div2\cdot3+4}{5^2-3^2\cdot2-7} = \frac{8+4\div2\cdot3+4}{25-9\cdot2-7}$$
$$= \frac{8+2\cdot3+4}{25-18-7}$$
$$= \frac{8+6+4}{25-18-7}$$
$$= \frac{14+4}{7-7}$$
$$= \frac{18}{0} \text{ which is undefined}$$

85.
$$\frac{8-[4-(3-1)^2]}{5-(-3)^2+4\div2} = \frac{8-[4-2^2]}{5-(-3)^2+4\div2}$$
$$= \frac{8-(4-4)}{5-9+4\div2}$$
$$= \frac{8-0}{5-9+4\div2}$$
$$= \frac{8-0}{5-9+2}$$
$$= \frac{8}{-4+2}$$
$$= \frac{8}{-2}$$
$$= -4$$

87.
$$-2|-3|-\sqrt{36}\div|2|+3^2 = -2(3)-6\div2+3^2$$
$$= -2(3)-6\div2+9$$
$$= -6-3+9$$
$$= -9+9$$
$$= 0$$

89.
$$\frac{6-|-4|-4|6-3|}{5-6\cdot2\div|-6|} = \frac{6-|-4|-4|3|}{5-6\cdot2\div6}$$
$$= \frac{6-4-4\cdot3}{5-6\cdot2\div6}$$
$$= \frac{6-4-12}{5-12\div6}$$
$$= \frac{2-12}{5-2}$$
$$= \frac{-10}{3} \text{ or } -\frac{10}{3}$$

91.
$$\frac{2}{5}\left[\sqrt[3]{27}-|-9|+4-3^2\right]^2 = \frac{2}{5}[3-(9)+4-9]^2$$
$$= \frac{2}{5}(3-9+4-9)^2$$
$$= \frac{2}{5}(-6+4-9)^2$$
$$= \frac{2}{5}(-2-9)^2$$
$$= \frac{2}{5}(-11)^2$$
$$= \frac{2}{5}(121)$$
$$= \frac{242}{5}$$

93.
$$\frac{24-5-4^2}{|-8|+4-2(3)}+\frac{4-(-3)^2+|4|}{3^2-4\cdot3+|-7|}$$
$$= \frac{24-5-16}{8+4-2(3)}+\frac{4-(9)+4}{9-4\cdot3+7}$$
$$= \frac{24-5-16}{8+4-6}+\frac{4-9+4}{9-12+7}$$
$$= \frac{19-16}{12-6}+\frac{-5+4}{-3+7}$$
$$= \frac{3}{6}+\frac{-1}{4}$$
$$= \frac{2}{4}+\frac{-1}{4}$$
$$= \frac{2-1}{4}$$
$$= \frac{1}{4}$$

95. Substitute 1 for *x*:
$$5x^2+3x = 5(2)^2+3(2)$$
$$= 5\cdot4+3(2)$$
$$= 20+6$$
$$= 26$$

97. Substitute 5 for x:
$$-9x^2 + 3x - 29 = -9(-1)^2 + 3(-1) - 29$$
$$= -9 \cdot 1 + 3(-1) - 29$$
$$= -9 + -3 - 29$$
$$= -12 - 29$$
$$= -41$$

99. Substitute -3 for x:
$$16(x+4)^3 - 25(x+4) = 16((-3)+4)^3 - 25((-3)+4)$$
$$= 16(1)^3 - 25(1)$$
$$= 16 \cdot 1 - 25 \cdot 1$$
$$= 16 - 25$$
$$= -9$$

101. Substitute 1 for x and -3 for y:
$$6x^2 + 3y^2 - 5 = 6(1)^2 + 3(-3)^3 - 5$$
$$= 6(1) + 3(-27) - 5$$
$$= 6 + (-81) - 5$$
$$= -75 - 5$$
$$= -80$$

103. Substitute 4 for a and -1 for b:
$$3(a+b)^2 + 4(a+b) - 6$$
$$= 3[4 + (-1)]^2 + 4[4 + (-1)] - 6$$
$$= 3(3)^2 + 4(3) - 6$$
$$= 3(9) + 4(3) - 6$$
$$= 27 + 12 - 6$$
$$= 39 - 6$$
$$= 33$$

105. Substitute 4 for x:
$$-6 - \{x - [2x - (x-3)]\}$$
$$= -6 - \{4 - [2 \cdot 4 - (4-3)]\}$$
$$= -6 - \{4 - [2 \cdot 4 - 1]\}$$
$$= -6 - \{4 - [8 - 1]\}$$
$$= -6 - [4 - (7)]$$
$$= -6 - (4 - 7)$$
$$= -6 - (-3)$$
$$= -6 + 3$$
$$= -3$$

107. Substitute 6 for a, -11 for b, and 3 for c:
$$\frac{-b + \sqrt{b^2 - 4ac}}{2a}$$
$$= \frac{-(-11) + \sqrt{(-11)^2 - 4(6)(3)}}{2(6)}$$
$$= \frac{11 + \sqrt{121 - 72}}{12}$$
$$= \frac{11 + \sqrt{49}}{12}$$
$$= \frac{11 + 7}{12}$$
$$= \frac{18}{12}$$
$$= \frac{3}{2}$$

109. The expression is $\dfrac{7y - 14}{2}$
Now substitute 6 for y:
$$\frac{7y - 14}{2} = \frac{7(6) - 14}{2}$$
$$= \frac{42 - 14}{2}$$
$$= \frac{28}{2}$$
$$= 14$$

111. The expression is $6(3x + 6) - 9$.
Now substitute 3 for x:
$$6(3x + 6) - 9 = 6(3 \cdot 3 + 6) - 9$$
$$= 6(9 + 6) - 9$$
$$= 6(15) - 9$$
$$= 90 - 9$$
$$= 81$$

113. The expression is $\left(\dfrac{x+3}{2y}\right)^2 - 3$
Now substitute 5 for x and 2 for y:
$$\left(\frac{x+3}{2y}\right)^2 - 3 = \left(\frac{5+3}{2 \cdot 2}\right)^2 - 3$$
$$= \left(\frac{5+3}{4}\right)^2 - 3$$
$$= \left(\frac{8}{4}\right)^2 - 3$$
$$= 2^2 - 3$$
$$= 4 - 3$$
$$= 1$$

115. **a.** 2000 means substitute 8 for x:

number of trips $= 0.065x^2 - 0.39x + 8.47$

$$= 0.065(8)^2 - 0.39(8) + 8.47$$
$$= 0.065(64) - 0.39(8) + 8.47$$
$$= 4.16 - 3.12 + 8.47$$
$$= 9.51$$

The number of trips made by public transportation in 2000 was approximately 9.51 billion.

b. 2010 means substitute 18 for x:

number of trips $= 0.065x^2 - 0.39x + 8.47$

$$= 0.065(18)^2 - 0.39(18) + 8.47$$
$$= 0.065(324) - 0.39(18) + 8.47$$
$$= 21.06 - 7.02 + 8.47$$
$$= 22.51$$

The number of trips made by public transportation in 2010 will be approximately 22.51 billion.

117. **a.** 10-year-olds means substitute 10 for x:

percent of children

$$= 0.23x^2 - 1.98x + 4.42$$
$$= 0.23(10)^2 - 1.98(10) + 4.42$$
$$= 0.23(100) - 1.98(10) + 4.42$$
$$= 23 - 19.8 + 4.42$$
$$= 7.62$$

The percent of all 10-year-olds who are latchkey kids is 7.62%.

b. 14-year-olds mean substitute 14 for x.

percent of children

$$= 0.23x^2 - 1.98x + 4.42$$
$$= 0.23(14)^2 - 1.98(14) + 4.42$$
$$= 0.23(196) - 1.98(14) + 4.42$$
$$= 45.08 - 27.72 + 4.42$$
$$= 21.78$$

The percent of all 14-year-olds who are latchkey kids is 21.78%.

119. **a.** 1991 means substitute 1 for x:

sales

$$= 0.062x^2 + 0.020x + 1.18$$
$$= 0.062(1)^2 + 0.020(1) + 1.18$$
$$= 0.062 + 0.020 + 1.18$$
$$= 1.262$$

The amount of sales of organically grown food in 1991 was about $1.262 billion.

b. 2001 means substitute 11 for x:

sales

$$= 0.062x^2 + 0.020x + 1.18$$
$$= 0.062(11)^2 + 0.020(11) + 1.18$$
$$= 7.502 + 0.22 + 1.18$$
$$= 8.902$$

The amount of sales of organically grown food in 2001 was about $8.902 billion.

121. **a.** 1989 means substitute 7 for x:

number $= 0.42x^2 - 3.44x + 5.80$

$$= 0.42(7)^2 - 3.44(7) + 5.80$$
$$= 0.42(49) - 3.44(7) + 5.80$$
$$= 20.58 - 24.08 + 5.80$$
$$= 2.30$$

In 1989, 2.30 million people used cellular phones.

b. 2002 means substitute 20 for x:

number $= 0.42x^2 - 3.44x + 5.80$

$$= 0.42(20)^2 - 3.44(20) + 5.80$$
$$= 0.42(400) - 3.44(20) + 5.80$$
$$168 - 68.8 + 5.80$$
$$= 105$$

In 2002, 105 million people used cellular phones.

123. $|a| = |-a|$ for all real numbers or R.

125. $|a| = 4$ for $a = 4$ or $a = -4$ since $|4| = 4$ and $|-4| = 4$.

127. Associative property of addition

Exercise Set 1.5

1. **a.** $a^m \cdot a^n = a^{m+n}$

3. **a.** $a^0 = 1$, $a \neq 0$

5. **a.** $(ab)^m = a^m b^m$

7. **a.** $\left(\dfrac{a}{b}\right)^m = \dfrac{a^m}{b^m}$, $b \neq 0$

9. $x^{-1} = 5$, $\dfrac{1}{x} = 5$, $\dfrac{1}{x} = \dfrac{5}{1}$

Cross multiply: $5x = 1$

Solve for x. $x = \dfrac{1}{5}$

11. a. The opposite of x is $-x$.

   The reciprocal of x is $\dfrac{1}{x}$.

b. x^{-1} or $\dfrac{1}{x}$

c. $-x$

13. $2^3 \cdot 2^2 = 2^{3+2}$

$\qquad = 3^5$

$\qquad = 32$

15. $\dfrac{3^7}{3^5} = 3^{7-5}$

$\qquad = 3^2$

$\qquad = 9$

17. $6^{-2} = \dfrac{1}{6^2}$

$\qquad = \dfrac{1}{36}$

19. $\dfrac{1}{2^{-3}} = \dfrac{2^3}{1}$ (using the Helpful Hint)

$\qquad = 2^3$

$\qquad = 8$

21. $13^0 = 1$

23. $\left(2^3\right)^2 = 2^{3 \cdot 2}$

$\qquad = 2^6$

$\qquad = 64$

25. $(2 \cdot 3)^2 = 2^2 \cdot 3^2$

$\qquad = 4 \cdot 9$

$\qquad = 36$

27. $\left(\dfrac{2}{3}\right)^4 = \dfrac{2^4}{3^4}$

$\qquad = \dfrac{16}{81}$

29. a. $3^{-2} = \dfrac{1}{3^2} = \dfrac{1}{9}$

b. $(-3)^{-2} = \dfrac{1}{(-3)^2} = \dfrac{1}{9}$

c. $-3^{-2} = -\dfrac{1}{3^2} = -\dfrac{1}{9}$

d. $-(-3)^{-2} = -\dfrac{1}{(-3)^2} = -\dfrac{1}{9}$

31. a. $\left(\dfrac{1}{2}\right)^{-1} = \left(\dfrac{2}{1}\right)^{1} = 2$

b. $\left(-\dfrac{1}{2}\right)^{-1} = \left(-\dfrac{2}{1}\right)^{1} = -2$

c. $-\left(\dfrac{1}{2}\right)^{-1} = -\left(\dfrac{2}{1}\right)^{1} = -2$

d. $-\left(-\dfrac{1}{2}\right)^{-1} = -\left(-\dfrac{2}{1}\right)^{1} = -(-2) = 2$

33. a. $5x^0 = 5 \cdot x^0 = 5 \cdot 1 = 5$

b. $-5x^0 = -5 \cdot x^0 = -5 \cdot 1 = -5$

c. $(-5x)^0 = 1$

d. $-(-5x)^0 = -1 \cdot (-5x)^0 = -1 \cdot 1 = -1$

35. a. $3xyz^0 = 3 \cdot x \cdot y \cdot z^0 = 3 \cdot x \cdot y \cdot 1 = 3xy$

b. $(3xyz)^0 = 1$

c. $3x(yz)^0 = 3x \cdot (yz)^0 = 3x \cdot 1 = 3x$

d. $3(xyz)^0 = 3 \cdot (xyz)^0 = 3 \cdot 1 = 3$

37. $5y^{-3} = 5 \cdot \dfrac{1}{y^3}$

$\qquad = \dfrac{5}{y^3}$

39. $\dfrac{1}{x^{-4}} = x^4$

41. $\dfrac{2a}{b^{-3}} = 2ab^3$

43. $\dfrac{5m^{-2}n^{-3}}{2} = \dfrac{5}{2m^2n^3}$

45. $\dfrac{5x^{-2}y^{-3}}{z^{-4}} = \dfrac{5z^4}{x^2y^3}$

47. $\dfrac{6^{-1}x^{-1}}{y} = \dfrac{1}{6^1x^1y}$

$\qquad = \dfrac{1}{6xy}$

49. $2^5 \cdot 2^{-6} = 2^{5+(-6)}$

$\qquad = 2^{-1}$

$\qquad = \dfrac{1}{2}$

51. $x^6 \cdot x^{-2} = x^{6+(-2)}$

$\qquad = x^4$

53. $\dfrac{6^5}{6^3} = 6^{5-3}$

$\qquad = 6^2$

$\qquad = 36$

55. $\dfrac{7^{-5}}{7^{-3}} = 7^{-5-(-3)} = 7^{-5+3} = 7^{-2} = \dfrac{1}{7^2} = \dfrac{1}{49}$

or, better yet

$\dfrac{7^{-5}}{7^{-3}} = \dfrac{1}{7^{-3-(-5)}} = \dfrac{1}{7^{-3+5}} = \dfrac{1}{7^2} = \dfrac{1}{49}$

57. $\dfrac{m^{-5}}{m^5} = m^{-5-5} = m^{-10} = \dfrac{1}{m^{10}}$

59. $\dfrac{5w^{-2}}{w^{-7}} = 5w^{-2-(-7)}$

$\qquad = 5w^{-2+7}$

$\qquad = 5w^5$

61. $3a^{-2} \cdot 4a^{-5} = 3 \cdot 4 \cdot a^{-2} \cdot a^{-5}$

$\qquad = 12a^{-2+(-5)}$

$\qquad = 12a^{-7}$

$\qquad = \dfrac{12}{a^7}$

63. $\left(-3p^{-2}\right)\left(-p^3\right) = (-3)(-1)p^{-2} \cdot p^3$

$\qquad = 3p^{-2+3}$

$\qquad = 3p^1$

$\qquad = 3p$

65. $\left(5r^2s^{-2}\right)\left(-2r^5s^2\right) = 5(-2)r^2 \cdot r^5 \cdot s^{-2} \cdot s^2$

$\qquad = -10r^{2+5} \cdot s^{-2+2}$

$\qquad = -10r^7s^0$

$\qquad = -10r^7$

67. $\left(2x^4y^7\right)\left(4x^3y^{-5}\right) = 2 \cdot 4 \cdot x^4 \cdot x^3 \cdot y^7 \cdot y^{-5}$

$\qquad = 8x^{4+3}y^{7+(-5)}$

$\qquad = 8x^7y^2$

69. $\dfrac{27x^5y^{-4}}{9x^3y^2} = \left(\dfrac{27}{9}\right)\dfrac{x^{5-3}}{y^{2-(-4)}}$

$\qquad = \dfrac{3x^2}{y^6}$

71. $\dfrac{9xy^{-4}z^3}{-3x^{-2}yz} = \left(\dfrac{9}{-3}\right)\dfrac{x^{1-(-2)}z^{3-1}}{y^{1-(-4)}}$

$\qquad = -\dfrac{3x^3z^2}{y^5}$

73. **a.** $3(a+b)^0 = 3 \cdot 1 = 3$

      b. $3a^0 + 3b^0 = 3 \cdot a^0 + 3 \cdot b^0 = 3 \cdot 1 + 3 \cdot 1 = 6$

      c. $(3a + 3b)^0 = 1$

      d. $-3a^0 + 3b^0 = -3 \cdot a^0 + 3 \cdot b^0 = -3 \cdot 1 + 3 \cdot 1 = 0$

75. **a.** $4^{-1} - 3^{-1} = \dfrac{1}{4} - \dfrac{1}{3} = \dfrac{3}{12} - \dfrac{4}{12} = -\dfrac{1}{12}$

      b. $4^{-1} + 3^{-1} = \dfrac{1}{4} + \dfrac{1}{3} = \dfrac{3}{12} + \dfrac{4}{12} = \dfrac{7}{12}$

c.
$$2 \cdot 4^{-1} + 3 \cdot 5^{-1} = 2 \cdot \frac{1}{4} + 3 \cdot \frac{1}{5}$$
$$= \frac{2}{4} + \frac{3}{5}$$
$$= \frac{10}{20} + \frac{12}{20}$$
$$= \frac{22}{20}$$
$$= \frac{11}{10} \text{ or } 1\frac{1}{10}$$

d.
$$(2 \cdot 4)^{-1} + (3 \cdot 5)^{-1} = 8^{-1} + 15^{-1}$$
$$= \frac{1}{8} + \frac{1}{15}$$
$$= \frac{15}{120} + \frac{8}{120}$$
$$= \frac{23}{120}$$

77.
$$\left(3^2\right)^2 = 3^{2 \cdot 2}$$
$$= 3^4$$
$$= 81$$

79.
$$\left(3^2\right)^{-2} = 3^{2 \cdot (-2)}$$
$$= 3^{-4}$$
$$= \frac{1}{81}$$

81.
$$\left(b^{-3}\right)^{-2} = b^{(-3)(-2)}$$
$$= b^6$$

83.
$$(-c)^3 = (-1 \cdot c)^3$$
$$= (-1)^3 \cdot c^3$$
$$= -1 \cdot c^3$$
$$= -c^3$$

85.
$$\left(-3x^{-3}\right)^2 = (-3)^2 \cdot \left(x^{-3}\right)^2$$
$$= 9 \cdot x^{-6}$$
$$= \frac{9}{x^6}$$

87.
$$5^{-1} + 2^{-1} = \frac{1}{5} + \frac{1}{2}$$
$$= \frac{2}{10} + \frac{5}{10}$$
$$= \frac{7}{10}$$

89.
$$3 \cdot 4^{-2} + 5 \cdot 8^{-1} = 3 \cdot \frac{1}{16} + 5 \cdot \frac{1}{8}$$
$$= \frac{3}{16} + \frac{5}{8}$$
$$= \frac{3}{16} + \frac{10}{16}$$
$$= \frac{13}{16}$$

91.
$$\left(\frac{4b}{3}\right)^{-2} = \left(\frac{3}{4b}\right)^2$$
$$= \frac{3^2}{(4b)^2}$$
$$= \frac{9}{16b^2}$$

93.
$$\left(4x^2y^{-2}\right)^2 = (4)^2 \left(x^2\right)^2 \left(y^{-2}\right)^2$$
$$= (4)^2 x^{2 \cdot 2} y^{(-2) \cdot 2}$$
$$= 16x^4 y^{-4}$$
$$= \frac{16x^4}{y^4}$$

95.
$$\left(3p^2q^{-4}\right)^{-3} = 3^{-3} p^{2(-3)} q^{(-4)(-3)}$$
$$= 3^{-3} p^{-6} q^{12}$$
$$= \frac{q^{12}}{3^3 p^6}$$
$$= \frac{q^{12}}{27 p^6}$$

97.
$$\left(-2g^{-4}h^3\right)^{-3} = (-2)^{-3}\, g^{(-4)(-3)} h^{3\cdot(-3)}$$
$$= (-2)^{-3}\, g^{12} h^{-9}$$
$$= \frac{g^{12}}{(-2)^3 h^9}$$
$$= \frac{g^{12}}{-8h^9}$$
$$= -\frac{g^{12}}{8h^9}$$

99.
$$\left(\frac{3j}{4k^2}\right)^2 = \frac{(3j)^2}{\left(4k^2\right)^2}$$
$$= \frac{3^2 j^2}{4^2 k^{2\cdot2}}$$
$$= \frac{9j^2}{16k^4}$$

101.
$$\left(\frac{2r^4 s^5}{r^2}\right)^3 = \left(2r^4 r^{-2} s^5\right)^3$$
$$= \left(2r^2 s^5\right)^3$$
$$= 2^3 r^{2\cdot3} s^{5\cdot3}$$
$$= 8r^6 s^{15}$$

103.
$$\left(\frac{4xy}{y^3}\right)^{-3} = \left(\frac{y^3}{4xy}\right)^3$$
$$= \left(\frac{y^3 y^{-1}}{4x}\right)^3$$
$$= \frac{\left(y^2\right)^3}{(4x)^3}$$
$$= \frac{y^{2\cdot3}}{4^3 x^3}$$
$$= \frac{y^6}{64x^3}$$

105.
$$\left(\frac{4x^{-2}y}{x^{-5}}\right)^3 = \left(4x^{-2} x^5 y\right)^3$$
$$= \left(4x^3 y\right)^3$$
$$= 4^3 x^{3\cdot3} y^3$$
$$= 64x^9 y^3$$

107.
$$\left(\frac{6x^2 y}{3xz}\right)^{-3} = \left(\frac{3xz}{6x^2 y}\right)^3$$
$$= \left(\frac{z}{2x^2 x^{-1} y}\right)^3$$
$$= \left(\frac{z}{2xy}\right)^3$$
$$= \frac{z^3}{2^3 x^3 y^3}$$
$$= \frac{z^3}{8x^3 y^3}$$

109.
$$\left(\frac{x^6 y^{-2}}{x^{-2} y^3}\right)^2 = \left(\frac{x^{6-(-2)}}{y^{3-(-2)}}\right)^2$$
$$= \left(\frac{x^8}{y^5}\right)^2$$
$$= \frac{\left(x^8\right)^2}{\left(y^5\right)^2}$$
$$= \frac{x^{16}}{y^{10}}$$

111.
$$\left(\frac{4x^{-1}y^{-2}z^3}{2xy^2 z^{-3}}\right)^{-2} = \left(\frac{2z^{3-(-3)}}{x^{1-(-1)} y^{2-(-2)}}\right)^{-2}$$
$$= \left(\frac{2z^6}{x^2 y^4}\right)^{-2}$$
$$= \left(\frac{x^2 y^4}{2z^6}\right)^2$$
$$= \frac{\left(x^2\right)^2 \left(y^4\right)^2}{2^2 \left(z^6\right)^2}$$
$$= \frac{x^4 y^8}{4z^{12}}$$

113.
$$\left(\frac{-a^3 b^{-1} c^{-3}}{2ab^3 c^{-4}}\right)^{-3} = \left(\frac{-a^{3-1} c^{-3-(-4)}}{2b^{3-(-1)}}\right)^{-3}$$
$$= \left(\frac{-a^2 c^1}{2b^4}\right)^{-3}$$
$$= \left(\frac{2b^4}{-a^2 c}\right)^{3}$$
$$= \frac{2^3 b^{4\cdot 3}}{-a^{2\cdot 3} c^3}$$
$$= -\frac{8b^{12}}{a^6 c^3}$$

115.
$$\frac{\left(3x^{-4} y^2\right)^3}{\left(2x^3 y^5\right)^3} = \frac{3^3 x^{-4\cdot 3} y^{2\cdot 3}}{2^3 x^{3\cdot 3} y^{5\cdot 3}}$$
$$= \frac{3^3 x^{-12} y^6}{2^3 x^9 y^{15}}$$
$$= \frac{27}{8x^{9-(-12)} y^{15-6}}$$
$$= \frac{27}{8x^{21} y^9}$$

117. $x^{2a} \cdot x^{5a+3} = x^{2a+5a+3}$
$$= x^{7a+3}$$

119. $w^{2a-5} \cdot w^{3a-2} = w^{2a-5+3a-2}$
$$= w^{5a-7}$$

121. $\dfrac{x^{2w+3}}{x^{w-4}} = x^{2w+3-(w-4)}$
$$= x^{2w+3-w+4}$$
$$= x^{w+7}$$

123. $\left(x^{3p+5}\right)\left(x^{2p-3}\right) = x^{3p+5+2p-3}$
$$= x^{5p+2}$$

125. $x^{-m}\left(x^{3m+2}\right) = x^{-m} x^{3m+2}$
$$= x^{-m+3m+2}$$
$$= x^{2m+2}$$

127.
$$\frac{25m^{a+b} n^{b-a}}{5m^{a-b} n^{a+b}} = \left(\frac{25}{5}\right)\frac{m^{a+b-(a-b)}}{n^{a+b-(b-a)}}$$
$$= \frac{5m^{a+b-a+b}}{n^{a+b-b+a}}$$
$$= \frac{5m^{2b}}{n^{2a}}$$

129. **a.** $x^4 > x^3$ when $x < 0$ or $x > 1$

b. $x^4 < x^3$ when $0 < x < 1$

c. $x^4 = x^3$ when $x = 0$ or $x = 1$

d. x^4 is not greater than x^3 when $0 \le x \le 1$

131. **a.** $(-1)^n = 1$ for any even number n because an even number of negative factors is positive.

b. $(-1)^n = -1$ for any odd number n because an odd number of negative factors is negative.

133. **a.**
$$\left(-\frac{2}{3}\right)^{-2} = \frac{1}{\left(-\frac{2}{3}\right)^2} = \frac{1}{\frac{4}{9}} = \frac{9}{4} \text{ or}$$
$$\left(-\frac{2}{3}\right)^{-2} = \left(-\frac{3}{2}\right)^2 = \frac{9}{4} \text{ by the negative}$$
exponent rule

Also, $\left(\frac{2}{3}\right)^{-2} = \frac{1}{\left(\frac{2}{3}\right)^2} = \frac{1}{\frac{4}{9}} = \frac{9}{4}$ or
$$\left(\frac{2}{3}\right)^{-2} = \left(\frac{3}{2}\right)^2 = \frac{9}{4} \text{ by the negative}$$
exponent rule

Thus, $\left(-\frac{2}{3}\right)^{-2} = \left(\frac{2}{3}\right)^{-2}$. So, yes they are equal.

b. Yes, because $x^{-2} = \dfrac{1}{x^2}$ and
$$(-x)^{-2} = \frac{1}{(-x)^2} = \frac{1}{x^2}$$

135. Let a represent the unknown exponent,

$$\left(\frac{x^2 y^{-2}}{x^{-3} y^a}\right)^2 = \left(x^{2-(-3)} y^{-2-a}\right)^2$$

$$= \left(x^5 y^{-2-a}\right)^2$$

$$= x^{10} y^{2(-2-a)}$$

$$= x^{10} y^{-4-2a}$$

Thus,

$$-4 - 2a = 2$$

$$2a = -4 - 2$$

$$2a = -6$$

$$a = -3$$

137. Let a and b represent the unknown exponents.

$$\left(\frac{x^a y^5 z^{-2}}{x^4 y^b z}\right)^{-1} = \left(\frac{y^{5-b}}{x^{4-a} z^{1-(-2)}}\right)^{-1}$$

$$= \frac{x^{4-a} z^3}{y^{5-b}}$$

Thus,

$$4 - a = 5$$

$$a = -1$$

and

$$5 - b = 2$$

$$b = 3$$

139.

$$\left(\frac{x^{5/8}}{x^{1/4}}\right)^3 = \left(x^{5/8 - 1/4}\right)^3$$

$$= \left(x^{3/8}\right)^3$$

$$= x^{(3/8)\cdot 3}$$

$$= x^{9/8}$$

141.

$$\frac{x^{1/2} y^{-3/2}}{x^5 y^{5/3}} = \frac{1}{x^{5-1/2} y^{5/3 - (-3/2)}}$$

$$= \frac{1}{x^{9/2} y^{19/6}}$$

145.

147. $\sqrt[3]{-125} = -5$ since $(-5)(-5)(-5) = -125$

Exercise Set 1.6

1. The form of a number in scientific notation is a number greater than or equal to 1 and less than 10 multiplied by a power of 10.

3. $1 \times 10^{-2} = 0.01$

$1 \times 10^{-3} = 0.001$

1×10^{-2} is greater than 1×10^{-3}.

5. $4700 = 4.7 \times 10^3$

7. $0.031 = 3.1 \times 10^{-2}$

9. $360,000 = 3.6 \times 10^5$

11. $0.00000186 = 1.86 \times 10^{-6}$

13. $5,780,000 = 5.78 \times 10^6$

15. $0.000101 = 1.01 \times 10^{-4}$

17. $3.1 \times 10^4 = 31,000$

19. $2.13 \times 10^{-5} = 0.0000213$

21. $9.17 \times 10^{-1} = 0.917$

23. $9 \times 10^6 = 9,000,000$

25. $2.07 \times 10^5 = 207,000$

27. $1 \times 10^6 = 1,000,000$

29. $\left(4 \times 10^5\right)\left(6 \times 10^2\right) = (4 \times 6)\left(10^5 \times 10^2\right)$

$$= 24 \times 10^7$$

$$= 240,000,000$$

31. $\dfrac{8.4 \times 10^{-6}}{4 \times 10^{-4}} = \left(\dfrac{8.4}{4}\right) \times 10^{-6-(-4)}$

$$= 2.1 \times 10^{-2}$$

$$= 0.021$$

33. $\dfrac{6.75 \times 10^{-3}}{2.5 \times 10^2} = \left(\dfrac{6.75}{2.5}\right) \times 10^{-3-2}$

$$= 2.7 \times 10^{-5}$$

$$= 0.000027$$

35. $\left(8.2 \times 10^5\right)\left(1.3 \times 10^{-2}\right)$

$$= (8.2 \times 1.3)\left(10^5 \times 10^{-2}\right)$$

$$= 10.66 \times 10^3$$

$$= 10,660$$

37. $\dfrac{1.68\times10^4}{5.6\times10^7}=\left(\dfrac{1.68}{5.6}\right)\times10^{4-7}$

$=0.3\times10^{-3}$

$=0.0003$

39. $\left(9.1\times10^{-4}\right)\left(6.3\times10^{-4}\right)$

$=(9.1\times6.3)\left(10^{-4}\times10^{-4}\right)$

$=57.33\times10^{-8}$

$=0.0000005733$

41. $(0.03)(0.0005)$

$=\left(3\times10^{-2}\right)\left(5\times10^{-4}\right)$

$=(3\times5)\left(10^{-2}\times10^{-4}\right)$

$=15\times10^{-6}$

$=1.5\times10^{-5}$

43. $\dfrac{35,000,000}{7000}=\dfrac{3.5\times10^7}{7.0\times10^3}$

$=\left(\dfrac{3.5}{7}\right)\times10^{7-3}$

$=0.5\times10^4$

$=5.0\times10^3$

45. $\dfrac{0.00046}{23,000}=\dfrac{4.6\times10^{-4}}{2.3\times10^4}$

$=\left(\dfrac{4.6}{2.3}\right)\times10^{-4-4}$

$=2\times10^{-8}$

47. $(47,000)(35,000,000)$

$=\left(4.7\times10^4\right)\left(3.5\times10^7\right)$

$=(4.7\times3.5)\left(10^4\times10^7\right)$

$=16.45\times10^{11}$

$=1.645\times10^{12}$

49. $\dfrac{672}{0.0021}=\dfrac{6.72\times10^2}{2.1\times10^{-3}}$

$=\left(\dfrac{6.72}{2.1}\right)\times10^{2-(-3)}$

$=3.2\times10^5$

51. $\dfrac{0.00153}{0.00051}=\dfrac{1.53\times10^{-3}}{5.1\times10^{-4}}$

$=\left(\dfrac{1.53}{5.1}\right)\times10^{-3+4}$

$=0.3\times10^1$

$=3.0\times10^0$

53. $\left(4.78\times10^9\right)\left(1.96\times10^5\right)$

$=(4.78\times1.96)\left(10^9\times10^5\right)$

$=9.3688\times10^{14}$

$\approx9.369\times10^{14}$

55. $\left(7.23\times10^{-3}\right)\left(1.37\times10^5\right)$

$=(7.23\times1.37)\left(10^{-3}\times10^5\right)$

$=9.905\times10^2$

57. $\dfrac{4.36\times10^{-4}}{8.17\times10^{-7}}=\left(\dfrac{4.36}{8.17}\right)\times10^{-4-(-7)}$

$=0.5337\times10^3$

$=5.337\times10^2$

59. $\left(4.89\times10^{15}\right)\left(7.91\times10^{-41}\right)$

$=(4.89\times7.91)\left(10^{15}\times10^{-41}\right)$

$=38.6799\times10^{-26}$

$=3.86799\times10^{-25}$

$\approx3.868\times10^{-25}$

61. $\left(7.71\times10^3\right)\left(9.14\times10^{-31}\right)$

$=(7.71\times9.14)\left(10^3\times10^{-31}\right)$

$=70.469\times10^{-28}$

$=7.047\times10^{-27}$

63. $\dfrac{1.50\times10^{35}}{4.5\times10^{-26}}=\left(\dfrac{1.50}{4.5}\right)\times10^{35-(-26)}$

$=0.3333\times10^{61}$

$=3.333\times10^{60}$

65. a. $\dfrac{1}{10}=10^{-1}$; Subtract 1 from the exponent.

b. $\dfrac{1}{100}=10^{-2}$; Subtract 2 from the exponent.

c. $\dfrac{1}{1\text{ million}} = \dfrac{1}{1,000,000} = 10^{-6}$; Subtract 6 from the exponent.

d. $\dfrac{6.58 \times 10^{-4}}{1\text{ million}} = 6.58 \times 10^{-4} \times 10^{-6}$
$= 6.58 \times 10^{-10}$

67. a. $5.25 \times 10^4 - 4.25 \times 10^4 = 1 \times 10^4$
It is off by 1×10^4 or 10,000.

b. $5.25 \times 10^5 - 5.25 \times 10^4$
$= 52.5 \times 10^4 - 5.25 \times 10^4$
$= 47.25 \times 10^4$
$= 4.725 \times 10^5$
It is off by 4.725×10^5 or 472,500.

c. The error in part b is more serious because 472,500 is greater than 10,000.

69. $\dfrac{93,000,000}{3100} = \dfrac{9.3 \times 10^7}{3.1 \times 10^3}$
$= \left(\dfrac{9.3}{3.1}\right) \times 10^{7-3}$
$= 3.0 \times 10^4$
$= 30,000$
It will take 30,000 hours to reach the sun.

71. a. $6.14 \times 10^9 - 2.81 \times 10^8$
$= 6.14 \times 10^9 - 0.281 \times 10^9$
$= 5.859 \times 10^9$
About 5.859×10^9 people will live outside of the United States.

b. $\dfrac{2.81 \times 10^8}{6.14 \times 10^9} = \left(\dfrac{2.81}{6.14} \cdot 10^{-1}\right)$
$\approx \left(0.458 \cdot 10^{-1}\right)$
≈ 0.0458
$\approx 4.58\%$

About 4.58% of the world's population lived in the United States in 2000.

73. $30 \times 5,900,000 = 3.0 \times 10^1 \times 5.9 \times 10^6$
$= (3.0 \times 5.9)\left(10^1 \times 10^6\right)$
$= 17.7 \times 10^7$
$= 1.77 \times 10^8$ red blood cells

75. a. $1.392 \times 10^8 \times 0.222$
$= 1.392 \times 10^8 \times 2.22 \times 10^{-1}$
$= (1.392 \times 2.22)\left(10^8 \times 10^{-1}\right)$
$\approx 3.0902 \times 10^7$
Approximately 3.0902×10^7 passengers enplaned at Chicago's airport.

b. $1.392 \times 10^8 \times 0.265$
$= 1.392 \times 10^8 \times 2.65 \times 10^{-1}$
$= (1.392 \times 2.65)\left(10^8 \times 10^{-1}\right)$
$\approx 3.689 \times 10^7$
Approximately 3.689×10^7 passengers enplaned at Atlanta's airport.

c. $\dfrac{3.689 \times 10^7}{3.0902 \times 10^7} = \left(\dfrac{3.689}{3.0902}\right) \times 10^{7-7}$
$\approx 1.193 \times 10^0$
≈ 1.193
The number of passengers that enplaned in Atlanta was approximately 1.193 times greater than the number enplaned in Chicago.

77. a. 1273 million − 285 million = 988 million. About 988 million more people lived in China than in the United States.

b. $\dfrac{1273\text{ million}}{6,137,000,000} = \dfrac{1.273 \times 10^9}{6.137 \times 10^9}$
$= \left(\dfrac{1.273}{6.137}\right) \times 10^{9-9}$
$\approx 0.2074 \times 10^0$
$= 20.74\%$
Approximately 20.74% of the worlds population lived in China.

c. $\dfrac{1273\text{ million}}{3.70 \times 10^6}$
$= \dfrac{1.273 \times 10^9}{3.70 \times 10^6}$
$= \left(\dfrac{1.273}{3.70}\right) \times 10^{9-6}$
$\approx 0.3441 \times 10^3$
≈ 344.1 people per square mile
The population density in China was approximately 344.1 people per sq. mile.

d. $\dfrac{285 \text{ million}}{3.62 \times 10^6}$

$= \dfrac{2.85 \times 10^8}{3.62 \times 10^6}$

$= \left(\dfrac{2.85}{3.62}\right) \times 10^{8-6}$

$\approx 0.787 \times 10^2$

≈ 78.7

The population density in the United States was approximately 78.7 people per square mile.

79. a. $\dfrac{1.86 \times 10^5 \text{ miles}}{1 \text{ second}} \cdot \dfrac{60 \text{ seconds}}{1 \text{ minute}} \cdot \dfrac{60 \text{ minutes}}{1 \text{ hour}} \cdot \dfrac{24 \text{ hours}}{1 \text{ day}} \cdot \dfrac{365 \text{ days}}{\text{year}}$

$= 1.86 \times 10^5 \times 6.0 \times 10^1 \times 6.0 \times 10^1 \times 2.4 \times 10^1 \times 3.65 \times 10^2$

$= (1.86 \times 6 \times 6 \times 2.4 \times 3.65)\left(10^5 \times 10^1 \times 10^1 \times 10^1 \times 10^2\right)$

$\approx 587 \times 10^{10}$

$\approx 5.87 \times 10^{12} \text{ miles}$

b. $\dfrac{93,000,000}{1.86 \times 10^5} = \dfrac{9.3 \times 10^7}{1.86 \times 10^5}$

$= \left(\dfrac{9.3}{1.86}\right) \times 10^{7-5}$

$= 5 \times 10^2$

$= 500 \text{ seconds or } 8\dfrac{1}{3} \text{ minutes}$

c. $\dfrac{6.25 \times 10^{16}}{0.5 \times 1.86 \times 10^5} \approx 6.72 \times 10^{11} \text{ seconds or } 21,309 \text{ years}$

Review Exercises

1. $\{4, 5, 6, 7\}$

2. $\{0, 3, 6, 9, \ldots\}$

3. Yes; the set of natural numbers is a subset of the set of whole numbers.

4. Yes; the set of rational numbers is a subset of the set of real numbers.

5. Yes; the set of irrational numbers is a subset of the set of real numbers.

6. No; the set of rational numbers is not a subset of the set of irrational numbers.

7. 4 and 6 are natural numbers.

8. 4, 6 and 0 are whole numbers.

9. –2, 4, 6 and 0 are integers.

10. $-2, 4, 6, \dfrac{1}{2}, 0, \dfrac{15}{27}, -\dfrac{1}{5},$ and 1.47 are rational numbers.

11. $\sqrt{7}$ and $\sqrt{3}$ are irrational numbers.

12. $-2, 4, 6, \frac{1}{2}, \sqrt{7}, \sqrt{3}, 0, \frac{15}{27}, -\frac{1}{5}$, and 1.47 are real numbers.

13. False; $\frac{0}{1} = 0$.

14. True; 0, –2, and 4 can be written with a denominator of 1.

15. True; division by 0 is undefined.

16. True; the set of real numbers contains both the rational and irrational numbers.

17. $A \cup B = \{1, 2, 3, 4, 5, 6, 8, 10\}$
    $A \cap B = \{2, 4, 6\}$

18. $A \cup B = \{2, 3, 4, 5, 6, 7, 8, 9\}$
    $A \cap B = \varnothing$ or $\{\ \}$

19. $A \cup B = \{1, 2, 3, 4, \ldots\}$
    $A \cap B = \varnothing$ or $\{\ \}$

20. $A \cup B = \{3, 4, 5, 6, 9, 10, 11, 12\}$
    $A \cap B = \{9, 10\}$

21.

22.

23.

24.

25. $-8 < 0$

26. $-4 < -3.9$

27. $1.06 < 1.6$

28. $|-3| = 3$
    $3 = 3$
    $|-3| = 3$

29. $|-4| = 4$
    $|-6| = 6$
    $|-4| < |-6|$

30. $13 = 13$
    $|-5| = 5$
    $13 > |-5|$

31. $\left|-\frac{2}{3}\right| = \frac{2}{3} = \frac{10}{15}$
    $\frac{3}{5} = \frac{9}{15}$
    $\left|-\frac{2}{3}\right| > \frac{3}{5}$

32. $-|-2| = -2$
    $-5 = -5$
    $-|-2| > -5$

33. $-\pi, -3, 3, \pi$

34. $0, \frac{3}{5}, 2.3, |-3|$

35. $-2, 3, |-5|, |-7|$

36. $-7, -3, |-3|, |-7|$

37. $-4, -|-3|, 5, 6$

38. $-3, 0, |1.6|, |-2.3|$

39. Distributive property

40. Commutative property of multiplication

41. Associative property of addition

42. Identity property of addition

43. Associative property of multiplication

44. Double negative property

45. Multiplicative property of zero

46. Inverse property of addition

47. Inverse property of multiplication

48. Identity property of multiplication

49. $7 + 3^2 - \sqrt{36} \div 2 = 7 + 9 - 6 \div 2$
    $= 7 + 9 - 3$
    $= 16 - 3$
    $= 13$

50. $-4 \div (-2) + 16 - \sqrt{49} = -4 \div (-2) + 16 - 7$
$$= 2 + 16 - 7$$
$$= 18 - 7$$
$$= 11$$

51. $(4 - 6) - (-3 + 5) + 12 = (-2) - (2) + 12$
$$= -2 - 2 + 12$$
$$= -4 + 12$$
$$= 8$$

52. $2|-7| - 4|-6| + 3$
$$= 2(7) - 4(6) + 3$$
$$= 14 - 24 + 3$$
$$= -10 + 3$$
$$= -7$$

53. $(6 - 9) \div (9 - 6) + 1 = -3 \div 3 + 1$
$$= \frac{-3}{3} + 1$$
$$= -1 + 1$$
$$= 0$$

54. $|6 - 3| \div 3 + 4 \cdot 8 - 12 = |3| \div 3 + 4 \cdot 8 - 12$
$$= 3 \div 3 + 4 \cdot 8 - 12$$
$$= 1 + 32 - 12$$
$$= 33 - 12$$
$$= 21$$

55. $\sqrt{9} + \sqrt[3]{64} + \sqrt[4]{16} = 3 + 4 + 2$
$$= 9$$

56. $3^2 - 6 \cdot 9 + 4 \div 2^2 - 3 = 9 - 6 \cdot 9 + 4 \div 4 - 3$
$$= 9 - 54 + 1 - 3$$
$$= -45 + 1 - 3$$
$$= -44 - 3$$
$$= -47$$

57. $4 - (2 - 9)^0 + 3^2 \div 1 + 3$
$$= 4 - (-7)^0 + 3^2 \div 1 + 3$$
$$= 4 - 1 + 9 \div 1 + 3$$
$$= 4 - 1 + 9 + 3$$
$$= 3 + 9 + 3$$
$$= 12 + 3$$
$$= 15$$

58. $5^2 + \left(-2 + 2^2\right)^3 + 1^4 = 5^2 + \left(-2 + 4\right)^3 + 1^4$
$$= 5^2 + (2)^3 + 1^4$$
$$= 25 + 8 + 1$$
$$= 33 + 1$$
$$= 34$$

59. $-3^2 + 14 \div 2 \cdot 3 - 6 = -9 + 14 \div 2 \cdot 3 - 6$
$$= -9 + 7 \cdot 3 - 6$$
$$= -9 + 21 - 6$$
$$= 12 - 6$$
$$= 6$$

60. $\left\{ \left[(9 \div 3)^2 - 1 \right]^2 \div 8 \right\}^3 = \left\{ \left[(3)^2 - 1 \right]^2 \div 8 \right\}^3$
$$= \left[(9 - 1)^2 \div 8 \right]^3$$
$$= \left[8^2 \div 8 \right]^3$$
$$= (64 \div 8)^3$$
$$= 8^3$$
$$= 512$$

61. $\dfrac{5 + 7 \div \left(3^2 - 2\right) + 4 \cdot 1}{\sqrt{81} + \sqrt{1} - 10} = \dfrac{5 + 7 \div (9 - 2) + 4 \cdot 1}{9 + 1 - 10}$
$$= \dfrac{5 + 7 \div (7) + 4 \cdot 1}{10 - 10}$$
$$= \dfrac{5 + 1 + 4}{0}$$
$$= \dfrac{10}{0} \text{ is undefined}$$

62.

$$\frac{-(4-6)^2 - 3(-2) + |-6|}{18 - 9 \div 3 \cdot 5}$$

$$= \frac{-(-2)^2 - 3(-2) + |-6|}{18 - 9 \div 3 \cdot 5}$$

$$= \frac{-4 - 3(-2) + |-6|}{18 - 9 \div 3 \cdot 5}$$

$$= \frac{-4 - 3(-2) + 6}{18 - 9 \div 3 \cdot 5}$$

$$= \frac{-4 + 6 + 6}{18 - 3 \cdot 5}$$

$$= \frac{-4 + 6 + 6}{18 - 15}$$

$$= \frac{2 + 6}{3}$$

$$= \frac{8}{3}$$

63. Substitute 2 for x:

$$
\begin{aligned}
2x^2 + 3x + 1 &= 2(2)^2 + 3(2) + 1 \\
&= 2(4) + 3(2) + 1 \\
&= 8 + 6 + 1 \\
&= 14 + 1 \\
&= 15
\end{aligned}
$$

64. Substitute -3 for a and -4 for b:

$$5a^2 - 7b^2$$

$$5(-3)^2 - 7(-4)^2$$

$$5(9) - 7(16)$$

$$45 - 112$$

$$-67$$

65. a. 1976 means substitute 7 for x.
dollars

$$= 50.86x^2 - 316.75x + 541.48$$
$$= 50.86(7)^2 - 316.75(7) + 541.48$$
$$= 50.86(49) - 316.75(7) + 541.48$$
$$= 2492.14 - 2217.25 + 541.48$$
$$= 816.37$$

In 1976, the amount spent was $816.37 million.

b. 2004 means substitute 14 for x.
dollars

$$= 50.86x^2 - 316.75x + 541.48$$
$$= 50.86(14)^2 - 316.75(14) + 541.48$$
$$= 50.86(196) - 316.75(14) + 541.48$$
$$= 9968.56 - 4434.5 + 541.48$$
$$= 6075.54$$

In 2004, the amount spent will be about $6,075.54 million.

66. a. 1980 means substitute 4 for x.
freight hauled

$$= 14.04x^2 + 1.96x + 712.05$$
$$= 14.04(4)^2 + 1.96(4) + 712.05$$
$$= 14.04(16) + 1.96(4) + 712.05$$
$$= 224.64 + 7.84 + 712.05$$
$$= 944.53$$

In 1980, the amount of freight hauled by trains was 944.53 ton-miles.

b. 2000 means substitute 8 for x.
freight hauled

$$= 14.04x^2 + 1.96x + 712.05$$
$$= 14.04(8)^2 + 1.96(8) + 712.05$$
$$= 14.04(64) + 1.96(8) + 712.05$$
$$= 898.56 + 15.68 + 712.05$$
$$= 1626.29$$

In 2000, the amount of freight hauled by trains was 1626.29 ton-miles.

67. $2^3 \cdot 2^2 = 2^{3+2} = 2^5 = 32$

68. $x^2 \cdot x^3 = x^{2+3}$
$$= x^5$$

69. $\dfrac{a^{12}}{a^4} = a^{12-4}$
$$= a^8$$

70. $\dfrac{y^{12}}{y^3} = y^{12-3}$
$$= y^9$$

71. $\dfrac{b^7}{b^{-2}} = b^{7-(-2)}$
$$= b^{7+2}$$
$$= b^9$$

72. $c^3 \cdot c^{-5} = c^{3+(-5)}$
$$= c^{-2}$$
$$= \frac{1}{c^2}$$

73.
$$5^{-2} \cdot 5^{-1} = 5^{-2+(-1)}$$
$$= 5^{-3}$$
$$= \frac{1}{5^3}$$
$$= \frac{1}{125}$$

74.
$$3x^0 = 3(1)$$
$$= 3$$

75.
$$\left(-2m^3\right)^2 = (-2)^2\left(m^3\right)^2$$
$$= 4m^{3 \cdot 2}$$
$$= 4m^6$$

76.
$$\left(\frac{5}{7}\right)^{-1} = \left(\frac{7}{5}\right)^1$$
$$= \frac{7}{5}$$

77.
$$\left(\frac{2}{3}\right)^{-3} = \left(\frac{3}{2}\right)^3$$
$$= \frac{3^3}{2^3}$$
$$= \frac{27}{8}$$

78.
$$\left(\frac{x}{y^2}\right)^{-1} = \left(\frac{y^2}{x}\right)^1$$
$$= \frac{y^2}{x}$$

79.
$$\left(5xy^3\right)\left(-3x^2y\right) = 5 \cdot (-3) \cdot x \cdot x^2 \cdot y^3 \cdot y$$
$$= -15x^{1+2}y^{3+1}$$
$$= -15x^3y^4$$

80.
$$\left(2v^3w^{-4}\right)\left(3v^{-6}w\right) = 2 \cdot 3 \cdot v^3 \cdot v^{-6} \cdot w^{-4} \cdot w^1$$
$$= 6 \cdot v^{3+(-6)} \cdot w^{-4+1}$$
$$= 6v^{-3}w^{-3}$$
$$= \frac{6}{v^3w^3}$$

81.
$$\frac{6x^{-3}y^5}{2x^2y^{-2}} = \frac{6y^{5-(-2)}}{2x^{2-(-3)}}$$
$$= \left(\frac{6}{2}\right)\frac{y^7}{x^5}$$
$$= \frac{3y^7}{x^5}$$

82.
$$\frac{12x^{-3}y^{-4}}{4x^{-2}y^5} = \left(\frac{12}{4}\right)\frac{1}{x^{-2-(-3)}y^{5-(-4)}}$$
$$= \frac{3}{xy^9}$$

83.
$$\frac{g^3h^{-6}j^{-9}}{g^{-2}h^{-1}j^5} = \frac{g^{3-(-2)}}{h^{-1-(-6)}j^{5-(-9)}}$$
$$= \frac{g^5}{h^5j^{14}}$$

84.
$$\frac{21m^{-3}n^{-2}}{7m^{-4}n^2} = \left(\frac{21}{7}\right)\frac{m^{-3-(-4)}}{n^{2-(-2)}}$$
$$= \frac{3m}{n^4}$$

85.
$$\left(\frac{5a^2b}{a}\right)^3 = \left(5a^{2-1}b\right)^3$$
$$= (5ab)^3$$
$$= 5^3a^3b^3$$
$$= 125a^3b^3$$

86.
$$\left(\frac{x^5y}{-3y^2}\right)^2 = \left(\frac{x^5}{-3y^{2-1}}\right)^2$$
$$= \left(\frac{x^5}{-3y}\right)^2$$
$$= \frac{\left(x^5\right)^2}{(-3)^2y^2}$$
$$= \frac{x^{5\cdot2}}{9y^2}$$
$$= \frac{x^{10}}{9y^2}$$

87.

$$\left(\frac{p^3 q^{-1}}{p^{-4} q^5}\right)^2 = \left(\frac{p^{3-(-4)}}{q^{5-(-1)}}\right)^2$$

$$= \left(\frac{p^7}{q^6}\right)^2$$

$$= \frac{p^{7 \cdot 2}}{q^{6 \cdot 2}}$$

$$= \frac{p^{14}}{q^{12}}$$

88.

$$\left(\frac{-2ab^{-3}}{c^2}\right)^3 = \left(\frac{-2a}{b^3 c^2}\right)^3$$

$$= \frac{(-2a)^3}{\left(b^3 c^2\right)^3}$$

$$= \frac{(-2)^3 \cdot a^3}{b^{3 \cdot 3} \cdot c^{2 \cdot 3}}$$

$$= -\frac{8a^3}{b^9 c^6}$$

89.

$$\left(\frac{6xy^3}{z^2}\right)^{-2} = \left(\frac{z^2}{6xy^3}\right)^2$$

$$= \frac{(z^2)^2}{6^2 x^2 (y^3)^2}$$

$$= \frac{z^{2 \cdot 2}}{36 x^2 y^{3 \cdot 2}}$$

$$= \frac{z^4}{36 x^2 y^6}$$

90.

$$\left(\frac{9m^{-2}n}{3mn}\right)^{-3} = \left[\left(\frac{9}{3}\right)\frac{n^{1-1}}{m^{1-(-2)}}\right]^{-3}$$

$$= \left(\frac{3}{m^3}\right)^{-3}$$

$$= \left(\frac{m^3}{3}\right)^3$$

$$= \frac{(m^3)^3}{3^3}$$

$$= \frac{m^9}{27}$$

91.

$$\left(-2m^2 n^{-3}\right)^{-2} = (-2)^{-2}\left(m^2\right)^{-2}\left(n^{-3}\right)^{-2}$$

$$= (-2)^{-2} m^{2 \cdot (-2)} n^{-3 \cdot (-2)}$$

$$= (-2)^{-2} m^{-4} n^6$$

$$= \frac{n^6}{(-2)^2 m^4}$$

$$= \frac{n^6}{4m^4}$$

92.

$$\left(\frac{15 x^5 y^{-3} z^{-2}}{-3 x^4 y^{-4} z^3}\right)^4 = \left[\left(\frac{15}{-3}\right)\frac{x^{5-4} y^{-3-(-4)}}{z^{3-(-2)}}\right]^4$$

$$= \left[\frac{-5xy}{z^5}\right]^4$$

$$= \frac{(-5)^4 x^4 y^4}{z^{5 \cdot 4}}$$

$$= \frac{625 x^4 y^4}{z^{20}}$$

93.

$$\left(\frac{2 x^{-1} y^5 z^4}{3 x^4 y^{-2} z^{-2}}\right)^{-2} = \left(\frac{2 y^{5-(-2)} z^{4-(-2)}}{3 x^{4-(-1)}}\right)^{-2}$$

$$= \left(\frac{2 y^7 z^6}{3 x^5}\right)^{-2}$$

$$= \left(\frac{3 x^5}{2 y^7 z^6}\right)^2$$

$$= \frac{3^2 x^{5 \cdot 2}}{2^2 y^{7 \cdot 2} z^{6 \cdot 2}}$$

$$= \frac{9 x^{10}}{4 y^{14} z^{12}}$$

94.

$$\left(\frac{8 x^{-2} y^{-2} z}{-x^4 y^{-4} z^3}\right)^{-1} = \left(\frac{8 y^{-2-(-4)}}{-x^{4-(-2)} z^{3-1}}\right)^{-1}$$

$$= \left(\frac{8 y^2}{-x^6 z^2}\right)^{-1}$$

$$= \left(\frac{-x^6 z^2}{8 y^2}\right)^1$$

$$= -\frac{x^6 z^2}{8 y^2}$$

95. $0.0000742 = 7.42 \times 10^{-5}$

96. $260,000 = 2.6 \times 10^5$

97. $183,000 = 1.83 \times 10^5$

98. $0.000001 = 1.0 \times 10^{-6}$

99. $\left(25 \times 10^{-3}\right)\left(1.2 \times 10^6\right) = (25 \times 1.2)\left(10^{-3} \times 10^6\right)$

$$= 30 \times 10^{-3+6}$$
$$= 30 \times 10^3$$
$$= 30,000$$

100. $\dfrac{18 \times 10^3}{9 \times 10^5} = \left(\dfrac{18}{9}\right) \times \left(\dfrac{10^3}{10^5}\right)$

$$= 2 \times 10^{3-5}$$
$$= 2 \times 10^{-2}$$
$$= 0.02$$

101. $\dfrac{4,000,000}{0.02} = \dfrac{4 \times 10^6}{2 \times 10^{-2}}$

$$= \left(\dfrac{4}{2}\right) \times \left(\dfrac{10^6}{10^{-2}}\right)$$
$$= 2 \times 10^{6-(-2)}$$
$$= 2 \times 10^8$$
$$= 200,000,000$$

102. $(0.004)(500,000) = \left(4 \times 10^{-3}\right)\left(5 \times 10^5\right)$

$$= (4 \times 5)\left(10^{-3} \times 10^5\right)$$
$$= 20 \times 10^{-3+5}$$
$$= 20 \times 10^2$$
$$= 2000$$

103. a. $\$2.64 \times 10^8 - \$1.51 \times 10^8$

$$= (\$2.64 - \$1.51) \times 10^8$$
$$= \$1.13 \times 10^8 \text{ or } \$113,000,000$$

b. $\$1.51 \times 10^8 - \$9.2 \times 10^7$

$$= \$1.51 \times 10^8 - \$0.92 \times 10^8$$
$$= (\$1.51 - \$0.92) \times 10^8$$
$$= \$0.59 \times 10^8$$
$$= \$5.9 \times 10^7 \text{ or } \$59,000,000$$

c.
a. $\dfrac{\$2.64 \times 10^8}{\$9.2 \times 10^7} = \left(\dfrac{\$2.64}{\$9.2}\right) \times 10^{8-7}$

$$\approx 0.287 \times 10^1$$
$$\approx 2.87$$

It was about 2.87 times larger.

104. a. $1.04 \times 10^{10} = 10,400,000,000$

b. $1.04 \times 10^{10} = 10.4 \times 10^9$
$$= 10.4 \text{ billion}$$

c. $\dfrac{1.04 \times 10^{10}}{20} = \dfrac{1.04 \times 10^{10}}{2.0 \times 10^1}$

$$= \left(\dfrac{1.04}{2.0}\right) \times 10^{10-1}$$
$$= 0.52 \times 10^9$$
$$= 5.2 \times 10^8$$

It traveled an average of 5.2×10^8 km or 520,000,000 km per year.

d. $1.04 \times 10^{10} \times 0.6$

$$= 1.04 \times 10^{10} \times 6 \times 10^{-1}$$
$$= (1.04 \times 6)\left(10^{10} \times 10^{-1}\right)$$
$$= 6.24 \times 10^9$$

It traveled about 6.24×10^9 miles or 6,240,000,000 miles.

Practice Test

1. $A = \{6, 7, 8, 9, \ldots\}$

2. False; π is a real number but it is not a rational number.

3. True; this is how the set of real numbers is defined.

4. $-\dfrac{3}{5}, 2, -4, 0, \dfrac{19}{12}, 2.57,$ and -1.92 are rational numbers.

5. $-\dfrac{3}{5}, 2, -4, 0, \dfrac{19}{12}, 2.57, \sqrt{8}, \sqrt{2},$ and -1.92 are real numbers.

6. $A \cup B = \{5, 7, 8, 9, 10, 11, 14\}$
   $A \cap B = \{8, 10\}$

7. $A \cup B = \{1, 3, 5, 7, \ldots\}$
$A \cap B = \{3, 5, 7, 9, 11\}$

8.

9.

10. $-|4|, -2, |3|, 6$

11. Associative property of addition

12. Commutative property of addition

13.
$$\left\{ 4 - \left[7 - 3^2 \div \left(3^2 - 2 \cdot 3 \right) \right] \right\}$$
$$= \left\{ 4 - \left[7 - 3^2 \div \left(9 - 2 \cdot 3 \right) \right] \right\}$$
$$= \left\{ 4 - \left[7 - 3^2 \div \left(9 - 6 \right) \right] \right\}$$
$$= \left\{ 4 - \left[7 - 3^2 \div \left(3 \right) \right] \right\}$$
$$= \left\{ 4 - \left[7 - 9 \div 3 \right] \right\}$$
$$= \left\{ 4 - \left[7 - 3 \right] \right\}$$
$$= \left\{ 4 - \left(4 \right) \right\}$$
$$= 0$$

14.
$$2^4 + 4^2 \div 2^3 \cdot \sqrt{25} + 7 = 16 + 16 \div 8 \cdot \sqrt{25} + 7$$
$$= 16 + 16 \div 8 \cdot 5 + 7$$
$$= 16 + 2 \cdot 5 + 7$$
$$= 16 + 10 + 7$$
$$= 33$$

15.
$$\frac{-3|4 - 8| \div 2 + 4}{-\sqrt{36} + 18 \div 3^2 + 4} = \frac{-3|-4| \div 2 + 4}{-\sqrt{36} + 18 \div 3^2 + 4}$$
$$= \frac{-3(4) \div 2 + 4}{-\sqrt{36} + 18 \div 3^2 + 4}$$
$$= \frac{-3(4) \div 2 + 4}{-6 + 18 \div 9 + 4}$$
$$= \frac{-12 \div 2 + 4}{-6 + 2 + 4}$$
$$= \frac{-6 + 4}{-6 + 2 + 4}$$
$$= \frac{-2}{-4 + 4}$$
$$= \frac{-2}{0}$$

which is undefined.

16.
$$\frac{-6^2 + 3(4 - |6|) \div 6}{4 - (-3) + 12 \div 4 \cdot 5} = \frac{-6^2 + 3(4 - 6) \div 6}{4 - (-3) + 12 \div 4 \cdot 5}$$
$$= \frac{-6^2 + 3(-2) \div 6}{4 - (-3) + 12 \div 4 \cdot 5}$$
$$= \frac{-36 + 3(-2) \div 6}{4 - (-3) + 12 \div 4 \cdot 5}$$
$$= \frac{-36 + (-6) \div 6}{4 + 3 + 3 \cdot 5}$$
$$= \frac{-36 + (-1)}{4 + 3 + 15}$$
$$= \frac{-37}{7 + 15}$$
$$= \frac{-37}{22}$$
$$= -\frac{37}{22}$$

17. Substitute 2 for x and 3 for y:
$$-x^2 + 2xy + y^2 = -(2)^2 + 2(2)(3) + (3)^2$$
$$= -4 + 2(2)(3) + 9$$
$$= -4 + 12 + 9$$
$$= 8 + 9$$
$$= 17$$

18. **a.** 1995 means substitute 5 for x:
Average Fed. Tax Return

$= 6.42x^2 + 13.9x + 970$

$= 6.42(5)^2 + 13.9(5) + 970$

$= 6.42(25) + 13.9(5) + 970$

$= 160.5 + 69.5 + 970$

$= 1200$

The average tax return in 1995 was approximately $1200.

b. 2002 means substitute 12 for x:
Average Fed. Tax Return

$= 6.42x^2 + 13.9x + 970$

$= 6.42(12)^2 + 13.9(12) + 970$

$= 6.42(144) + 13.9(12) + 970$

$= 924.48 + 166.8 + 970$

$= 2061.28$

The average tax return in 2002 will be approximately
$2061.28.

19. $3^{-2} = \dfrac{1}{3^2} = \dfrac{1}{9}$

20. $\left(\dfrac{4m^{-3}}{n^2}\right)^2 = \left(\dfrac{4}{m^3 n^2}\right)^2$

$= \dfrac{4^2}{m^{3\cdot 2} n^{2\cdot 2}}$

$= \dfrac{16}{m^6 n^4}$

21. $\dfrac{24a^2 b^{-3} c^0}{30a^3 b^2 c^{-2}} = \left(\dfrac{24}{30}\right) \dfrac{c^{0-(-2)}}{a^{3-2} b^{2-(-3)}}$

$= \dfrac{4c^2}{5ab^5}$

22. $\left(\dfrac{-3x^3 y^{-2}}{x^{-1} y^5}\right)^{-3} = \left(\dfrac{-3x^{3-(-1)}}{y^{5-(-2)}}\right)^{-3}$

$= \left(\dfrac{-3x^4}{y^7}\right)^{-3}$

$= \left(\dfrac{y^7}{-3x^4}\right)^3$

$= \dfrac{y^{7\cdot 3}}{(-3)^3 x^{4\cdot 3}}$

$= -\dfrac{y^{21}}{27x^{12}}$

23. $242,000,000 = 2.42 \times 10^8$

24. $\dfrac{3.12 \times 10^6}{1.2 \times 10^{-2}} = \left(\dfrac{3.12}{1.2}\right) \times 10^{6-(-2)}$

$= 2.6 \times 10^8$

$= 260,000,000$

25. **a.** $0.542 \times 1.02 \times 10^8$

$= 5.42 \times 10^{-1} \times 1.02 \times 10^8$

$= (5.42 \times 1.02)(10^{-1} \times 10^8)$

$\approx 5.528 \times 10^7$

b. $0.458 \times 1.02 \times 10^8$

$= 4.58 \times 10^{-1} \times 1.02 \times 10^8$

$= (4.58 \times 1.02)(10^{-1} \times 10^8)$

$\approx 4.672 \times 10^7$

$5.528 \times 10^7 - 4.672 \times 10^7$

$= (5.528 - 4.672) \times 10^7$

$= 0.856 \times 10^7$

c. $= 8.56 \times 10^6$

Chapter 2

Exercise Set 2.1

1. The terms of an expression are the parts added.

3. **a.** The coefficient of $\dfrac{x+y}{4}$ or $\dfrac{1}{4}(x+y)$ is $\dfrac{1}{4}$.

    b. The coefficient of $-(x+3)$ or $-1(x+3)$ is -1.

    c. The coefficient of $-\dfrac{3(x+2)}{5}$ or $-\dfrac{3}{5}(x+2)$ is $-\dfrac{3}{5}$.

5. **a.** Like terms have the same variables and exponents.

    b. No; $3x$ and $3x^2$ are not like terms because the exponent on x is different for each term.

7. $$2x+3=x+5$$
$$2(4)+3=4+5$$
$$8+3=4+5$$
$$11 \neq 9$$

   No, 4 is not a solution to the equation because substituting 4 for x results in a false equation.

9. The addition property of equality states that if $a = b$, then $a + c = b + c$.

11. **a.** An identity has infinitely many solutions

    b. Its solution set is **R**.

13. **b.** $$5x - 2(x-4) = 2(x-2)$$
$$5x - 2x + 8 = 2x - 4$$
$$3x + 8 = 2x - 4$$
$$3x - 2x + 8 = 2x - 2x - 4$$
$$x + 8 = -4$$
$$x + 8 - 8 = -4 - 8$$
$$x = -12$$

15. Symmetric property

17. Transitive property

19. Reflexive property

21. Addition property

23. Multiplication property

25. Multiplication property

27. $5c^3$ is degree three since the exponent is 3.

29. $3xy$ is degree two since $3xy$ can be written as $3x^1y^1$ and the sum of the exponents is $1 + 1 = 2$.

31. The degree of 6 is zero since 6 can be written as $6x^0$.

33. $-5x$ is degree one since $-5x$ can be written as $-5x^1$.

35. $5a^2b^4c$ is degree seven since $5a^2b^4c$ can be written as $5a^2b^4c^1$ and the sum of the exponents is $2 + 4 + 1 = 7$.

37. $3x^5y^6z$ is degree 12 since $3x^5y^6z$ can be written as $3x^5y^6z^1$ and the sum of the exponents is $5 + 6 + 1 = 12$.

39. $7r + 3b - 11x + 12y$ cannot be simplified since all the terms are "unlike".

41. $$5x^2 - 3x + 2x - 5$$
    Combine like terms
    $$= 5x^2 - x - 5$$

43. $$10.6c^2 - 2.3c + 5.9c - 1.9c^2$$
    Combine like terms
    $$= 8.7c^2 + 3.6c$$

45. $w^3 + w^2 - w + 1$ cannot be further simplified since all of the terms are "unlike".

47. $$6pq - 7pq + p + q$$
    Combine like terms
    $$= -pq + p + q$$

49. $$12\left(\frac{1}{6} + \frac{d}{4}\right) - d$$
    Distributive property
    $$= 12 \cdot \frac{1}{6} + 12 \cdot \frac{d}{4} - d$$
    $$= \frac{12}{6} + \frac{12d}{4} - d$$
    $$= 2 + 3d - d$$

29

Combine like terms
$= 2 + 2d$

51. $3\left(x + \dfrac{1}{2}\right) - \dfrac{1}{3}x + 5$

Distributive property

$= 3x + \dfrac{3}{2} - \dfrac{1}{3}x + 5$

$= 3x - \dfrac{1}{3}x + \dfrac{3}{2} + 5$

$= \dfrac{9}{3}x - \dfrac{1}{3}x + \dfrac{3}{2} + \dfrac{10}{2}$

Combine like terms

$= \dfrac{8}{3}x + \dfrac{13}{2}$

53. $4 - [6(3x + 2) - x] + 4$

Distributive property
$= 4 - [18x + 12 - x] + 4$
Combine like terms
$= 4 - [17x - 12] + 4$
Distributive property
$= 4 - 17x - 12 + 4$
$= 4 - 12 + 4 - 17x$
Combine like terms
$= -4 - 17x$
$= -17x - 4$

55. $4x - [3x - (5x - 4y)] + y$

Distributive property
$= 4x - [3x - 5x + 4y] + y$
Combine like terms
$= 4x - [-2x + 4y] + y$
Distributive property
$= 4x + 2x - 4y + y$
Combine like terms
$= 6x - 3y$

57. $5b - \{7[2(3b - 2) - (4b + 9)] - 2\}$

Distributive property inside [ ]
$= 5b - \{7[6b - 4 - 4b - 9] - 2\}$
$= 5b - \{7[6b - 4b - 4 - 9] - 2\}$
Combine like terms
$= 5b - [7(2b - 13) - 2]$
Distributive property
$= 5b - [14b - 91 - 2]$
Combine like terms
$= 5b - (14b - 93)$
Distributive property
$= 5b - 14b + 93$
Combine like terms
$= -9b + 93$

59. $-\{[2rs - 3(r + 2s)] - 2(2r^2 - s)\}$

Distributive property
$= -\{[2rs - 3r - 6s] - 4r^2 + 2s\}$

$= -\{2rs - 3r - 6s - 4r^2 + 2s\}$
$= -(2rs - 3r - 6s + 2s - 4r^2)$
Combine like terms
$= -(2rs - 3r - 4s - 4r^2)$
Distributive property
$= -2rs + 3r + 4s + 4r^2$
$= 4r^2 - 2rs + 3r + 4s$

61. $5a - 1 = 14$

$5a - 1 + 1 = 14 + 1$

$5a = 15$

$\dfrac{5a}{5} = \dfrac{15}{5}$

$a = 3$

63. $5x - 9 = 3(x - 2)$

$5x - 9 = 3x - 6$

$5x - 9 - 3x = 3x - 6 - 3x$

$2x - 9 = -6$

$2x - 9 + 9 = -6 + 9$

$2x = 3$

$\dfrac{2x}{2} = \dfrac{3}{2}$

$x = \dfrac{3}{2}$

65. $4x - 8 = -4(2x - 3) + 4$

$4x - 8 = -8x + 12 + 4$

$4x - 8 = -8x + 16$

$4x - 8 + 8x = -8x + 16 + 8x$

$12x - 8 = 16$

$12x - 8 + 8 = 16 + 8$

$12x = 24$

$\dfrac{12x}{12} = \dfrac{24}{12}$

$x = 2$

67. $-6(z - 1) = -5(z + 2)$

$-6z + 6 = -5z - 10$

$-6z + 6 + 6z = -5z - 10 + 6z$

$6 = 1z - 10$

$6 + 10 = 1z - 10 + 10$

$16 = z$

69.
$$-3(t-5) = 2(t-5)$$
$$-3t+15 = 2t-10$$
$$-3t+15-2t = 2t-10-2t$$
$$-5t+15 = -10$$
$$-5t+15-15 = -10-15$$
$$-5t = -25$$
$$\frac{-5t}{-5} = \frac{-25}{-5}$$
$$t = 5$$

71.
$$3x+4(x-2) = 4x-5$$
$$3x+4x-8 = 4x-5$$
$$7x-8 = 4x-5$$
$$7x-8-4x = 4x-5-4x$$
$$3x-8 = -5$$
$$3x-8+8 = -5+8$$
$$3x = 3$$
$$\frac{3x}{3} = \frac{3}{3}$$
$$x = 1$$

73.
$$2-(x+5) = 4x-8$$
$$2-x-5 = 4x-8$$
$$-x-3 = 4x-8$$
$$-x-3-4x = 4x-8-4x$$
$$-5x-3 = -8$$
$$-5x-3+3 = -8+3$$
$$-5x = -5$$
$$\frac{-5x}{-5} = \frac{-5}{-5}$$
$$x = 1$$

75.
$$p-(p+4) = 4(p-1)+2p$$
$$p-p-4 = 4p-4+2p$$
$$-4 = 6p-4$$
$$-4+4 = 6p-4+4$$
$$0 = 6p$$
$$\frac{0}{6} = \frac{6p}{6}$$
$$0 = p$$

77.
$$-3(y-1)+2y = 4(y-3)$$
$$-3y+3+2y = 4y-12$$
$$-y+3 = 4y-12$$
$$-y+3+y = 4y-12+y$$
$$3 = 5y-12$$
$$3+12 = 5y-12+12$$
$$15 = 5y$$
$$\frac{15}{5} = \frac{5y}{5}$$
$$3 = y$$

79.
$$6-(n+3) = 3n+5-2n$$
$$6-n-3 = 3n+5-2n$$
$$3-n = n+5$$
$$3-n+n = n+5+n$$
$$3 = 2n+5$$
$$3-5 = 2n+5-5$$
$$-2 = 2n$$
$$\frac{-2}{2} = \frac{2n}{2}$$
$$-1 = n$$
$$n = -1$$

81.
$$4(2x-2)-3(x+7) = -4$$
$$8x-8-3x-21 = -4$$
$$5x-29 = -4$$
$$5x-29+29 = -4+29$$
$$5x = 25$$
$$\frac{5x}{5} = \frac{25}{5}$$
$$x = 5$$

83.
$$-4(3-4x)-2(x-1) = 12x$$
$$-12+16x-2x+2 = 12x$$
$$14x-10 = 12x$$
$$14x-10-14x = 12x-14x$$
$$-10 = -2x$$
$$\frac{-10}{-2} = \frac{-2x}{-2}$$
$$5 = x$$
$$x = 5$$

85.
$$5(a+3)-a = -(4a-6)+1$$
$$5a+15-a = -4a+6+1$$
$$4a+15 = -4a+7$$
$$4a+15+4a = -4a+7+4a$$
$$8a+15 = 7$$
$$8a+15-15 = 7-15$$
$$8a = -8$$
$$\frac{8a}{8} = \frac{-8}{8}$$
$$a = -1$$

87.
$$5(x-2)-14x = x-5$$
$$5x-10-14x = x-5$$
$$-9x-10 = x-5$$
$$-9x-10+9x = x-5+9x$$
$$-10 = 10x-5$$
$$-10+5 = 10x-5+5$$
$$-5 = 10x$$
$$\frac{-5}{10} = \frac{10x}{10}$$
$$-\frac{1}{2} = x$$
$$x = -\frac{1}{2}$$

89.
$$2[3x-(4x-6)] = 5(x-6)$$
$$2(3x-4x+6) = 5x-30$$
$$6x-8x+12 = 5x-30$$
$$-2x+12 = 5x-30$$
$$-2x+12+2x = 5x-30+2x$$
$$12 = 7x-30$$
$$12+30 = 7x-30+30$$
$$42 = 7x$$
$$\frac{42}{7} = \frac{7x}{7}$$
$$6 = x$$
$$x = 6$$

91.
$$6-\{4[x-(3x-4)-x]+4\} = 2(x+3)$$
$$6-[4(x-3x+4-x)+4] = 2(x+3)$$
$$6-[4(-3x+4)+4] = 2(x+3)$$
$$4\{2-[(c+1)-2(c+1)]\} = -2c$$
$$4\{2-[c+1-2c-2]\} = -2c$$
$$4\{2-[-c-1]\} = -2c$$
$$4\{2+c+1\} = -2c$$
$$4\{c+3\} = -2c$$
$$4c+12 = -2c$$
$$4c+12+2c = -2c+2c$$
$$6c+12 = 0$$
$$6c+12-12 = 0-12$$
$$6c = 12$$
$$\frac{6c}{6} = \frac{12}{6}$$
$$c = 2$$

93.
$$-\{4(d+3)-5[3d-2(2d+7)]-8\} = -10d-6$$
$$-\{4(d+3)-5[3d-4d-14]-8\} = -10d-6$$
$$-\{4(d+3)-5[-d-14]-8\} = -10d-6$$
$$-\{4d+12+5d+70-8\} = -10d-6$$
$$-\{9d+74\} = -10d-6$$
$$-9d-74 = -10d-6$$
$$-9d-74+10d = -10d-6+10d$$
$$d-74 = -6$$
$$d-74+74 = -6+74$$
$$d = 68$$

95.
$$\frac{s}{4} = -16$$
$$4\left(\frac{s}{4}\right) = 4(-16)$$
$$s = -64$$

97.
$$\frac{4x-2}{3} = -6$$
$$3\left(\frac{4x-2}{3}\right) = 3(-6)$$
$$4x - 2 = -18$$
$$4x - 2 + 2 = -18 + 2$$
$$4x = -16$$
$$\frac{4x}{4} = \frac{-16}{4}$$
$$x = -4$$

99.
$$\frac{3}{4}t + \frac{7}{8}t = 39$$
$$8\left(\frac{3}{4}t + \frac{7}{8}t\right) = 8(39)$$
$$6t + 7t = 312$$
$$13t = 312$$
$$\frac{13t}{13} = \frac{312}{13}$$
$$t = 24$$

101.
$$4 - \frac{3}{4}x = 7$$
$$4 - \frac{3}{4}x - 4 = 7 - 4$$
$$-\frac{3}{4}x = 3$$
$$-4\left(-\frac{3}{4}x\right) = -4(3)$$
$$3x = -12$$
$$\frac{3x}{3} = \frac{-12}{3}$$
$$x = -4$$

103.
$$\frac{1}{2} = \frac{4}{5}x - \frac{1}{4}$$
$$20\left(\frac{1}{2}\right) = 20\left(\frac{4}{5}x - \frac{1}{4}\right)$$
$$10 = 16x - 5$$
$$10 + 5 = 16x - 5 + 5$$
$$15 = 16x$$
$$\frac{15}{16} = \frac{16x}{16}$$
$$\frac{15}{16} = x$$

105.
$$0.4n + 4.7 = 5.1n$$
$$0.4n + 4.7 - 0.4n = 5.1n - 0.4n$$
$$4.7 = 4.7n$$
$$\frac{4.7}{4.7} = \frac{4.7n}{4.7}$$
$$1.00 = n$$

107.
$$4.7x - 3.6(x-1) = 4.9$$
$$4.7x - 3.6x + 3.6 = 4.9$$
$$1.1x + 3.6 = 4.9$$
$$1.1x + 3.6 - 3.6 = 4.9 - 3.6$$
$$1.1x = 1.3$$
$$\frac{1.1x}{1.1} = \frac{1.3}{1.1}$$
$$x \approx 1.18$$

109.
$$5(z + 3.41) = -7.89(2z - 4) - 5.67$$
$$5z + 17.05 = -15.78z + 31.56 - 5.67$$
$$5z + 17.05 = -15.78z + 25.89$$
$$15.78z + 5z + 17.05 = -15.78z + 25.89 + 15.78z$$
$$20.78z + 17.05 = 25.89$$
$$20.78z + 17.05 - 17.04 = 25.89 - 17.04$$
$$20.78z = 8.85$$
$$\frac{20.78z}{20.78} = \frac{8.85}{20.78}$$
$$z \approx 0.43$$

111.
$$0.6(500 - 2.4x) = 3.6(2x - 4000)$$
$$300 - 1.44x = 7.2x - 14,400$$
$$300 - 1.44x + 1.44x = 7.2x - 14,400 + 1.44x$$
$$300 = 8.64x - 14,400$$
$$300 + 14,400 = 8.64x - 14,400 + 14,400$$
$$14,700 = 8.64x$$
$$\frac{14,700}{8.64} = \frac{8.64x}{8.64}$$
$$1701.39 \approx x$$
$$x \approx 1701.39$$

113.
$$1000(7.34q + 14.78) = 100(3.91 - 4.21q)$$
$$7340q + 14780 = 391 - 421q$$
$$7340q + 14780 + 421q = 391 - 421q + 421q$$
$$7761q + 14780 = 391$$
$$7761q + 14780 - 14780 = 391 - 14780$$
$$7761q = -14389$$
$$\frac{7761q}{7761} = \frac{-14389}{7761}$$
$$q = -1.85$$

115.
$$3(y + 3) - 4(2y - 7) = -5y + 2$$
$$3y + 9 - 8y + 28 = -5y + 2$$
$$-5y + 37 = -5y + 2$$
$$-5y + 37 + 5y = -5y + 2 + 5y$$
$$37 = 2$$

The solution set is $\varnothing$.
The equation is a contradiction.

117.
$$4(2x - 3) + 5 = -6(x - 4) + 12x - 31$$
$$8x - 12 + 5 = -6x + 24 + 12x - 31$$
$$8x - 7 = 6x - 7$$
$$8x - 7 + 7 = 6x - 7 + 7$$
$$8x = 6x$$
$$8x - 6x = 6x - 6x$$
$$2x = 0$$
$$x = 0$$

The solution set is {0}.
The equation is conditional.

The solution set is $\{-9\}$.
The equation is conditional.

119.
$$-(-b + 7) - 6(b + 3) = -5(b + 5)$$
$$b - 7 - 6b - 18 = -5b - 25$$
$$-5b - 25 = -5b - 25$$
$$-5b - 25 + 5b = -5b - 25 + 5b$$
$$-25 = -25$$

The solution set is R.
The equation is an identity.

121.
$$6(x - 1) = -3(2 - x) + 3x$$
$$6x - 6 = -6 + 3x + 3x$$
$$6x - 6 = -6 + 6x$$
$$6x - 6 - 6x = -6 + 6x - 6x$$
$$-6 = -6$$

The solution set is R.
The equation is an identity.

123.
$$-5(d - 4) + 3d - 5 = 3(d + 1 - 2d) + d$$
$$-5d + 20 + 3d - 5 = 3d + 3 - 6d + d$$
$$-2d + 15 = -2d + 3$$
$$-2d + 15 + 2d = -2d + 3 + 2d$$
$$15 = 3$$

The solution set is $\varnothing$.
The equation is a contradiction.

125. a. For first night, substitute 1 for n.
$$W = 5n + 5$$
$$W = 5(1) + 5$$
$$W = 10$$
Wait 10 minutes the first night.

b. For fourth night, substitute 4 for n.
$$W = 5n + 5$$
$$W = 5(4) + 5$$
$$W = 25$$
Wait 25 minutes the fourth night.

c. Substitute 30 for W and solve for n.
$$W = 5n + 5$$
$$30 = 5n + 5$$
$$30 - 5 = 5n + 5 - 5$$
$$25 = 5n$$
$$\frac{25}{5} = \frac{5n}{5}$$
$$5 = n$$
Wait 30 minutes the fifth night.

d.   Substitute 40 for W and solve for n.
$$W = 5n + 5$$
$$40 = 5n + 5$$
$$40 - 5 = 5n + 5 - 5$$
$$35 = 5n$$
$$\frac{35}{5} = \frac{5n}{5}$$
$$7 = n$$
Wait 40 minutes the seventh night.

127.   a.   For 2003, substitute 10 for x.
$$M = -1.26x + 75.34$$
$$= -1.26(10) + 75.34$$
$$= -12.6 + 75.34$$
$$= 62.74$$

The percent of total cars sold in the United States made by American automakers was 62.74%.

b.
$$M = -1.26x + 75.34$$
$$58.96 = -1.26x + 75.34$$
$$-16.38 = -1.26x$$
$$x = \frac{-16.38}{-1.26}$$
$$x = 13$$
$$13 + 1993 = 2006$$

The percent of total cars sold in the United States made by American automakers will be about 58.96% in 2006.

129.   a.   For 2003, substitute 7 for x.

$$P = 7x + 2170$$
$$P = 7(7) + 2170$$
$$P = 49 + 2170$$
$$P = 2219$$

The population was 2219 in 2003.

b.   For 2240, substitute 244 for x.

$$P = 7x + 2170$$
$$2240 = 7x + 2170$$
$$2240 - 2170 = 7x + 2170 - 2170$$
$$70 = 7x$$
$$\frac{70}{7} = \frac{7x}{7}$$
$$10 = x$$

$x = 10$ represents the year 2006.

The population was 2240 in 2006.

131.   Answers may vary. Possible answer:
$$2x + 3 = 8$$
$$14x = 35$$
$$x = \frac{5}{2}$$
All three equations can be written in the form $2x = 5$.

133.   Answers may vary. One possible answer is $x + 5 = x + 3$. Make sure that the variable terms "cancel" and leave a false statement.

135.   Answers may vary. One possible answer is $\frac{5}{2}x + 7 = 6 + 2x + 4$.

137. $2(x + 5) + n = 4x - 8$
Substitute -2 for x and solve for n.
$$2(-2 + 5) + n = 4(-2) - 8$$
$$2(3) + n = -8 - 8$$
$$6 + n = -16$$
$$6 + n - 6 = -16 - 6$$
$$n = -22$$

139. $* \; \triangle - \square = \odot \;$ for $\triangle$
$* \; \triangle - \square + \square = \odot + \square$
$* \; \triangle = \odot + \square$
$$* \; \frac{\triangle}{\triangle} = \frac{\odot + \square}{\triangle}$$
$$* \; = \frac{\odot + \square}{\triangle}$$

141. $\Delta(\odot + \square) = \otimes$ for Δ

$$\frac{\Delta(\odot + \square)}{\odot + \square} = \frac{\otimes}{\odot + \square}$$

$$\Delta = \frac{\otimes}{\odot + \square}$$

143. b. The definition of absolute value is
$$|a| = \begin{cases} a \text{ if } a \geq 0 \\ -a \text{ if } a < 0 \end{cases}$$

145. $\sqrt[3]{-64} = -4$ since $(-4)^3 = -64$

Exercise Set 2.2

1. A formula is an equation that is a mathematical model of a real-life situation.

3. 1. Understand
2. Translate
3. Carry out
4. Check
5. Answer

5. a.
$$16 = 2l + 2(3)$$
$$16 = 2l + 6$$
$$16 - 6 = 2l + 6 - 6$$
$$10 = 2l$$
$$\frac{10}{2} = \frac{2l}{2}$$
$$5 = l$$

b.
$$P = 2l + 2w$$
$$P - 2w = 2l + 2w - 2w$$
$$P - 2w = 2l$$
$$\frac{P - 2w}{2} = \frac{2l}{2}$$
$$\frac{P - 2w}{2} = l$$
$$l = \frac{P - 2w}{2}$$

c. No; the same procedure was used for each solution.

d.
$$l = \frac{P - 2w}{2}$$
$$l = \frac{16 - 2(3)}{2}$$
$$l = \frac{16 - 6}{2}$$
$$l = \frac{10}{2}$$
$$l = 5$$

They are the same.
The formula and the equation are equivalent when $P = 16$ and $w = 3$.

7. $E = IR$
$$= (1.2)(100)$$
$$= 120$$

9. $R = R_1 + R_2$
$$= 100 + 200$$
$$= 300$$

11. $A = \pi r^2$
$$= \pi(8)^2$$
$$= \pi(64)$$
$$\approx 201.06$$

13. $\bar{x} = \dfrac{x_1 + x_2 + x_3}{3}$
$$= \frac{40 + 120 + 80}{3}$$
$$= \frac{240}{3}$$
$$= 80$$

15. $A = P + Prt$
$$= 200 + 200(0.05)(2)$$
$$= 200 + 20$$
$$= 220$$

17. $m = \dfrac{y_2 - y_1}{x_2 - x_1}$
$$= \frac{4 - (-3)}{-2 - (-6)}$$
$$= \frac{4 + 3}{-2 + 6}$$
$$= \frac{7}{4}$$

19.
$$RT = \frac{R_1 R_2}{R_1 + R_2}$$
$$= \frac{100 \cdot 200}{100 + 200}$$
$$= \frac{20{,}000}{300}$$
$$\approx 66.67$$

21.
$$x = \frac{-b + \sqrt{b^2 - 4ac}}{2a}$$
$$= \frac{-(-5) + \sqrt{(-5)^2 - 4(2)(-12)}}{2(2)}$$
$$= \frac{5 + \sqrt{25 + 96}}{4}$$
$$= \frac{5 + \sqrt{121}}{4}$$
$$= \frac{5 + 11}{4}$$
$$= \frac{16}{4}$$
$$= 4$$

23.
$$A = p\left(1 + \frac{r}{n}\right)^{nt}$$
$$= 100\left(1 + \frac{0.06}{1}\right)^{1 \cdot 3}$$
$$= 100(1.06)^3$$
$$= 100(1.191016)$$
$$\approx 119.10$$

25.
$$3x + y = 5$$
$$3x + y - 3x = 5 - 3x$$
$$y = 5 - 3x$$
$$\text{or}$$
$$y = -3x + 5$$

27.
$$x - 4y = 13$$
$$x - 4y - x = -x + 13$$
$$-4y = -x + 13$$
$$\frac{-4y}{-4} = \frac{-x + 13}{-4}$$
$$y = \frac{1}{4}x - \frac{13}{4}$$

29.
$$6x - 2y = 16$$
$$6x - 2y - 6x = -6x + 16$$
$$-2y = -6x + 16$$
$$\frac{-2y}{-2} = \frac{-6x + 16}{-2}$$
$$y = 3x - 8$$

31.
$$\frac{3}{4}x - y = 1$$
$$4\left(\frac{3}{4}x - y\right) = 4 \cdot 1$$
$$3x - 4y = 4$$
$$3x - 4y - 3x = -3x + 4$$
$$-4y = -3x + 4$$
$$\frac{-4y}{-4} = \frac{-3x + 4}{-4}$$
$$y = \frac{3}{4}x - 1$$

33.
$$3(x - 2) + 3y = 6x$$
$$3x - 6 + 3y = 6x$$
$$3x - 6 + 3y - 3x = 6x - 3x$$
$$-6 + 3y = 3x$$
$$-6 + 3y + 6 = 3x + 6$$
$$3y = 3x + 6$$
$$\frac{3y}{3} = \frac{3x + 6}{3}$$
$$y = x + 2$$

35.
$$y + 1 = -\frac{4}{3}(x - 9)$$
$$3[y + 1] = 3\left[-\frac{4}{3}(x - 9)\right]$$
$$3y + 3 = -4(x - 9)$$
$$3y + 3 = -4x + 36$$
$$3y + 3 - 3 = -4x + 36 - 3$$
$$3y =$$
$$\frac{3y}{3} = \frac{-4x + 33}{3}$$
$$y = -\frac{4}{3} + 11$$

37. $d = rt$

$$\frac{d}{r} = \frac{rt}{r}$$

$$\frac{d}{r} = t \text{ or } t = \frac{d}{r}$$

39. $i = prt$

$$\frac{i}{pr} = \frac{prt}{pr}$$

$$\frac{i}{pr} = t \text{ or } t = \frac{i}{pr}$$

41. $P = 2l + 2w$

$$P - 2w = 2l + 2w - 2w$$

$$P - 2w = 2l$$

$$\frac{P - 2w}{2} = \frac{2l}{2}$$

$$\frac{P - 2w}{2} = l \text{ or } l = \frac{P - 2w}{2}$$

43. $V = lwh$

$$\frac{V}{lw} = \frac{lwh}{lw}$$

$$\frac{V}{lw} = h \text{ or } h = \frac{V}{lw}$$

45. $V = \pi r^2 h$

$$\frac{V}{\pi r^2} = \frac{\pi r^2 h}{\pi r^2}$$

$$\frac{V}{\pi r^2} = h \text{ or } h = \frac{V}{\pi r^2}$$

47. $V = \frac{1}{3}lwh$

$$3V = 3\left(\frac{1}{3}lwh\right)$$

$$3V = lwh$$

$$\frac{3V}{wh} = \frac{lwh}{wh}$$

$$\frac{3V}{wh} = l \text{ or } l = \frac{3v}{wh}$$

49. $y = mx + b$

$$y - b = mx + b - b$$

$$y - b = mx$$

$$\frac{y - b}{x} = \frac{mx}{x}$$

$$\frac{y - b}{x} = m \text{ or } m = \frac{y - b}{x}$$

51. $y - y_1 = m(x - x_1)$

$$\frac{y - y_1}{x - x_1} = \frac{m(x - x_1)}{x - x_1}$$

$$\frac{y - y_1}{x - x_1} = m \text{ or } m = \frac{y - y_1}{x - x_1}$$

53. $z = \dfrac{x - \mu}{\sigma}$

$$\sigma z = \sigma\left(\frac{x - \mu}{\sigma}\right)$$

$$\sigma z = x - \mu$$

$$\sigma z - x = x - \mu - x$$

$$\sigma z - x = -\mu \quad \text{or} \quad \mu = x - z\sigma$$

$$x - \sigma z = \mu$$

55. $P_1 = \dfrac{T_1 P_2}{T_2}$

$$T_2 P_1 = T_2\left(\frac{T_1 P_2}{T_2}\right)$$

$$T_2 P_1 = T_1 P_2$$

$$\frac{T_2 P_1}{P_1} = \frac{T_1 P_2}{P_1}$$

$$T_2 = \frac{T_1 P_2}{P_1}$$

57. $A = \dfrac{1}{2}h(b_1 + b_2)$

$$2A = 2\left[\frac{1}{2}h(b_1 + b_2)\right]$$

$$2A = h(b_1 + b_2)$$

$$\frac{2A}{b_1 + b_2} = \frac{h(b_1 + b_2)}{b_1 + b_2}$$

$$\frac{2A}{b_1 + b_2} = h \text{ or } h = \frac{2A}{b_1 + b_2}$$

59.
$$S = \frac{n}{2}(f + l)$$
$$2S = 2\left[\frac{n}{2}(f + l)\right]$$
$$2S = n(f + l)$$
$$\frac{2S}{f + l} = \frac{n(f + l)}{f + l}$$
$$\frac{2S}{f + l} = n \text{ or } n = \frac{2S}{f + l}$$

61.
$$C = \frac{5}{9}(F - 32)$$
$$\frac{9}{5}C = \frac{9}{5} \cdot \frac{5}{9}(F - 32)$$
$$\frac{9}{5}C = F - 32$$
$$\frac{9}{5}C + 32 = F - 32 + 32$$
$$\frac{9}{5}C + 32 = F \text{ or } F = \frac{9}{5}C + 32$$

63.
$$F = \frac{km_1 m_2}{d^2}$$
$$Fd^2 = d^2\left(\frac{km_1 m_2}{d^2}\right)$$
$$Fd^2 = km_1 m_2$$
$$\frac{Fd^2}{km_2} = \frac{km_1 m_2}{km_2}$$
$$\frac{Fd^2}{km_2} = m_1 \text{ or } m_1 = \frac{Fd^2}{km_2}$$

65. a. Let d = U.S. dollars, and p = Mexican pesos.
Then $p = 9.15d$.

    b. Solve $p = 9.15d$ for d.
$$p = 9.15d$$
$$\frac{p}{9.15} = \frac{9.15d}{9.15}$$
$$\frac{p}{9.15} = d \text{ or } d = \frac{p}{9.15}$$

    c. Answers will vary.

67.
$$i = prt$$
$$= 550(0.07)(4)$$
$$= 154$$
Paul must pay \$154 in simple interest.

69.
$$i = prt$$
$$4875 = (20000)(.0375)t$$
$$4875 = 750t$$
$$\frac{4875}{750} = \frac{750t}{750}$$
$$6.5 = t$$
The length of the loan was 6.5 years.

71. a.
$$A = \pi r^2$$
$$= \pi(1)^2$$
$$\approx 3.14 \text{ square inches}$$

    b.
$$A = \pi r^2$$
$$= \pi(5)^2$$
$$= 25\pi$$
$$\approx 78.54 \text{ square inches.}$$

73. a. 6 inches is 0.5 feet.
$$V = lwh$$
$$= 15(10)(0.5)$$
$$= 75 \text{ cubic feet}$$

    b. $\dfrac{75}{27} \approx 2.78$ cubic yards

    c. To get 2.78 cubic yards of concrete,
3 cubic yards must be purchased.
$3(\$35) = \$105$

75. The volume of a cylinder is given by $V = \pi r^2 h$.
Note that the radius is half the diameter so the
radius is 2.5 inches.

$$V = \pi r^2 h$$
$$= \pi(2.5)^2(6.25)$$
$$\approx 122.72 \text{ cubic inches}$$

For the volume of the box:

$$V = lwh$$
$$= (7)(5)(3.5)$$
$$= 122.5 \text{ cubic inches}$$

The cylinder has greater volume by about
$122.72 - 122.5 = 0.22$ cubic inches.

77. $A = p\left(1+\dfrac{r}{n}\right)^{nt}$

$= 10{,}000\left(1+\dfrac{0.06}{4}\right)^{4\cdot 2}$

$= 10{,}000(1.015)^8$

$\approx 11{,}264.93$

Beth will have $11,264.93 in her account.

79. Note that 36 months is 3 years so $t = 3$.

$A = p\left(1+\dfrac{r}{n}\right)^{nt}$

$= 4390\left(1+\dfrac{0.041}{2}\right)^{(2)(3)}$

$= 4390(1+0.0205)^6$

$= 4390(1.0205)^6$

≈ 4958.41

The certificate will be worth $4958.41 after 36 months.

81. $T_f = T_a(1-F)$

$0.035 = T_a(1-0.15)$

$0.035 = T_a(0.85)$

$\dfrac{0.035}{0.85} = T_a$

$T_a \approx 0.0412$

The equivalent taxable rate is 4.12%.

83. a. The 4.6% tax-free rate for Carlos:

$T_f = T_a(1-F)$

$0.046 = T_a(1-0.386)$

$0.046 = T_a(0.614)$

$\dfrac{0.046}{0.614} = T_a$

$T_a \approx 0.0749 = 7.49\%$

b. The 4.6% tax-free rate for Antonio:

$T_f = T_a(1-F)$

$0.046 = T_a(1-0.27)$

$0.046 = T_a(0.73)$

$\dfrac{0.046}{0.73} = T_a$

$T_a \approx 0.0630 = 6.30\%$

85. $w = 0.02c$

a. $c = 2600 - 2400 = 200$

$w = 0.02(200)$

$= 4$

Her weekly weight loss is 4 pounds per week.

b. $2 = 0.02c$

$\dfrac{2}{0.02} = c$

$c = 100$

$2400 + 100 = 2500$

She would have to burn 2500 calories per day to lose 2 pounds in a week.

87. a. $S = 100 - a$

b. $S = 100 - 60 = 40$

A 60-year-old should keep 40% in stocks.

89. $r = \dfrac{\frac{s}{t}}{\frac{t}{u}} = \dfrac{s}{t} \div \dfrac{t}{u} = \dfrac{s}{t} \cdot \dfrac{u}{t} = \dfrac{su}{t^2}$

In simplified form, it is $r = \dfrac{su}{t^2}$

a. $r = \dfrac{su}{t^2}$

$rt^2 = t^2\left(\dfrac{su}{t^2}\right)$

$rt^2 = su$

$\dfrac{rt^2}{u} = \dfrac{su}{u}$

$\dfrac{rt^2}{u} = s$ or $s = \dfrac{rt^2}{u}$

b. $r = \dfrac{su}{t^2}$

$rt^2 = t^2\left(\dfrac{su}{t^2}\right)$

$rt^2 = su$

$\dfrac{rt^2}{s} = \dfrac{su}{s}$

$\dfrac{rt^2}{s} = u$ or $u = \dfrac{rt^2}{s}$

91.
$$\frac{7+9\div\left(2^3+4\div4\right)}{|3-7|+\sqrt{5^2-3^2}}=\frac{7+9\div\left(8+4\div4\right)}{|3-7|+\sqrt{25-9}}$$
$$=\frac{7+9\div\left(8+1\right)}{|-4|+\sqrt{16}}$$
$$=\frac{7+9\div9}{4+4}$$
$$=\frac{7+1}{4+4}$$
$$=\frac{8}{8}$$
$$=1$$

93.
$$\frac{1}{4}t+\frac{1}{2}=1-\frac{1}{8}t$$
$$8\left(\frac{1}{4}t+\frac{1}{2}\right)=8\left(1-\frac{1}{8}t\right)$$
$$2t+4=8-t$$
$$2t+4+t=8-t+t$$
$$3t+4=8$$
$$3t+4-4=8-4$$
$$3t=4$$
$$\frac{3t}{3}=\frac{4}{3}$$
$$t=\frac{4}{3}$$

Exercise Set 2.3

1. Let $x=$ measure of angle B

$4x=$ measure of angle A

measure of angle A + measure of angle B = $90°$

$4x+x=90$

$5x=90$

$x=18$

Angle B is $18°$ and angle A is $4\times18°=72°$.

3.
$$B=4A$$
$$A+B=180$$
$$A+4A=180$$
$$5A=180$$
$$A=36$$
$$B=4A=4(36)=144$$
The measure of angle A is $36°$ and B is $144°$.

5. Let $x=$ smallest angle, then
$x+20=$ second angle
$2x=$ third angle
$$x+x+20+2x=180$$
$$4x+20=180$$
$$4x=160$$
$$x=40$$
$$x+20=40+20=60$$
$$2x=2(40)=80$$
The measures of the angles are $40°$, $60°$, and $80°$.

7. Let $x=$ the cost of the regular subscription.
$$x-0.25x=24$$
$$0.75x=24$$
$$\frac{0.75x}{0.75}=\frac{24}{0.75}$$
$$x=32$$

The cost of the original subscription was $32.

9. Let $x=$ number of rides.
$$1.80x=45$$
$$\frac{1.80x}{1.80}=\frac{45}{1.80}$$
$$x=25 \text{ rides}$$
Kate would need to ride the bus 25 times per month.

11. Let $n=$ number of miles.
$$0.20n+35=80$$
$$0.20n=45$$
$$\frac{0.20n}{0.20}=\frac{45}{0.20}$$
$$n=225 \text{ miles}$$
Tanya can drive 255 miles.

13. Let x = maximum price
$$x+0.04225x=650$$
$$1.04225x=650$$
$$x\approx623.65$$

The maximum price they can spend is $623.65.

15.   Let x = the number of golfing trips.

The cost of a social membership:

$50x + 25x + 1775 = 75x + 1775$

The cost of a golf membership:

$25x + 2425$

Set these two expressions equal to each other and solve for x.

$75x + 1775 = 25x + 2425$

$75x + 1775 - 25x = 25x + 2425 - 25x$

$50x + 1775 = 2425$

$50x + 1775 - 1775 = 2425 - 1775$

$50x = 650$

$x = 13$

He must go golfing 13 times per year for the two options to cost the same amount.

17. Let x = assets of SUI, then $2.7x$ = the assets of WMC.

$x + 2.7x = 636.4$

$3.7x = 636.4$

$x = 172$

$2.7x \rightarrow 2.7(172) = 464.4$

The assets of the SUI fund were about $172 million and the assets of the WMC fund were about $464.4 million.

19. Let x = the amount in billions of dollars spent by NASA on SAT, then $x + 0.10$ = the amount in billions of dollars spent by NASA on HSF. The total spent on SAT and HSF is 99.8% of $14.51 billion or (0.998)(14.51) billion dollars.

$x + (x + 0.10) = (0.998)(14.51)$

$2x + 0.10 = 14.48098$

$2x + 0.10 - 0.10 = 14.48098 - 0.10$

$2x = 14.38098$

$x \approx 7.19$

$x + 0.10 \rightarrow 7.19 + 0.10 = 7.29$

The amount spent on SAT was about $7.19 billion and the amount spent on HSF was about $7.29 billion.

21. Let x = stress steel can withstand. Then $3x + 6000$ = the stress a bone.

$(3x + 6000) - x = 18,000$

$2x + 6000 = 18,000$

$2x = 12,000$

$\dfrac{2x}{2} = \dfrac{12,000}{2}$

$x = 6000 \ \text{lb} / \text{in}^2$

The stress steel can withstand is 6000 lb/in^2 and the stress a bone can withstand is

$3(6000) + 6000 = 18,000 + 6000$

$= 24,000 \ \text{lb} / \text{in}^2$

23. Let x = price of lunch. Note that the tip is 15% of cost of the *meal plus the tax*. So the tip is $0.15(x + 0.07x)$.

$x + 0.07x + 0.15(x + 0.07x) = 20.00$

$x + 0.07x + 0.15x + 0.0105x = 20.00$

$1.2305x = 20.00$

$x \approx 16.25$

The maximum price of the lunch she can order is $16.25.

25. a. Let x = the pretax price of gasoline.

$m + 0.251m = 50.8$

$x + 0.68x = 4.29$

$1.68x = 4.29$

$x \approx 2.55$

The pretax price of gasoline was $2.55.

b. The amount spent on taxes per gallon is $4.29 - $2.55 = $1.74.

27. Since all of the metal counts seem to be described in terms of Australia's count, let x = the number of metals won by Australia. The other countries' metal counts can be described as follows:

   U.S. $\rightarrow 2x - 19$

   Russia $\rightarrow 2x - 28$

   China $\rightarrow x + 1$

   Germany $\rightarrow x - 1$

   We know that the total number of metals won by these countries was 359, therefore

   $x + (2x - 19) + (2x - 28) + (x + 1) + (x - 1) = 359$

   $7x - 47 = 359$

   $7x = 406$

   $x = 58 \rightarrow$ Autralia won 58 metals.

   U.S. $\rightarrow 2(58) - 19 = 97$ metals

   Russia $\rightarrow 2(58) - 28 = 88$ metals

   China $\rightarrow (58) + 1 = 59$ metals

   Germany $\rightarrow (58) - 1 = 57$ metals

29. Let m = the average monthly rent in 2001.

   $m + 0.133m = 1199$

   $1.133m = 1199$

   $m \approx 1058.25$

   The average monthly rent for a two-bedroom apartment in 2001 was about $1058.25.

31. **a.** Let x = number of months (or monthly payments) necessary for the accumulated payments under the original mortgage plan to equal the accumulated payments and closing cost under the other plan.

   $510x = 420.50x + 2500$

   $89.50x = 2500$

   $\dfrac{89.50x}{89.50} = \dfrac{2500}{89.50}$

   $x \approx 28$

   In about 28 months or 2.33 years, he would have paid the same amount under either plan.

   b. Yes, any time after 2.33 years makes the refinancing worth it.

33. Let s = the length of the smaller side. The lengths of the other two sides are $(s + 3)$ and $(2s - 3)$.

   The perimeter is the sum of the sides.

   $s + (s + 3) + (2s - 3) = 36$

   $4s = 36$

   $s = 9$

   The length of the smaller side is 9 in. The lengths of the other two sides are $(9 + 3) = 12$ in. and $(2(9) - 3) = 18 - 3 = 15$ in.

35. Let x = the measure of the smallest angle in degrees. The other two angle measurements are $(x + 12)$ and $(3x - 27)$. The sum of the measures of the interior angles is 180°, so

   $x + (x + 12) + (3x - 27) = 180$

   $5x - 15 = 180$

   $5x = 195$

   $x = 39$

   The smallest angle is 39°. The other angles are $39° + 12° = 51°$ and $3(39°) - 27° = 90°$.

37. Let x = the width. Then, $x + 3$ = length and since the perimeter is 22 feet, the equation is

   $P = 2l + 2w$

   $22 = 2(x + 3) + 2x$

   $22 = 2x + 6 + 2x$

   $22 = 4x + 6$

   $16 = 4x$

   $\dfrac{16}{4} = \dfrac{4x}{4}$

   $4 = x$

   The width is 4 feet and the length is $4 + 3 = 7$ feet.

39. Let h = height of each bookshelf. Then $h + 3$ is the width.

   $2h + 4(h + 3) = 30$

   $2h + 4h + 12 = 30$

   $6h = 18$

   $h = 3$

   $h + 3 = 6$

   The width is 6 feet and the height is 3 feet.

41. Let p = the original price of the calculator.

   $p - 0.10p - 5 = 49$

   $0.90p - 5 = 49$

   $0.90p = 54$

   $\dfrac{0.90p}{0.90} = \dfrac{54}{0.90}$

   $p = 60$

   The original price of the calculator was $60.

43. a. Let x = the original price of the kitchen.
Toys"R" Us sale price $\rightarrow x - 0.37x = 0.63x$

Wal-Mart sale price $\rightarrow x - 50$

These are equal so:

$x - 50 = 0.63x$

$x - 50 - 0.63x = 0.63x - 0.63x$

$0.37x - 50 = 0$

$0.37x = 50$

$x \approx 135.14$
The original price of the kitchen was
$135.14.

b. The sale price was $135.14 - $50 or $85.14.

45. Let x = energy cost.
$(9.75 + 73) - (20 + x) = 46.75$
$9.75 + 73 - 20 - x = 46.75$
$62.75 - x = 46.75$
$-x = -16$
$x = 16$
The energy cost is $16.

47. Let x = number of animals. Then $x + 100{,}000$ = number of plants,
$x + 290{,}000$ = number of non-beetle insects, and
$2x - 140{,}000$ = number of beetles.
$x + (x + 100{,}000) + (x + 290{,}000) + (2x - 140{,}000)$
$= 5x + 250{,}000$

$5x + 250{,}000 = 1{,}500{,}000$

$5x = 1{,}250{,}000$

$\dfrac{5x}{5} = \dfrac{1{,}250{,}000}{5}$

$x = 250{,}000$

There are 250,000 animal species. 250,000 + 100,000 = 350,000 plant species,
250,000 + 290,000 = 540,000 non-beetle insect species, and
2(250,000) – 140,000 = 360,000 beetle species

49. a. Let x be the score for the final exam.
$$\frac{70 + 83 + 97 + 84 + 74 + x + x}{7} = 80$$
$$\frac{408 + 2x}{7} = 80$$
$$7\left(\frac{408 + 2x}{7}\right) = 7(80)$$
$$408 + 2x = 560$$
$$2x = 152$$
$$\frac{2x}{x} = \frac{152}{2}$$
$$x = 76$$
Philip needs to score 76 points on the final exam to have an average score of 80 points.

b. Again, let x be the score for the final exam.
$$\frac{70 + 83 + 97 + 84 + 74 + 2x}{7} = 90$$
$$\frac{408 + 2x}{7} = 90$$
$$7\left(\frac{408 + 2x}{7}\right) = 7(90)$$
$$408 + 2x = 630$$
$$2x = 222$$
$$\frac{2x}{x} = \frac{222}{2}$$
$$x = 111$$
No, in order to have a final average of 90, Philip will need a score of 111 on the final exam. Since this is impossible, he must settle for a final grade lower than 90.

51. Answers will vary.

53. Let x = number of miles driven.
$3(28) + 0.15x + 0.04[3(28) + 0.15x] = 121.68$
Original Charge   4% Sales Tax
$84 + 0.15x + 0.04(84 + 0.15x) = 121.68$
$84 + 0.15x + 3.36 + 0.006x = 121.68$
$87.36 + 0.156x = 121.68$
$0.156x = 34.32$
$\dfrac{0.156x}{0.156} = \dfrac{34.32}{0.156}$
$x = 220$
Denise drove a total of 220 miles during the three days.

55. $2 + \left|-\dfrac{3}{5}\right| = 2 + \dfrac{3}{5} = \dfrac{10}{5} + \dfrac{3}{5} = \dfrac{13}{5}$

57. $\left|-\dfrac{5}{8}\right| \div |-2| = \dfrac{5}{8} \div 2 = \dfrac{5}{8} \cdot \dfrac{1}{2} = \dfrac{5}{16}$

59. $\left(2x^4 y^{-6}\right)^{-3} = 2^{-3}\left(x^4\right)^{-3}\left(y^{-6}\right)^{-3}$
$= \dfrac{1}{8}x^{-12}y^{18}$
$= \dfrac{y^{18}}{8x^{12}}$

Exercise Set 2.4

1.

	Rate	Time	Distance
Don	5	1.2	$5(1.2)$
Judy	4.5	1.2	$4.5(1.2)$

distance $= 5(1.2) + 4.5(1.2)$
$= 6 + 5.4$
$= 11.4$
The distance around the lake is 11.4 miles

3. Let t = time in hours

Balloon	Rate	Time	Distance
1	16	t	$16t$
2	14	t	$14t$

distance apart = balloon 1 dist. − balloon 2 dist.
$4 = 16t - 14t$
$4 = 2t$
$2 = t$
It will take 2 hours for the balloons to be 4 miles apart.

5. Let t = the time each are gleaning

	Rate	Time	Distance
Rodney	0.15	t	$0.15t$
Dennis	0.10	t	$0.10t$

$0.15t + 0.10t = 1.5$
$0.25t = 1.5$
$t = 6$
Rodney and Dennis will meet after 6 hours.

7. a. Let r = Wayne's speed

	Rate	Time	Distance
Laura	$2r$	3	$(2r)(3)$
Wayne	r	3	$3r$

After 3 hours, Laura is 18 miles ahead of Wayne:
$(2r)(3) = 3r + 18$
$6r = 3r + 18$
$3r = 18$
$r = 6$
Wayne's speed is 6 miles per hour.

b. Laura's speed is $2(6) = 12$ miles per hour.

9. a. Let t = time to reach bottom of canyon

	Rate	Time	Distance
Trip down	3.4	t	$3.4t$
Trip Up	1.2	$12 - t$	$1.2(12 - t)$

distance down = distance up
$3.4t = 1.2(12 - t)$
$3.4t = 14.4 - 1.2t$
$4.6t = 14.4$
$t \approx 3.13$
It took her about 3.13 hours to reach the bottom of the canyon.

b. total distance $= 2(\text{distance down})$
$= 2(3.4 \cdot 3.13)$
$= 2(10.642)$
$= 21.284$
The total distance traveled is about 21.3 miles.

11. Let t = time of operation for smaller machine

	Rate	Time	Amount
Smaller machine	400	t	$400t$
Larger machine	600	$t+2$	$600(t+2)$

$$400t + 600(t+2) = 15,000$$
$$400t + 600t + 1200 = 15,000$$
$$1000t = 13,800$$
$$t = 13.8$$

The smaller machine operated for 13.8 hours.

13. Let t = time needed for the parents to catch up with Lavon.

	Rate	Time	Distance
Parents	50	t	$50t$
Therese	35	$t+0.25$	$35(t+0.25)$

Since the distances traveled are the same,
$$50t = 35(t+0.25)$$
$$50t = 35t + 8.75$$
$$15t = 8.75$$
$$t = 0.58\overline{3} \text{ hours or 35 minutes}$$

It took the parents 35 minutes to catch Lavon.

15. Let x = amount invested at 3%. Assume that the interest is earned over a one-year period.

Account	Principal	Rate	Time	Interest
3%	x	0.03	1	$0.03x$
4.1%	$30,000 - x$	0.041	1	$0.041(30,000 - x)$

The total interest is $1091.73.
$$0.03x + 0.041(30000 - x) = 1091.73$$
$$0.03x + 1230 - 0.041x = 1091.73$$
$$-0.011x + 1230 = 1091.73$$
$$-.011x = -138.27$$
$$x = 12570$$

Thus, $12,570 was invested at 3% and the remaining amount of $30,000 – $12,570 = $17,430 was invested at 4.1%.

17. Let x = pounds of Kona coffee

Item	Cost	Pounds	Total
Kona	6.20	x	$6.20x$
Amaretto	5.80	18	$5.80(18)$
Mixture	6.10	$18+x$	$6.10(18+x)$

$$6.20x + 5.80(18) = 6.10(18 + x)$$
$$6.2x + 104.4 = 109.8 + 6.1x$$
$$0.1x = 5.4$$
$$x = 54$$

She should mix 54 pounds of Kona coffee with the amaretto coffee.

19. a. Let x = the number of shares invested in Johnson & Johnson stock.

	# of Shares	Price/Share	Total Value
J & J	x	56.88	$56.88x$
AOL	$2x$	27.36	$27.36(2x)$

The total amount invested is $250,000.
$$56.88x + 27.36(2x) = 250000$$
$$56.88x + 54.72x = 250000$$
$$111.6x = 250000$$
$$x \approx 2200 \text{ (to the nearest hundred)}$$
Bart should buy 2200 shares of Johnson & Johnson and 2(2200) = 4400 shares of AOL.

b. Bart's total purchase is

$$(2200)(\$56.88) + (4400)(\$27.36)$$
$$\$125,136 + \$120,384$$
$$\$245,520$$
Bart will have $250,000 - $245,520 = $4,480 left over after the purchase.

21. Let x = ounces of 12% solution

Solution	Strength	Ounces	Acid
Mail	12%	x	$0.12x$
Store	5%	40	$0.05(40)$
Mixture	8%	$x + 40$	$0.08(x + 40)$

$$0.12x + 0.05(40) = 0.08(x + 40)$$
$$0.12x + 2 = 0.08x + 3.2$$
$$0.04x = 1.2$$
$$x = 30$$
She should mix 30 ounces of the 12% vinegar.

23. Let x = number of teaspoons of 30% sauce.

Sauce	Strength	Teaspoons	Acid
#1	30%	x	$0.30x$
#2	80%	$4 - x$	$0.80(4 - x)$
Mixture	45%	4	$0.45(4)$

$$0.30x + 0.80(4 - x) = 0.45(4)$$
$$0.30x + 3.2 - 0.80x = 1.8$$
$$-0.50x = -1.4$$
$$x = 2.8$$
She should use 2.8 teaspoons of the 30% sauce and 4 − 2.8 = 1.2 teaspoons of the 80% sauce.

25. Let x = strength of the second solution.

Solution	Strength of Solution	No. of Milliliters	Amount
20%	0.20	200	0.20(200)
Unknown	x	100	$x(100)$
25%	0.25	300	0.25(300)

$$0.20(200) + x(100) = 0.25(300)$$
$$40 + 100x = 75$$
$$100x = 35$$
$$x = \frac{35}{100} = 0.35 \text{ or } 35\%$$

The strength of the unknown solution is 35%.

27. Let x = number of pounds of the striped sunflower seeds.

Type	Cost	No. of Pounds	Amount
Striped	$1.20	x	$1.20x$
Black	$1.60	$20 - x$	$1.60(20 - x)$
Mixture	$\frac{30}{20} = \$1.50$	20	30

$$1.20x + 1.60(20 - x) = 30$$
$$1.20x + 32 - 1.60x = 30$$
$$-0.40x + 32 = 30$$
$$-0.40x = -2$$
$$x = \frac{-2}{-0.40} = 5$$

5 pounds of the striped sunflower seeds should be mixed with $20 - 5 = 15$ pounds of the black oil sunflower seeds to produce the desired mixture.

29. Let t = time (in hours) before they meet.

	Rate	Time	Distance
Judy	45	t	$45t$
Kamilia	50	t	$50t$

Their combined distances are 2448 miles.
$$45t + 50t = 2448$$
$$95t = 2448$$
$$t \approx 25.77$$

They will meet after about 25.77 hours.

31. Let x = time needed for both pumps to empty the pool.

Pump	Rate	Time	Amount Pumped
1	10	t	$10t$
2	20	t	$20t$

The total amount of water pumped is 15,000 gallons.
$$10t + 20t = 15,000$$
$$30t = 15,000$$
$$t = \frac{15,000}{30} = 500 \text{ minutes}$$

It will take the pumps 500 minutes or $\frac{500}{60} = 8\frac{1}{3}$ hours to empty the pool.

33. Let x = amount of pure antifreeze to be added.

Type	Strength of Solution	No. of Quarts	Amount
Pure	1.00	x	$1.00x$
20%	0.20	10	$0.20(10)$
Mixture	0.50	$x + 10$	$0.50(x + 10)$

$$1.00x + 0.20(10) = 0.50(x + 10)$$
$$1.00x + 2 = 0.50x + 5$$
$$0.50x = 3$$
$$x = \frac{3}{0.50} = 6$$

Dureen Kelly should add 6 quarts of pure antifreeze to 10 quarts of 20% antifreeze to produce a mixture (solution) of 16 quarts of 50% antifreeze.

35. a. Let t = time before the jets meet.

	Rate	Time	Distance
Jet	800	t	$800t$
Refueling plane	520	$t + 2$	$520(t + 2)$

The distances traveled are equal.
$$800t = 520(t + 2)$$
$$800t = 520t + 1040$$
$$280t = 1040$$
$$t \approx 3.7143$$

The two planes will meet in approximately 3.71 hours.

b. $800t = 800(3.7143) = 2971.44$
The refueling will take place approximately 2971.4 miles from the base.

37. Let x = number of small paintings sold.

Item	Cost	Number	Amount
Small	60	x	$60x$
Large	180	$12 - x$	$180(12 - x)$

$$60x + 180(12 - x) = 1200$$
$$60x + 2160 - 180x = 1200$$
$$-120x = -960$$
$$x = 8$$
$$12 - x = 4$$

Peter Paul Rubin sold 8 small paintings and 4 large paintings.

39. Let x = amount of 80% solution needed.

Solution	Strength of Solution	No. of Ounces	Amount of Alcohol
80%	0.80	x	$0.80x$
Water	0	$128 - x$	$0(128 - x)$
6%	0.06	128	$0.06(128)$

$$0.80x + 0(128 - x) = 0.06(128)$$
$$0.80x = 7.68$$
$$x = \frac{7.68}{0.80} = 9.6$$

Herb should combine 9.6 ounces of the 80% solution with $128 - 9.6 = 118.4$ ounces of water to produce the desired solution.

41. Let x = amount of sirloin needed.

Type	Fat	No. of Ounces	Total Fat
Sirloin	1.2	x	$1.2x$
Veal	0.3	$64 - x$	$0.3(64 - x)$
Mixture	0.8	64	$0.8(64)$

$$1.2x + 0.3(64 - x) = 0.8(64)$$
$$1.2x + 19.2 - 0.3x = 51.2$$
$$0.9x + 19.2 = 51.2$$
$$0.9x = 32$$
$$x = \frac{32}{0.9} \approx 35.6$$

Sybil must combine about 35.6 ounces of sirloin with about $64 - 35.6 = 28.4$ ounces of veal to produce the desired meatloaf.

43. Let r = the rate Tyrone rides his bike.

Type	Rate	Time	Distance
Bike	r	$\frac{3}{4}$	$\frac{3}{4}r$
Car	$r + 14$	$\frac{1}{6}$	$\frac{1}{6}(r + 14)$

Both distances are the same.
$$\frac{1}{6}(r + 14) = \frac{3}{4}r$$
$$12\left[\frac{1}{6}(r + 14)\right] = 12\left(\frac{3}{4}r\right)$$
$$2(r + 14) = 3(3r)$$
$$2r + 28 = 9r$$
$$28 = 7r$$
$$\frac{28}{7} = r \text{ or } r = 4$$

The distance is $\frac{3}{4}r = \frac{3}{4}(4) = 3$ miles.

45. Let x = amount of water that needs to evaporate.
$$64(37) = 45(64 - x)$$
$$2368 = 2880 - 45x$$
$$-512 = -45x$$
$$\frac{-512}{-45} = x \text{ or } x \approx 11.4$$

About 11.4 ounces of water must evaporate to raise the salinity of the solution.

47. Answers will vary.

49. It is possible to determine the times for the 2nd and 3rd parts of the trip.

2nd Part: $t = \dfrac{d}{r} = \dfrac{31}{90} \approx 0.344$ hour

3rd Part: $t = \dfrac{d}{r} = \dfrac{68}{45} \approx 1.511$ hours

The time for the first part (Paris to Calais) is $3.000 - 0.344 - 1.511 = 1.145$ hours. The distance is
(130 mph)(1.145 hours) $\approx$ 149 miles

51. Let x be the amount of 20% solution which must be drained. Then, $16 - x$ is the amount remaining.

$$0.20(16 - x) + 1.00x = 0.50(16)$$
$$3.2 - 0.20x + 1.00x = 8$$
$$3.2 + 0.80x = 8$$
$$0.80x = 4.8$$
$$x = \frac{4.8}{0.80} = 6$$

Thus, 6 quarts must be drained before adding the same amount of antifreeze.

53.
$$0.6x + 0.22 = 0.4(x - 2.3)$$
$$0.6x + 0.22 = 0.4x - 0.92$$
$$0.6x - 0.4x + 0.22 = 0.4x - 0.4x - 0.92$$
$$0.2x + 0.22 = -0.92$$
$$0.2x + 0.22 - 0.22 = -0.92 - 0.22$$
$$0.2x = -1.14$$
$$\frac{0.2x}{0.2} = \frac{-1.14}{0.2}$$
$$x = -5.7$$

55.
$$\frac{3}{5}(x - 2) = \frac{2}{7}(2x + 3y)$$
$$35\left[\frac{3}{5}(x - 2)\right] = 35\left[\frac{2}{7}(2x + 3y)\right]$$
$$21(x - 2) = 10(2x + 3y)$$
$$21x - 42 = 20x + 30y$$
$$21x - 20x - 42 = 20x - 20x + 30y$$
$$x - 42 = 30y$$
$$\frac{x - 42}{30} = \frac{30y}{30}$$
$$\frac{x - 42}{30} = y \text{ or } y = \frac{x - 42}{30}$$

Exercise Set 2.5

1. It is necessary to change the direction of the inequality symbol when multiplying or dividing by a negative number.

3. a. Use open circles when the endpoints are not included.

   b. Use closed circles when the endpoints are included.

   c. Answers may vary. One possible answer is $x < 4$.

d. Answers may vary. One possible answer is $x \geq 4$.

5. $a < x < b$ means $a < x$ and $x < b.$.

7. a.
-2

   b. $(-2, \infty)$

   c. $\{x|x > -2\}$

9. a.
p

   b. $(-\infty, \pi]$

   c. $\{w|w \leq \pi\}$

11. a.
$-3 \qquad \frac{3}{4}$

   b. $\left(-3, \frac{3}{4}\right]$

   c. $\left\{q\middle|-3 < q \leq \frac{3}{4}\right\}$

13. a.
$-7 \qquad -4$

   b. $(-7, -4]$

   c. $\{x|-7 < x \leq -4\}$

15. $x - 7 > -4$
$$x > 3$$
3

17. $3 - x < -4$
$$-x < -7$$
Reverse the inequality
$$\frac{-x}{-1} > \frac{-7}{-1}$$
$$x > 7$$
7

19.
$$4.7x - 5.48 \geq 11.44$$
$$4.7x - 5.48 + 5.48 \geq 11.44 + 5.48$$
$$4.7x \geq 16.92$$
$$\frac{4.7x}{4.7} \geq \frac{16.92}{4.7}$$
$$x \geq 3.6$$

3.6

21. $4(x - 2) \leq 4x - 8$
$$4x - 8 \leq 4x - 8$$
$$-8 \leq -8$$
Since this is a true statement, the solution is the entire real number line.

0

23. $5b - 6 \geq 3(b + 3) + 2b$
$$5b - 6 \geq 3b + 9 + 2b$$
$$5b - 6 \geq 5b + 9$$
$$-6 \geq 9$$
Since this is a false statement, there is no solution.

0

25.
$$\frac{y}{3} + \frac{2}{5} \leq 4$$
$$15\left(\frac{y}{3}\right) + 15\left(\frac{2}{5}\right) \leq 15(4)$$
$$5y + 6 \leq 60$$
$$5y \leq 54$$
$$\frac{5y}{5} \leq \frac{54}{5}$$
$$y \leq \frac{54}{5}$$

$\frac{54}{5}$

27.
$$4 + \frac{4x}{3} < 6$$
$$\frac{4x}{3} < 2$$
$$3\left(\frac{4x}{3}\right) < 3(2)$$
$$4x < 6$$
$$\frac{4x}{4} < \frac{6}{4}$$
$$x < \frac{3}{2}$$
$$\left(-\infty, \frac{3}{2}\right)$$

29.
$$\frac{v - 5}{3} - v \geq -3(v - 1)$$
$$\frac{v - 5}{3} - v \geq -3v + 3$$
$$3\left(\frac{v - 5}{3} - v\right) \geq 3(-3v + 3)$$
$$v - 5 - 3v \geq -9v + 9$$
$$-2v - 5 \geq -9v + 9$$
$$7v \geq 14$$
$$v \geq 2 \quad \text{or} \quad [2,\infty)$$

31.
$$\frac{t}{3} - t + 2 \leq -\frac{4t}{3} + 3$$
$$3\left(\frac{t}{3} - t + 2\right) \leq 3\left(-\frac{4t}{3} + 3\right)$$
$$t - 3t + 6 \leq -4t + 9$$
$$-2t + 6 \leq -4t + 9$$
$$2t \leq 3$$
$$\frac{2t}{2} \leq \frac{3}{2}$$
$$t \leq \frac{3}{2} \quad \text{or} \quad \left(-\infty, \frac{3}{2}\right]$$

33. $-3x + 1 < 3[(x + 2) - 2x] - 1$
$$-3x + 1 < 3[x + 2 - 2x] - 1$$
$$-3x + 1 < 3[2 - x] - 1$$
$$-3x + 1 < 6 - 3x - 1$$
$$-3x + 1 < 5 - 3x$$
$$1 < 5 \quad \Rightarrow \quad \text{a true statement}$$
The solution set is $(-\infty, \infty)$.

35.
$$-2 \leq q + 3 < 4$$
$$-2 - 3 \leq q + 3 - 3 < 4 - 3$$
$$-5 \leq q < 1$$
$$[-5,1)$$

37. $-15 \le -3z \le 12$

Divide by -3 and reverse inequalities.

$$\frac{-15}{-3} \ge \frac{-3z}{-3} \ge \frac{12}{-3}$$

$5 \ge z \ge -4$

$-4 \le z \le 5$

$[-4, 5]$

39. $4 \le 2x - 4 < 7$

$4 + 4 \le 2x - 4 + 4 < 7 + 4$

$8 \le 2x < 11$

$\frac{8}{2} \le \frac{2x}{2} < \frac{11}{2}$

$4 \le x < \frac{11}{2}$

$\left[\frac{4}{2}, \frac{11}{2}\right)$

41. $14 \le 2 - 3g < 20$

$14 - 2 \le 2 - 3g - 2 < 20 - 2$

$12 \le -3g < 18$

Divide by -3 and reverse inequalities.

$$\frac{12}{-3} \ge \frac{-3g}{-3} > \frac{18}{-3}$$

$-4 \ge g > -6$

$-6 < g \le -4$

$(-6, -4]$

43. $5 \le \frac{3x + 1}{2} < 11$

$2(5) \le 2\left(\frac{3x + 1}{2}\right) < 2(11)$

$10 \le 3x + 1 < 22$

$10 - 1 \le 3x + 1 - 1 < 22 - 1$

$9 \le 3x < 21$

$\frac{9}{3} \le \frac{3x}{3} < \frac{21}{3}$

$3 \le x < 7$

$\{x \mid 3 \le x < 7\}$

45. $6 \le -3(2x - 4) < 12$

$6 \le -6x + 12 < 12$

$6 - 12 \le -6x + 12 - 12 < 12 - 12$

$-6 \le -6x < 0$

Divide by -6 and reverse inequalities

$$\frac{-6}{-6} \ge \frac{-6x}{-6} > \frac{0}{-6}$$

$1 \ge x > 0$

$0 < x \le 1$

$\{x \mid 0 < x \le 1\}$

47. $0 \le \frac{3(u - 4)}{7} \le 1$

$7(0) \le 7\left(\frac{3(u - 4)}{7}\right) \le 7(1)$

$0 \le 3(u - 4) \le 7$

$0 \le 3u - 12 \le 7$

$0 + 12 \le 3u - 12 + 12 \le 7 + 12$

$12 \le 3u \le 19$

$\frac{12}{3} \le \frac{3u}{3} \le \frac{19}{3}$

$4 \le u \le \frac{19}{3}$

$\left\{u \mid 4 \le u \le \frac{19}{3}\right\}$

49. $\{c \mid -3 < c \le 2\}$

51. $x < 2$

$x > 4$

$x < 2$ and $x > 4$

There is no overlap so the solution is the empty set, $\varnothing$.

53. $x + 1 < 3$ and $x + 1 > -4$

$\qquad x < 2$ and $x > -5$

$x > -5$

$x < 2$

$x < -2$ and $x > -5$ which is $-5 < x < 2$ or

$\{x \mid -5 < x < 2\}$

55. $2s + 3 < 7$ or $-3s + 4 \le -17$

$$2s < 4 \quad \text{or} \quad -3s \le -21$$
$$\frac{2s}{2} < \frac{4}{2} \quad \text{or} \quad \frac{-3s}{-3} \ge \frac{-21}{-3}$$
$$s < 2 \qquad\qquad s \ge 7$$

$s < 2$ or $s \ge 7$ which is $(-\infty, 2) \cup [7, \infty)$.

57. $4x + 5 \ge 5$ and $3x - 4 \le 2$

$$4x \ge 0 \quad \text{and} \quad 3x \le 6$$
$$x \ge 0 \quad \text{and} \quad x \le 2$$

$x \ge 0$

$x \le 2$

$x \ge 0$ and $x \le 2$ which is $0 \le x \le 2$

$[0, 2]$

59. $4 - x < -2$ $3x - 1 < -1$

$$-x < -6 \qquad\qquad 3x < 0$$
$$x > 6 \qquad\qquad\quad x < 0$$

$x > 6$

$x < 0$

$x > 6$ or $x < 0$

$(-\infty, \ 0) \cup (6, \infty)$

61. $2k + 5 > -1$ and $7 - 3k \le 7$

$$2k > -6 \qquad\qquad -3k \le 0$$
$$\frac{2k}{2} > \frac{-6}{2} \qquad\qquad \frac{-3k}{-3} \ge \frac{0}{-3}$$
$$k > -3 \qquad\qquad\quad k \ge 0$$

$k > -3$ and $k \ge 0 \implies k \ge 0$
In interval notation: $[0, \infty)$

63. **a.** $l + g \le 130$

   b. $g = 2w + 2d$
$$l + g \le 130$$
$$l + 2w + 2d \le 130$$

   c. $l = 40, \ w = 20.5$
$$l + 2w + 2d \le 130$$

$$l + 2w + 2d \le 130$$
$$40 + 2(20.5) + 2d \le 130$$
$$40 + 41 + 2d \le 130$$
$$81 + 2d \le 130$$
$$2d \le 49$$
$$d \le 24.5$$

The maximum depth is 24.5 inches.

65. Let x be the maximum number of boxes.
$$70x \le 800$$
$$x \le \frac{800}{70}$$
$$x \le 11.43$$

The maximum number of boxes is 11.

67. Let $x =$ the number of minutes she talks beyond the first 20 minutes.
$$0.99 + 0.07x \le 5.00$$
$$0.07x \le 4.01$$
$$\frac{0.07x}{0.07} \le \frac{4.01}{0.07}$$
$$x \le 57 \quad \text{(to nearest whole number)}$$

She can talk for 57 minutes beyond the first 20 minutes for a total of 77 minutes.

69. To make a profit, the cost must be less than the revenue: cost < revenue.
$$10,025 + 1.09x < 6.42x$$
$$10,025 < 5.33x$$
$$\frac{10,025}{5.33} < x$$
$$1880.86 < x$$

She needs to sell a minimum of 1881 books to make a profit.

71. Let $x =$ the number of additional ounces beyond the first ounce.
$$0.37 + 0.23x \le 10.00$$
$$0.23x \le 9.63$$
$$\frac{0.23x}{0.23} \le \frac{9.63}{0.23}$$
$$x \le 42 \quad \text{(rounded up)}$$

The maximum weight is 42 ounces.

73. Let x be the amount of sales in dollars.
$$300 + 0.10x > 400 + 0.08x$$
$$0.10x > 100 + 0.08x$$
$$0.02x > 100$$
$$x > \frac{100}{0.02}$$
$$x > 5000$$

She will earn more by plan 1 if her sales total more than $5000.

75. Let x be the minimum score for the sixth exam.

$$\frac{65 + 72 + 90 + 47 + 62 + x}{6} \geq 60$$

$$\frac{336 + x}{6} \geq 60$$

$$6\left(\frac{336 + x}{6}\right) \geq 6(60)$$

$$336 + x \geq 360$$

$$x \geq 24$$

She must make a 24 or higher on the sixth exam to pass the course.

77. Let x be the score on the fifth exam.

$$80 \leq \frac{87 + 92 + 70 + 75 + x}{5} < 90$$

$$80 \leq \frac{324 + x}{5} < 90$$

$$5(80) \leq 5\left(\frac{324 + x}{5}\right) < 5(90)$$

$$400 \leq 324 + x < 450$$

$$76 \leq x < 126$$

To receive a final grade of B, Ms. Mahoney must score 76 or higher on the fifth exam. That is, the score must be
$76 \leq x \leq 100$ (maximum grade is 100).

79. Let x be the value of the third reading.

$$7.2 < \frac{7.48 + 7.15 + x}{3} < 7.8$$

$$7.2 < \frac{14.63 + x}{3} < 7.8$$

$$3(7.2) < 3\left(\frac{14.63 + x}{3}\right) < 3(7.8)$$

$$21.6 < 14.63 + x < 23.4$$

$$6.97 < x < 8.77$$

Any value between 6.97 and 8.77 would result in a normal pH reading.

81. a. The taxable income of $128,479 places a married couple filing jointly in the 30.5% tax bracket. The tax is $24,393.75 plus 30.5% of the taxable income over $166,500.
The tax is

$24,393.75 + 0.305(128,479 - 109,250)$

$24,393.75 + 0.305(19,229)$

$24,393.75 + 5,864.85$

$30,258.60$

They will owe $30,258.60 in taxes.

b. The taxable income of $175,248 places a married couple filing jointly in the 35.5% tax bracket. The tax is $41,855.00 plus 35.5% of the taxable income over $166,500.
The tax is

$41,855.00 + 0.355(175,248 - 166,500)$

$41,855.00 + 0.355(8,748)$

$41,855.00 + 3,105.54$

$44,960.54$

They will owe $44,960.54 in taxes.

83. a. 1995, 1996, 1997, 1998, and 1999

b. 2000, 2001, 2002, 2003, 2004, and 2005

85. Answers may vary.

87. First find the average of 82, 90, 74, 76, and 68.

$$\frac{82 + 90 + 74 + 76 + 68}{5} = \frac{390}{5} = 78$$

This represents $\frac{2}{3}$ of the final grade.

Let x be the score from the final exam. Since this represents $\frac{1}{3}$ of the final grade, the inequality is

$$80 \leq \frac{2}{3}(78) + \frac{1}{3}x < 90$$

$$3(80) < 3\left[\frac{2}{3}(78) + \frac{1}{3}x\right] < 3(90)$$

$$240 \leq 2(78) + x < 270$$

$$240 \leq 156 + x < 270$$

$$84 \leq x < 114$$

Russell must score at least 84 points on the final exam to have a final grade of B. The range is $84 \leq x \leq 100$.

89. a. Answers may vary. One possible answer is: Write $x < 2x + 3 < 2x + 5$ as $x < 2x + 3$ and $2x + 3 < 2x + 5$

b. Solve each of the inequalities.

$\quad x < 2x + 3 \quad$ and $\quad 2x + 3 < 2x + 5$

$\quad -x < 3 \qquad\qquad\qquad 3 < 5$

$\quad x > -3 \qquad\qquad\qquad$ All real numbers

The final answer is $x > -3$ or $(-3, \infty)$.

91. a. $A \cup B = \{1, 2, 3, 4, 5, 6, 8, 9\}$

b. $A \cap B = \{1, 8\}$

93. Associative property of addition.

95.
$$R = L + (V - D)r$$
$$R = L + Vr - Dr$$
$$R - L + Dr = Vr$$
$$\frac{R - L + Dr}{r} = V \text{ or } V = \frac{R - L + Dr}{r}$$

Exercise Set 2.6

1. $|x| = a,\ a > 0$
    Set $x = a$ or $x = -a$.

3. $|x| < a,\ a > 0$
    Write $-a < x < a$.

5. $|x| > a,\ a > 0$
    Write $x < -a$ or $x > a$.

7. The solution to $|x| > 0$ is all real numbers except 0.
    The absolute value of any real number, except 0, is greater than 0, i.e., positive.

9. Set $x = y$ or $x = -y$.

11. If $a \neq 0$, and $k > 0$,

    a. $|ax + b| = k$ has 2 solutions.

    b. $|ax + b| < k$ has an infinite number of solutions.

    c. $|ax + b| > k$ has an infinite number of solutions.

13. a. $|x| = 5, \{-5, 5\}$, D

    b. $|x| < 5, \{x | -5 < x < 5\}$, B

    c. $|x| > 5, \{x | x < -5$ or $x > 5\}$, E

    d. $|x| \leq 5, \{x | -5 \leq x \leq 5\}$, C

    e. $|x| \geq 5, \{x | x \leq -5$ or $x \geq 5\}$, A

15. $|a| = 2$
    $a = 2$ or $a = -2$
    The solution set is $\{-2, 2\}$.

17. $|c| = \dfrac{1}{2}$
    $c = \dfrac{1}{2}$ or $c = -\dfrac{1}{2}$
    The solution set is $\left\{-\dfrac{1}{2}, \dfrac{1}{2}\right\}$.

19. $|d| = -\dfrac{3}{4}$
    There is no solution since the right side is a negative number and the absolute value can

never be equal to a negative number. The solution set $\varnothing$.

21. $|x + 5| = 7$
    $\begin{array}{ll} x + 5 = 7 & x + 5 = -7 \\ x = 2 \quad \text{or} & x = -12 \end{array}$
    The solution set is $\{-12, 2\}$.

23. $|4.5q + 22.5| = 0$
    $4.5q + 22.5 = 0$
    $4.5q = -22.5$
    $q = -5$
    The solution set is $\{-5\}$.

25. $|5 - 3x| = \dfrac{1}{2}$

    $\begin{array}{lll} 5 - 3x = \dfrac{1}{2} & \text{or} & 5 - 3x = -\dfrac{1}{2} \\[2mm] -3x = \dfrac{1}{2} - 5 & & -3x = -\dfrac{1}{2} - 5 \\[2mm] -3x = -\dfrac{9}{2} & & -3x = -\dfrac{11}{2} \\[2mm] -\dfrac{1}{3}(3x) = -\dfrac{1}{3}\left(-\dfrac{9}{2}\right) & & -\dfrac{1}{3}(-3x) = -\dfrac{1}{3}\left(-\dfrac{11}{2}\right) \\[2mm] x = \dfrac{3}{2} & & x = \dfrac{11}{6} \end{array}$

    The solution set is $\left\{\dfrac{3}{2}, \dfrac{11}{6}\right\}$.

27. $\left|\dfrac{x - 3}{4}\right| = 5$

    $\begin{array}{lll} \dfrac{x - 3}{4} = 5 & \text{or} & \dfrac{x - 3}{4} = -5 \\[2mm] 4\left(\dfrac{x - 3}{4}\right) = 4(5) & & 4\left(\dfrac{x - 3}{4}\right) = 4(-5) \\[2mm] x - 3 = 20 & & x - 3 = -20 \\[2mm] x = 23 & & x = -17 \end{array}$
    The solution set is $\{-17, 23\}$.

29. $\left|\dfrac{x - 3}{4}\right| + 4 = 4$
    $\left|\dfrac{x - 3}{4}\right| = 0$
    $\dfrac{x - 3}{4} = 0$
    $4\left(\dfrac{x - 3}{4}\right) = 4(0)$
    $x - 3 = 0$
    $x = 3$
    The solution set is $\{3\}$.

31. $|w| \leq 11$

$-11 \leq w \leq 11$

The solution set is $\{w|-11 \leq w \leq 11\}$.

33. $|q + 5| \leq 8$

$-8 \leq q + 5 \leq 8$

$-8 - 5 \leq q + 5 - 5 \leq 8 - 5$

$-13 \leq q \leq 3$

The solution set is $\{x|-13 \leq q \leq 3\}$.

35. $|5b - 15| < 10$

$-10 < 5b - 15 < 10$

$-10 + 15 < 5b - 15 + 15 < 10 + 15$

$5 < 5b < 25$

$\dfrac{5}{5} < \dfrac{5b}{5} < \dfrac{25}{5}$

$1 < b < 5$

The solution set is $\{b|1 < b < 5\}$.

37. $|2x + 3| - 5 \leq 10$

$|2x + 3| \leq 15$

$-15 \leq 2x + 3 \leq 15$

$-15 - 3 \leq 2x + 3 - 3 \leq 15 - 3$

$-18 \leq 2x \leq 12$

$\dfrac{-18}{2} \leq \dfrac{2x}{2} \leq \dfrac{12}{2}$

$-9 \leq x \leq 6$

The solution set is $\{x|-9 \leq x \leq 6\}$

39. $|3x - 7| + 5 < 11$

$|3x - 7| < 6$

$-6 < 3x - 7 < 6$

$-6 + 7 < 3x - 7 + 7 < 6 + 7$

$1 < 3x < 13$

$\dfrac{1}{3} < \dfrac{3x}{3} < \dfrac{13}{3}$

$\dfrac{1}{3} < x < \dfrac{13}{3}$

The solution set is $\left\{x\left|\dfrac{1}{3} < x < \dfrac{13}{3}\right.\right\}$.

41. $|2x - 6| + 5 \leq 2$

$|2x - 6| \leq -3$

There is no solution since the right side is negative whereas the left side is non-negative; zero or a positive number is never less than a negative number. The solution set is $\varnothing$.

43. $\left|\dfrac{1}{2}j + 3\right| < 6$

$-6 < \dfrac{1}{2}j + 3 < 6$

$-6 - 3 < \dfrac{1}{2}j + 3 - 3 < 6 - 3$

$-9 < \dfrac{1}{2}j < -3$

$2(-9) < 2\left(\dfrac{1}{2}j\right) < 2(-3)$

$-18 < j < -6$

The solution set is $\{j|-18 < j < 6\}$.

45. $\left|\dfrac{k}{4} - \dfrac{3}{8}\right| < \dfrac{7}{16}$

$-\dfrac{7}{16} < \dfrac{k}{4} - \dfrac{3}{8} < \dfrac{7}{16}$

$16\left(-\dfrac{7}{16}\right) < 16\left(\dfrac{k}{4} - \dfrac{3}{8}\right) < 16\left(\dfrac{7}{16}\right)$

$-7 < 4k - 6 < 7$

$-7 + 6 < 4k - 6 + 6 < 7 + 6$

$-1 < 4k < 13$

$-\dfrac{1}{4} < k < \dfrac{13}{4}$

The solution is $\left\{k\left|-\dfrac{1}{4} < k < \dfrac{13}{4}\right.\right\}$.

47. $|y| > 7$

$y < -7$ or $y > 7$

The solution set is $\{y|y < -7 \text{ or } y > 7\}$.

49. $|x + 4| > 5$

$x + 4 < -5$ or $x + 4 > 5$

$x < -9$ $x > 1$

The solution set is $\{x|x < -9 \text{ or } x > 1\}$.

51. $|7 - 3b| > 5$

$7 - 3b < -5$ or $7 - 3b > 5$

$-3b < -12$ $-3b > -2$

$\dfrac{-3b}{-3} > \dfrac{-12}{-3}$ $\dfrac{-3b}{-3} < \dfrac{-2}{-3}$

$b > 4$ $b < \dfrac{2}{3}$

The solution set is $\left\{ b \middle| b < \dfrac{2}{3} \text{ or } b > 4 \right\}$.

53. $\left| \dfrac{2h - 5}{3} \right| > 1$

$\dfrac{2h - 5}{3} < -1$ or $\dfrac{2h - 5}{3} > 1$

$3\left(\dfrac{2h - 5}{3}\right) < 3(-1)$ $3\left(\dfrac{2h - 5}{3}\right) > 3(1)$

$2h - 5 < -3$ $2h - 5 > 3$

$2h < 2$ $2h > 8$

$h < \dfrac{2}{2}$ $h > \dfrac{8}{2}$

$h < 1$ $h > 4$

The solution set is $\left\{ h \middle| h < 1 \text{ or } h > 4 \right\}$.

55. $|0.1x - 0.4| + 0.4 > 0.6$

$\quad |0.1x - 0.4| > 0.2$

$0.1x - 0.4 < -0.2$ or $0.1x - 0.4 > 0.2$

$0.1x < 0.2$ $0.1x > 0.6$

$x < \dfrac{0.2}{0.1}$ $x > \dfrac{0.6}{0.1}$

$x < 2$ $x > 6$

The solution set is $\{x | x < 2 \text{ or } x > 6\}$.

57. $\left| \dfrac{x}{2} + 4 \right| \geq 5$

$\dfrac{x}{2} + 4 \leq -5$ or $\dfrac{x}{2} + 4 \geq 5$

$2\left(\dfrac{x}{2} + 4\right) \leq 2(-5)$ $2\left(\dfrac{x}{2} + 4\right) \geq 2(5)$

$x + 8 \leq -10$ $x + 8 \geq 10$

$x \leq -18$ $x \geq 2$

The solution set is $\{x | x \leq -18 \text{ or } x \geq 2\}$.

59. $|7w + 3| - 6 \geq -6$

$\quad |7w + 3| \geq 0$

Observe that the absolute value of a number is always greater than or equal to 0. Thus, the solution is the set of real numbers or R.

61. $|4 - 2x| > 0$

$4 - 2x < 0$ or $4 - 2x > 0$

$-2x < -4$ $-2x > -4$

$x > \dfrac{-4}{-2}$ $x < \dfrac{-4}{-2}$

$x > 2$ $x < 2$

The solution set is $\{x | x < 2 \text{ or } x > 2\}$.

63. $|3p - 5| = |2p + 10|$

$3p - 5 = -(2p + 10)$ or $3p - 5 = 2p + 10$

$3p - 5 = -2p - 10$ $p - 5 = 10$

$5p - 5 = -10$ $p = 15$

$5p = -5$

$p = -1$

The solution set is $\{-1, 15\}$.

65. $|6x| = |3x - 9|$

$6x = -(3x - 9)$ or $6x = 3x - 9$

$6x = -3x + 9$ $3x = -9$

$9x = 9$ $x = \dfrac{-9}{3}$

$x = \dfrac{9}{9}$ $x = -3$

$x = 1$

The solution set is $\{-3, 1\}$.

67. $\left| \dfrac{2r}{3} + \dfrac{5}{6} \right| = \left| \dfrac{r}{2} - 3 \right|$

$\dfrac{2r}{3} + \dfrac{5}{6} = -\left(\dfrac{r}{2} - 3\right)$ or $\dfrac{2r}{3} + \dfrac{5}{6} = \dfrac{r}{2} - 3$

$\dfrac{2r}{3} + \dfrac{5}{6} = -\dfrac{r}{2} + 3$ $6\left(\dfrac{2r}{3} + \dfrac{5}{6}\right) = 6\left(\dfrac{r}{2} - 3\right)$

$6\left(\dfrac{2r}{3} + \dfrac{5}{6}\right) = 6\left(-\dfrac{r}{2} + 3\right)$ $4r + 5 = 3r - 18$

$4r + 5 = -3r + 18$ $r + 5 = -18$

$7r + 5 = 18$ $r = -23$

$7r = 13$

$r = \dfrac{13}{7}$

The solution set is $\left\{ -23, \dfrac{13}{7} \right\}$.

69. $\left|-\dfrac{3}{4}m+8\right|=\left|7-\dfrac{3m}{4}\right|$

$-\dfrac{3}{4}m+8=-\left(7-\dfrac{3m}{4}\right)$ or $-\dfrac{3}{4}m+8=7-\dfrac{3m}{4}$

$-\dfrac{3}{4}m+8=-7+\dfrac{3}{4}m$ $-\dfrac{3}{4}m+8=7-\dfrac{3}{4}m$

$-\dfrac{6}{4}m=-15$ $8=7$ False!

$m=10$

The solution set is $\{10\}$.

71. $|h|=1$

$h=1$ or $h=-1$

The solution set is $\{-1,\,1\}$.

73. $|q+6|>2$

$q+6<-2$ or $q+6>2$

$q<-8$ $q>-4$

The solution set is $\left\{q\,\middle|\,q<-8\ \text{or}\ q>-4\right\}$.

75. $|2w-7|\le 9$

$-9\le 2w-7\le 9$

$-9+7\le 2w-7+7\le 9+7$

$-2\le 2w\le 16$

$\dfrac{-2}{2}\le \dfrac{2w}{2}\le \dfrac{16}{2}$

$-1\le w\le 8$

The solution set is $\left\{w\,\middle|\,-1\le w\le 8\right\}$.

77. $|5a-1|=9$

$5a-1=-9$ or $5a-1=9$

$5a=-8$ $5a=10$

$a=-\dfrac{8}{5}$ $a=2$

The solution set is $\left\{-\dfrac{8}{5},\,2\right\}$.

79. $|5x+2|>0$

$5+2x<0$ or $5+2x>0$

$2x<-5$ $2x>-5$

$x<-\dfrac{5}{2}$ $x>-\dfrac{5}{2}$

The solution set is $\left\{x\,\middle|\,x<-\dfrac{5}{2}\ \text{or}\ x>-\dfrac{5}{2}\right\}$.

81. $|4+3x|\le 9$

$-9\le 4+3x\le 9$

$-13\le 3x\le 5$

$-\dfrac{13}{3}\le x\le \dfrac{5}{3}$

The solution set is $\left\{x\,\middle|\,-\dfrac{13}{3}\le x\le \dfrac{5}{3}\right\}$.

83. $|3n+8|-4=-10$

$|3n+8|=-6$

Since the right side is negative and the left side is non-negative, there is no solution since the absolute value can never equal a negative number. The solution set is $\varnothing$.

85. $\left|\dfrac{w+4}{3}\right|-1<3$

$\left|\dfrac{w+4}{3}\right|<4$

$-4<\dfrac{w+4}{3}<4$

$3(-4)<3\left(\dfrac{w+4}{3}\right)<3(4)$

$-12<w+4<12$

$-16<w<8$

The solution set is $\{w\,|-16<w<8\}$.

87. $\left|\dfrac{3x-2}{4}\right|+5\ge 5$

$\left|\dfrac{3x-2}{4}\right|\ge 0$

Since the absolute value of a number is always greater than or equal to zero, the solution is the set of all real numbers or R.

89. $|2x-8|=\left|\dfrac{1}{2}x+3\right|$

$2x-8=-\left(\dfrac{1}{2}x+3\right)$ or $2x-8=\dfrac{1}{2}x+3$

$2x-8=-\dfrac{1}{2}x-3$ $\dfrac{3}{2}x-8=3$

$\dfrac{5}{2}x-8=-3$ $\dfrac{3}{2}x=11$

$\dfrac{5}{2}x=5$ $\dfrac{2}{3}\left(\dfrac{3}{2}x\right)=\dfrac{2}{3}(11)$

$\dfrac{2}{5}\left(\dfrac{5}{2}x\right)=\dfrac{2}{5}(5)$ $x=\dfrac{22}{3}$

$x=2$

The solution set is $\left\{2,\,\dfrac{22}{3}\right\}$.

91. $\left|2-3x\right|=\left|4-\dfrac{5}{3}x\right|$

$$2-3x = -\left(4-\dfrac{5}{3}x\right) \qquad \text{or} \qquad 2-3x = 4-\dfrac{5}{3}x$$

$$2-3x = -4+\dfrac{5}{3}x \qquad\qquad -3x = 2-\dfrac{5}{3}x$$

$$-3x = -6+\dfrac{5}{3}x \qquad\qquad -\dfrac{4}{3}x = 2$$

$$-\dfrac{14}{3}x = -6 \qquad\qquad -\dfrac{3}{4}\left(-\dfrac{4}{3}x\right) = -\dfrac{3}{2}(2)$$

$$\left(-\dfrac{3}{14}\right)\left(-\dfrac{14}{3}\right)x = \left(-\dfrac{3}{14}\right)(-6) \qquad\qquad x = -\dfrac{3}{2}$$

$$x = \dfrac{9}{7}$$

The solution set is $\left\{-\dfrac{3}{2},\ \dfrac{9}{7}\right\}$.

93. a. $\left|t-0.089\right| \le 0.004$

$-0.004 \le t-0.089 \le 0.004$

$-0.004 + 0.089 \le t - 0.089 + 0.089 \le 0.004 +$

$0.085 \le t \le 0.093$
The solution is $[0.085, 0.093]$.

   b.   0.085 inches

   c.   0.093 inches

95. a. $\left|d-160\right| \le 28$

$-28 \le d-160 \le 28$
$-28 + 160 \le d-160 + 160 \le 28 + 160$
$132 \le d \le 188$
The solution is [132, 188]

   b.   The submarine can move between 132 feet and 188 feet below sea level, inclusive.

97. $\{-5, 5\}$ is the solution set of $\left|x\right| = 5$.

99. $\{x \mid x \le -5 \ \text{or} \ \ x \ge 5\}$ is the solution set of $\left|x\right| \ge 5$.

101. $\left|ax+b\right| \le 0$

$0 \le ax+b \le 0$
which is the same as
$ax+b = 0$

$ax = -b$

$x = -\dfrac{b}{a}$

103. a.   Set $ax+b = -c$ or $ax+b = c$ and solve each equation for x.

   b. $ax+b = -c \qquad \text{or} \qquad ax+b = c$

$ax = -c-b \qquad\qquad ax = c-b$

$x = \dfrac{-c-b}{a} \qquad\qquad x = \dfrac{c-b}{a}$

The solution is $x = \dfrac{-c-b}{a}$ or $x = \dfrac{c-b}{a}$.

105. a.   Write $ax+b < -c$ or $ax+b > c$ and solve each inequality for x.

   b. $ax+b < -c \qquad \text{or} \qquad ax+b > c$

$ax < -c-b \qquad\qquad ax > c-b$

$x < \dfrac{-c-b}{a} \qquad\qquad x > \dfrac{c-b}{a}$

The solution is $x < \dfrac{-c-b}{a}$ or $x > \dfrac{c-b}{a}$.

107. $\left|x-3\right| = \left|3-x\right|$

$x-3 = -(3-x) \quad \text{or} \quad x-3 = 3-x$

$x-3 = -3+x \qquad\qquad 2x-3 = 3$

$0 = 0 \qquad\qquad\qquad 2x = 6$

True $\qquad\qquad\qquad\qquad x = 3$

Since the first statement is always true all real values work. The solution set is R.

109. $\left|x\right| = x$

By definition $\left|x\right| = \begin{cases} x, & x \ge 0 \\ -x, & x < 0 \end{cases}$

Thus, $\left|x\right| = x$ when $x \ge 0$
The solution set is $\{x \mid x \ge 0\}$.

111. $|x + 1| = 2x - 1$

$x + 1 = -(2x - 1)$ or $x + 1 = 2x - 1$
$x + 1 = -2x + 1$ $1 = x - 1$
$3x + 1 = 1$ $2 = x$
$3x = 0$
$x = 0$

Checking both possible solutions, only $x = 2$ checks. The solution set is $\{2\}$.

113. $|x - 2| = -(x - 2)$

By the definition,

$|x - 2| = \begin{cases} x - 2, & x - 2 \ge 0 \\ -(x - 2), & x - 2 \le 0 \end{cases}$ or

$\begin{cases} x - 2, & x \ge 2 \\ -(x - 2), & x \le 2 \end{cases}$

Thus, $|x - 2| = -(x - 2)$ for $x \le 2$.
The solution set is $\{x | x \le 2\}$.

115. $x + |-x| = 6$

For $x \ge 0$: $x + |-x| = 6$
$x + x = 6$
$2x = 6$
$x = 3$

For $x < 0$: $x + |-x| = 6$
$x - x = 6$
$0 = 6$ False

The solution set is $\{3\}$.

117. $x - |x| = 6$

For $x \ge 0$: $x - |x| = 6$
$x - x = 6$
$0 = 6$ False

For $x < 0$: $x - |x| = 6$
$x - (-x) = 6$
$x + x = 6$
$2x = 6$
$x = 3$ Contradicts $x < 0$

There are no values of x, so the solution set is $\varnothing$.

119. $\dfrac{1}{3} + \dfrac{1}{4} \div \dfrac{2}{5}\left(\dfrac{1}{3}\right)^2 = \dfrac{1}{3} + \dfrac{1}{4} \div \dfrac{2}{5} \cdot \dfrac{1}{9}$

$= \dfrac{1}{3} + \dfrac{1}{4} \cdot \dfrac{5}{2} \cdot \dfrac{1}{9}$

$= \dfrac{1}{3} + \dfrac{5}{72}$

$= \dfrac{1}{3} \cdot \dfrac{24}{24} + \dfrac{5}{72}$

$= \dfrac{24}{72} + \dfrac{5}{72}$

$= \dfrac{29}{72}$

121. Let x be the time needed to swim across the lake. Then $1.5 - x$ is the time needed to make the return trip.

	Rate	Time	Distance
First Trip	2	x	$2x$
Return Trip	1.6	$1.5 - x$	$1.6(1.5 - x)$

The distances are the same.
$2x = 1.6(1.5 - x)$
$2x = 2.4 - 1.6x$
$3.6x = 2.4$
$x = \dfrac{2.4}{3.6} = \dfrac{2}{3}$

The total distance across the lake is
$2x = 2\left(\dfrac{2}{3}\right) = \dfrac{4}{3}$ or 1.33 miles.

Review Exercises

1. $23a^3 b^5$ has degree eight since the sum of the exponents is $3 + 5 = 8$.

2. $6x$ has degree one since $6x$ can be written as $6x^1$ and the only exponent is 1.

3. $-4xyz^5$ has degree seven since $-4xyz^5$ can be written as $-4x^1 y^1 z^5$ and the sum of the exponents is $1 + 1 + 5 = 7$.

4. $a(a + 3) - 4(a - 1)$
$a^2 + 3a - 4a + 4$
$a^2 - a + 4$

5. $x^2 + 2xy + 6x^2 - 4 = x^2 + 6x^2 + 2xy - 4$
$= 7x^2 + 2xy - 4$

6. $b^2 + b - 7$ cannot be simplified since there are no like terms.

7. $2[-(x - y) + 3x] - 5y + 6$
$= 2[-x + y + 3x] - 5y + 6$
$= 2[2x + y] - 5y + 6$
$= 4x + 2y - 5y + 6$
$= 4x - 3y + 6$

8. $5(c + 4) - 2c = -(c - 4)$
$5c + 20 - 2c = -c + 4$
$3c + 20 = -c + 4$
$4c + 20 = 4$
$4c = -16$
$c = -4$

9. $3(x + 2) - 6 = 4(x - 5)$
$3x + 6 - 6 = 4x - 20$
$3x + 0 = 4x - 20$
$3x = 4x - 20$
$3x - 4x = 4x - 4x - 20$
$-x = -20$
$\dfrac{-1x}{-1} = \dfrac{-20}{-1}$
$x = 20$

10.
$3 + \dfrac{x}{2} = \dfrac{5}{6}$
$6(3) + 6\left(\dfrac{x}{2}\right) = 6\left(\dfrac{5}{6}\right)$
$18 + 3x = 5$
$18 - 18 + 3x = 5 - 18$
$3x = -13$
$\dfrac{3x}{3} = \dfrac{-13}{3}$
$x = -\dfrac{13}{3}$

11.
$\dfrac{1}{2}(3t + 4) = \dfrac{1}{3}(4t + 1)$
$6\left(\dfrac{1}{2}(3t + 4)\right) = 6\left(\dfrac{1}{3}(4t + 1)\right)$
$3(3t + 4) = 2(4t + 1)$
$9t + 12 - 8t = 8t + 2 - 8t$
$t + 12 = 2$
$t + 12 - 12 = 2 - 12$
$t = -10$

12. $2\left(\dfrac{x}{2} - 4\right) = 3\left(x + \dfrac{1}{3}\right)$
$x - 8 = 3x + 1$
$x - 8 + 8 = 3x + 1 + 8$
$x = 3x + 9$
$x - 3x = 3x - 3x + 9$
$-2x = 9$
$\dfrac{-2x}{-2} = \dfrac{9}{-2}$
$x = -\dfrac{9}{2}$

13.
$3x - 4 = 6x + 4 - 3x$
$3x - 4 = 3x + 4$
$3x - 3x - 4 = 3x - 3x + 4$
$-4 = 4$
This is a false statement which means there is no solution.

14.
$2(x - 6) = 5 - \{2x - [4(x - 3) - 5]\}$
$2x - 12 = 5 - \{2x - [4x - 12 - 5]\}$
$2x - 12 = 5 - \{2x - [4x - 17]\}$
$2x - 12 = 5 - \{2x - 4x + 17\}$
$2x - 12 = 5 - \{-2x + 17\}$
$2x - 12 = 5 + 2x - 17$
$2x - 12 = 2x - 12$
$2x - 12 - 2x = 2x - 12 - 2x$
$12 = 12$
Since this is a true statement, the solution set is all real numbers, or R.

15. $m = \dfrac{y_2 - y_1}{x_2 - x_1} = \dfrac{(5) - (-2)}{(-8) - (6)} = \dfrac{5 + 2}{-8 - 6} = \dfrac{7}{-14} = -\dfrac{1}{2}$

16. $x = \dfrac{-b + \sqrt{b^2 - 4ac}}{2a}$
$= \dfrac{-10 + \sqrt{(10)^2 - 4(8)(-3)}}{2(8)}$
$= \dfrac{-10 + \sqrt{100 + 96}}{16}$
$= \dfrac{-10 + \sqrt{196}}{16}$
$= \dfrac{-10 + 14}{16}$
$= \dfrac{4}{16}$
$= \dfrac{1}{4}$

17.

$$h = \frac{1}{2}at^2 + v_0 t + h_0$$

$$= \frac{1}{2}(-32)(1)^2 + 0(2) + 80$$

$$= \frac{1}{2}(-32)(1) + 0 + 80$$

$$= -16(1) + 0 + 80$$

$$= -16 + 0 + 80$$

$$= 64$$

18.

$$z = \frac{\bar{x} - \mu}{\frac{\sigma}{\sqrt{n}}}$$

$$= \frac{60 - 64}{\frac{5}{\sqrt{25}}}$$

$$= \frac{60 - 64}{\frac{5}{5}}$$

$$= \frac{60 - 64}{1}$$

$$= -4$$

19.

$$E = IR$$

$$\frac{E}{I} = \frac{IR}{I}$$

$$\frac{E}{I} = R \text{ or } R = \frac{E}{I}$$

20.

$$A = \pi r^2 h$$

$$\frac{A}{\pi r^2} = \frac{\pi r^2}{\pi r^2}$$

$$\frac{A}{\pi r^2} = h \text{ or } h = \frac{A}{\pi r^2}$$

21.

$$P = 2l + 2w$$

$$P - 2l = 2l - 2l + 2w$$

$$P = 2l = 2w$$

$$\frac{P - 2l}{2} = \frac{2w}{2}$$

$$\frac{P - 2l}{2} = w \text{ or } w = \frac{P - 2l}{2}$$

22.

$$A = \frac{1}{2}bh$$

$$2(A) = 2\left(\frac{1}{2}bh\right)$$

$$2A = bh$$

$$\frac{2A}{b} = \frac{bh}{b}$$

$$\frac{2A}{b} = h \text{ or } h = \frac{2A}{b}$$

23.

$$y = mx + b$$

$$y - b = mx + b - b$$

$$y - b = mx$$

$$\frac{y - b}{x} = \frac{mx}{x}$$

$$\frac{y - b}{x} = m \text{ or } m = \frac{y - b}{x}$$

24.

$$2x - 3y = 5$$

$$2x - 2x - 3y = -2x + 5$$

$$-3y = -2x + 5$$

$$\frac{-3y}{-3} = \frac{-2x + 5}{-3}$$

$$y = \frac{-2x + 5}{-3} \text{ or } y = \frac{2x - 5}{3}$$

25.

$$R_T = R_1 + R_2 + R_3$$

$$R_T - R_1 - R_3 = R_1 + R_2 + R_3 - R_1 - R_3$$

$$R_T - R_1 - R_3 = R_2$$

$$\text{or } R_2 = R_T - R_1 - R_3$$

26.

$$S = \frac{3a + b}{2}$$

$$2(S) = 2\left(\frac{3a + b}{2}\right)$$

$$2S = 3a + b$$

$$2S - b = 3a + b - b$$

$$2S - b = 3a$$

$$\frac{2S - b}{3} = \frac{3a}{3}$$

$$\frac{2S - b}{3} = a \text{ or } a = \frac{2S - b}{3}$$

27.

$$K = 2(d + l)$$

$$K = 2d + 2l$$

$$K - 2d = 2d - 2d + 2l$$

$$K - 2d = 2l$$

$$\frac{K - 2d}{2} = \frac{2l}{2}$$

$$\frac{D - 2d}{2} = l \text{ or } l = \frac{K - 2d}{2}$$

28. Let x be the original price.

$$x - 0.75x = 5.50$$

$$0.25x = 5.50$$

$$\frac{0.25x}{0.25} = \frac{5.50}{0.25}$$

$$x = 22$$

The original price was $22.

29. Let x be the number of years for the population to reach 5800.
$$4750 + 350x = 5800$$
$$350x = 1050$$
$$x = \frac{1050}{350}$$
$$x = 3$$
It will take 3 years for the population to grow from 4750 people to 5800 people.

30. Let x be the amount of sales.
$$300 + 0.06x = 650$$
$$0.06x = 350$$
$$\frac{0.06x}{0.06} = \frac{350}{0.06}$$
$$x = 5833.33$$
Dawn's sales must be $5833.33.

31. Let x be the number of miles she drives.
$$3(24.99) = 3(19.99) + 0.10x$$
$$74.97 = 59.97 + 0.10x$$
$$15.00 = 0.10x$$
$$\frac{15.00}{0.10} = \frac{0.10x}{0.10}$$
$$150 = x$$
The costs would be the same if she drives 150 miles.

32. Let x be the regular price.
$$x - 0.40x - 20 = 120$$
$$0.60x - 20 = 120$$
$$0.60x = 140$$
$$\frac{0.60x}{0.60} = \frac{140}{0.60}$$
$$x \approx 233.33$$
The regular price was $233.33.

33. Let x = the amount invested at 3.5%. Then $5000 - x$ is the amount invested at 4.0%.

Account	Principal	Rate	Time	Interest
3.5%	x	0.035	1	$0.035x$
4.0%	$5000 - x$	0.04	1	$0.04(5000 - x)$

$$0.035x + 0.04(5000 - x) = 187.15$$
$$0.035x + 200 - 0.04x = 187.15$$
$$-0.005x + 200 = 187.15$$
$$-0.005x = -12.85$$
$$x = \frac{-12.85}{-0.005}$$
$$x = 2570$$
Thus, the Ari Klein invested $2,570 at 3.5% and $5,000 – $2,570 = $2,430 at 4.0%.

34. Let x = the amount of 20% solution.

Solution	Strength of Solution	No. of Gallons	Amount
20%	0.20	x	$0.20x$
60%	0.06	$250 - x$	$0.60(250 - x)$
Mixture	0.30	250	$0.30(250)$

$$0.20x + 0.60(250 - x) = 0.30(250)$$
$$0.20x + 150 - 0.60x = 75$$
$$-0.40x + 150 = 75$$
$$-0.40x = -75$$
$$x = \frac{-75}{-0.40}$$
$$x = 187.5$$
Dale must combine 187.5 gallons of the 20% solution with 250 – 187.5 = 62.5 gallons of the 60% solution to obtain the 30% solution.

35. Let t be the amount of time needed.

Type	Rate	Time	Distance
One Train	60	t	$60t$
Other Train	90	t	$90t$

The total distance is 400 miles.

$60t + 90t = 400$

$\qquad 150t = 400$

$\qquad\quad t = \dfrac{400}{150} = \dfrac{8}{3} = 2\dfrac{2}{3}$

In $2\dfrac{2}{3}$ hours, the trains are 400 miles apart.

36. a. Let x be the speed of Shuttle 1. Then $x + 300$ is the speed of Shuttle 2.

Type	Rate	Time	Distance
Shuttle 1	x	5.5	$5.5x$
Shuttle 2	$x + 300$	5.0	$5.0(x + 300)$

The distances are the same.

$5.5x = 5.0(x + 300)$

$5.5x = 5.0x + 1500$

$0.5x = 1500$

$\quad x = \dfrac{1500}{0.5} = 3000$

The speed of Shuttle 1 is 3000 mph.

b. The distance is $5.5(3000) = 16{,}500$ miles.

37. Let x be the amount of $6.00 coffee needed. Then $40 - x$ is the amount of $6.80 coffee needed.

Item	Cost per Pound	No. of Pounds	Total Value
$6.00 Coffee	$6.00	x	$6.00x$
$6.80 Coffee	$6.80	$40 - x$	$6.80(40 - x)$
Mixture	$6.50	40	$6.50(40)$

$6.00x + 6.80(40 - x) = 6.50(40)$

$6.00x + 272 - 6.80x = 260$

$\qquad -0.80x + 272 = 260$

$\qquad\qquad -0.80x = -12$

$\qquad\qquad\quad x = \dfrac{-12}{-0.80} = 15$

Mr. Tomlins needs to combine 15 pounds of $6.00 coffee with $40 - 15 = 25$ pounds of $6.80 coffee to produce the mixture.

38. Let x = the original price of the telephone.

$x - 0.20x = 24$

$\quad 0.80x = 24$

$\qquad x = \dfrac{24}{0.80} = 30$

The original price of the telephone was $30.

9. Let x be the time spent jogging. Then $4 - x$ is the time spent walking.

Trip	Rate	Time	Distance
Jogging	7.2	x	$7.2x$
Walking	2.4	$4 - x$	$2.4(4 - x)$

a. The distances are the same.
$$7.2x = 2.4(4 - x)$$
$$7.2x = 9.6 - 2.4x$$
$$9.6x = 9.6$$
$$x = \frac{9.6}{9.6} = 1$$
Thus, Nicole jogged for 1 hour and walked for $4 - 1 = 3$ hours.

b. The distance one-way is $7.2(1) = 7.2$ miles. The total distance is twice this value or $2(7.2) = 14.4$ miles.

40. Let x be the measure of the smallest angle. The measure of the other two angles are $x + 25$ and $2x - 5$.
$$x + (x + 25) + (2x - 5) = 180$$
$$4x + 20 = 180$$
$$4x = 160$$
$$x = \frac{160}{4} = 40$$
The measures of the angles are $40°$, $40 + 25 = 65°$, and $2(40) - 5 = 80 - 5 = 75°$.

41. Let x be the flow rate of the smaller hose.

Type	Rate	Time	Amount (No. of Gallons)
Smaller	r	3	$3r$
Larger	$1.5r$	5	$5(1.5r)$

The total number of gallons of water is 3150 gallons.
$$3r + 5(1.5r) = 3150$$
$$3r + 7.5r = 3150$$
$$10.5r = 3150$$
$$r = \frac{3150}{10.5} = 300$$
The flow rate for the smaller hose is 300 gallons per hour and the flow rate for the larger hose is $1.5(300) = 450$ gallons per hour.

42. Let $x =$ measure of one of the angles. Then the other angle measure is $2x - 15$. The sum of the measures of complementary angles is $90°$.
$$x + (2x - 15) = 90$$
$$3x - 15 = 90$$
$$3x = 105$$
$$x = \frac{105}{3}$$
$$x = 35$$
The measures of the angles are $35°$ and $2(35°) - 15° = 55°$.

43. Let x be the amount of 20% solution.

Solution	Strength of Solution	No. of Ounces	Amount
20%	0.20	x	$0.20x$
6%	0.06	10	$0.06(10)$
Mixture	0.12	$x + 10$	$0.12(x + 10)$

$$0.20x + 0.06(10) = 0.12(x + 10)$$
$$0.20x + 0.6 = 0.12x + 1.2$$
$$0.08x + 0.6 = 1.2$$
$$0.08x = 0.6$$
$$x = \frac{0.6}{0.08} = 7.5$$

The clothier must combine 7.5 ounces of the 20% solution with 10 ounces of the 6% solution to obtain the 12% solution.

44. Let x be the amount invested at 10%. Then $12,000 - x$ is the amount invested at 6%.

Account	Principal	Rate	Time	Interest
10%	x	0.10	1	$0.10x$
6%	$12,000 - x$	0.06	1	$0.06(12,000 - x)$

$$0.10x = 0.06(12,000 - x)$$
$$0.10x = 720 - 0.06x$$
$$0.16x = 720$$
$$x = \frac{720}{0.16} = 4500$$

Thus, Ken invested $4500 at 10% and $12000 - 4500 = \$7500$ at 6%.

45. Let x be the number of visits. The cost of the first plan = cost of second plan gives the equation
$40 + 1(x) = 25 + 4(x)$

$$40 + x = 25 + 4x$$
$$15 + x = 4x$$
$$15 = 3x$$
$$\frac{15}{3} = x \text{ or } x = 5$$

Erick needs to make more than 5 visits for the first plan to be advantageous.

46. Let x be the speed of the faster train. Then $x - 10$ is the speed of the slower train.

Train	Rate	Time	Distance
Faster	x	3	$3x$
Slower	$x - 10$	3	$3(x - 10)$

$$3x + 3(x - 10) = 270$$
$$3x + 3x - 30 = 270$$
$$6x - 30 = 270$$
$$6x = 300$$
$$x = \frac{300}{6} = 50$$

The speed of the faster train is 50 mph and the speed of the slower train is 40 mph.

47. $3z + 7 \le 13$

$3z \le 6$

$z \le 2$

48. $5 - 2w > -7$

$-2w > -12$

$\dfrac{-2w}{-2} < \dfrac{-12}{-2}$

$w < 6$

49. $2x + 4 > 9$

$2x > 5$

$x > \dfrac{5}{2}$

50. $16 \le 4x - 5$

$21 \le 4x$

$\dfrac{21}{4} \le x$

51. $\dfrac{4x + 3}{5} > -3$

$5\left(\dfrac{4x + 3}{5}\right) > 5(-3)$

$4x + 3 > -15$

$4x > -18$

$x > \dfrac{-18}{4}$

$x > -\dfrac{9}{2}$

52. $2(x - 3) > 3x + 4$

$2x - 6 > 3x + 4$

$2x - 10 > 3x$

$-10 > x$

53.

$-4(x - 2) \ge 6x + 4 - 10x$

$-4x + 8 \ge -4x + 4$

$8 \ge +4$ a true statement

The solution is all real numbers.

54. $\dfrac{x}{2} + \dfrac{3}{4} > x - \dfrac{x}{2} + 1$

$4\left(\dfrac{x}{2} + \dfrac{3}{4}\right) > 4\left(x - \dfrac{x}{2} + 1\right)$

$2x + 3 > 4x - 2x + 4$

$2x + 3 > 2x + 4$

$3 > 4$

This is a contradiction, so the solution is { }.

55. Let x be the maximum number of 40-pound boxes. Since the maximum load is 500 pounds, the total weight of the Joseph and boxes must be less than or equal to 500 pounds.

$180 + 40x \le 500$

$40x \le 320$

$x \le \dfrac{320}{40}$

$x \le 8$

The maximum number of boxes that Joseph can carry in the canoe is 8.

56. Let x be the number of additional minutes (beyond 3 minutes) of the phone call.

$4.50 + 0.95x \le 8.65$

$0.95x \le 4.15$

$x \le \dfrac{4.15}{0.95}$

$x \le 4.4$

The customer can talk for 3 minutes plus an additional 4 minutes for a total of 7 minutes.

57. Let x be the number of weeks (after the first week) needed to lose 27 pounds.

$3 + 1.5x \ge 27$

$1.5x \ge 24$

$x \ge \dfrac{24}{1.5}$

$x \ge 16$

The number of weeks is 16 plus the initial week for a total of 17 weeks.

58. Let x be the grade from the 5th exam. The inequality is

$$80 \le \frac{94 + 73 + 72 + 80 + x}{5} < 90$$

$$80 \le \frac{319 + x}{5} < 90$$

$$5(80) \le 5\left(\frac{319 + x}{5}\right) < 5(90)$$

$$400 \le 319 + x < 450$$

$$400 - 319 \le 319 + x < 450 - 319$$

$$81 \le x < 131$$

(must use 100 here since it is not possible to score 131)

Thus, Jekeila needs to score 81 or higher on the 5th exam to receive a B.

$$\{x | 81 \le x \le 100\}$$

59.
$$1 < x - 4 < 7$$
$$1 + 4 < x - 4 + 4 < 7 + 4$$
$$5 < x < 11$$
$$(5, 11)$$

60.
$$7 < p + 10 \le 15$$
$$7 - 10 < p + 10 - 10 \le 15 - 10$$
$$-3 < p \le 5$$
$$(-3, 5]$$

61.
$$3 < 2x - 4 < 8$$
$$3 + 4 < 2x - 4 + 4 < 8 + 4$$
$$7 < 2x < 12$$
$$\frac{7}{2} < \frac{2x}{2} < \frac{12}{2}$$
$$\frac{7}{2} < x < 6$$
$$\left(\frac{7}{2}, 6\right)$$

62.
$$-12 < 6 - 3x < -2$$
$$-12 - 6 < 6 - 6 - 3x < -2 - 6$$
$$18 < -3x < -8$$
$$\frac{-18}{-3} > \frac{-3x}{-3} > \frac{-8}{-3}$$
$$6 > x > \frac{8}{3}$$
$$\frac{8}{3} < x < 6$$
$$\left(\frac{8}{3}, 6\right)$$

63.
$$-1 < \frac{5}{9}x + \frac{2}{3} \le \frac{11}{9}$$
$$9(-1) < 9\left(\frac{5}{9}x + \frac{2}{3}\right) \le 9\left(\frac{11}{9}\right)$$
$$-9 < 5x + 6 \le 11$$
$$-9 - 6 < 5x + 6 - 6 \le 11 - 6$$
$$-15 < 5x \le 5$$
$$\frac{-15}{5} < \frac{5x}{5} \le \frac{5}{5}$$
$$-3 < x \le 1$$
$$(-3, 1]$$

64.
$$-8 < \frac{4 - 2x}{3} < 0$$
$$3(-8) < 3\left(\frac{4 - 2x}{3}\right) < 3(0)$$
$$-24 < 4 - 2x < 0$$
$$-24 - 4 < 4 - 4 - 2x < 0 - 4$$
$$-28 < -2x < -4$$
$$\frac{-28}{-2} > \frac{-2x}{-2} > \frac{-4}{-2}$$
$$14 > x > 2$$
$$2 < x < 14$$
$$(2, 14)$$

65.
$$h \le 2 \quad \text{and} \quad 7h - 4 > -25$$
$$h \le 2 \quad \text{and} \quad 7h > -21$$
$$h \le 2 \quad \text{and} \quad h > -3$$

$h \le 2$

$h > -3$

$x \le 2$ and $x > -3$ which is $-3 < h \le 2$

$$\{h | -3 < h \le 2\}$$

66. $2x - 1 > 5$　or　$3x - 2 \le 7$

　　　　$2x > 6$　or　　$3x \le 9$

　　　　$x > 3$　or　　　$x \le 3$

$x > 3$

3

$x \le 3$

3

$x > 3$ or $x \le 3$

0

which is the entire real number line or R.

67. $4x - 5 < 11$　and　$-3x - 4 \ge 8$

　　　　$4x < 16$　and　　　$-3x \ge 12$

　　　　$x < 4$　and　　　　$x \le -4$

$x \le 4$

4

$x \le -4$

-4

$x \le -4$ and $x < 4$ which is $x \le -4$

-4

$\{x | x \le -4\}$

68. $\dfrac{7 - 2g}{3} \le -5$　or　$\dfrac{3 - g}{8} > 1$

　　$7 - 2g \le -15$　or　$3 - g > 8$

　　　$-2g \le -22$　or　　$-g > 5$

　　　　$g \ge 11$　or　　$g \le -5$

$g \le -5$

$g \ge 11$

$g \le -5$ or $g \ge 11$

$\{g | g \le -5$ or $g \ge 11\}$

69. $|a| = 2$

$a = 2$ or $a = -2$
The solution set is $\{-2, 2\}$.

70. $|x| < 3$
$-3 < x < 3$
The solution set is $\{x | -3 < x < 3\}$.

71. $|x| \ge 4$
$x \le -4$ or $x \ge 4$
The solution set is $\{x | x \le -4$ or $x \ge 4\}$.

72. $|l + 5| = 11$

　$l + 5 = -11$　or　$l + 5 = 11$

　　$l = -16$　　　　　$l = 6$

The solution set is $\{-16, 6\}$.

73. $|x - 2| \ge 5$

　$x - 2 \le -5$　or　$x - 2 \ge 5$

　　$x \le -3$　　　　　$x \ge 7$

The solution set is $\{x | x \le -3$ or $x \ge 7\}$.

74. $|4 - 2x| = 5$

　$4 - 2x = 5$　　or　$4 - 2x = -5$

　　$-2x = 1$　　　　　　$-2x = -9$

　　$x = \dfrac{1}{-2}$　　　　　$x = \dfrac{-9}{-2}$

　　$x = -\dfrac{1}{2}$　　　　　$x = \dfrac{9}{2}$

The solution set is $\left\{-\dfrac{1}{2}, \dfrac{9}{2}\right\}$.

75. $|-2q + 9| < 7$

　　$-7 < -2q + 9 < 7$

　$-7 - 9 < -2q + 9 - 9 < 7 - 9$

　　$-16 < -2q < -2$

　　$\dfrac{-16}{-2} > \dfrac{-2q}{-2} > \dfrac{-2}{-2}$

　　$8 > q > 1$

　　$1 < q < 8$

The solution set is $\{q | 1 < q < 8\}$.

76. $\left|\dfrac{2x - 3}{5}\right| = 1$

　$\dfrac{2x - 3}{5} = 1$　or　$\dfrac{2x - 3}{5} = -1$

　$2x - 3 = 5$　　　$2x - 3 = -5$

　　$2x = 8$　　　　　$2x = -2$

　　$x = 4$　　　　　　$x = -1$

The solution set is $\{-1, 4\}$.

77. $\left|\dfrac{x - 4}{3}\right| < 6$

　$-6 < \dfrac{x - 4}{3} < 6$

　$3(-6) < 3\left(\dfrac{x - 4}{3}\right) < 3(6)$

　$-18 < x - 4 < 18$
　$-14 < x < 22$
The solution set is $\{x | -14 < x < 22\}$.

78. $|3x - 4| = |x + 3|$

$3x - 4 = -(x + 3)$ or $3x - 4 = x + 3$

$3x - 4 = -x - 3$ $2x - 4 = 3$

$4x - 4 = -3$ $2x = 7$

$4x = 1$ $x = \dfrac{7}{2}$

$x = \dfrac{1}{4}$

The solution set is $\left\{\dfrac{1}{4},\ \dfrac{7}{2}\right\}$.

79. $|2x - 3| + 4 \ge -10$

$|2x - 3| \ge -14$

Since the right side is negative and the left side is non-negative, the solution is the entire real number line since the absolute value of a number is always greater than a negative number. The solution set is all real numbers or R.

80. $|3c + 8| - 5 \le 2$

$|3c + 8| \le 7$

$-7 \le 3c + 8 \le 7$

$-7 - 8 \le 3c + 8 - 8 \le 7 - 8$

$-15 \le 3c \le -1$

$\dfrac{-15}{3} \le \dfrac{3c}{3} \le \dfrac{-1}{3}$

$-5 \le c \le -\dfrac{1}{3}$

$\left[-5, -\dfrac{1}{3}\right]$

81. $3 < 2x - 5 \le 9$

$3 + 5 < 2x - 5 + 5 \le 9 + 5$

$8 < 2x \le 14$

$\dfrac{8}{2} < \dfrac{2x}{2} \le \dfrac{14}{2}$

$4 < x \le 7$

The solution is (4, 7].

82. $-6 \le \dfrac{3 - 2x}{4} < 5$

$4(-6) \le 4\left(\dfrac{3 - 2x}{4}\right) < 4(5)$

$-24 \le 3 - 2x < 20$

$-27 \le -2x < 17$

$\dfrac{-27}{-2} \ge \dfrac{-2x}{-2} > \dfrac{17}{-2}$

$\dfrac{27}{2} \ge x > -\dfrac{17}{2}$

$-\dfrac{17}{2} < x \le \dfrac{27}{2}$

The solution is $\left(-\dfrac{17}{2},\ \dfrac{27}{2}\right]$.

83. $2p - 5 < 7$ or $9 - 3p \le 12$

$2p < 12$ or $-3p \le 3$

$p < 6$ or $p \ge -1$

$-1 \le p < 6$

The solution is $[-1, 6)$.

84. $x - 3 \le 4$ or $2x - 5 > 9$

$x - 3 + 3 \le 4 + 3$ $2x - 5 + 5 > 9 + 5$

$x \le 7$ $2x > 14$

$x > 7$

The solution is $(-\infty, \infty)$.

85. $-10 < 3(x - 4) \le 12$

$-10 < 3x - 12 \le 12$

$-10 + 12 < 3x - 12 + 12 \le 12 + 12$

$2 < 3x \le 24$

$\dfrac{2}{3} < x \le 8$

The solution is $\left(\dfrac{2}{3},\ 8\right]$.

Practice Test

1. $-4a^2bc^4$ is degree seven since $-4a^2bc^4$ can be written as $-4a^2b^1c^4$ and the sum of the exponents is $2 + 1 + 4 = 7$.

2. $2p - 3q + 2pq - 6p(q - 3) - 4p$

$= 2p - 3q + 2pq - 6pq + 18p - 4p$

$= (2p + 18p - 4p) - 3q + (2pq - 6pq)$

$= 16p - 3q - 4pq$

3. $4x - \{3 - [2(x - 2) - 5x]\}$

$= 4x - [3 - (2x - 4 - 5x)]$

$= 4x - [3 - (-3x - 4)]$

$= 4x - (3 + 3x + 4)$

$= 4x - (7 + 3x)$

$= 4x - 7 - 3x$

$= x - 7$

4.
$$7(d+2) = 3(2d-4)$$
$$7d+14 = 6d-12$$
$$7d+14-6d = 6d-12-6d$$
$$d+14 = -12$$
$$d+14-14 = -12-14$$
$$d = -26$$

5.
$$\frac{r}{6}+\frac{2}{3} = \frac{8}{9}$$
$$18\left(\frac{r}{6}+\frac{2}{3}\right) = 18\left(\frac{8}{9}\right)$$
$$3r+12 = 16$$
$$3r+12-12 = 16-12$$
$$3r = 4$$
$$\frac{3r}{3} = \frac{4}{3}$$
$$r = \frac{4}{3}$$

6.
$$-2(x+3) = 4\{3[x-(3x+7)]+2\}$$
$$-2x-6 = 4\{3[x-3x-7]+2\}$$
$$-2x-6 = 4\{3[-2x-7]+2\}$$
$$-2x-6 = 4\{-6x-21+2\}$$
$$-2x-6 = 4\{-6x-19\}$$
$$-2x-6 = -24x-76$$
$$-2x-6+24x = -24x-76+24x$$
$$22x-6 = -76$$
$$22x-6+6 = -76+6$$
$$22x = -70$$
$$\frac{22x}{22} = \frac{-70}{22}$$
$$x = -\frac{35}{11}$$

7. $7x-6(2x-4) = 3-(5x-6)$
$$7x-12x+24 = 3-5x+6$$
$$-5x+24 = -5x+9$$
$$-5x+24+5x = -5x+9+5x$$
$$24 = 9$$
This is a false statement which means there is no solution. $\varnothing$

8. $-\frac{1}{2}(4x-6) = \frac{1}{3}(3-6x)+2$
$$-2x+3 = 1-2x+2$$
$$-2x+3 = -2x+3$$
$$-2x+3+2x = -2x+3+2x$$
$$3 = 3$$
This is always true which means the solution is any real number or R.

9. $S_n = \dfrac{a_1(1-r^n)}{1-r}$

$$S_3 = \frac{3\left[1-\left(\frac{1}{3}\right)^3\right]}{1-\frac{1}{3}} = \frac{3\left[1-\frac{1}{27}\right]}{1-\frac{1}{3}} = \frac{3\left(\frac{26}{27}\right)}{\frac{2}{3}}$$
$$= \frac{\frac{26}{9}}{\frac{2}{3}} = \frac{26}{9}\cdot\frac{3}{2} = \frac{13}{3}$$

10.
$$c = \frac{a-3b}{2}$$
$$2(c) = 2\left(\frac{a-3b}{2}\right)$$
$$2c = a-3b$$
$$2c-a = a-a-3b$$
$$2c-a = -3b$$
$$\frac{2c-a}{-3} = \frac{-3b}{-3}$$
$$\frac{2c-a}{-3} = b \text{ or } b = \frac{a-2c}{3}$$

11.
$$A = \frac{1}{2}h(b_1+b_2)$$
$$2(A) = 2\left[\frac{1}{2}h(b_1+b_2)\right]$$
$$2A = h(b_1+b_2)$$
$$2A = hb_1+hb_2$$
$$2A-hb_1 = hb_1-hb_1+hb_2$$
$$2A-hb_1 = hb_2$$
$$\frac{2A-hb_1}{h} = \frac{hb_2}{h}$$
$$\frac{2A-hb_1}{h} = b_2 \text{ or } b_2 = \frac{2A-hb_1}{h}$$

12. Let x be the cost of the clubs before tax, then $0.07x$ is the tax.
$$x+0.07x = 668.75$$
$$1.07x = 668.75$$
$$x = \frac{668.75}{1.07}$$
$$x = 625$$
The cost of the clubs before tax is $625.

13. Let x = the number of visits Jay can make.   Jay can visit the health club 80 times.

$$240 + 2x = 400$$
$$2x = 160$$
$$x = 80$$

14. Let x = the number of hours in which the will be 147 miles apart.

Person	Rate	Time	Distance
Jeffrey	15	x	$15x$
Roberto	20	x	$20x$

The total distance is the sum of the distances they traveled.
$$15x + 20x = 147$$
$$35x = 147$$
$$x = \frac{147}{35}$$
$$x = 4.2$$

In 4.2 hours, the cyclists will be 147 miles apart.

15. Let x be the amount of 12% solution.

Solution	Strength of Solution	No. of Liters	Amount of Salt
12%	0.12	x	$0.12x$
25%	0.25	10	$0.25(10)$
20%	0.20	$x + 10$	$0.20(x + 10)$

$$0.12x + 0.25(10) = 0.20(x + 10)$$
$$0.12x + 2.50 = 0.20x + 2.00$$
$$0.12x + 0.50 = 0.20x$$
$$0.50 = 0.08x$$
$$\frac{0.50}{0.08} = x$$
$$6.25 = x$$

Combine 6.25 liters of the 12% solution with 10 liters of the 25% solution to obtain the mixture.

16. Let x be the amount invested at 8%. Then $12,000 - x$ is the amount invested at 7%.

Account	Principal	Rate	Interest
8%	x	0.08	$0.08x$
7%	$12,000 - x$	0.07	$0.07(12,000 - x)$

The total interest is $910.
$$0.08x + 0.07(12,000 - x) = 910$$
$$0.08x + 840 - 0.07x = 910$$
$$0.01x + 840 = 910$$
$$0.01x = 70$$
$$x = \frac{70}{0.01}$$
$$x = 7000$$

Thus, $7000 was invested at 8% and the remaining amount of $12000 - 7000 = \$5000$ was invested at 7%.

17. $3(2q+4) < 5(q-1)+7$

$6q+12 < 5q-5+7$

$6q+12 < 5q+2$

$q+12 < 2$

$q < -10$

18. $\dfrac{6-2x}{5} \ge -12$

$5\left(\dfrac{6-2x}{5}\right) \ge 5(-12)$

$6-2x \ge -60$

$-2x \ge -66$

$\dfrac{-2x}{-2} \le \dfrac{-66}{-2}$

$x \le 33$

19. $x-3 \le 4$ and $2x-4 > 5$

$x-3+3 \le 4+3$ $2x-4+4 > 5+4$

$x \le 7$ $2x > 9$

$x > \dfrac{9}{2}$

The solution is $\left(\dfrac{9}{2},\ 7\right]$.

20. $1 \le \dfrac{2u-5}{3} < 7$

$3(1) \le 3\left(\dfrac{2u-5}{3}\right) < 3(7)$

$3 \le 2u-5 < 21$

$3+5 \le 2u-5+5 < 21+5$

$8 \le 2u < 26$

$4 \le u < 13$

The solution is [4, 13).

21. $|2b+5| = 9$

$2b+5 = -9$ or $2b+5 = 9$

$2b = -14$ $2b = 4$

$b = -7$ $b = 2$

The solution set is {−7, 2}.

22. $|2x-3| = \left|\dfrac{1}{2}x-10\right|$

$2x-3 = -\left(\dfrac{1}{2}x-10\right)$ or $2x-3 = \dfrac{1}{2}x-10$

$2x-3 = -\dfrac{1}{2}x+10$ $\dfrac{3}{2}x-3 = -10$

$\dfrac{5}{2}x-3 = 10$ $\dfrac{3}{2}x = -7$

$\dfrac{5}{2}x = 13$ $\dfrac{2}{3}\left(\dfrac{3}{2}x\right) = \dfrac{2}{3}(-7)$

$\dfrac{2}{5}\left(\dfrac{5}{2}x\right) = \dfrac{2}{5}(13)$ $x = -\dfrac{14}{3}$

$x = \dfrac{26}{5}$

The solution set is $\left\{-\dfrac{14}{3},\ \dfrac{26}{5}\right\}$.

23. $|4z+12| = 0$

$4z+12 = 0$

$4z = -12$

$z = -3$

The solution set is {−3}.

24. $|2x-3|+1 > 6$

$|2x-3| > 5$

$2x-3 < -5$ or $2x-3 > 5$

$2x < -2$ $2x > 8$

$x < -1$ $x > 4$

The solution set is $\{x \mid x < -1 \text{ or } x > 4\}$.

25. $\left|\dfrac{2x-3}{4}\right| \le \dfrac{1}{2}$

$-\dfrac{1}{2} \le \dfrac{2x-3}{4} \le \dfrac{1}{2}$

$4\left(-\dfrac{1}{2}\right) \le 4\left(\dfrac{2x-3}{4}\right) \le 4\left(\dfrac{1}{2}\right)$

$-2 \le 2x-3 \le 2$

$1 \le 2x \le 5$

$\dfrac{1}{2} \le x \le \dfrac{5}{2}$

The solution set is $\left\{x \mid \dfrac{1}{2} \le x \le \dfrac{5}{2}\right\}$.

Cumulative Review Test

1. **a.** $A \cup B = \{1,2,3,5,7,9,11,13,15\}$

   b. $A \cap B = \{3,5,7,11,13\}$

2. **a.** Commutative property of addition

   b. Associative property of multiplication

   c. Distributive property

3. $-4^2 + (-6)^2 \div (2^3 - 2)^2$
   $= -4^2 + (-6)^2 \div (8-2)^2$
   $= -4^2 + (-6)^2 \div (6)^2$
   $= -16 + 36 \div 36$
   $= -16 + 1$
   $= -15$

4. Substitute -1 for a and -2 for b.
   $a^2b^3 + ab^2 - 3b$
   $= (-1)^2(-2)^3 + (-1)(-2)^2 - 3(-2)$
   $= (1)(-8) + (-1)(4) - 3(-2)$
   $= -8 + (-4) - (-6)$
   $= -8 + (-4) + 6$
   $= -12 + 6$
   $= -6$

5. $\dfrac{8 - \sqrt[3]{27} \cdot 3 \div 9}{|-5| - [5 - (12 \div 4)]^2} = \dfrac{8 - \sqrt[3]{27} \cdot 3 \div 9}{|-5| - [5-3]^2}$
   $= \dfrac{8 - \sqrt[3]{27} \cdot 3 \div 9}{|-5| - 2^2}$
   $= \dfrac{8 - 3 \cdot 3 \div 9}{5 - 4}$
   $= \dfrac{8 - 9 \div 9}{5 - 4}$
   $= \dfrac{8 - 1}{5 - 4}$
   $= \dfrac{7}{1}$
   $= 7$

6. $(2x^4y^3)^{-2} = \left(\dfrac{1}{2x^4y^3}\right)^2$
   $= \dfrac{1^2}{2^2 x^{4\cdot2} y^{3\cdot2}}$
   $= \dfrac{1}{4x^8y^6}$

7. $\left(\dfrac{3m^2n^{-4}}{m^{-3}n^2}\right)^2 = \left(\dfrac{3m^{2-(-3)}}{n^{2-(-4)}}\right)^2$
   $= \left(\dfrac{3m^5}{n^6}\right)^2$
   $= \dfrac{3^2m^{5\cdot2}}{n^{6\cdot2}}$
   $= \dfrac{9m^{10}}{n^{12}}$

8. $\dfrac{5.704 \times 10^5}{1.045 \times 10^3} = \dfrac{5.704}{1.045} \times 10^{5-3}$
   $\approx 5.458 \times 10^2$
   ≈ 545.8

   The land area of Alaska is about 545.8 times larger than that of Rhode Island.

9. $-3(y+7) = 2(-2y-8)$
   $-3y - 21 = -4y - 16$
   $y - 21 = -16$
   $y = 5$

10. $1.2(x-3) = 2.4x - 4.98$
    $1.2x - 3.6 = 2.4x - 4.98$
    $1.2x = 2.4x - 1.38$
    $-1.2x = -1.38$
    $x = \dfrac{-1.38}{-1.2}$
    $x = 1.15$

11. $\dfrac{2m}{3} - \dfrac{1}{6} = \dfrac{4}{9}m$
    $18\left(\dfrac{2m}{3} - \dfrac{1}{6}\right) = 18\left(\dfrac{4}{9}m\right)$
    $12m - 3 = 8m$
    $4m - 3 = 0$
    $4m = 3$
    $m = \dfrac{3}{4}$

12. A conditional equation is true only under specific conditions. An identity is true for all values of the variable. A contradiction is never true. Answers may vary. One possible answer is: $3x + 4 = 13$ is a conditional linear equation.
$3(x + 7) = 2(x + 10) + x + 1$ is an identity.
$3x + 4 = 3x + 8$ is a contradiction.

13.
$$x = \frac{-b + \sqrt{b^2 - 4ac}}{2a}$$
$$= \frac{-(-8) + \sqrt{(-8)^2 - 4(3)(-3)}}{2(3)}$$
$$= \frac{-(-8) + \sqrt{64 + 36}}{6}$$
$$= \frac{-(-8) + \sqrt{100}}{6}$$
$$= \frac{8 + 10}{6}$$
$$= \frac{18}{6}$$
$$= 3$$

14.
$$y - y_1 = m(x - x_1)$$
$$\frac{y - y_1}{m} = \frac{m(x - x_1)}{m}$$
$$\frac{y - y_1}{m} = x - x_1$$
$$\frac{y - y_1}{m} + x_1 = x$$
$$x = \frac{y - y_1}{m} + x_1 \text{ or } x = \frac{y - y_1 + mx_1}{m}$$

15. a.
$$-4 < \frac{5x - 2}{3} < 2$$
$$3(-4) < 3\left(\frac{5x - 2}{3}\right) < 3(2)$$
$$-12 < 5x - 2 < 6$$
$$-12 + 2 < 5x - 2 + 2 < 6 + 2$$
$$-10 < 5x < 8$$
$$\frac{-10}{5} < \frac{5x}{5} < \frac{8}{5}$$
$$-2 < x < \frac{8}{5}$$

b. $\left\{x \middle| -2 < x < \frac{8}{5}\right\}$

c. $\left(-2, \frac{8}{5}\right)$

16. $|3h - 1| = 8$
$$3h - 1 = -8 \quad \text{or} \quad 3h - 1 = 8$$
$$3h = -7 \qquad\qquad 3h = 9$$
$$h = -\frac{7}{3} \qquad\qquad h = 3$$
Solution is $\left\{-\frac{7}{3}, 3\right\}$.

17. $|2x - 4| - 6 \geq 18$
$$|2x - 4| \geq 24$$
$$2x - 4 \leq -24 \quad \text{or} \quad 2x - 4 \geq 24$$
$$2x \leq -20 \qquad\qquad 2x \geq 28$$
$$x \leq -10 \qquad\qquad x \geq 14$$
The solution set is $\{x | x \leq -10 \text{ or } x \geq 14\}$.

18. Let x be the original price.
$$x - 0.40x = 21$$
$$0.60x = 21$$
$$x = \frac{21}{0.60}$$
$$x = 35$$
The original price was $35.

19. Let x be the speed of the car traveling south. Then $x + 10$ is the speed of the car traveling north.

Car	Rate	Time	Distance
South	x	3	$3x$
North	$x + 10$	3	$3(x + 10)$

The total distance is 270 miles.
$$3x + 3(x + 10) = 270$$
$$3x + 3x + 30 = 270$$
$$6x + 30 = 270$$
$$6x = 240$$
$$x = \frac{240}{6}$$
$$x = 40$$
The speed of the car traveling south is 40 mph and the speed of the car traveling north is $40 + 10 = 50$ mph.

20. Let x = the number of pounds of cashews.. Then $40 - x$ is the number of pounds of peanuts.

	Cost	Pounds	Cost
cashews	6.50	x	$6.50x$
peanuts	2.50	$40 - x$	$2.50(40 - x)$
mixture	4.00	40	$4.00(40)$

$$6.50x + 2.50(40 - x) = 4.00(40)$$
$$6.50x + 100 - 2.50x = 160$$
$$4.00x + 100 = 160$$
$$4.00x = 60$$
$$x = 15$$

Molly should combine 15 pounds of cashews with 40 lbs − 15 lbs = 25 lbs of peanuts.

Chapter 3

Exercise Set 3.1

1. a. The graph of any linear equation looks like a straight line.

  b. Two points are needed to graph a linear equation.
  Two points uniquely determine a straight line.

3. If a set of points is collinear, they are in a straight line.

5. $A(3, 1)$, $B(-6, 0)$, $C(2, -4)$, $D(-2, -4)$, $E(0, 3)$, $F(-8, 1)$, $G\left(\dfrac{3}{2}, -1\right)$

7.

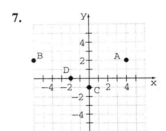

9. I

11. IV

13. II

15. III

17. $y = 2x - 5$

$21 \overset{?}{=} 2(2) - 5$

$21 \overset{?}{=} 4 - 5$

$21 \neq -1$ false

No, (2, 21) is not a solution to $y = 2x - 5$.

19. $y = |x| + 2$

$(-2) \overset{?}{=} |-4| + 2$

$-2 \overset{?}{=} 4 + 2$

$-2 \neq 6$ false

No, (−4, −2) is not a solution to $y = |x| + 2$.

21. $s = 2r^2 - r - 5$

$5 \overset{?}{=} 2(-2)^2 - (-2) - 5$

$5 \overset{?}{=} 8 + 2 - 5$

$5 = 5$ true

Yes, (−2, 5) is a solution to $s = 2r^2 - r - 5$.

23. $-a^2 + 2b^2 = -2$

$-(2)^2 + 2(1)^2 \overset{?}{=} -2$

$-(4) + 2(1) \overset{?}{=} -2$

$-4 + 2 \overset{?}{=} -2$

$-2 = -2$ true

Yes, (2, 1) is a solution to $-a^2 + 2b^2 = -2$.

25. $2x^2 + 4x - y = 0$

$2\left(\dfrac{1}{2}\right)^2 + 4\left(\dfrac{1}{2}\right) - \left(\dfrac{3}{2}\right) \overset{?}{=} 0$

$2\left(\dfrac{1}{4}\right) + 4\left(\dfrac{1}{2}\right) - \left(\dfrac{3}{2}\right) \overset{?}{=} 0$

$\dfrac{1}{2} + 2 - \dfrac{3}{2} \overset{?}{=} 0$

$1 \neq 0$ false

No, $\left(\dfrac{1}{2}, \dfrac{3}{2}\right)$ is not a solution to $2x^2 + 4x - y = 0$.

27.

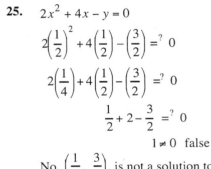

29.

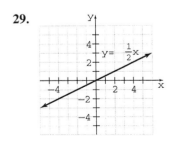

31.

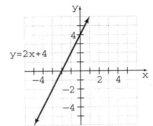

$y=2x+4$

33. $y=-3x-5$

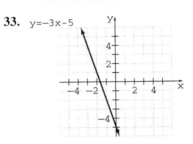

35.

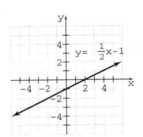

$y=\frac{1}{2}x-1$

37.

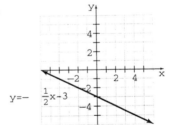

$y=-\frac{1}{2}x-3$

39.

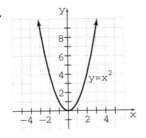

$y=x^2$

41.

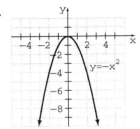

$y=-x^2$

43.

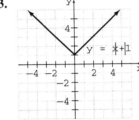

$y = |x|+1$

45.

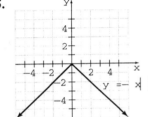

$y =- |x|$

47.

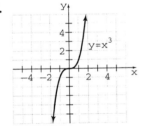

$y=x^3$

49.

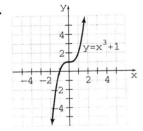

$y=x^3+1$

51.

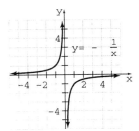

53.

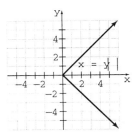

55.

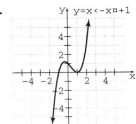

57.

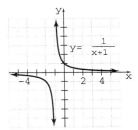

59.

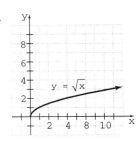

61.

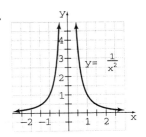

63.

$$y = \frac{x^2}{x+1}$$

$$\left(\frac{1}{12}\right) \overset{?}{=} \frac{\left(\frac{1}{3}\right)^2}{\left(\frac{1}{3}\right)+1}$$

$$\frac{1}{12} \overset{?}{=} \frac{\frac{1}{9}}{\frac{4}{3}}$$

$$\frac{1}{12} \overset{?}{=} \frac{1}{9} \cdot \frac{3}{4}$$

$$\frac{1}{12} \overset{?}{=} \frac{1}{12} \quad \text{true}$$

Yes, $\left(\frac{1}{3}, \frac{1}{12}\right)$ is on the graph of

the equation $y = \frac{x^2}{x+1}$.

65 a.

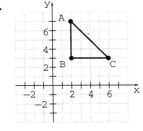

b.   area $= \frac{1}{2}bh$

$= \frac{1}{2}(4)(4)$

$= 8$

The area is 8 square units.

67. a. The estimated shipments for 1999 is 115 million.

b. The estimated shipments for 2003 is 190 million.

c. Estimated shipments of personal computers are greater than 140 million units for the years 2001, 2002, and 2003.

d. Yes, the increase in worldwide shipments of personal computers from 1999 to 2003 appears to be approximately linear. Worldwide shipments of personal computers appear to be increasing at approximately 19 million units per year from 1999 to 2003.

69.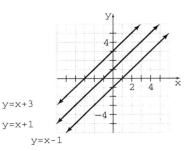

a. Each graph crosses the *y*-axis at the point corresponding to the constant term in the graph's equation.

b. Yes, all the equations seem to have the same slant or slope.

71.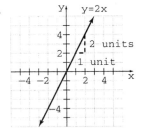

For each unit change in *x*, *y* changes 2 units. Therefore, the rate of change of *y* with respect to *x* is 2.

73.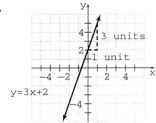

For each unit change in *x*, *y* changes 3 units. Therefore, the rate of change of *y* with respect to *x* is 3.

75. Starting at $(3, -6)$:
For a unit change, *x* changes from 3 to $3 + 1 = 4$.
At the same time, *y* changes from -6 to $-6 + 4 = -2$
So, $(4, -2)$ is a solution to the equation starting at $(4, -2)$:
For a unit change, *x* changes from 4 to $4 + 1 = 5$.
At the same time, *y* changes from -2 to $-2 + 4 = 2$.
So, $(5, 2)$ is a solution to the equation.
Answers may vary. One possible answer is the points $(4, -2)$ and $(5, 2)$.

77. c

79. a

81. d

83. b

85. b

87. d

89. b

91. d

93.

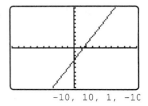

-10, 10, 1, -1C

X	**Y1**
0	-3
1	-1
2	1
3	3
4	5
5	7
6	9

Y₁◻2X-3

95.

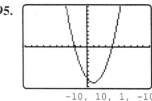

-10, 10, 1, -1C

X	**Y1**
0	-8
1	-9
2	-8
3	-5
4	0
5	7
6	16

Y₁◻X²-2X-8

97.

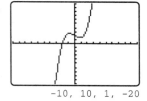

-10, 10, 1, -20

X	**Y1**
0	4
1	3
2	8
3	25
4	60
5	119
6	208

Y₁◻X^3-2X+4

99.

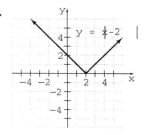

103.

$$\frac{-b + \sqrt{b^2 - 4ac}}{2a} = \frac{-(7) + \sqrt{(7)^2 - 4(2)(-15)}}{2(2)}$$

$$= \frac{-7 + \sqrt{169}}{4}$$

$$= \frac{-7 + 13}{4}$$

$$= \frac{3}{2}$$

105.

$$-4 \le \frac{4 - 3x}{2} < 5$$

$$2(-4) \le 4 - 3x < 2(5)$$

$$-8 \le 4 - 3x < 10$$

$$-8 - 4 \le -3x < 10 - 4$$

$$-12 \le -3x < 6$$

$$\frac{-12}{-3} \ge x > \frac{6}{-3}$$

$$4 \ge x > -2$$

$$-2 < x \le 4$$

$$\{x | -2 < x \le 4\}$$

Exercise Set 3.2

1. A function is a correspondence between a first set of elements, the domain, and a second set of elements, the range, such that each element of the domain corresponds to exactly one element in the range.

3. Yes, all functions are also relations. A function is a set of ordered pairs so it is a relation.

5. If each vertical line drawn through any part of the graph intersects the graph in at most one point, the graph represents a function.

7. The range is the set of values for the dependent variable.

9. Domain: $\{x \mid x \ne 0\}$

   The denominator cannot be zero.

   Range: $\{y \mid y \ne 0\}$

   All values of y except $y = 0$ are represented in the function.

11. Domain: R or $(-\infty, \infty)$

    There are no restrictions on values of x that can be used.

    Range: $\{y | y \ge 0\}$

    The absolute value of any number is never negative.

13. If y depends on x, then x is the independent variable.

15. a. Yes, the relation is a function.

    b. Domain: {3, 5, 10}, Range: {6, 10, 20}

17. a. Yes, the relation is a function.

    b. Domain: {Cameron, Tyrone, Vishnu}, Range:{1, 2}

19. a. No, the relation is not a function.

    b. Domain: {1990, 2001, 2002}, Range: {20, 34, 37}

21. a. A function

    b. Domain: {1, 2, 3, 4, 5}, Range: {1, 2, 3, 4, 5}

23. a. A function

    b. Domain: {1, 2, 3, 4, 5, 7}, Range: {−1, 0, 2, 4, 5}

25. a. Not a function

    b. Domain: {1, 2, 3}, Range: {1, 2, 4, 5, 6}

27. a. Not a function

    b. Domain: {0, 1, 2}, Range: {−7, −1, 2, 3}

29. a. A function

    b. Domain: R, Range: R

    c. $x = 2$

31. a. Not a function

    b. Domain: $\{x \mid 0 \le x \le 2\}$, Range: $\{y \mid -3 \le y \le 3\}$

    c. ≈ 1.5

33. a. Not a function

    b. Domain: $\{x \mid -4 \le x \le 4\}$, Range: $\{y \mid -2 \le y \le 2\}$

    c. $x = 0$

35. a. Not a function

    b. Domain: R, Range: R

    c. $x = 2$

37. a. A function

    b. Domain: {1, 2, 3}, Range: {1}

    c. No values of x

39. a. A function

    b. Domain: $\{x \mid -20 \le x \le 10\}$, Range: $\{y \mid -2 \le y \le 2\}$

    c. $x = -17.5$ or $x = -7.5$ or $x = 2.5$

41. a. $f(2) = -2(2) + 5 = -4 + 5 = 1$

    b. $f(-3) = -2(-3) + 5 = 6 + 5 = 11$

43. a. $h(0) = (0)^2 - (0) - 6 = -6$

    b. $h(-1) = (-1)^2 - (-1) - 6 = 1 + 1 - 6 = -4$

45. a. $r(1) = -(1)^3 - 2(1)^2 + (1) + 4$
$$= -1 - 2 + 1 + 4 = 2$$

    b. $r(1) = -(-2)^3 - 2(-2)^2 + (-2) + 4$
$$= -(-8) - 2(4) + (-2) + 4$$
$$= 8 - 8 - 2 + 4$$
$$= 2$$

47. a. $h(6) = |5 - 2(6)|$
$$= |5 - 12|$$
$$= |-7|$$
$$= 7$$

    b. $h\left(\dfrac{5}{2}\right) = \left|5 - 2\left(\dfrac{5}{2}\right)\right|$
$$= |5 - 5|$$
$$= 0$$

49. a.
$$s(-2) = \sqrt{(-2)+2}$$
$$= \sqrt{0}$$
$$= 0$$

b.
$$s(7) = \sqrt{(7)+2}$$
$$= \sqrt{9}$$
$$= 3$$

51. a.
$$g(0) = \frac{(0)^3 - 2}{(0) - 2}$$
$$= \frac{-2}{-2}$$
$$= 1$$

b.
$$g(2) = \frac{(2)^3 - 2}{(2) - 2}$$
$$= \frac{8-2}{0} \quad \text{undefined}$$

53. a. $A(2) = 6(2) = 12$
The area is 12 square feet.

b. $A(4.5) = 6(4.5) = 27$
The area is 27 square feet.

55. a. $A(r) = \pi r^2$

b. $A(10) = \pi(10)^2 = 100\pi \approx 314.2$
The area is about 314.2 square yards.

57. a. $C(F) = \frac{5}{9}(F - 32)$

b. $C(-40) = \frac{5}{9}(-40 - 32) = \frac{5}{9}(-72) = -40$
The Celsius temperature that corresponds to
$-40°F$ is $-40°C$.

59. a. $T(3) = -0.03(3)^2 + 1.5(3) + 14$
$$= -0.27 + 4.5 + 14$$
$$= 18.23$$
The temperature is $18.23°C$.

b. $T(12) = -0.03(12)^2 + 1.5(12) + 14$
$$= -4.32 + 18 + 14$$
$$= 27.68$$
The temperature is $27.68°C$.

61. a. $T(4) = -0.02(4)^2 - 0.34(4) + 80$
$$= -0.32 - 1.36 + 80$$
$$= 78.32$$
The temperature is $78.32°$.

b. $T(12) = -0.02(12)^2 - 0.34(12) + 80$
$$= -2.88 - 4.08 + 80$$
$$= 73.04$$
The temperature is $73.04°$.

63. a. $T(6) = \frac{1}{3}(6)^3 + \frac{1}{2}(6)^2 + \frac{1}{6}(6)$
$$= 72 + 18 + 1$$
$$= 91$$
91 oranges

b. $T(8) = \frac{1}{3}(8)^3 + \frac{1}{2}(8)^2 + \frac{1}{6}(8)$
$$= \frac{512}{3} + 32 + \frac{4}{3}$$
204 oranges

65. Answers will vary. One possible interpretation: The person warms up slowly, possibly by walking for 5 minutes, then begins jogging slowly over a period of 5 minutes. For the next 15 minutes, the person jogs at a steady pace. For the next 5 minutes, he walks slowly and his heart rate decreases to his normal resting heart rate. The rate stays the same for the next 5 minutes.

67. Answers will vary. One possible interpretation: The man walks on level ground, about 30 feet above sea level, for 5 minutes. For the next 5 minutes he walks uphill to 45 feet above sea level. For 5 minutes he walks on level ground then walks quickly downhill for 3 minutes to an elevation of 20 feet above sea level. For 7 minutes he walks on level ground. Then he walks quickly uphill.

69. Answers may vary. One possible interpretation: A woman drives in stop-and-go traffic for 5 minutes. Then she drives on the highway for 15 minutes, gets off onto a country road for a few minutes, stops for a couple of minutes, and returns to stop-and-go traffic.

71. a. Yes, it passes the vertical line test.

b. The independent variable is the year.

c. $f(2000)$ is about \$115 billion.

d.
$$\text{percent increase} = \frac{115 - 80}{80} \times 100$$
$$= .4375 \times 100 \qquad \text{The}$$
$$= 43.75$$
percent increase from 1997 through 2000 was about 43.75%.

73. a. Yes, it passes the vertical line test.

b. Yes, it passes the vertical line test.

c. No, the graph does not appear to be a straight line.

d. Yes, the graph does seem to be a straight line.

e. $f(t) = \$80$ billion for $t = 1999$.

f. $g(t) = \$18$ billion for $t = 2000$.

75. a.

b. No, the points don't lie on a straight line.

c. The cost of a 30-second commercial in 2000 was about \$2,000,000.

77. a.

b.
$$f(40,000) = -0.00004(40,000) + 4.25$$
$$= -1.6 + 4.25$$
$$= 2.65$$
The cost of a bushel of soybeans if 40,000 bushels are produced is approximately \$2.65 per bushel.

81.
$$E = a_1 p_1 + a_2 p_2 + a_3 p_3$$
$$E - a_1 p_1 - a_3 p_3 = a_2 p_2$$
$$p_2 = \frac{E - a_1 p_1 - a_3 p_3}{a_2}$$

83.
$$\left| \frac{x-4}{3} \right| + 2 = 4$$
$$\left| \frac{x-4}{3} \right| = 2$$
$$\frac{x-4}{3} = -2 \quad \text{or} \quad \frac{x-4}{3} = 2$$
$$x - 4 = -6 \qquad\qquad x - 4 = 6$$
$$x = -2 \qquad\qquad\quad x = 10$$
The solution set is $\{-2, 10\}$.

Exercise Set 3.3

1. The standard form of a linear equation is $ax + by = c$, where a, b, and c are real numbers, and a and b are not both 0.

3. To find the x-intercept, set $y = 0$ and solve for x. To find the y-intercept, set $x = 0$ and solve for y.

5. The graph of $x = a$, for any real number a, will be a vertical line.

7. The graph of $f(x) = b$, for any real number b, will be a horizontal line.

9. To solve an equation in one variable, graph both sides of the equation. The solution is the x-coordinate of the intersection.

11.
$$y = -2x + 4$$
$$2x + y = 4$$

13.
$$3(x - 2) = 4(y - 5)$$
$$3x - 6 = 4y - 20$$
$$3x - 4y = -14$$

15. $y = -2x + 4$

For the y-intercept, set $x = 0$ and solve for y:

$y = -2x + 4$

$y = -2x + 4$

$y = 0 + 4$

$y = 4$

The y-intercept is at $(0, 4)$.

For the x-intercept, set $y = 0$ and solve for x:

$y = -2x + 4$

$0 = -2x + 4$

$-4 = -2x$

$\dfrac{-4}{-2} = y$

$2 = x$

The x-intercept is at $(2, 0)$.

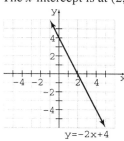

17. $y = 2x + 3$

For the y-intercept, set $x = 0$ and solve for y:

$y = 2x + 3$

$y = 2(0) + 3$

$y = 0 + 3$

$y = 3$

The y-intercept is at $(0, 3)$.

For the x-intercept, set $y = 0$ and solve for x:

$y = 2x + 3$

$0 = 2x + 3$

$-3 = 2x$

$-\dfrac{3}{2} = x$

The x-intercept is at $\left(-\dfrac{3}{2},\ 0\right)$.

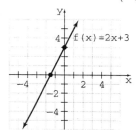

19. $2y = 4x + 6$

For the y-intercept, set $x = 0$ and solve for y:

$2y = 4x + 6$

$2y = 4(0) + 6$

$2y = 0 + 6$

$y = 3$

The y-intercept is at $(0, 3)$.

For the x-intercept, set $y = 0$ and solve for y:

$2y = 4x + 6$

$2(0) = 4x + 6$

$0 = 4x + 6$

$-6 = 4x$

$\dfrac{-6}{4} = x$

$-\dfrac{3}{2} = x$

The x-intercept is at $\left(-\dfrac{3}{2}, 0\right)$.

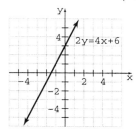

21. $\dfrac{4}{3}x = y - 3$

For the y-intercept, set $x = 0$ and solve for y:

$\dfrac{4}{3}(0) = y - 3$

$0 = y - 3$

$3 = y$

The y-intercept is at $(0, 3)$.

For the x-intercept, set $y = 0$ and solve for x:

$\dfrac{4}{3}x = (0) - 3$

$\dfrac{4}{3}x = -3$

$3\left(\dfrac{4}{3}x\right) = 3(-3)$

$4x = -9$

$x = -\dfrac{9}{4}$

The *x*-intercept is at $\left(-\dfrac{9}{4},\ 0\right)$.

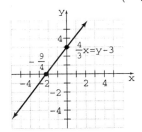

23. $15x + 30y = 60$
For the *y*-intercept, set $x = 0$ and solve for *y*:
$15(0) + 30y = 60$

$$0 + 30y = 60$$

$$30y = 60$$

$$y = 2$$

The *y*-intercept is at (0, 2).
For the *x*-intercept, set $y = 0$ and solve for *x*:
$15x + y(0) = 60$

$$15x + 0 = 60$$

$$15x = 60$$

$$x = 4$$

The *x*-intercept is at (4, 0).

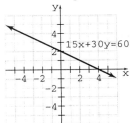

25. $0.25x + 0.50y = 1.00$
For the *y*-intercept, set $x = 0$ and solve for *y*:
$0.25x + 0.50y = 1.00$
$0.25(0) + 0.50y = 1.00$
$0 + 0.50y = 1.00$
$0.50y = 1.00$

$$y = \frac{1.00}{0.50} = 2$$

The *y*-intercept is at (0, 2).
For the *x*-intercept, set $y = 0$ and solve for *x*:
$0.25x + 0.50y = 1.00$
$0.25x + 0.50(0) = 1.00$
$0.25x + 0 = 1.00$
$0.25x = 1.00$

$$x = \frac{1.00}{0.25} = 4$$

The *x*-intercept is (4, 0).

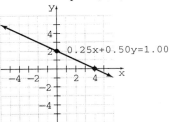

27. $120x - 360y = 720$
For the *y*-intercept, set $x = 0$ and solve for *y*:
$120x - 360y = 720$
$120(0) - 360y = 720$
$0 - 360y = 720$
$-360y = 720$

$$y = \frac{720}{-360} = -2$$

The *y*-intercept is at (0, –2).
For the *x*-intercept, set $y = 0$ and solve for *x*:
$120x - 360y = 720$
$120x - 360(0) = 720$
$120x - 0 = 720$
$120x = 720$

$$x = \frac{720}{120} = 6$$

The *x*-intercept is 6 and the point is (6, 0).

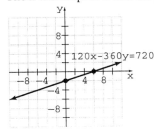

29. Multiply each term by the least common multiple, 12.

$$\frac{1}{3}x + \frac{1}{4}y = 12$$

$$12\left(\frac{1}{3}x\right) + 12\left(\frac{1}{4}y\right) = 12(12)$$

$$4x + 3y = 144$$

For the y-intercept, set $x = 0$ and solve for y:

$$4x + 3y = 144$$
$$4(0) + 3y = 144$$
$$0 + 3y = 144$$
$$3y = 144$$
$$y = \frac{144}{3} = 48$$

The y-intercept is at $(0, 48)$.

For the x-intercept, set $y = 0$ and solve for x:

$$4x + 3y = 144$$
$$4x + 3(0) = 144$$
$$4x + 0 = 144$$
$$4x = 144$$
$$x = \frac{144}{4} = 36$$

The x-intercept is at $(36, 0)$.

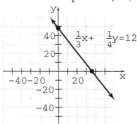

31. The equation is $y = -2x$. To graph, plot a few points.

x	Calculation	y
0	$-2(0)$	0
1	$-2(1)$	-2
-1	$-2(-1)$	2

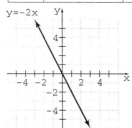

33. The equation is $f(x) = \frac{1}{3}x$. To graph, plot a few points. Pick multiples of 3 for easier calculation.

x	Calculation	$f(x)$
0	$\frac{1}{3}(0)$	0
3	$\frac{1}{3}(3)$	1
-3	$\frac{1}{3}(-3)$	-1

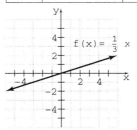

35. Solve for y and make a table of values.

$$2x + 4y = 0$$
$$4y = -2x$$
$$y = -\frac{1}{2}x$$

x	Calculation	y
0	$-\frac{1}{2}(0)$	0
2	$-\frac{1}{2}(2)$	-1
-2	$-\frac{1}{2}(-2)$	1

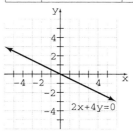

37. Solve for y and make a table of values.
$$4x - 6y = 0$$
$$-6y = -4x$$
$$y = \frac{2}{3}x$$

x	Calculation	y
0	$\frac{2}{3}(0)$	0
3	$\frac{2}{3}(3)$	2
−3	$\frac{2}{3}(-3)$	−2

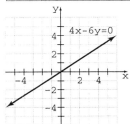

39. $y = 4$
This is a horizontal line 4 units above the x-axis.

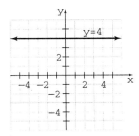

41. $x = -4$
This is a vertical line 4 units to the left of the y-axis.

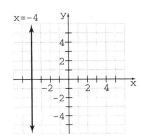

43. $y = -1.5$
This is a horizontal line 1.5 units below the x-axis.

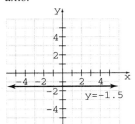

45. $x = \frac{5}{2}$
This is vertical line $\frac{5}{2}$ units to the right of the y-axis.

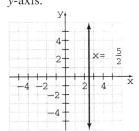

47. $x = 0$
This is a vertical line corresponding to the y-axis.

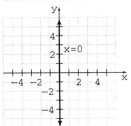

49. The equation is $d = 30t$. To graph, plot a few points.

t	Calculation	d
0	30(0)	0
1	30(1)	30
4	30(4)	120

51. a. $p = 60x - 80,000$. To graph, plot a few points.

x	Calculation	p
0	$60(0) - 80,000$	$-80,000$
2500	$60(2500) - 80,000$	$70,000$
5000	$60(5000) - 80,000$	$220,000$

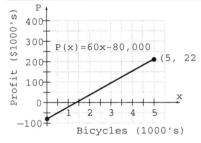

b. To break even, the profit would be zero. That is, set $p = 0$ and solve for x:
$0 = 60x - 80,000$
$-60x = -80,000$
$x = \dfrac{-80,000}{-60} \approx 1333$
The company must sell about 1,300 bicycles to break even.

c. To earn a profit of $150,000, set $p = 150,000$ and solve for x.
$150,000 = 60x - 80,000$
$230,000 = 60x$
$\dfrac{230,000}{60} = x$ or $x = 3833$
The company must sell about 3,800 bicycles to make a $150,000 profit.

53. a. $s(x) = 500 + 0.15x$

b. To graph, plot a few points.

x	Calculation	s
0	$500 + 0.15(0)$	500
1000	$500 + 0.15(1000)$	650
5000	$500 + 0.15(5000)$	1250

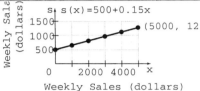

c. For weekly sales of $2500,
$s(2500) = 500 + 0.15(2500)$
$= 500 + 375$
$= 875$
Her salary is $875.

d. For a salary of $1025, set $s = 1025$ and solve for x.
$1025 = 500 + 0.15x$
$525 = 0.15x$
$3500 = x$
Her weekly sales are $3500.

55. a. There is only one y-value for each x-value.

b. The independent variable is length. The dependent variable is weight.

c. Yes, the graph of weight versus length is approximately linear.

d. The weight of the average girl who is 85 centimeters long is 11.5 kilograms.

e. The average length of a girl with a weight of 7 kilograms is 65 centimeters.

f. For a girl 95 centimeters long, the weights 12.0–15.5 kilograms are considered normal.

g. As the lengths increase, the normal range of weights increases. Yes, this is expected: as the girl grows, it is reasonable that her weight would increase with her length.

57. The x- and y-intercepts of a graph will be the same when the graph goes through the origin.

59. Answers may vary. One possible answer is,
$f(x) = 4$ is a function whose graph has no
x-intercept but has a y-intercept of $(0, 4)$.

61. The x- and y-intercepts
will both be 0.

63. a.

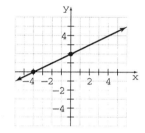

b. vertical change $= 2 - 0 = 2$

c. horizontal change $= 0 - (-4) = 4$

d. $\dfrac{\text{vertical change}}{\text{horizontal change}} = \dfrac{2}{4} = \dfrac{1}{2}$
The ratio represents the slope of the line.

65. Graph $f(x) = 3x + 2$ and $g(x) = 2x + 3$, and find
the intersection.

The solution is $x = 1$.

67. Graph $f(x) = 0.3(x + 5)$ and $g(x) = -0.6(x + 2)$,
and find the intersection.

The solution is $x = -3$.

69. The x-intercept is $(-3.2, 0)$. The y-intercept is
$(0, 6.4)$.

71. To use the graphing calculator, we must rewrite
the equation in the form $y = f(x)$.
$-4x - 3.2y = 8$
$\qquad -3.2y = 4x + 8$
$\qquad\qquad y = -\dfrac{1}{3.2}(4x + 8)$

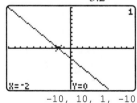

$-10, \ 10, \ 1, \ -10$
The x-intercept is $(-2, 0)$.
The y-intercept is $(0, -2.5)$.

73. $4\{2 - 3[(1-4) - 5]\} - 2$
$\quad 4\{2 - 3[(-3) - 5]\} - 2$
$\quad\quad 4\{2 - 3[-8]\} - 2$
$\quad\quad 4\{2 - (-24)\} - 2$
$\quad\quad\quad 4\{26\} - 2$
$\quad\quad\quad\quad 104 - 2$
$\quad\quad\quad\quad\quad 102$

75. a. Answers will vary.

b. $|x - a| = b$
$x - a = -b \qquad$ or $\quad x - a = b$
$\quad x = a - b \quad$ or $\qquad x = a + b$

77. a. Answers will vary.

b. $|x - a| > b$
$x - a < -b \qquad$ or $\quad x - a > b$
$\quad x < a - b \quad$ or $\qquad x > a + b$

Exercise Set 3.4

1. Select two points on the line. Then find $\dfrac{\Delta y}{\Delta x}$, the
ratio of the vertical change (or rise) to the
horizontal change (or run) between the two
points.

3. The line rises going from left to right.

5. The horizontal change on a vertical line is zero,
and we cannot divide by zero. So the slope is
undefined.

7. To get the slope-intercept form from the standard
form, solve for y in terms of x.

9. a. If a graph is translated down 3 units, it is
lowered or moved down 3 units.

b. If the y-intercept is -3 and the graph is
translated down 3 units, the new y-intercept
will be at $y = -3 - 3 = -6$. The new
y-intercept is $(0, -6)$.

11. When the slope is given as a rate of change it
means the change in y for a unit change in x.

13. $m = \dfrac{9 - 5}{0 - 2} = \dfrac{4}{-2} = -2$

15. $m = \dfrac{4-2}{1-5} = \dfrac{2}{-4} = -\dfrac{1}{2}$

17. $m = \dfrac{0-5}{2-(-3)} = \dfrac{-5}{5} = -1$

19. $m = \dfrac{-1-2}{4-4} = \dfrac{-3}{0}$, undefined

21. $m = \dfrac{4-4}{-1-(-3)} = \dfrac{0}{2} = 0$

23. $m = \dfrac{-3-3}{7-(-2)} = \dfrac{-6}{9} = -\dfrac{2}{3}$

25. $\dfrac{b-2}{4-3} = 1$

    $\dfrac{b-2}{1} = 1$

    $b - 2 = 1$

    $b = 3$

27. $\dfrac{k-3}{1-5} = \dfrac{1}{2}$

    $\dfrac{k-3}{-4} = \dfrac{1}{2}$

    $-4\left(\dfrac{k-3}{-4}\right) = -4\left(\dfrac{1}{2}\right)$

    $k - 3 = -2$

    $k = 1$

29. $\dfrac{-4-2}{3-x} = 2$

    $\dfrac{-6}{3-x} = 2$

    $(3-x)\left(\dfrac{-6}{3-x}\right) = (3-x)\cdot 2$

    $-6 = 6 - 2x$

    $-12 = -2x$

    $\dfrac{-12}{-2} = x$

    $x = 6$

31. $\dfrac{-1-(-2)}{r-2} = -\dfrac{1}{2}$

    $\dfrac{1}{r-2} = -\dfrac{1}{2}$

    $2(r-2)\left(\dfrac{1}{r-2}\right) = 2(r-2)\left(-\dfrac{1}{2}\right)$

    $2 = (r-2)(-1)$

    $2 = -r + 2$

    $r = 0$

33. The slope is negative and y decreases 6 units when x increases 2 units. Thus, $m = -\dfrac{6}{2} = -3$. The line crosses the y-axis at 0 so $b = 0$. Hence, $m = -3$ and $b = 0$ and the equation of the line is $y = -3x + 0$ or $y = -3x$.

35. The slope is negative and y decreases 1 unit when x increases 3 units. Thus, $m = -\dfrac{1}{3}$. The line crosses the y-axis at 2 so $b = 2$. Hence, $m = -\dfrac{1}{3}$ and $b = 2$ and the equation of the line is $y = -\dfrac{1}{3}x + 2$.

37. The slope is undefined since the change in x is 0. The equation of this vertical line is $x = -2$.

39. The line is horizontal so $m = 0$. The line crosses the y-axis at 3 so $b = 3$. Hence, $m = 0$ and $b = 3$ and the equation of the line is $y = 3$

41. The slope is negative and y decreases 15 units when x increases 10 units. Thus, $m = -\dfrac{15}{10} = -\dfrac{3}{2}$. The line crosses the y-axis at 15 so $b = 15$. Hence, $m = -\dfrac{3}{2}$ and $b = 15$ and the equation of the line is $y = -\dfrac{3}{2}x + 15$.

43. The equation $y = -x + 2$ is given in slope-intercept form . The slope is -1 and the

y-intercept is (0, 2).

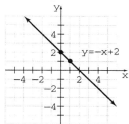

45. $5x + 15y = 30$

$$15y = -5x + 30$$

$$y = \frac{-5x + 30}{15}$$

$$y = -\frac{1}{3}x + 2$$

The slope is $-\frac{1}{3}$ and the *y*-intercept is (0, 2).

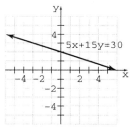

47. $-50x + 20y = 40$

$$20y = 50x + 40$$

$$y = \frac{50x + 40}{20}$$

$$y = \frac{5}{2}x + 2$$

The slope is $\frac{5}{2}$ and the *y*-intercept is (0, 2).

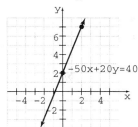

49. $f(x) = -2x + 1$

The slope is -2 and the *y*-intercept is (0, 1).

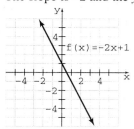

51. $h(x) = -\frac{3}{4}x + 2$

The slope is $-\frac{3}{4}$ and the *y*-intercept is (0, 2).

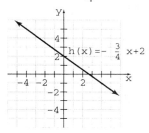

53. a. 2

b. 4

c. 1

d. 3

55. If the slopes are the same and the *y*-intercepts are different, the lines are parallel.

57. Begin with $y = mx + b$. If $m = \frac{4}{3}$ and (6, 3) is a point on the graph, then

$$y = \frac{4}{3}x + b$$

$$3 = \frac{4}{3}(6) + b$$

$$3 = 8 + b$$

$$-5 = b$$

The *y*-intercept is (0, −5).

59. a. The slope is 3 and the *y*-intercept is (0, 1), so the equation is $y = 3x + 1$.

b. The slope is 3 and the *y*-intercept is (0, −5), so the equation is $y = 3x - 5$.

61. a.   The slope of the translated graph is 1.

 b.   Using the y-intercept $b = -1$ is translated up 3 units, the y-intercept of the translated graph is at $y = -1 + 3 = 2$. The new y-intercept is $(0, 2)$.

 c.   Using $m = 1$ and $b = 2$, the equation of the translated graph is $y = x + 2$.

63.   First, rewrite the equation in the slope-intercept form by solving for y in terms of x.
$$3x - 2y = 6$$
$$-2y = -3x + 6$$
$$y = \frac{-3x + 6}{-2}$$
$$y = \frac{3}{2}x - 3$$
Thus, $m = \frac{3}{2}$ and $b = -3$. If the graph is translated down 4 units, then the y-intercept of the translated graph is at $y = -3 - 4 = -7$. Therefore, the equation of the translated graph is $y = \frac{3}{2}x - 7$.

65. $m = \dfrac{2 - 4}{-4 - 6} = \dfrac{-2}{-10} = \dfrac{1}{5}$

 Thus, for a unit change in x, y changes $\dfrac{1}{5}$ or 0.2 unit.

67. a, b.

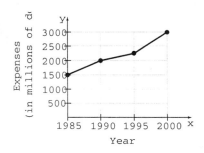

 c.   From 1985 to 1990,
$$m = \frac{2012 - 1600}{1990 - 1985} = \frac{412}{5} \approx 82.4$$
From 1990 to 1995,
$$m = \frac{2257 - 2012}{1995 - 1990} = \frac{245}{5} = 49$$
From 1995 - 2000,
$$m = \frac{2876 - 2257}{2000 - 1995} = \frac{619}{5} = 123.8$$

 d.   The greatest average rate of change occurred during the period 1995 to 2000, because the largest slope corresponds to these years.

69. a.   If x is the number of years after age 20, two points on the graph are $(0, 200)$ and $(50, 150)$. The slope is
$$m = \frac{150 - 200}{50 - 0} = \frac{-50}{50} = -1$$
and the y-intercept is $(0, 200)$, so $b = 200$. Thus, the equation for the line is $h(x) = -1 \cdot x + 200$, or
$$h(x) = -x + 200.$$

 b.   For a 34-year-old man, $x = 34 - 20 = 14$. Therefore,
$$h(x) = -x + 200$$
$$h(14) = -14 + 200 = 186$$
186 beats per minute is the maximum recommended heart rate.

71. a.   Note that $t = 0$ represents 1996 and that $t = 4$ represents 2000. Therefore, two ordered pairs of the function are $(0, 36.5)$ and $(4, 31.1)$. The slope of the line is
$$m = \frac{31.1 - 36.5}{2000 - 1996} = \frac{-5.4}{4} = -1.35$$
Since the slope is $m = -1.35$ and the y-intercept is $(0, 36.5)$, the linear function is
$$N(t) = -1.35t + 36.5.$$

 b.   Note that $t = 2$ represents 1998.
$$N(2) = -1.35(2) + 36.5$$
$$= -2.7 + 36.5$$
$$= 33.8$$
The number of people below the poverty threshold in 1998 was about 33.8 million.

 c.   Note that $t = 9$ represents 2005.
$$N(9) = -1.35(9) + 36.5$$
$$= -12.15 + 36.5$$
$$= 24.35$$
The number of people below the poverty threshold in 2005 will be about 24.35 million.

 d.   Set the function equal to 25 and solve for t.
$$-1.35t + 36.5 = 25$$
$$-1.35t = -11.5$$
$$t = \frac{-11.5}{-1.35}$$
$$t \approx 8.5$$
The number of people below the poverty threshold will reach 25 million sometime during the eighth year which is the year 2004.

73. a. Note that $t = 0$ represents 1975 and that $t = 25$ represents 2000. Therefore, two ordered pairs of the function are (0, 7156) and (25, 5890). The slope of the line is

$$m = \frac{5890 - 7156}{2000 - 1975} = \frac{-1266}{25} = -50.64$$

Since the slope is $m = -50.64$ and the y-intercept is (0, 7156), the linear function is $n(t) = -50.64t + 7156$.

b. Note that $t = 20$ represents 1995.

$$n(20) = -50.64(20) + 7156$$

$$= -1012.8 + 7156$$

$$= 6143.2$$

There were about 6,143 hospitals in the United States in 1995.

c. Note that $t = 30$ represents 2005.

$$n(30) = -50.64(30) + 7156$$

$$= -1519.2 + 7156$$

$$= 5636.8$$

There will be about 5,637 hospitals in the United States in 2005.

d. Set the function equal to 5000 and solve for t.

$$-50.64t + 7156 = 5000$$

$$-50.64t = -2156$$

$$t = \frac{-2156}{-50.64}$$

$$t \approx 42.6$$

The number of hospitals in the United States will drop to 5000 during the forty-second year after 1975 which is the year 2017.

75. a. Note that $t = 0$ represents 1995 and that $t = 5$ represents 2000. Therefore, two ordered pairs of the function are (0, \$110,500) and (5, \$139,000). The slope of the line is

$$m = \frac{139000 - 110500}{2000 - 1995} = \frac{28500}{5} = 5700$$

Since the slope is $m = 5700$ and the y-intercept is (0, 110500), the linear function is $P(t) = 5700t + 110500$.

b. Note that $t = 2$ represents 1997.

$$P(2) = 5,700(2) + 110,500$$

$$= 11,400 + 110,500$$

$$= 121,900$$

The median home sale price in 1997 was about \$121,900.

c. Note that $t = 15$ represents 2010.

$$P(15) = 5,700(15) + 110,500$$

$$= 85500 + 110,500$$

$$= 196,000$$

The median home sale price in 2010 will be about \$196,000.

d. Set the function equal to 200,000 and solve for t.

$$5700t + 110,500 = 200,000$$

$$5700t = 89,500$$

$$t = \frac{89,500}{5,700}$$

$$t \approx 15.7$$

The median home sale price will reach \$200,000 during the fifteen year after 1995 which is the year 2010.

77. The y-intercept of $y = 3x + 6$ is 6; on the screen, the y-intercept is not 6. The y-intercept is wrong.

79. The slope of $y = \frac{1}{2}x + 4$ is $\frac{1}{2}$; on the screen, the slope is not $\frac{1}{2}$. The slope is wrong.

81. There are 91 steps and the total vertical distance is 1292.2 in. Therefore, the average height of a step is $\frac{1292.2}{91} = 14.2$ inches.

If the slope is 2.21875 and the average height, or "rise", is 14.2 inches., the average width, or "run" is found as follows:

$$\text{slope} = \frac{\text{rise}}{\text{run}}$$

$$m = \frac{\text{height}}{\text{width}}$$

$$2.21875 = \frac{14.2}{\text{width}}$$

$$\text{width} = \frac{14.2}{2.21875} = 6.4$$

The average width is 6.4 inches.

85. Multiply both sides by LCM, 60.

$$\frac{3}{4}x + \frac{1}{5} = \frac{2}{3}(x-2)$$

$$60\left(\frac{3}{4}x + \frac{1}{5}\right) = 60 \cdot \frac{2}{3}(x-2)$$

$$15 \cdot 3x + 12 = 20 \cdot 2(x-2)$$

$$45x + 12 = 40x - 80$$

$$45x - 40x = -12 - 80$$

$$5x = -92$$

$$x = -\frac{92}{5}$$

87. Let r be the rate of the second, slower train, in miles per hour. Then the first train travels at $r + 15$ miles per hour. The first train travels for a total of 6 hours at which time it is $6(r + 15)$ miles from Chicago. The second train travels for 3 hours at which time it is $3r$ miles from Chicago. If they are 270 miles apart, we have

$$6(r + 15) = 3r + 270$$

$$6r + 90 = 3r + 270$$

$$6r - 3r = 270 - 90$$

$$3r = 180$$

$$r = 60$$

The first train travels at $r + 15 = 60 + 15$, or 75 miles per hour, and the second train travels at $r = 60$, or 60 miles per hour.

Exercise Set 3.5

1. The point-slope form of linear equation is $y - y_1 = m(x - x_1)$ where m is the slope of the line and (x_1, y_1) is a point on the line.

3. Two lines are perpendicular if their slopes are negative reciprocals, or if one line is horizontal and the other is vertical.

5. $y - y_1 = m(x - x_1)$

$$y - 1 = 2(x - 1)$$

$$y - 1 = 2x - 2$$

$$y = 2x - 1$$

7. $y - y_1 = m(x - x_1)$

$$y - (-1) = -\frac{1}{2}(x - 4)$$

$$y + 1 = -\frac{1}{2}x + 2$$

$$y = -\frac{1}{2}x + 1$$

9. $y - y_1 = m(x - x_1)$

$$y - (-5) = \frac{1}{2}(x - (-1))$$

$$y + 5 = \frac{1}{2}(x + 1)$$

$$y + 5 = \frac{1}{2}x + \frac{1}{2}$$

$$y = \frac{1}{2}x - \frac{9}{2}$$

11. $m = \dfrac{-6-6}{4-(-4)} = \dfrac{-12}{8} = -\dfrac{3}{2}$

Use $m = -\dfrac{3}{2}$ and $(x_1, y_1) = (-4, 6)$.

$$y - y_1 = m(x - x_1)$$

$$y - 6 = -\frac{3}{2}(x - (-4))$$

$$y - 6 = -\frac{3}{2}(x + 4)$$

$$y - 6 = -\frac{3}{2}x - 6$$

$$y = -\frac{3}{2}x$$

13. $m = \dfrac{-2-(-3)}{6-4} = \dfrac{-2+3}{2} = \dfrac{1}{2}$

Use $m = \dfrac{1}{2}$ and $(x_1, y_1) = (4, -3)$.

$$y - y_1 = m(x - x_1)$$

$$y - (-3) = \frac{1}{2}(x - 4)$$

$$y + 3 = \frac{1}{2}x - 2$$

$$y = \frac{1}{2}x - 5$$

15. $m_1 = \dfrac{2-0}{0-2} = \dfrac{2}{-2} = -1$

$m_2 = \dfrac{5-0}{0-5} = \dfrac{5}{-5} = -1$

Since their slopes are equal, l_1 and l_2 are parallel.

17. $m_1 = \dfrac{7-1}{5-1} = \dfrac{6}{4} = \dfrac{3}{2}$

$m_2 = \dfrac{4-(-1)}{1-(-1)} = \dfrac{5}{2}$

Since their slopes are different and since the product of their slopes is not -1, l_1 and l_2 are neither parallel nor perpendicular.

19. $m_1 = \dfrac{-2-2}{-1-3} = \dfrac{-4}{-4} = 1$

$m_2 = \dfrac{-1-0}{3-2} = \dfrac{-1}{1} = -1$

Since the product of their slopes is -1, the lines are perpendicular.

21. $y = \dfrac{1}{5}x + 1$, so $m_1 = \dfrac{1}{5}$

$y = -5x + 2$, so $m_2 = -5$

Since the product of their slopes is -1, the lines are perpendicular.

23. $\begin{array}{ll} 4x + 2y = 8 & 8x = 4 - 4y \\ 2y = -4x + 8 & 4y = -8x + 4 \\ y = -2x + 4 & y = -2x + 1 \\ m_1 = -2 & m_2 = -2 \end{array}$

Since their slopes are equal, the lines are parallel.

25. $\begin{array}{ll} 4x + 2y = 6 & -x + 4y = 4 \\ 2y = -4x + 6 & 4y = x + 4 \\ y = -2x + 3 & y = \dfrac{1}{4}x + 1 \\ m_1 = -2 & \\ & m_2 = \dfrac{1}{4} \end{array}$

Since their slopes are different and since the product of their slopes is not -1, the lines are neither parallel nor perpendicular.

27. $\begin{array}{ll} y = \dfrac{1}{2}x - 6 & -3y = 6x + 9 \\ & y = -2x - 3 \\ m_1 = \dfrac{1}{2} & m_2 = -2 \end{array}$

Since the product of their slopes is -1, the lines are perpendicular.

29. $y = \dfrac{1}{2}x + 3$

$m_1 = \dfrac{1}{2}$

$-2x + 4y = 8$

$4y = 2x + 8$

$y = \dfrac{1}{2}x + 2$

$m_2 = \dfrac{1}{2}$

Since the slopes are equal, the lines are parallel.

31. $\begin{array}{ll} x - 3y = -9 & y = 3x + 6 \\ -3y = -x - 9 & m_2 = 3 \\ y = \dfrac{1}{3}x + 3 & \\ m_1 = \dfrac{1}{3} & \end{array}$

Since the slopes are different and since the

product of their slopes is not -1, the lines are neither parallel nor perpendicular.

33. The slope of the given line, $y = 2x + 4$, is $m_1 = 2$. So $m_2 = 2$. Now use the point-slope form with $m = 2$ and $(x_1, y_1) = (2, 5)$ to obtain the slope-intercept form.

$y - y_1 = m(x - x_1)$

$y - 5 = 2(x - 2)$

$y - 5 = 2x - 4$

$y = 2x + 1$

35. Find the slope of the given line.

$2x - 5y = 7$

$-5y = -2x + 7$

$y = \dfrac{2}{5}x - \dfrac{7}{5}$

$m_1 = \dfrac{2}{5}$, so $m_2 = \dfrac{2}{5}$ Now use the point-slope form with $m = \dfrac{2}{5}$ and $(x_1, y_1) = (-3, -5)$ to obtain the standard form.

$y - y_1 = m(x - x_1)$

$y - (-5) = \dfrac{2}{5}\left(x - (-3)\right)$

$y + 5 = \dfrac{2}{5}(x + 3)$

$y + 5 = \dfrac{2}{5}x + \dfrac{6}{5}$

$5(y + 5) = 5\left(\dfrac{2}{5}x + \dfrac{6}{5}\right)$

$5y + 25 = 2x + 6$

$-2x + 5y = -19$

$2x - 5y = 19$

37. Find the slope of the line with the given intercepts.

$m = \dfrac{5 - 0}{0 - 3} = -\dfrac{5}{3}$

With $m = -\dfrac{5}{3}$ and y-intercept $(0, 5)$ the slope-intercept form of the equation is $y = -\dfrac{5}{3}x + 5$.

39. The slope of the given line $f(x) = \frac{1}{3}x + 1$ is
$m_1 = \frac{1}{3}$. So $m_2 = -3$. Now use the point-slope
form with $m = -3$ and $(x_1, y_1) = (5, -1)$ to
obtain the function notation.

$$y - y_1 = m(x - x_1)$$
$$y - (-1) = -3(x - 5)$$
$$y + 1 = -3x + 15$$
$$y = -3x + 14$$
$$f(x) = -3x + 14$$

41. Find the slope of the line with the given
intercepts.
$$m_1 = \frac{-3 - 0}{0 - 2} = \frac{3}{2}$$
So m_2 is the negative reciprocal, or
$$m_2 = -\frac{1}{m_1} = -\frac{1}{\frac{3}{2}} = -\frac{2}{3}.$$

Now use the point-slope form with $m = -\frac{2}{3}$ and
$(x_1, y_1) = (6, 2)$ and obtain the slope-intercept
form.
$$y - y_1 = m(x - x_1)$$
$$y - 2 = -\frac{2}{3}(x - 6)$$
$$y - 2 = -\frac{2}{3}x + 4$$
$$y = -\frac{2}{3}x + 6$$

43. a. To find the function, use the points
(2.5, 210) and (6, 370) to determine the
slope.
$$m = \frac{370 - 210}{6 - 2.5} = \frac{160}{3.5} \approx 45.7$$
Now use the point-slope form with $m = 45.7$
and $(s_1, C_1) = (2.5, 210)$
$$C - C_1 = m(s - s_1)$$
$$C - 210 = 45.7(s - 2.5)$$
$$C - 210 = 45.7s - 114.25$$
$$C = 45.7s + 95.75$$
$$C(s) = 45.7s + 95.8$$

b. For a speed of 5 miles per hour:
$$C(s) = 45.7s + 95.8$$
$$C(5) = 45.7(5) + 95.8$$
$$= 228.5 + 95.8$$
$$= 324.3$$
The average person will burn about 324.3
calories.

45. a. To find the function, use the points
(200, 50) and (300, 30) to determine the
slope.
$$m = \frac{30 - 50}{300 - 200} = \frac{-20}{100} = -0.20$$
Now use the point-slope form with $m =$
-0.20 and $(p_1, d_1) = (200, 50)$
$$d - d_1 = m(p - p_1)$$
$$d - 50 = -0.20(p - 200)$$
$$d - 50 = -0.20p + 40$$
$$d = -0.20p + 90$$
$$d(p) = -0.20p + 90$$

b. For a price of \$260:
$$d(p) = -0.20p + 90$$
$$d(260) = -0.20(260) + 90$$
$$= -52 + 90$$
$$= 38$$
The demand will be 38 DVD players.

c. Set the function equal to 45 and solve for p.
$$d(p) = -0.20p + 90$$
$$45 = -0.20p + 90$$
$$0.20p = 45$$
$$p = 225$$
In order to have a demand of 45 DVD
players, the price should be \$225.

47. a. To find the function, use the points
(2.00, 130) and (4.00, 320) to determine the
slope.
$$m = \frac{320 - 130}{4.00 - 2.00} = \frac{190}{2.00} = 95$$
Now use the point-slope form with $m = 95$
and $(p_1, s_1) = (2.00, 130)$
$$s - s_1 = m(p - p_1)$$
$$s - 130 = 95(p - 2.00)$$
$$s - 130 = 95p - 190$$
$$s = 95p - 60$$
$$s(p) = 95p - 60$$

b. For a price of \$2.80:
$$s(p) = 95p - 60$$
$$s(2.80) = 95(2.80) - 60$$
$$= 266 - 60$$
$$= 206$$
The supply will be 206 kites.

c. Set the function equal to 225 and solve for p.

$$s(p) = 95p - 60$$
$$225 = 95p - 60$$
$$285 = 95p$$
$$p = 3$$

In order to have a supply of 225 kites, the price should be $3.00.

49. a. To find the function, use the points (45, 40) and (90, 25) to determine the slope.

$$m = \frac{25 - 40}{90 - 45} = \frac{-15}{45} = -\frac{1}{3}$$

Now use the point-slope form with $m = -\frac{1}{3}$ and $(s_1, m_1) = (45, 40)$

$$m - m_1 = m(s - s_1)$$
$$m - 40 = -\frac{1}{3}(s - 45)$$
$$m - 40 = -\frac{1}{3}s + 15$$
$$m = -\frac{1}{3}s + 55$$
$$m(s) = -\frac{1}{3}s + 55$$

b. For a speed of 60 mph:

$$m(s) = -\frac{1}{3}s + 55$$
$$m(60) = -\frac{1}{3}(60) + 55$$
$$= -20 + 55$$
$$= 35$$

The car's gas mileage will be 35 mpg.

c. Set the function equal to 30 and solve for s.

$$m(s) = -\frac{1}{3}s + 55$$
$$30 = -\frac{1}{3}s + 55$$
$$-25 = -\frac{1}{3}s$$
$$s = 75$$

In order to have a gas mileage of 30 mpg, the speed should be 75 mph.

51. a. To find the function, use the points (10, 3477) and (20, 4168) to determine the slope.

$$m = \frac{4168 - 3477}{20 - 10} = \frac{691}{10} = 69.1$$

Now use the point-slope form with $m = 69.1$ and $(s_1, p_1) = (10, 3477)$

$$p - p_1 = m(s - s_1)$$
$$p - 3477 = 69.1(s - 10)$$
$$p - 3477 = 69.1s - 691$$
$$p = 69.1s + 2786$$
$$p(s) = 69.1s + 2786$$

b. For 18 years of service:

$$p(s) = 69.1s + 2786$$
$$p(18) = 69.1(18) + 2786$$
$$= 1243.8 + 2786$$
$$= 4029.8$$

The monthly salary will be $4,029.80.

c. Set the function equal to 4000 and solve for

$$p(s) = 69.1s + 2786$$
$$4000 = 69.1s + 2786$$
s. $$1214 = 69.1s$$
$$s \approx 17.6$$

In order to have a monthly salary of $4,000, one would need about 18 years of service.

53. a. To find the function, use the points (50, 36.0) and (70, 18.7) to determine the slope.

$$m = \frac{18.7 - 36.0}{70 - 50} = \frac{-17.3}{20} = -0.865$$

Now use the point-slope form with $m = -0.865$ and $(a_1, y_1) = (50, 36.0)$

$$y - y_1 = m(a - a_1)$$
$$y - 36.0 = -0.865(a - 50)$$
$$y - 36.0 = -0.865a + 43.25$$
$$y = -0.865a + 79.25$$
$$y(a) = -0.865a + 79.25$$

b. For a person who is currently 37 years old:

$$y(a) = -0.865a + 79.25$$
$$y(37) = -0.865(37) + 79.25$$
$$= -32.005 + 79.25$$
$$= 47.245$$

The additional life expectancy will be about 47.2 years.

c. Set the function equal to 25 and solve for s.

$$y(a) = -0.865a + 79.25$$

$$25 = -0.865a + 79.25$$

$$-54.25 = -0.865a$$

$$a \approx 62.7$$

In order to have an additional life expectancy of 25 years, one would need to be currently about 62.7 years old..

55. a. To find the function, use the points $(18, 14)$ and $(36, 17.4)$ to determine the slope.

$$m = \frac{17.4 - 14}{36 - 18} = \frac{3.4}{18} \approx 0.189$$

Now use the point-slope form with $m = 0.189$ and $(a_1, \ w_1) = (18, 14)$

$$w - w_1 = m(a - a_1)$$

$$w - 14 = 0.189(a - 18)$$

$$w - 14 = 0.189a - 3.402$$

$$w = 0.189a + 10.598$$

$$w(a) = 0.189a + 10.6$$

b. For a 22-month-old boy who is in the 95th percentile for weight:

$$w(a) = 0.189a + 10.6$$

$$w(22) = 0.189(22) + 10.6$$

$$= 4.158 + 10.6$$

$$= 14.758$$

The boy will weigh about 14.158 kg.

59. When dividing or multiplying both sides of an inequality by a negative number, reverse the direction of the inequality symbol.

61. D:{3, 4, 5, 6}, R:{−2, −1, 2, 3}

Exercise Set 3.6

1. Yes, $f(x) + g(x) = (f + g)(x)$ for all values of x. This is how addition of functions is defined.

3. $f(x)/g(x) = (f/g)(x)$ provided $g(x) \neq 0$. This is because division by zero is undefined.

5. No, $(f - g)(x) \neq (g - f)(x)$ for all values of x since subtraction is not commutative. For example, if $f(x) = x^2 + 1$ and $g(x) = x$, then

$$(f - g)(x) = f(x) - g(x)$$

$$= (x^2 + 1) - (x)$$

$$= x^2 - x + 1$$

$$(g - f)(x) = g(x) - f(x)$$

$$= (x) - (x^2 + 1)$$

$$= -x^2 + x - 1$$

So $(f - g)(x) \neq (g - f)(x)$.

7. a. $(f + g)(-2) = f(-2) + g(-2) = -3 + 5 = 2$

b. $(f - g)(-2) = f(-2) - g(-2) = -3 - 5 = -8$

c. $(f \cdot g)(-2) = f(-2) \cdot g(-2) = (-3) \cdot (5) = -15$

d. $(f/g)(-2) = f(-2)/g(-2) = \dfrac{-3}{5} = -\dfrac{3}{5}$

9. a. $(f + g)(x) = f(x) + g(x)$

$$= (x + 1) + (x^2 + x)$$

$$= x^2 + 2x + 1$$

b. $(f + g)(a) = a^2 + 2a + 1$

c. $(f + g)(2) = (2)^2 + 2(2) + 1$

$$= 4 + 4 + 1$$

$$= 9$$

11. a. $(f + g)(x) = f(x) + g(x)$

$$= (-3x^2 + x - 4) + (x^3 + 3x^2)$$

$$= x^3 + x - 4$$

b. $(f + g)(a) = a^3 + a - 4$

c. $(f + g)(2) = (2)^3 + (2) - 4$

$$= 8 + 2 - 4$$

$$= 6$$

13. a. $(f + g)(x) = f(x) + g(x)$
$$= (4x^3 - 3x^2 - x) + (3x^2 + 4)$$
$$= 4x^3 - x + 4$$

   b. $(f + g)(a) = 4a^3 - a + 4$

   c. $(f + g)(2) = 4(2)^3 - (2) + 4$
$$= 32 - 2 + 4$$
$$= 34$$

15. $f(3) = (3)^2 - 4 = 5$
$g(3) = -5(3) + 3 = -12$
$f(3) + g(3) = 5 + (-12) = -7$

17. $f(-2) = (-2)^2 - 4 = 0$
$g(-2) = -5(-2) + 3 = 13$
$f(-2) - g(-2) = 0 - 13 = -13$

19. $f(3) = 3^2 - 4 = 5$
$g(3) = -5(3) + 3 = -12$
$f(3) \cdot g(3) = 5(-12) = -60$

21.
$$f\left(\frac{3}{5}\right) = \left(\frac{3}{5}\right)^2 - 4 = -\frac{91}{25}$$
$$g\left(\frac{3}{5}\right) = -5\left(\frac{3}{5}\right) + 3 = 0$$
$$f\left(\frac{3}{5}\right) / g\left(\frac{3}{5}\right) \text{ is undefined since } g\left(\frac{3}{5}\right) = 0.$$

23. $f(-3) = (-3)^2 - 4 = 5$
$g(-3) = -5(-3) + 3 = 18$
$g(-3) - f(-3) = 18 - 5 = 13$

25. $f(0) = 0^2 - 4 = -4$
$g(0) = -5(0) + 3 = 3$
$g(0) / f(0) = 3 / -4 = -\frac{3}{4}$

27. $(f + g)(x) = f(x) + g(x)$
$$= (2x^2 - x) + (x - 6)$$
$$= 2x^2 - 6$$

29. $(f + g)(0) = 2(0)^2 - 6$
$$= 0 - 6$$
$$= -6$$

31. $(f - g)(-3) = f(-3) - g(-3)$
$$= \left(2 \cdot (-3)^2 - (-3)\right) - \left((-3) - 6\right)$$
$$= 21 - (-9)$$
$$= 30$$

33. $(f \cdot g)(0) = f(0) \cdot g(0)$
$f(0) = 2(0)^2 - (0) = 0$
$g(0) = (0) - 6 = -6$
$f(0) \cdot g(0) = 0 \cdot (-6) = 0$

35. $(f/g)(-1) = f(-1)/g(-1)$
$f(-1) = 2(-1)^2 - (-1) = 3$
$g(-1) = (-1) - 6 = -7$
$f(-1) / g(-1) = 3 / (-7) = -\frac{3}{7}$

37. $(g/f)(5) = g(5)/f(5)$
$f(5) = 2(5)^2 - 5 = 45$
$g(5) = 5 - 6 = -1$
$g(5) / f(5) = (-1) / 45 = -\frac{1}{45}$

39. $(g - f)(x) = g(x) - f(x)$
$$= (x - 6) - (2x^2 - x)$$
$$= -2x^2 + 2x - 6$$

41. $(f + g)(0) = f(0) + g(0) = 2 + 1 = 3$

43. $(f \cdot g)(2) = f(2) \cdot g(2) = 4 \cdot (-1) = -4$

45. $(g - f)(-1) = g(-1) - f(-1) = 2 - 1 = 1$

47. $(g/f)(4) = g(4)/f(4) = 1/0$, undefined

49. $(f + g)(3) = f(3) + g(3) = 1 + 3 = 4$

51. $(f \cdot g)(1) = f(1) \cdot g(1) = 0 \cdot 1 = 0$

53. $(f/g)(4) = f(4) / g(4) = 3/1 = -3$

55. $(g/f)(2) = g(2)/f(2) = 2/(-1) = -2$

57. a. The total expenditures, T, is the sum of the private expenditures, r, and the public expenditures, u.

   b. The total amount of expenditures increased the least during 1970 - 1980.

   c. The total amount of expenditures increased the most during 1990 - 2000.

59. **a.** There were about 6,200,000 people who were aged receiving Medicare hospital insurance in 2000.

     b. There were about 1,000,000 people who were disabled receiving Medicare hospital insurance in 2000.

     c. There was a total of about 7,200,000 people receiving Medicare hospital insurance in 2000.

61. If $(f + g)(a) = 0$, then, $f(a)$ and $g(a)$ must either be opposites or both be equal to 0.

63. If $(f - g)(a) = 0$, then $f(a) = g(a)$.

65. If $(f/g)(a) < 0$, then $f(a)$ and $g(a)$ must have opposite signs.

67.

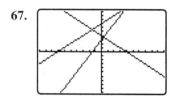

$$-10, \ 10, \ 1, \ -10$$

69.

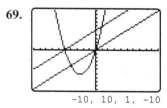

$$-10, \ 10, \ 1, \ -10$$

73. $1,630,000 = 1.63 \times 10^6$

75. Let the pre-tax cost of the washing machine be x.
$$x + 0.06x = 477$$
$$1.06x = 477$$
$$x = \frac{477}{1.06}$$
$$x = 450$$
The pre-tax cost of the washing machine was $450.

77. Set $y = 0$ to find the x-intercept.
$$3x - 4(0) = 12$$
$$3x = 12$$
$$x = 4$$
The x-intercept is $(4, 0)$. Set $x = 0$ to find the y-intercept.
$$3(0) - 4y = 12$$
$$-4y = 12$$
$$y = -3$$

The y-intercept is $(0, -3)$.

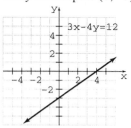

Exercise Set 3.7

1. The inequalities $>$ and $<$ do not include the corresponding equation; the points on the line satisfy only the equation.

3. $(0, 0)$ cannot be used as a test point if the line passes through the origin.

5. $x > 1$
Graph the line $x = 1$ (vertical line) using a dashed line. For the check point, select $(0, 0)$:
$x > 1$
$0 > 1 \leftarrow$ Substitute 0 for x
Since this is a false statement, shade the region which does not contain $(0, 0)$.

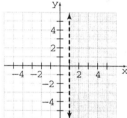

7. $y < -2$
Graph the line $y = -2$ (horizontal line) using a dashed line. For the check point, select $(0, 0)$.
$y < -2$
$0 < -2 \leftarrow$ Substitute 0 for y.
Since this is a false statement, shade the region which does not contain $(0, 0)$.

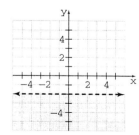

9. $y \geq -\dfrac{1}{2}x$

Graph the line $y = -\dfrac{1}{2}x$ using a solid line. For the check point, select $(0, 2)$.

$y \geq -\dfrac{1}{2}x$

$2 \geq -\dfrac{1}{2}(0) \leftarrow$ Substitute 0 for x, 2 for y

$2 \geq 0$

Since this is a true statement, shade the region which contains the point $(0, 2)$.

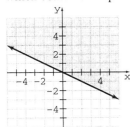

11. $y < 2x + 1$

Graph the line $y = 2x + 1$ using a dashed line. For the check point, select $(0, 0)$.

$y < 2x + 1$

$0 < 2(0) + 1 \leftarrow$ Substitute 0 for x and y

$0 < 1$

Since this is a true statement, shade the region which contains the point $(0, 0)$.

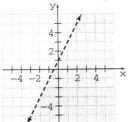

13. $y > 2x - 1$

Graph the line $y = 2x - 1$ using a dashed line. For the check point, select $(0, 0)$.

$y > 2x - 1$

$0 > 2(0) - 1 \leftarrow$ Substitute 0 for x and y

$0 > -1$

Since this is a true statement, shade the region which contains the point $(0, 0)$.

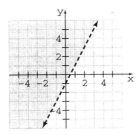

15. $y \geq \dfrac{1}{2}x - 3$

Graph the line $y = \dfrac{1}{2}x - 3$ using a solid line. For the check point, select $(0, 0)$.

$y \geq \dfrac{1}{2}x - 3$

$0 \geq \dfrac{1}{2}(0) - 3 \leftarrow$ Substitute 0 for x and y

$0 \geq -3$

Since this is a true statement, shade the region which contains the point $(0, 0)$.

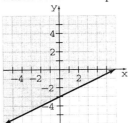

17. $2x - 3y \geq 12$

$-3y \geq -2x + 12$

$\dfrac{-3y}{-3} \leq \dfrac{-2x + 12}{-3}$

$y \leq \dfrac{2}{3}x - 4$

Graph the line $y = \dfrac{2}{3}x - 4$ using a solid line. For the check point, select $(0, 0)$.

$y \leq \dfrac{2}{3}x - 4$

$(0) \leq \dfrac{2}{3}(0) - 4 \leftarrow$ Substitute 0 for x and y

$0 \leq -4$

Since this is a false statement, shade the region

which does not contain the point (0, 0).

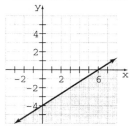

19. $y \leq -3x + 5$

Graph the line $y = -3x + 5$ using a solid line.
For the check point, select (0, 0).
$y \leq -3x + 5$
$0 \leq -3(0) + 5 \leftarrow$ Substitute 0 for x and y
$0 \leq 5$
Since this is a true statement, shade the region
which contains the point (0, 0).

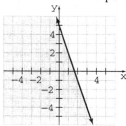

21. $2x + y < 4$

Graph the line $2x + y = 4$ using a dashed line.
For the check point, select (0, 0).
$2x + y < 4$
$2(0) + 0 < 4 \leftarrow$ Substitute 0 for x and y
$0 < 4$
Since this is a true statement, shade the region
which contains the point (0, 0).

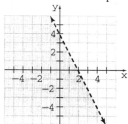

23. $10 \geq 5x - 2y$

Graph the line $10 = 5x - 2y$ using a solid line.
For the check point, select (0, 0).
$10 \geq 5x - 2y$
$10 \geq 5(0) - 2(0) \leftarrow$ Substitute 0 for x and y
$10 \geq 0$
Since this is a true statement, shade the region

which contains the point (0, 0).

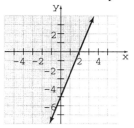

25. a, b.

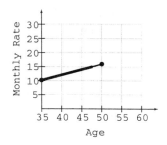

   c. The age at which the rate first exceeds $15
per month is 47.

27. a, b.

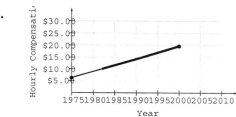

   c. 1982 was the year that the average hourly
wage first exceeded $10 per hour.

29. a.

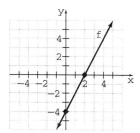

   b.

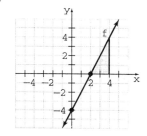

31. $y < |x|$

Graph the equation $y = |x|$ using a dashed line.
For the check point, select (0, 2).
$y < |x|$
$2 < (0) \leftarrow$ Substitute 0 for x and 2 for y
$2 < 0$
Since this is a false statement, shade the region which does not contain the point (0, 2).

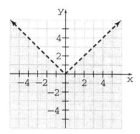

33. $y < x^2 - 4$

Graph the equation $y = x^2 - 4$ using a dashed line. For the check point, select (0, 0).
$y < x^2 - 4$
$0 < 0^2 - 4 \leftarrow$ Substitute 0 for x and y
$0 < -4$
Since this is a false statement, shade the region which does not contain the point (0, 0).

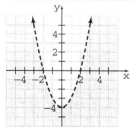

35. $C = \bar{x} + Z\dfrac{\sigma}{\sqrt{n}}$

$C = 80 + 1.96\dfrac{3}{\sqrt{25}}$

$C = 80 + 1.96\left(\dfrac{3}{5}\right)$

$C = 80 + 1.176$

$C = 81.176$

37. $f(x) = -x^2 + 3$

$f(-1) = -(-1)^2 + 3$

$\qquad = -1 + 3$

$\qquad = 2$

39. $(x_1, y_1) = (-4, 7)$ and $(x_2, y_2) = (2, -1)$

$m = \dfrac{-1 - 7}{2 - (-4)} = \dfrac{-8}{6} = -\dfrac{4}{3}$

Review Exercises

1.

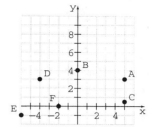

2. $y = \dfrac{1}{2}x$

x	y
-2	$y = 0.5(-2) = -1$
0	$y = 0.5(0) = 0$
2	$y = 0.5(2) = 1$

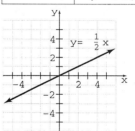

3. $y = -2x - 1$

x	y
0	$y = -2(0) - 1 = -1$
1	$y = -2(1) - 1 = -3$
2	$y = -2(2) - 1 = -4$

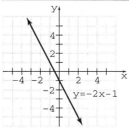

4. $y = \dfrac{1}{2}x + 3$

x	y
0	$y = \frac{1}{2}(0) + 3 = 3$
-2	$y = \frac{1}{2}(-2) + 3 = 2$
-4	$y = \frac{1}{2}(-4) + 3 = 1$

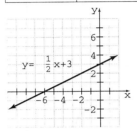

5. $y = -\dfrac{3}{2}x + 1$

x	y
-2	$y = -\frac{3}{2}(-2) + 1 = 4$
0	$y = -\frac{3}{2}(0) + 1 = 1$
2	$y = -\frac{3}{2}(2) + 1 = -2$

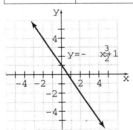

6. $y = x^2$

x	y
-3	$y = (-3)^2 = 9$
-1	$y = (-1) =^2 -1$
0	$y = 0^2 = 0$
2	$y = 2^2 = 4$

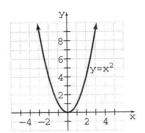

7. $y = x^2 - 1$

x	y
-3	$y = (-3)^2 - 1 = 8$
-1	$y = (-1)^2 - 1 = 0$
0	$y = 0^2 - 1 = 0$
1	$y = 1^2 - 1 = 0$
2	$y = 2^2 - 1 = 3$

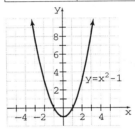

8. $y = |x|$

x	y
-4	$y = |-4| = 4$
-1	$y = |-1| = 1$
0	$y = |0| = 0$
2	$y = |2| = 2$

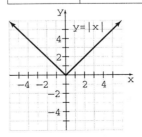

9. $y = |x| - 1$

x	y
-4	$y = |-4| - 1 = 3$
-1	$y = |-1| - 1 = 0$
0	$y = |0| - 1 = -1$
2	$y = |2| - 1 = 1$

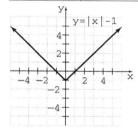

10. $y = x^3$

x	y
-2	$y = (-2)^3 = -8$
-1	$y = (-1)^3 = -1$
0	$y = 0^3 = 0$
1	$y = 1^3 = 1$
2	$y = 2^3 = 8$

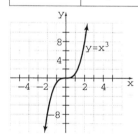

11. $y = x^3 + 4$

x	y
-2	$y = (-2)^3 + 4 = -4$
-1	$y = (-1)^3 + 4 = 3$
0	$y = 0^3 + 4 = 4$
1	$y = 1^3 + 4 = 5$

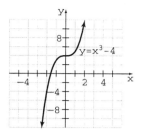

12. A function is a correspondence where each member of the domain corresponds to exactly one member of the range.

13. No, every relation is not a function.
$\{(4, 2), (4, -2)\}$ is a relation but not a function.
Yes, every function is a relation because it is a set of ordered pairs.

14. Yes, each member of the domain corresponds to exactly one member of the range.

15. No, the domain element 2 corresponds to more than one member of the range (5 and -5).

16. a. No, the relation is not a function.

    b. Domain: $\{x|-1 \le x \le 1\}$
         Range: $\{y|-1 \le y \le 1\}$

17. a. No, the relation is not a function.

    b. Domain: $\{x|-2 \le x \le 2\}$
         Range: $\{y|-1 \le y \le 1\}$

18. a. Yes, the relation is a function.

    b. Domain: R
         Range: $\{y|y \le 0\}$

19. a. Yes, the relation is a function.

    b. Domain: R
         Range: R

20. $f(x) = -x^2 + 3x - 5$

    a. $f(2) = -(2)^2 + 3(2) - 5 = -4 + 6 - 5 = -3$

    b. $f(h) = -h^2 + 3h - 5$

21. $g(t) = 2t^3 - 3t^2 + 1$

a. $g(-1) = 2(-1)^3 - 3(-1)^2 + 1$
$$= -2 - 3 + 1$$
$$= -4$$

b. $g(a) = 2a^3 - 3a^2 + 1$

22. Answers will vary. One possible interpretation: Car speeds up to 50 mph. Stays at 50 mph for about 11 minutes. Speeds up to about 68 mph. Stays at that speed for 5 minutes. Stops quickly. Stays stopped for 5 minutes. In stop and go traffic for 5 minutes.

23. $N(x) = 40x - 0.2x^2$

a. $N(20) = 40(20) - 0.2(20)^2$
$$= 800 - 80$$
$$= 720$$
720 baskets of apples are produced by 20 trees.

b. $N(50) = 40(50) - 0.2(50)^2$
$$= 2000 - 500$$
$$= 1500$$
1500 baskets of apples are produced by 50 trees.

24. $h(t) = -16t^2 + 100$

a. $h(1) = -16(1)^2 + 100 = 84$
After 1 second, the height of the ball is 84 feet.

b. $h(2) = -16(2)^2 + 100 = 36$
After 2 seconds, the height of the ball is 36 feet.

25.
$3x - 4y = 6$
To find the *x*-intercept, set $y = 0$.
$3x - 4(0) = 6$
$$3x = 6$$
$$x = 2$$
The *x*-intercept is (2, 0).
To find the *y*-intercept , set $x = 0$.
$3(0) - 4y = 6$
$$y = -\frac{3}{2}$$

The *y*-intercept is $\left(0, -\frac{3}{2}\right)$.

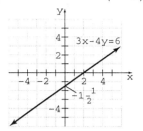

26. $\frac{2}{3}x = \frac{1}{4}y + 20$
To find the *x*-intercept, set $y = 0$.
$$\frac{2}{3}x = \frac{1}{4}(0) + 20$$
$$\frac{2}{3}x = 20$$
$$\frac{3}{2}\left(\frac{2}{3}x\right) = \frac{3}{2}(20)$$
$$x = 30$$
The *x*-intercept is (30, 0).
To find the *y*-intercept, set $x = 0$.
$$\frac{2}{3}(0) = \frac{1}{4}y + 20$$
$$0 = \frac{1}{4}y + 20$$
$$-20 = \frac{1}{4}y$$
$$4(-20) = 4\left(\frac{1}{4}y\right)$$
$$-80 = y$$
The *y*-intercept is (0 –80).

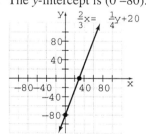

27. $f(x) = 4$ is a horizontal line 4 units above the x-axis.

x	y
−2	4
0	4
2	4

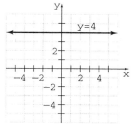

28. $x = -2$ is a vertical line 2 units to the left of the y-axis.

x	y
−2	2
−2	0
−2	−2

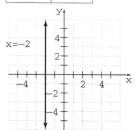

29. a. $p = 0.1x - 5000$

x	y
0	$p = 0.1(0) - 5000 = -5000$
50,000	$p = 0.1(50,000) - 5000 = 0$
100,000	$p = 0.1(100,000) - 5000 = 5000$

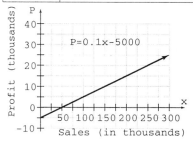

b. Approximately 50,000 bagels are sold when the comany breaks even.

c. Approximately 250,000 bagels are sold for $20,000 profit.

30. The principle is $12,000 and the time is one year. Use the decimal form of the interest rate.
$I = 12,000r$

31. $y = \dfrac{1}{2}x - 3$

$m = \dfrac{1}{2}, b = -3$

32. $f(x) = -2x + 1$

$m = -2, b = 1$

33. $3x + 5y = 12$
Solve for y.
$5y = -3x + 12$
$y = \dfrac{-3x + 12}{5}$
$y = -\dfrac{3}{5}x + \dfrac{12}{5}$
$m = -\dfrac{3}{5}, b = \dfrac{12}{5}$

34. $3x + 4y = 10$
Solve for y.
$4y = -3x + 10$
$y = \dfrac{-3x + 10}{4}$
$y = -\dfrac{3}{4}x + \dfrac{5}{2}$
$m = -\dfrac{3}{4}, b = \dfrac{5}{2}$

35. $x = -2$ is a vertical line so m is undefined and there is no y-intercept.

36. $y = 6$ is a horizontal line so that $m = 0$ and $b = 6$.

37. $m = \dfrac{7-5}{-2-2} = \dfrac{2}{-4} = -\dfrac{1}{2}$

38. $m = \dfrac{3-1}{-2-4} = \dfrac{2}{-6} = -\dfrac{1}{3}$

39. This is a horizontal line ($m = 0$) having a
y-intercept of 3.
The equation is $y = 3$.

40. This is a vertical line (m is undefined) having an
x-intercept of 2. The equation is $x = 2$.

41. The slope is negative and y changes 2 units when
x changes 4 units. Thus, $m = -\dfrac{2}{4} = -\dfrac{1}{2}$. Hence,

$m = -\dfrac{1}{2}$ and $b = 2$.

$y = -\dfrac{1}{2}x + 2$

42. a. The slope of the translated graph is the same
as the slope of the original graph: $m = -2$.

   b. The y-intercept of the translated graph is the
4 less than the y-intercept of the original
graph: $3 - 4 = -1$. The y-intercept is $(0, -1)$.

   c. The equation of the translated graph is
$y = -2x - 1$.

43. Use the point-slope form.
$y - y_1 = m(x - x_1)$
$y - (-8) = \dfrac{4}{3}(x - (-6))$
$y + 8 = \dfrac{4}{3}(x + 6)$
$y + 8 = \dfrac{4}{3}x + 8$
$y = \dfrac{4}{3}x$
The y-intercept is $(0, 0)$.

44. a.

b. 1970 to 1980:
$m_1 = \dfrac{510 - 346}{1980 - 1970} = \dfrac{164}{10} = 16.4$
1980 to 1990:
$m_2 = \dfrac{552 - 510}{1990 - 1980} = \dfrac{42}{10} = 4.2$
1990 to 2000:
$m_3 = \dfrac{317 - 552}{2000 - 1990} = \dfrac{-235}{10} = -23.5$

c. The number of reported cases of typhoid
fever increased the most during the 10-year
period of 1970 – 1980.

45. First, find the slope.
$m = \dfrac{98.2 - 35.6}{2070 - 1980} = \dfrac{62.6}{90} \approx 0.7$
Let t be the number of years since 1980. Use the
point-slope form with $m = 0.7$ and
$(t_1, n_1) = (0, 35.6)$.
$n - m_1 = m(t - t_1)$
$n - 35.6 = 0.7(t - 0)$
$n - 35.6 = 0.7t$
$n = 0.7t + 35.6$
$n(t) = 0.7t + 35.6$

46. Write each equation in slope-intercept form by
solving for y.

$2x - 3y = 10$ $y = \dfrac{2}{3}x - 4$
$-3y = -2x + 10$
$\dfrac{-3y}{-3} = \dfrac{-2x + 10}{-3}$
$y = \dfrac{2}{3}x - \dfrac{10}{3}$

Since $m = \dfrac{2}{3}$ for both lines, the lines are parallel.

47. Write each equation in slope-intercept form by
solving for y.
$2x - 3y = 9$ $-3x - 2y = 6$
$-3y = -2x + 9$ $-2y = 3x + 6$
$y = \dfrac{-2x + 9}{-3}$ $y = \dfrac{3x + 6}{-2}$
$y = \dfrac{2}{3}x - 3$ $y = -\dfrac{3}{2}x - 3$

Since the slopes are $\dfrac{2}{3}$ and $-\dfrac{3}{2}$ which are
negative reciprocals, the lines are perpendicular.

48. Write each equation in slope-intercept form by solving for y.

$$4x - 2y = 10 \qquad\qquad -2x + 4y = -8$$
$$-2y = -4x + 10 \qquad\qquad 4y = 2x - 8$$
$$y = \frac{-4x + 10}{-2} \qquad\qquad y = \frac{2x - 8}{4}$$
$$y = 2x - 5 \qquad\qquad\qquad y = \frac{1}{2}x - 2$$

Since the slopes are 2 and $\frac{1}{2}$ which are neither equal nor negative reciprocals, the lines are neither parallel nor perpendicular.

49. Use the point-slope form with $m = \frac{1}{2}$ and $(x_1, \ y_1) = (4, 5)$.

$$y - 5 = \frac{1}{2}(x - 4)$$
$$y - 5 = \frac{1}{2}x - 2$$
$$y = \frac{1}{2}x + 3$$

50. First, find the slope: $m = \dfrac{-4 - 1}{2 - (-3)} = \dfrac{-5}{5} = -1$.

Now, use the point-slope form with $m = -1$ and $(x_1, \ y_1) = (-3, \ 1)$.

$$y - 1 = -1\left(x - (-3)\right)$$
$$y - 1 = -1\left(x + 3\right)$$
$$y - 1 = -x - 3$$
$$y = -x - 2$$

51. The slope of the line $y = -\frac{2}{3}x + 1$ is $m = -\frac{2}{3}$. Since the new line is parallel to this line, its slope is also $m = -\frac{2}{3}$. Use the slope-intercept form with $m = -\frac{2}{3}$ and y-intercept of $(0, 4)$.

$$y = -\frac{2}{3}x + 4$$

52. To find the slope of the line $5x - 2y = 7$, solve for y.

$$-2y = -5x + 7$$
$$y = \frac{-5x + 7}{-2}$$
$$y = \frac{5}{2}x - \frac{7}{2}$$

The slope of this line is $\frac{5}{2}$, and since the new

line is parallel to this line, its slope is also $\frac{5}{2}$.

Use the point-slope form with $m = \frac{5}{2}$ and $(x_1, y_1) = (2, \ 3)$.

$$y - 3 = \frac{5}{2}(x - 2)$$
$$y - 3 = \frac{5}{2}x - 5$$
$$y = \frac{5}{2}x - 2$$

53. The slope of the line $y = \frac{3}{5}x + 5$ is $\frac{3}{5}$. Since the new line is perpendicular to this line, its slope is $-\frac{5}{3}$. Use the point-slope form with $m = -\frac{5}{3}$ and $(x_1, \ y_1) = (-3, 1)$.

$$y - 1 = -\frac{5}{3}[x - (-3)]$$
$$y - 1 = -\frac{5}{3}(x + 3)$$
$$y - 1 = -\frac{5}{3}x - 5$$
$$y = -\frac{5}{3}x - 4$$

54. To find the slope of the line $4x - 2y = 8$, solve for y.

$$-2y = -4x + 8$$
$$y = \frac{-4x + 8}{-2}$$
$$y = 2x - 4$$

The slope of this line is 2. Since the new line is perpendicular to this line, its slope is $-\frac{1}{2}$. Use the point-slope form with $m = -\frac{1}{2}$ and $(x_1, \ y_1) = (4, 2)$.

$$y - 2 = -\frac{1}{2}(x - 4)$$
$$y - 2 = -\frac{1}{2}x + 2$$
$$y = -\frac{1}{2}x + 4$$

55. $m_1 = \dfrac{3 - (-3)}{4 - 0} = \dfrac{3 + 3}{4 - 0} = \dfrac{6}{4} = \dfrac{3}{2}$

$m_2 = \dfrac{-1 - (-2)}{1 - 2} = \dfrac{-1 + 2}{1 - 2} = \dfrac{1}{-1} = -1$

Since the slopes are neither the same nor negative reciprocals, the lines are neither parallel nor perpendicular.

56. $m_1 = \dfrac{2-3}{3-2} = \dfrac{-1}{1} = -1$

$m_2 = \dfrac{1-4}{4-1} = \dfrac{-3}{3} = -1$

Since the slopes are the same, the lines are parallel.

57. $m_1 = \dfrac{0-3}{4-1} = \dfrac{-3}{3} = -1$

$m_2 = \dfrac{2-3}{5-6} = \dfrac{-1}{-1} = 1$

Since the slopes are negative reciprocals, the lines are perpendicular.

58. $m_1 = \dfrac{5-3}{-3-2} = \dfrac{2}{-5} = -\dfrac{2}{5}$

$m_2 = \dfrac{-2-2}{-4-(-1)} = \dfrac{-2-2}{-4+1} = \dfrac{-4}{-3} = \dfrac{4}{3}$

Since the slopes are neither the same nor negative reciprocals, the lines are neither parallel nor perpendicular.

59. a. First, find the slope of the linear function using the points (35, 10.76) and (50, 19.91)
$m = \dfrac{19.91-10.76}{50-35} = \dfrac{9.15}{15} = 0.61$
Use the point-slope form with $m = 0.61$ and $(a_1, r_1) = (35, 10.76)$
$r - r_1 = m(a - a_1)$
$r - 10.76 = 0.61(a - 35)$
$r - 10.76 = 0.61a - 21.35$
$r = 0.61a - 10.59$
$r(a) = 0.61a - 10.59$

b. For a 42-year-old man:
$r(a) = 0.61a - 10.59$
$r(42) = 0.61(42) - 10.59$
$= 15.03$
The monthly rate is about $15.03.

60. a. First, find the slope of the linear function using the points (30, 489) and (50, 525)
$m = \dfrac{525-489}{50-30} = \dfrac{36}{20} = 1.8$
Use the point-slope form with $m = 1.8$ and $(r_1, C_1) = (30, 489)$
$C - C_1 = m(r - r_1)$
$C - 489 = 1.8(r - 30)$
$C - 489 = 1.8r - 54$
$C = 1.8r + 435$
$C(r) = 1.8r + 435$

b. For a rate of 40 yards per minute:
$C(r) = 1.8r + 435$
$C(40) = 1.8(40) + 435$
$= 507$
The number of calories burned is 507.

c. Set the function equal to 600 and solve for r.
$C(r) = 1.8r + 435$
$600 = 1.8r + 435$
$1.8r = 165$
$r \approx 91.7$
The person needs to swim at a speed of about 91.7 yards per minute.

61. $(f+g)(x) = f(x) + g(x)$
$= (x^2 - 3x + 4) + (2x - 5)$
$= x^2 - x - 1$

62. $(f+g)(3) = f(3) + g(3)$
$= (3)^2 - 3 - 1$
$= 9 - 3 - 1$
$= 5$

63. $(g-f)(x) = (2x-5) - (x^2 - 3x + 4)$
$= -x^2 + 5x - 9$

64. $(g-f)(-1) = g(-1) - f(-1)$
$= -(-1)^2 + 5(-1) - 9$
$= -1 - 5 - 9$
$= -15$

65. $(f \cdot g)(-1) = f(-1) \cdot g(-1)$
$= ((-1)^2 - 3(-1) + 4) \cdot (2(-1) - 5)$
$= 8(-7)$
$= -56$

66. $(f \cdot g)(5) = f(5) \cdot g(5)$
$= (5^2 - 3(5) + 4) \cdot (2(5) - 5)$
$= 14(5)$
$= 70$

67. $(f/g)(1) = f(1)/g(1)$
$= (1^2 - 3(1) + 4)/(2(1) - 5)$
$= 2/-3$
$= -\dfrac{2}{3}$

68. $(f/g)(2) = f(2)/g(2)$
$= (2^2 - 3(2) + 4)/(2(2) - 5)$
$= 2(-1)$
$= -2$

69. a. The number of morning newspapers in 1960 was about 300.

   b. The number of morning newspapers in 2000 was about 750.

   c. The number of evening newspapers in 1960 was about 1450.

   d. The number of evening newspapers in 2000 was about 750.

   e. The number of daily newspapers in 1960 was about 1750.

   f. The number of daily newspapers in 2000 was about 1500.

70. a. $c(2000)$ was about 490 million.

   b. $t(2000)$ was about 190 million.

   c. $(c + t)(2000)$ was about 680 million.

71. $y \geq -3$
Graph the line $y = -3$ using a solid line. For the check point, select $(0, 0)$.
$y \geq -3$
$0 \geq -3 \leftarrow$ Substitute 0 for y
Since this is a true statement, shade the region which contains $(0, 0)$.

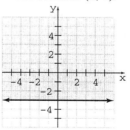

72. $x < 4$
Graph the line $x = 4$ using a dashed line. For the check point, select $(0, 0)$.
$x < 4$
$0 < 4 \leftarrow$ Substitute 0 for x
Since this is a true statement, shade the region

which contains $(0, 0)$.

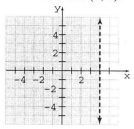

73. $y \leq 4x - 3$
Graph the line $y = 4x - 3$ using a solid line. For the check point, select $(0, 0)$.
$y \leq 4x - 3$
$0 \leq 4(0) - 3 \leftarrow$ Substitute 0 for x and y
$0 \leq -3$
Since this is a false statement, shade the region which does not contain $(0, 0)$.

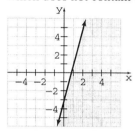

74. $y < \dfrac{1}{3}x - 2$

Graph the line $y = \dfrac{1}{3}x - 2$ using a dashed line.

For the check point, select $(0, 0)$.

$y < \dfrac{1}{3}x - 2$

$0 < \dfrac{1}{3}(0) - 2 \leftarrow$ Substitute 0 for x and y

$0 < -2$
Since this is a false statement, shade the region which does not contain $(0, 0)$.

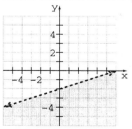

Practice Test

1. $y = -2x + 1$

x	y
-1	$y = -2(-1) + 1 = 3$
0	$y = -2(0) + 1 = 1$
1	$y = -2(1) + 1 = -1$

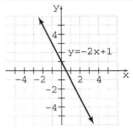

2. $y = \sqrt{x}$

x	y
-1	$y = \sqrt{-1}$ undefined
0	$y = \sqrt{0} = 0$
1	$y = \sqrt{1} = 1$
4	$y = \sqrt{4} = 2$

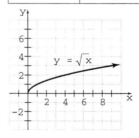

3. $y = x^2 - 4$

x	y
-2	$y = (-2)^2 - 4 = 0$
-1	$y = (-1)^2 - 4 = -3$
0	$y = (0)^2 - 4 = -4$
1	$y = (1)^2 - 4 = -3$
2	$y = (2)^2 - 4 = 0$

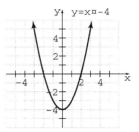

4. $y = |x|$

x	y
-3	$y = |-3| = 3$
0	$y = |0| = 0$
4	$y = |4| = 4$

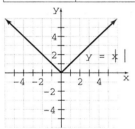

5. A function is a correspondence where each member in the domain corresponds with exactly one member in the range.

6. Yes, because each member in the domain corresponds with exactly one member in the range.

7. Yes, it is a function.
Domain: R
Range: $\left\{ y \middle| y \le 4 \right\}$

8. No, it is not a function.
Domain: $\left\{ x \middle| -3 \le x \le 3 \right\}$
Range: $\left\{ y \middle| -2 \le y \le 2 \right\}$

9. $f(x) = 3x^2 - 6x + 2$
$f(-2) = 3(-2)^2 - 6(-2) + 2 = 12 + 12 + 2 = 26$

10. $-10x + 5y = 20$
To find the *x*-intercept, set $y = 0$.
$-10x + 5(0) = 20$
$$-10x = 20$$
$$x = \frac{20}{-10}$$
$$x = -2$$
The *x*-intercept is (–2, 0).
To find the *y*-intercept, set $x = 0$.
$-10(0) + 5y = 20$
$$5y = 20$$
$$y = 4$$
The *y*-intercept is (0, 4).

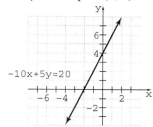

11. $\dfrac{x}{5} - \dfrac{y}{4} = 1$
To find the *x*-intercept, set $y = 0$.
$\dfrac{x}{5} - \dfrac{0}{4} = 1$
$$\frac{x}{5} = 1$$
$$x = 5$$
The *x*-intercept is (5, 0).
To find the *y*-intercept, set $x = 0$.
$\dfrac{0}{5} - \dfrac{y}{4} = 1$
$$-\frac{y}{4} = 1$$
$$-4\left(-\frac{y}{4}\right) = -4(1)$$
$$y = -4$$
The *y*-intercept is (0, –4).

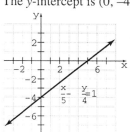

12. $f(x) = -3$ is a horizontal line 3 units below the *x*-axis.

x	*y*
–2	–3
0	–3
2	–3

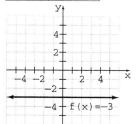

13. $x = 4$ is a vertical line 4 units to the right of the *y*-axis.

x	*y*
4	–2
4	0
4	2

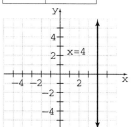

14. a. $p(x) = 10.2x - 50,000$

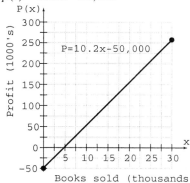

b. The company breaks even when $p(x) = 0$.
$10.2x - 50,000 = 0$
$$10.2x = 50,000$$
$$x = \frac{50,000}{10.2} = 4900$$
The company breaks even when it sells 4900 books.

c. $10.2x - 50,000 = 100,000$
$$10.2x = 150,000$$
$$x = \frac{150,000}{10.2} \approx 14,700$$
The company needs to sell about 14,700 books to break even.

15. To determine the slope and y-intercept, solve for y.
$4x - 3y = 9$
$$-3y = -4x + 9$$
$$y = \frac{-4x + 9}{-3}$$
$$y = \frac{4}{3}x - 3$$
$m = \frac{4}{3},\ b = -3$

16. $m = \frac{4-1}{3-2} = \frac{3}{1} = 3$
Use the point-slope form with $m = 3$ and $(x_1,\ y_1) = (2, 1)$.
$y - y_1 = m(x - x_1)$
$$y - 1 = 3(x - 2)$$
$$y - 1 = 3x - 6$$
$$y = 3x - 5$$

17. The slope of $y = \frac{1}{2}x + 1$ is $m_1 = \frac{1}{2}$. Any line perpendicular to this line has slope $m_2 = -2$. Use the point-slope form with $m = -2$ and $(x_1,\ y_1) = (5, -3)$.
$y - y_1 = m(x - x_1)$
$$y - (-3) = -2(x - 5)$$
$$y + 3 = -2x + 10$$
$$y = -2x + 7$$

18. For the year 2050, $t = 2050 - 2000 = 50$. The points are $(0, 274.634)$ and $(50, 393.931)$.

$m = \dfrac{393.931 - 274.634}{50 - 0}$
$= \dfrac{119.297}{50}$
$= 2.38594$
≈ 2.386
Use the point-slope form with $m = 2.386$ and $(t_1,\ p_1) = (0, 274.634)$.
$p - p_1 = m(t - t_1)$
$$p - 274.634 = 2.386(t - 0)$$
$$p - 274.634 = 2.386t$$
$$p = 2.386t + 274.634$$
$$p(t) \approx 2.386t + 274.634$$

19. Write each equation in slope-intercept form by solving for y.

$2x - 3y = 6$
$$-3y = -2x + 6$$
$$y = \frac{-2x + 6}{-3}$$
$$y = \frac{2}{3}x - 2$$

$4x + 8 = 6y$
$$\frac{4x + 8}{6} = y$$
$$\frac{4}{6}x + \frac{8}{6} = y$$
$$y = \frac{2}{3}x + \frac{4}{3}$$

Since the slopes are the same, the lines are parallel.

20. a. Let t represent the number of years since 1970. Then $t = 0$ represents 1970 and $t = 30$ represents 2000. Find the slope of the linear function using the points $(0, 362)$ and $(30, 266)$.
$m = \dfrac{266 - 362}{30 - 0} = \dfrac{-96}{30} = -3.2$
Use the point-slope form with $m = -3.2$ and $(t_1,\ r_1) = (0, 362)$
$r - r_1 = m(t - t_1)$
$$r - 362 = -3.2(t - 0)$$
$$r - 362 = -3.2t$$
$$r = -3.2t + 362$$
$$r(t) = -3.2t + 362$$

b. For 1995, use $t = 25$:
$r(t) = -3.2t + 362$
$$r(25) = -3.2(25) + 362$$
$$= 282$$
There were 282 deaths due to heart disease per 100,000 people in 1995.

c. For 2010, use $t = 40$:

$$r(t) = -3.2t + 362$$

$$r(40) = -3.2(40) + 362$$

$$= 234$$

There will be about 234 deaths due to heart disease per 100,000 people in 2010.

21. $(f + g)(3) = f(3) + g(3)$

$$= (2(3)^2 - 3) + (3 - 5)$$

$$= 15 - 2 = 13$$

22. $(f / g)(-1) = f(-1) / g(-1)$

$$= (2(-1)^2 - (-1)) / ((-1) - 5)$$

$$= 3 / (-6) = -\frac{1}{2}$$

23. $f(a) = 2a^2 - a$

24. a. The total number of tons of paper to be used in 2010 will be about 44 million tons.

   b. The number of tons of paper to be used by businesses in 2010 will be about 18 million tons.

   c. The number of tons of paper to be used for reference, print media, and household use in 2010 will be about $44 - 18 = 26$, or 26 million tons.

25. Graph the line $y = 3x - 2$ using a dashed line. For the check point, select $(0, 0)$.

$$y < 3x - 2$$

$0 < 3 \cdot 0 - 2 \leftarrow$ Substitute 0 for x and y

$$0 < -2$$

Since the statement is false, shade the region that does not contain $(0, 0)$.

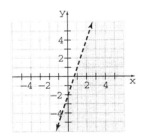

Cumulative Review Test

1. a. $A \cap B = \{3, 5, 7\}$

   b. $A \cup B = \{1, 2, 3, 5, 7, 9, 11, 13\}$

2. a. None of the numbers are natural numbers.

   b. $-6, -4, -\sqrt{2}, 0, \frac{1}{3}, \sqrt{3}, 4.67,$ and $\frac{37}{2}$ are real numbers.

3. $2 - \{3[6 - 4(6^2 \div 4)]\} = 2 - \{3[6 - 4(36 \div 4)]\}$

$$= 2 - \{3[6 - 4(9)]\}$$

$$= 2 - \{3[6 - 36]\}$$

$$= 2 - \{3[-30]\}$$

$$= 2 - \{-90\}$$

$$= 2 + 90$$

$$= 92$$

4. $\left(\dfrac{4x^2}{y^{-3}}\right)^2 = (4x^2 y^3)^2 = 4^2 (x^2)^2 (y^3)^2 = 16x^4 y^6$

5. $\left(\dfrac{2x^4 y^{-2}}{4xy^3}\right)^3 = \left(\dfrac{x^3}{2y^5}\right)^3 = \dfrac{(x^3)^3}{2^3 (y^5)^3} = \dfrac{x^9}{8y^{15}}$

6. a. Property Taxes:

   $= 30.7\%$ of 1.576×10^9

   $= 0.307 \times 1.576 \times 10^9$

   $= 0.483832 \times 10^9$

   $= 4.83832 \times 10^8$ or $483,832,000

   b. Federal Grants:

   $= 14.2\%$ of 1.576×10^9

   $= 0.142 \times 1.576 \times 10^9$

   $= 0.223792 \times 10^9$

   $= 2.23792 \times 10^8$ or $223,792,000

   c. State Shared Taxes % − State Grants %:

   $= 10.3\% - 9.4\% = 0.9\%$

   Difference in Amount of Taxes Obtained:

   $= 0.9\% \times 1.576 \times 10^9$

   $= 0.009 \times 1.576 \times 10^9$

   $= 0.014184 \times 10^9$

   $= 1.4184 \times 10^7$ or $14,184,000

7.
$$2(x+4)-5=-3[x-(2x+1)]$$
$$2x+8-5=-3[x-2x-1]$$
$$2x+3=-3[-x-1]$$
$$2x+3=3x+3$$
$$x=0$$

8.
$$\frac{4}{5}-\frac{x}{3}=10$$
$$15\left(\frac{4}{5}-\frac{x}{3}\right)=15(10)$$
$$12-5x=150$$
$$-5x=138$$
$$x=-\frac{138}{5}$$

9.
$$5x-\{4-[2(x-4)]-5\}=5x-\{4-[2x-8]-5\}$$
$$=5x-\{4-2x+8-5\}$$
$$=5x-\{-2x+7\}$$
$$=5x+2x-7$$
$$=7x-7$$

10.
$$A=\frac{1}{2}h(b_1+b_2)$$
$$2A=h(b_1+b_2)$$
$$\frac{2A}{h}=b_1+b_2$$
$$\frac{2A}{h}-b_2=b_1$$
$$b_1=\frac{2A}{h}-b_2$$

11. Let x be amount of 15% hydrogen peroxide solution.

Solution	Strength	Amount	Salt
15%	0.15	x	$0.15x$
4%	0.04	10	$0.04(10)$
Mixture	0.10	$x+10$	$0.10(x+10)$

$$0.15x+0.04(10)=0.10(x+10)$$
$$0.15x+0.4=0.10x+1$$
$$0.15x-0.10x=1-0.4$$
$$0.05x=0.6$$
$$x=\frac{0.6}{0.05}$$
$$x=12$$
12 gallons of the 15% hydrogen peroxide solution must be added.

12.
$$3(x-4)<6(2x+3)$$
$$3x-12<12x+18$$
$$3x-12x<18+12$$
$$-9x<30$$
$$\frac{-9x}{-9}>\frac{30}{-9}$$
$$x>-\frac{10}{3}$$

13.
$$-4<3x-7<8$$
$$-4+7<3x-7+7<8+7$$
$$3<3x<15$$
$$\frac{3}{3}<\frac{3x}{3}<\frac{15}{3}$$
$$1<x<5$$

14.
$$|3x+5|=|2x-10|$$

$$3x+5=2x-10 \quad \text{or} \quad 3x+5=-(2x-10)$$
$$3x-2x=-10-5 \qquad\qquad 3x+5=-2x+10$$
$$x=-15 \qquad\qquad\qquad 3x+2x=10-5$$
$$5x=5$$
$$x=1$$
$$\{-15,1\}$$

The solution set is $\left\{\frac{4}{3},\frac{12}{5}\right\}$.

15.
$$|2x-1|\le 3$$
$$-3\le 2x-1\le 3$$
$$-3+1\le 2x-1+1\le 3+1$$
$$-2\le 2x\le 4$$
$$\frac{-2}{2}\le\frac{2x}{2}\le\frac{4}{2}$$
$$-1\le x\le 2$$
The solution set is $\{x|-1\le x\le 2\}$.

16. Set up a table of values to find some points on the line $y = -\dfrac{3}{2}x - 4$.

x	y
-4	$-\dfrac{3}{2}(-4) - 4 = 2$
-2	$-\dfrac{3}{2}(-2) - 4 = -1$
0	$-\dfrac{3}{2}(0) - 4 = -4$

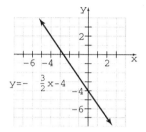

17. a. The graph is not a function.

   b. Domain: $\{x | x \le 2\}$; Range: R

18. Let $(x_1, y_1) = (-5, 3)$ and $(x_2, y_2) = (4, -1)$.
$$m = \frac{y_2 - y_1}{x_2 - x_1} = \frac{-1 - 3}{4 - (-5)} = \frac{-4}{9}$$

19. Write each equation in slope-intercept form by solving for y.

$$2x - 5y = 6 \qquad\qquad 5x - 2y = 9$$
$$-5y = -2x + 6 \qquad -2y = -5x + 9$$
$$y = \frac{-2x + 6}{-5} \qquad y = \frac{-5x + 9}{-2}$$
$$y = \frac{2}{5}x - \frac{6}{5} \qquad y = \frac{5}{2}x - \frac{9}{2}$$

Since the slopes are $\dfrac{2}{5}$ and $\dfrac{5}{2}$ which are neither equal nor negative reciprocals, the lines are neither parallel nor perpendicular.

20. $(f + g)(x) = f(x) + g(x)$
$$= (x^2 + 3x - 2) + (4x - 6)$$
$$= x^2 + 7x - 8$$

Chapter 4

Exercise Set 4.1

1. The solution to a system of linear equations is the point(s) that satisfy all equations in the system.

3. A dependent system of equations is a system of equations that has an infinite number of solutions.

5. A consistent system of equations has a solution.

7. Compare the slopes and y-intercepts of the equations. If the slopes are different, the system is consistent. If the slopes and y-intercepts are the same, the system is dependent. If the slopes are the same and the y-intercepts are different, the system is inconsistent.

9. You will get a true statement, like $0 = 0$.

11. $y = 2x + 4$ and $y = 2x - 1$

   a. $(0, 4)$ does not satisfy the second equation since the left side is 4, whereas the right side is $2(0) - 1 = 0 - 1 = -1$.

   b. $(3, 10)$ does not satisfy the second equation since the left side is 10, whereas the right side is
   $2(3) - 1 = 6 - 1 = 5$

13. $x + y = 25$ and $0.25x + 0.45y = 7.50$

   a. $(5, 20)$ does not satisfy the second equation and is therefore not a solution to the system.
   1st equation: 2nd equation:
   $(5) + (20) = 25$ $0.25(5) + 0.45(20) = 7.50$
   $25 = 25$ $10.25 \neq 7.50$

   b. $(18.75, 6.25)$ satisfies both equations and is therefore a solution to the system.

   1st equation: 2nd equation:
   $(18.75) + (6.25) = 25$ $0.25(18.75) + 0.45(6.25) = 7.50$
   $25 = 25$ $7.50 = 7.50$

15. $x + 2y - z = -5$
    $2x - y + 2z = 8$
    $3x + 3y + 4z = 5$

   a. $(1, 3, -2)$ does not satisfy the first equation since the left side is
   $1 + 2(3) - (-2) = 1 + 6 + 2 = 9$, whereas the right side is -5.

   b. $(1, -2, 2)$ satisfies all three equations. For the first equation, the left side is
   $1 + 2(-2) - (2) = 1 - 4 - 2 = -5$ and the right side is -5. For the second equation, the left side is $2(1) - (-2) + 2(2) = 2 + 2 + 4 = 8$ and the right side is 8. Finally, for the third equation, the left side is
   $3(1) + 3(-2) + 4(2) = 3 - 6 + 8 = 5$ and the right side is 5.

17. Write each equation in slope-intercept form.
   $$-6x + 3y = 1 \qquad\qquad 4y + 12 = -6x$$
   $$3y = 6x + 1 \qquad\qquad 4y = -6x - 12$$
   $$y = 2x + \frac{1}{3} \qquad\qquad y = -\frac{3}{2}x - 3$$

   Since the slope of the first line is 2 and the slope of the second line is $-\frac{3}{2}$, the slopes are different so that the lines intersect to produce one solution. This is a consistent system.

19. Multiply the first equation through by 12.
   $$\frac{x}{3} + \frac{y}{4} = 1 \qquad \text{and} \quad 4x + 3y = 12$$
   $$12\left(\frac{x}{3} + \frac{y}{4}\right) = 12(1)$$
   $$4x + 3y = 12$$

   Since both equations are identical, the line is the same for both of them to produce an infinite number of solutions. This is a dependent system.

21. Write each equation in slope-intercept form.
   $$3x - 3y = 9 \qquad\qquad 2x - 2y = -4$$
   $$-3y = -3x + 9 \qquad\qquad -2y = -2x - 4$$
   $$y = x - 3 \qquad\qquad y = x + 2$$

   Since the slope of each line is 1, but the y-intercepts are different ($b = -3$ for the first equation, $b = 2$ for the second equation), the two lines are parallel and produce no solution. This is an inconsistent system.

23. Write each equation in slope-intercept form.

$$y = \frac{3}{2}x + \frac{1}{2}$$

$$3x - 2y = -\frac{1}{2}$$

$$-2y = -3x - \frac{1}{2}$$

$$y = \frac{3}{2}x + \frac{1}{4}$$

Since the slope of each line is $\frac{3}{2}$, but the

y-intercepts are different ($b = \frac{1}{2}$ for the first

equation, $b = \frac{1}{4}$ for the second equation) the two

lines are parallel and produce no solution. This is an inconsistent system.

25. Graph the equations $y = x + 5$ and $y = -x + 3$.

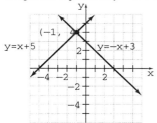

The lines intersect and the point of intersection is $(-1, 4)$. This is a consistent system.

27. Graph the equations $y = 4x - 1$ and $2y = 8x + 6$.

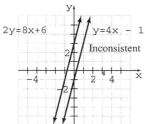

The lines are parallel. The system is inconsistent and there is no solution.

29. Graph the equations $2x + 3y = 6$ and $4x = -6y + 12$.

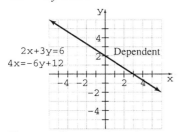

The equations produce the same line. The system is dependent and there are an infinite number of solutions.

31. Graph the equations $x + 3y = 4$ and $x = 1$.

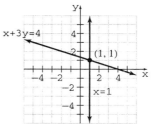

The lines intersect and the point of intersection is $(1, 1)$. This is a consistent system.

33. Graph the equations $y = -5x + 5$ and $y = 2x - 2$.

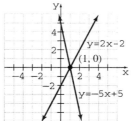

The lines intersect and the point of intersection is $(1, 0)$. This is a consistent system.

35. Graph the equations $2x - y = -4$ and $2y = 4x - 6$.

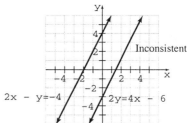

The lines are parallel and do not intersect. The system is inconsistent and there is no solution.

37. $x + 3y = -1$

$y = x + 1$

Substitute $x + 1$ for y in the first equation.

$x + 3(x + 1) = -1$

$x + 3x + 3 = -1$

$4x = -4$

$x = -1$

Now, substitute -1 for x in the second equation.

$y = (-1) + 1$

$= 0$

The solution is $(-1, 0)$.

39. $x = 2y + 3$

$y = x$

Substitute x for y in first equation.

$x = 2(x) + 3$

$-x = 3$

$x = -3$

Now, substitute -3 for x in the second equation.
$x = y$

$-3 = y$

The solution is $(-3, -3)$.

41. $a + 3b = 5$

$2a - b = 3$

Solve the first equation for a.
$a + 3b = 5$

$a = -3b + 5$

Substitute $-3b + 5$ for a in the second equation.
$2(-3b + 5) - b = 3$

$-6b + 10 - b = 3$

$-7b = -7$

$b = 1$

Now, substitute 1 for b in the first equation.
$a + 3(1) = 5$

$a = 2$

The solution is $(2, 1)$.

43. $y + \frac{1}{2}x = 0$

$x + 4y - 1 = 0$

Solve for y in the first equation then substitute that expression into the second equation.

$y + \frac{1}{2}x = 0 \Rightarrow y = -\frac{1}{2}x$

$x + 4\left(-\frac{1}{2}x\right) - 1 = 0$

$x - 2x - 1 = 0$

$-x = 1$

$x = -1$

Substitue $x = -1$ into the first equation.

$y + \frac{1}{2}(-1) = 0$

$y - \frac{1}{2} = 0$

$y = \frac{1}{2}$

The solution is $\left(-1, \frac{1}{2}\right)$.

45. $a - \frac{1}{2}b = 2$

$b = 2a - 4$

Substitute $2a - 4$ for b in the first equation.

$a - \frac{1}{2}(2a - 4) = 2$

$a - a + 2 = 2$

$2 = 2$

Since this is an identity, there are an infinite number of solutions. This is a dependent system.

47. $5x - 2y = -7$

$y = \frac{5}{2}x + 1$

Substitute $\frac{5}{2}x + 1$ into y in the first equation.

$5x - 2\left(\frac{5}{2}x + 1\right) = -7$

$5x - 5x - 2 = -7$

$-2 \neq -7$

Since this is a contradiction, there is no solution. This is an inconsistent system.

49. $5x - 4y = -7$

$x - \frac{3}{5}y = -2$

First, solve the second equation for x.

$x - \frac{3}{5}y = -2$

$x = \frac{3}{5}y - 2$

Now substitute $\frac{3}{5}y - 2$ for x in the first equation.

$5\left(\frac{3}{5}y - 2\right) - 4y = -7$

$3y - 10 - 4y = -7$

$-10 - y = -7$

$-y = 3$

$y = -3$

Finally, substitute -3 for y in the equation $x = \frac{3}{5}y - 2$.

$x = \frac{3}{5}(-3) - 2$

$x = -\frac{9}{5} - 2$

$x = -\frac{9}{5} - \frac{10}{5}$

$x = -\frac{19}{5}$

The solution is $\left(-\frac{19}{5}, -3\right)$.

51. $\frac{1}{2}x - \frac{1}{3}y = 2$

$\frac{1}{4}x + \frac{2}{3}y = 6$

Solve the first equation for y.

$\frac{1}{2}x - \frac{1}{3}y = 2$

$-\frac{1}{3}y = -\frac{1}{2}x + 2$

$y = \frac{3}{2}x - 6$

Substitute $\frac{3}{2}x - 6$ for y in the second equation.

$\frac{1}{4}x + \frac{2}{3}\left(\frac{3}{2}x - 6\right) = 6$

$\frac{1}{4}x + x - 4 = 6$

$\frac{5}{4}x - 4 = 6$

$\frac{5}{4}x = 10$

$x = \frac{4}{5}(10) = 8$

Substitute 8 for x in the equation $y = \frac{3}{2}x - 6$.

$y = \frac{3}{2}(8) - 6 = 12 - 6 = 6$

The solution is $(8, 6)$.

52. $\frac{1}{2}x + \frac{1}{3}y = 13$

$\frac{1}{5}x + \frac{1}{8}y = 5$

Solve the first equation for x.

$\frac{1}{2}x + \frac{1}{3}y = 13$

$\frac{1}{2}x = -\frac{1}{3}y + 13$

$x = -\frac{2}{3}y + 26$

Substitute $-\frac{2}{3}y + 26$ for x in the second

equation.

$\frac{1}{5}\left(-\frac{2}{3}y + 26\right) + \frac{1}{8}y = 5$

$-\frac{2}{15}y + \frac{26}{5} + \frac{1}{8}y = 5$

$-\frac{1}{120}y + \frac{26}{5} = 5$

$-\frac{1}{120}y = -\frac{1}{5}$

$y = (-120)\left(-\frac{1}{5}\right) = 24$

Substitute 24 for y in the equation

$x = -\frac{2}{3}y + 26.$

$x = -\frac{2}{3}(24) + 26 = -16 + 26 = 10$

The solution is $(10, 24)$.

53. $x + y = 7$

          $\underline{x - y = -3}$

Add: $2x \quad\quad = 4$

          $x \quad\quad = 2$

Substitute 2 for x in the first equation.

$(2) + y = 7$

$y = 5$

The solution is $(2, 5)$.

55. $4x - 3y = 1$

        $\underline{5x + 3y = -10}$

Add: $9x \quad\quad = -9$

          $x = -1$

Substitute -1 for x in the second

equation.

$5(-1) + 3y = -10$

$-5 + 3y = -10$

$3y = -5$

$y = -\frac{5}{3}$

The solution is $\left(-1, -\frac{5}{3}\right)$.

57. $10m - 2n = 6$

$-5m + n = -3$

To eliminate m, multiply the second
equation by 2 and then add.

$10m - 2n = 6$

$2[-5m + n = -3]$

gives

        $10m - 2n = 6$

        $\underline{-10m + 2n = -6}$

Add: $0 = 0$

Since this is an identity, there are an
infinite number of solutions. This is a
dependent system.

59. $2c - 5d = 1$

$-4c + 10d = 6$

To eliminate c, multiply the first equation by 2 and then add.

$2[2c - 5d = 1]$

$-4c + 10d = 6$

gives

$$4c - 10d = 2$$
$$\underline{-4c + 10d = 6}$$

Add: $0 = 8$

Since $0 = 8$ is a false statement, the system has no solution. It is an inconsistent system.

61. $3p - 2q = 1$

$2p + 5q = 7$

To eliminate q, multiply the first equation by 5, multiply the second equation by 2, and then add:

$5[3p - 2q = 1]$

$2[2p + 5q = 7]$

gives

$$15p - 10q = \ 5$$
$$\underline{4p + 10q = 14}$$

Add: $19p \qquad = 19$

$p \ = \ 1$

Substitute 1 for p in the second equation.

$2(1) + 5q = 7$

$2 + 5q = 7$

$5q = 5$

$q = 1$

The solution is $(1, 1)$.

63. $5s - 3t = 7$

$t = s + 1$

Write the system in standard form.

$5s - 3t = 7$

$-s + t = 1$

To eliminate s, multiply the second equation by 5 and then add.

$5s - 3t = 7$

$5[-s + t = 1]$

gives

$$5s - 3t = \ 7$$
$$\underline{-5s + 5t = \ 5}$$

Add: $2t = 12$

$t = \ 6$

Substitute 6 for t in the second

equation.

$(6) = s + 1$

$s = 5$

The solution is $(5, 6)$.

65. $2x - y = \ 8$
$$\underline{3x + y = \ 6}$$

Add: $5x \qquad = 14$

$$x = \frac{14}{5}$$

Substitute $\frac{14}{5}$ for x in the second equation.

$3x + y = 6$

$3\left(\dfrac{14}{5}\right) + y = 6$

$\dfrac{42}{5} + y = 6$

$y = 6 - \dfrac{42}{5}$

$y = \dfrac{30}{5} - \dfrac{42}{5}$

$y = -\dfrac{12}{5}$

The solution is $\left(\dfrac{14}{5}, -\dfrac{12}{5}\right)$.

67. $3x - 4y = 5$

$\qquad 2x = 5y - 3$

Write the system in standard form.

$3x - 4y = 5$

$2x - 5y = -3$

To eliminate x, multiply the first equation by -2 and the second equation by 3 and then add.

$-2[3x - 4y = 5]$

$3[2x - 5y = -3]$

gives

$$-6x + \ 8y = -10$$
$$\underline{6x - 15y = \ -9}$$

Add: $-7y = -19$

$$y = \frac{-19}{-7}$$

$$= \frac{19}{7}$$

Substitute $\dfrac{19}{7}$ for y in the second equation.

$$2x = 5y - 3$$
$$2x = 5\left(\frac{19}{7}\right) - 3$$
$$2x = \frac{95}{7} - 3$$
$$2x = \frac{74}{4}$$
$$x = \frac{1}{2}\left(\frac{74}{7}\right) = \frac{37}{7}$$

The solution is $\left(\frac{37}{7}, \frac{19}{7}\right)$.

69. $0.2x + 0.5y = 1.6$
$$-0.3x + 0.4y = -0.1$$

To eliminate x, multiply the first equation by 3 and the second equation by 2 and then add.
$$3[0.2x + 0.5y = 1.6]$$
$$2[-0.3x + 0.4y = -0.1]$$
gives
$$0.6x + 1.5y = 4.8$$
$$\underline{-0.6x + 0.8y = -0.2}$$
$$\text{Add:} \quad 2.3y = 4.6$$
$$y = \frac{4.6}{2.3} = 2$$

Now, substitute 2 for y in the first equation.
$$0.2x + 0.5y = 1.6$$
$$0.2x + 0.5(2) = 1.6$$
$$0.2x + 1 = 1.6$$
$$0.2x = 0.6$$
$$x = \frac{0.6}{0.2} = 3$$

The solution is (3, 2).

71. $2.1m - 0.6n = 8.4$
$$-1.5m - 0.3n = -6.0$$

To eliminate n, multiply the second equation by -2 and then add.
$$2.1m - 0.6n = 8.4$$
$$-2[-1.5x - 0.3y = -6.0]$$
gives
$$2.1m - 0.6n = 8.4$$
$$\underline{3.0m + 0.6n = 12.0}$$
$$\text{Add:} \quad 5.1m \quad\quad = 20.40$$
$$m = \frac{20.40}{5.1} = 4$$

Substitute 4 for m into the second equation.
$$-1.5m - 0.3n = -6.0$$
$$-1.5(4) - 0.3n = -6.0$$
$$-6.0 - 0.3n = -6.0$$
$$-0.3n = 0$$
$$n = 0$$

The solution is (4, 0).

73. $\frac{1}{2}x - \frac{1}{3}y = 1$
$$\frac{1}{4}x - \frac{1}{9}y = \frac{2}{3}$$

To clear fractions, multiply the first equation by 6 and the second equation by 36:
$$6\left[\frac{1}{2}x - \frac{1}{3}y = 1\right]$$
$$36\left[\frac{1}{4}x - \frac{1}{9}y = \frac{2}{3}\right]$$
gives
$$3x - 2y = 6$$
$$9x - 4y = 24$$

To eliminate y, multiply the first equation by -2 and then add.
$$-2[3x - 2y = 6]$$
$$9x - 4y = 24$$
gives
$$-6x + 4y = -12$$
$$\underline{9x - 4y = 24}$$
$$\text{Add:} \quad 3x \quad\quad = 12$$
$$x = 4$$

Substitute 4 for x in the equation $3x - 2y = 6$.
$$3(4) - 2y = 6$$
$$12 - 2y = 6$$
$$6 - 2y = 0$$
$$6 = 2y$$
$$3 = y$$

The solution is (4, 3).

75. $\frac{1}{5}x + \frac{1}{2}y = 4$
$$\frac{2}{3}x - y = \frac{8}{3}$$

To clear fractions and to eliminate x, multiply the first equation by 10 and the second equation by -3 and then add.
$$10\left[\frac{1}{5}x + \frac{1}{2}y = 4\right]$$
$$-3\left[\frac{2}{3}x - y = \frac{8}{3}\right]$$
gives
$$2x + 5y = 40$$
$$\underline{-2x + 3y = -8}$$
$$\text{Add:} \quad\quad 8y = 32$$
$$y = 4$$

Substitute 4 for y in the equation $2x + 5y = 40$.
$$2x + 5(4) = 40$$
$$2x + 20 = 40$$
$$2x = 20$$
$$x = 10$$

The solution is (10, 4).

77. Answers will vary. The system should involve a variable that has a coefficient of 1.

79. $W(t) = 0.12t + 20.3$

$M(t) = 0.1t + 22.8$

Here, the $W(t)$ and the $M(t)$ can each be replaced with the variable y. Rewrite as a system of equations in y and t.

$y = 0.12t + 20.3$

$y = 0.1t + 22.8$

This system can be solved using any of the methods described in the text. Here, we use substitution to solve the system by substituting $0.1t + 22.8$ into the y in the first equation.

$0.1t + 22.8 = 0.12t + 20.3$

$-0.02t = -2.5$

$t = 125$

Because t represents the number of years since 1960, $t = 125$ represents $1960 + 125 = 2085$. The average age at first marriage for men and women will be the same in 2085.

81. Multiply the first equation by 2. The resulting equations are identical.

83. a. If a system has more than one solution, then it must have an infinite number of solutions. All of these solutions must lie on the same line.

b. Slope is $m = \dfrac{11-3}{-6-(-4)} = \dfrac{8}{-2} = -4$. Use the

point-slope form with $m = -\dfrac{1}{2}$ and

$(x_1, y_1) = (-4, 3)$.

$y - y_1 = m(x - x_1)$

$y - 3 = -4(x - (-4))$

$y - 3 = -4(x + 4)$

$y - 3 = -4x - 16$

$y = -4x - 13$

The y-intercept is $(0, -13)$.

c. Yes, the graph of a non-vertical line is a function.

85. Answers may vary. One example is

$\begin{array}{l} x + y = 1 \\ 2x + 2y = 2 \end{array}$.

87. a. Answers may vary. One example is

$\begin{array}{l} x + y = 7 \\ x - y = -3 \end{array}$.

b. Choose coefficients for x and y, then use the given coordinates to find the constants.

89. $Ax + 4y = -8$

$3x - By = 21$

Since the solution is $(2, -3)$, substitute 2 for x and -3 for y.

$A(2) + 4(-3) = -8$

$3(2) - B(-3) = 21$

or

$2A - 12 = -8$

$6 + 3B = 21$

This is a system of two equations in the two unknowns A and B. To solve, solve each equation for the unknown variable. In the first equation, solve for A.

$2A - 12 = -8$

$2A = 4$

$A = \dfrac{4}{2} = 2$

In the second equation, solve for B.

$6 + 3B = 21$

$3B = 15$

$B = \dfrac{15}{3} = 5$

Thus, $A = 2$ and $B = 5$.

91. $f(x) = mx + b$

Substitute $(2, 6)$ and $(-1, -6)$ into the equation to get a system.

$6 = 2m + b$

$-6 = -m + b$

Multiply the second equation by -1 and add.

$\begin{array}{l} 6 = 2m + b \\ \underline{6 = m - b} \\ 12 = 3m \end{array}$

$4 = m$

Substitute 4 for m in the first equation and solve for b.

$6 = 2(4) + b$

$-2 = b$

Thus, $m = 4$ and $b = -2$.

93. The system is dependent or one graph is not in the viewing window.

95. $\dfrac{x+2}{2} - \dfrac{y+4}{3} = 4$

$\dfrac{x+y}{2} = \dfrac{1}{2} + \dfrac{x-y}{3}$

Start by writing each equation in standard form after clearing fractions.

$$6\left(\frac{x+2}{2}\right) - 6\left(\frac{y+4}{3}\right) = 6(4)$$
$$6\left(\frac{x+y}{2}\right) = 6\left(\frac{1}{2}\right) + 6\left(\frac{x-y}{3}\right)$$

$$3(x+2) - 2(y+4) = 24$$
$$3(x+y) = 3 + 2(x-y)$$

$$3x + 6 - 2y - 8 = 24$$
$$3x + 3y = 3 + 2x - 2y$$

$$3x - 2y = 26 \quad (1)$$
$$x + 5y = 3 \quad (2)$$

To eliminate x, multiply equation (2) by -3 and then add to equation (1).
$$3x - 2y = 26$$
$$-3[x + 5y = 3]$$
gives
$$3x - 2y = 26$$
$$\underline{-3x - 15y = -9}$$
Add: $\quad -17y = 17$
$$y = \frac{17}{-17} = -1$$

Now, substitute -1 for y in equation (2).
$$x + 5(-1) = 3$$
$$x - 5 = 3$$
$$x = 8$$
The solution is $(8, -1)$.

97. Rewrite the system using the hint.
$$3 \cdot \frac{1}{a} + 4 \cdot \frac{1}{b} = -1$$
$$\frac{1}{a} + 6 \cdot \frac{1}{b} = 2$$
Now let $x = \frac{1}{a}$ and $y = \frac{1}{b}$.
$$3x + 4y = -1 \quad (1)$$
$$x + 6y = 2 \quad (2)$$
Multiply equation (2) by -3 and add.
$$3x + 4y = -1$$
$$-3[x + 6y = 2]$$
gives
$$3x + 4y = -1$$
$$\underline{-3x - 18y = -6}$$
Add: $\quad -14y = -7$
$$y = \frac{-7}{-14} = \frac{1}{2}$$

Substitute $\frac{1}{2}$ for y in equation (2).
$$x + 6\left(\frac{1}{2}\right) = 2$$
$$x + 3 = 2$$
$$x = -1$$

Now find the values of a and b.
$$x = \frac{1}{a}$$
$$-1 = \frac{1}{a}$$
$$a = -1$$
$$y = \frac{1}{b}$$
$$\frac{1}{2} = \frac{1}{b}$$
$$b = 2$$
The solution is $(-1, 2)$.

99. $4ax + 3y = 19$
$\quad -ax + y = 4$
Solve the second equation for y.
$$-ax + y = 4$$
$$y = ax + 4$$
Substitute $ax + 4$ for y in the first equation.
$$4ax + 3y = 19$$
$$4ax + 3(ax + 4) = 19$$
$$4ax + 3ax + 12 = 19$$
$$7ax + 12 = 19$$
$$7ax = 7$$
$$x = \frac{7}{7a} = \frac{1}{a}$$
Now substitute $\frac{1}{a}$ for x in the equation $y = ax + 4$.
$$y = a\left(\frac{1}{a}\right) + 4$$
$$y = 1 + 4$$
$$y = 5$$
The solution is $\left(\frac{1}{a}, 5\right)$.

103. a. Yes, the set of real numbers includes the set of rational numbers.

b. Yes, the set of real numbers includes the set of irrational numbers.

105. $|x - 4| = |4 - x|$
$\quad x - 4 = 4 - x \quad$ or $\quad x - 4 = -(4 - x)$
$\quad 2x - 4 = 4 \qquad\qquad x - 4 = -4 + x$
$\quad 2x = 8 \qquad\qquad\quad -4 = -4$
$\quad x = 4$
This means that the solution is all real numbers or R.

107. No, the points $(-3, 4)$ and $(-3, 2)$ have the same first coordinate but different second coordinates.

Exercise Set 4.2

1. The graph will be a plane.

3.
$$x = 1$$
$$2x - y = 4$$
$$-3x + 2y - 2z = 1$$
Substitute 1 for x in the second equation.
$$2(1) - y = 4$$
$$2 - y = 4$$
$$-y = 2$$
$$y = -2$$
Substitute 1 for x and -2 for y in the third equation.
$$-3(1) + 2(-2) - 2z = 1$$
$$-3 - 4 - 2z = 1$$
$$-7 - 2z = 1$$
$$-2z = 8$$
$$z = -4$$
The solution is (1, −2, −4).

5.
$$5x - 6z = -17$$
$$3x - 4y + 5z = -1$$
$$2z = -6$$
Solve the third equation for z.
$$2z = -6$$
$$z = -3$$
Substitute −3 for z in the first equation.
$$5x - 6z = -17$$
$$5x - 6(-3) = -17$$
$$5x + 18 = -17$$
$$5x = -35$$
$$x = -7$$
Substitute −7 for x and −3 for z in the second equation.
$$3x - 4y + 5z = -1$$
$$3(-7) - 4y + 5(-3) = -1$$
$$-21 - 4y - 15 = -1$$
$$-4y - 36 = -1$$
$$-4y = 35$$
$$y = \frac{35}{-4} = -\frac{35}{4}$$
The solution is $\left(-7, -\dfrac{-35}{4}, -3\right)$.

7.
$$x + 2y = 6$$
$$3y = 9$$
$$x + 2z = 12$$
Solve the second equation for y.
$$3y = 9$$
$$y = 3$$
Substitute 3 for y in the first equation.

$$x + 2y = 6$$
$$x + 2(3) = 6$$
$$x + 6 = 6$$
$$x = 0$$
Substitute 0 for x in the third equation.
$$x + 2z = 12$$
$$0 + 2z = 12$$
$$2z = 12$$
$$z = 6$$
The solution is (0, 3, 6).

9.
$$x - 2y = -3 \quad (1)$$
$$3x + 2y = 7 \quad (2)$$
$$2x - 4y + z = -6 \quad (3)$$
To eliminate y between equations (1) and (2), add equations (1) and (2).

$$x - 2y = -3$$
$$\underline{3x + 2y = \ 7}$$
Add: $\qquad 4x = \ 4$
$$x = 1$$
Substitute 1 for x in equation (1).
$$(1) - 2y = -3$$
$$-2y = -4$$
$$y = 2$$
Substitute 1 for x, and 2 for y in equation (3).
$$2(1) - 4(2) + z = -6$$
$$2 - 8 + z = -6$$
$$-6 + z = -6$$
$$z = 0$$
The solution is (1, 2, 0).

11.
$$2y + 4z = 6 \quad (1)$$
$$x + y + 2z = 0 \quad (2)$$
$$2x + y + z = 4 \quad (3)$$
To eliminate x between equations (2) and (3), multiply equation (2) by −2 and then add.
$$-2[x + y + 2z = 0]$$
$$2x + y + z = 4$$
gives
$$-2x - 2y - 4z = \ 0$$
$$2x + y \ + z = \ 4$$
Add: $\qquad -y - 3z = \ 4 \quad (4)$
To eliminate y between equations (1) and (4), multiply equation (4) by 2 and then add.
$$2y + 4z = 6$$
$$2[-y - 3z = 4]$$
gives

128

$$2y + 4z = 6$$
$$\underline{-2y - 6z = 8}$$

Add: $-2z = 14$
$$z = -7$$

Substitute –7 for z in equation (1).
$$2y + 4(-7) = 6$$
$$2y - 28 = 6$$
$$2y = 34$$
$$y = 17$$

Substitute 17 for y, and –7 for z in equation (3).
$$2x + (17) + (-7) = 4$$
$$2x + 10 = 4$$
$$2x = -6$$
$$x = -3$$
The solution is (–3, 17, –7).

13. $3p + 2q = 11$ (1)
     $4q - r = 6$ (2)
     $2p + 2r = 2$ (3)

To eliminate r between equations (2) and (3), multiply equation (2) by 2 and add to equation (3).
$$2[4q - r = 6]$$
$$2p + 2r = 2$$
gives
$$8q - 2r = 12$$
$$\underline{2p + 2r = 2}$$
Add: $2p + 8q = 14$ (4)

Equations (1) and (4) are two equations in two unknowns. To eliminate q, multiply equation (1) by –4 and add to equation (4).
$$4[3p + 2q = 11]$$
$$2p + 8q = 14$$
gives
$$-12p - 8q = -44$$
$$\underline{2p + 8q = 14}$$
Add: $-10p = -30$
$$p = 3$$

Substitute 3 for p in equation (1).
$$3p + 2q = 11$$
$$3(3) + 2q = 11$$
$$9 + 2q = 11$$
$$2q = 2$$
$$q = 1$$

Substitute 3 for p in equation (3).
$$2p + 2r = 2$$
$$2(3) + 2r = 2$$
$$6 + 2r = 2$$
$$2r = -4$$
$$r = -2$$
The solution is (3, 1, –2).

15. $p + q + 4 = 4$ (1)
     $p - 2q - r = 1$ (2)
     $2p - q - 2r = -1$ (3)

To eliminate q between equations (1) and (3), simply add.
$$p + q + r = 4$$
$$\underline{2p - q - 2r = -1}$$
Add: $3p - r = 3$ (4)

To eliminate q between equations (1) and (2), multiply equation (1) by 2 and then add.
$$2[p + q + r = 4]$$
$$p - 2q - r = 1$$
gives
$$2p + 2q + 2r = 8$$
$$\underline{p - 2q - r = 1}$$
Add: $3p + r = 9$ (5)

Equations (4) and (5) are two equations in two unknowns.
$$3p - r = 3$$
$$3p + r = 9$$

To eliminate r, simply add these two equations.
$$3p - r = 3$$
$$\underline{3p + r = 9}$$
Add: $6p = 12$
$$p = 2$$

Substitute 2 for p in equation (5).
$$3p + r = 9$$
$$3(2) + r = 9$$
$$6 + r = 9$$
$$r = 3$$

Substitute 2 for p and 3 for r in equation (1).
$$p + q + r = 4$$
$$2 + q + 3 = 4$$
$$q + 5 = 4$$
$$q = -1$$
The solution is (2, –1, 3).

17. $2x - 2y + 3z = 5$ (1)
     $2x + y - 2z = -1$ (2)
     $4x - y - 3z = 0$ (3)

To eliminate y between equations (2) and (3), simply add.
$$2x + y - 2z = -1$$
$$\underline{4x - y - 3z = 0}$$
Add: $6x - 5z = -1$ (4)

To eliminate y between equations (1) and (2), multiply equation (2) by 2 and then add.
$$2x - 2y + 3z = 5$$
$$2[2x + y - 2z = -1]$$
gives
$$2x - 2y + 3z = 5$$
$$\underline{4x + 2y - 4z = -2}$$
Add: $6x - z = 3$ (5)

Equations (4) and (5) are two equations in two unknowns.

$6x - 5z = -1$

$6x - z = 3$

To eliminate x, multiply equation (5) by -1 and then add.

$6x - 5z = -1$

$-1[6x - z = 3]$

gives

$$6x - 5z = -1$$
$$\underline{-6x + z = -3}$$

Add: $-4z = -4$

$z = 1$

Substitute 1 for z in equation (5).

$6x - z = 3$

$6x - 1 = 3$

$6x = 4$

$x = \dfrac{4}{6} = \dfrac{2}{3}$

Substitute $\dfrac{2}{3}$ for x and 1 for z in equation (2).

$2x + y - 2z = -1$

$2\left(\dfrac{2}{3}\right) + y - 2(1) = -1$

$\dfrac{4}{3} + y - 2 = -1$

$y - \dfrac{2}{3} = -1$

$y = -1 + \dfrac{2}{3} = -\dfrac{1}{3}$

The solution is $\left(\dfrac{2}{3}, -\dfrac{1}{3}, 1\right)$.

19. $r - 2s + t = 2$ (1)

$2r + 2s - t = -2$ (2)

$2r - s - 2t = 1$ (3)

To eliminate s between equations (1) and (2), by adding equations (1) and (2).

$$r - 2s + t = 2$$
$$\underline{2r + 2s - t = -2}$$

Add: $3r = 0$

$r = 0$

To eliminate s between equations (2) and (3), multiply equation (3) by 2 and then add.

$2r + 2s - t = -2$

$2[2r - s - 2t = 1]$

gives

$2r + 2s - t = -2$

$\underline{4r - 2s - 4t = 2}$

Add: $6r - 5t = 0$ (4)

Substitute 0 for r into equation (4) and solve for t.

$6(0) - 5t = 0$

$0 - 5t = 0$

$t = 0$

Finally, substitute 0 for r and 0 for t into equation (1)

$(0) - 2s + (0) = 2$

$-2s = 2$

$s = -1$

The solution is $(0, -1, 0)$.

21. $2a + 2b - c = 2$ (1)

$3a + 4b + c = -4$ (2)

$5a - 2b - 3c = 5$ (3)

To eliminate c between equations (1) and (2), simply add.

$$2a + 2b - c = 2$$
$$\underline{3a + 4b + c = -4}$$

Add: $5a + 6b = -2$ (4)

To eliminate c between equations (2) and (3), multiply equation (2) by 3 and then add.

$3[3a + 4b + c = -4]$

$5a - 2b - 3c = 5$

gives

$$9a + 12b + 3c = -12$$
$$\underline{5a - 2b - 3c = 5}$$

Add: $14a + 10b = -7$ (5)

Equations (4) and (5) are two equations in two unknowns.

$5a + 6b = -2$

$14a + 10b = -7$

To eliminate b, multiply equation (4) by -5 and multiply equation (5) by 3 and then add.

$-5[5a + 6b = -2]$

$3[14a + 10b = -7]$

gives

$$-25a - 30b = 10$$
$$\underline{42a + 30b = -21}$$

Add: $17a = -11$

$a = -\dfrac{11}{17}$

Substitute $-\dfrac{11}{17}$ for a in equation (4).

$$5a + 6b = -2$$

$$5\left(-\frac{11}{17}\right) + 6b = -2$$

$$-\frac{55}{17} + 6b = -2$$

$$6b = -2 + \frac{55}{17}$$

$$b = \frac{1}{6} \cdot \frac{21}{17} = \frac{7}{34}$$

Substitute $-\dfrac{11}{17}$ for a and $\dfrac{7}{34}$ for b in equation (2).

$$3a + 4b + c = -4$$

$$3\left(-\frac{11}{17}\right) + 4\left(\frac{7}{34}\right) + c = -4$$

$$-\frac{33}{17} + \frac{14}{17} + c = -4$$

$$-\frac{19}{17} + c = -4$$

$$c = -4 + \frac{19}{17}$$

$$c = -\frac{49}{17}$$

The solution is $\left(-\dfrac{11}{17}, \dfrac{7}{34}, -\dfrac{49}{17}\right)$.

23.
$$-x + 3y + z = 0 \quad (1)$$
$$-2x + 4y - z = 0 \quad (2)$$
$$3x - y + 2z = 0 \quad (3)$$

To eliminate z between equations (1) and (2), simply add.

$$-x + 3y + z = 0$$
$$\underline{-2x + 4y - z = 0}$$
Add: $\quad -3x + 7y \quad\quad = 0 \quad (4)$

To eliminate z between equations (2) and (3), multiply equation (2) by 2 and then add.
$$2[-2x + 4y - z] = 0$$
$$3x - y + 2z = 0$$
gives
$$-4x + 8y - 2z = 0$$
$$\underline{3x - \;\; y + 2z = 0}$$
Add: $\quad -x + 7y \quad\quad = 0 \quad (5)$

Equations (4) and (5) are two equations in two unknowns.
$$-3x + 7y = 0$$
$$-x + 7y = 0$$

To eliminate y, multiply equation (4) by -1 and then add.
$$-1[-3x + 7y = 0]$$
$$-x + 7y = 0$$
gives

$$3x - 7y = 0$$
$$\underline{-x + 7y = 0}$$
Add: $\;\; 2x \quad\quad = 0$
$$x = 0$$
Substitute 0 for x in equation (5).
$$-x + 7y = 0$$
$$-0 + 7y = 0$$
$$7y = 0$$
$$y = 0$$
Finally, substitute 0 for x and 0 for y into equation (1).
$$-x + 3y + z = 0$$
$$-0 + 3(0) + z = 0$$
$$0 + z = 0$$
$$z = 0$$
The solution is $(0, 0, 0)$.

25. $\quad -\dfrac{1}{4}x + \dfrac{1}{2}y - \dfrac{1}{2}z = -2 \quad (1)$

$\qquad \dfrac{1}{2}x + \dfrac{1}{3}y - \dfrac{1}{4}z = 2 \quad (2)$

$\qquad \dfrac{1}{2}x - \dfrac{1}{2}y + \dfrac{1}{4}z = 1 \quad (3)$

To clear fractions, multiply equation (1) by 4, equation (2) by 12, and equation (3) by 4.

$$4\left(-\frac{1}{4}x + \frac{1}{2}y - \frac{1}{2}z = -2\right)$$

$$12\left(\frac{1}{2}x + \frac{1}{3}y - \frac{1}{4}z = 2\right)$$

$$4\left(\frac{1}{2}x - \frac{1}{2}y + \frac{1}{4}z = 1\right)$$

gives
$$-x + 2y - 2z = -8 \quad (4)$$
$$6x + 4y - 3z = 24 \quad (5)$$
$$2x + 2y + z = 4 \quad (6)$$

To eliminate y between equations (4) and (6), simply add.
$$-x + 2y - 2z = -8$$
$$\underline{2x - 2y + \;\; z = \;\; 4}$$
Add: $\;\; x \quad\quad - z = -4 \quad (7)$

To eliminate y between equations (5) and (6), multiply equation (6) by 2 and then add to equation (5).
$$6x + 4y - 3z = 24$$
$$2[2x - 2y + z = 4]$$
gives
$$6x + 4y - 3z = 24$$
$$\underline{4x - 4y + 2z = \;\; 8}$$
Add: $\; 10x \quad\quad - z = 32 \quad (8)$

Equations (7) and (8) are two equations in two unknowns.
$$x - z = -4$$
$$10x - z = 32$$

To eliminate z, multiply equation (7) by -1 and then add.
$$-1[x - z = -4]$$
$$10x - z = 32$$
gives

Substitute 4 for x in equation (7).
$$x - z = -4$$
$$4 - z = -4$$
$$-z = -8$$
$$z = 8$$
Finally, substitute 4 for x and 8 for z in equation (4).
$$-x + 2y - 2z = -8$$
$$-4 + 2y - 2(8) = -8$$
$$-4 + 2y - 16 = -8$$
$$2y - 20 = -8$$
$$2y = 12$$
$$y = \frac{12}{2} = 6$$
The solution is (4, 6, 8).

27.
$$x - \frac{2}{3}y - \frac{2}{3}z = -2 \quad (1)$$
$$\frac{2}{3}x + y - \frac{2}{3}z = \frac{1}{3} \quad (2)$$
$$-\frac{1}{4}x + y - \frac{1}{4}z = \frac{3}{4} \quad (3)$$
To clear fractions, multiply equation (1) by 3, equation (2) by 3, and equation (3) by 4. The resulting system is
$$3\left(x - \frac{2}{3}y - \frac{2}{3}z = -2\right)$$
$$3\left(\frac{2}{3}x + y - \frac{2}{3}z = \frac{1}{3}\right)$$
$$4\left(-\frac{1}{4}x + y - \frac{1}{4}z = \frac{3}{4}\right)$$
gives
$$3x - 2y - 2z = -6 \quad (4)$$
$$2x + 3y - 2z = 1 \quad (5)$$
$$-x + 4y - z = 3 \quad (6)$$
To eliminate x between equations (4) and (6), multiply equation (6) by 3 and then add.
$$3x - 2y - 2z = -6$$
$$3[-x + 4y - z = 3]$$
gives
$$3x - 2y - 2z = -6$$
$$-3x + 12y - 3z = 9$$
Add: $10y - 5z = 3 \quad (7)$

To eliminate x between equations (5) and (6), multiply equation (6) by 2 and then add.
$$2x + 3y - 2z = 1$$
$$2[-x + 4y - z = 3]$$
gives
$$2x + 3y - 2z = 1$$
$$-2x + 8y - 2z = 6$$
Add: $11y - 4z = 7 \quad (8)$
Equations (7) and (8) are two equations in two unknowns.
$$10y - 5z = 3$$
$$11y - 4z = 7$$
To eliminate z, multiply equation (7) by -4 and equation (8) by 5 and then add.
$$-4[10y - 5z = 3]$$
$$5[11y - 4z = 7]$$
gives
$$-40y + 20z = -12$$
$$55y - 20z = 35$$
Add: $15y = 23$
$$y = \frac{23}{15}$$
Substitute $\frac{23}{15}$ for y into equation (7).
$$10y - 5z = 3$$
$$10\left(\frac{23}{15}\right) - 5z = 3$$
$$\frac{46}{3} - 5z = 3$$
$$-5z = 3 - \frac{46}{3}$$
$$-5z = -\frac{37}{3}$$
$$z = \left(-\frac{1}{5}\right)\left(-\frac{37}{3}\right) = \frac{37}{15}$$
Substitute $\frac{23}{15}$ for y and $\frac{37}{15}$ for z in equation (6).

$$-x + 4y - z = 3$$
$$-x + 4\left(\frac{23}{15}\right) - \frac{37}{15} = 3$$
$$-x + \frac{92}{15} - \frac{37}{15} = 3$$
$$-x + \frac{55}{15} = 3$$
$$-x + \frac{11}{3} = 3$$
$$-x = 3 - \frac{11}{3}$$
$$-x = -\frac{2}{3}$$
$$x = \frac{2}{3}$$

The solution is $\left(\frac{2}{3}, \frac{23}{15}, \frac{37}{15}\right)$.

29. Multiply each equation by 10.
$$10(0.2x + 0.3y + 0.3z = 1.1)$$
$$10(0.4x - 0.2y + 0.1z = 0.4)$$
$$10(-0.1x - 0.1y + 0.3z = 0.4)$$
gives
$$2x + 3y + 3z = 11 \quad (1)$$
$$4x - 2y + z = 4 \quad (2)$$
$$-x - y + 3z = 4 \quad (3)$$
To eliminate multiply equation (2) by -3 and then add.
$$2x + 3y + 3z = 11$$
$$3[4x - 2y + z = 4]$$
gives
$$\begin{array}{r} 2x + 3y + 3z = 11 \\ -12x + 6y - 3z = -12 \\ \hline \end{array}$$
Add: $-10x + 9y \quad\quad = -1 \quad (4)$
To eliminate z between equations (1) and (3) multiply equation (1) by -1 and then add.
$$-1[2x + 3y + 3z = 11]$$
$$-x - y + 3z = 4$$
gives
$$\begin{array}{r} -2x - 3y - 3z = -11 \\ -x - y + 3z = 4 \\ \hline \end{array}$$
Add: $-3x - 4y \quad\quad = -7 \quad (5)$
Equations (4) and (5) are two equations in two unknowns.
$$-10x + 9y = -1$$
$$-3x - 4y = -7$$
To eliminate y, multiply equation (4) by -3 and equation (5) by 10.
$$-3[-10 + 9y = -1]$$
$$10[-3x - 4y = -7]$$
gives

$$\begin{array}{r} 30x - 27y = 3 \\ -30x - 40y = -70 \\ \hline \end{array}$$
Add: $\quad\quad -67y = -67$
$$y = 1$$
Substitute 1 for y in equation (4).
$$-10x + 9y = -1$$
$$-10x + 9(1) = -1$$
$$-10x = -10$$
$$x = 1$$
Substitute 1 for x and 1 for y in equation (1).
$$2x + 3y + 3z = 11$$
$$2(1) + 3(1) + 3z = 11$$
$$5 + 3z = 11$$
$$3z = 6$$
$$z = 2$$
The solution is $(1, 1, 2)$.

31. $2x + y + 2z = 1 \quad (1)$
$\quad\; x - 2y - z = 0 \quad (2)$
$\quad\; 3x - y + z = 2 \quad (3)$
To eliminate z between equations (2) and (3), simply add.
$$\begin{array}{r} x - 2y - z = 0 \\ 3x - y + z = 2 \\ \hline \end{array}$$
Add: $4x - 3y \quad\quad = 2 \quad (4)$
To eliminate z between equations (1) and (2), multiply equation (2) by 2 and then add.
$$2x + y + 2z = 1$$
$$2[x - 2y - z = 0]$$
gives
$$\begin{array}{r} 2x + y + 2z = 1 \\ 2x - 4y - 2z = 0 \\ \hline \end{array}$$
Add: $4x - 3y \quad\quad = 1 \quad (5)$
Equations (4) and (5) are two equations in two unknowns.
$$4x - 3y = 2$$
$$4x - 3y = 1$$
To eliminate x, multiply equation (4) by -1 and then add.
$$-1[4x - 3y = 2]$$
$$4x - 3y = 1$$
gives
$$\begin{array}{r} -4x + 3y = -2 \\ 4x - 3y = 1 \\ \hline \end{array}$$
Add: $\quad\quad\quad 0 = -1 \quad$ False
Since this is a false statement, there is no solution and the system is inconsistent.

33.
$$x - 4y - 3z = -1 \quad (1)$$
$$2x - 10y - 7z = 5 \quad (2)$$
$$-3x + 12y + 9z = 3 \quad (3)$$

To eliminate x between equations (1) and (2), multiply equation (1) by -2 and then add.
$$-2[x - 4y - 3z = -1]$$
$$2x - 10y - 7z = 5$$
gives
$$-2x + 8y + 6z = 2$$
$$\underline{2x - 10y - 7z = 5}$$
Add: $\qquad -2y - z = 7 \quad (4)$

To eliminate x between equations (1) and (3), multiply equation (1) by 3 and then add.
$$3[x - 4y - 3z = -1]$$
$$-3x + 12y + 9z = 3$$
gives
$$3x - 12y - 9z = -3$$
$$\underline{-3x + 12y + 9z = 3}$$
Add: $\qquad 0 = 0$

Since $0 = 0$ is a true statement, the system is dependent and therefore has infinitely many solutions.

35.
$$x + 3y + 2z = 6 \quad (1)$$
$$x - 2y - z = 8 \quad (2)$$
$$-3x - 9y - 6z = -4 \quad (3)$$

To eliminate x between equations (1) and (3), multiply equation (1) by 3 and then add.
$$3[x + 3y + 2z = 6]$$
$$-3x - 9y - 6z = -4$$
gives
$$3x + 9y + 6z = 18$$
$$\underline{-3x - 9y - 6z = -4}$$
Add: $\qquad 0 = 14$

Since $0 = 14$ is a false statement, the system is inconsistent.

37. No point is common to all three planes. Therefore, the system is inconsistent.

39. One point is common to all three planes. There is one solution and the system is consistent.

41. a. Yes, if two or more of the planes are parallel, there will be no solution.

   b. Yes, three planes may intersect at a single point.

   c. No, the possibilities are no solution, one solution, or infinitely many solutions.

43. $Ax + By + Cz = -2$
Substitute $(-1, 2, -1)$, $(-1, 1, 2)$, and $(1, -2, 2)$ into the equation forming three equations in the three unknowns A, B, and C.
$$A(-1) + B(2) + C(-1) = 1$$
$$A(-1) + B(1) + C(2) = 1$$
$$A(1) + B(-2) + C(2) = 1$$
gives
$$-A + 2B - C = 1 \quad (1)$$
$$-A + B + 2C = 1 \quad (2)$$
$$A - 2B + 2C = 1 \quad (3)$$
To eliminate A between equations (1) and (2), multiply equation (2) by -1 and then add.
$$-A + 2B - C = 1$$
$$-1[-A + B + 2C = 1]$$
gives
$$-A + 2B - C = 1$$
$$\underline{A - B - 2C = -1}$$
Add: $\qquad B - 3C = 0 \quad (4)$
To eliminate A between equations (1) and (3), simply add.
$$-A + 2B - C = 1$$
$$\underline{A - 2B + 2C = 1}$$
Add: $\qquad C = 2$

Substitute 2 for C in equation (4).
$$B - 3(2) = 0$$
$$B - 6 = 0$$
$$B = 6$$
Substitute 6 for B and 2 for C in equation (23).
$$A - 2(6) + 2(2) = 1$$
$$A - 12 + 4 = 1$$
$$A - 8 = 1$$
$$A = 9$$
Therefore, $A = 9$, $B = 6$, $C = 2$. and the equation is $9x + 6y + 2z = 1$.

45. One example is
$$x + y + z = 10$$
$$x + 2y + z = 11$$
$$x + y + 2z = 16$$
Choose coefficients for x, y, and z, then use the given coordinates to find the constants.

47. a. $y = ax^2 + bx + c$
For the point $(1, -1)$,
let $y = -1$ and $x = 1$.
$$-1 = a(1)^2 + b(1) + c$$
$$-1 = a + b + c \quad (1)$$
For the point $(-1, -5)$,

let $y = -5$ and $x = -1$.
$-5 = a(-1)^2 + b(-1) + c$
$-5 = a - b + c$ (2)
For the point (3, 11),
let $y = 11$ and $x = 3$.
$11 = a(3)^2 + b(3) + c$
$11 = 9a + 3b + c$ (3)
Equations (1), (2), and (3) give us a system of three equations.
$a + b + c = -1$ (1)
$a - b + c = -5$ (2)
$9a + 3b + c = 11$ (3)
To eliminate a and c between equations (1) and (2) multiply equation (2) by -1 and then add.
$a + b + c = -1$
$-1[a - b + c = -5]$
gives
$a + b + c = -1$
$\underline{-a + b - c = 5}$
Add: $2b = 4$
$b = 2$
Substitute 2 for b in equations (1) and (3).
Equation (1) becomes
$a + b + c = -1$
$a + 2 + c = -1$
$a + c = -3$ (4)
Equation (3) becomes
$9a + 3b + c = 11$
$9a + 3(2) + c = 11$
$9a + c = 5$ (5)
Equations (4) and (5) are two equations in two unknowns. To eliminate c, multiply equation (4) by -1 and then add.
$-1[a + c = -3]$
$9a + c = 5$
gives
$-a - c = 3$
$\underline{9a + c = 5}$
Add: $8a = 8$
$a = 1$
Finally, substitute 1 for a in equation (4).
$a + c = -3$
$1 + c = -3$
$c = -4$
Thus, $a = 1$, $b = 2$, and $c = -4$.

b. The quadratic equation is $y = x^2 + 2x - 4$. This is the equation determined by the values found in part a.

49. $3p + 4q = 11$ (1)
$2p + r + s = 9$ (2)
$q - s = -2$ (3)
$p + 2q - r = 2$ (4)
To eliminate r between equations (2) and (4), simply add.
$2p + r + s = 9$
$\underline{p + 2q - r = 2}$
Add: $3p + 2q + s = 11$ (5)
To eliminate s between equations (3) and (5), simply add.
$q - s = -2$
$\underline{3p + 2q + s = 11}$
Add: $3p + 3q = 9$ (6)
Equations (1) and (6) give us a system of two equations in two unknowns.
To eliminate p, multiply equation (6) by -1 and then add.
$3p + 4q = 11$
$-1[3p + 3q = 9]$
gives
$3p + 4q = 11$
$\underline{-3p - 3q = -9}$
Add: $ q = 2$
Substitute 2 for q in equation (3).
$q - s = -2$
$2 - s = -2$
$-s = -4$
$s = 4$
Substitute 2 for q in equation (1).
$3p + 4q = 11$
$3p + 4(2) = 11$
$3p + 8 = 11$
$3p = 3$
$p = 1$
Finally, substitute 1 for p and 4 for s in equation (2).
$2p + r + s = 9$
$2(1) + r + 4 = 9$
$r + 6 = 9$
$r = 3$
The solution is (1, 2, 3, 4).

51. Let t be the time for Margie.

Then, $t - \dfrac{1}{6}$ is the time for David.

	rate	time	distance
David	5	$t - \dfrac{1}{6}$	$5\left(t - \dfrac{1}{6}\right)$
Margie	3	t	$3t$

a. The distances traveled are the same.

$$5\left(t - \frac{1}{6}\right) = 3t$$

$$5t - \frac{5}{6} = 3t$$

$$5t = 3t + \frac{5}{6}$$

$$2t = \frac{5}{6}$$

$$t = \frac{1}{2}\left(\frac{5}{6}\right) = \frac{5}{12} \text{ hr}$$

or $\dfrac{5}{12}(60) = 25$ min

b. The distance is

$$3t = 3\left(\frac{5}{12}\right) = \frac{15}{12} = 1\frac{1}{4}$$

or 1.25 miles.

53. $\left|\dfrac{3x-4}{2}\right| - 1 < 5$

$\left|\dfrac{3x-4}{2}\right| < 6$

$$-6 < \frac{3x-4}{2} < 6$$

$$2(-6) < 2\left(\frac{3x-4}{2}\right) < 2(6)$$

$$-12 < 3x - 4 < 12$$

$$-12 + 4 < 3x - 4 + 4 < 12 + 4$$

$$-8 < 3x < 16$$

$$-\frac{8}{3} < \frac{3x}{3} < \frac{16}{3}$$

$$-\frac{8}{3} < x < \frac{16}{3}$$

The solution is $\left\{x \middle| -\dfrac{8}{3} < x < \dfrac{16}{3}\right\}$.

54. $\left|2x - \dfrac{1}{2}\right| = -5$

There is no solution since the right side is a negative number and the left side is non-negative and it is not possible for a non-negative quantity

to be equal to a negative number. The solution is $\varnothing$.

Exercise Set 4.3

1. Let x = number who visited Disneyland

y = number who visited Magic Kingdom

$x + y = 27.1$

$y = x + 2.5$

Substitute $x + 2.5$ for y in the first equation.

$x + (x + 2.5) = 27.1$

$$2x + 2.5 = 27.1$$

$$2x = 24.6$$

$$x = 12.3$$

Substitute 12.3 for x in the second equation.

$y = (12.3) + 2.5$

$y = 14.8$

14.8 million people visited Magic Kingdom and 12.3 million people visited Disneyland.

3. Let F = grams of fat in fries

H = grams of fat in hamburger

$F = 3H + 4$

$F - H = 46$

Substitute $3H + 4$ for F in the second equation.

$F - H = 46$

$3H + 4 - H = 46$

$2H = 42$

$H = 21$

Substitute 21 for H in the first equation.

$F = 3H + 4$

$F = 3(21) + 4$

$F = 63 + 4$

$F = 67$

The hamburger has 21 grams of fat and the fries have 67 grams of fat.

5. Let x be the measure of the larger angle and y be the measure of the smaller angle.

$x + y = 90$

$x = 2y + 15$

Substitute $2y + 15$ for x in the first equation.

$x + y = 90$

$2y + 15 + y = 90$

$3y + 15 = 90$

$3y = 75$

$y = 25$

Now, substitute 25 for y in the second equation.

$x = 2y + 15$

$x = 2(25) + 15$

$x = 50 + 15$

$x = 65$

The two angles measure 25° and 65°.

7. Let A and B be the measures of the two angles.
$A + B = 180$
$A = 3B - 28$
Substitute $3B - 28$ for A in the first equation.
$A + B = 180$
$3B - 28 + B = 180$
$4B - 28 = 180$
$4B = 208$
$B = 52$
Now substitute 52 for B in the second equation.
$A = 3B - 28$
$A = 3(52) - 28$
$A = 128$
The two angles measure 52° and 128°.

9. Let t = team's rowing speed in still water
$c =$ speed of current
$t + c = 15.6$

$t - c = 8.8$
Add the equations to eliminate variable c.
$t + c = 15.6$

$\underline{t - c = 8.8}$

$2t = 24.4$

$t = 12.2$

Substitute 12.2 for t in the first equation.
$(12.2) + c = 15.6$

$c = 3.4$
The team's speed in still air is 12.2 mph and the speed of the current is 3.4 mph.

11. Let x be the weekly salary and y be the commission rate.
$x + 4000y = 660$
$x + 6000y = 740$

Multiply the first equation by -1 and then add.
$-1[x + 4000y = 660]$
$x + 6000y = 740$
gives
$-x - 4000y = -660$
$\underline{x + 6000y = 740}$
Add: $ 2000y = 80$
$y = \dfrac{80}{2000} = 0.04$
Substitute 0.04 for y in the first equation.
$x + 4000y = 660$
$x + 4000(0.04) = 660$
$x + 160 = 660$
$x = 500$ dollars
Her weekly salary is $500 and the commission rate is 4%.

13. Let x be the amount of 5% solution and y be the amount of 30% solution.
$x + y = 3$

$0.05x + 0.30y = 0.20(3)$
Solve the first equation for x.
$x = 3 - y$
Substitute $3 - y$ for x in the second equation.
$0.05x + 0.30y = 0.20(3)$

$0.05(3 - y) + 0.30y = 0.6$

$0.15 - 0.05y + 0.30y = 0.6$

$0.25y = 0.45$

$y = 1.8$
Substitute 1.8 for y in the first equation.
$x + y = 3$

$x + 1.8 = 3$

$x = 1.2$
Pola should mix 1.2 ounces of the 5% solution with 1.8 ounces of the 30% solution.

15. Let x = gallons of concentrate (18% solution) and y = gallons of water (0% solution).
$x + y = 200$
$0.18x + 0y = 0.009(200)$
Solve the second equation for x.
$0.18x + 0y = 0.009(200)$
$0.18x = 1.8$
$x = 10$
Substitute 10 for x in the first equation.
$x + y = 200$
$10 + y = 200$
$y = 190$
The mixture should contain 10 gallons of concentrate and 190 gallons of water.

17. Let x = pounds of birdseed
and y = pounds of sunflower seeds
$0.59x + 0.89y = 0.76(40)$
$x + y = 40$
Solve the second equation for y.
$y = 40 - x$
Substitute $40 - x$ for y in the first equation.
$0.59x + 0.89y = 0.76(40)$
$0.59x + 0.89(40 - x) = 30.4$
$0.59x + 35.6 - 0.89x = 30.4$
$-0.3x = -5.2$
$x = 17\dfrac{1}{3}$

Substitute $17\dfrac{1}{3}$ for x in the second equation.

$$x + y = 40$$

$$17\frac{1}{3} + y = 40$$

$$y = 22\frac{2}{3}$$

Angela Leinenbach should mix $17\frac{1}{3}$ pounds of birdseed at \$0.59 per pound with $22\frac{2}{3}$ pounds of sunflower seeds at \$0.89 per pound.

19. Let x be the number of the \$4.00 adult tickets sold and y be the number of the \$1.50 children's tickets sold.

$$x + y = 225$$

$$4.00x + 1.50y = 500$$

Solve the first equation for x.

$$x + y = 225$$

$$x = 225 - y$$

Substitute $225 - y$ for x in the second equation.

$$4.00(225 - y) + 1.50y = 500$$

$$900 - 4.00y + 1.50y = 500$$

$$-2.50y = -400$$

$$y = 160$$

Substitute 160 for y in the equation $x = 225 - y$.

$$x = 225 - (160)$$

$$x = 65$$

65 adult tickets and 160 children's tickets were sold.

21. Let x = amount invested at 5% and y = amount invested at 6%

$$x + y = 10,000$$

$$0.05x + 0.06y = 540$$

Solve the first equation for y.

$$y = 10,000 - x$$

Substitute $10,000 - x$ for y in the second equation.

$$0.05x + 0.06y = 540$$

$$0.05x + 0.06(10,000 - x) = 540$$

$$0.05x + 600 - 0.06x = 540$$

$$-0.01x = -60$$

$$x = 6000$$

Substitute 6000 for x in the first equation.

$$x + y = 10,000$$

$$6000 + y = 10,000$$

$$y = 4000$$

Mr. and Mrs. McAdams invested \$6000 at 5% and \$4000 at 6%.

23. Let x be the amount of the whole milk (3.25% fat) and y be the amount of the skim milk (0% fat).

$$x + y = 260$$

$$0.0325x + 0y = 0.02(260)$$

Solve the second equation for x.

$$0.0325x + 0y = 0.02(260)$$

$$0.0325x = 5.2$$

$$x = 160$$

Now substitute 160 for x in the first equation.

$$(160) + y = 260$$

$$y = 100$$

Becky needs to mix 160 gallons of the whole milk with 100 gallons of skim milk to produce 100 gallons of 2% fat milk.

25. Let x = pounds of *Season's Choice* birdseed at \$1.79/lb
and y = pounds of *Garden Mix* birdseed at \$1.19/lb

$$1.79x + 1.19y = 28.00$$

$$x + y = 20$$

Solve the second equation for y.

$$y = 20 - x$$

Substitute $20 - x$ for y in the first equation.

$$1.79x + 1.19(20 - x) = 28.00$$

$$1.79x + 23.80 - 1.19x = 28.00$$

$$0.60x = 4.20$$

$$x = 7$$

Substitute 7 for x in the second equation.

$$(7) + y = 20$$

$$y = 13$$

The class should buy 7 pounds *of Season's Choice* and 13 pounds of *Garden Mix*.

27. Let x be the rate of the slower car and y the rate of the faster car.

$$4x + 4y = 420$$

$$y = x + 5$$

Substitute $x + 5$ for y in the first equation.

$$4x + 4y = 420$$

$$4x + 4(x + 5) = 420$$

$$4x + 4x + 20 = 420$$

$$8x + 20 = 420$$

$$8x = 400$$

$$x = 50$$

Now substitute 50 for x in the second equation.

$$y = x + 5$$

$$y = 50 + 5$$

$$y = 55$$

The rate of the slower car is 50 mph and the rate of the faster car is 55 mph.

29. Let x be the amount of time traveled at 65 mph and y be the amount of time traveled at 50 mph.

$$x + y = 11.4$$
$$65x + 50y = 690$$

Solve the first equation for x

$$x = 11.4 - y$$

Now substitute $11.4 - y$ into x in the second equation.

$$65(11.4 - y) + 50y = 690$$
$$741 - 65y + 50y = 690$$
$$-15y = -51$$
$$y = 3.4$$

Substitute 3.4 for y in the first equation.

$$x + (3.4) = 11.4$$
$$x = 8$$

Cabrina traveled for 8 hours at 65 mph and Dabney traveled for 3.4 hours at 50 mph.

31. Let x the number of grams of Mix A and y be the number of grams of Mix B.

$$0.1x + 0.2y = 20$$
$$0.06x + 0.02y = 6$$

To solve, multiply the second equation by -10 and then add.

$$0.1x + 0.2y = 20$$
$$-10[0.06x + 0.02y = 6]$$

gives

$$0.1x + 0.2y = 20$$
$$-0.6x - 0.2y = -60$$

Add: $-0.5x = -40$

$$x = \frac{-40}{-0.5} = 80$$

Now substitute 80 for x in the first equation.

$$0.1x + 0.2y = 20$$
$$0.1(80) + 0.2y = 20$$
$$8 + 0.2y = 20$$
$$0.2y = 12$$
$$y = \frac{12}{0.2} = 60$$

The scientist should feed each animal 80 grams of Mix A and 60 grams of Mix B.

33. Let x be the amount of the first alloy and y be the amount of the second alloy.

$$0.7x + 0.4y = 0.6(300)$$
$$0.3x + 0.6y = 0.4(300)$$

To solve, multiply the first equation by 3 and the second equation by -2 and then add.

$$3[0.7x + 0.4y = 0.6(300)]$$
$$-2[0.3x + 0.6y = 0.4(300)]$$

gives

$$2.1x + 1.2y = 540$$
$$-0.6x - 1.2y = -240$$

Add: $1.5x = 300$

$$x = \frac{300}{1.5} = 200$$

Now substitute 200 for x in the first equation.

$$0.7x + 0.4y = 0.6(300)$$
$$0.7(200) + 0.4y = 0.6(300)$$
$$140 + 0.4y = 180$$
$$0.4y = 40$$
$$y = \frac{40}{0.4} = 100$$

200 grams of the first alloy should be combined with 100 grams of the second alloy to produce the desired mixture.

35. Let x = speed of Melissa's car and y = speed of Tom's car

$$x = y + 15$$
$$\frac{150}{x} = \frac{120}{y}$$

Substitute $y + 15$ for x in the second equation.

$$\frac{150}{y + 15} = \frac{120}{y}$$
$$150y = 120y + 1800$$
$$30y = 1800$$
$$y = 60$$

Substitute 60 for y in the first equation.

$$x = y + 15$$
$$x = 60 + 15$$
$$x = 75$$

Tom traveled at 60 mph and Melissa traveled at 75 mph.

37. $E(t) = 3.62t + 12.6$

$$P(t) = -3.62t + 87.4$$
$$3.62t + 12.6 = -3.62t + 87.4$$
$$7.24t = 74.8$$
$$t \approx 10.3$$

They will be equal approximately 10 years after 1996 or in 2006.

39. a. Let c = cost
and m = minutes
Plan 1: $c = 0.05m + 8.95$
Plan 2: $c = 0.07m + 5.95$

b.

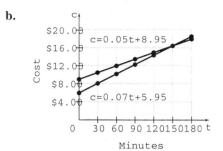

c. The cost is the same at about 150 minutes.

$$0.05m + 8.95 = 0.07m + 5.95$$

d. $$-0.02m = -3.00$$
$$m = 150$$

41. a. Let x = pieces of personal mail
y = number of bills and statements
z = number of advertisements
$x + y + z = 24$
$$y = 2x - 2$$
$$z = 5x + 2$$

b. Substitute $2x - 2$ for y and $5x + 2$ for z in the first equation.
$$x + y + z = 24$$
$$x + 2x - 2 + 5x + 2 = 24$$
$$8x = 24$$
$$x = 3$$
Substitute 3 for x in the second and third equations.

$y = 2x - 2$	$z = 5x + 2$
$y = 2(3) - 2$	$z = 5(3) + 2$
$y = 4$	$z = 17$

An average American household receives 3 pieces of personal mail, 4 bills and statements, and 17 advertisements per week.

43. a. Let x = number of land mines in Iraq
y = number of land mines in Angola
z = number of land mines in Iran
$x + y + z = 41$
$$z = 3x - 14$$
$$y = 2x - 5$$

b. Substitute $3x - 14$ for z and $2x - 5$ for y in the first equation.

$$x + y + z = 41$$
$$x + 2x - 5 + 3x - 14 = 41$$
$$6x = 60$$
$$x = 10$$
Substitute 10 for x in the second and third equations.

$z = 3x - 14$	$y = 2x - 5$
$z = 3(10) - 14$	$y = 2(10) - 5$
$z = 16$	$y = 15$

The number of land mines in the countries is
Iraq: 10 million
Angola: 15 million
Iran: 16 million.

45. a. Let x, y, and z be the measures of the three angles.
$$x + y + z = 180$$
$$x = \frac{2}{3}y$$
$$z = 3y - 30$$

b. Substitute $\frac{2}{3}y$ for x and $3y - 30$ for z in the first equation.
$$x + y + z = 180$$
$$\frac{2}{3}y + y + 3y - 30 = 180$$
$$\frac{14}{3}y - 30 = 180$$
$$\frac{14}{3}y = 210$$
$$\frac{3}{14}\left(\frac{14}{3}y\right) = \frac{3}{14}(210)$$
$$y = 45$$
Substitute 45 for y in the second equation.
$$x = \frac{2}{3}y$$
$$x = \frac{2}{3}(45)$$
$$x = 30$$
Substitute 45 for y in the third equation.
$$z = 3y - 30$$
$$z = 3(45) - 30$$
$$z = 135 - 30$$
$$z = 105$$
The three angles are 30°, 45°, and 105°.

47. a. Let x be the amount invested at 3%, y be the amount invested at 5%, and z be the amount invested at 6%.
$$y = 2x \quad (1)$$
$$x + y + z = 10{,}000 \quad (2)$$
$$0.03x + 0.05y + 0.06z = 525 \quad (3)$$

b. Substitute $2x$ for y in equation (2).
$$x + y + z = 10,000$$
$$x + 2x + z = 10,000$$
$$3x + z = 10,000 \quad (4)$$
Substitute $2x$ for y in equation (3).
$$0.03x + 0.05y + 0.06z = 525$$
$$0.03x + 0.05(2x) + 0.06z = 525$$
$$0.03x + 0.10x + 0.06z = 525$$
$$0.13x + 0.06z = 525 \quad (5)$$
Equations (4) and (5) are a system of two equations in two unknowns.
$$3x + z = 10,000$$
$$0.13x + 0.06z = 525$$
To eliminate z, multiply equation (4) by -3 and equation (5) by 50 and add.
$$-3[3x + z = 10,000]$$
$$50[0.13x + 0.06x = 525]$$
gives
$$-9x - 3z = -30,000$$
$$6.5x + 3z = 26,250$$
Add: $\overline{\quad -2.5x = -3750 \quad}$
$$x = \frac{-3750}{-2.5} = 1500$$
Substitute 1500 for x in equation (4).
$$3x + z = 10,000$$
$$3(1500) + z = 10,000$$
$$4500 + z = 10,000$$
$$z = 5500$$
Substitute 1500 for x and 5500 for z in equation (2).
$$x + y + z = 10,000$$
$$1500 + y + 5500 = 10,000$$
$$y + 7000 = 10,000$$
$$y = 3000$$
Marion invested $1500 at 3%, $3000 at 5%, and $5500 at 6%.

49. a. Let x be the amount of the 10% solution, y be the amount of the 12% solution, and z be the amount of the 20% solution.
$$x + y + z = 8 \quad (1)$$
$$0.10x + 0.12y + 0.20z = (0.13)8 \quad (2)$$
$$z = x - 2 \quad (3)$$

b. Substitute $x - 2$ for z in equation (1).
$$x + y + z = 8$$
$$x + y + (x - 2) = 8$$
$$2x + y - 2 = 8$$
$$2x + y = 10 \quad (4)$$
Substitute $x - 2$ for z in equation (2).
$$0.10x + 0.12y + 0.20z = (0.13)8$$
$$0.10x + 0.12y + 0.20(x - 2) = (0.13)8$$
$$0.10x + 0.12y + 0.20x - 0.40 = 1.04$$
$$0.30x + 0.12y = 1.44 \quad (5)$$

Equations (4) and (5) are a system of two equations in two unknowns.
$$2x + y = 10$$
$$0.30x + 0.12y = 1.44$$
To solve, multiply equation (5) by 100 and equation (4) by -12 and then add.
$$-12[2x + y = 10]$$
$$100[0.30x + 0.12y = 1.44]$$
gives
$$-24x - 12y = -120$$
$$30x + 12y = 144$$
Add: $\overline{\quad 6x \qquad\quad = 24 \quad}$
$$x = 4$$
Substitute 4 for x in equation (4).
$$2x + y = 10$$
$$2(4) + y = 10$$
$$8 + y = 10$$
$$y = 2$$
Finally, substitute 4 for x in equation (3).
$$z = x - 2$$
$$z = 4 - 2$$
$$z = 2$$
The mixture consists of 4 liters of the 10% solution, 2 liters of the 12% solution, and 2 liters of the 20% solution.

51. a. Let x be the number of children's chairs, y be the number of standard chairs, and z be the number of executive chairs.
$$5x + 4y + 7z = 154 \quad (1)$$
$$3x + 2y + 5 = 94 \quad (2)$$
$$2x + 2y + 4z = 76 \quad (3)$$

b. To eliminate y between equations (1) and (2), multiply equation (2) by -2 and add.
$$5x + 4y + 7z = 154$$
$$-2[3x + 2y + 5z = 94]$$
gives
$$5x + 4y + 7z = 154$$
$$-6x - 4y - 10z = -188$$
Add: $\overline{\quad -x \qquad - 3z = -34 \quad (4)}$
To eliminate y between equations (2) and (3), multiply equation (3) by -1 and add.
$$3x + 2y + 5z = 94$$
$$-1[2x + 2y + 4z = 76]$$
gives
$$3x + 2y + 5z = 94$$
$$-2x - 2y - 4z = -76$$
Add: $\overline{\quad x \qquad\quad + z = 18 \quad (5)}$
Equations (4) and (5) are a system of two equations in two unknowns. To eliminate x, simply add.

$$-x - 3z = -34$$
$$x + z = 18$$

Add: $-2z = -16$

$$z = \frac{-16}{-2} = 8$$

Substitute 8 for z in equation (5).
$$x + z = 18$$
$$x + 8 = 18$$
$$x = 10$$

Substitute 10 for x and 8 for z in equation (3).

$$2x + 2y + 4z = 76$$
$$2(10) + 2y + 4(8) = 76$$
$$20 + 2y + 32 = 76$$
$$2y + 52 = 76$$
$$2y = 24$$
$$y = 12$$

The Donaldson Furniture Company should produce 10 children's chairs, 12 standard chairs, and 8 executive chairs.

53.
$$I_A + I_B + I_C = 0 \quad (1)$$
$$-8I_B + 10I_C = 0 \quad (2)$$
$$4I_A - 8I_B = 6 \quad (3)$$

To eliminate I_A between equations (1) and (3), multiply equation (1) by –4 and add.
$$-4[I_A + I_B + C = 0]$$
$$4I_A - 8I_B = 6$$

gives
$$-4I_A - 4I_B - 4I_C = 0$$
$$4I_A - 8I_B = 6$$

Add: $-12I_B - 4I_C = 6$

or $-6I_B - 2I_C = 3 \quad (4)$

Equations (4) and (2) are a system of two equations in two unknowns.
$$-8I_B + 10I_C = 0$$
$$-6I_B - 2I_C = 3$$

Multiply equation (4) by 5 and add this result to equation (2).
$$-8I_B + 10I_C = 0$$
$$5[-6I_B - 2I_C = 3]$$

gives
$$-8I_B + 10I_C = 0$$
$$-30I_B - 10I_C = 15$$

Add: $-38I_B = 15$

$$I_B = \frac{15}{-38} = -\frac{15}{38}$$

Substitute $-\frac{15}{38}$ for I_B in equation (2).

$$-8I_B + 10I_C = 0$$
$$-8\left(-\frac{15}{38}\right) + 10I_C = 0$$
$$\frac{120}{38} + 10I_C = 0$$
$$10I_C = -\frac{120}{38}$$
$$\frac{1}{10}(10I_C) = \frac{1}{10}\left(-\frac{120}{38}\right)$$
$$I_C = -\frac{12}{38} = -\frac{6}{19}$$

Finally, substitute $-\frac{15}{38}$ for I_B in equation (3).
$$4I_A - 8I_B = 6$$
$$4I_A - 8\left(-\frac{15}{38}\right) = 6$$
$$4I_A + \frac{120}{38} = 6$$
$$4I_A = 6 - \frac{120}{38}$$
$$4I_A = 6 - \frac{60}{19}$$
$$4I_A = \frac{114}{19} - \frac{60}{19}$$
$$4I_A = \frac{54}{19}$$
$$\frac{1}{4}(4I_A) = \frac{1}{4}\left(\frac{54}{19}\right)$$
$$I_A = \frac{27}{38}$$

The current in branch A is $\frac{27}{38}$, the current in branch B is $-\frac{15}{38}$ and the current in branch C is $-\frac{6}{19}$.

57.
$$4 - 2[(x - 5) + 2x] = -(x + 6)$$
$$4 - 2(x - 5 + 2x) = -x - 6$$
$$4 - 2(3x - 5) = -x - 6$$
$$4 - 6x + 10 = -x - 6$$
$$-6x + 14 = -x - 6$$
$$-6x + x = -6 - 14$$
$$-5x = -20$$
$$x = 4$$

59. The slope is
$$m = \frac{-4 - (-8)}{6 - 2} = \frac{-4 + 8}{6 - 2} = \frac{4}{4} = 1$$
Use the point-slope form with $m = 1$ and

$(x_1, y_1) = (6, -4).$
$y - y_1 = m(x - x_1)$
$y - (-4) = 1(x - 6)$
$y + 4 = x - 6$
$y = x - 10$

Exercise Set 4.4

1. A square matrix has the same number of rows and columns.

3. The next step is to change the −1 in the second row to 1 by multiplying the second row of numbers by −1.

5. Switch row (2) and row (3) in order to continuing placing ones along the diagonal.

7. Dependent

9. $\begin{bmatrix} 5 & -10 & | & -15 \\ 3 & 1 & | & -4 \end{bmatrix} \Rightarrow \begin{bmatrix} 1 & -2 & | & -3 \\ 3 & 1 & | & -4 \end{bmatrix} \frac{1}{5}R_1$

11. $\begin{bmatrix} 4 & 7 & 2 & | & -1 \\ 3 & 2 & 1 & | & -5 \\ 1 & 1 & 3 & | & -8 \end{bmatrix} \Rightarrow \begin{bmatrix} 1 & 1 & 3 & | & -8 \\ 3 & 2 & 1 & | & -5 \\ 4 & 7 & 2 & | & -1 \end{bmatrix}$ switch R_1 and R_2

13. $\begin{bmatrix} 1 & 3 & | & 12 \\ -3 & 8 & | & -6 \end{bmatrix} \Rightarrow \begin{bmatrix} 1 & 3 & | & 12 \\ 0 & 17 & | & 30 \end{bmatrix} 3R_1 + R_2$

15. $\begin{bmatrix} 1 & 0 & 8 & | & \frac{1}{4} \\ 5 & 2 & 2 & | & -2 \\ 6 & -3 & 1 & | & 0 \end{bmatrix} \Rightarrow$
$\begin{bmatrix} 1 & 0 & 8 & | & \frac{1}{4} \\ 0 & 2 & -38 & | & -\frac{13}{4} \\ 6 & -3 & 1 & | & 0 \end{bmatrix} -5R_1 + R_2$

17. $x + 3y = 3$
$-x + y = -3$
$\begin{bmatrix} 1 & 3 & | & 3 \\ -1 & 1 & | & -3 \end{bmatrix}$
$\begin{bmatrix} 1 & 3 & | & 3 \\ 0 & 4 & | & 0 \end{bmatrix} R_1 + R_2$
$\begin{bmatrix} 1 & 3 & | & 3 \\ 0 & 1 & | & 0 \end{bmatrix} \frac{1}{4}R_2$
The system is
$x + 3y = 3$
$y = 0$
Substitute 0 for y in the first equation.

$x + 3y = 3$
$x + 3(0) = 3$
$x + 0 = 3$
$x = 3$
The solution is $(3, 0)$.

19. $x + 3y = 4$
$-4x - y = 6$
$\begin{bmatrix} 1 & 3 & | & 4 \\ -4 & -1 & | & 6 \end{bmatrix}$
$\begin{bmatrix} 1 & 3 & | & 4 \\ 0 & 11 & | & 22 \end{bmatrix} 4R_1 + R_2$
$\begin{bmatrix} 1 & 3 & | & 4 \\ 0 & 1 & | & 2 \end{bmatrix} \frac{1}{11}R_2$
The system is
$x + 3y = 4$
$y = 2$
Substitute 2 for y in the first equation.
$x + 3(2) = 4$
$x + 6 = 4$
$x = -2$
The solution is $(-2, 2)$.

21. $5a - 10b = -10$
$2a + b = 1$
$\begin{bmatrix} 5 & -10 & | & -10 \\ 2 & 1 & | & 1 \end{bmatrix}$
$\begin{bmatrix} 1 & -2 & | & -2 \\ 2 & 1 & | & 1 \end{bmatrix} \frac{1}{5}R_1$
$\begin{bmatrix} 1 & -2 & | & -2 \\ 0 & 5 & | & 5 \end{bmatrix} -2R_1 + R_2$
$\begin{bmatrix} 1 & -2 & | & -2 \\ 0 & 1 & | & 1 \end{bmatrix} \frac{1}{5}R_2$
The system is
$a - 2b = -2$
$b = 1$
Substitute 1 for b in the first equation.
$a - 2(1) = -2$
$a - 2 = -2$
$a = 0$
The solution is $(0, 1)$.

23.
$$2x - 5y = -6$$
$$-4x + 10y = 12$$

$$\begin{bmatrix} 2 & -5 & | & -6 \\ -4 & 10 & | & 12 \end{bmatrix}$$

$$\begin{bmatrix} 1 & -\frac{5}{2} & | & -3 \\ -4 & 10 & | & 12 \end{bmatrix} \frac{1}{2}R_1$$

$$\begin{bmatrix} 1 & -\frac{5}{2} & | & -3 \\ 0 & 0 & | & 0 \end{bmatrix} 4R_1 + R_2$$

Since the last row contains all 0's, this is a dependent system of equations.

25.
$$12x + 10y = -14$$
$$4x - 3y = -11$$

$$\begin{bmatrix} 12 & 10 & | & -14 \\ 4 & -3 & | & -11 \end{bmatrix}$$

$$\begin{bmatrix} 1 & \frac{5}{6} & | & -\frac{7}{6} \\ 4 & -3 & | & -11 \end{bmatrix} \frac{1}{12}R_1$$

$$\begin{bmatrix} 1 & \frac{5}{6} & | & -\frac{7}{6} \\ 0 & -\frac{19}{3} & | & -\frac{19}{3} \end{bmatrix} -4R_1 + R_2$$

$$\begin{bmatrix} 1 & \frac{5}{6} & | & -\frac{7}{6} \\ 0 & 1 & | & 1 \end{bmatrix} -\frac{3}{19}R_2$$

The system is
$$x + \frac{5}{6}y = -\frac{7}{6}$$
$$y = 1$$

Substitute 1 for y in the first equation.
$$x + \frac{5}{6}y = -\frac{7}{6}$$
$$x + \frac{5}{6}(1) = -\frac{7}{6}$$
$$x + \frac{5}{6} = -\frac{7}{6}$$
$$x = -\frac{12}{6}$$
$$x = -2$$
The solution is (–2, 1).

27.
$$-3x + 6y = 5$$
$$2x - 4y = 8$$

$$\begin{bmatrix} -3 & 6 & | & 5 \\ 2 & -4 & | & 8 \end{bmatrix}$$

$$\begin{bmatrix} 1 & -2 & | & -\frac{5}{3} \\ 2 & -4 & | & 8 \end{bmatrix} -\frac{1}{3}R_1$$

$$\begin{bmatrix} 1 & -2 & | & -\frac{5}{3} \\ 0 & 0 & | & \frac{34}{3} \end{bmatrix} -2R_1 + R_2$$

Since the last row contains zeros on the left and a nonzero number on the right, this is an inconsistent system and there is no solution.

29.
$$9x - 8y = 4$$
$$-3x + 4y = -1$$

$$\begin{bmatrix} 9 & -8 & | & 4 \\ -3 & 4 & | & -1 \end{bmatrix}$$

$$\begin{bmatrix} 1 & -\frac{8}{9} & | & \frac{4}{9} \\ -3 & 4 & | & -1 \end{bmatrix} \frac{1}{9}R_1$$

$$\begin{bmatrix} 1 & -\frac{8}{9} & | & \frac{4}{9} \\ 0 & \frac{4}{3} & | & \frac{1}{3} \end{bmatrix} 3R_1 + R_2$$

$$\begin{bmatrix} 1 & -\frac{8}{9} & | & \frac{4}{9} \\ 0 & 1 & | & \frac{1}{4} \end{bmatrix} \frac{3}{4}R_2$$

The system is
$$x - \frac{8}{9}y = \frac{4}{9}$$
$$y = \frac{1}{4}$$

Substitute $\frac{1}{4}$ for y in the first equation.
$$x - \frac{8}{9}y = \frac{4}{9}$$
$$x - \frac{8}{9}\left(\frac{1}{4}\right) = \frac{4}{9}$$
$$x - \frac{2}{9} = \frac{4}{9}$$
$$x = \frac{4}{9} + \frac{2}{9}$$
$$x = \frac{6}{9}$$
$$x = \frac{2}{3}$$

The solution is $\left(\frac{2}{3}, \frac{1}{4}\right)$.

31.
$$10m = 8n + 15$$
$$16n = -15m - 2$$
Write the system in standard form.
$$10m - 8n = 15$$
$$15m + 16n = -2$$

$$\begin{bmatrix} 10 & -8 & | & 15 \\ 15 & 16 & | & -2 \end{bmatrix}$$

$$\begin{bmatrix} 1 & -\frac{4}{5} & | & \frac{3}{2} \\ 15 & 16 & | & -2 \end{bmatrix} \frac{1}{10}R_1$$

$$\begin{bmatrix} 1 & -\frac{4}{5} & | & \frac{3}{2} \\ 0 & 28 & | & -\frac{49}{2} \end{bmatrix} -15R_1 + R_2$$

$$\begin{bmatrix} 1 & -\frac{4}{5} & | & \frac{3}{2} \\ 0 & 1 & | & -\frac{7}{8} \end{bmatrix} \frac{1}{28}R_2$$

The system can be written as
$$m - \frac{4}{5}n = \frac{3}{2}$$
$$n = -\frac{7}{8}$$
Substitute $-\frac{7}{8}$ for n in the first equation.
$$m - \frac{4}{5}n = \frac{3}{2}$$
$$m - \frac{4}{5}\left(-\frac{7}{8}\right) = \frac{3}{2}$$
$$m + \frac{7}{10} = \frac{3}{2}$$
$$m = \frac{3}{2} - \frac{7}{10}$$
$$m = \frac{15}{10} - \frac{7}{10}$$
$$m = \frac{8}{10}$$
$$m = \frac{4}{5}$$
The solution is $\left(\frac{4}{5}, -\frac{7}{8}\right)$.

33. $x - 3y + 2z = 5$
$2x + 5y - 4z = -3$
$-3x + y - 2z = -11$

$$\begin{bmatrix} 1 & -3 & 2 & | & 5 \\ 2 & 5 & -4 & | & -3 \\ -3 & 1 & -2 & | & -11 \end{bmatrix}$$

$$\begin{bmatrix} 1 & -3 & 2 & | & 5 \\ 0 & 11 & -8 & | & -13 \\ -3 & 1 & -2 & | & -11 \end{bmatrix} -2R_1 + R_2$$

$$\begin{bmatrix} 1 & -3 & 2 & | & 5 \\ 0 & 11 & -8 & | & -13 \\ 0 & -8 & 4 & | & 4 \end{bmatrix} 3R_1 + R_3$$

$$\begin{bmatrix} 1 & -3 & 2 & | & 5 \\ 0 & 1 & -\frac{8}{11} & | & -\frac{13}{11} \\ 0 & -8 & 4 & | & 4 \end{bmatrix} \frac{1}{11}R_2$$

$$\begin{bmatrix} 1 & -3 & 2 & | & 5 \\ 0 & 1 & -\frac{8}{11} & | & -\frac{13}{11} \\ 0 & 0 & -\frac{20}{11} & | & -\frac{60}{11} \end{bmatrix} 8R_2 + R_3$$

$$\begin{bmatrix} 1 & -3 & 2 & | & 5 \\ 0 & 1 & -\frac{8}{11} & | & -\frac{13}{11} \\ 0 & 0 & 1 & | & 3 \end{bmatrix} -\frac{11}{20}R_3$$

The system is

$x - 3y + 2z = 5$
$$y - \frac{8}{11}z = -\frac{13}{11}$$
$$z = 3$$
Substitute 3 for z in the second equation.
$$y - \frac{8}{11}(3) = -\frac{13}{11}$$
$$y - \frac{24}{11} = -\frac{13}{11}$$
$$y = \frac{11}{11}$$
$$y = 1$$
Substitute 1 for y and 3 for z in the first equation.
$$x - 3(1) + 2(3) = 5$$
$$x - 3 + 6 = 5$$
$$x + 3 = 5$$
$$x = 2$$
The solution is $(2, 1, 3)$.

35. $x + 2y = 5$
$y - z = -1$
$2x - 3z = 0$
Write the system in standard form.
$x + 2y + 0z = 5$
$0x + y - z = -1$
$2x + 0y - 3z = 0$

$$\begin{bmatrix} 1 & 2 & 0 & | & 5 \\ 0 & 1 & -1 & | & -1 \\ 2 & 0 & -3 & | & 0 \end{bmatrix}$$

$$\begin{bmatrix} 1 & 2 & 0 & | & 5 \\ 0 & 1 & -1 & | & -1 \\ 0 & -4 & -3 & | & -10 \end{bmatrix} -2R_1 + R_3$$

$$\begin{bmatrix} 1 & 2 & 0 & | & 5 \\ 0 & 1 & -1 & | & -1 \\ 0 & 0 & -7 & | & -14 \end{bmatrix} 4R_2 + R_3$$

$$\begin{bmatrix} 1 & 2 & 0 & | & 5 \\ 0 & 1 & -1 & | & -1 \\ 0 & 0 & 1 & | & 2 \end{bmatrix} -\frac{1}{7}R_3$$

The system is
$x + 2y = 5$
$y - z = -1$
$z = 2$
Substitute 2 for z in the second equation.
$y - z = -1$
$y - 2 = -1$
$y = 1$
Substitute 1 for y in the first equation.

$$x + 2y = 5$$
$$x + 2(1) = 5$$
$$x + 2 = 5$$
$$x = 3$$

The solution is $(3, 1, 2)$.

37.
$$x - 2y + 4z = 5$$
$$-3x + 4y - 2z = -8$$
$$4x + 5y - 4z = -3$$

$$\begin{bmatrix} 1 & -2 & 4 & 5 \\ -3 & 4 & -2 & -8 \\ 4 & 5 & -4 & -3 \end{bmatrix}$$

$$\begin{bmatrix} 1 & -2 & 4 & 5 \\ 0 & -2 & 10 & 7 \\ 4 & 5 & -4 & -3 \end{bmatrix} 3R_1 + R_2$$

$$\begin{bmatrix} 1 & -2 & 4 & 5 \\ 0 & -2 & 10 & 7 \\ 0 & 13 & -20 & -23 \end{bmatrix} -4R_1 + R_3$$

$$\begin{bmatrix} 1 & -2 & 4 & 5 \\ 0 & 1 & -5 & -\frac{7}{2} \\ 0 & 13 & -20 & -23 \end{bmatrix} -\frac{1}{2}R_2$$

$$\begin{bmatrix} 1 & -2 & 4 & 5 \\ 0 & 1 & -5 & -\frac{7}{2} \\ 0 & 0 & 45 & \frac{45}{2} \end{bmatrix} -13R_2 + R_3$$

$$\begin{bmatrix} 1 & -2 & 4 & 5 \\ 0 & 1 & -5 & -\frac{7}{2} \\ 0 & 0 & 1 & \frac{1}{2} \end{bmatrix} \frac{1}{45}R_3$$

The system is
$$x - 2y + 4z = 5$$
$$y - 5z = -\frac{7}{2}$$
$$z = \frac{1}{2}$$

Substitute $\frac{1}{2}$ for z in the second equation.
$$y - 5\left(\frac{1}{2}\right) = -\frac{7}{2}$$
$$y - \frac{5}{2} = -\frac{7}{2}$$
$$y = -\frac{2}{2}$$
$$y = -1$$

Substitute -1 for y and $\frac{1}{2}$ for z in the first equation.

$$x - 2(-1) + 4\left(\frac{1}{2}\right) = 5$$
$$x + 2 + 2 = 5$$
$$x + 4 = 5$$
$$x = 1$$

The solution is $\left(1, -1, \frac{1}{2}\right)$.

39.
$$2x - 5y + z = 1$$
$$3x - 5y + z = 2$$
$$-4x + 10y - 2z = -2$$

$$\begin{bmatrix} 2 & -5 & 1 & 1 \\ 3 & -5 & 1 & 2 \\ -4 & 10 & -2 & -2 \end{bmatrix}$$

$$\begin{bmatrix} 1 & -\frac{5}{2} & \frac{1}{2} & \frac{1}{2} \\ 3 & -5 & 1 & 2 \\ -4 & 10 & -2 & -2 \end{bmatrix} \frac{1}{2}R_1$$

$$\begin{bmatrix} 1 & -\frac{5}{2} & \frac{1}{2} & \frac{1}{2} \\ 0 & \frac{5}{2} & -\frac{1}{2} & \frac{1}{2} \\ -4 & 10 & -2 & -2 \end{bmatrix} -3R_1 + R_2$$

$$\begin{bmatrix} 1 & -\frac{5}{2} & \frac{1}{2} & \frac{1}{2} \\ 0 & \frac{5}{2} & -\frac{1}{2} & \frac{1}{2} \\ 0 & 0 & 0 & 0 \end{bmatrix} 4R_1 + R_3$$

Since there is a row of all zeros, the system is dependent.

41.
$$4p - q + r = 4$$
$$-6p + 3q - 2r = -5$$
$$2p + 5q - r = 7$$

$$\begin{bmatrix} 4 & -1 & 1 & 4 \\ -6 & 3 & -2 & -5 \\ 2 & 5 & -1 & 7 \end{bmatrix}$$

$$\begin{bmatrix} 1 & -\frac{1}{4} & \frac{1}{4} & 1 \\ -6 & 3 & -2 & -5 \\ 2 & 5 & -1 & 7 \end{bmatrix} \frac{1}{4}R_1$$

$$\begin{bmatrix} 1 & -\frac{1}{4} & \frac{1}{4} & 1 \\ 0 & \frac{3}{2} & -\frac{1}{2} & 1 \\ 2 & 5 & -1 & 7 \end{bmatrix} 6R_1 + R_2$$

$$\begin{bmatrix} 1 & -\frac{1}{4} & \frac{1}{4} & 1 \\ 0 & \frac{3}{2} & -\frac{1}{2} & 1 \\ 0 & \frac{11}{2} & -\frac{3}{2} & 5 \end{bmatrix} -2R_1 + R_3$$

$$\begin{bmatrix} 1 & -\frac{1}{4} & \frac{1}{4} & \Big| & 1 \\ 0 & 1 & -\frac{1}{3} & \Big| & \frac{2}{3} \\ 0 & \frac{11}{2} & -\frac{3}{2} & \Big| & 5 \end{bmatrix} \frac{2}{3}R_2$$

$$\begin{bmatrix} 1 & -\frac{1}{4} & \frac{1}{4} & \Big| & 1 \\ 0 & 1 & -\frac{1}{3} & \Big| & \frac{2}{3} \\ 0 & 0 & \frac{1}{3} & \Big| & \frac{4}{3} \end{bmatrix} -\frac{11}{2}R_2 + R_3$$

$$\begin{bmatrix} 1 & -\frac{1}{4} & \frac{1}{4} & \Big| & 1 \\ 0 & 1 & -\frac{1}{3} & \Big| & \frac{2}{3} \\ 0 & 0 & 1 & \Big| & 4 \end{bmatrix}$$

The system is
$$x - \frac{1}{4}y + \frac{1}{4}z = 1$$
$$y - \frac{1}{3}z = \frac{2}{3}$$
$$z = 4$$

Substitute 4 for z in the second equation.
$$y - \frac{1}{3}z = \frac{2}{3}$$
$$y - \frac{1}{3}(4) = \frac{2}{3}$$
$$y - \frac{4}{3} = \frac{2}{3}$$
$$y = \frac{6}{3}$$
$$y = 2$$

Substitute 2 for y and 4 for z in the first equation.
$$x - \frac{1}{4}y + \frac{1}{4}z = 1$$
$$x - \frac{1}{4}(2) + \frac{1}{4}(4) = 1$$
$$x - \frac{1}{2} + 1 = 1$$
$$x + \frac{1}{2} = 1$$
$$x = \frac{1}{2}$$

The solution is $\left(\frac{1}{2}, 2, 4\right)$.

43.
$$2x - 4y + 3z = -12$$
$$3x - y + 2z = -3$$
$$-4x + 8y - 6z = 10$$

$$\begin{bmatrix} 2 & -4 & 3 & \Big| & -12 \\ 3 & -1 & 2 & \Big| & -3 \\ -4 & 8 & -6 & \Big| & 10 \end{bmatrix}$$

$$\begin{bmatrix} 1 & -2 & \frac{3}{2} & \Big| & -6 \\ 3 & -1 & 2 & \Big| & -3 \\ -4 & 8 & -6 & \Big| & 10 \end{bmatrix} \frac{1}{2}R_1$$

$$\begin{bmatrix} 1 & -2 & \frac{3}{2} & \Big| & -6 \\ 0 & 5 & -\frac{5}{2} & \Big| & 15 \\ -4 & 8 & -6 & \Big| & 10 \end{bmatrix} -3R_1 + R_2$$

$$\begin{bmatrix} 1 & -2 & \frac{3}{2} & \Big| & -6 \\ 0 & 5 & -\frac{5}{2} & \Big| & 15 \\ 0 & 0 & 0 & \Big| & -14 \end{bmatrix} 4R_1 + R_3$$

Since the last row contains zeros on the left and a nonzero number on the right, the system is inconsistent and there is no solution.

45.
$$5x - 3y + 4z = 22$$
$$-x - 15y + 10z = -15$$
$$-3x + 9y - 12z = -6$$

$$\begin{bmatrix} 5 & -3 & 4 & \Big| & 22 \\ -1 & -15 & 10 & \Big| & -15 \\ -3 & 9 & -12 & \Big| & -6 \end{bmatrix}$$

$$\begin{bmatrix} 1 & -\frac{3}{5} & \frac{4}{5} & \Big| & \frac{22}{5} \\ -1 & -15 & 10 & \Big| & -15 \\ -3 & 9 & -12 & \Big| & -6 \end{bmatrix} \frac{1}{5}R_1$$

$$\begin{bmatrix} 1 & -\frac{3}{5} & \frac{4}{5} & \Big| & \frac{22}{5} \\ 0 & -\frac{78}{5} & \frac{54}{5} & \Big| & -\frac{53}{5} \\ -3 & 9 & -12 & \Big| & -6 \end{bmatrix} R_1 + R_2$$

$$\begin{bmatrix} 1 & -\frac{3}{5} & \frac{4}{5} & \Big| & \frac{22}{5} \\ 0 & -\frac{78}{5} & \frac{54}{5} & \Big| & -\frac{53}{5} \\ 0 & \frac{36}{5} & -\frac{48}{5} & \Big| & \frac{36}{5} \end{bmatrix} 3R_1 + R_3$$

$$\begin{bmatrix} 1 & -\frac{3}{5} & \frac{4}{5} & \Big| & \frac{22}{5} \\ 0 & 1 & -\frac{9}{13} & \Big| & \frac{53}{78} \\ 0 & \frac{36}{5} & -\frac{48}{5} & \Big| & \frac{36}{5} \end{bmatrix} -\frac{5}{78}R_2$$

$$\begin{bmatrix} 1 & -\frac{3}{5} & \frac{4}{5} & \Big| & \frac{22}{5} \\ 0 & 1 & -\frac{9}{13} & \Big| & \frac{53}{78} \\ 0 & 0 & -\frac{60}{13} & \Big| & \frac{30}{13} \end{bmatrix} -\frac{36}{5}R_2 + R_3$$

$$\begin{bmatrix} 1 & -\frac{3}{5} & \frac{4}{5} & \Big| & \frac{22}{5} \\ 0 & 1 & -\frac{9}{13} & \Big| & \frac{53}{78} \\ 0 & 0 & 1 & \Big| & -\frac{1}{2} \end{bmatrix}$$

The system is
$$x - \frac{3}{5}y + \frac{4}{5}z = \frac{22}{5}$$
$$y - \frac{9}{13}z = \frac{53}{78}$$
$$z = -\frac{1}{2}$$

Substitute $-\dfrac{1}{2}$ for z in the second equation.

$$y - \frac{9}{13}z = \frac{53}{78}$$

$$y - \frac{9}{13}\left(-\frac{1}{2}\right) = \frac{53}{78}$$

$$y + \frac{9}{26} = \frac{53}{78}$$

$$y = \frac{53}{78} - \frac{27}{78}$$

$$y = \frac{26}{78}$$

$$y = \frac{1}{3}$$

Substitute $\dfrac{1}{3}$ for y and $-\dfrac{1}{2}$ for z in the first equation.

$$x - \frac{3}{5}y + \frac{4}{5}z = \frac{22}{5}$$

$$x - \frac{3}{5}\left(\frac{1}{3}\right) + \frac{4}{5}\left(-\frac{1}{2}\right) = \frac{22}{5}$$

$$x - \frac{1}{5} - \frac{2}{5} = \frac{22}{5}$$

$$x - \frac{3}{5} = \frac{22}{5}$$

$$x = \frac{25}{5}$$

$$x = 5$$

The solution is $\left(5, \dfrac{1}{3}, -\dfrac{1}{2}\right)$.

47. No, this is the same as switching the order of the equations.

49. Let $x =$ smallest angle
$y =$ remaining angle
$z =$ largest angle
$$z = x + 55$$
$$z = y + 20$$
$$x + y + z = 180$$
Write the system in standard form:
$$x - z = -55$$
$$y - z = -20$$
$$x + y + z = 180$$

$$\begin{bmatrix} 1 & 0 & -1 & | & -55 \\ 0 & 1 & -1 & | & -20 \\ 1 & 1 & 1 & | & 180 \end{bmatrix}$$

$$\begin{bmatrix} 1 & 0 & -1 & | & -55 \\ 0 & 1 & -1 & | & -20 \\ 0 & 1 & 2 & | & 235 \end{bmatrix} -1R_1 + R_3$$

$$\begin{bmatrix} 1 & 0 & -1 & | & -55 \\ 0 & 1 & -1 & | & -20 \\ 0 & 0 & 3 & | & 255 \end{bmatrix} -1R_2 + R_3$$

$$\begin{bmatrix} 1 & 0 & -1 & | & -55 \\ 0 & 1 & -1 & | & -20 \\ 0 & 0 & 1 & | & 85 \end{bmatrix} \tfrac{1}{3}R_3$$

The system is
$$x - z = -55$$
$$y - z = -20$$
$$z = 85$$
Substitute 85 for z in the second equation.
$$y - z = -20$$
$$y - 85 = -20$$
$$y = 65$$
Substitute 85 for z in the first equation.
$$x - z = -55$$
$$x - 85 = -55$$
$$x = 30$$
The angles are $30°$, $65°$, and $85°$.

51. Let $x =$ amount Chiquita controls,
$y =$ amount Dole controls,
$z =$ amount Del Monte controls
$$x = z + 12$$
$$y = 2z - 3$$
$$x + y + z = 65$$
Write the system in standard form.
$$x - z = 12$$
$$y - 2z = -3$$
$$x + y + z = 65$$

$$\begin{bmatrix} 1 & 0 & -1 & | & 12 \\ 0 & 1 & -2 & | & -3 \\ 1 & 1 & 1 & | & 65 \end{bmatrix}$$

$$\begin{bmatrix} 1 & 0 & -1 & | & 12 \\ 0 & 1 & -2 & | & -3 \\ 0 & 1 & 2 & | & 53 \end{bmatrix} -1R_1 + R_3$$

$$\begin{bmatrix} 1 & 0 & -1 & | & 12 \\ 0 & 1 & -2 & | & -3 \\ 0 & 0 & 4 & | & 56 \end{bmatrix} -1R_2 + R_3$$

$$\begin{bmatrix} 1 & 0 & -1 & | & 12 \\ 0 & 1 & -2 & | & -3 \\ 0 & 0 & 1 & | & 14 \end{bmatrix} \tfrac{1}{4}R_3$$

The system is
$$x - z = 12$$
$$y - 2z = -3$$
$$z = 14$$
Substitute 14 for z in the second equation.

$$y - 2z = -3$$
$$y - 2(14) = -3$$
$$y - 28 = -3$$
$$y = 25$$

Substitute 14 for z in the first equation.

$$x - z = 12$$
$$x - 14 = 12$$
$$x = 26$$

Thus, Del Monte controls 14% of the bananas, Dole controls 25% and Chiquita controls 26%, with the remaining $100\% - 65\% = 35\%$ being controlled by "other."

53. a. $A \cup B = \{1, 2, 3, 4, 5, 6, 9, 10\}$

   b. $A \cap B = \{4, 6\}$

55. A graph is the set of points whose coordinates satisfy an equation.

Exercise Set 4.5

1. Answers will vary.

3. If $D = 0$ and either D_x, D_y, or D_z is not equal to 0, the system is inconsistent.

5. $x = \dfrac{D_x}{D} = \dfrac{-8}{4} = -2$

   $y = \dfrac{D_y}{D} = \dfrac{-2}{4} = -\dfrac{1}{2}$

   The solution is $\left(-2, -\dfrac{1}{2}\right)$.

7. $\begin{vmatrix} 2 & 3 \\ 1 & 5 \end{vmatrix} = (2)(5) - (1)(3) = 10 - 3 = 7$

9. $\begin{vmatrix} \frac{1}{2} & 3 \\ 2 & -4 \end{vmatrix} = \frac{1}{2}(-4) - (2)(3) = -2 - 6 = -8$

11. $\begin{vmatrix} 3 & 2 & 0 \\ 0 & 5 & 3 \\ -1 & 4 & 2 \end{vmatrix} = 3\begin{vmatrix} 5 & 3 \\ 4 & 2 \end{vmatrix} - 0\begin{vmatrix} 2 & 0 \\ 4 & 2 \end{vmatrix} + (-1)\begin{vmatrix} 2 & 0 \\ 5 & 3 \end{vmatrix}$

   $= 3(10 - 12) - 0(4 - 0) - 1(6 - 0)$
   $= 3(-2) - 0(4) - 1(6)$
   $= -6 - 0 - 6$
   $= -12$

13. $\begin{vmatrix} 2 & 3 & 1 \\ 1 & -3 & -6 \\ -4 & 5 & 9 \end{vmatrix}$

   $= 2\begin{vmatrix} -3 & -6 \\ 5 & 9 \end{vmatrix} - 1\begin{vmatrix} 3 & 1 \\ 5 & 9 \end{vmatrix} + (-4)\begin{vmatrix} 3 & 1 \\ -3 & -6 \end{vmatrix}$
   $= 2[-27 - (-30)] - 1(27 - 5) - 4[-18 - (-3)]$
   $= 2(3) - 1(22) - 4(-15)$
   $= 6 - 22 + 60$
   $= 44$

15. $x + 3y = 1$
   $-2x - 3y = 4$

   To solve, first calculate D, D_x, and D_y.

   $D = \begin{vmatrix} 1 & 3 \\ -2 & -3 \end{vmatrix} = (1)(-3) - (-2)(3) = -3 - (-6) = 3$

   $D_x = \begin{vmatrix} 1 & 3 \\ 4 & -3 \end{vmatrix}$
   $= (1)(-3) - (4)(3)$
   $= -3 - 12$
   $= -15$

   $D_y = \begin{vmatrix} 1 & 1 \\ -2 & 4 \end{vmatrix} = (1)(4) - (-2)(1) = 4 - (-2) = 6$

   $x = \dfrac{D_x}{D} = \dfrac{-15}{3} = -5$ and $y = \dfrac{D_y}{D} = \dfrac{6}{3} = 2$

   The solution is $(-5, 2)$.

17. $x - 2y = -1$
   $x + 3y = 9$

   To solve, first calculate D, D_x, and D_y.

   $D = \begin{vmatrix} 1 & -2 \\ 1 & 3 \end{vmatrix} = (1)(3) - (1)(-2) = 3 + 2 = 5$

   $D_x = \begin{vmatrix} -1 & -2 \\ 9 & 3 \end{vmatrix}$
   $= (-1)(3) - (9)(-2)$
   $= -3 + 18$
   $= 15$

   $D_y = \begin{vmatrix} 1 & -1 \\ 1 & 9 \end{vmatrix} = (1)(9) - (1)(-1) = 9 + 1 = 10$

   $x = \dfrac{D_x}{D} = \dfrac{15}{5} = 3$ and $y = \dfrac{D_y}{D} = \dfrac{10}{5} = 2$

   The solution is $(3, 2)$.

19. $5p - 7q = -21$
$-4p + 3q = 22$

To solve, first calculate D, D_p, and D_q.

$D = \begin{vmatrix} 5 & -7 \\ -4 & 3 \end{vmatrix}$

$= (5)(3) - (-4)(-7)$

$= 15 - 28$

$= -13$

$D_p = \begin{vmatrix} -21 & -7 \\ 22 & 3 \end{vmatrix}$

$= (-21)(3) - (22)(-7)$

$= -63 - (-154)$

$= 91$

$D_q = \begin{vmatrix} 5 & -21 \\ -4 & 22 \end{vmatrix}$

$= (5)(22) - (-4)(-21)$

$= 110 - 84$

$= 26$

$p = \dfrac{D_p}{D} = \dfrac{91}{-13} = -7$ and $q = \dfrac{D_q}{D} = \dfrac{26}{-13} = -2$

The solution is $(-7, -2)$.

21. $4x = -5y - 2$
$-2x = y + 4$

Rewrite the system in standard form:
$4x + 5y = -2$

$2x + y = -4$

Now calculate D, D_x, and D_y.

$D = \begin{vmatrix} 4 & 5 \\ 2 & 1 \end{vmatrix} = (4)(1) - (2)(5) = 4 - 10 = -6$

$D_x = \begin{vmatrix} -2 & 5 \\ -4 & 1 \end{vmatrix}$

$= (-2)(1) - (-4)(5)$

$= -2 - (-20)$

$= 18$

$D_y = \begin{vmatrix} 4 & -2 \\ 2 & -4 \end{vmatrix}$

$= (4)(-4) - (2)(-2)$

$= -16 - (-4)$

$= -12$

$x = \dfrac{D_x}{D} = \dfrac{18}{-6} = -3$ and $y = \dfrac{D_y}{D} = \dfrac{-12}{-6} = 2$

The solution is $(-3, 2)$.

23. $x + 5y = 3$
$2x + 10y = 6$

To solve, first calculate D, D_x, and D_y.

$D = \begin{vmatrix} 1 & 5 \\ 2 & 10 \end{vmatrix} = (1)(10) - (2)(5) = 10 - 10 = 0$

$D_x = \begin{vmatrix} 3 & 5 \\ 6 & 10 \end{vmatrix} = (3)(10) - (6)(5) = 30 - 30 = 0$

$D_y = \begin{vmatrix} 1 & 3 \\ 2 & 6 \end{vmatrix} = (1)(6) - (2)(3) = 6 - 6 = 0$

Since $D = 0$, $D_x = 0$, and $D_y = 0$, the system is dependent so there are an infinite number of solutions.

25. $3r = -4s - 6$
$3s = -5r + 1$

Rewrite the system in standard form.
$3r + 4s = -6$
$5r + 3s = 1$

Now calculate D, D_r, and D_s.

$D = \begin{vmatrix} 3 & 4 \\ 5 & 3 \end{vmatrix} = (3)(3) - (5)(4) = 9 - 20 = -11$

$D_r = \begin{vmatrix} -6 & 4 \\ 1 & 3 \end{vmatrix}$

$= (-6)(3) - (1)(4)$

$= -18 - 4$

$= -22$

$D_s = \begin{vmatrix} 3 & -6 \\ 5 & 1 \end{vmatrix}$

$= (3)(1) - (5)(-6)$

$= 3 + 30$

$= 33$

$r = \dfrac{D_r}{D} = \dfrac{-22}{-11} = 2$ and $s = \dfrac{D_s}{D} = \dfrac{33}{-11} = -3$

The solution is $(2, -3)$.

27. $5x - 5y = 3$
$x - y = -2$

To solve, first calculate D, D_x, and D_y.

$D = \begin{vmatrix} 5 & -5 \\ 1 & -1 \end{vmatrix} = (5)(-1) - (1)(-5) = -5 + 5 = 0$

$D_x = \begin{vmatrix} 3 & -5 \\ -2 & -1 \end{vmatrix}$

$= (3)(-1) - (-2)(-5)$

$= -3 - 10$

$= -13$

Since $D = 0$ and $D_x \neq 0$, the system is inconsistent, so there is no solution.

29. $6.3x - 4.5y = -9.9$
$-9.1x + 3.2y = -2.2$

Here, you can work with decimals in the determinants. If you do not want to use decimals, then you need to multiply each equation by 10 to clear the decimals.

First, calculate D, D_x, and D_y.

$D = \begin{vmatrix} 6.3 & -4.5 \\ -9.1 & 3.2 \end{vmatrix}$

$= (6.3)(3.2) - (-9.1)(-4.5)$

$= 20.16 - 40.95$

$= -20.79$

$D_x = \begin{vmatrix} -9.9 & -4.5 \\ -2.2 & 3.2 \end{vmatrix}$

$= (-9.9)(3.2) - (-2.2)(-4.5)$

$= -31.68 - 9.90$

$= -41.58$

$D_y = \begin{vmatrix} 6.3 & -9.9 \\ -9.1 & -2.2 \end{vmatrix}$

$= (6.3)(-2.2) - (-9.1)(-9.9)$

$= -13.86 - 90.09$

$= -103.95$

$x = \dfrac{D_x}{D} = \dfrac{-41.58}{-20.79} = 2$ and

$y = \dfrac{D_y}{D} = \dfrac{-103.95}{-20.79} = 5$

The solution is (2, 5).

31. $x + y + z = 2$
$0x - 3y + 4z = 11$
$-3x + 4y - 2z = -11$

To solve, first calculate D, D_x, D_y, and D_z.

$D = \begin{vmatrix} 1 & 1 & 1 \\ 0 & -3 & 4 \\ -3 & 4 & -2 \end{vmatrix}$ (using first column)

$= 1\begin{vmatrix} -3 & 4 \\ 4 & -2 \end{vmatrix} - 0\begin{vmatrix} 1 & 1 \\ 4 & -2 \end{vmatrix} + (-3)\begin{vmatrix} 1 & 1 \\ -3 & 4 \end{vmatrix}$

$= 1(6 - 16) - 0(-2 - 4) - 3(4 + 3)$

$= 1(-10) - 0(-6) - 3(7)$

$= -10 - 0 - 21$

$= -31$

$D_x = \begin{vmatrix} 2 & 1 & 1 \\ 11 & -3 & 4 \\ -11 & 4 & -2 \end{vmatrix}$ (using first row)

$= 2\begin{vmatrix} -3 & 4 \\ 4 & -2 \end{vmatrix} - 1\begin{vmatrix} 11 & 4 \\ -11 & -2 \end{vmatrix} + 1\begin{vmatrix} 11 & -3 \\ -11 & 4 \end{vmatrix}$

$= 2(6 - 16) - 1(-22 + 44) + 1(44 - 33)$

$= 2(-10) - 1(22) + 1(11)$

$= -20 - 22 + 11$

$= -31$

$D_y = \begin{vmatrix} 1 & 2 & 1 \\ 0 & 11 & 4 \\ -3 & -11 & -2 \end{vmatrix}$ (using first column)

$= 1\begin{vmatrix} 11 & 4 \\ -11 & -2 \end{vmatrix} - 0\begin{vmatrix} 2 & 1 \\ -11 & -2 \end{vmatrix} + (-3)\begin{vmatrix} 2 & 1 \\ 11 & 4 \end{vmatrix}$

$= 1(-22 + 44) - 0(-4 + 11) - 3(8 - 11)$

$= 1(22) - 0(7) - 3(-3)$

$= 22 - 0 + 9$

$= 31$

$D_z = \begin{vmatrix} 1 & 1 & 2 \\ 0 & -3 & 11 \\ -3 & 4 & -11 \end{vmatrix}$ (using first column)

$= 1\begin{vmatrix} -3 & 11 \\ 4 & -11 \end{vmatrix} - 0\begin{vmatrix} 1 & 2 \\ 4 & -11 \end{vmatrix} + (-3)\begin{vmatrix} 1 & 2 \\ -3 & 11 \end{vmatrix}$

$= 1(33 - 44) - 0(-11 - 8) - 3(11 + 6)$

$= 1(-11) - 0(-19) - 3(17)$

$= -11 - 0 - 51$

$= -62$

$x = \dfrac{D_x}{D} = \dfrac{-31}{-31} = 1$, $y = \dfrac{D_y}{D} = \dfrac{31}{-31} = 1$, and

$z = \dfrac{D_z}{D} = \dfrac{-62}{-31} = 2$

The solution is (1, −1, 2).

33.
$$3x - 5y - 4z = -4$$
$$4x + 2y + 0z = 1$$
$$0x + 6y - 4z = -11$$

To solve, first calculate D, D_x, D_y, and D_z.

$$D = \begin{vmatrix} 3 & -5 & -4 \\ 4 & 2 & 0 \\ 0 & 6 & -4 \end{vmatrix} \text{ (using the first row)}$$

$$= 3\begin{vmatrix} 2 & 0 \\ 6 & -4 \end{vmatrix} - (-5)\begin{vmatrix} 4 & 0 \\ 0 & -4 \end{vmatrix} + (-4)\begin{vmatrix} 4 & 2 \\ 0 & 6 \end{vmatrix}$$

$$= 3(-8 - 0) + 5(-16 - 0) - 4(24 - 0)$$
$$= 3(-8) + 5(-16) - 4(24)$$
$$= -24 - 80 - 96$$
$$= -200$$

$$D_x = \begin{vmatrix} -4 & -5 & -4 \\ 1 & 2 & 0 \\ -11 & 6 & -4 \end{vmatrix} \text{ (using the first row)}$$

$$= -4\begin{vmatrix} 2 & 0 \\ 6 & -4 \end{vmatrix} - (-5)\begin{vmatrix} 1 & 0 \\ -11 & -4 \end{vmatrix} + (-4)\begin{vmatrix} 1 & 2 \\ -11 & 6 \end{vmatrix}$$

$$= -4(-8 - 0) + 5(-4 + 0) - 4(6 + 22)$$
$$= -4(-8) + 5(-4) - 4(28)$$
$$= 32 - 20 - 112$$
$$= -100$$

$$D_y = \begin{vmatrix} 3 & -4 & -4 \\ 4 & 1 & 0 \\ 0 & -11 & -4 \end{vmatrix} \text{ (using the first row)}$$

$$= 3\begin{vmatrix} 1 & 0 \\ -11 & -4 \end{vmatrix} - (-4)\begin{vmatrix} 4 & 0 \\ 0 & -4 \end{vmatrix} + (-4)\begin{vmatrix} 4 & 1 \\ 0 & -11 \end{vmatrix}$$

$$= 3(-4 + 0) + 4(-16 - 0) - 4(-44 - 0)$$
$$= 3(-4) + 4(-16) - 4(-44)$$
$$= -12 - 64 + 176$$
$$= 100$$

$$D_z = \begin{vmatrix} 3 & -5 & -4 \\ 4 & 2 & 1 \\ 0 & 6 & -11 \end{vmatrix} \text{ (using the first row)}$$

$$= 3\begin{vmatrix} 2 & 1 \\ 6 & -11 \end{vmatrix} - (-5)\begin{vmatrix} 4 & 1 \\ 0 & -11 \end{vmatrix} + (-4)\begin{vmatrix} 4 & 2 \\ 0 & 6 \end{vmatrix}$$

$$= 3(-22 - 6) + 5(-44 - 0) - 4(24 - 0)$$
$$= 3(-28) + 5(-44) - 4(24)$$
$$= -84 - 220 - 96$$
$$= -400$$

$$x = \frac{D_x}{D} = \frac{-100}{-200} = \frac{1}{2}, \ y = \frac{D_y}{D} = \frac{100}{-200} = -\frac{1}{2}, \text{ and}$$
$$z = \frac{D_z}{D} = \frac{-400}{-200} = 2$$

The solution is $\left(\frac{1}{2}, -\frac{1}{2}, 2\right)$.

35.
$$x + 4y - 3z = -6$$
$$2x - 8y + 5z = 12$$
$$3x + 4y - 2z = -3$$

To solve, first calculate D, D_x, D_y, and D_z

$$D = \begin{vmatrix} 1 & 4 & -3 \\ 2 & -8 & 5 \\ 3 & 4 & -2 \end{vmatrix} \text{ (using the first row)}$$

$$= 1\begin{vmatrix} -8 & 5 \\ 4 & -2 \end{vmatrix} - 4\begin{vmatrix} 2 & 5 \\ 3 & -2 \end{vmatrix} + (-3)\begin{vmatrix} 2 & -8 \\ 3 & 4 \end{vmatrix}$$

$$= 1(16 - 20) - 4(-4 - 15) - 3(8 + 24)$$
$$= 1(-4) - 4(-19) - 3(32)$$
$$= -4 + 76 - 96$$
$$= -24$$

$$D_x = \begin{vmatrix} -6 & 4 & -3 \\ 12 & -8 & 5 \\ -3 & 4 & -2 \end{vmatrix} \text{ (using the first row)}$$

$$= -6\begin{vmatrix} -8 & 5 \\ 4 & -2 \end{vmatrix} - 4\begin{vmatrix} 12 & 5 \\ -3 & -2 \end{vmatrix} + (-3)\begin{vmatrix} 12 & -8 \\ -3 & 4 \end{vmatrix}$$

$$= -6(16 - 20) - 4(-24 + 15) - 3(48 - 24)$$
$$= -6(-4) - 4(-9) - 3(24)$$
$$= 24 + 36 - 72$$
$$= -12$$

$$D_y = \begin{vmatrix} 1 & -6 & -3 \\ 2 & 12 & 5 \\ 3 & -3 & -2 \end{vmatrix} \text{ (using the first row)}$$

$$= 1\begin{vmatrix} 12 & 5 \\ -3 & -2 \end{vmatrix} - (-6)\begin{vmatrix} 2 & 5 \\ 3 & -2 \end{vmatrix} + (-3)\begin{vmatrix} 2 & 12 \\ 3 & -3 \end{vmatrix}$$

$$= 1(-24 + 15) + 6(-4 - 15) - 3(-6 - 36)$$
$$= 1(-9) + 6(-19) - 3(-42)$$
$$= -9 - 114 + 126$$
$$= 3$$

$$D_z = \begin{vmatrix} 1 & 4 & -6 \\ 2 & -8 & 12 \\ 3 & 4 & -3 \end{vmatrix} \text{ (using the first row)}$$

$$= 1\begin{vmatrix} -8 & 12 \\ 4 & -3 \end{vmatrix} - 4\begin{vmatrix} 2 & 12 \\ 3 & -3 \end{vmatrix} + (-6)\begin{vmatrix} 2 & -8 \\ 3 & 4 \end{vmatrix}$$

$$= 1(24 - 48) - 4(-6 - 36) - 6(8 + 24)$$

$$= 1(-24) - 4(-42) - 6(32)$$

$$= -24 + 168 - 192$$

$$= -48$$

$$x = \frac{D_x}{D} = \frac{-12}{-24} = \frac{1}{2}, \ y = \frac{D_y}{D} = \frac{3}{-24} = -\frac{1}{8}, \text{ and}$$

$$z = \frac{D_z}{D} = \frac{-48}{-24} = 2.$$

The solution is $\left(\frac{1}{2}, -\frac{1}{8}, 2\right)$.

37. $a - b + 2c = 3$
$a - b + c = 1$
$2a + b + 2c = 2$
To solve, first calculate D, D_a, D_b, and D_c.

$$D = \begin{vmatrix} 1 & -1 & 2 \\ 1 & -1 & 1 \\ 2 & 1 & 2 \end{vmatrix}$$

$$= 1\begin{vmatrix} -1 & 1 \\ 1 & 2 \end{vmatrix} - 1\begin{vmatrix} -1 & 2 \\ 1 & 2 \end{vmatrix} + 2\begin{vmatrix} -1 & 2 \\ -1 & 1 \end{vmatrix}$$

$$= 1(-2 - 1) - 1(-2 - 2) + 2(-1 + 2)$$

$$= 1(-3) - 1(-4) + 2(1)$$

$$= -3 + 4 + 2$$

$$= 3$$

$$D_a = \begin{vmatrix} 3 & -1 & 2 \\ 1 & -1 & 1 \\ 2 & 1 & 2 \end{vmatrix}$$

$$= 3\begin{vmatrix} -1 & 1 \\ 1 & 2 \end{vmatrix} - 1\begin{vmatrix} -1 & 2 \\ 1 & 2 \end{vmatrix} + 2\begin{vmatrix} -1 & 2 \\ -1 & 1 \end{vmatrix}$$

$$= 3(-2 - 1) - 1(-2 - 2) + 2(-1 + 2)$$

$$= 3(-3) - 1(-4) + 2(1)$$

$$= -9 + 4 + 2$$

$$= -3$$

$$D_b = \begin{vmatrix} 1 & 3 & 2 \\ 1 & 1 & 1 \\ 2 & 2 & 2 \end{vmatrix}$$

$$= 1\begin{vmatrix} 1 & 1 \\ 2 & 2 \end{vmatrix} - 1\begin{vmatrix} 3 & 2 \\ 2 & 2 \end{vmatrix} + 2\begin{vmatrix} 3 & 2 \\ 1 & 1 \end{vmatrix}$$

$$= 1(2 - 2) - 1(6 - 4) + 2(3 - 2)$$

$$= 1(0) - 1(2) + 2(1)$$

$$= 0 - 2 + 2$$

$$= 0$$

$$D_c = \begin{vmatrix} 1 & -1 & 3 \\ 1 & -1 & 1 \\ 2 & 1 & 2 \end{vmatrix}$$

$$= 1\begin{vmatrix} -1 & 1 \\ 1 & 2 \end{vmatrix} - 1\begin{vmatrix} -1 & 3 \\ 1 & 2 \end{vmatrix} + 2\begin{vmatrix} -1 & 3 \\ -1 & 1 \end{vmatrix}$$

$$= 1(-2 - 1) - 1(-2 - 3) + 2(-1 + 3)$$

$$= 1(-3) - 1(-5) + 2(2)$$

$$= -3 + 5 + 4$$

$$= 6$$

$$a = \frac{D_a}{D} = \frac{-3}{3} = -1, \ b = \frac{D_b}{D} = \frac{0}{3} = 0, \text{ and}$$

$$c = \frac{D_c}{D} = \frac{6}{3} = 2$$

The solution is $(-1, 0, 2)$.

39. $a + 2b + c = 1$
$a - b + c = 1$
$2a + b + 2c = 2$
To solve, first calculate D, D_a, D_b, and D_c.

$$D = \begin{vmatrix} 1 & 2 & 1 \\ 1 & -1 & 1 \\ 2 & 1 & 2 \end{vmatrix}$$

$$= 1\begin{vmatrix} -1 & 1 \\ 1 & 2 \end{vmatrix} - 1\begin{vmatrix} 2 & 1 \\ 1 & 2 \end{vmatrix} + 2\begin{vmatrix} 2 & 1 \\ -1 & 1 \end{vmatrix}$$

$$= 1(-2 - 1) - 1(4 - 1) + 2(2 + 1)$$

$$= 1(-3) - 1(3) + 2(3)$$

$$= -3 - 3 + 6$$

$$= 0$$

$$D_a = \begin{vmatrix} 1 & 2 & 1 \\ 1 & -1 & 1 \\ 2 & 1 & 2 \end{vmatrix}$$

$$= 1\begin{vmatrix} -1 & 1 \\ 1 & 2 \end{vmatrix} - 1\begin{vmatrix} 2 & 1 \\ 1 & 2 \end{vmatrix} + 2\begin{vmatrix} 2 & 1 \\ -1 & 1 \end{vmatrix}$$

$$= 1(-2 - 1) - 1(4 - 1) + 2(2 + 1)$$

$$= 1(-3) - 1(3) + 2(3)$$

$$= -3 - 3 + 6$$

$$= 0$$

$$D_b = \begin{vmatrix} 1 & 1 & 1 \\ 1 & 1 & 1 \\ 2 & 2 & 2 \end{vmatrix}$$

$$= 1\begin{vmatrix} 1 & 1 \\ 2 & 2 \end{vmatrix} - 1\begin{vmatrix} 1 & 1 \\ 2 & 2 \end{vmatrix} + 2\begin{vmatrix} 1 & 1 \\ 1 & 1 \end{vmatrix}$$

$$= 1(2 - 2) - 1(2 - 2) + 2(1 - 1)$$

$$= 1(0) - 1(0) + 2(0)$$

$$= 0 - 0 + 0$$

$$= 0$$

$$D_c = \begin{vmatrix} 1 & 2 & 1 \\ 1 & -1 & 1 \\ 2 & 1 & 2 \end{vmatrix}$$

$$= 1\begin{vmatrix} -1 & 1 \\ 1 & 2 \end{vmatrix} - 1\begin{vmatrix} 2 & 1 \\ 1 & 2 \end{vmatrix} + 2\begin{vmatrix} 2 & 1 \\ -1 & 1 \end{vmatrix}$$

$$= 1(-2-1)-1(4-1)+2(2+1)$$
$$= 1(-3)-1(3)+2(3)$$
$$= -3-3+6$$
$$= 0$$

Since $D = 0$, $D_a = 0$, $D_b = 0$, and $D_c = 0$, there are an infinite number of solutions to the system and it is a dependent system.

41. $1.1x + 2.3y - 4.0z = -9.2$
$-2.3x + 0y + 4.6z = 6.9$
$0x - 8.2y - 7.5z = -6.8$

Here, you can work with decimals in the determinants. If you do not want to use decimals, then you need to multiply each equation by 10 to clear the decimals. To solve, first calculate D, D_x, D_y, and D_z.

$$D = \begin{vmatrix} 1.1 & 2.3 & -4.0 \\ -2.3 & 0 & 4.6 \\ 0 & -8.2 & -7.5 \end{vmatrix}$$

$$= 1.1\begin{vmatrix} 0 & 4.6 \\ -8.2 & -7.5 \end{vmatrix} - (-2.3)\begin{vmatrix} 2.3 & -4.0 \\ -8.2 & -7.5 \end{vmatrix} + 0\begin{vmatrix} 2.3 & -4.0 \\ 0 & 4.6 \end{vmatrix}$$

$$= 1.1(0+37.72)+2.3(-17.25-32.8)+0(10.58-0)$$
$$= 1.1(37.72)+2.3(-50.05)+0(10.58)$$
$$= 41.492-115.115+0$$
$$= -73.623$$

$$D_x = \begin{vmatrix} -9.2 & 2.3 & -4.0 \\ 6.9 & 0 & 4.6 \\ -6.8 & -8.2 & -7.5 \end{vmatrix}$$

$$= -9.2\begin{vmatrix} 0 & 4.6 \\ -8.2 & -7.5 \end{vmatrix} - 6.9\begin{vmatrix} 2.3 & -4.0 \\ -8.2 & -7.5 \end{vmatrix} + (-6.8)\begin{vmatrix} 2.3 & -4.0 \\ 0 & 4.6 \end{vmatrix}$$

$$= -9.2(0+37.72)-6.9(-17.25-32.8)-6.8(10.58-0)$$
$$= -9.2(37.72)-6.9(-50.05)-6.8(10.58)$$
$$= -347.024+345.345-71.944$$
$$= -73.623$$

$$D_y = \begin{vmatrix} 1.1 & -9.2 & -4.0 \\ -2.3 & 6.9 & 4.6 \\ 0 & -6.8 & -7.5 \end{vmatrix}$$

$$= 1.1\begin{vmatrix} 6.9 & 4.6 \\ -6.8 & -7.5 \end{vmatrix} - (-2.3)\begin{vmatrix} -9.2 & -4.0 \\ -6.8 & -7.5 \end{vmatrix} + 0\begin{vmatrix} -9.2 & -4.0 \\ 6.9 & 4.6 \end{vmatrix}$$

$$= 1.1(-51.75+31.28)+2.3(69-27.2)+0(-42.32+27.6)$$
$$= 1.1(-20.47)+2.3(41.8)+0(-14.72)$$
$$= -22.517+96.14+0$$
$$= 73.623$$

$$D_z = \begin{vmatrix} 1.1 & 2.3 & -9.2 \\ -2.3 & 0 & 6.9 \\ 0 & -8.2 & -6.8 \end{vmatrix}$$

$$= 1.1\begin{vmatrix} 0 & 6.9 \\ -8.2 & -6.8 \end{vmatrix} - (-2.3)\begin{vmatrix} 2.3 & -9.2 \\ -8.2 & -6.8 \end{vmatrix} + 0\begin{vmatrix} 2.3 & -9.2 \\ 0 & 6.9 \end{vmatrix}$$

$$= 1.1(0 + 56.58) + 2.3(-15.64 - 75.44) + 0(15.87 - 0)$$

$$= 1.1(56.58) + 2.3(-91.08) + 0(15.87)$$

$$= 62.238 - 209.484 + 0$$

$$= 147.246$$

$x = \dfrac{D_x}{D} = \dfrac{-73.623}{-73.623} = 1$, $y = \dfrac{D_y}{D} = \dfrac{73.623}{-73.623} = -1$, and $z = \dfrac{D_z}{D} = \dfrac{-147.246}{-73.623} = 2$

The solution is $(1, -1, 2)$.

43. $-6x + 3y - 9z = -8$
$5x + 2y - 3z = 1$
$2x - y + 3z = -5$

To solve, first calculate D, D_x, D_y, and D_z.

$$D = \begin{vmatrix} -6 & 3 & -9 \\ 5 & 2 & -3 \\ 2 & -1 & 3 \end{vmatrix} \text{ (using the first row)}$$

$$= -6\begin{vmatrix} 2 & -3 \\ -1 & 3 \end{vmatrix} - 3\begin{vmatrix} 5 & -3 \\ 2 & 3 \end{vmatrix} + (-9)\begin{vmatrix} 5 & 2 \\ 2 & -1 \end{vmatrix}$$

$$= -6(6 - 3) - 3(15 + 6) - 9(-5 - 4)$$

$$= -6(3) - 3(21) - 9(-9)$$

$$= -18 - 63 + 81$$

$$= 0$$

$$D_x = \begin{vmatrix} -8 & 3 & -9 \\ 1 & 2 & -3 \\ -5 & -1 & 3 \end{vmatrix} \text{ (using the first row)}$$

$$= -8\begin{vmatrix} 2 & -3 \\ -1 & 3 \end{vmatrix} - 3\begin{vmatrix} 1 & -3 \\ -5 & 3 \end{vmatrix} + (-9)\begin{vmatrix} 1 & 2 \\ -5 & -1 \end{vmatrix}$$

$$= -8(6 - 3) - 3(3 - 15) - 9(-1 + 10)$$

$$= -8(3) - 3(-12) - 9(9)$$

$$= -24 + 36 - 81$$

$$= -69$$

Since $D = 0$ and $D_x = -69 \neq 0$, there is no solution to the system and it is an inconsistent system.

45. $2x + \dfrac{1}{2}y - 3z = 5$
$-3x + 2y + 2z = 1$
$4x - \dfrac{1}{4}y - 7z = 4$

To clear the system of fractions, multiply the first equation by 2 and the third equation by 4.
$4x + y - 6z = 10$

$-3x + 2y + 2z = 1$

$16x - y - 28z = 16$

To solve, first calculate D, D_x, D_y, and D_z.

$$D = \begin{vmatrix} 4 & 1 & -6 \\ -3 & 2 & 2 \\ 16 & -1 & -28 \end{vmatrix} \text{ (use the first row)}$$

$$= 4\begin{vmatrix} 2 & 2 \\ -1 & -28 \end{vmatrix} - 1\begin{vmatrix} -3 & 2 \\ 16 & -28 \end{vmatrix} + (-6)\begin{vmatrix} -3 & 2 \\ 16 & -1 \end{vmatrix}$$

$$= 4(-56 + 2) - 1(84 - 32) - 6(3 - 32)$$

$$= 4(-54) - 1(52) - 6(-29)$$

$$= -216 - 52 + 174$$

$$= -94$$

$$D_x = \begin{vmatrix} 10 & 1 & -6 \\ 1 & 2 & 2 \\ 16 & -1 & -28 \end{vmatrix} \text{ (use the first row)}$$

$$= 10\begin{vmatrix} 2 & 2 \\ -1 & -28 \end{vmatrix} - 1\begin{vmatrix} 1 & 2 \\ 16 & -28 \end{vmatrix} + (-6)\begin{vmatrix} 1 & 2 \\ 16 & -1 \end{vmatrix}$$

$$= 10(-56 + 2) - 1(-28 - 32) - 6(-1 - 32)$$

$$= 10(-54) - 1(-60) - 6(-33)$$

$$= -540 + 60 + 198$$

$$= -282$$

$$D_y = \begin{vmatrix} 4 & 10 & -6 \\ -3 & 1 & 2 \\ 16 & 16 & -28 \end{vmatrix} \text{ (use the first row)}$$

$$= 4\begin{vmatrix} 1 & 2 \\ 16 & -28 \end{vmatrix} - 10\begin{vmatrix} -3 & 2 \\ 16 & -28 \end{vmatrix} + (-6)\begin{vmatrix} -3 & 1 \\ 16 & 16 \end{vmatrix}$$

$$= 4(-28 - 32) - 10(84 - 32) - 6(-48 - 16)$$

$$= 4(-60) - 10(52) - 6(-64)$$

$$= -240 - 520 + 384$$

$$= -376$$

$$D_z = \begin{vmatrix} 4 & 1 & 10 \\ -3 & 2 & 1 \\ 16 & -1 & 16 \end{vmatrix} \text{ (use the first row)}$$

$$= 4\begin{vmatrix} 2 & 1 \\ -1 & 16 \end{vmatrix} - 1\begin{vmatrix} -3 & 1 \\ 16 & 16 \end{vmatrix} + 10\begin{vmatrix} -3 & 2 \\ 16 & -1 \end{vmatrix}$$

$$= 4(32 + 1) - 1(-48 - 16) + 10(3 - 32)$$

$$= 4(33) - 1(-64) + 10(-29)$$

$$= 132 + 64 - 290$$

$$= -94$$

$$x = \frac{D_x}{D} = \frac{-282}{-94} = 3, \ y = \frac{D_y}{D} = \frac{-376}{-94} = 4,$$

$$z = \frac{D_z}{D} = \frac{-94}{-94} = 1$$

The solution is (3, 4, 1).

47. $0.2x - 0.1y - 0.3z = -0.1$
$0.2x - 0.1y + 0.1z = -0.9$
$0.1x + 0.2y - 0.4z = 1.7$
To clear decimals multiply each equation by 10.
$2x - y - 3x = -1$
$2x - y + z = -9$
$x + 2y - 4z = 17$
To solve, first calculate D, D_x, D_y, and D_z.

$$D = \begin{vmatrix} 2 & -1 & -3 \\ 2 & -1 & 1 \\ 1 & 2 & -4 \end{vmatrix}$$

$$= 2\begin{vmatrix} -1 & 1 \\ 2 & -4 \end{vmatrix} - 2\begin{vmatrix} -1 & -3 \\ 2 & -4 \end{vmatrix} + 1\begin{vmatrix} -1 & -3 \\ -1 & 1 \end{vmatrix}$$

$$= 2(4 - 2) - 2(4 + 6) + 1(-1 - 3)$$

$$= 2(2) - 2(10) + 1(-4)$$

$$= 4 - 20 - 4$$

$$= -20$$

$$D_x = \begin{vmatrix} -1 & -1 & -3 \\ -9 & -1 & 1 \\ 17 & 2 & -4 \end{vmatrix}$$

$$= -1\begin{vmatrix} -1 & 1 \\ 2 & -4 \end{vmatrix} - (-9)\begin{vmatrix} -1 & -3 \\ 2 & -4 \end{vmatrix} + 17\begin{vmatrix} -1 & -3 \\ -1 & 1 \end{vmatrix}$$

$$= -1(4 - 2) + 9(4 + 6) + 17(-1 - 3)$$

$$= -1(2) + 9(10) + 17(-4)$$

$$= -2 + 90 - 68$$

$$= 20$$

$$D_y = \begin{vmatrix} 2 & -1 & -3 \\ 2 & -9 & 1 \\ 1 & 17 & -4 \end{vmatrix}$$

$$= 2\begin{vmatrix} -9 & 1 \\ 17 & -4 \end{vmatrix} - 2\begin{vmatrix} -1 & -3 \\ 17 & -4 \end{vmatrix} + 1\begin{vmatrix} -1 & -3 \\ -9 & 1 \end{vmatrix}$$

$$= 2(36 - 17) - 2(4 + 51) + 1(-1 - 27)$$

$$= 2(19) - 2(55) + 1(-28)$$

$$= 38 - 110 - 28$$

$$= -100$$

$$D_z = \begin{vmatrix} 2 & -1 & -1 \\ 2 & -1 & -9 \\ 1 & 2 & 17 \end{vmatrix}$$

$$= 2\begin{vmatrix} -1 & -9 \\ 2 & 17 \end{vmatrix} - 2\begin{vmatrix} -1 & -1 \\ 2 & 17 \end{vmatrix} + 1\begin{vmatrix} -1 & -1 \\ -1 & -9 \end{vmatrix}$$

$$= 2(-17 + 18) - 2(-17 + 2) + 1(9 - 1)$$

$$= 2(1) - 2(-15) + 1(8)$$

$$= 2 + 30 + 8$$

$$= 40$$

$$x = \frac{D_x}{D} = \frac{20}{-20} = -1, \ y = \frac{D_y}{D} = \frac{-100}{-20} = 5, \text{ and}$$

$$z = \frac{D_z}{D} = \frac{40}{-20} = -2$$

The solution is (-1, 5, -2).

49. $\begin{vmatrix} a_1 & b_1 \\ a_2 & b_2 \end{vmatrix} = a_1 b_2 - a_2 b_1$

$\begin{vmatrix} a_2 & b_2 \\ a_1 & b_1 \end{vmatrix} = a_2 b_1 - a_1 b_2$

The second result is the negative of the first result. Thus, the second determinant has the opposite sign.

51. 0

53. 0

55. Yes, the determinant will become the opposite of the original value.

57.
$$\begin{vmatrix} 4 & 6 \\ -2 & y \end{vmatrix} = 32$$
$$(4)(y) - (-2)(6) = 32$$
$$4y + 12 = 32$$
$$4y = 20$$
$$y = \frac{20}{4} = 5$$

59.
$$\begin{vmatrix} 4 & 7 & y \\ 3 & -1 & 2 \\ 4 & 1 & 5 \end{vmatrix} = -35$$
$$4\begin{vmatrix} -1 & 2 \\ 1 & 5 \end{vmatrix} - 3\begin{vmatrix} 7 & y \\ 1 & 5 \end{vmatrix} + 4\begin{vmatrix} 7 & y \\ -1 & 2 \end{vmatrix} = -35$$
$$4(-5 - 2) - 3(35 - y) + 4(14 + y) = -35$$
$$4(-7) - 3(35 - y) + 4(14 + y) = -35$$
$$-28 - 105 + 3y + 56 + 4y = -35$$
$$-77 + 7y = -35$$
$$7y = 42$$
$$y = 6$$

61. a. To eliminate y, multiply the first equation by b_2 and the second equation by $-b_1$ and then add.
$$b_2[a_1 x + b_1 y = c_1]$$
$$-b_1[a_2 x + b_2 y = c_2]$$
gives
$$a_1 b_2 x + b_1 b_2 y = c_1 b_2$$
$$\underline{-a_2 b_1 x - b_1 b_2 y = -c_2 b_1}$$
Add: $(a_1 b_2 - a_2 b_1)x \quad = c_1 b_2 - c_2 b_1$
$$x = \frac{c_1 b_2 - c_2 b_1}{a_1 b_2 - a_2 b_1}$$

b. To eliminate x, multiply the first equation by $-a_2$ and the second equation by a_1 and then add.
$$-a_2[a_1 x + b_1 y = c_1]$$
$$a_1[a_2 x + b_2 y = c_2]$$
gives
$$-a_1 a_2 x - a_2 b_1 y = -a_2 c_1$$
$$\underline{a_1 a_2 x + a_1 b_2 y = a_1 c_2}$$
Add: $(a_1 b_2 - a_2 b_1)y = a_1 c_2 - a_2 c_1$
$$y = \frac{a_1 c_2 - a_2 c_1}{a_1 b_2 - a_2 b_1}$$

63. $3x + 4y = 8$
Solve for y.
$$4y = -3x + 8$$
$$y = -\frac{3}{4}x + 2$$

x	y
-4	$y = -\frac{3}{4}(-4) + 2 = 3 + 2 = 5$
0	$y = -\frac{3}{4}(0) + 2 = 0 + 2 = 2$
4	$y = -\frac{3}{4}(4) + 2 = -3 + 2 = -1$

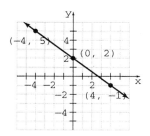

65. $3x + 4y = 8$
Solve for y.
$$4y = -3x + 8$$
$$y = -\frac{3}{4}x + 2$$
The slope is $-\frac{3}{4}$ and the y-intercept is 2.

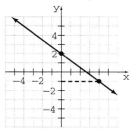

Exercise Set 4.6

1. Answers will vary.

3. Yes, the points along the two boundary lines are ordered pairs which are solutions to both inequalities.

5. $2x - y < 4$

$y \geq -x + 2$

For $2x - y < 4$, graph the line $2x - y = 4$ using a dashed line. For the check point, select $(0, 0)$:
$2x - y < 4$

$2(0) - (0) < 4$

$0 < 4$ True

Since this is a true statement, shade the region which contains the point $(0, 0)$. This is the region "above" the line.

For $y \geq -x + 2$, graph the line
$y = -x + 2$ using a solid line. For the check point, select $(0, 0)$:
$y \geq -x + 2$

$(0) \geq -(0) + 2$

$0 \geq 2$ False

Since this is a false statement, shade the region which does not contain the point $(0, 0)$. This is the region "above" the line. To obtain the final region, take the intersection of the above two regions.

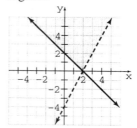

7. $y < 3x - 2$

$y \leq -2x + 3$

For $y < 3x - 2$, graph the line $y = 3x - 2$ using a dashed line. For the check point, select $(0, 0)$:
$y < 3x - 2$

$(0) < 3(0) - 2$

$0 < -2$ False

Since this is a false statement, shade the region which does not contain the point $(0, 0)$. This is the region "below" the line.

For $y \leq -2x + 3$, graph the line $y = -2x + 3$ using a solid line. For the check point, select $(0, 0)$:
$y \leq -2x + 3$

$(0) \leq -2(0) + 3$

$0 \leq 3$ True

Since this is a true statement, shade the region which contains the point $(0, 0)$. This is the region "below" the line. To obtain the final region, take

the intersection of the above two regions.

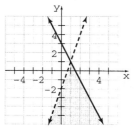

9. $y < x$

$y \geq 3x + 2$

For $y < x$, graph the line $y = x$ using a dashed line. For the check point, select $(1, 0)$:
$y < x$

$0 < 1$ True

Since this is a true statement, shade the region which contains the point $(1, 0)$. This is the region "below" the line.

For $y \geq 3x + 2$, graph the line $y = 3x + 2$ using a solid line. For the check point, select $(0, 0)$:
$y \geq 3x + 2$

$(0) \geq 3(0) + 2$

$0 \geq 2$ False

Since this is a false statement, shade the region which does not contain the point $(0, 0)$. This is the region "above" the line. To obtain the final region, take the intersection of the above two regions.

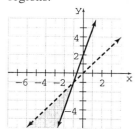

11. $-3x + 2y \geq -5$

$y \leq -4x + 7$

For $-3x + 2y \geq -5$, graph the line $-3x + 2y = -5$ using a solid line. For the check point, select $(0, 0)$:
$-3x + 2y \geq -5$

$-3(0) + 2(0) \geq -5$

$0 \geq -5$ True

Since this is a true statement, shade the region which contains the point $(0, 0)$. This is the region "above" the line.

    For $y \leq -4x + 7$, graph the line $y = -4x + 7$ using a solid line. For the check point, select $(0, 0)$:

$y \le -4x + 7$

$(0) \le -4(0) + 7$

$0 \le 7$ True

Since this is a true statement, shade the region which contains the point (0, 0). This is the region "below" the line.

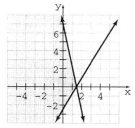

13. $-4x + 5y < 20$

$x \ge -3$

For $-4x + 5y < 20$, graph the line $-4x + 5y = 20$ using a dashed line. For the check point, select (0, 0):

$-4x + 5y < 20$

$-4(0) + 5(0) < 20$

$0 < 20$ True

Since this is a true statement, shade the region which contains the point (0, 0). This is the region "below" the line.

For $x \ge -3$, the graph is the line $x = -3$ along with the region to the right of $x = -3$. To obtain the final region, take the intersection of the above two regions.

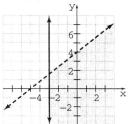

15. $x \le 4$

$y \ge -2$

For $x \le 4$, the graph is the line $x = 4$ along with the region to the left of $x = 4$. For $y \ge -2$, the graph is the line $y = -2$ along with the region above the line $y = -2$. To obtain the final region, take the intersection of the above two regions.

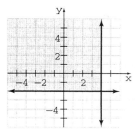

17. $5x + 2y > 10$

$3x - y > 3$

For $5x + 2y > 10$, graph the line $5x + 2y = 10$ using a dashed line. For the check point, select (0, 0):

$5x + 2y > 10$

$5(0) + 2(0) > 10$

$0 > 10$ False

Since this is a false statement, shade the region which does not contain the point (0, 0). This is the region "above" the line.

For $3x - y > 3$, graph the line $3x - y = 3$ using a dashed line. For the check point, select (0, 0):

$3x - y > 3$

$3(0) - 0 > 3$

$0 > 3$ False

Since this is a false statement, shade the region which does not contain the point (0, 0). This is the region "below" the line. To obtain the final region, take the intersection of the above two regions.

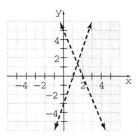

19. $-2x > y + 4$

$-x < \dfrac{1}{2}y - 1$

For $-2x > y + 4$, graph the line $-2x = y + 4$ using a dashed line. For the check point, select (0, 0):

$-2x > y + 4$

$-2(0) > 0 + 4$

$0 > 4$ False

Since this is a false statement, shade the region which does not contain the point (0, 0). This is the region "below" the line.

For $-x < \dfrac{1}{2}y - 1$, graph the line $-x = \dfrac{1}{2}y - 1$ using a dashed line. For the check point, select (0, 0):

$-x < \dfrac{1}{2}y - 1$

$-0 < \dfrac{1}{2}(0) - 1$

$0 < -1$ \qquad False

Since this is a false statement, shade the region which does not contain the point (0, 0). This is the region "above" the line. To obtain the final region take the intersection of the above two regions. Since the regions do not overlap, the final result is the empty set which means there is no solution.

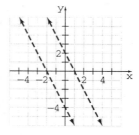

21. $y < 3x - 4$

$6x \geq 2y + 8$

Solve the second inequality for y.

$\quad 6x \geq 2y + 8$

$6x - 2y > 8$

$\quad -2y \geq -6x + 8$

$\quad\quad y \leq 3x - 4$

The second inequality is now identical to the first except that the second inequality includes the line.

For $y < 3x - 4$, graph the line $y = 3x - 4$ using a dashed line. For the check point, select (0, 0):

$y < 3x - 4$

$0 < 3(0) - 4$

$0 < -4$ \qquad False

Since this is a false statement, shade the region which does not contain the point (0, 0). This is the region "below" the line.

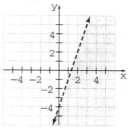

23. $x \geq 0$

$y \geq 0$

$2x + 3y \leq 6$

$4x + y \leq 4$

The first two inequalities indicate that the region

must be in the first quadrant. For $2x + 3y \leq 6$, the graph is the line $2x + 3y = 6$ along with the region below this line. For $4x + y \leq 4$, the graph is the line $4x + y = 4$ along with the region below this line. To obtain the final region, take the intersection of these regions.

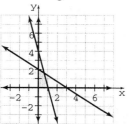

25. $x \geq 0$

$y \geq 0$

$x + y \leq 6$

$7x + 4y \leq 28$

The first two inequalities indicate that the region must be in the first quadrant. For $x + y \leq 6$, the graph is the line $x + y = 6$ along with the region below this line. For $7x + 4y \leq 28$, the graph is the line $7x + 4y = 28$ along with the region below the line. To obtain the final region, take the intersection of these regions.

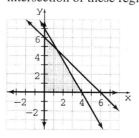

27. $x \geq 0$

$y \geq 0$

$3x + 2y \leq 18$

$2x + 4y \leq 20$

The first two inequalities indicate that the region must be in the first quadrant.
For $3x + 2y \leq 18$, the graph is the line $3x + 2y = 18$ along with the region below this line. For $2x + 4y \leq 20$, the graph is the line $2x + 4y = 20$ along with the region below the line. To obtain the final region, take the intersection of these regions. The final answer is

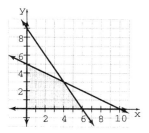

29. $x \geq 0$

$y \geq 0$

$x \leq 4$

$x + y \leq 6$

$x + 2y \leq 8$

The first two inequalities indicate that the region must be in the first quadrant. The third inequality indicates that the region must be on or to the left of the line $x = 4$. For $x + y \leq 6$, the graph is the line $x + y = 6$ along with the region below this line. For $x + 2y \leq 8$, the graph is the line $x + 2y = 8$ along with the region below the line. To obtain the final region, take the intersection of these regions.

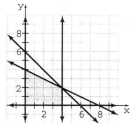

31. $x \geq 0$

$y \geq 0$

$x \leq 15$

$40x + 25y \leq 1000$

$5x + 30y \leq 900$

The first two inequalities indicate that the region must be in the first quadrant. The third inequality indicates that the region must be on or to the left of the line $x = 15$. For $40x + 25y \leq 1000$, the graph is the line $40x + 25y = 1000$ along with the region below this line. For $5x + 30y \leq 900$, the graph is the line $5x + 30y = 900$ along with the region below this line. To obtain the final region, take the intersection of these regions.

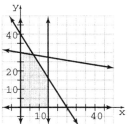

33. $|x| > 1$

$y < x$

For $|x| > 1$, the graph is the region to the right of the dashed line $x = 1$ and to the left of the dashed lines $x = -1$. For $y < x$, the graph is the region below the dashed line $y = x$. To obtain the final region, take the intersection of the above two regions.

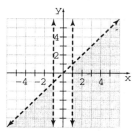

35. $|x| \geq 1$

$|y| \geq 2$

For $|x| \geq 1$, the graph is the region to the left of the solid line $x = -1$ along with the region to the right of the solid line $x = 1$. For $|y| \geq 2$, the graph is the region above the solid line $y = 2$ along with the region below the solid line $y = -2$. To obtain the final region, take the intersection of these regions.

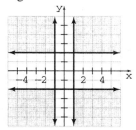

37. $|y| > 2$

$y \leq x + 3$

For $|y| > 2$, the graph is the region above the dashed line $y = 2$ along with the region below the dashed line $y = -2$. For $y \leq x + 3$, the graph is the region below the solid line $y = x + 3$. To obtain the final region, take the intersection of these regions.

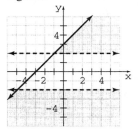

39. $|y| < 4$

$y \geq -2x + 2$

For $|y| < 4$, the graph is the region between the dashed lines $y = -4$ and $y = 4$. For $y \geq -2x + 2$, the graph is the region above the solid line $y = -2x + 2$. To obtain the final region, take the intersection of these regions.

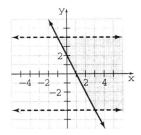

41. $|x + 2| < 3$

$|y| > 4$

$|x + 2| < 3$ can be written as

$-3 < x + 2 < 3$

$-5 < x < 1$

For $|x + 2| < 3$, the graph is the region between the dashed lines $x = -5$ and $x = 1$. For $|y| > 4$, the graph is the region above the dashed line $y = 4$ along with the region below the dashed line $y = -4$. To obtain the final region, take the intersection of these regions.

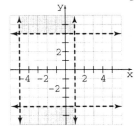

43. $|x - 3| \leq 4$

$|y + 2| \leq 1$

$|x - 3| \leq 4$ can be written as

$-4 \leq x - 3 \leq 4$

$-1 \leq x \leq 7$

For $|x - 3| \leq 4$, the graph is the region between the solid lines $x = -1$ and $x = 7$.

$|y + 2| \leq 1$ can be written as

$-1 \leq y + 2 \leq 1$

$-3 \leq y \leq -1$

For $|y + 2| \leq 1$, the graph is the region between the solid lines $y = -3$ and $y = -1$. To obtain the final region, take the intersection of these

regions.

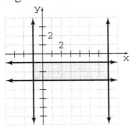

45. If the boundary lines are parallel, there may be no solution. For example, the system $y < x$ and $y > x + 1$ has no solution.

47. There are no solutions. Opposite sides of the same line are being shaded, but not the line itself.

49. There are an infinite number of solutions. Both inequalities include the line $5x - 2y = 3$.

51. There are an infinite number of solutions. The lines are parallel but the same side of each line is being shaded.

53 $y \geq x^2$

$y \leq 4$

For $y \geq x^2$, graph the equation $y = x^2$ using a solid line. For the check point, select $(0, 1)$.

$y \geq x^2$

$(1) \geq (0)^2$

$1 \geq 0$ True

Since this is a true statement, shade the region which contains the point $(0, 1)$. This is the region "above" the graph of $y \geq x^2$.

For $y \leq 4$, the graph is the region below the solid line $y = 4$. To obtain the final region, take the intersection of these regions.

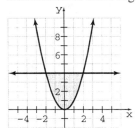

55. $y < |x|$

$y < 4$

For $y < |x|$, graph the equation $y = |x|$ using a dashed line. For the check point, select $(0, 3)$.

$y < |x|$

$3 < |0|$

$3 < 0$ False

Since this is a false statement, shade the region which does not contain the point (0, 3). This is the region below the graph of $y = |x|$.

For $y < 4$, the graph is the region below the dashed line $y = 4$. To obtain the final region, take the intersection of these regions.

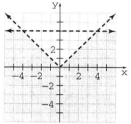

57.

$$f_1d_1 + f_2d_2 = f_3d_3$$
$$f_1d_1 - f_1d_1 + f_2d_2 = f_3d_3 - f_1d_1$$
$$f_2d_2 = f_3d_3 - f_1d_1$$
$$\frac{f_2d_2}{d_2} = \frac{f_3d_3 - f_1d_1}{d_2}$$
$$f_2 = \frac{f_3d_3 - f_1d_1}{d_2}$$

59. Domain: R
     Range: R

Review Exercises

1. Write each equation in slope-intercept form.

$$2x - 3y = -1 \qquad -4x + 6y = 1$$
$$-3y = -2x - 1 \qquad 6y = 4x + 1$$
$$y = \frac{2}{3}x + \frac{1}{3} \qquad y = \frac{2}{3}x + \frac{1}{6}$$

Since the slope of each line is $\frac{2}{3}$ but the y-intercepts are different ($b = \frac{1}{3}$ for first equation, $b = \frac{1}{6}$ for second equation), the two lines are parallel and produce no solution. This is an inconsistent system.

2. Both equations are already written in slope-intercept form.

$$y = -4x + 2$$
$$y = 3x - 12$$

Since the slope of the first line is –4 and the slope of the second line is 3, the slopes are

different so that the lines intersect to produce one solution. This is a consistent system.

3. Write each equation in slope-intercept form.

$y = \frac{1}{2}x + 4$ is already in this form.

$$x + 2y = 8$$
$$2y = -x + 8$$
$$y = -\frac{1}{2}x + 4$$

Since the slope of the first line is $\frac{1}{2}$ and the slope of the second line is $-\frac{1}{2}$, the slopes are different so that the lines intersect to produce one solution. This is a consistent system.

4. Write each equation in slope-intercept form.

$$6x = 4y - 8 \qquad\qquad 4" = 6" + 8$$
$$6x + 8 = 4y \qquad\qquad 4" - 8 = 6"$$
$$\frac{6x + 8}{4} = y \qquad\qquad \frac{4" - 8}{6} = "$$
$$\frac{3}{2}x + 2 = y \qquad\qquad \frac{2}{3}" - \frac{4}{3} = "$$

Since the slope of the first line is $\frac{3}{2}$ and the slope of the second line is $\frac{2}{3}$, the slopes are different so that the lines intersect to produce one solution. This is a consistent system.

5. Graph the equations $y = x + 3$ and $y + 2x + 5$.

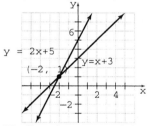

The lines intersect and the point of intersection is (–2, 1).

6. Graph the equations $x = -2$ and $y = 3$.

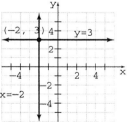

The lines intersect and the point of intersection is (–2, 3).

7. Graph the equations $2x + 2y = 8$ and
   $2x - y = -4$.

   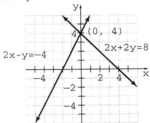

   The lines intersect and the point of intersection is
   $(0, 4)$.

8. Graph the equations $2y = 2x - 6$ and
   $\frac{1}{2}x - \frac{1}{2}y = \frac{3}{2}$.

   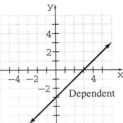

   Both equations produce the same line. This is a
   dependent system.

9. $y = -4x + 2$

   $y = 3x - 12$

   Substitute $3x - 12$ for y in the first equation.
   $$y = -4x + 2$$
   $$3x - 12 = -4x + 2$$
   $$7x - 12 = 2$$
   $$7x = 14$$
   $$x = 2$$
   Now, substitute 2 for x in the first equation.
   $$y = -4x + 2$$
   $$y = -4(2) + 2$$
   $$y = -8 + 2$$
   $$y = -6$$
   The solution is $(2, -6)$.

10. $4x - 3y = -1$

    $y = -3x - 4$

    Substitute $-3x - 4$ for y in the first equation.
    $$4x - 3(-3x - 4) = -1$$
    $$4x + 9x + 12 = -1$$
    $$13x + 13 = -1$$
    $$13x = -13$$
    $$x = -1$$

Now, substitute -1 for x in the second equation.
$$y = -3x - 4$$
$$y = -3(-1) - 4$$
$$y = 3 - 4$$
$$y = -1$$
The solution is $(-1, -1)$.

11. $a = 2b - 8$
        $2b - 5a = 0$
    Substitute $2b - 8$ for a in the second equation.
    $$2b - 5a = 0$$
    $$2b - 5(2b - 8) = 0$$
    $$2b - 10b + 40 = 0$$
    $$-8b + 40 = 0$$
    $$-8b = -40$$
    $$b = \frac{-40}{-8} = 5$$
    Now, substitute 5 for b in the first equation.
    $$a = 2b - 8$$
    $$a = 2(5) - 8$$
    $$a = 10 - 8$$
    $$a = 2$$
    The solution is $(2, 5)$.

12. $3x + y = 17$
        $\frac{1}{2}x - \frac{3}{4}y = 1$
    First multiply the second equation by 4 to
    eliminate fractions.
    $$3x + y = 17$$
    $$4\left(\frac{1}{2}x - \frac{3}{4}y = 1\right)$$
    gives
    $3x + y = 17 \leftarrow$ first equation
    $2x - 3y = 4 \leftarrow$ second equation
    Now, solve the first equation for y.
    $$3x + y = 17$$
    $$y = -3x + 17$$
    Substitute $-3x + 17$ for y in the second equation.
    $$2x - 3y = 4$$
    $$2x - 3(-3x + 17) = 4$$
    $$2x + 9x - 51 = 4$$
    $$11x - 51 = 4$$
    $$11x = 55$$
    $$x = \frac{55}{11} = 5$$
    Finally, substitute 5 for x in the equation

$y = -3x + 17.$
$y = -3x + 17$
$y = -3(5) + 17$
$y = -15 + 17$
$y = 2$
The solution is $(5, 2)$.

13.

$$x - 2y = 5$$
$$2x + 2y = 4$$

Add: $3x \quad\quad = 9$

$$x = 3$$

Substitute 3 for x in the first equation.
$(3) - 2y = 5$
$\quad -2y = 2$
$\quad\quad y = -1$
The solution is $(3, -1)$.

14.

$$-2x - y = 5$$
$$2x + 2y = 6$$

Add: $y = 11$

Substitute 11 for y in the first equation.
$-2x - (11) = 5$
$\quad\quad -2x = 16$
$\quad\quad\quad x = -8$
The solution is $(-8, 11)$.

15. $2a + 3b = 7$

$a - 2b = -7$
To eliminate a, multiply the second equation by
-2 and then add.
$2a + 3b = 7$
$-2[a - 2b = -7]$
gives

$$2a + 3b = 7$$
$$-2a + 4b = 14$$

Add: $7b = 21$

$$b = 3$$

Substitute 3 for b in the second equation.
$a - 2(3) = -7$
$\quad a - 6 = -7$
$\quad\quad a = -1$
The solution is $(-1, 3)$.

16. $0.4x - 0.3y = 1.8$

$-0.7x + 0.5y = -3.1$
To eliminate y, multiply the first equation by 5
and the second equation by 3 and then add.

$5[0.4x - 0.3y = 1.8]$
$3[-0.7x + 0.5y = -3.1]$
gives

$$2.0x - 1.5y = 9$$
$$-2.1x + 1.5y = -9.3$$

Add: $-0.1x \quad\quad = -0.3$

$$x = \frac{-0.3}{-0.1} = 3$$

Substitute 3 for x in the first equation.
$0.4(3) - 0.3y = 1.8$
$\quad 1.2 - 0.3y = 1.8$
$\quad\quad -0.3y = 0.6$
$$y = \frac{0.6}{-0.3}$$
$\quad\quad y = -2$
The solution is $(3, -2)$.

17. $4r - 3s = 8$

$2r + 5s = 8$
To eliminate r, multiply the second equation by
-2 and then add.
$4r - 3s = 8$
$-2[2r + 5s = 8]$
gives

$$4r - 3s = 8$$
$$-4r - 10s = -16$$

Add: $-13s = -8$

$$s = \frac{-8}{-13} = \frac{8}{13}$$

Substitute $\dfrac{8}{13}$ for s in the first equation.
$4r - 3s = 8$
$$4r - 3\left(\frac{8}{13}\right) = 8$$
$$4r - \frac{24}{13} = 8$$
$$4r = 8 + \frac{24}{13}$$
$$4r = \frac{104}{13} + \frac{24}{13}$$
$$4r = \frac{128}{13}$$
$$r = \frac{128}{13} \cdot \frac{1}{4}$$
$$r = \frac{32}{13}$$

The solution is $\left(\dfrac{32}{15}, \dfrac{8}{13}\right)$.

18. $-2m + 3n = 15$
$\quad\;\; 3m + 3n = 10$
To eliminate n, multiply the second equation by -1 and then add.
$\quad -2m + 3n = 15$
$\quad -1[3m + 3n = 10]$
gives
$\qquad\quad -2m + 3n = \;\;\; 15$
$\qquad\quad \underline{-3m - 3n = -10}$
Add: $\;\; -5m \qquad\;\; = \;\;\; 5$
$$m = \frac{5}{-5} = -1$$
Substitute -1 for m in the second equation.
$\quad 3m + 3n = 10$
$\quad 3(-1) + 3n = 10$
$\quad\;\; -3 + 3n = 10$
$\qquad\quad 3n = 13$
$$n = \frac{13}{3}$$
The solution is $\left(-1, \dfrac{13}{3}\right)$.

19. $x + \dfrac{2}{5}y = \dfrac{9}{5}$
$\quad x - \dfrac{3}{2}y = -2$
To clear fractions and to eliminate x, multiply the first equation by 10 and the second equation by -10 and then add.
$$10\left(x + \frac{2}{5}y = \frac{9}{5}\right)$$
$$-10\left(x - \frac{3}{2}y = -2\right)$$
gives
$\qquad\quad 10x + \;\; 4y = 18$
$\qquad\quad \underline{-10x + 15y = 20}$
Add: $\qquad\quad 19y = 38$
$\qquad\qquad\quad\; y = 2$
Now substitute 2 for y in the equation
$10x + 4y = 18$.
$\quad 10x + 4y = 18$
$\quad 10x + 4(2) = 18$
$\quad\;\; 10x + 8 = 18$
$\qquad\;\; 10x = 10$
$\qquad\qquad x = 1$
The solution is $(1, 2)$.

20. $2x + 2y = 8$
$\qquad\;\; y = 4x - 3$
Write the system in standard form and divide the first equation by 2.
$\quad x + y = 4$
$\quad -4x + y = -3$

To eliminate x, multiply the first equation by 4 and then add.
$\quad 4[x + y = 4]$
$\quad -4x + y = -3$
gives
$\qquad\quad 4x + 4y = 16$
$\qquad\quad \underline{-4x + \;\; y = -3}$
Add: $\qquad\;\; 5y = 13$
$$y = \frac{13}{5}$$
Substitute $\dfrac{13}{5}$ for y in the first equation.
$\quad x + y = 4$
$\quad x + \dfrac{13}{5} = 4$
$\qquad\quad x = 4 - \dfrac{13}{5}$
$\qquad\quad x = \dfrac{20}{5} - \dfrac{13}{5}$
$\qquad\quad x = \dfrac{7}{5}$
The solution is $\left(\dfrac{7}{5}, \dfrac{13}{5}\right)$.

21. $\qquad y = -\dfrac{3}{4}x + \dfrac{5}{2}$
$\quad x + \dfrac{5}{4}y = \dfrac{7}{2}$
Write the system in standard form.
$\quad \dfrac{3}{4}x + y = \dfrac{5}{2}$
$\quad x + \dfrac{5}{4}y = \dfrac{7}{2}$
To clear fractions and to eliminate x, multiply the first equation by 16 and the second equation by -12 and then add.
$$16\left[\frac{3}{4}x + y = \frac{5}{2}\right]$$
$$-12\left[x + \frac{5}{4}y = \frac{7}{2}\right]$$
gives
$\qquad\quad 12x + 16y = \;\;\; 40$
$\qquad\quad \underline{-12x - 15y = -42}$
Add: $\qquad\qquad\quad y = -2$
Now, substitute -2 for y in the equation
$x + \dfrac{5}{4}y = \dfrac{7}{2}$ and then solve for x.

$$x + \frac{5}{4}y = \frac{7}{2}$$

$$x + \frac{5}{4}(-2) = \frac{7}{2}$$

$$x - \frac{5}{2} = \frac{7}{2}$$

$$x = \frac{5}{2} + \frac{7}{2}$$

$$x = \frac{12}{2}$$

$$x = 6$$

The solution is $(6, -2)$.

22. $2x - 5y = 12$

$$x - \frac{4}{3}y = -2$$

To clear fractions and to eliminate x, multiply the first equation by -3 and the second equation by 6 and then add.

$$-3[2x - 5y = 12]$$

$$6\left[x - \frac{4}{3}y = -2\right]$$

gives

$$\begin{aligned} -6x + 15y &= -36 \\ 6x - 8y &= -12 \end{aligned}$$

Add: $7y = -48$

$$y = -\frac{48}{7}$$

Now substitute $-\frac{48}{7}$ for y in the first equation.

$$2x - 5y = 12$$

$$2x - 5\left(-\frac{48}{7}\right) = 12$$

$$2x + \frac{240}{7} = 12$$

$$2x = 12 - \frac{240}{7}$$

$$2x = \frac{84}{7} - \frac{240}{7}$$

$$2x = -\frac{156}{7}$$

$$x = \frac{1}{2}\left(-\frac{156}{7}\right) = -\frac{78}{7}$$

The solution is $\left(-\frac{78}{7}, -\frac{48}{7}\right)$.

23. $2x + y = 4$

$$x + \frac{1}{2}y = 2$$

To eliminate y, multiply the second equation by -2 and then add.

$$2x + y = 4$$

$$-2\left[x + \frac{1}{2}y = 2\right]$$

gives

$$\begin{aligned} 2x + y &= 4 \\ -2x - y &= -4 \end{aligned}$$

Add: $0 = 0$ True

The system has an infinite number of solutions.

24. $2x = 4y + 5$

$$2y = x - 6$$

Write the system in standard form.

$$2x - 4y = 5$$

$$-x + 2y = -6$$

To eliminate x, multiply the second equation by 2 and then add.

$$2x - 4y = 5$$

$$2[-x + 2y = -6]$$

gives

$$\begin{aligned} 2x - 4y &= 5 \\ -2x + 4y &= -12 \end{aligned}$$

Add: $0 = -7$ False

Since this a false statement, there is no solution to the system. The system is inconsistent.

25.

$$\begin{aligned} x - 2y - 4z &= 13 && (1) \\ 3y + 2z &= -2 && (2) \\ 5z &= -20 && (3) \end{aligned}$$

Solve equation (3) for z.

$$5z = -20$$

$$z = -4$$

Substitute -4 for z in equation (2).

$$3y + 2(-4) = -2$$

$$3y - 8 = -2$$

$$3y = 6$$

$$y = 2$$

Substitute -4 for z and 2 for y in equation (1).

$$x - 2(2) - 4(-4) = 13$$

$$x - 4 + 16 = 13$$

$$x + 12 = 13$$

$$x = 1$$

The solution is $(1, 2, -4)$.

26.
$$2a + b - 2c = 5$$
$$3b + 4c = 1$$
$$3c = -6$$
Solve the third equation for c.
$$3c = -6$$
$$c = -2$$
Substitute -2 for c in the second equation.
$$3b + 4(-2) = 1$$
$$3b - 8 = 1$$
$$3b = 9$$
$$b = 3$$
Substitute 3 for b and -2 for c in the first equation.
$$2a + (3) - 2(-2) = 5$$
$$2a + 3 + 4 = 5$$
$$2a + 7 = 5$$
$$2a = -2$$
$$a = -1$$
The solution is $(-1, 3, -2)$.

27.
$$x + 2y + 3z = 3 \quad (1)$$
$$-2x - 3y - z = 5 \quad (2)$$
$$4x + 2y + 5z = -8 \quad (3)$$
To eliminate x between equations (1) and (2), multiply equation (1) by 2 and then add.
$$2[x + 2y + 3z = 3]$$
$$-2x - 3y - z = 5$$
gives
$$2x + 4y + 6z = 6$$
$$\underline{-2x - 3y - z = 5}$$
Add: $\qquad y + 5z = 11 \quad (4)$
To eliminate x between equations (2) and (3), multiply equation (2) by 2 and then add.
$$2[-2x - 3y - z = 5]$$
$$4x + 2y + 5z = -8$$
gives
$$-4x - 6y - 2z = 10$$
$$\underline{4x + 2y + 5z = -8}$$
Add: $\quad -4y + 3z = 2 \quad (5)$
Equations (4) and (5) are two equations in two unknowns.
$$y + 5z = 11 \quad (4)$$
$$-4y + 3z = 2 \quad (5)$$
To eliminate y, multiply equation (4) by 4 and then add.
$$4[y + 5z = 11]$$
$$-4y + 3z = 2$$
gives

28.
$$4y + 20z = 44$$
$$\underline{-4y + 3z = 2}$$
Add: $\qquad 23z = 46$
$$z = 2$$
Substitute 2 for z in equation (4).
$$y + 5(2) = 11$$
$$y + 10 = 11$$
$$y = 1$$
Finally, substitute 1 for y and 2 for z in equation (1).
$$x + 2(1) + 3(2) = 3$$
$$x + 2 + 6 = 3$$
$$x + 8 = 3$$
$$x = -5$$
The solution is $(-5, 1, 2)$.

$$-x - 4y + 2z = 1 \quad (1)$$
$$2x + 2y + z = 0 \quad (2)$$
$$-3x - 2y - 5z = 5 \quad (3)$$
To eliminate y between equations (1) and (2), multiply equation (2) by 2 and add.
$$-x - 4y + 2z = 1$$
$$2[2x + 2y + z = 0]$$
gives
$$-x - 4y + 2z = 1$$
$$\underline{4x + 4y + 2z = 0}$$
Add: $\quad 3x + 4z = 1 \quad (4)$
To eliminate y between equations (2) and (3), simply add.
$$2x + 2y + z = 0$$
$$\underline{-3x - 2y - 5z = 5}$$
Add: $\quad -x - 4z = 5 \quad (5)$
Equations (4) and (5) are two equations in two unknowns.
$$3x + 4z = 1 \quad (4)$$
$$-x - 4z = 5 \quad (5)$$
To eliminate z, simply add equations (4) and (5).
$$3x + 4z = 1$$
$$\underline{-x - 4z = 5}$$
Add: $\quad 2x = 6$
$$x = 3$$
Substitute 3 for x in equation (4).
$$3(3) + 4z = 1$$
$$9 + 4z = 1$$
$$4z = -8$$
$$z = -2$$
Finally, substitute 3 for x and -2 for z in equation

(1).
$$-(3) - 4y + 2(-2) = 1$$
$$-3 - 4y - 4 = 1$$
$$-7 - 4y = 1$$
$$-4y = 8$$
$$y = -2$$
The solution is $(3, -2, -2)$.

29. $3y - 2z = -4$ (1)
$3x - 5z = -7$ (2)
$2x + y = 6$ (3)
To eliminate y between equations (1) and (3), multiply equation (3) by -3 and then add.
$$3y - 2z = -4$$
$$-3[2x + y = 6]$$
gives
$$\begin{array}{r} 3y - 2z = -4 \\ -6x - 3y \quad\quad = -18 \\ \hline \end{array}$$
Add: $-6x \quad - 2z = -22$
or
$-3x - z = -11$ (4)
Equations (4) and (2) are two equations into two unknowns. To eliminate x, simply add.
$$\begin{array}{r} 3x - 5z = -7 \\ -3x - \; z = -11 \\ \hline \end{array}$$
Add: $\quad\quad -6z = -18$
$$z = 3$$
Substitute 3 for z in equation (2).
$$3x - 5z = -7$$
$$3x - 5(3) = -7$$
$$3x - 15 = -7$$
$$3x = 8$$
$$x = \frac{8}{3}$$
Substitute $\frac{8}{3}$ for x in equation (3).
$$2x + y = 6$$
$$2\left(\frac{8}{3}\right) + y = 6$$
$$\frac{16}{3} + y = 6$$
$$y = 6 - \frac{16}{3}$$
$$y = \frac{18}{3} - \frac{16}{3}$$
$$y = \frac{2}{3}$$
The solution is $\left(\frac{8}{3}, \frac{2}{3}, 3\right)$.

30. $3a + 2b - 5c = 19$ (1)
$2a - 3b + 3c = -15$ (2)
$5a - 4b - 2c = -2$ (3)
To eliminate b between equations (1) and (2), multiply equation (1) by 3 and equation (2) by 2 and then add.
$3[3a + 2b - 5c = 19]$
$2[2a - 3b + 3c = -15]$
gives
$$\begin{array}{r} 9a + 6b - 15c = 57 \\ 4a - 6b + 6c = -30 \\ \hline \end{array}$$
Add: $13a \quad\quad - 9c = 27$ (4)
To eliminate b between equations (1) and (3), multiply equation (1) by 2 and then add.
$2[3a + 2b - 5c = 19]$
$5a - 4b - 2c = -2$
gives
$$\begin{array}{r} 6a + 4b - 10c = 38 \\ 5a - 4b - 2c = -2 \\ \hline \end{array}$$
Add: $11a \quad\quad - 12c = 36$ (5)
Equations (4) and (5) are two equations into two unknowns.
$13a - 9c = 27$
$11a - 12c = 36$
To eliminate c, multiply equation (4) by 4 and equation (5) by -3 and then add.
$4[13a - 9c = 27]$
$-3[11a - 12c = 36]$
gives
$$\begin{array}{r} 52a - 36c = 108 \\ -33a + 36c = -108 \\ \hline \end{array}$$
Add: $19a \quad\quad = 0$
$$a = 0$$
Substitute 0 for a in equation (4).
$$13a - 9c = 27$$
$$13(0) - 9c = 27$$
$$-9c = 27$$
$$c = \frac{27}{-9} = -3$$
Finally, substitute 0 for a and -3 for c in equation (1).
$$3a + 2b - 5c = 19$$
$$3(0) + 2b - 5(-3) = 19$$
$$0 + 2a + 15 = 19$$
$$2a + 15 = 19$$
$$2a = 4$$
$$a = \frac{4}{2} = 2$$
The solution is $(0, 2, -3)$.

31.
$$x - y + 3z = 1 \quad (1)$$
$$-x + 2y - 2z = 1 \quad (2)$$
$$x - 3y + z = 2 \quad (3)$$

To eliminate x between equations (1) and (2), simply add.
$$x - y + 3z = 1$$
$$\underline{-x + 2y - 2z = 1}$$
Add: $\quad y + z = 2 \quad (4)$

To eliminate x between equations (2) and (3), simply add.
$$-x + 2y - 2z = 1$$
$$\underline{x - 3y + z = 2}$$
Add: $-y - z = 3 \quad (5)$

Equations (4) and (5) are two equations in two unknowns. To eliminate y and z simply add.
$$y + z = 2$$
$$\underline{-y - z = 3}$$
Add: $\quad 0 = 5 \quad$ False

Since this is a false statement, there is no solution to the system. This is an inconsistent system.

32. $-2x + 2y - 3z = 6 \quad (1)$
$\quad 4x - y + 2z = -2 \quad (2)$
$\quad 2x + y - z = 4 \quad (3)$

To eliminate x between equations (1) and (2), multiply equation (1) by 2 and then add.
$$2[-2x + 2y - 3z = 6]$$
$$4x - y + 2z = -2$$
gives
$$-4x + 4y - 6z = 12$$
$$\underline{4x - y + 2z = -2}$$
Add: $\quad 3y - 4z = 10 \quad (4)$

To eliminate x between equations (1) and (3), simply add.
$$-2x + 2y - 3z = 6$$
$$\underline{2x + y - z = 4}$$
Add: $\quad 3y - 4z = 10 \quad (5)$

Equations (4) and (5) are two equations in two unknowns.
$$3y - 4z = 10$$
$$3y - 4z = 10$$
Since they are identical, there are an infinite number of solutions. This is a dependent system.

33. Let x be Jennifer's age and y be Dennis' age.
$$y = x + 10$$
$$x + y = 66$$
Substitute $x + 10$ for y in the second equation.

$$x + (x + 10) = 66$$
$$2x + 10 = 66$$
$$2x = 56$$
$$x = 28$$
Now substitute 28 for x in the first equation.
$$y = (28) + 10$$
$$y = 38$$
Jennifer is 28 years old and Dennis is 38 years old.

34. Let x be the speed of the plane in still air and y be the speed of the wind.
$$x + y = 560$$
$$x - y = 480$$
To eliminate y, simply add.
$$x + y = 560$$
$$\underline{x - y = 480}$$
Add: $2x = 1040$
$\quad\quad x = 520$
Substitute 520 for x in the first equation.
$$x + y = 560$$
$$(520) + y = 560$$
$$y = 40$$
The speed of the plane in still air is 520 mph and the speed of the wind is 40 mph.

35. Let x be the amount of 20% acid solution and y be the amount of 50% acid solution.
$$x + y = 6$$
$$0.2x + 0.5y = 0.4(6)$$
To clear decimals, multiply the second equation by 10.
$$x + y = 6$$
$$2x + 5y = 24$$
Solve the first equation for y.
$$x + y = 6$$
$$y = -x + 6$$
Substitute $-x + 6$ for y in the second equation.
$$2x + 5y = 24$$
$$2x + 5(-x + 6) = 24$$
$$2x - 5x + 30 = -24$$
$$-3x + 30 = 24$$
$$-3x = -6$$
$$x = \frac{-6}{-3} = 2$$
Finally, substitute 3 for x in the equation $y = -x + 6$.
$$y = -x + 6$$
$$y = -3 + 6$$
$$y = 4$$

James should combine 2 liters of the 20% acid solution to 4 liters of the 50% acid solution.

36. Let x be the number of adult tickets and y be the number of children's tickets.
$$x + y = 650$$
$$15x + 11y = 8790$$
To solve, multiply the first equation by -11 and then add.
$$-11[x + y = 650]$$
$$15x + 11y = 8790$$
gives
$$-11x - 11y = -7150$$
$$\underline{15x + 11y = 8790}$$
Add: $4x = 1640$
$$x = \frac{1640}{4} = 410$$
Substitute 410 for x in the first equation.
$$x + y = 650$$
$$410 + y = 650$$
$$y = 240$$
Thus, 410 adult tickets and 240 children's tickets were sold.

37. Let x = age at first time and y = age at second time.
$$y = 2x - 5$$
$$x + y = 118$$
Substitute $2x - 5$ for y in the second equation.
$$x + y = 118$$
$$x + 2x - 5 = 118$$
$$3x - 5 = 118$$
$$3x = 123$$
$$x = 41$$
Substitute 41 for x in the first equation.
$$y = 2x - 5$$
$$y = 2(41) - 5$$
$$y = 82 - 5$$
$$y = 77$$
His ages were 41 years and 77 years.

38. Let x be the amount invested at 7%, y the amount invested at 5%, and z the amount invested at 3%.
$$x + y + z = 40,000 \quad (1)$$
$$y = x - 5000 \quad (2)$$
$$0.07x + 0.05y + 0.03z = 2300 \quad (3)$$
Substitute $x - 5000$ for y in equations (1) and (3).
Equation (1) becomes
$$x + y + z = 40,000$$
$$x + x - 5000 + z = 40,000$$
$$2x + z = 45,000 \quad (4)$$
Equation (3) becomes

$$0.07x + 0.05y + 0.03z = 2300$$
$$0.07x + 0.05(x - 5000) + 0.03z = 2300$$
$$0.07x + 0.05x - 250 + 0.03z = 2300$$
$$0.12x + 0.03z = 2550 \quad (5)$$
Equation (4) and (5) are a system of two equations in two unknowns. Solve equation (4) for z.
$$2x + z = 45,000$$
$$z = -2x + 45,000$$
Substitute $-2x + 45,000$ for z in equation (5).
$$0.12x + 0.03z = 2550$$
$$0.12x + 0.03(-2x + 45,000) = 2550$$
$$0.12x - 0.06x + 1350 = 2550$$
$$0.06x = 1200$$
$$x = 20,000$$
Now substitute 20,000 for x in equation (2).
$$y = x - 5000$$
$$y = 20,000 - 5000 = 15,000$$
Finally, substitute 20,000 for x and 15,000 for y in equation (1).
$$x + y + z = 40,000$$
$$20,000 + 15,000 + z = 40,000$$
$$35,000 + z = 40,000$$
$$z = 5000$$
Thus, \$20,000 was invested at 7%, \$15,000 at 5%, and \$5000 at 3%.

39.
$$x + 5y = 1$$
$$-2x - 8y = -6$$
$$\begin{bmatrix} 1 & 5 & | & 1 \\ -2 & -8 & | & -6 \end{bmatrix}$$
$$\begin{bmatrix} 1 & 5 & | & 1 \\ 0 & 2 & | & -4 \end{bmatrix} 2R_1 + R_2$$
$$\begin{bmatrix} 1 & 5 & | & 1 \\ 0 & 1 & | & -2 \end{bmatrix} \frac{1}{2}R_2$$
The system is
$$x + 5y = 1$$
$$y = -2$$
Substitute -2 for y in the first equation.
$$x + 5(-2) = 1$$
$$x - 10 = 1$$
$$x = 11$$
The solution is $(11, -2)$.

40. $2x - 3y = 3$

$2x + 4y = 10$

$\begin{bmatrix} 2 & -3 & | & 3 \\ 2 & 4 & | & 10 \end{bmatrix}$

$\begin{bmatrix} 1 & \frac{-3}{2} & | & \frac{3}{2} \\ 2 & 4 & | & 10 \end{bmatrix} \frac{1}{2}R_1$

$\begin{bmatrix} 1 & \frac{-3}{2} & | & \frac{3}{2} \\ 0 & 7 & | & 7 \end{bmatrix} -2R_1 + R_2$

$\begin{bmatrix} 1 & \frac{-3}{2} & | & \frac{3}{2} \\ 0 & 1 & | & 1 \end{bmatrix} \frac{1}{7}R_2$

The system is

$x - \frac{3}{2}y = \frac{3}{2}$

$y = 1$

Substitute 1 for y in the first equation.

$x - \frac{3}{2}(1) = \frac{3}{2}$

$x - \frac{3}{2} = \frac{3}{2}$

$x = \frac{6}{2}$

$x = 3$

The solution is (3, 1).

41. $y = 2x - 4$

$4x = 2y + 8$

Write the system in standard form.

$-2x + y = -4$

$4x - 2y = 8$

$\begin{bmatrix} -2 & 1 & | & -4 \\ 4 & -2 & | & 8 \end{bmatrix}$

$\begin{bmatrix} 1 & -\frac{1}{2} & | & 2 \\ 4 & -2 & | & 8 \end{bmatrix} -\frac{1}{2}R_1$

$\begin{bmatrix} 1 & -\frac{1}{4} & | & 2 \\ 0 & 0 & | & 0 \end{bmatrix} -4R_1 + R_2$

Since the last row is all zeros, the system is dependent.

42. $2x - y - z = 5$

$x + 2y + 3z = -2$

$3x - 2y + z = 2$

$\begin{bmatrix} 2 & -1 & -1 & | & 5 \\ 1 & 2 & 3 & | & -2 \\ 3 & -2 & 1 & | & 2 \end{bmatrix}$

$\begin{bmatrix} 1 & -\frac{1}{2} & -\frac{1}{2} & | & \frac{5}{2} \\ 1 & 2 & 3 & | & -2 \\ 3 & -2 & 1 & | & 2 \end{bmatrix} \frac{1}{2}R_1$

$\begin{bmatrix} 1 & -\frac{1}{2} & -\frac{1}{2} & | & \frac{5}{2} \\ 0 & \frac{5}{2} & \frac{7}{2} & | & -\frac{9}{2} \\ 3 & -2 & 1 & | & 2 \end{bmatrix} -1R_1 + R_2$

$\begin{bmatrix} 1 & -\frac{1}{2} & -\frac{1}{2} & | & \frac{5}{2} \\ 0 & \frac{5}{2} & \frac{7}{2} & | & -\frac{9}{2} \\ 0 & -\frac{1}{2} & \frac{5}{2} & | & -\frac{11}{2} \end{bmatrix} -3R_1 + R_3$

$\begin{bmatrix} 1 & -\frac{1}{2} & -\frac{1}{2} & | & \frac{5}{2} \\ 0 & 1 & \frac{7}{5} & | & -\frac{9}{5} \\ 0 & -\frac{1}{2} & \frac{5}{2} & | & -\frac{11}{2} \end{bmatrix} \frac{2}{5}R_2$

$\begin{bmatrix} 1 & -\frac{1}{2} & -\frac{1}{2} & | & \frac{5}{2} \\ 0 & 1 & \frac{7}{5} & | & -\frac{9}{5} \\ 0 & 0 & \frac{16}{5} & | & -\frac{32}{5} \end{bmatrix} \frac{1}{2}R_2 + R_3$

$\begin{bmatrix} 1 & -\frac{1}{2} & -\frac{1}{2} & | & \frac{5}{2} \\ 0 & 1 & \frac{7}{5} & | & -\frac{9}{5} \\ 0 & 0 & 1 & | & -2 \end{bmatrix} \frac{5}{16}R_3$

The system is

$x - \frac{1}{2}y - \frac{1}{2}z = \frac{5}{2}$

$y + \frac{7}{5}z = -\frac{9}{5}$

$z = -2$

Substitute –2 for z in the second equation.

$y + \frac{7}{5}z = -\frac{9}{5}$

$y + \frac{7}{5}(-2) = -\frac{9}{5}$

$y - \frac{14}{5} = -\frac{9}{5}$

$y = \frac{5}{5} = 1$

Substitute 1 for y and –2 for z in the first equation.

$x - \frac{1}{2}y - \frac{1}{2}z = \frac{5}{2}$

$x - \frac{1}{2}(1) - \frac{1}{2}(-2) = \frac{5}{2}$

$x - \frac{1}{2} + 1 = \frac{5}{2}$

$x + \frac{1}{2} = \frac{5}{2}$

$x = \frac{4}{2} = 2$

The solution is (2, 1, –2).

43.
$$3a - b + c = 2$$
$$2a - 3b + 4c = 4$$
$$a + 2b - 3c = -6$$

$$\begin{bmatrix} 3 & -1 & 1 & | & 2 \\ 2 & -3 & 4 & | & 4 \\ 1 & 2 & -3 & | & -6 \end{bmatrix}$$

$$\begin{bmatrix} 1 & -\frac{1}{3} & \frac{1}{3} & | & \frac{2}{3} \\ 2 & -3 & 4 & | & 4 \\ 1 & 2 & -3 & | & -6 \end{bmatrix} \frac{1}{3} R_1$$

$$\begin{bmatrix} 1 & -\frac{1}{3} & \frac{1}{3} & | & \frac{2}{3} \\ 0 & -\frac{7}{3} & \frac{10}{3} & | & \frac{8}{3} \\ 1 & 2 & -3 & | & -6 \end{bmatrix} -2R_1 + R_2$$

$$\begin{bmatrix} 1 & -\frac{1}{3} & \frac{1}{3} & | & \frac{2}{3} \\ 0 & -\frac{7}{3} & \frac{10}{3} & | & \frac{8}{3} \\ 0 & \frac{7}{3} & -\frac{10}{3} & | & -\frac{20}{3} \end{bmatrix} -1R_1 + R_3$$

$$\begin{bmatrix} 1 & -\frac{1}{3} & \frac{1}{3} & | & \frac{2}{3} \\ 0 & 1 & -\frac{10}{7} & | & -\frac{8}{7} \\ 0 & \frac{7}{3} & -\frac{10}{3} & | & -\frac{20}{3} \end{bmatrix} -\frac{3}{7} R_2$$

$$\begin{bmatrix} 1 & -\frac{1}{3} & \frac{1}{3} & | & \frac{2}{3} \\ 0 & 1 & -\frac{10}{7} & | & -\frac{8}{7} \\ 0 & 0 & 0 & | & -4 \end{bmatrix}$$

Since the last row has all zeros on the left side and a nonzero number on the right side, the system is inconsistent.

44.
$$x + y + z = 3$$
$$3x + 2y = 1$$
$$y - 3z = -10$$

$$\begin{bmatrix} 1 & 1 & 1 & | & 3 \\ 3 & 2 & 0 & | & 1 \\ 0 & 1 & -3 & | & -10 \end{bmatrix}$$

$$\begin{bmatrix} 1 & 1 & 1 & | & 3 \\ 0 & -1 & -3 & | & -8 \\ 0 & 1 & -3 & | & -10 \end{bmatrix} -3R_1 + R_2$$

$$\begin{bmatrix} 1 & 1 & 1 & | & 3 \\ 0 & 1 & 3 & | & 8 \\ 0 & 1 & -3 & | & -10 \end{bmatrix} -1R_2$$

$$\begin{bmatrix} 1 & 1 & 1 & | & 3 \\ 0 & 1 & 3 & | & 8 \\ 0 & 0 & -6 & | & -18 \end{bmatrix} -1R_2 + R_3$$

$$\begin{bmatrix} 1 & 1 & 1 & | & 3 \\ 0 & 1 & 3 & | & 8 \\ 0 & 0 & 1 & | & 3 \end{bmatrix} -\frac{1}{6} R_3$$

The system is
$$x + y + z = 3$$
$$y + 3z = 8$$
$$z = 3$$

Substitute 3 for z in the second equation.
$$y + 3z = 8$$
$$y + 3(3) = 8$$
$$y + 9 = 8$$
$$y = -1$$

Substitute -1 for y and 3 for z in the first equation.
$$x + y + z = 3$$
$$x - 1 + 3 = 3$$
$$x + 2 = 3$$
$$x = 1$$

The solution is $(1, -1, 3)$.

45.
$$7x - 8y = -10$$
$$-5x + 4y = 2$$

To solve, first calculate D, D_x, and D_y.

$$D = \begin{vmatrix} 7 & -8 \\ -5 & 4 \end{vmatrix}$$
$$= (7)(4) - (-5)(-8)$$
$$= 28 - 40$$
$$= -12$$

$$D_x = \begin{vmatrix} -10 & -8 \\ 2 & 4 \end{vmatrix}$$
$$= (-10)(4) - (2)(-8)$$
$$= -40 + 16$$
$$= -24$$

$$D_y = \begin{vmatrix} 7 & -10 \\ -5 & 2 \end{vmatrix}$$
$$= (7)(2) - (-5)(-10)$$
$$= 14 - 50$$
$$= -36$$

$$x = \frac{D_x}{D} = \frac{-24}{-12} = 2 \text{ and } y = \frac{D_y}{D} = \frac{-36}{-12} = 3$$

The solution is $(2, 3)$.

46.
$$x + 4y = 5$$
$$-2x - 2y = 2$$
To solve, first calculate D, D_x, and D_y.

$$D = \begin{vmatrix} 1 & 4 \\ -2 & -2 \end{vmatrix}$$
$$= (1)(-2) - (-2)(4)$$
$$= -2 + 8$$
$$= 6$$

$$D_x = \begin{vmatrix} 5 & 4 \\ 2 & -2 \end{vmatrix}$$
$$= (5)(-2) - (2)(4)$$
$$= -10 - 8$$
$$= -18$$

$$D_y = \begin{vmatrix} 1 & 5 \\ -2 & 2 \end{vmatrix}$$
$$= (1)(2) - (-2)(5)$$
$$= 2 + 10$$
$$= 12$$

$$x = \frac{D_x}{D} = \frac{-18}{6} = -3 \text{ and } y = \frac{D_y}{D} = \frac{12}{6} = 2$$
The solution is $(-3, 2)$.

47.
$$4m + 3n = 2$$
$$7m - 2n = -11$$
To solve, first calculate D, D_m, and D_n.

$$D = \begin{vmatrix} 4 & 3 \\ 7 & -2 \end{vmatrix}$$
$$= (4)(-2) - (7)(3)$$
$$= -8 - 21$$
$$= -29$$

$$D_m = \begin{vmatrix} 2 & 3 \\ -11 & -2 \end{vmatrix}$$
$$= (2)(-2) - (-11)(3)$$
$$= -4 + 33$$
$$= 29$$

$$D_n = \begin{vmatrix} 4 & 2 \\ 7 & -11 \end{vmatrix}$$
$$= (4)(-11) - (7)(2)$$
$$= -44 - 14$$
$$= -58$$

$$m = \frac{D_m}{D} = \frac{29}{-29} = -1 \text{ and } n = \frac{D_n}{D} = \frac{-58}{-29} = 2.$$
The solution is $(-1, 2)$.

48.
$$p + q + r = 5$$
$$2p + q - r = -5$$
$$-p + 2q - 3r = -4$$
To solve, calculate D, D_p, D_q, and D_r.

$$D = \begin{vmatrix} 1 & 1 & 1 \\ 2 & 1 & -1 \\ -1 & 2 & -3 \end{vmatrix}$$
$$= 1\begin{vmatrix} 1 & -1 \\ 2 & -3 \end{vmatrix} - 1\begin{vmatrix} 2 & -1 \\ -1 & -3 \end{vmatrix} + 1\begin{vmatrix} 2 & 1 \\ -1 & 2 \end{vmatrix}$$
$$= 1(-3 + 2) - 1(-6 - 1) + 1(4 + 1)$$
$$= 1(-1) - 1(-7) + 1(5)$$
$$= -1 + 7 + 5$$
$$= 11$$

$$D_p = \begin{vmatrix} 5 & 1 & 1 \\ -5 & 1 & -1 \\ -4 & 2 & -3 \end{vmatrix}$$
$$= 5\begin{vmatrix} 1 & -1 \\ 2 & -3 \end{vmatrix} - 1\begin{vmatrix} -5 & -1 \\ -4 & -3 \end{vmatrix} + 1\begin{vmatrix} -5 & 1 \\ -4 & 2 \end{vmatrix}$$
$$= 5(-3 + 2) - 1(15 - 4) + 1(-10 + 4)$$
$$= 5(-1) - 1(11) + 1(-6)$$
$$= -5 - 11 - 6$$
$$= -22$$

$$D_q = \begin{vmatrix} 1 & 5 & 1 \\ 2 & -5 & -1 \\ -1 & -4 & -3 \end{vmatrix}$$
$$= 1\begin{vmatrix} -5 & -1 \\ -4 & -3 \end{vmatrix} - 5\begin{vmatrix} 2 & -1 \\ -1 & -3 \end{vmatrix} + 1\begin{vmatrix} 2 & -5 \\ -1 & -4 \end{vmatrix}$$
$$= 1(15 - 4) - 5(-6 - 1) + 1(-8 - 5)$$
$$= 1(11) - 5(-7) + 1(-13)$$
$$= 11 + 35 + 13$$
$$= 33$$

$$D_r = \begin{vmatrix} 1 & 1 & 5 \\ 2 & 1 & -5 \\ -1 & 2 & -4 \end{vmatrix}$$
$$= 1\begin{vmatrix} 1 & -5 \\ 2 & -4 \end{vmatrix} - 1\begin{vmatrix} 2 & -5 \\ -1 & -4 \end{vmatrix} + 5\begin{vmatrix} 2 & 1 \\ -1 & 2 \end{vmatrix}$$
$$= 1(-4 + 10) - 1(-8 - 5) + 5(4 + 1)$$
$$= 1(6) - 1(-13) + 5(5)$$
$$= 6 + 13 + 25$$
$$= 44$$

$$p = \frac{D_p}{D} = \frac{-22}{11} = -2, \ q = \frac{D_q}{D} = \frac{33}{11} = 3, \text{ and}$$

$$r = \frac{D_r}{D} = \frac{44}{11} = 4$$

The solution is $(-2, 3, 4)$.

49. $-2a + 3b - 4c = -7$

    $a + b + c = 4$

  $-2a - 3b + 4c = 3$

To solve, calculate D, D_a, D_b, and D_c.

$$D = \begin{vmatrix} -2 & 3 & -4 \\ 1 & 1 & 1 \\ -2 & -3 & 4 \end{vmatrix}$$

$$= -2\begin{vmatrix} 1 & 1 \\ -3 & 4 \end{vmatrix} - 3\begin{vmatrix} 1 & 1 \\ -2 & 4 \end{vmatrix} + (-4)\begin{vmatrix} 1 & 1 \\ -2 & -3 \end{vmatrix}$$

$$= -2(4+3) - 3(4+2) - 4(-3+2)$$

$$= -2(7) - 3(6) - 4(-1)$$

$$= -14 - 18 + 4$$

$$= -28$$

$$D_a = \begin{vmatrix} -7 & 3 & -4 \\ 4 & 1 & 1 \\ 3 & -3 & 4 \end{vmatrix}$$

$$= -7\begin{vmatrix} 1 & 1 \\ -3 & 4 \end{vmatrix} - 3\begin{vmatrix} 4 & 1 \\ 3 & 4 \end{vmatrix} + (-4)\begin{vmatrix} 4 & 1 \\ 3 & -3 \end{vmatrix}$$

$$= -7(4+3) - 3(16-3) - 4(-12-3)$$

$$= -7(7) - 3(13) - 4(-15)$$

$$= -49 - 39 + 60$$

$$= -28$$

$$D_b = \begin{vmatrix} -2 & -7 & -4 \\ 1 & 4 & 1 \\ -2 & 3 & 4 \end{vmatrix}$$

$$= -2\begin{vmatrix} 4 & 1 \\ 3 & 4 \end{vmatrix} - (-7)\begin{vmatrix} 1 & 1 \\ -2 & 4 \end{vmatrix} + (-4)\begin{vmatrix} 1 & 4 \\ -2 & 3 \end{vmatrix}$$

$$= -2(16-3) + 7(4+2) - 4(3+8)$$

$$= -2(13) + 7(6) - 4(11)$$

$$= -26 + 42 - 44$$

$$= -28$$

$$D_c = \begin{vmatrix} -2 & 3 & -7 \\ 1 & 1 & 4 \\ -2 & -3 & 3 \end{vmatrix}$$

$$= -2\begin{vmatrix} 1 & 4 \\ -3 & 3 \end{vmatrix} - 3\begin{vmatrix} 1 & 4 \\ -2 & 3 \end{vmatrix} + (-7)\begin{vmatrix} 1 & 1 \\ -2 & -3 \end{vmatrix}$$

$$= -2(3+12) - 3(3+8) - 7(-3+2)$$

$$= -2(15) - 3(11) - 7(-1)$$

$$= -30 - 33 + 7$$

$$= -56$$

$$a = \frac{D_a}{D} = \frac{-28}{-28} = 1, \ b = \frac{D_b}{D} = \frac{-28}{-28} = 1, \text{ and}$$

$$c = \frac{D_c}{D} = \frac{-56}{-28} = 2$$

The solution is $(1, 1, 2)$.

50. $y + 3z = 4$

    $-x - y + 2z = 0$

      $x + 2y + z = 1$

To solve, first calculate D, D_x, D_y, and D_z.

$$D = \begin{vmatrix} 0 & 1 & 3 \\ -1 & -1 & 2 \\ 1 & 2 & 1 \end{vmatrix}$$

$$= 0\begin{vmatrix} -1 & 2 \\ 2 & 1 \end{vmatrix} - (-1)\begin{vmatrix} 1 & 3 \\ 2 & 1 \end{vmatrix} + 1\begin{vmatrix} 1 & 3 \\ -1 & 2 \end{vmatrix}$$

$$= 0(-1-4) + 1(1-6) + 1(2+3)$$

$$= 0(-5) + 1(-5) + 1(5)$$

$$= 0 - 5 + 5$$

$$= 0$$

$$D_x = \begin{vmatrix} 4 & 1 & 3 \\ 0 & -1 & 2 \\ 1 & 2 & 1 \end{vmatrix}$$

$$= 4\begin{vmatrix} -1 & 2 \\ 2 & 1 \end{vmatrix} - 0\begin{vmatrix} 1 & 3 \\ 2 & 1 \end{vmatrix} + 1\begin{vmatrix} 1 & 3 \\ -1 & 2 \end{vmatrix}$$

$$= 4(-1-4) - 0(1-6) + 1(2+3)$$

$$= 4(-5) - 0(-5) + 1(5)$$

$$= -20 + 0 + 5$$

$$= -15$$

Since $D = 0$ and $D_x = -15$, the system is inconsistent.

51. $-x + 3y > 6$

    $2x - y \le 2$

For $-x + 3y > 6$, graph the line $-x + 3y = 6$ using a dashed line. For the check point, select $(0, 0)$:

$$-x + 3y > 6$$

$$-0 + 3(0) > 6$$

$$0 > 6 \qquad \text{False}$$

Since this is a false statement, shade the region

which does not contain the point (0, 0).
For $2x - y \le 2$, graph the line $2x - y = 2$ using a
solid line. For the check point, select (0, 0):

$$2x - y \le 2$$
$$2(0) - 0 \le 2$$
$$0 \le 2 \qquad \text{True}$$

Since this is a true statement, shade the region
which contains the point (0, 0).
To obtain the final region, take the intersection
of the above two regions.

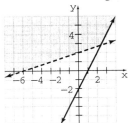

52. $5x - 2y \le 10$
$3x + 2y > 6$

For $5x - 2y \le 10$, graph the line $5x - 2y = 10$
using a solid line. For the check point, select (0,
0):

$$5x - 2y \le 10$$
$$5(0) - 2(0) \le 10$$
$$0 \le 10 \qquad \text{True}$$

Since this is a true statement, shade the region
which contains the point (0, 0).
For $3x + 2y > 6$, graph the line $3x + 2y = 6$ using
a dashed line. For the check point, select (0, 0):

$$3x + 2y > 6$$
$$3(0) + 2(0) > 6$$
$$0 > 6 \qquad \text{False}$$

Since this is a false statement, shade the region
which does not contain the point (0, 0). To
obtain the final region, take the intersection of
the above two regions.

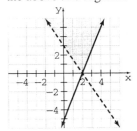

53. $y > 2x + 3$
$y < -x + 4$

For $y > 2x + 3$, graph the line $y = 2x + 3$ using a
dashed line. For the check point, select (0, 0):

$$y > 2x + 3$$
$$0 > 2(0) + 3$$
$$0 > 3 \qquad \text{False}$$

Since this is a false statement, shade the region

which does not contain the point (0, 0).
For $y < -x + 4$, graph the line
$y = -x + 4$ using a dashed line. For the check
point, select (0, 0):

$$y < -x + 4$$
$$0 < -0 + 4$$
$$0 < 4 \qquad \text{True}$$

Since this is a true statement, shade the region
which contains the point (0, 0). To obtain the
final region, take the intersection of the above
two regions.

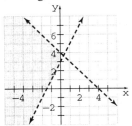

54. $x > -2y + 4$
$$y < -\frac{1}{2}x - \frac{3}{2}$$

For $x > -2y + 4$, graph the line $x = -2y + 4$ using
a dashed line. For the check point, select (0, 0):

$$x > -2y + 4$$
$$0 > -2(0) + 4$$
$$0 > 4 \qquad \text{False}$$

Since this is a false statement, shade the region
which does not contain the point (0, 0).
For $y < -\frac{1}{2}x - \frac{3}{2}$, graph the line $y = -\frac{1}{2}x - \frac{3}{2}$

using a dashed line. For the check point, select
(0, 0):

$$y < -\frac{1}{2}x - \frac{3}{2}$$
$$0 < -\frac{1}{2}(0) - \frac{3}{2}$$
$$0 < -\frac{3}{2} \qquad \text{False}$$

Since this is a false statement, shade the region
which does not contain the point
(0, 0). To obtain the final region, take the
intersection of the above two regions. The
regions do not overlap, so there are no solutions.

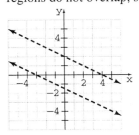

55. $x \geq 0$
$y \geq 0$
$x + y \leq 6$
$4x + y \leq 8$

The first two inequalities indicate that the solution must be in the first quadrant. For $x + y \leq 6$, the graph is the line $x + y = 6$ along with the region below this line. For $4x + y \leq 8$, the graph is the line $4x + y = 8$ along with the region below this line. To obtain the final region, take the intersection of these regions.

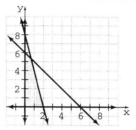

56. $x \geq 0$
$y \geq 0$
$2x + y \leq 6$
$4x + 5y \leq 20$

The first two inequalities indicate that the solution must be in the first quadrant. For $2x + y \leq 6$, graph the line $2x + y = 6$ along with the region below this line. For $4x + 5y \leq 20$, graph the line $4x + 5y = 20$ along with the region below this line. To obtain the final region, take the intersection of these regions.

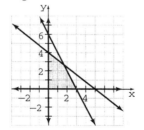

57. $|x| \leq 3$
$|y| > 2$

For $|x| \leq 3$, the graph is the region between the solid lines $x = -3$ and $x = 3$. For $|y| > 2$, the graph is the region above the dashed line $y = 2$ along with the region below the dashed line $y = -2$. To obtain the final region, take the intersection of these regions.

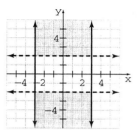

58. $|x| > 4$
$|y - 2| \leq 3$

For $|x| > 4$, the graph is the region to the left of dashed line $x = -4$ along with the region to the right of the dashed line $x = 4$.
$|y - 2| \leq 3$ can be written as
$-3 \leq y - 2 \leq 3$
$-1 \leq y \leq 5$
For $|y - 2| \leq 3$, the graph is the region between the solid lines $y = -1$ and $y = 5$. To obtain the final region, take the intersection of these regions.

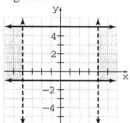

Practice Test

1. Answers will vary.

2. Write both equations in slope-intercept form.

$$5x + 2y = 4 \qquad\qquad \begin{aligned} 5x &= 3y - 7 \\ -3y &= -5x - 7 \end{aligned}$$
$$2y = -5x + 4 \qquad\qquad y = \frac{-5x - 7}{-3}$$
$$y = \frac{-5x + 4}{2} \qquad\qquad y = \frac{5}{3}x + \frac{7}{3}$$
$$y = -\frac{5}{2}x + 2$$

Since the slope of the first line is $-\frac{5}{2}$ and the slope of the second line is $\frac{5}{3}$, the slopes are different so that the lines intersect to produce one solution. This is a consistent system.

3. Write both equations in slope-intercept form.

$5x + 3y = 9$

$3y = -5x + 9$

$y = \dfrac{-5x + 9}{3}$

$y = -\dfrac{5}{3}x + 3$

$2y = -\dfrac{10}{3}x + 6$

$\dfrac{1}{2}(2y) = \dfrac{1}{2}\left(-\dfrac{10}{3}x + 6\right)$

$y = -\dfrac{5}{3}x + 3$

Since the equations are identical, there is an infinite number of solutions and this is a dependent system.

4. Write both equations in slope-intercept form.

$5x - 4y = 6$

$-4y = -5x + 6$

$y = \dfrac{-5x + 6}{-4}$

$y = \dfrac{5}{4}x - \dfrac{3}{2}$

$-10x + 8y = -10$

$8y = 10x - 10$

$y = \dfrac{10x - 10}{8}$

$y = \dfrac{5}{4}x - \dfrac{5}{4}$

Since the slope of each line is $\dfrac{5}{4}$, but the y-intercepts are different $\left(b = -\dfrac{3}{2}\right.$ for the first equation, $b = -\dfrac{5}{4}$ for the second equation$\left.\right)$, the two lines are parallel and produce no solution. This is an inconsistent system.

5. Graph the equations $y = 3x - 2$ and $y = -2x + 8$.

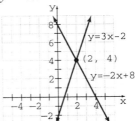

The lines intersect and the point of intersection is (2, 4).

6. Graph the equations $y = -x + 6$ and $y = 2x + 3$.

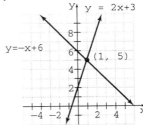

The lines intersect and the point of intersection is (1, 5).

7. $y = -3x + 4$

$y = 5x - 4$

Substitute $-3x + 4$ for y in the second equation.

$-3x + 4 = 5x - 4$

$-8x = -8$

$x = 1$

Substitute 1 for x in the first equation.

$y = -3(1) + 4$

$y = -3 + 4$

$y = 1$

The solution is (1, 1).

8. $2a + 4b = 2$

$5a + b = -13$

Solve the second equation for b.

$5a + b = -13$

$b = -5a - 13$

Substitute $-5a - 13$ for b in the first equation.

$2a + 4(-5a - 13) = 2$

$2a - 20a - 52 = 2$

$-18a - 52 = 2$

$-18a = 54$

$a = -3$

Substitute -3 for a in the equation $b = -5a - 13$.

$b = -5(-3) - 13$

$b = 15 - 13$

$b = 2$

The solution is (–3, 2).

9. $4x + 3y = 10$

$6x + y = 1$

To eliminate y, multiply the second equation by -3 and then add.

$4x + 3y = 10$

$-3[6x + y = 1]$

gives

$4x + 3y = 10$

$-18x - 3y = -3$

Add: $-14x \qquad = 7$

$x = \dfrac{7}{-14} = -\dfrac{1}{2}$

Substitute $-\dfrac{1}{2}$ for x in the second equation.

$6\left(-\dfrac{1}{2}\right) + y = 1$

$-3 + y = 1$

$y = 4$

The solution is $\left(-\dfrac{1}{2}, 4\right)$.

10.
$$0.3x = 0.2y + 0.4$$
$$-1.2x + 0.8y = -1.6$$
Write the system in standard form.
$$0.3x - 0.2y = 0.4$$
$$-1.2x + 0.8y = -1.6$$
To eliminate x, multiply the first equation by 4 and then add.
$$4[0.3x - 0.2y = 0.4]$$
$$-1.2x + 0.8y = -1.6$$
gives
$$1.2x - 0.8y = 1.6$$
$$\underline{-1.2x + 0.8y = -1.6}$$
Add: $0 = 0$ True

Since this is a true statement, there are an infinite number of solutions and this is a dependent system.

11. $\dfrac{3}{2}a + b = 6$

$a - \dfrac{5}{2}b = -4$

To clear fractions, multiply both equations by 2.
$$2\left[\dfrac{3}{2}a + b = 6\right]$$
$$2\left[a - \dfrac{5}{2}b = -4\right]$$
gives
$$3a + 2b = 12$$
$$2a - 5b = -8$$
Now, to eliminate b, multiply the first equation by 5 and the second equation by 2 and then add.
$$5[3a + 2b = 12]$$
$$2[2a - 5b = -8]$$
gives
$$15a + 10b = 60$$
$$\underline{4a - 10b = -16}$$
Add: $19a \qquad\;\; = 44$
$$a = \dfrac{44}{19}$$
Substitute $\dfrac{44}{19}$ for a in the first equation.

$$\dfrac{3}{2}a + b = 6$$
$$\dfrac{3}{2}\left(\dfrac{44}{19}\right) + b = 6$$
$$\dfrac{66}{19} + b = 6$$
$$b = 6 - \dfrac{66}{19}$$
$$b = \dfrac{114}{19} - \dfrac{66}{19}$$
$$b = \dfrac{48}{19}$$
The solution is $\left(\dfrac{44}{19}, \dfrac{48}{19}\right)$.

12.
$$x + y + z = 2 \quad (1)$$
$$-2x - y + z = 1 \quad (2)$$
$$x - 2y - z = 1 \quad (3)$$
To eliminate z between equations (1) and (3) simply add.
$$x + y + z = 2$$
$$\underline{x - 2y - z = 1}$$
Add: $2x - y \qquad = 3 \quad (4)$

To eliminate z between equations (2) and (3) simply add.
$$-2x - y + z = 1$$
$$\underline{x - 2y - z = 1}$$
Add: $-x - 3y \qquad = 2 \quad (5)$

Equations (4) and (5) are two equations in two unknowns.
$$2x - y = 3$$
$$-x - 3y = 2$$
To eliminate x, multiply equation (5) by 2 and then add.
$$2x - y = 3$$
$$2[-x - 3y = 2]$$
gives
$$2x - y = 3$$
$$\underline{-2x - 6y = 4}$$
Add: $-7y = 7$
$$y = \dfrac{7}{-7} = -1$$
Substitute -1 for y in equation (4).
$$2x - y = 3$$
$$2x - (-1) = 3$$
$$2x + 1 = 3$$
$$2x = 2$$
$$x = \dfrac{2}{2} = 1$$
Finally, substitute 1 for x and -1 for y in equation (1).

$x + y + z = 2$
$1 - 1 + z = 2$
$0 + z = 2$
$z = 2$
The solution is $(1, -1, 2)$.

13. $-2x + 3y + 7z = 5$
$3x - 2y + z = -2$
$x - 6y + 5z = -13$

The augmented matrix is $\begin{bmatrix} -2 & 3 & 7 & | & 5 \\ 3 & -2 & 1 & | & -2 \\ 1 & -6 & 5 & | & -13 \end{bmatrix}$

14. $\begin{bmatrix} 6 & -2 & 4 & | & 4 \\ 4 & 3 & 5 & | & 6 \\ 2 & -1 & 4 & | & -3 \end{bmatrix}$

$\begin{bmatrix} 6 & -2 & 4 & | & 4 \\ 0 & 5 & -3 & | & 12 \\ 2 & -1 & 4 & | & -3 \end{bmatrix} -2R_3 + R_2$

15. $x - 3y = 7$
$3x + 5y = 7$

$\begin{bmatrix} 1 & -3 & | & 7 \\ 3 & 5 & | & 7 \end{bmatrix}$

$\begin{bmatrix} 1 & -3 & | & 7 \\ 0 & 14 & | & -14 \end{bmatrix} -3R_1 + R_2$

$\begin{bmatrix} 1 & -3 & | & 7 \\ 0 & 1 & | & -1 \end{bmatrix} \frac{1}{14}R_2$

The system is
$x - 3y = 7$
$y = -1$
Substitute -1 for y in the first equation.
$x - 3(-1) = 7$
$x + 3 = 7$
$x = 4$
The solution is $(4, -1)$.

16. $x - 2y + z = 7$
$-2x - y - z = -7$
$3x - 2y + 2z = 15$

$\begin{bmatrix} 1 & -2 & 1 & | & 7 \\ -2 & -1 & -1 & | & -7 \\ 3 & -2 & 2 & | & 15 \end{bmatrix}$

$\begin{bmatrix} 1 & -2 & 1 & | & 7 \\ 0 & -5 & 1 & | & 7 \\ 3 & -2 & 2 & | & 15 \end{bmatrix} 2R_1 + R_2$

$\begin{bmatrix} 1 & -2 & 1 & | & 7 \\ 0 & -5 & 1 & | & 7 \\ 0 & 4 & -1 & | & -6 \end{bmatrix} -3R_1 + R_3$

$\begin{bmatrix} 1 & -2 & 1 & | & 7 \\ 0 & 1 & -\frac{1}{5} & | & -\frac{7}{5} \\ 0 & 4 & -1 & | & -6 \end{bmatrix} -\frac{1}{5}R_2$

$\begin{bmatrix} 1 & -2 & 1 & | & 7 \\ 0 & 1 & -\frac{1}{5} & | & -\frac{7}{5} \\ 0 & 0 & -\frac{1}{5} & | & -\frac{2}{5} \end{bmatrix} -4R_2 + R_3$

$\begin{bmatrix} 1 & -2 & 1 & | & 7 \\ 0 & 1 & -\frac{1}{5} & | & -\frac{7}{5} \\ 0 & 0 & 1 & | & 2 \end{bmatrix} -5R_3$

The system is
$x - 2y + z = 7$
$y - \frac{1}{5}z = -\frac{7}{5}$
$z = 2$
Substitute 2 for z in the second equation.
$y - \frac{1}{5}z = -\frac{7}{5}$
$y - \frac{1}{5}(2) = -\frac{7}{5}$
$y - \frac{2}{5} = -\frac{7}{5}$
$y = -1$
Substitute -1 for y and 2 for z in the first equation.
$x - 2y + z = 7$
$x - 2(-1) + 2 = 7$
$x + 2 + 2 = 7$
$x + 4 = 7$
$x = 3$
The solution is $(3, -1, 2)$.

17. $\begin{vmatrix} 3 & -1 \\ 4 & -2 \end{vmatrix} = (3)(-2) - (4)(-1)$
$= -6 - (-4)$
$= -6 + 4$
$= -2$

18. $\begin{vmatrix} 8 & 2 & -1 \\ 3 & 0 & 5 \\ 6 & -3 & 4 \end{vmatrix} = 8\begin{vmatrix} 0 & 5 \\ -3 & 4 \end{vmatrix} - 3\begin{vmatrix} 2 & -1 \\ -3 & 4 \end{vmatrix} + 6\begin{vmatrix} 2 & -1 \\ 0 & 5 \end{vmatrix}$
$= 8(0 + 15) - 3(8 - 3) + 6(10 - 0)$
$= 8(15) - 3(5) + 6(10)$
$= 120 - 15 + 60$
$= 165$

19. $4x + 3y = -6$

$-2x + 5y = 16$

To solve, first calculate D, D_x, and D_y.

$D = \begin{vmatrix} 4 & 3 \\ -2 & 5 \end{vmatrix}$

$= (4)(5) - (-2)(3)$

$= 20 + 6$

$= 26$

$D_x = \begin{vmatrix} -6 & 3 \\ 16 & 5 \end{vmatrix}$

$= (-6)(5) - (16)(3)$

$= -30 - 48$

$= -78$

$D_y = \begin{vmatrix} 4 & -6 \\ -2 & 16 \end{vmatrix}$

$= (4)(16) - (-2)(-6)$

$= 64 - 12$

$= 52$

$x = \dfrac{D_x}{D} = \dfrac{-78}{26} = -3$ and $y = \dfrac{D_y}{D} = \dfrac{52}{26} = 2$.

The solution is $(-3, 2)$.

20. $2r - 4s + 3t = -1$

$-3r + 5s - 4t = 0$

$-2r + s - 3t = -2$

To solve, first calculate D, D_r, D_s, and D_t.

$D = \begin{vmatrix} 2 & -4 & 3 \\ -3 & 5 & -4 \\ -2 & 1 & -3 \end{vmatrix}$

$= 2\begin{vmatrix} 5 & -4 \\ 1 & -3 \end{vmatrix} - (-4)\begin{vmatrix} -3 & -4 \\ -2 & -3 \end{vmatrix} + 3\begin{vmatrix} -3 & 5 \\ -2 & 1 \end{vmatrix}$

$= 2(-15 + 4) + 4(9 - 8) + 3(-3 + 10)$

$= 2(-11) + 4(1) + 3(7)$

$= -22 + 4 + 21$

$= 3$

$D_r = \begin{vmatrix} -1 & -4 & 3 \\ 0 & 5 & -4 \\ -2 & 1 & -3 \end{vmatrix}$

$= -1\begin{vmatrix} 5 & -4 \\ 1 & -3 \end{vmatrix} - (-4)\begin{vmatrix} 0 & -4 \\ -2 & -3 \end{vmatrix} + 3\begin{vmatrix} 0 & 5 \\ -2 & 1 \end{vmatrix}$

$= -1(-15 + 4) + 4(0 - 8) + 3(0 + 10)$

$= -1(-11) + 4(-8) + 3(10)$

$= 11 - 32 + 30$

$= 9$

$D_s = \begin{vmatrix} 2 & -1 & 3 \\ -3 & 0 & -4 \\ -2 & -2 & -3 \end{vmatrix}$

$= 2\begin{vmatrix} 0 & -4 \\ -2 & -3 \end{vmatrix} - (-1)\begin{vmatrix} -3 & -4 \\ -2 & -3 \end{vmatrix} + 3\begin{vmatrix} -3 & 0 \\ -2 & -2 \end{vmatrix}$

$= 2(0 - 8) + 1(9 - 8) + 3(6 - 0)$

$= 2(-8) + 1(1) + 3(6)$

$= -16 + 1 + 18$

$= 3$

$D_t = \begin{vmatrix} 2 & -4 & -1 \\ -3 & 5 & 0 \\ -2 & 1 & -2 \end{vmatrix}$

$= 2\begin{vmatrix} 5 & 0 \\ 1 & -2 \end{vmatrix} - (-4)\begin{vmatrix} -3 & 0 \\ -2 & -2 \end{vmatrix} + (-1)\begin{vmatrix} -3 & 5 \\ -2 & 1 \end{vmatrix}$

$= 2(-10 - 0) + 4(6 - 0) - 1(-3 + 10)$

$= 2(-10) + 4(6) - 1(7)$

$= -20 + 24 - 7$

$= -3$

$r = \dfrac{D_r}{D} = \dfrac{9}{3} = 3$, $s = \dfrac{D_s}{D} = \dfrac{3}{3} = 1$,

$t = \dfrac{D_t}{D} = \dfrac{-3}{3} = -1$

The solution is $(-1, -1, 2)$.

21. Let x be the number of pounds of cashews and y be the number of pounds of peanuts.

$x + y = 20$

$7x + 5.5y = 20(6)$

Solve the first equation for y.

$x + y = 20$

$y = -x + 20$

Substitute $-x + 20$ for y in the second equation.

$$7x + 5.5y = 20(6)$$
$$7x + 5.5(-x + 20) = 20(6)$$
$$7x - 5.5x + 110 = 120$$
$$1.5x + 110 = 120$$
$$1.5x = 10$$
$$x = \frac{10}{1.5} \cdot \frac{10}{10} = \frac{100}{15} = \frac{20}{3} \text{ or } 6\frac{2}{3}$$

Thus, Dick should mix $6\frac{2}{3}$ lb of cashews with

$20 - 6\frac{2}{3} = 13\frac{1}{3}$ lb of peanuts to obtain the

desired mixture.

22. Let x = amount of 6% solution
y = amount of 15% solution
$$x + y = 10$$
$$0.06x + 0.15y = 0.09(10)$$

The system can be written as
$$x + y = 10$$
$$6x + 15y = 90$$

Solve the first equation for y.
$$y = 10 - x$$

Substitute $10 - x$ for y in the second equation.
$$6x + 15y = 90$$
$$6x + 15(10 - x) = 90$$
$$6x + 150 - 15x = 90$$
$$-9x = -60$$
$$x = \frac{-60}{-9} = \frac{20}{3} = 6\frac{2}{3}$$

Substitute $6\frac{2}{3}$ for x into $y = 10 - x$

$$y = 10 - 6\frac{2}{3}$$
$$y = 3\frac{1}{3}$$

She should mix $6\frac{2}{3}$ liters of 6% solution and

$3\frac{1}{3}$ liters of 15% solution.

23. Let x = smallest number
y = remaining number
z = largest number
$$x + y + z = 25$$
$$z = 3x$$
$$y = 2x + 1$$

Substitute $2x + 1$ for y and $3x$ for z in the first equation.
$$x + y + z = 25$$
$$x + 2x + 1 + 3x = 25$$
$$6x = 24$$
$$x = 4$$

Substitute 4 for x in the third equation.

$$y = 2x + 1$$
$$y = 2(4) + 1$$
$$y = 9$$

Substitute 4 for x in the second equation.
$$z = 3x$$
$$z = 3(4)$$
$$z = 12$$

The three numbers are 4, 9, and 12.

24. $3x + 2y < 9$
$-2x + 5y \le 10$

For $3x + 2y < 9$, graph the line $3x + 2y = 9$ using a dashed line. For the check point, select $(0, 0)$.
$$3x + 2y < 9$$
$$3(0) + 2(0) < 9$$
$$0 < 9 \qquad \text{True}$$

Since this is a true statement, shade the region which contains the point $(0, 0)$. this is the region "below" the line.

For $-2x + 5y \le 10$, graph the line $-2x + 5y = 10$ using a solid line. For the check point, select $(0, 0)$.
$$-2x + 5y \le 10$$
$$-2(0) + 5(0) \le 10$$
$$0 \le 10 \qquad \text{True}$$

Since this is a true statement, shade the region which contains the point $(0, 0)$. this is the region "below" the line. To obtain the final region, take the intersection of the above two regions.

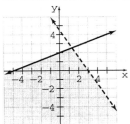

25. $|x| > 3$
$|y| \le 1$

For $|x| > 3$, the graph is the region to the left of the dashed line $x = -3$ along with the region to the right of the dashed line $x = 3$.

For $|y| \le 1$, the graph is the region between the solid lines $y = -1$ and $y = 1$. To obtain the final region, take the intersection of these regions.

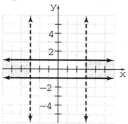

Cumulative Review Test

1.

$$16 \div \left\{ 4\left[3 + \left(\frac{5+10}{5} \right)^2 \right] - 32 \right\}$$

$$16 \div \left\{ 4\left[3 + \left(\frac{15}{5} \right)^2 \right] - 32 \right\}$$

$$16 \div \left\{ 4\left[3 + (3)^2 \right] - 32 \right\}$$

$$16 \div \left\{ 4[3 + 9] - 32 \right\}$$

$$16 \div \left\{ 4[12] - 32 \right\}$$

$$16 \div \left\{ 48 - 32 \right\}$$

$$16 \div \left\{ 16 \right\}$$

$$1$$

2. a. 9 and 1 are natural numbers.

b. $\frac{1}{2}$, –4, 9, 0, –4.63, and 1 are rational numbers.

c. $\frac{1}{2}$, –4, 9, 0, $\sqrt{3}$, –4.63, and 1 are real numbers.

3. $-|-8|,\ -1,\ \frac{5}{8},\ \frac{3}{4},\ |-4|,\ |-10|$

4. $-[3 - 2(x - 4)] = 3(x - 6)$
$-[3 - 2x + 8] = 3(x - 6)$
$-(-2x + 11) = 3(x - 6)$
$2x - 11 = 3x - 18$
$-11 = x - 18$
$7 = x$
$x = 7$

5. $\frac{2}{3}x - \frac{5}{6} = 2$

$$6\left(\frac{2}{3}x - \frac{5}{6} \right) = 6(2)$$

$$4x - 5 = 12$$

$$4x = 17$$

$$x = \frac{17}{4}$$

6. $|2x - 3| - 4 = 5$

$$|2x - 3| = 9$$

$2x - 3 = -9$ or $2x - 3 = 9$
$2x = -6$ $2x = 12$
$x = -3$ $x = 6$

7. $M = \frac{1}{2}(a + x)$

$$2[M] = 2\left[\frac{1}{2}(a + x) \right]$$

$$2M = a + x$$

$$2M - a = x \text{ or } x = 2M - a$$

8. $0 < \dfrac{3x - 2}{4} \le 8$

$$4(0) < 4\left(\frac{3x - 2}{4} \right) \le 4(8)$$

$$0 < 3x - 2 \le 32$$

$$0 + 2 < 3x - 2 + 2 \le 32 + 2$$

$$2 < 3x \le 34$$

$$\frac{2}{3} < \frac{3x}{3} \le \frac{34}{3}$$

$$\frac{2}{3} < x \le \frac{34}{3}$$

The solution set is $\left\{ x \left| \dfrac{2}{3} < x \le \dfrac{34}{3} \right. \right\}$.

9. $\left(\dfrac{3x^2 y^{-2}}{y^3} \right)^{-2} = \left(\dfrac{y^3}{3x^2 y^{-2}} \right)^2$

$$= \left(\frac{y^5}{3x^2} \right)^2$$

$$= \frac{y^{5 \cdot 2}}{3^2 x^{2 \cdot 2}}$$

$$= \frac{y^{10}}{9x^4}$$

10. $2y = 3x - 8$

$y = \dfrac{3x - 8}{2}$

$y = \dfrac{3}{2}x - 4$

x	y
0	$y = \frac{3}{2}(0) - 4 = 0 - 4 = -4$
2	$y = \frac{3}{2}(2) - 4 = 3 - 4 = -1$
4	$y = \frac{3}{2}(4) - 4 = 6 - 4 = 2$

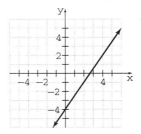

11. $2x - 3y = 8$

To find the slope, solve for y.
$2x - 3y = 8$

$-3y = -2x + 8$

$y = \dfrac{-2x + 8}{-3}$

$y = \dfrac{2}{3}x - \dfrac{8}{3}$

The slope of this line is $\dfrac{2}{3}$. Since the new line is

parallel to this line, its slope is also $\dfrac{2}{3}$. Use the

point-slope form with $m = \dfrac{2}{3}$ and

$(x_1, y_1) = (2, 3)$.

$y - y_1 = m(x - x_1)$

$y - 3 = \dfrac{2}{3}(x - 2)$

$y - 3 = \dfrac{2}{3}x - \dfrac{4}{3}$

$y = \dfrac{2}{3}x - \dfrac{4}{3} + 3$

$y = \dfrac{2}{3}x - \dfrac{4}{3} + \dfrac{9}{3}$

$y = \dfrac{2}{3}x + \dfrac{5}{3}$

12. $6x - 3y < 12$

Graph the line $6x - 3y = 12$ using a dashed line.
For the check point, select $(0, 0)$.

$6x - 3y < 12$
$6(0) - 3(0) < 12$
$0 - 0 < 12$
$0 < 12$ True

Since this is a true statement, shade the region containing the point $(0, 0)$.

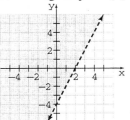

13. a. It is a function since it passes the vertical line test.

b. It is a function since it passes the vertical line test.

c. It is not a function since it fails the vertical line test.

14. a. $f(x) = \dfrac{x + 3}{x^2 - 9}$

$f(-4) = \dfrac{(-4) + 3}{(-4)^2 - 9}$

$f(-4) = \dfrac{-1}{16 - 9}$

$f(-4) = -\dfrac{1}{7}$

b. $f(h) = \dfrac{h + 3}{h^2 - 9}$

c. $f(3) = \dfrac{(3) + 3}{(3)^2 - 9}$

$f(3) = \dfrac{6}{9 - 9}$

$f(3) = \dfrac{6}{0}$ undefined

15. $3x + y = 6$
$y = 2x + 1$

Substitute $2x + 1$ for y in the first equation.
$3x + y = 6$
$3x + 2x + 1 = 6$
$5x + 1 = 6$
$5x = 5$
$x = \dfrac{5}{5} = 1$

Substitute 1 for x in the second equation.
$y = 2x + 1$
$y = 2(1) + 1$
$y = 2 + 1$
$y = 3$
The solution is $(1, 3)$.

16. $2p + 3q = 11$
$-3p - 5q = -16$
To eliminate p, multiply the first equation by 3 and the second equation by 2 and then add.
$3[2p + 3q = 11]$
$2[-3p - 5q = -16]$
gives
$$6p + 9q = 33$$
$$\underline{-6p - 10q = -32}$$
Add: $\qquad -q = 1$
$$q = -1$$
Substitute -1 for q in the first equation.
$2p + 3(-1) = 11$
$2p - 3 = 11$
$2p = 14$
$p = 7$
The solution is $(7, -1)$.

17. $x - 2y = 0 \quad (1)$
$2x + z = 7 \quad (2)$
$y - 2z = -5 \ (3)$
To eliminate z between equations (2) and (3), multiply equation (2) by 2 and then add.
$2[2x + z = 7]$
$y - 2z = -5$
gives
$$4x \qquad + 2z = 14$$
$$\underline{\quad y - 2z = -5}$$
Add: $4x + y \qquad = 9 \quad (4)$
Equations (4) and (1) are two equations in two unknowns:
$x - 2y = 0$
$4x + y = 9$
To eliminate y, multiply equation (4) by 2 and then add.
$x - 2y = 0$
$2[4x + y = 9]$
gives
$$x - 2y = 0$$
$$\underline{8x + 2y = 18}$$
Add: $9x \qquad = 18$
$$x = \frac{18}{9} = 2$$
Substitute 2 for x in equation (4).

$4x + y = 9$
$4(2) + y = 9$
$8 + y = 9$
$y = 1$
Finally, substitute 2 for x in equation (2).
$2x + z = 7$
$2(2) + z = 7$
$4 + z = 7$
$z = 3$
The solution is $(2, 1, 3)$.

18. Let x be the measure of the smallest angle. Then $9x$ is the measure of the largest angle and $x + 70$ is the measure of the remaining angle. The sum of the measures of the three angles is 180°.
$x + (x + 70) + 9x = 180$
$\qquad\qquad 11x + 70 = 180$
$\qquad\qquad\qquad 11x = 110$
$$x = \frac{110}{11} = 10$$
$x + 70 = 10 + 70 = 80$
$9x = 9(10) = 90$
The three angles are 10°, 90°, and 80°.

19. Let t be the time for Judy to catch up to Dawn.

	rate	time	distance
Judy	6	t	$6t$
Dawn	4	$t + \dfrac{1}{2}$	$4\left(t + \tfrac{1}{2}\right)$

$6t = 4\left(t + \dfrac{1}{2}\right)$
$6t = 4t + 2$
$2t = 2$
$t = \dfrac{2}{2} = 1$

It takes 1 hour for Judy to catch up to Dawn.

20. Let x be the number of \$20 tickets sold. Then $1000 - x$ is the number of \$16 tickets sold.
$20x + 16(1000 - x) = 18,400$
$20x + 16,000 - 16x = 18,400$
$\qquad 4x + 16,000 = 18,400$
$\qquad\qquad\qquad 4x = 2400$
$$x = \frac{2400}{4} = 600$$
Thus, 600 \$20 tickets and $1000 - 600 = 400$ \$16 tickets were sold for the concert.

Chapter 5

Exercise Set 5.1

1. The terms are the parts that are added or subtracted.

3. A polynomial is a finite sum of terms in which all variables have whole number exponents and no variable appears in a denominator.

5. The leading coefficient is the coefficient of the leading term.

7. **a.** It is the same as that of the highest-degree term.

   b. The degree of $-4x^4 + 6x^3y^4 + z^5$ is the same as the degree of the highest-degree term $\left(6x^3y^4\right)$. The degree is $3 + 4 = 7$.

9. **a.** A polynomial is linear if its degree is 0 or 1.

   b. Answers will vary. One example is $x + 4$

11. **a.** A polynomial is cubic if it has degree 3 and is in one variable.

   b. Answers will vary. One example is $x^3 + x - 4$

13. Answers will vary. One example is $x^5 + x + 1$

15. Since -6 has only one term, it is a monomial.

17. The polynomial $5y$ has only term, it is a monomial.

19. Since $5x^{-3}$ has a negative exponent. It is not a polynomial.

21. Since $3x^{1/2} + 2xy$ has a fractional exponent, it is not a polynomial.

23. $-5 - 4x - x^2 = -x^2 - 4x - 5$; degree two

25. $9y^2 + 3xy + 10x^2 = 10x^2 + 3xy + 9y^2$; degree two

27. $-2x^4 + 5x^2 - 4$ is already in descending order; degree four

29. $x^4 + 3x^6 - 2x - 10 = 3x^6 + x^4 - 2x - 10$

   a. $3x^6$: The degree of the polynomial is 6.

   b. $3x^6$: The leading coefficient is 3.

31. $4x^2y^3 + 6xy^4 + 9xy^5$
   $= 9xy^5 + 6xy^4 + 4x^2y^3$

   a. $9xy^5$ or $9x^1y^5$: The degree of the polynomial is $1 + 5 = 6$.

   b. $9xy^5$: The leading coefficient is 9.

33. $-\dfrac{1}{3}m^4n^5p^8 + \dfrac{3}{5}m^3p^6 - \dfrac{5}{9}n^4p^6q$

   a. $-\dfrac{1}{3}m^4n^5p^8$: The degree of the polynomial is $4 + 5 + 8 = 17$.

   b. $-\dfrac{1}{3}m^4n^5p^8$: The leading coefficient is $-\dfrac{1}{3}$.

35. $P(x) = x^2 - 6x + 1$
   $P(2) = 2^2 - 6(2) + 1$
   $\qquad = 4 - 12 + 1$
   $\qquad = -7$

37. $P(x) = 2x^2 - 3x - 6$
   $P\left(\dfrac{1}{2}\right) = 2\left(\dfrac{1}{2}\right)^2 - 3\left(\dfrac{1}{2}\right) - 6$
   $\qquad = \dfrac{1}{2} - \dfrac{3}{2} - 6$
   $\qquad = -7$

39. $P(x) = 0.2x^3 + 1.6x^2 - 2.3$
   $P(0.4) = 0.2(0.4)^3 + 1.6(0.4)^2 - 2.3$
   $\qquad = 0.0128 + 0.256 - 2.3$
   $\qquad = -2.0312$

41. $\left(x^2 + 3x - 7\right) + \left(6x - 5\right) = x^2 + 5x - 7 + 6x - 5 \leftarrow$ Remove parentheses

$\qquad\qquad\qquad = x^2 + 5x + 6x - 7 - 5 \leftarrow$ Rearrange terms

$\qquad\qquad\qquad = x^2 + 11x - 12 \qquad\quad \leftarrow$ Combine like terms

43. $\left(x^2 - 8x + 2\right) - \left(5x + 9\right) = x^2 - 8x + 2 - 5x - 9 \leftarrow$ Remove parentheses

$\qquad\qquad\qquad = x^2 - 8x - 5x + 2 - 9 \leftarrow$ Rearrange terms

$\qquad\qquad\qquad = x^2 - 13x - 7 \qquad\quad \leftarrow$ Combine like terms

45. $\left(4y^2 + 9y - 1\right) - \left(2y^2 + 10\right) = 4y^2 + 9y - 1 - 2y^2 - 10 \leftarrow$ Remove parentheses

$\qquad\qquad\qquad\quad = 4y^2 - 2y^2 + 9y - 1 - 10 \leftarrow$ Rearrange terms

$\qquad\qquad\qquad\quad = 2y^2 + 9y - 11 \qquad\qquad \leftarrow$ Combine like terms

47. $\left(-\dfrac{5}{9}a + 8\right) + \left(-\dfrac{2}{3}a^2 - \dfrac{1}{4}a - 1\right) = -\dfrac{5}{9}a + 8 - \dfrac{2}{3}a^2 - \dfrac{1}{4}a - 1 \quad \leftarrow$ Remove parentheses

$\qquad\qquad\qquad\qquad = -\dfrac{2}{3}a^2 - \dfrac{5}{9}a - \dfrac{1}{4}a + 8 - 1 \quad \leftarrow$ Rearrange terms

$\qquad\qquad\qquad\qquad = -\dfrac{2}{3}a^2 - \dfrac{20}{36}a - \dfrac{9}{36}a + 8 - 1 \leftarrow$ Common denominator

$\qquad\qquad\qquad\qquad = -\dfrac{2}{3}a^2 - \dfrac{29}{36}a + 7 \qquad\qquad \leftarrow$ Combine like terms

49. $\left(1.4x^2 + 1.6x - 8.3\right) - \left(4.9x^2 + 3.7x + 11.3\right)$

$\quad = 1.4x^2 + 1.6x - 8.3 - 4.9x^2 - 3.7x - 11.3 \leftarrow$ Remove parentheses

$\quad = 1.4x^2 - 4.9x^2 + 1.6x - 3.7x - 8.3 - 11.3 \leftarrow$ Rearrange terms

$\quad = -3.5x^2 - 2.1x - 19.6 \qquad\qquad\qquad \leftarrow$ Combine like terms

51. $\left(-\dfrac{1}{3}x^3 + \dfrac{1}{4}x^2y + 8xy^2\right) + \left(-x^3 - \dfrac{1}{2}x^2y + xy^2\right)$

$\quad = -\dfrac{1}{3}x^3 + \dfrac{1}{4}x^2y + 8xy^2 - x^3 - \dfrac{1}{2}x^2y + xy^2 \leftarrow$ Remove parentheses

$\quad = -\dfrac{1}{3}x^3 - x^3 + \dfrac{1}{4}x^2y - \dfrac{1}{2}x^2y + 8xy^2 + xy^2 \leftarrow$ Rearrange terms

$\quad = -\dfrac{4}{3}x^3 - \dfrac{1}{4}x^2y + 9xy^2 \qquad\qquad\qquad \leftarrow$ Combine like terms

53. $\left(3a - 6b + 5c\right) - \left(-2a + 4b - 8c\right) = 3a - 6b + 5c + 2a - 4b + 8c \leftarrow$ Remove parentheses

$\qquad\qquad\qquad\qquad = 3a + 2a - 6b - 4b + 5c + 8c \leftarrow$ Rearrange terms

$\qquad\qquad\qquad\qquad = 5a - 10b + 13c \qquad\qquad \leftarrow$ Combine like terms

55. $\left(3a^2b - 6ab + 5b^2\right) - \left(4ab - 6b^2 - 5a^2b\right) = 3a^2b - 6ab + 5b^2 - 4ab + 6b^2 + 5a^2b \leftarrow$ Remove parentheses

$\qquad\qquad\qquad\qquad\qquad = 3a^2b + 5a^2b - 6ab - 4ab + 5b^2 + 6b^2 \leftarrow$ Rearrange terms

$\qquad\qquad\qquad\qquad\qquad = 8a^2b - 10ab + 11b^2 \qquad\qquad \leftarrow$ Combine like terms

57. $\left(8r^2 - 5t^2 + 2rt\right) + \left(-6rt + 2t^2 - r^2\right) = 8r^2 - 5t^2 + 2rt - 6rt + 2t^2 - r^2$ ← Remove parentheses

$$= 8r^2 - r^2 + 2rt - 6rt - 5t^2 + 2t^2 \quad \leftarrow \text{Rearrange terms}$$

$$= 7r^2 - 4rt - 3t^2 \quad\quad\quad \leftarrow \text{Combine like terms}$$

59. $6x^2 - 2x - \left[3x - \left(4x^2 - 9\right)\right] = 6x^2 - 2x - \left[3x - 4x^2 + 9\right]$ ← Remove parentheses

$$= 6x^2 - 2x - 3x + 4x^2 - 9 \quad \leftarrow \text{Remove brackets}$$

$$= 6x^2 + 4x^2 - 2x - 3x - 9 \quad \leftarrow \text{Rearrange terms}$$

$$= 10x^2 - 5x - 9 \quad\quad\quad \leftarrow \text{Combine like terms}$$

61. $5w - 6w^2 - \left[\left(3w - 2w^2\right) - \left(4w + w^2\right)\right] = 5w - 6w^2 - \left[3w - 2w^2 - 4w - w^2\right]$ ← Remove parentheses

$$= 5w - 6w^2 - \left[3w - 4w - 2w^2 - w^2\right] \quad \leftarrow \text{Rearrange terms}$$

$$= 5w - 6w^2 - \left(-w - 3w^2\right) \quad \leftarrow \text{Combine like terms}$$

$$= 5w - 6w^2 + w + 3w^2 \quad \leftarrow \text{Remove parenthesess}$$

$$= -6w^2 + 3w^2 + 5w + w \quad \leftarrow \text{Rearrange terms}$$

$$= -3w^2 + 6w \quad\quad\quad \leftarrow \text{Combine like terms}$$

63. $(7x + 3) - (4x - 11) = 7x + 3 - 4x + 11$ ← Remove parentheses

$$= 7x - 4x + 3 + 11 \leftarrow \text{Rearrange terms}$$

$$= 3x + 14 \quad\quad \leftarrow \text{Combine like terms}$$

65. $\left(-2x^2 + 4x - 12\right) + \left(-x^2 - 2x\right) = -2x^2 + 4x - 12 - x^2 - 2x$ ← Remove parentheses

$$= -2x^2 - x^2 + 4x - 2x - 12 \leftarrow \text{Rearrange terms}$$

$$= -3x^2 + 2x - 12 \quad\quad \leftarrow \text{Combine like terms}$$

67. $\left(-4.2a^2 - 9.6a\right) - \left(0.2a^2 - 3.9a + 26.4\right)$

$$= -4.2a^2 - 9.6a - 0.2a^2 + 3.9a - 26.4$$

$$= -4.2a^2 - 0.2a^2 - 9.6a + 3.9a - 26.4$$

$$= -4.4a^2 - 5.7a - 26.4$$

69. $\left(-\dfrac{1}{2}x^2y + xy^2 + \dfrac{3}{5}\right) - \left(5x^2y + \dfrac{5}{9}\right)$

$$= -\dfrac{1}{2}x^2y + xy^2 + \dfrac{3}{5} - 5x^2y - \dfrac{5}{9}$$

$$= -\dfrac{1}{2}x^2y - 5x^2y + xy^2 + \dfrac{3}{5} - \dfrac{5}{9}$$

$$= -\dfrac{11}{2}x^2y + xy^2 + \dfrac{2}{45}$$

71. $\left(3x^{2r} - 7x^r + 1\right) + \left(2x^{2r} - 3x^r + 2\right)$

$$= 3x^{2r} - 7x^r + 1 + 2x^{2r} - 3x^r + 2$$

$$= 3x^{2r} + 2x^{2r} - 7x^r - 3x^r + 1 + 2$$

$$= 5x^{2r} - 10x^r + 3$$

73. $\left(x^{2s} - 8x^s + 6\right) - \left(2x^{2s} - 4x^s - 9\right)$

$$= x^{2s} - 8x^s + 6 - 2x^{2s} + 4x^s + 9$$

$$= x^{2s} - 2x^{2s} - 8x^s + 4x^s + 6 + 9$$

$$= -x^{2s} - 4x^s + 15$$

75. $\left(7b^{4n} - 5b^{2n} + 1\right) - \left(3b^{3n} - b^{2n}\right)$

$$= 7b^{4n} - 5b^{2n} + 1 - 3b^{3n} + b^{2n}$$

$$= 7b^{4n} - 3b^{3n} - 5b^{2n} + b^{2n} + 1$$

$$= 7b^{4n} - 3b^{3n} - 4b^{2n} + 1$$

77. The perimeter of a square is $P = 4s$.

$$P = 4\left(x^2 + 2x + 5\right)$$
$$= 4x^2 + 8x + 20$$

79. The perimeter of a triangle is $P = s_1 + s_2 + s_3$.

$$P = \left(x^2 + 3x + 1\right) + \left(x^2 + 2x + 5\right) + \left(x^2 - x + 13\right)$$
$$= 3x^2 + 4x + 19$$

81. The perimeter of a trapezoid is the sum of its sides.

$$P = (5x - 1) + \left(x^2 + 8\right) + (4x + 1) + \left(x^2 + 3x + 1\right)$$
$$= 2x^2 + 12x + 9$$

83. No; answers will vary.

85. No; answers will vary.

87. $A(r) = \pi r^2$

$$A(6) = \pi 6^2$$
$$A = \pi(36)$$
$$A \approx 113.10 \text{ in}^2$$

89. $h = P(t) = -16t^2 + 1250$

$$h = P(6) = -16(6)^2 + 1250 = 674$$

The object is 674 feet from the ground.

91. a. $R(x) = 2x^2 - 60x$, $C(x) = 8050 - 420x$
$P(x) = R(x) - C(x)$

$$P(x) = \left(2x^2 - 60x\right) - (8050 - 420x)$$
$$P(x) = 2x^2 - 60x0 - 8050 + 420x$$
$$P(x) = 2x^2 + 360x - 8050$$

b. $P(100) = 2(100)^2 + 360(100) - 8050$

$$= 20{,}000 + 36{,}000 - 8050$$
$$= 47{,}950$$

The profit is $47,950.

93. $y = x^2 + 3x - 4$ is graph c.
The coefficient of the leading term is positive, so the graph opens up. The y-intercept is –4.

95. $y = -x^3 + 2x - 6$ is graph c.
The coefficient of the leading term is negative, so that eliminates graphs (a) and (b).

97. a. $f(t) = 1.55t^2 - 22.03t + 133.65$

$$t = 2001 - 1993 = 8$$
$$f(8) = 1.55(8)^2 - 22.03(8) + 113.65$$
$$= 99.2 - 176.24 + 113.65$$
$$= 36.61 \text{ thousand}$$

The number of car thefts in New York City in 2001 was about 36,610.

b. Yes

99. $C(t) = 0.31t^2 + 0.59t + 9.61$

$$t = 2012 - 1997 = 15$$
$$C(15) = 0.31(15)^2 + 0.59(15) + 9.61$$
$$= 69.75 + 8.85 + 9.61$$
$$= 88.21 \text{ thousand or } 88{,}210$$

The cost in 2012 is $88,210.

101. a. $y_1 = x^3$
$y_2 = x^3 - 3x^2 - 3$

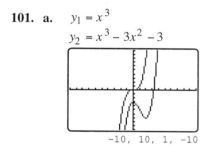

-10, 10, 1, -10

b. increase

c. Answers will vary.

d. decrease

e. Answers will vary.

103. $y = -x^4 + 3x^3 - 5$ is graph b.
The leading coefficient is negative, therefore eliminating graph (c). The y-intercept is –5.

107. $\sqrt[4]{81} = 3$ since $3^4 = 81$

109. Let t be the number of hours for the two machines to produce 540 buckets.
$40t + 50t = 540$

$$90t = 540$$
$$t = 6$$

It will take the two machines 6 hours to produce 540 buckets.

111. The system is
$$-4s + 3t = 16 \quad (1)$$
$$2t - 2u = 2 \quad (2)$$
$$-s + 6u = -2 \quad (3)$$
To eliminate the u in equation (3), multiply equation (2) by 3 and add to equation (3):
$$3[2t - 2u = 2]$$
$$-s + 6u = -2$$
gives:
$$6t - 6u = 6$$
$$\underline{-s + \quad 6u = -2}$$
$$-s + 6t \quad = 4 \quad (4)$$
Equations (1) and (4) form a system of equations in s and t. Solve this system.
$$-4s + 3t = 16 \quad (1)$$
$$-s + 6t = 4 \quad (4)$$
Multiply equation (4) by –4 and add to equation

(1).
$$-4s + 3t = 16$$
$$-4[-s + 6t = 4]$$
gives:
$$-4s + 3t = 16$$
$$\underline{4s - 24t = -16}$$
$$-21t = 0$$
$$t = 0$$
Substitute 0 for t in equation (4) and solve for s.
$$-s + 6(0) = 4$$
$$-s = 4$$
$$s = -4$$
Substitute 0 for t in equation (2) and solve for u.
$$2(0) - 2u = 2$$
$$-2u = 2$$
$$u = -1$$
The solution is $(-4, 0, -1)$.

Exercise Set 5.2

1. Answers will vary.

3. a. Answers will vary.

b. $(4 + x)(x^2 - 6x + 3)$
$$= 4(x^2 - 6x + 3) + x(x^2 - 6x + 3)$$
$$= 4x^2 - 24x + 12 + x^3 - 6x^2 + 3x$$
$$= x^3 - 2x^2 - 21x + 12$$

5. a. Answers will vary.

b. Answers will vary. One example is $(x + 4)(x - 4)$

c. Answers will vary.

d. Answers will vary. One example is $x^2 - 16$

7. Yes, answers may vary.

9. $(4xy)(6xy^4) = 4 \cdot 6 \cdot x \cdot x \cdot y \cdot y^4$
$$= 24x^{1+1}y^{1+4}$$
$$= 24x^2y^5$$

11. $\left(\frac{5}{9}x^2y^5\right)\left(\frac{1}{5}x^5y^3z^2\right) = \frac{5}{9} \cdot \frac{1}{5} \cdot x^2 \cdot x^5 \cdot y^5 \cdot y^3 \cdot z^2$
$$= \frac{1}{9}x^{2+5}y^{5+3}z^2$$
$$= \frac{1}{9}x^7y^8z^2$$

13. $-3x^2y\left(-2x^4y^2 + 3xy^3 + 4\right) = \left(-3x^2y\right)\left(-2x^4y^2\right) + \left(-3x^2y\right)\left(3xy^3\right) + \left(-3x^2y\right)(4)$
$$= 6x^6y^3 - 9x^3y^4 - 12x^2y$$

15. $\frac{2}{3}yz\left(3x + 4y - 9y^2\right) = \left(\frac{2}{3}yz\right)(3x) + \left(\frac{2}{3}yz\right)(4y) + \left(\frac{2}{3}yz\right)\left(-9y^2\right)$
$$= 2xyz + \frac{8}{3}y^2z - 6y^3z$$

17. $0.3\left(2x^2 - 5x + 7y\right) = 0.3\left(2x^2\right) + 0.3(-5x) + 0.3(7y)$
$$= 0.6x^2 - 1.5x + 2.1y$$

19. $0.3a^5b^4\left(9.5a^6b - 4.6a^4b^3 + 1.2ab^5\right) = 0.3a^5b^4\left(9.5a^6b\right) + 0.3a^5b^4\left(-4.6a^4b^3\right) + 0.3a^5b^4\left(1.2ab^5\right)$
$$= (0.3)(9.5)a^{5+6}b^{4+1} + 0.3(-4.6)a^{5+4}b^{4+3} + 0.3(1.2)a^{5+1}b^{4+5}$$
$$= 2.85a^{11}b^5 - 1.38a^9b^7 + 0.36a^6b^9$$

21. $(4x - 6)(3x - 5) = (4x)(3x) + (4x)(-5) + (-6)(3x) + (-6)(-5)$
$$= 12x^2 - 20x - 18x + 30$$
$$= 12x^2 - 38x + 30$$

23. $\left(4 - x\right)\left(3 + 2x^2\right) = (4)(3) + (4)\left(2x^2\right) + (-x)(3) + (-x)\left(2x^2\right)$
$$= 12 + 8x^2 - 3x - 2x^3$$
$$= -2x^3 + 8x^2 - 3x + 12 \leftarrow \text{Rearrange terms}$$

25. $\left(\frac{1}{2}x + 2y\right)\left(2x - \frac{1}{3}y\right) = \left(\frac{1}{2}x\right)(2x) + \left(\frac{1}{2}x\right)\left(-\frac{1}{3}y\right) + (2y)(2x) + (2y)\left(-\frac{1}{3}y\right)$
$$= x^2 - \frac{1}{6}xy + 4xy - \frac{2}{3}y^2$$
$$= x^2 + \frac{23}{6}xy - \frac{2}{3}y^2$$

27. $(0.3a + 5b)(2a - 0.7b) = \left(0.3a\right)\left(2a\right) + \left(0.3a\right)\left(-0.7b\right) + \left(5b\right)\left(2a\right) + \left(5b\right)\left(-0.7b\right)$
$$= 0.6a^2 - 0.21ab + 10ab - 3.5b^2$$
$$= 0.6a^2 + 9.79ab - 3.5b^2$$

29.
$$x^2 + 3x + 1$$
$$\underline{\qquad\qquad x - 2}$$
$$\underline{-2x^2 - 6x - 2} \qquad \leftarrow \text{Multiply top expression by } -2$$
$$\underline{x^3 + 3x^2 + x} \qquad\qquad \leftarrow \text{Multiply top expression by } x$$
$$x^3 + x^2 - 5x - 2 \qquad \leftarrow \text{Add like terms}$$

31.

$$2a^2 - ab + 2b^2$$
$$\underline{a - 3b}$$
$$-6a^2b + 3ab^2 - 6b^3 \qquad \leftarrow \text{Multiply top expression by } a$$
$$\underline{2a^3 - a^2b + 2ab^2} \qquad \leftarrow \text{Multiply top expression by } x$$
$$2a^3 - 7a^2b + 5ab^2 - 6b^3 \qquad \leftarrow \text{Add like terms}$$

33.

$$x^3 + -x^2 + 3x + 7$$
$$\underline{x + 1}$$
$$x^3 + -x^2 + 3x + 7 \qquad \leftarrow \text{Multiply top expression by } 1$$
$$\underline{x^4 + -x^3 + 3x^2 + 7x} \qquad \leftarrow \text{Multiply top expression by } x$$
$$x^4 \qquad + 2x^2 + 10x + 7 \qquad \leftarrow \text{Add like terms}$$

35.

$$5x^3 + 4x^2 - 6x + 2$$
$$\underline{x + 5}$$
$$25x^3 + 20x^2 - 30x + 10 \qquad \leftarrow \text{Multiply top expression by } 5$$
$$\underline{5x^4 + 4x^3 - 6x^2 + 2x} \qquad \leftarrow \text{Multiply top expression by } x$$
$$5x^4 + 29x^3 + 14x^2 - 28x + 10 \qquad \leftarrow \text{Add like terms}$$

37.

$$3m^2 - 2m + 4$$
$$\underline{m^2 - 3m - 5}$$
$$-15m^2 + 10m - 20 \qquad \leftarrow \text{Multiply top expression by } -5$$
$$-9m^3 + 6m^2 - 12m \qquad \leftarrow \text{Multiply top expression by } -3m$$
$$\underline{3m^4 - 2m^3 + 4m^2} \qquad \leftarrow \text{Multiply top expression by } m^2$$
$$3m^4 - 11m^3 - 5m^2 - 2m - 20 \qquad \leftarrow \text{Add like terms}$$

39. $(2x-1)^3 = (2x-1)(2x-1)(2x-1)$

$$= \left[(2x)^2 - 2(2x)(1) + 1^2\right](2x-1)$$

$$= \left(4x^2 - 4x + 1\right)(2x-1)$$

To complete the solution, multiply vertically

$$4x^2 - 4x + 1$$
$$\underline{2x - 1}$$
$$-4x^2 + 4x - 1$$
$$\underline{8x^3 - 8x^2 + 2x}$$
$$8x^3 - 12x^2 + 6x - 1$$

41.

$$5r^2 - rs + 2s^2$$
$$\underline{2r^2 - s^2}$$
$$-5r^2s^2 + rs^3 - 2s^4 \qquad \leftarrow \text{Multiply top expression by } -s^2$$
$$\underline{10r^4 - 2r^3s + 4r^2s^2} \qquad \leftarrow \text{Multiply top expression by } 2r^2$$
$$10r^4 - 2r^3s - r^2s^2 + rs^3 - 2s^4 \qquad \leftarrow \text{Add like terms}$$

43. $(x+2)(x+2) = (x+2)^2$
$$= (x)^2 + 2(x)(2) + (2)^2$$
$$= x^2 + 4x + 4$$

45. $(2x-3)(2x-3) = (2x-3)^2$
$$= (2x)^2 + 2(2x)(-3) + (-3)^2$$
$$= 4x^2 - 12x + 9$$

47. $(4x-3y)^2 = (4x)^2 - 2(4x)(3y) + (3y)^2$
$$= 16x^2 - 24xy + 9y^2$$

49. $(5m^2 + 2n)(5m^2 - 2n) = (5m^2)^2 - (2n)^2$
$$= 25m^4 - 4n^2$$

51. $[y + (4-2x)]^2 = (y)^2 + 2(y)(4-2x) + (4-2x)^2$
$$= y^2 + 8y - 4xy + 16 - 16x + 4x^2$$

53. $[5x + (2y+3)]^2$
$$= (5x)^2 + 2(5x)(2y+3) + (2y+3)^2$$
$$= 25x^2 + 10x(2y+3) + (2y+3)^2$$
$$= 25x^2 + 20xy + 30x + 4y^2 + 12y + 9$$

55. $[a + (b+2)][a - (b+2)] = (a)^2 - (b+2)^2$
$$= a^2 - (b^2 + 4b + 4)$$
$$= a^2 - b^2 - 4b - 4$$

57. $2xy(x^2 + xy + 3y^2) = (2xy)(x^2) + (2xy)(xy) + (2xy)(3y^2)$
$$= 2x^3y + 2x^2y^2 + 6xy^3$$

59. $\frac{1}{2}xy^2(4x^2 + 3xy - 7y^2) = \left(\frac{1}{2}xy^2\right)(4x^2) + \left(\frac{1}{2}xy^2\right)(3xy) + \left(\frac{1}{2}xy^2\right)(-7y^2)$
$$= 2x^3y^2 + \frac{3}{2}x^2y^3 - \frac{7}{2}xy^4$$

61. $-\frac{3}{5}xy^3z^2\left(-xy^2z^5 - 5xy + \frac{1}{6}xz^7\right) = \left(-\frac{3}{5}xy^3z^2\right)(-xy^2z^5) + \left(-\frac{3}{5}xy^3z^2\right)(-5xy) + \left(-\frac{3}{5}xy^3z^2\right)\left(\frac{1}{6}xz^7\right)$
$$= \frac{3}{5}x^2y^5z^7 + 3x^2y^4z^2 - \frac{1}{10}x^2y^3z^9$$

63. $(3a+4)(7a-6) = (3a)(7a) + (3a)(-6) + (4)(7a) + (4)(-6)$
$$= 21a^2 - 18a + 28a - 24$$
$$= 21a^2 + 10a - 24$$

65. $\left(8x + \dfrac{1}{4}\right)\left(8x - \dfrac{1}{4}\right) = (8x)^2 - \left(\dfrac{1}{4}\right)^2$

$$= 64x^2 - \dfrac{1}{16}$$

67. $(2x - 9y)^2 = (2x)^2 + 2(2x)(-9y) + (-9y)^2$

$$= 4x^2 - 36xy + 81y^2$$

69.　　　　$2x^2 + 4x - 3$
　　　　　　　　$x + 3$

　　　　$\overline{6x^2 + 12x - 9}$ ← Multiply top expression by 3
$\underline{2x^3 + 4x^2 - 3x}$ ← Multiply top expression by x
$2x^3 + 10x^2 + 9x - 9$ ← Add like terms

71.　　　　　$3p^2 + 4pq - 2q^2$
　　　　　　　　　　$2p - 3q$

　　$\overline{-9p^2q - 12pq^2 + 6q^3}$ ← Multiply top expression by $-3q$
$\underline{6p^3 + 8p^2q - 4pq^2}$ ← Multiply top expression by $2p$
$6p^3 - p^2q - 16pq^2 + 6q^3$ ← Add like terms

73. $\left[(3x + 2) + y\right]\left[(3x + 2) - y\right]$

$$= (3x + 2)^2 - y^2$$

$$= (3x)^2 + 2(3x)(2) + 2^2 - y^2$$

$$= 9x^2 + 12x + 4 - y^2$$

75. $(a + b)(a - b)\left(a^2 - b^2\right)$

$$= \left(a^2 - b^2\right)\left(a^2 - b^2\right)$$

$$= \left(a^2\right)^2 - 2\left(a^2\right)\left(b^2\right) + \left(b^2\right)^2$$

$$= a^4 - 2a^2b^2 + b^4$$

77. $(x - 4)(6 + x)(2x - 8)$

$$= \left(6x + x^2 - 24 - 4x\right)(2x - 8)$$

$$= \left(x^2 + 2x - 24\right)(2x - 8)$$

$$= x^2(2x - 8) + 2x(2x - 8) - 24(2x - 8)$$

$$= 2x^3 - 8x^2 + 4x^2 - 16x - 48x + 192$$

$$= 2x^3 - 4x^2 - 64x + 192$$

79　a. $(f \cdot g)(x) = f(x) \cdot g(x)$

$$= (x - 5)(x + 4)$$

$$= x^2 + 4x - 5x - 20$$

$$= x^2 - x - 20$$

b. $(f \cdot g)(4) = 4^2 - 4 - 20$

$$= 16 - 4 - 20$$

$$= -8$$

81.　a. $(f \cdot g)(x)$

$$= f(x) \cdot g(x)$$

$$= \left(2x^2 + 6x - 4\right)(5x + 3)$$

$$= 2x^2(5x + 3) + 6x(5x + 3) - 4(5x + 3)$$

$$= 10x^3 + 6x^2 + 30x^2 + 18x - 20x - 12$$

$$= 10x^3 + 36x^2 - 2x - 12$$

b. $(f \cdot g)(4) = 10(4)^3 + 36(4)^2 - 2(4) - 12$

$$= 640 + 576 - 8 - 12$$

$$= 1196$$

83. a. $(f \cdot g)(x) = f(x) \cdot g(x)$
$$= \left(-x^2 + 3x\right)\left(x^2 + 2\right)$$
$$= -x^4 - 2x^2 + 3x^3 + 6x$$
$$= -x^4 + 3x^3 - 2x^2 + 6x$$

  b. $(f \cdot g)(4) = -4^4 + 3(4)^3 - 2(4)^2 + 6(4)$
$$= -256 + 192 - 32 + 24$$
$$= -72$$

85. The area is the sum of the three component areas:
$$(x)(x) + (2)(x) + (3)(x)$$
$$x^2 + 2x + 3x$$
$$x^2 + 5x$$

87. The area is the sum of the area of the large square and the area of small square $= x^2 + y^2$

89. a. The sum of the areas of the four pieces is
$$x^2 + 5x + 3x + 15 = x^2 + 8x + 15$$

  b. The area is length 3 width
$$= (x + 5)(x + 3)$$
$$= x^2 + 5x + 3x + 15$$
$$= x^2 + 8x + 15$$

91. The area is
length × width $= (6 + x)(6 - x)$.
$$= 6^2 - x^2$$
$$= 36 - x^2$$

93. a. The area of the larger rectangle is
$$(2x + 3)(x + 4) = 2x^2 + 8x + 3x + 12$$
$$= 2x^2 + 11x + 12$$
The area of the smaller rectangle is
$(2x)(x) = 2x^2$.
The area of the shaded portion is the area of the larger rectangle – area of the smaller rectangle.
shaded portion $= \left(2x^2 + 11x + 12\right) - 2x^2$
$$= 11x + 12$$

  b. Since the area of the shaded portions is 67 sq in., set $11x + 12$ equal to 67 and then solve:
$$11x + 12 = 67$$
$$11x = 55$$
$$x = \frac{55}{11} = 5$$
Now, the dimensions of the larger rectangle are
$2(5) + 3 = 10 + 3 = 13$ inches by

$5 + 4 = 9$ inches.
The area is $(13)(9) = 117$ square inches. Also, the dimensions of the smaller rectangle are $2(5)$ $= 10$ by 5 in.
The area is $(10)(5) = 50$ sq in.

95. $x^2 - 25 = x^2 - 5^2 = (x - 5)(x + 5)$

97. $x^2 + 12x + 36 = x^2 + 2(6x) + 6^2$
$$= (x + 6)(x + 6)$$

99. $a(x - n)^3 = a(x - n)(x - n)(x - n)$

101. a. Answers will vary. One example is Observe that the length is $a + b$ and the width is $a + b$. Since the area is the product of the length and the width, this gives
$$\text{area} = (a + b)(a + b) = (a + b)^2$$

  b. The sum of the area of the four pieces is
$$(a)(a) + (a)(b) + (b)(a) + (b)(b)$$
$$= a^2 + ab + ab + b^2$$
$$= a^2 + 2ab + b^2$$

  c. $(a + b)^2 = a^2 + 2ab + b^2$

  d. The are the same

103. $A = P\left(1 + \dfrac{r}{n}\right)^{nt}$

  a. $A = P\left(1 + \dfrac{r}{1}\right)^{1 \cdot t}$
$$A = P(1 + r)^t$$

  b. $A = 1000(1 + 0.06)^2$
$$= 1000(1.06)^2$$
$$= 1123.6$$
The amount is \$1123.60.

105. $f(x) = x^2 + 3x + 4$

Then $f(a+b) = (a+b)^2 - 3(a+b) + 5$ ← Replace x by $a + b$

$$= a^2 + 2ab + b^2 - 3a - 3b + 5$$

107. $3x^t\left(5x^{2t-1} + 6x^{3t}\right) = \left(3x^t\right)\left(5x^{2t-1}\right) + \left(3x^t\right)\left(6x^{3t}\right)$

$$= 15x^{t+(2t-1)} + 18x^{t+3t}$$

$$= 15x^{3t-1} + 18x^{4t}$$

109. $\left(6x^m - 5\right)\left(2x^{2m} - 3\right) = \left(6x^m\right)\left(2x^{2m}\right) + \left(6x^m\right)(-3) + (-5)\left(2x^{2m}\right) + (-5)(-3)$

$$= 12x^{m+2m} - 18x^m - 10x^{2m} + 15$$

$$= 12x^{3m} - 18x^m - 10x^{2m} + 15$$

111. $\left(y^{a-b}\right)^{a+b} = y^{(a-b)(a+b)}$

$$= y^{a^2-b^2}$$

113. First, find

$(x - 3y)^2 = (x)^2 - 2(x)(3y) + (3y)^2$

$$= x^2 - 6xy + 9y^2$$

Then,

$(x - 3y)^4 = \left[(x - 3y)^2\right]^2 = \left(x^2 - 6xy + 9y^2\right)^2$

$$\begin{array}{r} x^2 - 6xy + 9y^2 \\ \underline{x^2 - 6xy + 9y^2} \\ 9x^2y^2 - 54xy^3 + 81y^4 \\ -6x^3y + 36x^2y^2 - 54xy^3 \\ \underline{x^4 - 6x^3y + 9x^2y^2} \\ x^4 - 12x^3y + 54x^2y^2 - 108xy^3 + 81y^4 \end{array}$$

115. a. Answers will vary. Possible answer.
Graph $y_1 = \left(x^2 + 2x + 3\right)(x + 2)$ and
$y_2 = x^3 + 4x^2 + 7x + 6$.
If they coincide, then the multiplication is correct.

b.

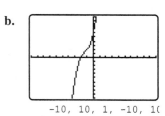

−10, 10, 1, −10, 1(

It is correct.

117. $\left[(y+1) - (x+2)\right]^2 = \left[y + 1 - x - 2\right]^2$

$$= \left[(y - x) - 1\right]^2$$

$$= (y - x)^2 - 2(y - x)(1) + (1)^2$$

$$= y^2 - 2xy + x^2 - 2y + 2x + 1$$

119. $\dfrac{4}{5} - \left(\dfrac{3}{4} - \dfrac{2}{3}\right) = \dfrac{4}{5} - \dfrac{3}{4} + \dfrac{2}{3}$

$$= \dfrac{4 \cdot 12}{5 \cdot 12} - \dfrac{3 \cdot 15}{4 \cdot 15} + \dfrac{2 \cdot 20}{3 \cdot 20}$$

$$= \dfrac{48}{60} - \dfrac{45}{60} + \dfrac{40}{60}$$

$$= \dfrac{43}{60}$$

121. $-12 < 3x - 5 \le -4$

$$-12 + 5 < 3x - 5 + 5 \le -4 + 5$$

$$-7 < 3x \le 1$$

$$\dfrac{-7}{3} < \dfrac{3x}{3} \le \dfrac{1}{3}$$

$$-\dfrac{7}{3} < x \le \dfrac{1}{3} \Rightarrow \left(-\dfrac{7}{3}, \dfrac{1}{3}\right]$$

Exercise Set 5.3

1. a. Answers will vary.

b. $\dfrac{5x^4 - 6x^3 - 4x^2 - 12x + 7}{3x}$.

$$= \dfrac{5x^4}{3x} - \dfrac{6x^3}{3x} - \dfrac{4x^2}{3x} - \dfrac{12x}{3x} + \dfrac{7}{3x}$$

$$= \dfrac{5}{3}x^3 - 2x^2 - \dfrac{4}{3}x - 4 + \dfrac{7}{3x}$$

3. Yes; answers will vary.

5. Place them in descending order of the variable.

7. **a.** Answers will vary.

   b.
$$\begin{array}{r|rrr} 5 & 1 & 3 & -4 \\ & & 5 & 40 \\ \hline & 1 & 8 & 36 \end{array} \leftarrow \text{Remainder}$$

   Thus, $\dfrac{x^2+3x-4}{x-5} = x+8+\dfrac{36}{x-5}$

9. To find the remainder, use synthetic division:
$$\begin{array}{r|rrr} -2 & 1 & 11 & 21 \\ & & -2 & -18 \\ \hline & 1 & 9 & 3 \end{array}$$

   The remainder is 3. Since the remainder is not zero, $x+2$ is not a factor.

11. $\dfrac{4x+18}{2} = \dfrac{4x}{2}+\dfrac{18}{2} = 2x+9$

13. $\dfrac{4x^2+2x}{2x} = \dfrac{4x^2}{2x}+\dfrac{2x}{2x} = 2x+1$

15. $\dfrac{5y^3+6y^2-9y}{3y} = \dfrac{5y^3}{3y}+\dfrac{6y^2}{3y}-\dfrac{9y}{3y}$
$$= \dfrac{5}{3}y^2+2y-3$$

17. $\dfrac{4x^5-6x^4+12x^3-8x^2}{4x^2}$
$$= \dfrac{4x^5}{4x^2}-\dfrac{6x^4}{4x^2}+\dfrac{12x^3}{4x^2}-\dfrac{8x^2}{4x^2}$$
$$= x^3-\dfrac{3}{2}x^2+3x-2$$

19. $\dfrac{8x^2y^2-10xy^3-5y}{2y^2} = \dfrac{8x^2y^2}{2y^2}-\dfrac{10xy^3}{2y^2}-\dfrac{5y}{2y^2}$
$$= 4x^2-5xy-\dfrac{5}{2y}$$

21. $\dfrac{9x^2y-12x^3y^2+7y^3}{2xy^2} = \dfrac{9x^2y}{2xy^2}-\dfrac{12x^3y^2}{2xy^2}+\dfrac{7y^3}{2xy^2}$
$$= \dfrac{9x}{2y}-6x^2+\dfrac{7y}{2x}$$

23. $\dfrac{3xyz+6xyz^2-9x^3y^5z^7}{6xy}$
$$= \dfrac{3xyz}{6xy}+\dfrac{6xyz^2}{6xy}-\dfrac{9x^3y^5z^7}{6xy}$$
$$= \dfrac{z}{2}+z^2-\dfrac{3}{2}x^2y^4z^7$$

25.
$$\begin{array}{r} x+2 \\ x+1{\overline{\smash{\big)}\,x^2+3x+2}} \end{array}$$
$$\begin{array}{r} \underline{x^2+x} \qquad \leftarrow x(x+1) \\ 2x+2 \\ \underline{2x+2} \quad \leftarrow 2(x+1) \\ 0 \quad \leftarrow \text{Remainder} \end{array}$$

   Thus, $\dfrac{x^2+3x+2}{x+1} = x+2$

27.
$$\begin{array}{r} 2x+3 \\ x+4{\overline{\smash{\big)}\,2x^2+11x+12}} \end{array}$$
$$\begin{array}{r} \underline{2x^2+8x} \qquad \leftarrow 2x(x+4) \\ 3x+12 \\ \underline{3x+12} \leftarrow 3(x+4) \\ 0 \leftarrow \text{Remainder} \end{array}$$

   Thus, $\dfrac{2x^2+11x+12}{x+4} = 2x+3$

29.
$$\begin{array}{r} 3x+2 \\ 2x-1{\overline{\smash{\big)}\,6x^2+x-2}} \end{array}$$
$$\begin{array}{r} \underline{6x^2-3x} \qquad \leftarrow 3x(2x-1) \\ 4x-2 \\ \underline{4x-2} \leftarrow 2(2x-1) \\ 0 \leftarrow \text{Remainder} \end{array}$$

   Thus, $\dfrac{6x^2+x-2}{2x-1} = 3x+2$

31.
$$\begin{array}{r} x+5 \\ x+1{\overline{\smash{\big)}\,x^2+6x+7}} \end{array}$$
$$\begin{array}{r} \underline{x^2+x} \qquad \leftarrow x(x+1) \\ 5x+7 \\ \underline{5x+5} \leftarrow 5(x+1) \\ 2 \leftarrow \text{Remainder} \end{array}$$

   Thus, $\dfrac{x^2+6x+7}{x+1} = x+5+\dfrac{2}{x+1}$

33.

$$b-2 \overline{\smash{\big)}2b^2+b-9} \quad \begin{array}{c} 2b+5 \end{array}$$

$$\underline{2b^2-4b} \quad \leftarrow 2b(b-2)$$
$$5b-9$$
$$\underline{5b-10} \quad \leftarrow 5(b-2)$$
$$1 \quad \leftarrow \text{Remainder}$$

Thus, $\dfrac{2b^2+b-9}{b-2} = 2b+5+\dfrac{1}{b-2}$

35.

$$2x-3 \overline{\smash{\big)}8x^2+6x-25} \quad \begin{array}{c} 4x+9 \end{array}$$

$$\underline{8x^2-12x} \quad \leftarrow 4x(2x-3)$$
$$18x-25$$
$$\underline{18x-27} \quad \leftarrow 9(2x-3)$$
$$2 \quad \leftarrow \text{Remainder}$$

Thus, $\dfrac{8x^2+6x-25}{2x-3} = 4x+9+\dfrac{2}{2x-3}$

37.

$$2x-5 \overline{\smash{\big)}4x^2+0x-25} \quad \begin{array}{c} 2x+5 \end{array} \quad \leftarrow \text{Write } 4x^2-25$$
$$\text{as } 4x^2+0x-25$$
$$\underline{4x^2-10x} \quad \leftarrow 2x(2x-5)$$
$$10x-25$$
$$\underline{10x-25} \quad \leftarrow 5(2x-5)$$
$$0 \quad \leftarrow \text{Remainder}$$

Thus $\dfrac{4x^2-25}{2x-5} = 2x+5$

39.

$$x+1 \overline{\smash{\big)}x^3+3x^2+5x+4} \quad \begin{array}{c} x^2+2x+3 \end{array}$$

$$\underline{x^3+\;\;x^2} \quad \leftarrow x(x+1)$$
$$2x^2+5x$$
$$\underline{2x^2+2x} \quad \leftarrow 2x(x+1)$$
$$3x+4$$
$$\underline{3x+3} \quad \leftarrow 3(x+1)$$
$$1 \quad \leftarrow \text{Remainder}$$

Thus, $\dfrac{x^3+3x^2+5x+4}{x+1} = x^2+2x+3+\dfrac{1}{x+1}$

41.

$$3b+2 \overline{\smash{\big)}9b^3-3b^2-3b+4} \quad \begin{array}{c} 3b^2-3b+1 \end{array}$$

$$\underline{9b^3+6b^2} \quad \leftarrow 3b^2(3b+2)$$
$$-9b^2-3b$$
$$\underline{-9b^2-6b} \quad \leftarrow -3b(3b+2)$$
$$3b+4$$
$$\underline{3b+2} \quad \leftarrow 1(3b+2)$$
$$2 \quad \leftarrow \text{Remainder}$$

Thus, $\dfrac{9b^3-3b^2-3b+4}{3b+2} = 3b^2-3b+1+\dfrac{2}{3b+2}$

43.

$$x+4 \overline{\smash{\big)}2x^3+0x^2+6x-4} \quad \begin{array}{c} 2x^2-8x+38 \end{array}$$

$$\underline{2x^3+8x^2} \quad \leftarrow 2x^2(x+4)$$
$$-8x^2+6x$$
$$\underline{-8x^2-32x} \quad \leftarrow -8x(x+4)$$
$$38x-4$$
$$\underline{38x+152} \quad \leftarrow 38(x+4)$$
$$-156 \leftarrow \text{Remainder}$$

Thus,
$$\dfrac{2x^3+6x-4}{x+4} = 2x^2-8x+38-\dfrac{156}{x+4}$$

45.

$$
x^2 + 0x - 2 \overline{\smash{\big)}\, 3x^5 + 0x^4 + 0x^3 + 4x^2 - 12x - 8} \quad \begin{array}{r} 3x^3 \qquad\qquad + 6x + 4 \end{array}
$$

$$
\underline{3x^5 + 0x^4 - 6x^3} \qquad \leftarrow 3x^3(x^2 + 0x - 2)
$$

$$
6x^3 + 4x^2 - 12x
$$

$$
\underline{6x^3 + 0x^2 - 12x} \qquad \leftarrow 6x(x^2 + 0x - 2)
$$

$$
4x^2 + 0x - 8
$$

$$
\underline{4x^2 + 0x - 8} \leftarrow 4(x^2 + 0x - 2)
$$

$$
0 \leftarrow \text{Remainder}
$$

Thus, $\dfrac{3x^5 + 4x^2 - 12x - 8}{x^2 - 2} = 3x^3 + 6x + 4$

47.

$$
3x^3 - 8x^2 + 0x - 5 \overline{\smash{\big)}\, 3x^4 + 4x^3 - 32x^2 - 5x - 20} \quad \begin{array}{r} x + 4 \end{array}
$$

$$
\underline{3x^4 - 8x^3 + 0x^2 - 5x} \qquad \leftarrow x\left(3x^3 - 8x^2 + 0x - 5\right)
$$

$$
12x^3 - 32x^2 + 0x - 20
$$

$$
\underline{12x^3 - 32x^2 + 0x - 20} \leftarrow 4\left(3x^3 - 8x^2 + 0x - 5\right)
$$

$$
0 \leftarrow \text{Remainder}
$$

Thus, $\dfrac{3x^4 + 4x^3 - 32x^2 - 5x - 20}{3x^3 - 8x^2 - 5} = x + 4$

49.

$$
c^2 - c + 5 \overline{\smash{\big)}\, 2c^4 - 8c^3 + 19c^2 - 33c + 15} \quad \begin{array}{r} 2c^2 - 6c + 3 \end{array}
$$

$$
\underline{2c^4 - 2c^3 + 10c^2} \qquad \leftarrow 2c^2(c^2 - c + 5)
$$

$$
-6c^3 + 9c^2 - 33c
$$

$$
\underline{-6c^3 + 6c^2 - 30c} \leftarrow -6c(c^2 - c + 5)
$$

$$
3c^2 - 3c + 15
$$

$$
\underline{3c^2 - 3c + 15} \leftarrow 3(c^2 - c + 5)
$$

$$
0 \leftarrow \text{Remainder}
$$

Thus $\dfrac{2c^4 - 8c^3 + 19c^2 - 33c + 15}{c^2 - c + 5} = 2c^2 - 6c + 3$

51.

$$
\begin{array}{r|rrr}
-1 & 1 & 7 & 6 \\
   &   & -1 & -6 \\
\hline
   & 1 & 6 & 0
\end{array}
$$

Thus, $\dfrac{x^2 + 7x + 6}{x + 1} = x + 6$

53.

$$
\begin{array}{r|rrr}
-2 & 1 & 5 & 6 \\
   &   & -2 & -6 \\
\hline
   & 1 & 3 & 0
\end{array}
$$

Thus, $\dfrac{x^2 + 5x + 6}{x + 2} = x + 3$

55.

$$
\begin{array}{r|rrr}
4 & 1 & -11 & 28 \\
  &   & 4 & -28 \\
\hline
  & 1 & -7 & 0
\end{array}
$$

Thus, $\dfrac{x^2 - 11x + 28}{x - 4} = x - 7$

57.

$$
\begin{array}{r|rrr}
3 & 1 & 5 & -12 \\
  &   & 3 & 24 \\
\hline
  & 1 & 8 & 12
\end{array}
$$

Thus, $\dfrac{x^2 + 5x - 12}{x - 3} = x + 8 + \dfrac{12}{x - 3}$

59.

$$
\begin{array}{r|rrr}
4 & 3 & -7 & -10 \\
 & & 12 & 20 \\
\hline
 & 3 & 5 & 10
\end{array}
$$

Thus, $\dfrac{3x^2 - 7x - 10}{x - 4} = 3x + 5 + \dfrac{10}{x - 4}$

61.

$$
\begin{array}{r|rrrr}
1 & 4 & -3 & 2 & 0 \\
 & & 4 & 1 & 3 \\
\hline
 & 4 & 1 & 3 & 3
\end{array}
$$

Thus, $\dfrac{4x^3 - 3x^2 + 2x}{x - 1} = 4x^2 + x + 3 + \dfrac{3}{x - 1}$

63.

$$
\begin{array}{r|rrrr}
-3 & 3 & 7 & -4 & 18 \\
 & & -9 & 6 & -6 \\
\hline
 & 3 & -2 & 2 & 12
\end{array}
$$

Thus, $\dfrac{3c^3 + 7c^2 - 4c + 18}{c + 3} = 3c^2 - 2c + 2 + \dfrac{12}{c + 3}$

65.

$$
\begin{array}{r|rrrrr}
1 & 1 & 0 & 0 & 0 & -1 \\
 & & 1 & 1 & 1 & 1 \\
\hline
 & 1 & 1 & 1 & 1 & 0
\end{array}
$$

Thus, $\dfrac{y^4 - 1}{y - 1} = y^3 + y^2 + y + 1$

67.

$$
\begin{array}{r|rrrrr}
-4 & 1 & 0 & 0 & 0 & 16 \\
 & & -4 & 16 & -64 & 256 \\
\hline
 & 1 & -4 & 16 & -64 & 272
\end{array}
$$

Thus, $\dfrac{x^4 + 16}{x + 4} = x^3 - 4x^2 + 16x - 64 + \dfrac{272}{x + 4}$

69.

$$
\begin{array}{r|rrrrrr}
-1 & 1 & 1 & 0 & 0 & 0 & -10 \\
 & & -1 & 0 & 0 & 0 & 0 \\
\hline
 & 1 & 0 & 0 & 0 & 0 & -10
\end{array}
$$

Thus, $\dfrac{x^5 + x^4 - 10}{x + 1} = x^4 - \dfrac{10}{x + 1}$

71.

$$
\begin{array}{r|rrrrrr}
-1 & 1 & 4 & 0 & 0 & 0 & -12 \\
 & & -1 & -3 & 3 & -3 & 3 \\
\hline
 & 1 & 3 & -3 & 3 & -3 & -9
\end{array}
$$

Thus, $\dfrac{b^5 + 4b^4 - 10}{b + 1} = b^4 + 3b^3 - 3b^2 + 3b - 3 - \dfrac{9}{b + 1}$

73.

$$
\begin{array}{r|rrrr}
\frac{1}{3} & 3 & 2 & -4 & 1 \\
 & & 1 & 1 & -1 \\
\hline
 & 3 & 3 & -3 & 0
\end{array}
$$

Thus, $\dfrac{3x^3 + 2x^2 - 4x + 1}{x - \frac{1}{3}} = 3x^2 + 3x - 3$

75.

$$
\begin{array}{r|rrrrr}
\frac{1}{2} & 2 & -1 & 2 & -3 & 1 \\
 & & 1 & 0 & 1 & -1 \\
\hline
 & 2 & 0 & 2 & -2 & 0
\end{array}
$$

Thus, $\dfrac{2x^4 - x^3 + 2x^2 - 3x + 1}{x - \frac{1}{2}} = 2x^3 + 2x - 2$

77. To find the remainder, use synthetic division:

$$
\begin{array}{r|rrr}
2 & 4 & -5 & 4 \\
 & & 8 & 6 \\
\hline
 & 4 & 3 & 10
\end{array}
$$

The remainder is 10.

79. To find the remainder, use synthetic division:

$$
\begin{array}{r|rrrr}
2 & 1 & -2 & 4 & -8 \\
 & & 2 & 0 & 8 \\
\hline
 & 1 & 0 & 4 & 0
\end{array}
$$

The remainder is 0 which means that $x - 2$ is a factor.

81. To find the remainder, use synthetic division.

$$
\begin{array}{r|rrrr}
\frac{1}{2} & -2 & -6 & 2 & -4 \\
 & & -1 & -\frac{7}{2} & -\frac{3}{4} \\
\hline
 & -2 & -7 & -\frac{3}{2} & -\frac{19}{4} \text{ or } -4.75
\end{array}
$$

The remainder is $-\dfrac{19}{4}$ or -4.75.

83. Width $= \dfrac{\text{area}}{\text{length}} = \dfrac{6x^2 - 8x - 8}{2x - 4}$

$$2x - 4 \overline{\smash{\big)}\ 6x^2 - 8x - 8} \quad \overset{\textstyle 3x + 2}{}$$

$$\underline{6x^2 - 12x} \leftarrow 3x(2x - 4)$$
$$4x - 8$$
$$\underline{4x - 8} \leftarrow 2(2x - 4)$$
$$0 \leftarrow \text{Remainder}$$

Thus the width is $3x + 2$.

85. To compare the areas, compare the lengths and widths of the two figures (rectangles).

Length: observe that $12x + 24$ is six times $2x + 4$

Width: observe that $\dfrac{1}{2}x + 4$ is $\dfrac{1}{2}$ of $x + 8$

The area of the larger rectangle is $\dfrac{1}{2}(6) = 3$

times the area of the smaller rectangle.

87. No; answers will vary.

89. Answers will vary. One example is If the remainder is 0, $x - a$ is a factor.

91. $\dfrac{P(x)}{x - 4} = x + 2$

$P(x) = (x - 4)(x + 2)$

$P(x) = x^2 - 2x - 8$

93. $\dfrac{P(x)}{x + 4} = x + 5 + \dfrac{4}{x + 4}$

$P(x) = (x + 4)\left(x + 5 + \dfrac{4}{x + 4}\right)$

$\quad = x(x + 4) + 5(x + 4) + \dfrac{4}{x + 4}(x + 4)$

$\quad = x^2 + 4x + 5x + 20 + 4$

$\quad = x^2 + 9x + 24$

95. $x - 2y \overline{\smash{\big)}\ 2x^3 - x^2 y - 7xy^2 + 2y^3} \quad \overset{\textstyle 2x^2 + 3xy - y^2}{}$

$$\underline{2x^3 - 4x^2 y} \qquad\qquad \leftarrow 2x^2(x - 2y)$$
$$3x^2 y - 7xy^2$$
$$\underline{3x^2 y - 6xy^2} \qquad \leftarrow 3xy(x - 2y)$$
$$-xy^2 + 2y^3$$
$$\underline{-xy^2 + 2y^3} \leftarrow -y^2(x - 2y)$$
$$0 \leftarrow \text{Remainder}$$

Thus, $\dfrac{2x^3 - x^2 y - 7xy^2 + 2y^3}{x - 2y} = 2x^2 + 3xy - y^2$

97. $2x - 3 \overline{\smash{\big)}\ 2x^2 + 2x - 2} \quad \overset{\textstyle x + \frac{5}{2}}{}$

$$\underline{2x^2 - 3x} \qquad \leftarrow x(2x - 3)$$
$$5x - 2$$
$$\underline{5x - \dfrac{15}{2}} \leftarrow \dfrac{5}{2}(2x - 3)$$
$$\dfrac{11}{2} \leftarrow \text{Remainder}$$

Thus, $\dfrac{2x^2 + 2x - 2}{2x - 3} = x + \dfrac{5}{2} + \dfrac{11}{2(2x - 3)}$

99. Two of the dimensions are r and $2r + 2$. This product is $r(2r + 2) = 2r^2 + 2r$. To find the third side, divide the volume by the above product. That is,

the third side $= \dfrac{\text{volume}}{\text{product of two sides}}$

$$= \dfrac{2r^3 + 4r^2 + 2r}{2r^2 + 2r}$$

$$2r^2 + 2r \overline{\smash{\big)}\ 2r^3 + 4r^2 + 2r} \quad \overset{\textstyle r + 1}{}$$

$$\underline{2r^3 + 2r^2} \qquad \leftarrow r(2r^2 + 2r)$$
$$2r^2 + 2r$$
$$\underline{2r^2 + 2r} \leftarrow 1(2r^2 + 2r)$$
$$0 \leftarrow \text{Remainder}$$

Thus, the third side is $w = r + 1$.

101. The polynomial is the product of $x - 3$ with $x^2 - 3x + 4$ plus the remainder of 2.

$$x^2 - 3x + 4$$
$$\underline{x - 3}$$
$$-3x^2 + 9x - 12$$
$$\underline{x^3 - 3x^2 + 4x}$$
$$x^3 - 6x^2 + 13x - 12$$

Now, add on the remainder of 2 to get $x^3 - 6x^2 + 13x - 10$ for the polynomial.

103.
$$\frac{4x^{n+1} + 2x^n - 3x^{n-1} - x^{n-2}}{2x^n} = \frac{4x^{n+1}}{2x^n} + \frac{2x^n}{2x^n} - \frac{3x^{n-1}}{2x^n} - \frac{x^{n-2}}{2x^n}$$

$$= 2x^{n+1-n} + x^{n-n} - \frac{3}{2}x^{n-1-n} - \frac{1}{2}x^{n-2-n}$$

$$= 2x + x^0 - \frac{3}{2}x^{-1} - \frac{1}{2}x^{-2}$$

$$= 2x + 1 - \frac{3}{2x} - \frac{1}{2x^2}$$

105. Let $P(x) = x^{100} + x^{99} + \dots + x + 1$. To determine if $x - 1$ is a factor, compute $P(1)$. If it is 0, then $x - 1$ is a factor. Now,

$$P(1) = 1^{100} + 1^{99} + 1^{98} + 1^{97} + \dots + 1^2 + 1^1 + 1$$
$$= 1 + 1 + 1 + 1 + \dots + 1 + 1 + 1 = 101$$

Note: Here you are adding up the number 1 a total of 101 times. Since $P(1) = 101$ which is not zero, then $x - 1$ is not a factor.

107. Let $P(x) = x^{99} + x^{98} + \dots + x + 1$. To determine if $x + 1$ is a factor, compute $P(-1)$. If it is 0, then $x + 1$ is a factor. Now,

$$P(-1) = (-1)^{99} + (-1)^{98} + (-1)^{97} + (-1)^{96} + \dots + (-1)^3 + (-1)^2 + (-1) + 1$$
$$= -1 + 1 - 1 + 1 + \dots - 1 + 1 - 1 + 1$$
$$= \quad 0 + 0 + \dots + \quad 0 \quad + 0 = 0$$

Since $P(-1) = 0$, $x + 1$ is a factor.

109. a.

$$-\tfrac{5}{3} \Big| \begin{array}{cccc} 9 & 9 & 5 & 12 \\ & -15 & 10 & -25 \\ \hline 9 & -6 & 15 & -13 \end{array}$$

Now, divide $9x^2 - 6x + 15$ by 3 to get $3x^2 - 2x + 5$.

Thus,

$$\frac{9x^3 + 9x^2 + 5x + 12}{3x + 5}$$

$$= 3x^2 - 2x + 5 - \frac{13}{3x + 5}$$

b. Because we are expressing the remainder in terms of $3x + 5$ rather than $x + \dfrac{5}{3}$, the denominator of the remainder is altered rather than the numerator.

111. Let x be the measure of smallest angle. Then the other angle measures are $2x$ and $x + 60$.

$$x + 2x + x + 60 = 180$$
$$4x + 60 = 180$$
$$4x = 120$$
$$x = 30$$

The smallest angle is 30°.

The next angle is $2 \times 30° = 60°$.

The last angle is $30° + 60° = 90°$.

113. $f(x) = x^2 - 4, \;\; g(x) = -5x + 3$

$$f(6) = (6)^2 - 4 = 36 - 4 = 32$$
$$g(6) = -5(6) + 3 = -30 + 3 = -27$$
$$f(6) \cdot g(6) = (32)(-27) = -864$$

Exercise Set 5.4

1. Determine if all the terms contain a greatest common factor and, if so, factor it out.

3. a. Answers will vary.

    b. The greatest common factor is $2x^2 y$.

    c. $2x^2 y\left(3y^4 - x + 6x^7 y^2\right)$

5. a. Answers will vary.

    b. $6x^3 - 2xy^3 + 3x^2 y^2 - y^5$

$$= 2x\left(3x^2 - y^3\right) + y^2\left(3x^2 - y^3\right)$$

$$= \left(2x + y^2\right)\left(3x^2 - y^3\right)$$

7.

The lowest power of x is 1. The lowest power of y is 4. Therefore the GCF is xy^4.

9. $7n+7 = 7 \cdot n + 7 \cdot 1 = 7(n+1)$

11. $2x^2 - 4x + 8 = 2 \cdot x^2 + 2 \cdot (-2x) + 2(4)$
$$= 2(x^2 - 2x + 4)$$

13. $12y^2 - 16y + 24 = 4 \cdot 3y^2 - 4 \cdot 4y + 4 \cdot 6$
$$= 4(3y^2 - 4y + 6)$$

15. $9x^4 - 3x^3 + 11x^2 = x^2 \cdot 9x^2 + x^2(-3x) + x^2 \cdot 11$
$$= x^2(9x^2 - 3x + 11)$$

17. $-24a^7 + 9a^6 - 3a^2$
$$= -3a^2 \cdot 8a^5 - 3a^2(-3a^4) - 3a^2 \cdot 1$$
$$= -3a^2(8a^5 - 3a^4 + 1)$$

19. $3x^2 y + 6x^2 y^2 + 3xy = 3xy \cdot x + 3xy \cdot 2xy + 3xy \cdot 1$
$$= 3xy(x + 2xy + 1)$$

21. $80a^5 b^4 c - 16a^4 b^2 c^2 + 8a^2 c$
$$= 8a^2 c \cdot 10a^3 b^4 + 8a^2 c(-2a^2 b^2 c) + 8a^2 c(1)$$
$$= 8a^2 c(10a^3 b^4 - 2a^2 b^2 c + 1)$$

23. $9p^4 q^5 r - 3p^2 q^2 r^2 + 6pq^5 r^3$
$$= 3pq^2 r \cdot 3p^3 q^3 + 3pq^2 r(-pr) + 3pq^2 r(2q^3 r^2)$$
$$= 3pq^2 r(3p^3 q^3 - pr + 2q^3 r^2)$$

25. $-52p^2 q^2 - 16pq^3 + 26r$
$$= -2 \cdot 26p^2 q^2 - 2 \cdot 8pq^3 - 2(-13r)$$
$$= -2(26p^2 q^2 + 8pq^3 - 13r)$$

27. $-8x + 4 = -4(2x) - 2(-1)$
$$= -4(2x - 1)$$

29. $-x^2 + 4x - 12 = -(x^2 - 4x + 12)$

31. $-3r^2 - 6r + 9 = -3(r^2 + 2r - 3)$

33. $-6r^4 s^3 + 4r^2 s^4 + 2rs^5$
$$= -2(3r^4 s^3 - 2r^2 s^4 - rs^5)$$
$$= -2rs^3(3r^3 - 2rs - s^2)$$

35. $-a^4 b^2 c + 5a^3 bc^2 + a^2 b$
$$= -a^2 b(a^2 bc) - a^2 b(-5ac^2) - a^2 b(-1)$$
$$= -a^2 b(a^2 bc - 5ac^2 - 1)$$

37. $x(a+3) + 1(a+3) = (x+1)(a+3)$

39. $3c(x-4) + 2(x-4) = (3c+2)(x-4)$

41. $(x-2)(3x+5) - (x-2)(5x-4)$
$$= (x-2)(3x+5-5x+4)$$
$$= (x-2)(-2x+9)$$
$$= -(x-2)(2x-9)$$

43. $(2a+4)(a-3) - (2a+4)(2a-1)$
$$= (2a+4)(a-3-2a+1)$$
$$= (2a+4)(-a-2)$$
$$= -2(a+2)(a+2)$$

45. $x^2 + 3x - 5x - 15 = x(x+3) - 5(x+3)$
$$= (x-5)(x+3)$$

47. $8y^2 - 4y - 20y + 10 = 2(4y^2 - 2y - 10y + 5)$
$$= 2[2y(2y-1) - 5(2y-1)]$$
$$= 2(2y-5)(2y-1)$$

49. $ax + ay + bx + by = a(x+y) + b(x+y)$
$$= (a+b)(x+y)$$

51. $x^3 - 3x^2 + 4x - 12 = x^2(x-3) + 4(x-3)$
$$= (x^2+4)(x-3)$$

53. $10m^2 - 12mn - 25mn + 30n^2$
$$= 2m(5m-6n) - 5n(5m-6n)$$
$$= (2m-5n)(5m-6n)$$

55. $5a^3 + 15a^2 - 10a - 30 = 5[a^3 + 3a^2 - 2a - 6]$
$$= 5[a^2(a+3) - 2(a+3)]$$
$$= 5(a^2-2)(a+3)$$

57.
$$c^5 - c^4 + c^3 - c^2 = c^2\left(c^3 - c^2 + c - 1\right)$$
$$= c^2\left[c^2(c-1) + 1(c-1)\right]$$
$$= c^2\left(c^2 + 1\right)(c-1)$$

59.
$$A_1 - A_2 = 6x(2x+1) - 5(2x+1)$$
$$= (2x+1)(6x-5)$$

61.
$$A_1 - A_2 = \left(3x^2 + 12x\right) - (2x - 8)$$
$$= 3x(x+4) - 2(x+4)$$
$$= (x+4)(3x-2)$$

63.
$$V_1 - V_2 = 9x(3x+2) - 5(3x+2)$$
$$= (3x+2)(9x-5)$$

65. a.
$$h(t) = -16t^2 + 128t$$
$$h(3) = -16(3)^2 + 128(3)$$
$$= -16(9) + 128(3)$$
$$= -144 + 384$$
$$= 240$$
The height after 3 seconds is 240 feet.

b.
$$h(t) = -16t^2 + 128t$$
$$h(t) = -16t(t) - 16t(-8)$$
$$h(t) = -16t(t - 8)$$

c.
$$h(3) = -16(3)(3 - 8)$$
$$= -48(-5)$$
$$= 240 \text{ feet}$$

67. a.
$$A = \pi r^2 + 2rl$$
$$= \pi(20)^2 + 2(20)(40)$$
$$= 400\pi + 1600$$
$$\approx 2856.64$$
The area is about 2856.64 ft^2.

b.
$$A = \pi r^2 + 2rl$$
$$A = r(\pi r) + r(2l)$$
$$A = r(\pi r + 2l)$$

c.
$$A = 20(\pi \cdot 20 + 2 \cdot 40)$$
$$A \approx 2856.64 \text{ ft}^2$$

69. a. Sale price is
$$(x + 0.06x) - 0.06(x + 0.06x)$$
$$= (1 - 0.06)(x + 0.06x)$$
$$= (0.94)(1.06x)$$

b. Now, $(0.94)(1.06x) = 0.9964x$ upon multiplication. This represents 99.64% of the 2002 price which means that the new price is slightly lower than the price of the 2002 model.

71. a. Final price is
$$(x + 0.15x) - 0.20(x + 0.15x)$$
$$= 0.80(x + 0.15x)$$

b.
$$(x + 0.15x) - 0.20(x + 0.15x)$$
$$= (1 - 0.20)(x + 0.15x)$$
$$= 0.80(1.15x)$$
$$= 0.92x$$
The sale price is 92% of the regular price.

73.
$$5a(3x-2)^5 + 4(3x-2)^4 = 5a(3x-2) \cdot (3x-2)^4 + 4 \cdot (3x-2)^4$$
$$= (3x-2)^4\left[5a(3x-2) + 4\right]$$
$$= (3x-2)^4(15ax - 10a + 4)$$

75.
$$4x^2(x-3)^3 - 6x(x-3)^2 + 4(x-3) = 2(x-3)\left[2x^2(x-3)^2 - 3x(x-3) + 2\right] \quad \leftarrow (2x-3) \text{ is a common factor}$$
$$= 2(x-3)\left[2x^2\left(x^2 - 6x + 9\right) - 3x(x-3) + 2\right]$$
$$= 2(x-3)\left(2x^4 - 12x^3 + 18x^2 - 3x^2 + 9x + 2\right)$$
$$= 2(x-3)\left(2x^4 - 12x^3 + 15x^2 + 9x + 2\right)$$

77. $ax^2 + 2ax - 3a + bx^2 + 2bx - 3b$
$= ax^2 + bx^2 + 2ax + 2bx - 3a - 3b$
$= x^2(a+b) + 2x(a+b) - 3(a+b)$
$= (x^2 + 2x - 3)(a+b)$

79. $x^{6m} - 2x^{4m} = x^{4m} \cdot x^{2m} - x^{4m} \cdot 2$
$= x^{4m}(x^{2m} - 2)$

81. $3x^{4m} - 2x^{3m} + x^{2m}$
$= x^{2m} \cdot 3x^{2m} - x^{2m} \cdot 2x^m + x^{2m} \cdot 1$
$= x^{2m}(3x^{2m} - 2x^m + 1)$

83. $a^r b^r + c^r b^r - a^r d^r - c^r d^r$
$= b^r(a^r + c^r) - d^r(a^r + c^r)$
$= (b^r - d^r)(a^r + c^r)$

85. a. $6x^3 - 3x^2 + 9x = 3x(2x^2) + 3x(-x) + 3x(3)$
$= 3x(2x^2 - x + 3)$

Yes

b. 0

c. Answers will vary.

87. a. They should be the same graph.

b. $y_1 = 8x^3 - 16x^2 - 4x$
$y_2 = 4x(2x^2 - 4x - 1)$

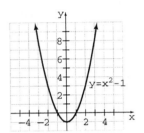

$-10, 10, 1, -20$

c. Answers will vary.

d. The factoring is not correct.

89. $\dfrac{\left(\left|\frac{1}{2}\right| - \left|-\frac{1}{3}\right|\right)^2}{-\left|\frac{1}{3}\right| \cdot \left|-\frac{2}{5}\right|} = \dfrac{\left(\frac{1}{2} - \frac{1}{3}\right)^2}{-\left(\frac{1}{3}\right)\left(\frac{2}{5}\right)}$ ← Do abs.vals first

$= \dfrac{\left(\frac{3}{6} - \frac{2}{6}\right)^2}{-\left(\frac{1}{3}\right)\left(\frac{2}{5}\right)}$ ← Simplify numerator

$= \dfrac{\left(\frac{1}{6}\right)^2}{-\left(\frac{1}{3}\right)\left(\frac{2}{5}\right)}$ ← Simplify numerator

$= \dfrac{\frac{1}{36}}{-\left(\frac{1}{3}\right)\left(\frac{2}{5}\right)}$ ← Simplify numerator

$= \dfrac{\frac{1}{36}}{-\frac{2}{15}}$ ← Multiply denominator

$= \dfrac{1}{36}\left(-\dfrac{15}{2}\right)$ ← Perform division

$= -\dfrac{15}{72} = -\dfrac{5}{24}$

91. This graph is a translation of the parent graph $y = x^2$. The parent graph is shifted down one unit.

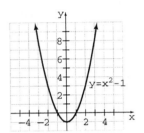

93. $(7a - 3)(-2a^2 - 4a + 1)$
$7a(-2a^2) + 7a(-4a) + 7a(1) - 3(-2a^2) - 3(-4a) - 3(1)$
$-14a^3 - 28a^2 + 7a + 6a^2 + 12a - 3$
$-14a^3 - 22a^2 + 19a - 3$

Exercise Set 5.5

1. Factor out the greatest common factor if it is present.

3. a. Answers will vary.

b. $6x^2 - x - 12$
Observe that $6(-12) = -72$. The two numbers whose product is -72 and whose sum is -1 are -9 and 8, since $(-9)(8) = -72$ and $-9 + 8 = -1$. Then the middle term, $-x$, can be written as $-x = -9x + 8x$ and the factorization is
$6x^2 - x - 12 = 6x^2 - 9x + 8x - 12$
$= 3(2x - 3) + 4(2x - 3)$
$= (3x + 4)(2x - 3)$

5. No. You must first factor out the GCF.
$$2x^2 + 8x + 6 = 2\left(x^2 + 4x + 3\right)$$
$$= 2(x+3)(x+1)$$

7. No. You must first factor out the GCF.
$$3x^3 + 6x^2 - 24x = 3x\left(x^2 + 2x - 8\right)$$
$$= 3x(x+4)(x-2)$$

9. Both are +.

11. One is +, one is –.

13. $x^2 + 7x + 12$
The two numbers whose product is 12 and whose sum is 7 are 3 and 4, since (3)(4) = 12 and 3 + 4 = 7. Thus, $x^2 + 7x + 12 = (x+3)(x+4)$.

15. $b^2 - 10b + 9$
The two numbers whose product is 9 and whose sum is –10 are –1 and –9, since (–1)(–9) = 9 and (–1) + (–9) = –10. Thus,
$$b^2 - 10b + 9 = (b-1)(b-9)$$

17. $c^2 - 12c + 36$
The two numbers whose product is 36 and whose sum is –12 are –6 and –6, since (–6)(–6) = 36 and –6 + (–6) = –12. Thus,
$$c^2 - 12c + 36 = (c-6)(c-6) = (c-6)^2.$$

19. $y^2 - 18y + 81$
The two numbers whose product is 81 and whose sum is –18 are –9 and –9, since (–9)(–9) = 81 and –9 + (–9) = –18. Thus,
$$y^2 - 18y + 81 = (y-9)(y-9) = (y-9)^2.$$

21. $x^2 - 34x + 64$
The two numbers whose product is 64 and whose sum is –34 are –2 and –32, since (–2)(–32) = 64 and –2 + (–32) = –34. Thus,
$$x^2 - 34x + 64 = (x-2)(x-32).$$

23. $x^2 - 13x - 30$
The two numbers whose product is –30 and whose sum is –13 are 2 and –15, since (2)(–15) = –30 and 2 – 15 = –13. Thus,
$$x^2 - 13x - 30 = (x+2)(x-15).$$

25. $-a^2 + 18a - 45$ can be written as $-(a^2 - 18a + 45)$. Now, factor $a^2 - 18a + 45$.
The two numbers whose product is 45 and whose sum is –18 are –3 and –15, since (–3)(–15) = 45

and –3 + (–15) = –18. Thus,
$$-(a^2 - 18a + 45) = -(a-3)(a-15).$$

27. $x^2 + xy + 6y^2$
Notice that there are no two rational numbers whose product is 6 and whose sum is 1. Therefore the polynomial is prime and cannot be factored.

29. $m^2 - 7mn + 10n^2$
The two numbers whose product is 10 and whose sum is –7 are –5 and –2, since (–5)(–2) = 10 and –5 + (–2) = –7. Thus,
$$m^2 - 7mn + 10n^2 = (m-2n)(m-5n).$$

31. $4r^2 + 12r - 16$
$$= 4\left(r^2 + 3r - 4\right) \leftarrow 4 \text{ is a common factor}$$
Now factor $r^2 + 3r - 4$. The two numbers whose product is –4 and whose sum is 3 are 4 and –1, since (4)(–1) = –4 and 4 + (–1) = 3. Now,
$r^2 + 3r - 4 = (r+4)(r-1)$ and the answer is
$$4r^2 + 12r - 16 = 4(r+4)(r-1).$$

33. $x^3 - 3x^2 - 18x$
$$= x\left(x^2 - 3x - 18\right) \leftarrow x \text{ is a common factor}$$
Now, factor $x^2 - 3x - 18$. The two numbers whose product is –18 and whose sum is –3 are –6 and 3 since, (–6)(3) = –18 and –6 + 3 = –3. Thus, $x^2 - 3x - 18 = (x-6)(x+3)$ and the answer is $x^3 - 3x^2 - 18x = x(x-6)(x+3)$.

35. $5a^2 - 8a + 3$
Observe that (5)(3) = 15. The two numbers whose product is 15 and whose sum is –8 are –5 and –3, since (–5)(–3) = 15 and (–5) + (–3) = –8. Now the middle term, –8a, can be written as –5a – 3a and the factorization is
$$5a^2 - 8a + 3 = 5a^2 - 5a - 3a + 3$$
$$= 5a(a-1) - 3(a-1)$$
$$= (5a-3)(a-1)$$

37. $3x^2 - 3x - 6 = 3\left(x^2 - x - 2\right)$
Now factor $\left(x^2 - x - 2\right)$. The two numbers whose product is –2 and sum is –1 are –2 and 1, since (–2)(–1) = –2 and –2 + 1 = –1. Thus
$$3x^2 - 3x - 6 = 3\left(x^2 - x - 2\right)$$
$$= 3(x-2)(x+1)$$

39. $6c^2 - 13c - 63$

Observe that $6(-63) = -378$. The two numbers whose product is -378 and whose sum is -13 are -27 and 14, since $(-27)(14) = -378$ and $-27 + 14 = -13$. Now the middle term $-13c$ can be written as $-27c + 14c$ and the factorization is
$$6c^2 - 13c - 63 = 6c^2 - 27c + 14c - 63$$
$$= 3c(2c - 9) + 7(2c - 9)$$
$$= (3c + 7)(2c - 9)$$

41. $8b^2 - 2b - 3$

Observe that $(8)(-3) = -24$. The two numbers whose product is -24 and whose sum is -2 are -6 and 4, since $(-6)(4) = -24$ and $-6 + 4 = -2$. Now the middle term, $-2b$, can be written as $-6b + 4b$ and the factorization is
$$8b^2 - 2b - 3 = 8b^2 - 6b + 4b - 3$$
$$= 2b(4b - 3) + 1(4b - 3)$$
$$= (4b - 3)(2b + 1)$$

43. $6c^2 + 11c - 10$

Observe that $(6)(-10) = -60$. The two numbers whose product is -60 and whose sum is 11 are 15 and -4, since $(15)(-4) = -60$ and $15 + (-4) = 11$. Now the middle term, $11c$, can be written as $15c + -4c$ and the factorization is
$$6c^2 + 11c - 10 = 6c^2 + 15c - 4c - 10$$
$$= 3c(2c + 5) - 2(2c + 5)$$
$$= (2c + 5)(3c - 2)$$

45. $16p^2 - 16pq - 12q^2 = 4\left(4p^2 - 4pq - 3q^2\right)$

[4 is a common factor]

Now, factor $4p^2 - 4pq - 3q^2$. Observe that $(4)(-3) = -12$. The two numbers whose product is -12 and whose sum is -4 are -6 and 2, since $(-6)(2) = -12$ and $-6 + 2 = -4$. Now, the middle term, $-4pq$, can be written as $-6pq + 2pq$ and the factorization is
$$4p^2 - 4pq - 3q^2 = 4p^2 - 6pq + 2pq - 3q^2$$
$$= 2p(2p - 3q) + q(2p - 3q)$$
$$= (2p + q)(2p - 3q)$$
Thus, $16p^2 - 16pq - 12q^2 = 4(2p + q)(2p - 3q)$.

47. $4x^2 + 4xy + 9y^2$

Observe that $(4)(9) = 36$. Notice that there are no two rational numbers whose product is 36 and whose sum is 4. Therefore the polynomial is prime and cannot be factored.

49. $18a^2 + 18ab - 8b^2 = 2\left(9a^2 + 9ab - 4b^2\right)$

Now, factor $9a^2 + 9ab - 4b^2$. Observe that $(9)(-4) = -36$. The two numbers whose product is -36 and whose sum is 9 are 12 and -3, since $(12)(-3) = -36$ and $12 + (-3) = 9$. Then the middle term, $9ab$, can be written as $9ab = 12ab - 3ab$ and the factorization is
$$9a^2 + 9ab - 4b^2 = 9a^2 + 12ab - 3ab - 4b^2$$
$$= 3a(3a + 4b) - b(3a + 4b)$$
$$= (3a - b)(3a + 4b)$$
Thus, $18a^2 + 18ab - 8b^2 = 2(3a - b)(3a + 4b)$.

51. $9y^2 - 104y - 48$

Observe that $9(-48) = -432$. The two numbers whose product is -432 and whose sum is -104 are -108 and 4, since $-108(4) = -432$ and $-108 + 4 = -104$. The middle term can be written as $-104y = -108y + 4y$ and the factorization is
$$9y^2 - 104y - 48 = 9y^2 - 108y + 4y - 48$$
$$= 9y(y - 12) + 4(y - 12)$$
$$= (9y + 4)(y - 12)$$

53. $100b^2 - 90b + 20 = 10(10b^2 - 9b + 2)$

Now, factor $10b^2 - 9b + 2$. Observe that $(10)(2) = 20$. The two numbers whose product is 20 and whose sum is -9 are -4 and -5, since $(-4)(-5) = 20$ and $-4 + (-5) = -9$. Then the middle term, $-9b$, can be written as $-4b - 5b$ and the factorization is
$$10b^2 - 9b + 2 = 10b^2 - 4b - 5b + 2$$
$$= 2b(5b - 2) - 1(5b - 2)$$
$$= (2b - 1)(5b - 2)$$
Thus, $100b^2 - 90b + 20 = 10(2b - 1)(5b - 2)$.

55. $a^3b^5 - a^2b^5 - 12ab^5$
$= ab^5(a^2 - a - 12) \leftarrow ab^5$ is a common factor

Now, factor $a^2 - a - 12$. The two numbers whose product is -12 and whose sum is -1 are -4 and 3, since $(-4)(3) = -12$ and $-4 + 3 = -1$. Thus,
$$a^2 - ab - 12 = (a - 4)(a + 3)$$
and the answer is
$$a^3b^5 - a^2b^5 - 12ab^5 = ab^5(a - 4)(a + 3).$$

57. $3b^4c - 18b^3c^2 + 27b^2c^3 = 3b^2c(b^2 - 6bc + 9c^2)$
[$3b^2c$ is a common factor.]
Now factor $b^2 - 6bc + 9c^2$. The two numbers whose product is 9 and whose sum is -6 are -3

and –3, since $(-3)(-3) = 9$ and $-3 + (-3) = -6$.
Thus,
$b^2 - 6bc + 9c^2 = (b - 3c)(b - 3c)$
and the answer is
$3b^4 c - 18b^3 c^2 + 27b^2 c^3 = 3b^2 c(b - 3c)(b - 3c)$
$= 3b^2 c(b - 3c)^2$

59. $8m^8 n^3 + 4m^7 n^4 - 24m^6 n^5$
$= 4m^6 n^3 (2m^2 + mn - 6n^2) \leftarrow 4m^6 n^3$ is a
common factor.

Now factor $2m^2 + mn - 6n^2$. Observe that
$(2)(-6) = -12$. The two numbers whose product
is –12 and whose sum is 1 are 4 and –3, since
$(4)(-3) = -12$ and $4 + (-3) = 1$. Then the middle
term, *mn*, can be written as $4mn - 3mn$ and the
factorization is

$2m^2 + mn - 6n^2 = 2m^2 + 4mn - 3mn - 6n^2$
$= 2m(m + 2n) - 3n(m + 2n)$
$= (2m - 3n)(m + 2n)$
Thus,
$8m^8 n^3 + 4m^7 n^4 - 24m^6 n^5$
$= 4m^6 n^3 (m + 2n)(2m - 3n)$

61. $30x^2 - x - 20$
Observe that $(30)(-20) = -600$. The two numbers
whose product is –600 and whose sum is –1 are
–25 and 24, since $(-25)(24) = -600$ and
$-25 + 24 = -1$. Then the middle term, $-x$, can be
written as $-25x + 24x$ and the factorization is
$30x^2 - x - 20 = 30x^2 - 25x + 24x - 20$
$= 5x(6x - 5) + 4(6x - 5)$.
$= (5x + 4)(6x - 5)$

63. $8x^4 y^4 + 24x^3 y^4 - 32x^2 y^4 = 8x^2 y^4 (x^2 + 3x - 4)$ $\left[8x^2 y^4 \text{ is a common factor} \right]$

Now, factor $x^2 + 3x - 4$. The two numbers whose product is –4 and whose sum is 3 are 4 and –1, since
$(4)(-1) = -4$ and $4 + (-1) = 3$. Thus, $8x^4 y^4 + 2x^3 y^4 - 32x^2 y^4 = 8x^2 y^4 (x + 4)(x - 1)$.

65. $x^4 + x^2 - 6 = (x^2)^2 + x^2 - 6$
$= y^2 + y - 6 \qquad \leftarrow$ Replace x^2 by y
$= (y + 3)(y - 2) \qquad \leftarrow$ Use 3 and -2 since $(3)(-2) = -6,\ 3 + (-2) = 1$
$= (x^2 + 3)(x^2 - 2) \qquad \leftarrow$ Replace y by x^2

67. $b^4 + 9b^2 + 20 = (b^2)^2 + 9b^2 + 20$
$= u^2 + 9u + 20 \qquad \leftarrow$ Replace b^2 by u
$= (u + 4)(u + 5) \qquad \leftarrow$ Use 4 and 5 since $(4)(5) = 20, 4 + 5 = 9$
$= (b^2 + 4)(b^2 + 5) \qquad \leftarrow$ Replace u by b^2

69. $6a^4 + 5a^2 - 25 = 6(a^2)^2 + 5a^2 - 25$
$= 6w^2 + 5w - 25 \qquad \leftarrow$ Replace a^2 by w
$= 6w^2 - 10w + 15w - 25 \qquad \leftarrow$ Use $-10w + 15w$ for $5w$ since $(-10)(15) = -150, -10 + 15 = 5$
$= 2w(3w - 5) + 5(3w - 5) \qquad \leftarrow$ Factor by grouping
$= (2w + 5)(3w - 5)$
$= (2a^2 + 5)(3a^2 - 5) \qquad \leftarrow$ Replace w by a^2

71. $4(x+1)^2 + 8(x+1) + 3 = 4y^2 + 8y + 3$ ← Replace $x+1$ by y
$$= 4y^2 + 6y + 2y + 3$$ ← Use $6y + 2y$ for $8y$ since $(6)(2) = 12$, and $6 + 2 = 8$
$$= 2y(2y+3) + 1(2y+3)$$
$$= (2y+1)(2y+3)$$
$$= [2(x+1)+1][2(x+1)+3]$$ ← Replace y by $x+1$
$$= (2x+2+1)(2x+2+3)$$
$$= (2x+3)(2x+5)$$

73. $6(a+2)^2 - 7(a+2) - 5 = 6y^2 - 7y - 5$ ← Replace $a+2$ by y
$$= 6y^2 + 3y - 10y - 5$$ ← Use $3y - 10y$ for $-7y$ since $(3)(-10) = -30$ and $3 + (-10) = -7$
$$= 3y(2y+1) - 5(2y+1)$$
$$= (3y-5)(2y+1)$$
$$= [3(a+2)-5][2(a+2)+1]$$ ← Replace y by $a+2$
$$= (3a+6-5)(2a+4+1)$$
$$= (3a+1)(2a+5)$$

75. $x^2y^2 + 9xy + 14 = (xy)^2 + 9xy + 14$
$$= w^2 + 9w + 14$$ ← Replace xy by w
$$= (w+2)(w+7)$$ ← Use 2 and 7 since $(2)(7) = 14, 2 + 7 = 9$
$$= (xy+2)(xy+7)$$ ← Replace w by xy

77. $2x^2y^2 - 9xy - 11 = 2(xy)^2 - 9xy - 11$
$$= 2w^2 - 9w - 11$$ ← Replace xy by w
$$= 2w^2 + 2w - 11w - 11$$ ← Use $2w - 11w$ for $-9w$ since $(2)(-11) = -22$ and $2 + (-11) = -9$
$$= 2w(w+1) - 11(w+1)$$
$$= (2w-11)(w+1)$$
$$= (2xy-11)(xy+1)$$ ← Replace w by xy

79. $2y^2(5-y) - 7y(5-y) + 5(5-y)$
$$= (5-y)(2y^2 - 7y + 5)$$ ← $5-y$ is a common factor
$$= (5-y)(2y^2 - 2y - 5y + 5)$$ ← Use $-2y - 5y$ for $-7y$ since $(-2)(-5) = 10$ and $-2 + (-5) = -7$
$$= (5-y)[2y(y-1) - 5(y-1)]$$ ← Factor by grouping
$$= (5-y)(2y-5)(y-1)$$

81. $2p^2(p-3) + 7p(p-3) + 6(p-3)$
$$= (p-3)(2p^2 + 7p + 6)$$ ← $p-3$ is a common factor
$$= (p-3)(2p^2 + 4p + 3p + 6)$$ ← Use $4p + 3p$ for $7p$ since $(4)(3) = 12$ and $4 + 3 = 7$
$$= (p-3)[2p(p+2) + 3(p+2)]$$ ← Factor by grouping
$$= (p-3)(2p+3)(p+2)$$

83. $a^6 - 7a^3 - 30 = \left(a^3\right)^2 - 7a^3 - 30$

$\qquad = b^2 - 7b - 30 \quad \leftarrow$ Replace a^3 by b

$\qquad = (b-10)(b+3) \quad \leftarrow$ Use -10 and 3 since $(-10)(3) = -30$ and $-10 + 3 = -7$

$\qquad = \left(a^3 - 10\right)\left(a^3 + 3\right) \quad \leftarrow$ Replace b by a^3

85. $x^2(x+3) + 3x(x+3) + 2(x+3) = (x+3)\left(x^2 + 3x + 2\right) \quad \leftarrow x+3$ is a common factor

$\qquad\qquad\qquad\qquad\qquad\qquad\qquad = (x+3)(x+2)(x+1) \quad \leftarrow$ Use 2 and 1 since $(2)(1) = 2$ and $2 + 1 = 3$

87. $5a^5b^2 - 8a^4b^3 + 3a^3b^4$

$\quad = a^3b^2\left(5a^2 - 8ab + 3b^2\right) \quad \leftarrow a^3b^2$ is a common factor

$\quad = a^3b^2\left[5a^2 - 5ab - 3ab + 3b^2\right] \quad \leftarrow$ Use $-5ab - 3ab$ for $8ab$ since $(-5)(-3) = -15, \ -5 + (-3) = -8$

$\quad = a^3b^2\left[5a(a-b) - 3b(a-b)\right] \quad \leftarrow$ Factor by grouping

$\quad = a^3b^2(5a - 3b)(a - b)$

89. $A_1 - A_2 = (x+5)(x+2) - (2)(2)$

$\qquad\qquad = x^2 + 2x + 5x + 10 - 4$

$\qquad\qquad = x^2 + 7x + 6$

$\qquad\qquad = (x+6)(x+1)$

91. $A_1 - A_2 = (x+4)(x+5) - (2)(1)$

$\qquad\qquad = x^2 + 5x + 4x + 20 - 3$

$\qquad\qquad = x^2 + 9x + 18$

$\qquad\qquad = (x+6)(x+3)$

93. To find the polynomial multiply the factors.

$(2x+3y)(x-4y) = 2x(x-4y) + 3y(x-4y)$

$\qquad\qquad\qquad = 2x^2 - 8xy + 3xy - 12y^2$

$\qquad\qquad\qquad = 2x^2 - 5xy - 12y^2$

95. To find the other factor, simply divide
$x^2 + 3x - 18$ by $x - 3$.

$$\begin{array}{r} x + 6 \\ x-3{\overline{\smash{\big)}\,x^2 + 3x - 18}} \end{array}$$

$\qquad \dfrac{x^2 - 3x}{} \qquad \leftarrow x(x-3)$

$\qquad \quad 6x - 18$

$\qquad \quad \dfrac{6x - 18}{} \qquad \leftarrow 6(x-3)$

$\qquad\qquad\quad 0 \qquad \leftarrow$ Remainder

The other factor is $x + 6$.

97. a. Answers will vary.

$\quad$ **b.** $30x^2 + 23x - 40 = 30x^2 - 25x + 48x - 40$

$\qquad\qquad\qquad\qquad\quad = 5x(6x - 5) + 8(6x - 5)$

$\qquad\qquad\qquad\qquad\quad = (5x + 8)(6x - 5)$

$\qquad\quad 49x^2 - 98x + 13 = 49x^2 - 7x - 91x + 13$

$\qquad\qquad\qquad\qquad\quad = 7x(7x - 1) - 13(7x - 1)$

$\qquad\qquad\qquad\qquad\quad = (7x - 13)(7x - 1)$

99. To factor $2x^2 + bx - 5$, the factors must be of the form

$\quad (2x - 5)(x + 1)$ which gives $2x^2 - 3x - 5$

$\quad$ or $(2x - 1)(x + 5)$ which gives $2x^2 + 9x - 5$

$\quad$ or $(2x + 5)(x - 1)$ which gives $2x^2 + 3x - 5$

$\quad$ or $(2x + 1)(x - 5)$ which gives $2x^2 - 9x - 5$

$\quad$ Therefore $b = \pm 3, \ \pm 9$.

101. To factor $x^2 + bx + 5$, the factors must be of the form $(x + 1)(x + 5)$ which gives $x^2 + 6x + 5$ or $(x - 1)(x - 5)$ which gives $x^2 - 6x + 5$. Therefore, $b = 6$ or -6.

103. a. $b^2 - 4ac = (-8)^2 - 4(1)(15) = 64 - 60 = 4$
a perfect square

b. $x^2 - 8x + 15 = x^2 - 5x - 3x + 15$
$= x(x - 5) - 3(x - 5)$
$= (x - 3)(x - 5)$

105. a. $b^2 - 4ac = (-4)^2 - 4(1)(6) = 16 - 24 = -8$
not a perfect square

b. Not factorable

107. Answers will vary. One example is $x^2 + 2x + 1$

109.
$4a^{2n} - 4a^n - 15 = 4(a^n)^2 - 4a^n - 15$
$= 4y^2 - 4y - 15$ ← Replace a^n by y
$= 4y^2 - 10y + 6y - 15$
$= 2y(2y - 5) + 3(2y - 5)$
$= (2y + 3)(2y - 5)$
$= (2a^n + 3)(2a^n - 5)$ ← Replace y by a^n

111. $x^2(x + y)^2 - 7xy(x + y)^2 + 12y^2(x + y)^2 = (x + y)^2(x^2 - 7xy + 12y^2)$
$= (x + y)^2(x^2 - 3xy - 4xy + 12y^2)$
$= (x + y)^2[x(x - 3y) - 4y(x - 3y)]$
$= (x + y)^2(x - 4y)(x - 3y)$

113. $x^{2n} + 3x^n - 10 = (x^n)^2 + 3(x^n) - 10$
$= y^2 + 3y - 10$ ← Replace x^n with y
$= y^2 - 2y + 5y - 10$
$= y(y - 2) + 5(y - 2)$
$= (y + 5)(y - 2)$
$= (x^n + 5)(x^n - 2)$ ← Replace y with x^n

115. a. Answers will vary.

b.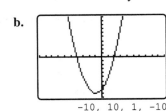
-10, 10, 1, -10

The graphs of $y_1 = x^2 + 2x - 8$ and
$y_2 = (x + 4)(x - 2)$ are the same. The
factoring is correct.

117. $F = \frac{9}{5}C + 32$
$F - 32 = \frac{9}{5}C$
$\frac{5}{9}(F - 32) = \frac{5}{9}\left(\frac{9}{5}C\right)$
$\frac{5}{9}(F - 32) = C$ or $C = \frac{5}{9}(F - 32)$

119.

$$\begin{vmatrix} 3 & -2 & -1 \\ 2 & 3 & -2 \\ 1 & -4 & 1 \end{vmatrix}$$

$$= 3\begin{vmatrix} 3 & -2 \\ -4 & 1 \end{vmatrix} - (-2)\begin{vmatrix} 2 & -2 \\ 1 & 1 \end{vmatrix} + (-1)\begin{vmatrix} 2 & 3 \\ 1 & -4 \end{vmatrix}$$

$$= 3(3-8) + 2(2+2) - 1(-8-3)$$

$$= 3(-5) + 2(4) - 1(-11)$$

$$= -15 + 8 + 11$$

$$= 4$$

121. $2x^3 + 4x^2 - 5x - 10 = 2x^2(x+2) - 5(x+2)$

$$= (x+2)(2x^2 - 5)$$

Exercise Set 5.6

1.   **a.**   Answers will vary.

      b. $x^2 - 16 = x^2 - 4^2 = (x+4)(x-4)$

3.   Answers will vary.

5. $a^3 + b^3 = (a+b)(a^2 - ab + b^2)$

7.   No. $(x+7)(x-7) = x^2 - 7x + 7x - 49$

$$= x^2 - 49$$

$$\neq x^2 + 14x - 49$$

9.   No. $(x-9)^2 = (x-9)(x-9)$

$$= x^2 - 9x - 9x + 81$$

$$= x^2 - 18x + 81$$

$$\neq x^2 - 81$$

11. $x^2 - 81 = (x)^2 - (9)^2 = (x+9)(x-9)$

13. $a^2 - 100 = (a)^2 - (10)^2 = (a+10)(a-10)$

15. $1 - 36b^2 = (1)^2 - (6b)^2 = (1+6b)(1-6b)$

17. $25 - 16y^4 = (5)^2 - \left(4y^2\right)^2$

$$= \left(5 + 4y^2\right)\left(5 - 4y^2\right)$$

19. $\frac{1}{25} - y^2 = \left(\frac{1}{5}\right)^2 - (y)^2 = \left(\frac{1}{5} + y\right)\left(\frac{1}{5} - y\right)$

21. $x^2 y^2 - 121c^2 = (xy)^2 - (11c)^2$

$$= (xy + 11c)(xy - 11c)$$

23. $0.4x^2 - 0.9 = (0.2x)^2 - (0.3)^2$

$$= (0.2x + 0.3)(0.2x - 0.3)$$

25. $36 - (x-6)^2 = (6)^2 - (x-6)^2$

$$= [6 + (x-6)][6 - (x-6)]$$

$$= (6 + x - 6)(6 - x + 6)$$

$$= x(12 - x)$$

27. $a^2 - (3b+2)^2 = [a + (3b+2)][a - (3b+2)]$

$$= (a + 3b + 2)(a - 3b - 2)$$

29. $x^2 + 10x + 25 = x^2 + 2(x)(5) + 5^2$

$$= (x+5)^2$$

31. $4 + 4a + a^2 = 2^2 + 2(2)(a) + a^2$

$$= (2+a)^2$$

33. $4x^2 - 20xy + 25y^2 = (2x)^2 - 2(2x)(5y) + (5y)^2$

$$= (2x - 5y)^2$$

35. $0.81x^2 - 0.36x + 0.04$

$$= (0.9x)^2 - 2(0.9)(0.2)x + (0.2)^2$$

$$= (0.9x - 0.2)^2$$

37. $y^4 + 4y^2 + 4 = \left(y^2\right)^2 + 2\left(y^2\right)(2) + 2^2$

$$= \left(y^2 + 2\right)^2$$

39. $(x+y)^2 + 2(x+y) + 1$

$$= (x+y)^2 + 2(x+y)(1) + 1^2$$

$$= [(x+y) + 1]^2$$

$$= (x + y + 1)^2$$

41. $(y-3)^2 + 8(y-3) + 16$

$= (y-3)^2 + 2(y-3)(4) + 4^2$

$= [(y-3)+4]^2$

$= (y-3+4)^2$

$= (y+1)^2$

43. $x^2 + 6x + 9 - y^2 = (x+3)^2 - (y)^2$

$= [(x+3)+y][(x+3)-y]$

$= (x+3+y)(x+3-y)$

45. $25 - (x^2 + 4x + 4) = (5)^2 - (x+2)^2$

$= [5+(x+2)][5-(x+2)]$

$= (5+x+2)(5-x-2)$

$= (x+7)(3-x)$

47. $9 - (c^2 - 8c + 16) = 3^2 - (c-4)^2$

$= [3+(c-4)][3-(c-4)]$

$= (3+c-4)(3-c+4)$

$= (c-1)(7-c)$

49. $y^4 - 6y^2 + 9 = (y^2)^2 - 2(y^2)(3) + 3^2$

$= (y^2 - 3)^2$

51. $x^3 - 27 = (x)^3 - (3)^3$

$= (x-3)\left[x^2 + x(3) + 3^2\right]$

$= (x-3)\left(x^2 + 3x + 9\right)$

53. $64 - a^3 = (4)^3 - (a)^3$

$= (4-a)\left[4^2 + 4(a) + a^2\right]$

$= (4-a)\left(16 + 4a + a^2\right)$

55. $p^3 - 27a^3 = (p)^3 - (3a)^3$

$= (p-3a)\left((p)^2 + (p)(3a) + (3a)^2\right)$

$= (p-3a)\left(p^2 + 3ap + 9a^2\right)$

57. $27y^3 - 8x^3 = (3y)^3 - (2x)^3$

$= (3y-2x)\left[(3y)^2 + (3y)(2x) + (2x)^2\right]$

$= (3y-2x)\left(9y^2 + 6xy + 4x^2\right)$

59. $32a^3 - 108b^3$

$= 4\left(8a^3 - 27b^3\right)$

$= 4\left[(2a)^3 - (3b)^3\right]$

$= 4(2a-3b)\left[(2a)^2 + (2a)(3b) + (3b)^2\right]$

$= 4(2a-3b)\left(4a^2 + 6ab + 9b^2\right)$

61. $2b^3 - 250c^3 = 2\left(b^3 - 125c^3\right)$

$= 2\left[(b)^3 - (5c)^3\right]$

$= 2(b-5c)\left[b^2 + b(5c) + (5c)^2\right]$

$= 2(b-5c)\left(x^2 + 5bc + 25c^2\right)$

63. $(x+1)^3 + 1$

$= (x+1)^3 + (1)^3$

$= \left[(x+1)+1\right]\left[(x+1)^2 - (x+1)(1) + 1^2\right]$

$= (x+2)\left(x^2 + 2x + 1 - x - 1 + 1\right)$

$= (x+2)\left(x^2 + x + 1\right)$

65. $(a-b)^3 - 27$

$= (a-b)^3 - (3)^3$

$= \left[(a-b)-3\right]\left[(a-b)^2 + (a-b)(3) + 3^2\right]$

$= (a-b-3)\left(a^2 - 2ab + b^2 + 3a - 3b + 9\right)$

67. $b^3 - (b+3)^3$

$= \left[b - (b+3)\right]\left[b^2 + b(b+3) + (b+3)^2\right]$

$= (b-b-3)\left(b^2 + b^2 + 3b + b^2 + 6b + 9\right)$

$= (-3)\left(3b^2 + 9b + 9\right)$

$= (-3)\cdot 3\left(b^2 + 3b + 3\right)$

$= -9\left(b^2 + 3b + 3\right)$

69. $121y^4 - 49x^2 = \left(11y^2\right)^2 - (7x)^2$

$= \left(11y^2 + 7x\right)\left(11y^2 - 7x\right)$

71. $16y^2 - 81x^2 = (4y)^2 - (9x)^2$
$$= (4y + 9x)(4y - 9x)$$

73. $25x^4 - 81y^6 = (5x^2)^2 - (9y^3)^2$
$$= (5x^2 + 9y^3)(5x^2 - 9y^3)$$

75. $x^3 - 64 = (x)^3 - (4)^3$
$$= (x - 4)\left[x^2 + x(4) + 4^2\right]$$
$$= (x - 4)(x^2 + 4x + 16)$$

77. $9x^2y^2 + 24xy + 16 = (3xy)^2 + 2(3xy)(4) + (4)^2$
$$= (3xy + 4)^2$$

79. $a^4 + 2a^2b^2 + b^4 = (a^2)^2 + 2(a^2)(b^2) + (b^2)^2$
$$= (a^2 + b^2)^2$$

81. $x^2 - 2x + 1 - y^2 = (x - 1)^2 - (y)^2$
$$= \left[(x - 1) + y\right]\left[(x - 1) - y\right]$$
$$= (x - 1 + y)(x - 1 - y)$$

83. $(x + y)^3 + 1$
$$= (x + y)^3 + (1)^3$$
$$= \left[(x + y) + 1\right]\left[(x + y)^2 - (x + y)(1) + 1^2\right]$$
$$= (x + y + 1)(x^2 + 2xy + y^2 - x - y + 1)$$

85. $(m + n)^2 - (2m - n)^2$
$$= \left[(m + n) + (2m - n)\right]\left[(m + n) - (2m - n)\right]$$
$$= (3m)(-m + 2n)$$
$$= 3m(-m + 2n)$$

87. $V_1 - V_2 = (3x)^3 - (2)^3$
$$= (3x - 2)\left((3x)^2 + (3x)(2) + (2)^2\right)$$
$$= (3x - 2)(9x^2 + 6x + 4)$$

89. $V_1 - V_2 = (6a)^3 - (b)^3$
$$= (6a - b)\left((6a)^2 + (6a)(b) + (b)^2\right)$$
$$= (6a - b)(36a^2 + 6ab + b^2)$$

91. $V_1 + V_2 = (4x)^3 + (3a)^3$
$$= (4x + 3a)\left((4x)^2 - (4x)(3a) + (3a)^2\right)$$
$$= (4x + 3a)(16x^2 - 12ax + 9a^2)$$

93. Area of larger square is $(a)(a) = a^2$.
Area of smaller square is $(b)(b) = b^2$.

   a. Area of shaded region is $a^2 - b^2$.

   b. In factored form, the area is
   $a^2 - b^2 = (a + b)(a - b)$.

95. Volume of larger solid is $(6a)(a)(a) = 6a^3$.
Volume of smaller solid is $(6a)(b)(b) = 6ab^2$.

   a. Volume of shaded region is $6a^3 - 6ab^2$.

   b. In factored form, the volume is
   $6a^3 - 6ab^2 = 6a(a^2 - b^2)$
   $$= 6a(a + b)(a - b).$$

97. Volume of larger sphere is $\frac{4}{3}\pi R^3$.

Volume of smaller sphere is $\frac{4}{3}\pi r^3$.

   a. Volume of shaded region is $\frac{4}{3}\pi R^3 - \frac{4}{3}\pi r^3$.

   b. In factored form the volume is
   $\frac{4}{3}\pi R^3 - \frac{4}{3}\pi r^3 = \frac{4}{3}\pi(R^3 - r^3)$
   $$= \frac{4}{3}\pi(R - r)(R^2 + Rr + r^2).$$

99. Express $4x^2 + bx + 9$ as $(2x)^2 + bx + (3)^2$. Now,
$bx = 2(2x)(3)$ or $bx = -2(2x)(3)$
$bx = 12$ $\qquad\qquad bx = -12x$
$b = 12$ $\qquad\qquad\quad b = -12$

101. Express c as a^2. Then $25x^2 + 20x + c$ becomes
$25x^2 + 20x + a^2$ or $(5x)^2 + 20x + (a)^2$. But,
$20x = 2(5x)(a)$
$20x = 10xa$
$\dfrac{20x}{10x} = a$
$\quad 2 = a$
Now, $a = 2$ and $c = a^2 = (2)^2 = 4$.

103. a. Find an expression whose square is
$25x^2 - 30x + 9$.

b. $A(x) = \left[s(x)\right]^2$
$A(x) = 25x^2 - 30x + 9$
$\quad\quad = (5x - 3)^2$
Therefore $s(x) = 5x - 3$

c. $s(2) = 5(2) - 3 = 10 - 3 = 7$

105. $x^2 + 64 = \left(x^4 + 16x^2 + 64\right) - 16x^2$
$= \left(x^2 + 8\right)^2 - (4x)^2$
$\left(x^2 + 8 + 4x\right)\left(x^2 + 8 - 4x\right)$
$= \left(x^2 + 4x + 8\right)\left(x^2 - 4x + 8\right)$

107. $P(x) = x^2$
$P(a + h) - P(a) = (a + h)^2 - a^2$
$\quad\quad\quad\quad\quad = a^2 + 2ah + h^2 - a^2$
$\quad\quad\quad\quad\quad = 2ah + h^2$
$\quad\quad\quad\quad\quad = h(2a + h)$

109. a. The area is $4 \cdot 4 = 16$

b. The sum is $x^2 + 8x + 16$

c. $x^2 + 8x + 16 = (x + 4)^2$

111. $64x^{4a} - 9y^{6a} = \left(8x^{2a}\right)^2 - \left(3y^{3a}\right)^2$
$= \left(8x^{2a} + 3y^{3a}\right)\left(8x^{2a} - 3y^{3a}\right)$

113. $a^{2n} - 16a^n + 64 = \left(a^n\right)^2 - 2\left(a^n\right)(8) + (8)^2$
$= \left(a^n - 8\right)^2$

115. $x^{3n} - 8 = \left(x^n\right)^3 - 2^3$
$= \left(x^n - 2\right)\left[\left(x^n\right)^2 + \left(x^n\right)(2) + (2)^2\right]$
$= \left(x^n - 2\right)\left(x^{2n} + 2x^n + 4\right)$

117. $y_1 = 2x^2 - 18$
$y_2 = 2(x + 3)(x - 3)$

$-10, 10, 1, -30$
The factoring is correct because the graphs are
the same.

119. a. $x^6 - 1 = \left(x^3\right)^2 - 1^2 = \left(x^3 - 1\right)\left(x^3 + 1\right)$

b. $x^6 - 1 = \left(x^2\right)^3 - 1^3$
$= \left(x^2 - 1\right)\left[\left(x^2\right)^2 + \left(x^2\right)(1) + (1)^2\right]$
$= \left(x^2 - 1\right)\left(x^4 + x^2 + 1\right)$

c. $x^6 - 1$
$= \left(x^3 - 1\right)\left(x^3 + 1\right)$
$= (x - 1)\left(x^2 + x + 1\right)(x + 1)\left(x^2 - x + 1\right)$
$= (x - 1)(x + 1)\left(x^2 + x + 1\right)\left(x^2 - x + 1\right)$
$= \left(x^2 - 1\right)\left(x^4 + x^2 + 1\right)$ upon multiplication

121. $-2\left[3x - (2y - 1) - 5x\right] + y$
$-2\left[3x - 2y + 1 - 5x\right] + y$
$-2\left[-2x - 2y + 1\right] + y$
$4x + 4y - 2 + y$
$4x + 5y - 2$

123.   Let x be the measure of the smallest angle. The measure of the largest angle will be $2x$. The measure of the remaining angle will be $x +10$.

$x+(x+10)+(2x)=90$

$4x+10=90$

$4x=80$

$x = 20$

     The measures of the angles are $20°$, $30°$, and $40°$.

125. $12x^2 - 9xy + 4xy - 3y^2$

$3x(4x - 3y) + y(4x - 3y)$

$(4x - 3y)(3x + y)$

Exercise Set 5.7

1. a.   Factor out the GCF if it is present. If the remaining polynomial is the difference of two squares, difference of two cubes, or the sum of two cubes, use the following factoring formulas.

$a^2 - b^2 = (a +b)(a - b)$

$a^3 - b^3 = (a - b)(a^2 + ab + b^2)$

$a^3 + b^3 = (a + b)(a^2 - ab + b^2)$

     b.   Factor out the GCF if it is present. If the remaining polynomial is a perfect square, use the special factoring formulas:

$a^2 + 2ab + b^2 = (a + b)^2$

$a^2 - 2ab + b^2 = (a - b)^2$

     c.   Factor out the GCF if it is present. Factor the remaining polynomial using the method of grouping.

3. $3x^2 - 75 = 3(x^2 - 25)$ $\leftarrow$ 3 is a common factor

$\qquad\quad = 3(x+5)(x-5)$ $\leftarrow$ Factor $x^2 - 25$ as difference of squares

5. $10s^2 + 19s - 15 = 10s^2 + 25s - 6s - 15$ $\leftarrow$ Use $19s = 25s - 6s$

$\qquad\qquad\qquad\quad = 5s(2s + 5) - 3(2s + 5)$

$\qquad\qquad\qquad\quad = (5s - 3)(2s + 5)$

7. $-8r^2 + 26r - 15 = -(8r^2 - 26r + 15)$ $\leftarrow$ -1 is a common factor

$\qquad\qquad\qquad\quad = -(8r^2 - 20r - 6r + 15)$ $\leftarrow$ Use $-26r = -20r - 6r$

$\qquad\qquad\qquad\quad = -[4r(2r - 5) - 3(2r - 5)]$

$\qquad\qquad\qquad\quad = -(4r - 3)(2r - 5)$

9. $0.4x^2 - 0.036 = 0.4(x^2 - 0.09)$ $\leftarrow 0.4$ is a common factor

$\qquad\qquad\qquad = 0.4(x^2 - 0.3^2)$ $\leftarrow$ Difference of two squares

$\qquad\qquad\qquad = 0.4(x + 0.3)(x - 0.3)$

11. $6x^5 - 54x = 6x\left(x^4 - 9\right)$ $\leftarrow$ $6x$ is a common factor

$\qquad = 6x\left[\left(x^2\right)^2 - (3)^2\right]$ $\leftarrow$ Difference of two squares

$\qquad = 6x\left(x^2 + 3\right)\left(x^2 - 3\right)$

13. $3x^6 - 3x^5 + 12x^5 - 12x^4 = 3x^4\left(x^2 - x + 4x - 4\right)$ $\leftarrow$ $3x^4$ is a common factor

$\qquad\qquad = 3x^4\left[x(x-1) + 4(x-1)\right]$ $\leftarrow$ Factor by grouping

$\qquad\qquad = 3x^4(x+4)(x-1)$

15. $5x^4y^2 + 20x^3y^2 + 15x^3y^2 + 60x^2y^2 = 5x^2y^2\left(x^2 + 4x + 3x + 12\right)$ $\leftarrow$ $5x^2y^2$ is a common factor

$\qquad\qquad = 5x^2y^2\left[x(x+4) + 3(x+4)\right]$ $\leftarrow$ Factor by grouping

$\qquad\qquad = 5x^2y^2(x+3)(x+4)$

17. $x^4 - x^2y^2 = x^2\left(x^2 - y^2\right)$ $\leftarrow$ x^2 is a common factor

$\qquad = x^2(x+y)(x-y)$ $\leftarrow$ Difference of two squares

19. $x^7y^2 - x^4y^2 = x^4y^2\left(x^3 - 1\right)$ $\leftarrow$ x^4y^2 is a common factor

$\qquad = x^4y^2(x-1)\left(x^2 + x + 1\right)$ $\leftarrow$ Difference of two cubes

21. $x^5 - 16x = x\left(x^4 - 16\right)$ $\leftarrow$ x is a common factor

$\qquad = x\left[\left(x^2\right)^2 - (4)^2\right]$ $\leftarrow$ Difference of two squares

$\qquad = x\left(x^2 + 4\right)\left(x^2 - 4\right)$ $\leftarrow$ Difference of two squares on $x^2 - 4$

$\qquad = x\left(x^2 + 4\right)(x+2)(x-2)$

23. $2x^6 + 16y^3 = 2\left(x^6 + 8y^3\right)$ $\leftarrow$ 2 is a common factor

$\qquad = 2\left[\left(x^2\right)^3 + (2y)^3\right]$ $\leftarrow$ Sum of two cubes

$\qquad = 2\left(x^2 + 2y\right)\left[\left(x^2\right)^2 - \left(x^2\right)(2y) + (2y)^2\right]$ $\leftarrow$ Simplify

$\qquad = 2\left(x^2 + 2y\right)\left(x^4 - 2x^2y + 4y^2\right)$

25. $2(a+b)^2 - 50 = 2\left[(a+b)^2 - 25\right]$ $\leftarrow$ 2 is a common factor

$\qquad = 2\left[(a+b)+5\right]\left[(a+b)-5\right]$ $\leftarrow$ Difference of two squares

$\qquad = 2(a+b+5)(a+b-5)$ $\leftarrow$ Simplify

27. $6x^2 + 36xy + 54y^2 = 6\left(x^2 + 6xy + 9y^2\right)$ ← 6 is a common factor

$$= 6\left[x^2 + 2(x)(3y) + (3y)^2\right]$$ ← Perfect square trinomial

$$= 6(x + 3y)^2$$

29. $(x + 2)^2 - 4 = \left[(x + 2) + 2\right]\left[(x + 2) - 2\right]$ ← Difference of two squares

$$= (x + 2 + 2)(x + 2 - 2)$$ ← Simplify

$$= (x + 4)(x) \text{ or } x(x + 4)$$

31. $(2a + b)(2a - 3b) - (2a + b)(a - b) = (2a + b)\left[(2a - 3b) - (a - b)\right]$ ← $(2a + b)$ is a common factor

$$= (2a + b)(2a - 3b - a + b)$$ ← Simplify

$$= (2a + b)(a - 2b)$$

33. $(y + 5)^2 + 4(y + 5) + 4 = (y + 5)^2 + 2(y + 5)(2) + (2)^2$ ← Perfect square trinomial

$$= \left[(y + 5) + 2\right]^2$$

$$= (y + 7)^2$$

35. $45a^4 - 30a^3 + 5a^2 = 5a^2\left(9a^2 - 6a + 1\right)$ ← $5a^2$ is a common factor

$$= 5a^2\left[(3a)^2 - 2(3a)(1) + 1^2\right]$$ ← Perfect square trinomial

$$= 5a^2(3a - 1)^2$$

37. $x^3 + \dfrac{1}{64} = x^3 + \left(\dfrac{1}{4}\right)^3$ ← Sum of two cubes

$$= \left(x + \dfrac{1}{4}\right)\left[x^2 - x\left(\dfrac{1}{4}\right) + \left(\dfrac{1}{4}\right)^2\right]$$

$$= \left(x + \dfrac{1}{4}\right)\left[x^2 - \dfrac{x}{4} + \dfrac{1}{16}\right]$$

39. $3x^3 + 2x^2 - 27x - 18 = x^2(3x + 2) - 9(3x + 2)$ ← Factor by grouping

$$= \left(x^2 - 9\right)(3x + 2)$$ ← Difference of two squares

$$= (x + 3)(x - 3)(3x + 2)$$

41. $a^3b - 64ab^3 = ab\left(a^2 - 64b^2\right)$ ← ab is a common factor

$$= ab\left[a^2 - (8b)^2\right]$$ ← Difference of two squares

$$= ab(a + 8b)(a - 8b)$$

43. $81 - (x^2 + 2xy + y^2) = 81 - (x + y)^2$ ← Perfect square trinomial

$$= \left[9 + (x + y)\right]\left[9 - (x + y)\right]$$ ← Difference of two squares

$$= (9 + x + y)(9 - x - y)$$ ← Simplify

45. $24x^2 - 34x + 12 = 2\left(12x^2 - 17x + 6\right)$ ← 2 is a common factor

$\qquad\qquad\qquad\quad = 2\left(12x^2 - 8x - 9x + 6\right)$ ← Use $-17x = -8x - 9x$

$\qquad\qquad\qquad\quad = 2\left[4x(3x - 2) - 3(3x - 2)\right]$ ← Factor by grouping

$\qquad\qquad\qquad\quad = 2(4x - 3)(3x - 2)$

47. $16x^2 + 34x - 15 = 16x^2 + 40x - 6x - 15$ ← Use $-34x = 40x - 6x$

$\qquad\qquad\qquad\quad = 8x(2x + 5) - 3(2x + 5)$ ← Factor by grouping

$\qquad\qquad\qquad\quad = (8x - 3)(2x - 5)$

49. $x^4 - 16 = \left(x^2\right)^2 - (4)^2$ ← Difference of two squares

$\qquad\qquad = \left(x^2 + 4\right)\left(x^2 - 4\right)$ ← Difference of two squares $(x^2 - 4)$

$\qquad\qquad = \left(x^2 + 4\right)(x + 2)(x - 2)$

51. $5bc - 10cx - 7by + 14xy = 5c(b - 2x) - 7y(b - 2x)$ ← Factor by grouping

$\qquad\qquad\qquad\qquad\qquad = (5c - 7y)(b - 2x)$ ← $(b - 2x)$ is a common factor

53. $3x^4 - x^2 - 4 = 3\left(x^2\right)^2 - x^2 - 4$

$\qquad\qquad\qquad = 3\left(x^2\right)^2 - 4x^2 + 3x^2 - 4$ ← Use $-x^2 = -4x^2 + 3x^2$

$\qquad\qquad\qquad = x^2\left(3x^2 - 4\right) + 1\left(3x^2 - 4\right)$ ← Factor by grouping

$\qquad\qquad\qquad = \left(x^2 + 1\right)\left(3x^2 - 4\right)$ ← $\left(3x^2 - 4\right)$ is a common factor

55. $y^2 - \left(x^2 - 12x + 36\right) = y^2 - (x - 6)^2$ ← Perfect square trinomial

$\qquad\qquad\qquad\qquad = \left[y + (x - 6)\right]\left[y - (x - 6)\right]$ ← Difference of two squares

$\qquad\qquad\qquad\qquad = (y + x - 6)(y - x + 6)$ ← Simplify

57. $2(y + 4)^2 + 5(y + 4) - 12 = 2x^2 + 5x - 12$ ← Replace $y + 4$ with x

$\qquad\qquad\qquad\qquad\quad = 2x^2 + 8x - 3x - 12$ ← Use $5x = 8x - 3x$

$\qquad\qquad\qquad\qquad\quad = 2x(x + 4) - 3(x + 4)$ ← Factor by grouping

$\qquad\qquad\qquad\qquad\quad = (2x - 3)(x + 4)$ ← $x + 4$ is a common factor

$\qquad\qquad\qquad\qquad\quad = \left[2(y + 4) - 3\right]\left[(y + 4) + 4\right]$ ← Replace x with $y + 4$

$\qquad\qquad\qquad\qquad\quad = (2y + 8 - 3)(y + 8)$ ← Simplify

$\qquad\qquad\qquad\qquad\quad = (2y + 5)(y + 8)$ ← Simplify

59. $a^2 + 12ab + 36b^2 - 16c^2 = (a + 6b)^2 - (4c)^2$ ← Perfect square trinomial

$\qquad\qquad\qquad\qquad\quad = \left[(a + 6b) + 4c\right]\left[(a + 6b) - 4c\right]$ ← Difference of two squares

$\qquad\qquad\qquad\qquad\quad = (a + 6b + 4c)(a + 6b - 4c)$ ← Simplify

61. $6x^4y + 15x^3y - 9x^2y = 3x^2y\left(2x^2 + 5x - 3\right)$ ← $3x^2y$ is a common factor

$\qquad\qquad = 3x^2y\left(2x^2 - x + 6x - 3\right)$ ← Use $5x = -x + 6x$

$\qquad\qquad = 3x^2y\left[x(2x-1) + 3(2x-1)\right]$ ← Factor by grouping

$\qquad\qquad = 3x^2y(x+3)(2x-1)$ ← $2x+1$ is a common factor

63. $x^4 - 2x^2y^2 + y^4 = \left(x^2\right)^2 - 2\left(x^2\right)\left(y^2\right) + \left(y^2\right)^2$ ← Perfect square trinomial

$\qquad\qquad = \left(x^2 - y^2\right)^2$ ← Difference of two squares

$\qquad\qquad = \left[(x+y)(x-y)\right]^2$

$\qquad\qquad = (x+y)^2(x-y)^2$

65. $a^2 + b^2$ is not factorable, (e)

67. $a^3 + b^3 = (a+b)\left(a^2 - ab + b^2\right)$, (a)

69. $a^3 - b^3 = (a-b)\left(a^2 + ab + b^2\right)$, (f)

71. $a^3 + b^3 = (a+b)\left(a^2 - ab + b^2\right)$, (c)

73. $P = 2\left(x^2 + 3\right) + 2(5x+3)$

$\qquad = 2x^2 + 6 + 10x + 6$

$\qquad = 2x^2 + 10x + 12$

$\qquad = 2\left(x^2 + 5x + 6\right)$

$\qquad = 2(x+3)(x+2)$

75. $A = x^2 + 4x + 4x + (3)(4)$

$\qquad = x^2 + 8x + 12$

$\qquad = (x+6)(x+2)$

77. $A = (x+5)(x+4) - (4)(3)$

$\qquad = x^2 + 4x + 5x + 20 - 12$

$\qquad = x^2 + 9x + 8$

$\qquad = (x+8)(x+1)$

79. $V = (5x)^3 - (3)^3$

$\qquad = (5x-3)\left((5x)^2 + (5x)(3) + (3)^2\right)$

$\qquad = (5x-3)\left(25x^2 + 15x + 9\right)$

81. The area of larger rectangle is $a(a+b)$.
The area of center rectangle is $b(a+b)$.

   a.   The area of shaded region is
$a(a+b) - b(a+b) = a^2 - b^2$.

   b.   In factored form, the area is
$a(a+b) - b(a+b) = (a-b)(a+b)$

83.   **a.**   The area of the shaded region is the sum of
the areas of the three regions. This is
$(a)(a) + (2b)(a) + (b)(b) = a^2 + 2ab + b^2$.

   b.   In factored form, the area is
$a^2 + 2ab + b^2 = (a+b)^2$.

85. The area of the left side is $b(a-b)$.
The area of the right side is $b(a-b)$.
The area of the front side is $a(a-b)$.
The area of the back side is $a(a-b)$.

   a.   The surface area is $2a(a-b) + 2b(a-b)$.

   b.   In factored form, the area is
$2a(a-b) + 2b(a-b) = 2(a+b)(a-b)$.

87.   **a.**   Answers will vary.

   b.   Answers will vary.

89.   **a.** $x^{-3} - 2x^{-4} - 3x^{-5} = x^{-5}\left(x^2 - 2x - 3\right)$

   b. $x^{-5}\left(x^2 - 2x - 3\right) = x^{-5}(x-3)(x+1)$

91. a.
$$5x^{1/2} + 2x^{-1/2} - 3x^{-3/2}$$
$$= 5x^{-3/2}x^2 + 2x^{-3/2}x^1 - 3x^{-3/2}$$
$$= x^{-3/2}\left(5x^2 + 2x - 3\right)$$

b. $x^{-3/2}(5x^2 + 2x - 3) = x^{-3/2}(5x - 3)(x + 1)$

93. $\left|\dfrac{6+2z}{3}\right| > 2$

$\dfrac{6+2z}{3} < -2$ or $\dfrac{6+2z}{3} > 2$

$6 + 2z < -6$ $6 + 2z > 6$

$2z < -12$ $2z > 0$

$z < -6$ $z > 0$

$\{z | z < -6 \text{ or } z > 0\}$

95.
$$x^2 - x + 4$$
$$\underline{5x + 4}$$
$$4x^2 - 4x + 16$$
$$\underline{5x^3 - 5x^2 + 20x}$$
$$5x^3 - x^2 + 16x + 16$$

Exercise Set 5.8

1. The degree of a polynomial function is the same as the degree of the leading term.

3. $ax^2 + bx + c = 0$ is the standard form of a quadratic equation.

5. a. The zero factor property only holds when one side of the equation is 0.

b. $(x + 3)(x + 4) = 2$
$$x^2 + 7x + 12 = 2$$
$$x^2 + 7x + 10 = 0$$
$$(x + 5)(x + 2) = 0$$
$$x + 5 = 0 \quad \text{or} \quad x + 2 = 0$$
$$x = -5 \qquad\qquad x = -2$$
The solutions are –2 and –5.

7. a. Answers will vary. Possible answer: Factor the polynomial, set the factors equal to 0, and then solve.

b.
$$-x - 20 = -12x^2$$
$$12x^2 - x - 20 = 0$$
$$(3x - 4)(4x + 5) = 0$$
$$3x - 4 = 0 \quad \text{or} \quad 4x + 5 = 0$$
$$3x = 4 \quad \text{or} \quad 4x = -5$$
$$x = \frac{4}{3} \quad \text{or} \quad x = -\frac{5}{4}$$
The solutions are $\frac{4}{3}, -\frac{5}{4}$.

9. a. The two shorter sides of a right triangle are called the legs.

b. The longest side of a right triangle is called the hypotenuse.

11. –8 and –2; answers will vary.

13. Yes, the graph of the function may be such that the graph never crosses the x-axis.

15. Yes, the graph of the function may be such that the graph touches the x-axis at two points.

17. $x(x - 4) = 0$
$$x = 0 \quad \text{or} \quad x - 4 = 0$$
$$x = 4$$
The solutions are 0, 4.

19. $3x(x - 1) = 0$
$$3x = 0 \quad \text{or} \quad x - 1 = 0$$
$$x = 0 \qquad\qquad x = 1$$
The solutions are 0, 1.

21. $2(x + 1)(x - 7) = 0$
$$x + 1 = 0 \quad \text{or} \quad x - 7 = 0$$
$$x = -1 \qquad\qquad x = 7$$
The solutions are –1, 7.

23. $x(x - 9)(x + 4) = 0$
$$x = 0 \quad \text{or} \quad x - 9 = 0 \quad \text{or} \quad x + 4 = 0$$
$$x = 0 \qquad\qquad x = 9 \qquad\qquad x = -4$$

The solutions are 0, 9, –4.

25. $(2x+3)(4x+5)=0$

$2x+3=0$ or $4x+5=0$

$2x=-3$ $4x=-5$

$x=-\dfrac{3}{2}$ $x=-\dfrac{5}{4}$

The solutions are $-\dfrac{3}{2}, -\dfrac{5}{4}$.

27. $4x^2=12x$

$4x^2-12x=0$

$4x(x-3)=0$

$4x=0$ or $x-3=0$

$x=0$ or $\quad x=3$

The solutions are 0, 3.

29. $x^2+5x=0$

$x(x+5)=0$

$x=0$ or $x+5=0$

$x=-5$

The solutions are 0, −5.

31. $-x^2+6x=0$

$x(-x+6)=0$

$x=0$ or $-x+6=0$

$x=6$

The solutions are 0, 6.

33. $3x^2=15x$

$3x^2-15x=0$

$3x(x-5)=0$

$3x=0$ or $x-5=0$

$x=0$ $x=5$

The solutions are 0, 5.

35. $x^2-6x+5=0$

$(x-5)(x-1)=0$

$x-5=0$ or $x-1=0$

$x=5$ $x=1$

The solutions are 5, 1.

37. $x^2+x-12=0$

$(x+4)(x-3)=0$

$x+4=0$ or $x-3=0$

$x=-4$ $x=3$

The solutions are −4, 3.

39. $x^2+8x+16=0$

$(x+4)(x+4)=0$

$x+4=0$ or $x+4=0$

$x=-4$ $x=-4$

The solution is −4.

41. $x(x-12)=-20$

$x^2-12x=-20$

$x^2-12x+20=0$

$(x-10)(x-2)=0$

$x-10=0$ or $x-2=0$

$x=10$ $x=2$

The solutions are 10, 2.

43. $2x^2=-14x-12$

$2x^2+14x+12=0$

$2(x^2+7x+6)=0$

$2(x+6)(x+1)=0$

$x+6=0$ or $x+1=0$

$x=-6$ $x=-1$

The solutions are −6, −1.

45. $3x^2-6x-72=0$

$3(x^2-2x-24)=0$

$3(x-6)(x+4)=0$

$x-6=0$ or $x+4=0$

$x=6$ $x=-4$

The solutions are 6, −4.

47. $x^3-3x^2=18x$

$x^3-3x^2-18x=0$

$x(x^2-3x-18)=0$

$x(x-6)(x+3)=0$

$x=0$ or $x-6=0$ or $x+3=0$

$x=6$ $x=-3$

The solutions are 0, 6, −3.

49.
$$12a^2 = 16a + 3$$
$$12a^2 - 16a - 3 = 0$$
$$(2a - 3)(6a + 1) = 0$$
$$2a - 3 = 0 \quad \text{or} \quad 6a + 1 = 0$$
$$2a = 3 \qquad\qquad 6a = -1$$
$$a = \frac{3}{2} \qquad\qquad a = -\frac{1}{6}$$

The solutions are $\dfrac{3}{2}, \ -\dfrac{1}{6}$.

51. $4c^3 + 4c^2 - 48c = 0$
$$4c\left(c^2 + c - 12\right) = 0$$
$$4c(c + 4)(c - 3) = 0$$
$$4c = 0 \quad \text{or} \quad c + 4 = 0 \quad \text{or} \quad c - 3 = 0$$
$$c = 0 \qquad\quad c = -4 \qquad\qquad c = 3$$

The solutions are 0, –4, 3.

53. $x^2 - 36 = 0$
$$(x + 6)(x - 6) = 0$$
$$x + 6 = 0 \quad \text{or} \quad x - 6 = 0$$
$$x = -6 \qquad\qquad x = 6$$

The solutions are –6, 6.

55.
$$4x^2 = 9$$
$$4x^2 - 9 = 0$$
$$(2x + 3)(2x - 3) = 0$$
$$2x + 3 = 0 \quad \text{or} \quad 2x - 3 = 0$$
$$2x = -3 \qquad\qquad 2x = 3$$
$$x = -\frac{3}{2} \qquad\qquad x = \frac{3}{2}$$

The solutions are $-\dfrac{3}{2}, \dfrac{3}{2}$.

57.
$$25x^3 - 16x = 0$$
$$x\left(25x^2 - 16\right) = 0$$
$$x\left[(5x)^2 - 4^2\right] = 0$$
$$x(5x + 4)(5x - 4) = 0$$
$$x = 0 \quad \text{or} \quad 5x + 4 = 0 \quad \text{or} \quad 5x - 4 = 0$$
$$5x = -4 \qquad\qquad 5x = 4$$
$$x = -\frac{4}{5} \qquad\qquad x = \frac{4}{5}$$

The solutions are $0, \ -\dfrac{4}{5}, \dfrac{4}{5}$.

59.
$$-x^2 = 2x - 99$$
$$-x^2 - 2x + 99 = 0$$
$$x^2 + 2x - 99 = 0$$
$$(x + 11)(x - 9) = 0$$
$$x + 11 = 0 \quad \text{or} \quad x - 9 = 0$$
$$x = -11 \qquad\qquad x = 9$$

The solutions are –11, 9.

61.
$$(x + 4)^2 - 16 = 0$$
$$[(x + 4) + 4][(x + 4) - 4] = 0$$
$$(x + 8)(x) = 0$$
$$x + 8 = 0 \quad \text{or} \quad x = 0$$
$$x = -8$$

The solutions are –8, 0.

63.
$$(2x + 5)^2 - 9 = 0$$
$$[(2x + 5) + 3][(2x + 5) - 3] = 0$$
$$(2x + 8)(2x + 2) = 0$$
$$2(x + 4)[2(x + 1)] = 0$$
$$4(x + 4)(x + 1) = 0$$
$$x + 4 = 0 \quad \text{or} \quad x + 1 = 0$$
$$x = -4 \qquad\qquad x = -1$$

The solutions are –4, –1.

65. $6a^2 - 12 - 4a = 19a - 32$
$$6a^2 - 23a + 20 = 0$$
$$(3a - 4)(2a - 5) = 0$$
$$3a - 4 = 0 \quad \text{or} \quad 2a - 5 = 0$$
$$3a = 4 \qquad\qquad 2a = 5$$
$$a = \frac{4}{3} \qquad\qquad a = \frac{5}{2}$$

The solutions are $\dfrac{4}{3}, \dfrac{5}{2}$.

67. $2b^3 + 16b^2 = -30b$
$$2b^3 + 16b^2 + 30b = 0$$
$$2b\left(b^2 + 8b + 15\right) = 0$$
$$2b(b + 5)(b + 3) = 0$$
$$2x = 0 \quad \text{or} \quad x + 5 = 0 \quad \text{or} \quad x + 3 = 0$$
$$x = 0 \qquad\qquad x = -5 \qquad\qquad x = -3$$

The solutions are 0, –5, –3.

68. $(a-1)(3a+2) = 4a$

$$3a^2 - a - 2 = 4a$$
$$3a^2 - 5a - 2 = 0$$
$$(3a+1)(a-2) = 0$$
$$3a+1 = 0 \quad \text{or} \quad a-2 = 0$$
$$3a = -1 \qquad\qquad a = 2$$
$$a = -\frac{1}{3}$$

The solutions are $-\frac{1}{3}$, 2.

69. $f(x) = 3x^2 + 7x + 9$

$$7 = 3a^2 + 7a + 9$$
$$0 = 3a^2 + 7a + 2$$
$$0 = (3a+1)(a+2)$$
$$3a+1 = 0 \quad \text{or} \quad a+2 = 0$$
$$a = -\frac{1}{3} \qquad\qquad a = -2$$

The values of a are $-\frac{1}{3}$, -2.

71. $g(x) = 10x^2 - 31x + 19$

$$4 = 10a^2 - 31a + 19$$
$$0 = 10a^2 - 31a + 15$$
$$0 = (5a-3)(2a-5)$$
$$5a-3 = 0 \quad \text{or} \quad 2a-5 = 0$$
$$a = \frac{3}{5} \qquad\qquad a = \frac{5}{2}$$

The values of a are $\frac{3}{5}, \frac{5}{2}$.

73. $r(x) = x^2 - x$

$$30 = a^2 - a$$
$$0 = a^2 - a - 30$$
$$0 = (a+5)(a-6)$$
$$a+5 = 0 \quad \text{or} \quad a-6 = 0$$
$$a = -5 \qquad\qquad a = 6$$

The values of a are –5, and 6.

75. $y = x^2 + 2x - 24$

Set $y = 0$ and solve the resulting equation.

$$x^2 + 2x - 24 = 0$$
$$(x+6)(x-4) = 0$$
$$x+6 = 0 \quad \text{or} \quad x-4 = 0$$
$$x = -6 \qquad\qquad x = 4$$

The x-intercepts are –6 and 4.

77. $y = x^2 + 16x + 64$

Set $y = 0$ and solve the resulting equation.

$$x^2 + 16x + 64 = 0$$
$$(x+8)^2 = 0$$
$$x+8 = 0$$
$$x = -8$$

The x-intercept is –8.

79. $y = 6x^3 - 23x^2 + 20x$

Set $y = 0$ and solve the resulting equation.

$$6x^3 - 23x^2 + 20x = 0$$
$$x\left(6x^2 - 23x + 20\right) = 0$$
$$x(3x-4)(2x-5) = 0$$
$$x = 0 \quad \text{or} \quad 3x-4 = 0 \quad \text{or} \quad 2x-5 = 0$$
$$3x = 4 \qquad\qquad 2x = 5$$
$$x = \frac{4}{3} \qquad\qquad x = \frac{5}{2}$$

The x-intercepts are 0, $\frac{4}{3}$, and $\frac{5}{2}$.

81.
$$(x+3)^2 + (x+2)^2 = (x+4)^2$$
$$\left(x^2+6x+9\right) + \left(x^2+4x+4\right) = x^2 + 8x + 16$$
$$x^2 + 2x - 3 = 0$$
$$(x+3)(x-1) = 0$$
$$x+3 = 0 \quad \text{or} \quad x-1 = 0$$
$$x = -3 \qquad\qquad x = 1$$

Since $x = -3$ would result in negative length for the small side, we must reject this solution. Therefore $x = 1$.

83.
$$(x+3)^2 + (x+10)^2 = (x+11)^2$$
$$\left(x^2+6x+9\right) + \left(x^2+20x+100\right) = x^2 + 22x + 12$$
$$x^2 + 4x - 12 = 0$$
$$(x+6)(x-2) = 0$$
$$x+6 = 0 \quad \text{or} \quad x-2 = 0$$
$$x = -6 \qquad\qquad x = 2$$

Since $x = -6$ would result in negative length for the small side, we must reject this solution. Therefore $x = 2$.

85.
$$(x)^2 + (x+7)^2 = (x+9)^2$$
$$\left(x^2\right) + \left(x^2 + 14x + 49\right) = x^2 + 18x + 81$$
$$x^2 - 4x - 32 = 0 \qquad \text{Since}$$
$$(x-8)(x+4) = 0$$
$$x - 8 = 0 \quad \text{or} \quad x + 4 = 0$$
$$x = 8 \qquad\qquad x = -4$$

$x = -4$ would result in negative length for the small side, we must reject this solution. Therefore $x = 8$.

87.
$$y = x^2 - 5x + 6$$
$$0 = (x-2)(x-3)$$
$$x - 2 = 0 \quad \text{or} \quad x - 3 = 0$$
$$x = 2 \qquad\qquad x = 3$$

The x-intercepts are 2 and 3.
Graph (d) matches this equation.

89.
$$y = x^2 + 5x + 6$$
$$0 = (x+2)(x+3)$$
$$x + 2 = 0 \quad \text{or} \quad x + 3 = 0$$
$$x = -2 \qquad\qquad x = -3$$

The x-intercepts are -3 and -2.
Graph (b) matches this equation.

91.
$$y = (x-2)(x-5)$$
$$y = x^2 - 7x - 10$$

93.
$$y = (x-4)(x+1)$$
$$y = x^2 - 3x - 4$$

95.
$$y = (6x+5)(x-2)$$
$$y = 6x^2 - 7x - 10$$

97. Let w = width,
then $2w + 1$ = length
surface area = width · length
$$10 = w(2w+1)$$
$$0 = 2w^2 + w - 10$$
$$0 = (2w+5)(w-2)$$
$$2w + 5 = 0 \quad \text{or} \quad w - 2 = 0$$
$$w = -\frac{5}{2} \qquad\qquad w = 2$$

Since width cannot be negative, the width is 2 feet and the length is $2(2) + 1 = 5$ feet.

99. Let b = length of base,
then $b + 6$ = height
$$\text{area} = \frac{1}{2} \cdot \text{base} \cdot \text{height}$$

$$80 = \frac{1}{2} b(b+6)$$
$$160 = b(b+6)$$
$$0 = b^2 + 6b - 160$$
$$0 = (b+16)(b-10)$$
$$b + 16 = 0 \quad \text{or} \quad b - 10 = 0$$
$$b = -16 \qquad\qquad b = 10$$

Since the base length cannot be negative, the base is 10 feet and the height is $10 + 6 = 16$ feet.

101. Let x = width of frame.
picture area = total area – frame area
$$414 = 28(23) - \left[2x(28-x) + 2x(23-x)\right]$$
$$414 = 644 - \left(56x - 2x^2 + 46x - 2x^2\right)$$
$$414 = 644 - 102x + 4x^2$$
$$0 = 4x^2 - 102x + 230$$
$$0 = 2\left(2x^2 - 51x + 115\right)$$
$$0 = 2(2x-5)(x-23)$$
$$2x - 5 = 0 \quad \text{or} \quad x - 23 = 0$$
$$x = \frac{5}{2} \qquad\qquad x = 23$$

The width cannot be 23 cm, therefore the width is $\frac{5}{2}$ cm.

103. Let w = width of mulch border.
area of extra mulch = total area – garden area
$$2w(30+w) + 2w(20+w) = 936 - 20(30)$$
$$60w + 2w^2 + 40w + 2w^2 = 936 - 600$$
$$4w^2 + 100w = 336$$
$$4w^2 + 100w - 336 = 0$$
$$4\left(w^2 + 25w - 84\right) = 0$$
$$4(w-3)(w+28) = 0$$
$$w - 3 = 0 \quad \text{or} \quad w + 28 = 0$$
$$w = 3 \qquad\qquad w = -28$$

The width cannot be negative. Therefore the width is 3 feet.

105. $h(t) = -16t^2 + 32t$
$$0 = -16t^2 + 32t$$
$$0 = -16t(t-2)$$
$$-16t = 0 \quad \text{or} \quad t - 2 = 0$$
$$t = 0 \qquad\qquad t = 2$$

The spurt of water will return to the jet's height in 2 seconds.

107. Let x = the distance that Tim had traveled and $x + 7$ = the distance that Bob had traveled.

$$(x)^2 + (x+7)^2 = 13^2$$
$$x^2 + x^2 + 14x + 49 = 169$$
$$2x^2 + 14x - 120 = 0$$
$$2(x^2 + 7x - 60) = 0$$
$$2(x+12)(x-5) = 0$$
$$x + 12 = 0 \quad \text{or} \quad x - 5 = 0$$
$$x = -12 \qquad\quad x = 5$$

Since the distance must be positive, Tim had traveled 5 miles and Bob had traveled 5 + 7 = 12 miles.

109. Let x = height from the ground where the wire is attached, then $x + 8$ = length of the wire

$$c^2 = a^2 + b^2$$
$$(x+8)^2 = x^2 + 12^2$$
$$x^2 + 16x + 64 = x^2 + 144$$
$$16x + 64 = 144$$
$$16x = 80$$
$$x = 5$$
$$x + 8 = 13$$

The height is 5 feet, so the wire is 13 feet.

111. $R(x) = C(x)$

$$60x - x^2 = 7x + 150$$
$$x^2 - 53x + 150 = 0$$
$$(x-50)(x-3) = 0$$
$$x - 50 = 0 \quad \text{or} \quad x - 3 = 0$$
$$x = 50 \quad \text{or} \qquad x = 3$$

Reject 3 because it was stated in the problem that $x \geq 10$. The company must sell 50 bicycles to break even.

113. Let x = length of side of original cardboard.
Volume = length · width · height

$$162 = (x-4)(x-4) \cdot 2$$
$$162 = 2(x^2 - 8x + 16)$$
$$0 = x^2 - 8x - 65$$
$$0 = (x-13)(x+5)$$
$$x - 13 = 0 \quad \text{or} \quad x + 5 = 0$$
$$x = 13 \qquad\quad x = -5$$

Disregard a negative length. The original cardboard measures 13 in. by 13 in.

115. a. $V = a^3 - ab^2$

b. $V = a(a^2 - b^2)$
$$V = a(a-b)(a+b)$$

c.
$$1620 = 12(12 - b)(12 + b)$$
$$135 = (12 - b)(12 + b)$$
$$135 = 144 - b^2$$
$$b^2 = 9$$
$$b = \pm 3$$
Then, $b = 3$ in.

117. a. The x-intercepts are $x = -5$ and $x = -2$. The factors are $x + 5$ and $x + 2$. One possible representation for the function is
$$f(x) = (x+5)(x+2) = x^2 + 7x + 10.$$

b. The quadratic equation can be $x^2 + 7x + 10 = 0$.

c. There are an infinite number. For this, express $f(x)$ as $f(x) = a(x^2 + 7x + 10)$ where a is any real number except 0.

d. There are an infinite number. For this, use $a(x^2 + 7x + 10) = 0$ where a is any real number except 0. The solution is $x = -2$ or $x = -5$.

119. a. Answers will vary. One example is: No x-intercepts

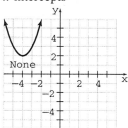

One x-intercept

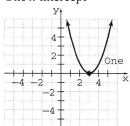

Two x-intercepts

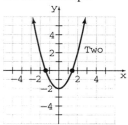

b. $ax^2 + bx + c$ could have no x-intercepts, one x-intercept, or two x-intercepts. If the graph does not cross the x-axis, there are no x-intercepts (no real solutions). If the vertex is located on the x-axis, then there is one intercept (one real solution). If the graph crosses the x-axis at two different points, then there are two

121. $d(s) = -0.31s^2 + 59.82s - 2180.22$

$545 = -0.31s^2 + 59.82s - 2180.22$

$y_1 = 545$

$y_2 = -0.31s^2 + 59.82s - 2180.22$

```
Intersection
X=73.721949  Y=545
```

60, 80, 2, 400, 600

The intersection is approximately (73.721949, 545). The car was traveling approximately 73.721949 mph.

123. $x^4 - 13x^2 = -36$

$x^4 - 13x^2 + 36 = 0$

$\left(x^2\right)^2 - 13x^2 + 36 = 0$

$y^2 - 13y + 36 = 0$ ← Replace x^2 with y

$(y - 9)(y - 4) = 0$

$y - 9 = 0$ or $y - 4 = 0$

$x^2 - 9 = 0$ or $x^2 - 4 = 0$ ← Replace y with x^2

$(x - 3)(x + 3) = 0$ $(x - 2)(x + 2) = 0$

$x - 3 = 0$ $x + 3 = 0$ $x - 2 = 0$ $x + 2 = 0$

$x = 3$ $x = -3$ $x = 2$ $x = -2$

The solutions are 3, –3, 2, –2.

125. $xy' + yy' = 1$

$y'(x + y) = 1$

$\dfrac{y'(x + y)}{(x + y)} = \dfrac{1}{(x + y)}$

$y' = \dfrac{1}{x + y}$

127. $2xyy' - xy = x - 3y'$

$2xyy' + 3y' = x + xy$

$y'(2xy + 3) = x + xy$

$\dfrac{y'(2xy + 3)}{(2xy + 3)} = \dfrac{x + xy}{(2xy + 3)}$

$y' = \dfrac{x + xy}{(2xy + 3)}$

129.

$$-1 < \frac{4(3x-2)}{3} \le 5$$

$$3(-1) < 3\left(\frac{4(3x-2)}{3}\right) \le 3(5)$$

$$-3 < 4(3x-2) \le 15$$

$$-3 < 12x - 8 \le 15$$

$$5 < 12x \le 23$$

$$\frac{5}{12} < x \le \frac{23}{12}$$

131. $f(x) = -x^2 + 3x, \quad g(x) = x^2 + 2$

$$(f \cdot g)(x) = \left(-x^2 + 3x\right)\left(x^2 + 2\right)$$

$$(f \cdot g)(4) = \left(-(4)^2 + 3(4)\right)\left((4)^2 + 2\right)$$

$$= (-16 + 12)(16 + 2)$$

$$= (-4)(18)$$

$$= -72$$

Review Exercises

1. $3x^2 + 2$

  a. Binomial (2 terms)

  b. $3x^2 + 2$

  c. The degree is 2.

2. $5x + 4x^3 - 9$

  a. Trinomial (3 terms)

  b. $4x^3 + 5x - 9$

  c. The degree is 3.

3. $8x - x^{-1} + 6$ is not a polynomial due to the negative exponent.

4. $-3 - 10x^2 y + 6xy^3 + 2x^4$

  a. Polynomial

  b. $2x^4 - 10x^2 y + 6xy^3 - 3$

  c. The degree is 4.

5. $\left(x^2 - 5x + 6\right) + (2x + 3)$

$$= x^2 - 5x + 6 + 2x + 3$$

$$= x^2 - 3x + 9$$

6. $\left(7x^2 + 2x - 5\right) - \left(2x^2 - 9x - 1\right)$

$$= 7x^2 - 2x^2 + 2x + 9x - 5 + 1$$

$$= 5x^2 + 11x - 4$$

7. $(2a - 3b - 2) - (-a + 5b - 8)$

$$= 2a + a - 3b - 5b - 2 + 8$$

$$= 3a - 8b + 6$$

8. $\left(4x^3 - 4x^2 - 2x\right) + \left(2x^3 + 4x^2 - 7x + 10\right)$

$$= 4x^3 + 2x^3 - 4x^2 + 4x^2 - 2x - 7x + 10$$

$$= 6x^3 - 9x + 10$$

9. $\left(3x^2 y + 6xy - 5y^2\right) - \left(4y^2 + 3xy\right)$

$$= 3x^2 y + 6xy - 5y^2 - 4y^2 - 3xy$$

$$= 3x^2 y + 6xy - 3xy - 5y^2 - 4y^2$$

$$= 3x^2 y + 3xy - 9y^2$$

10. $\left(-8ab + 2b^2 - 3a\right) + \left(-b^2 + 5ab + a\right)$

$$= -8ab + 5ab + 2b^2 - b^2 - 3a + a$$

$$= -3ab + b^2 - 2a$$

11. $\left(x^2 - 3x + 5\right) + \left(4x^2 + 10x - 9\right)$

$$= x^2 + 4x^2 - 3x + 10x + 5 - 9$$

$$= 5x^2 + 7x - 4$$

12. $\left(-7a^2 b - ab\right) - \left(3a^2 b - 5ab\right)$

$$= -7a^2 b - 3a^2 b - ab + 5ab$$

$$= -10a^2 b + 4ab$$

13. $P(x) = 2x^2 - 3x + 13$

$$P(2) = 2(2)^2 - 3(2) + 13$$

$$= 8 - 6 + 13$$

$$= 15$$

14. $P(x) = x^3 - 3x^2 + 4x - 9$

$P(-3) = (-3)^3 - 3(-3)^2 + 4(-3) - 9$

$\quad = -27 - 27 - 12 - 9$

$\quad = -75$

15. $P = \left(x^2 - x + 7\right) + \left(x^2 + 1\right) + \left(x^2 + x + 19\right)$

$\quad = x^2 + x^2 + x^2 - x + x + 7 + 1 + 19$

$\quad = 3x^2 + 27$

16. $P = (13x + 8) + \left(x^2 + 7\right) + (9x + 5) + \left(x^2 + 2x + 3\right)$

$\quad = x^2 + x^2 + 13x + 9x + 2x + 8 + 7 + 5 + 3$

$\quad = 2x^2 + 24x + 23$

17. **a.** $t = 2010 - 1997 = 13$

$\quad R(t) = 0.78t^2 + 20.28t + 385.0$

$\quad R(13) = 0.78(13)^2 + 20.28(13) + 385.0$

$\quad R(13) = 780.46$

The receipts in 2010 are estimated to be $780.46 billion.

b. Yes, the graph supports the answer.

18. **a.** $t = 2010 - 1997 = 13$

$\quad G(t) = 1.74t^2 + 7.32t + 383.91$

$\quad G(13) = 1.74(13)^2 + 7.32(13) + 383.91$

$\quad G(13) = 773.13$

The outlays in 2010 are estimated to be $773.13 billion.

b. Yes, the graph supports the answer.

19. $2x\left(3x^2 - 7x + 5\right)$

$= (2x)\left(3x^2\right) + (2x)(-7x) + (2x)(5)$

$= 6x^3 - 14x^2 + 10x$

20. $-3xy^2\left(x^3 + xy^4 - 6y^5\right)$

$= \left(-3xy^2\right)\left(x^3\right) + \left(-3xy^2\right)\left(xy^4\right) + \left(-3xy^2\right)\left(-6y^5\right)$

$= -3x^4y^2 - 3x^2y^6 + 18xy^7$

21. $(3x - 5)(2x + 1)$

$= (3x)(2x) + (3x)(1) + (-5)(2x) + (-5)(1)$

$= 6x^2 + 3x - 10x - 5$

$= 6x^2 - 7x - 5$

22. $(5a + 9)(10a - 3)$

$= (5a)(10a) + (5a)(-3) + (9)(10a) + (9)(-3)$

$= 50a^2 - 15a + 90a - 27$

$= 50a^2 + 75a - 27$

23. $(x + 8y)^2 = (x)^2 + 2(x)(8y) + (8y)^2$

$\quad = x^2 + 16xy + 64y^2$

24. $(a - 11b)^2 = (a)^2 - 2(a)(11b) + (11b)^2$

$\quad = a^2 - 22ab + 121b^2$

25. $(2xy - 1)(5x + 4y)$

$= (2xy)(5x) + (2xy)(4y) + (-1)(5x) + (-1)(4y)$

$= 10x^2y + 8xy^2 - 5x - 4y$

26. $(2pq - r)(3pq + 7r)$

$= (2pq)(3pq) + (2pq)(7r) + (-r)(3pq) + (-r)(7r)$

$= 6p^2q^2 + 14pqr - 3pqr - 7r^2$

$= 6p^2q^2 + 11pqr - 7r^2$

27. $(2a + 9b)^2 = (2a)^2 + 2(2a)(9b) + (9b)^2$

$\quad = 4a^2 + 36ab + 81b^2$

28. $(3x - 2y)^2 = (3x)^2 - 2(3x)(2y) + (2y)^2$

$\quad = 9x^2 - 12xy + 4y^2$

29. $(7x + 5y)(7x - 5y) = (7x)^2 - (5y)^2$

$\quad = 49x^2 - 25y^2$

30. $\left(2a - 5b^2\right)\left(2a + 5b^2\right) = (2a)^2 - \left(5b^2\right)^2$

$\quad = 4a^2 - 25b^4$

31. $(5xy + 6)(5xy - 6) = (5xy)^2 - (6)^2$

$\quad = 25x^2y^2 - 36$

32. $\left(9a^2 - 2b^2\right)\left(9a^2 + 2b^2\right) = (9a^2)^2 - \left(2b^2\right)^2$

$\quad = 81a^4 - 4b^4$

33.

$$[(x+3y)+2]^2$$
$$= (x+3y)^2 + 2(x+3y)(2) + (2)^2$$
$$= (x)^2 + 2(x)(3y) + (3y)^2 + 4(x+3y) + 4$$
$$= x^2 + 6xy + 9y^2 + 4x + 12y + 4$$

34.

$$[(2p-q)-5]^2$$
$$= (2p-q)^2 - 2(2p-q)(5) + (5)^2$$
$$= (2p)^2 - 2(2p)(q) + (q)^2 - 10(2p-q) + 25$$
$$= 4p^2 - 4pq + q^2 - 20p + 10q + 25$$

35.

$$
\begin{array}{r}
3x^2 + 4x - 6 \\
2x - 3 \\
\hline
-9x^2 - 12x + 18 \\
6x^3 + 8x^2 - 12x \\
\hline
6x^3 - x^2 - 24x + 18
\end{array}
$$

36.

$$
\begin{array}{r}
4x^3 + 0x^2 + 6x - 5 \\
x + 3 \\
\hline
12x^3 + 0x^2 + 18x - 15 \\
4x^4 + 0x^3 + 6x^2 - 5x \\
\hline
4x^4 + 12x^3 + 6x^2 + 13x - 15
\end{array}
$$

37.

$$A = (x)(x) + (5)(x) + (3)(x) + (5)(2)$$
$$= x^2 + 5x + 3x + 10$$
$$= x^2 + 8x + 10$$

38.

$$A = (x)(x) + (y)(x) + (z)(x) + (4)(y)$$
$$= x^2 + xy + xz + 4y$$

39.

a.
$$(f \cdot g)(x) = f(x) \cdot g(x)$$
$$= (x+2)(x-3)$$
$$= x^2 + 2x - 3x - 6$$
$$= x^2 - x - 6$$

b. $(f \cdot g)(3) = 3^2 - 3 - 6$
$$= 9 - 3 - 6$$
$$= 0$$

40.

a.
$$(f \cdot g)(x) = f(x)g(x)$$
$$= (2x-4)(x^2 - 3)$$
$$= 2x^3 - 6x - 4x^2 + 12$$
$$= 2x^3 - 4x^2 - 6x + 12$$

b. $(f \cdot g)(3) = 2(3)^3 - 4(3)^2 - 6(3) + 12$
$$= 54 - 36 - 18 + 12$$
$$= 12$$

41.

a.
$$(f \cdot g)(x) = f(x) \cdot g(x)$$
$$= (x^2 + x - 3)(x-2)$$
$$= x^3 - 2x^2 + x^2 - 2x - 3x + 6$$
$$= x^3 - x^2 - 5x + 6$$

b. $(f \cdot g)(3) = 3^3 - 3^2 - 5(3) + 6$
$$= 27 - 9 - 15 + 6$$
$$= 9$$

42.

a.
$$(f \cdot g)(x) = f(x) \cdot g(x)$$
$$= (x^2 - 2)(x^2 + 2)$$
$$= x^4 - 4$$

b. $(f \cdot g)(3) = 3^4 - 4$
$$= 77$$

43.

$$\frac{6x^2 + 9x + 12}{3} = \frac{6x^2}{3} + \frac{9x}{3} + \frac{12}{3}$$
$$= 2x^2 + 3x + 4$$

44.

$$\frac{7a^2 - 16a + 20}{4} = \frac{7a^2}{4} - \frac{16a}{4} + \frac{20}{4}$$
$$= \frac{7}{4}a^2 - 4a + 5$$

45.

$$\frac{21y^3 + 6y + 2}{3y} = \frac{21y^3}{3y} + \frac{6y}{3y} + \frac{2}{3y} = 7y^2 + 2 + \frac{2}{3y}$$

46.

$$\frac{45pq - 25q^2 - 10q}{5q} = \frac{45pq}{5q} - \frac{25q^2}{5q} - \frac{10q}{5q}$$
$$= 9p - 5q - 2$$

47.

$$\frac{4x^3y^2 + 8x^2y^3 + 12xy^4}{8xy^3}$$
$$= \frac{4x^3y^2}{8xy^3} + \frac{8x^2y^3}{8xy^3} + \frac{12xy^4}{8xy^3}$$
$$= \frac{x^2}{2y} + x + \frac{3y}{2}$$

48.

$$
\begin{array}{r}
4x-3 \\
2x+5\overline{)8x^2+14x-15}
\end{array}
$$

$$
\underline{8x^2+20x} \leftarrow 4x(2x+5)
$$
$$
-6x-15
$$
$$
\underline{-6x-15} \leftarrow -3(2x+5)
$$
$$
0
$$

Thus, $\dfrac{8x^2+14x-15}{2x+5}=4x-3$

49.

$$
\begin{array}{r}
x^3-2x^2+\ 3x+7 \\
2x+1\overline{)2x^4-3x^3+4x^2+17x+7}
\end{array}
$$

$$
\underline{2x^4+x^3}
$$
$$
-4x^3+4x^2
$$
$$
\underline{-4x^3-2x^2}
$$
$$
6x^2+17x
$$
$$
\underline{6x^2+\ 3x}
$$
$$
14x+7
$$
$$
\underline{14x+7}
$$
$$
0
$$

50.

$$
\begin{array}{r}
2a^3+a^2-3a-4 \\
2a-1\overline{)4a^4+0a^3-7a^2-5a+4}
\end{array}
$$

$$
\underline{4a^4-2a^3}
$$
$$
2a^3-7a^2
$$
$$
\underline{2a^3-a^2}
$$
$$
-6a^2-5a
$$
$$
\underline{-6a^2+3a}
$$
$$
-8a+4
$$
$$
\underline{-8a+4}
$$
$$
0
$$

Thus, $\dfrac{4a^4-7a^2-5a+4}{2a-1}=2a^3+a^2-3a-4$

51.

$$
\begin{array}{r}
x+\ 4 \\
x-3\overline{)x^2+x-18}
\end{array}
$$

$$
\underline{x^2-3x} \leftarrow x(x-3)
$$
$$
4x-18
$$
$$
\underline{4x-12} \leftarrow 4(x-3)
$$
$$
-6
$$

Thus, $\dfrac{x^2+x-18}{x-3}=x+4-\dfrac{6}{x-3}$

52.

$$
\begin{array}{r}
2x^2+3x-4 \\
2x+3\overline{)4x^3+12x^2+x-10}
\end{array}
$$

$$
\underline{4x^3+6x^2}
$$
$$
6x^2+x
$$
$$
\underline{6x^2+9x}
$$
$$
-8x-10
$$
$$
\underline{-8x-12}
$$
$$
2
$$

Thus,

$$
\dfrac{4x^3+12x^2+x-10}{2x+3}=2x^2+3x-4+\dfrac{2}{2x+3}
$$

53.

$$
\begin{array}{r|rrrr}
3 & 3 & -2 & 0 & 10 \\
  &   & 9 & 21 & 63 \\
\hline
  & 3 & 7 & 21 & 73
\end{array}
$$

Thus, $\dfrac{3x^3-2x^2+10}{x-3}=3x^2+7x+21+\dfrac{73}{x-3}$

54.

$$
\begin{array}{r|rrrrrr}
-1 & 2 & 0 & -10 & 0 & 1 & -1 \\
   &   & -2 & 2 & 8 & -8 & 7 \\
\hline
   & 2 & -2 & -8 & 8 & -7 & 6
\end{array}
$$

Thus, $\dfrac{2y^5-10y^3+y-1}{y+1}$

$$
=2y^4-2y^3-8y^2+8y-7+\dfrac{6}{y+1}
$$

55.

$$
\begin{array}{r|rrrrrr}
2 & 1 & 0 & 0 & 0 & 0 & -20 \\
  &   & 2 & 4 & 8 & 16 & 32 \\
\hline
  & 1 & 2 & 4 & 8 & 16 & 12
\end{array}
$$

Thus,

$$
\dfrac{x^5-20}{x-2}=x^4+2x^3+4x^2+8x+16+\dfrac{12}{x-2}
$$

56.

$$
\begin{array}{r|rrrr}
\frac{1}{2} & 2 & 1 & 5 & -3 \\
            &   & 1 & 1 & 3 \\
\hline
            & 2 & 2 & 6 & 0
\end{array}
$$

Thus,

$$
\dfrac{2x^3+x^2+5x-3}{x-\frac{1}{2}}=2x^2+2x+6
$$

57. To find the remainder, use synthetic division:

$$
\begin{array}{r|rrr}
3 & 1 & -4 & 11 \\
  &   & 3 & -3 \\
\hline
  & 1 & -1 & 8
\end{array}
$$

Thus, the remainder is 8.

58. To find the remainder, use synthetic division:

$$\begin{array}{r|rrrr} -4 & 2 & -6 & 3 & 0 \\ & & -8 & 56 & -236 \\ \hline & 2 & -14 & 59 & -236 \end{array}$$

Thus, the remainder is -236.

59. To find the remainder, use synthetic division:

$$\begin{array}{r|rrrr} \frac{1}{3} & 3 & 0 & 0 & -6 \\ & & 1 & \frac{1}{3} & \frac{1}{9} \\ \hline & 3 & 1 & \frac{1}{3} & -\frac{53}{9} \end{array} \text{ or } -5.\overline{8}$$

Thus, the remainder is $-\dfrac{53}{9}$ or $-5.\overline{8}$.

60. To find the remainder, use synthetic division:

$$\begin{array}{r|rrrrr} -2 & 2 & 0 & -6 & 0 & -8 \\ & & -4 & 8 & -4 & 8 \\ \hline & 2 & -4 & 2 & -4 & 0 \end{array}$$

Since the remainder is 0, then $x + 2$ is a factor.

61. $4x^2 + 8x + 24 = 4\left(x^2 + 2x + 6\right)$

62. $15x^4 + 6x^3 - 12x^4 y^3 = 3x^3\left(5x + 2 - 4xy^3\right)$

63. $10a^3 b^3 - 12a^2 b^6 = 2a^2 b^3\left(5a - 6b^3\right)$

64. $12xy^4 z^3 + 6x^2 y^3 z^2 - 15x^3 y^2 z^3$
$= 3xy^2 z^2\left(4y^2 z + 2xy - 5x^2 z\right)$

65. $5x^2 - xy + 20xy - 4y^2$
$= x\left(5x - y\right) + 4y\left(5x - y\right)$
$= \left(x + 4y\right)\left(5x - y\right)$

66. $12a^2 - 8ab + 15ab - 10b^2$
$= 4a\left(3a - 2b\right) + 5b\left(3a - 2b\right)$
$= \left(4a + 5b\right)\left(3a - 2b\right)$

67. $\left(2x - 3\right)\left(2x + 1\right) - \left(2x - 3\right)\left(x - 8\right)$
$= \left(2x - 3\right)\left[\left(2x + 1\right) - \left(x - 8\right)\right]$
$= \left(2x - 3\right)\left(2x + 1 - x + 8\right)$
$= \left(2x - 3\right)\left(x + 9\right)$

68. $7x\left(3x - 5\right) + 3\left(3x - 5\right)^2$
$= \left(3x - 5\right)\left[7x + 3\left(3x - 5\right)\right]$
$= \left(3x - 5\right)\left(7x + 9x - 15\right)$
$= \left(3x - 5\right)\left(16x - 15\right)$

69. $A = 13x\left(5x + 2\right) - 7\left(5x + 2\right)$
$= \left(5x + 2\right)\left(13x - 7\right)$

70. $A = \left(14x^2 + 18x\right) - \left(7x + 9\right)$
$= 2x\left(7x + 9\right) - 1\left(7x + 9\right)$
$= \left(7x + 9\right)\left(2x - 1\right)$

71. $V = 9x\left(17x + 3\right) - 7\left(17x + 3\right)$
$= \left(17x + 3\right)\left(9x - 7\right)$

72. $V = \left(20x^2 + 25x\right) - \left(8x + 10\right)$
$= 5x\left(4x + 5\right) - 2\left(4x + 5\right)$
$= \left(4x + 5\right)\left(5x - 2\right)$

73. $x^2 + 8x + 12 = \left(x + 6\right)\left(x + 2\right)$ ← Use 6 and 2: $(6)(2) = 12$, $6 + 2 = 8$

74. $x^2 + 2x - 15 = \left(x + 5\right)\left(x - 3\right)$ ← Use 5 and -3: $(5)(-3) = -15$, $5 + (-3) = 2$

75. $x^2 - 4x - 21 = \left(x - 7\right)\left(x + 3\right)$ ← Use -7 and 3: $(-7)(3) = -21$, $(-7) + 3 = -4$

76. $x^2 - 10x + 16 = \left(x - 8\right)\left(x - 2\right)$ ← Use -8 and -2: $(-8)(-2) = 16$, $(-8) + (-2) = -10$

77. $-x^2 + 12x + 45 = -\left(x^2 - 12x - 45\right) = -\left(x - 15\right)\left(x + 3\right)$ ← Use -15 and 3: $(-15)(3) = -45$, $-15 + 3 = -12$

78. $-x^2 + 13x - 12 = -\left(x^2 - 13x + 12\right) = -\left(x - 12\right)\left(x - 1\right)$ ← Use -12 and -1: $(-12)(-1) = 12$, $-12 + (-1) = -13$

79.
$$2x^3 + 13x^2 + 6x = x\left(2x^2 + 13x + 6\right)$$
$$= x\left(2x^2 + 12x + x + 6\right) \quad \leftarrow \text{ Use } 12x + x = 13x$$
$$= x\left[2x(x+6) + 1(x+6)\right]$$
$$= x(x+6)(2x+1)$$

80.
$$8x^3 + 10x^2 - 25x = x\left(8x^2 + 10x - 25\right)$$
$$= x\left(8x^2 + 20x - 10x - 25\right) \quad \leftarrow \text{ Use } 20x - 10x = 10x$$
$$= x\left[4x(2x+5) - 5(2x+5)\right]$$
$$= x(4x-5)(2x+5)$$

81.
$$4a^3 - 9a^2 + 5a = a\left(4a^2 - 9a + 5\right)$$
$$= a\left(4a^2 - 4a - 5a + 5\right) \quad \leftarrow \text{Use } -4a - 5a = -9a$$
$$= a\left[4a(a-1) - 5(a-1)\right]$$
$$= a(4a-5)(a-1)$$

82.
$$12y^4 + 61y^3 + 5y^2 = y^2\left(12y^2 + 61y + 5\right)$$
$$= y^2\left(12y^2 + 60y + y + 5\right) \quad \leftarrow \text{ Use } 60y + y = 61y$$
$$= y^2\left[12y(y+5) + 1(y+5)\right]$$
$$= y^2(12y+1)(y+5)$$

83. $x^2 - 15xy - 54y^2 = (x - 18y)(x + 3y)$ $\leftarrow$ Use -18 and 3: $(-18)(3) = -54, -18 + 3 = -15$

84.
$$6p^2 - 19pq + 10q^2 = 6p^2 - 15pq - 4pq + 10q^2 \quad \leftarrow \text{ Use } -15pq - 4pq = -19pq$$
$$= 3p(2p - 5q) - 2q(2p - 5q)$$
$$= (2p - 5q)(3p - 2q)$$

85.
$$x^4 + 8x^2 + 15 = y^2 + 8y + 15 \quad \leftarrow \text{ Replace } x^2 \text{ by } y$$
$$= (y+5)(y+3) \quad \leftarrow \text{ Use } 5 \text{ and } 3: (5)(3) = 15, \, 5+3=8$$
$$= \left(x^2 + 5\right)\left(x^2 + 3\right) \quad \leftarrow \text{ Replace } y \text{ by } x^2$$

86.
$$x^4 + 2x^2 - 63 = y^2 + 2y - 63 \quad \leftarrow \text{ Replace } x^2 \text{ by } y$$
$$= (y+9)(y-7) \quad \leftarrow \text{ Use } 9 \text{ and } -7: (9)(-7) = -63, \, 9+(-7) = 2$$
$$= \left(x^2 + 9\right)\left(x^2 - 7\right) \quad \leftarrow \text{ Replace } y \text{ by } x^2$$

87.
$$(x+5)^2 + 10(x+5) + 24 = w^2 + 10w + 24 \quad \leftarrow \text{ Replace } x + 5 \text{ by } w$$
$$= (w+6)(w+4)$$
$$= \left[(x+5)+6\right]\left[(x+5)+4\right] \quad \leftarrow \text{ Replace } w \text{ by } x+5$$
$$= (x+11)(x+9)$$

88. $(x-2)^2 - (x-2) - 20 = w^2 - w - 20$ ← Replace $x-2$ by w

$= (w-5)(w+4)$

$= [(x-2)-5][(x-2)+4]$ ← Replace w by $x-2$

$= (x-7)(x+2)$

89. $A = (x+9)(x+2) - (4)(2)$

$= x^2 + 9x + 2x + 18 - 8$

$= x^2 + 11x + 10$

$= (x+1)(x+10)$

90. $A = (x+8)(x+4) - (4)(3)$

$= x^2 + 8x + 4x + 32 - 12$

$= x^2 + 12x + 20$

$= (x+2)(x+10)$

91. $x^2 - 49 = x^2 - 7^2$

$= (x+7)(x-7)$

92. $x^2 - 100 = x^2 - 10^2$

$= (x+10)(x-10)$

93. $x^4 - 16 = (x^2)^2 - 4^2$

$= (x^2+4)(x^2-4)$

$= (x^2+4)(x^2-2^2)$

$= (x^2+4)(x+2)(x-2)$

94. $x^4 - 81 = (x^2)^2 - 9^2$

$= (x^2+9)(x^2-9)$

$= (x^2+9)(x^2-3^2)$

$= (x^2+9)(x+3)(x-3)$

95. $4a^2 + 4a + 1 = (2a)^2 + 2(2a)(1) + (1)^2$

$= (2a+1)^2$

96. $4y^2 - 12y + 9 = (2y)^2 - 2(2y)(3) + (3)^2$

$= (2y-3)^2$

97. $(x+2)^2 - 9 = (x+2)^2 - 3^2$

$= [(x+2)+3][(x+2)-3]$

$= (x+5)(x-1)$

98. $(3y-1)^2 - 25$

$= (3y-1)^2 - 5^2$

$= [(3y-1)+5][(3y-1)-5]$

$= (3y+4)(3y-6)$ ← GCF of 2nd factor is 3

$= 3(3y+4)(y-2)$

99. $p^4 + 16p^2 + 64 = (p^2)^2 + 2(p^2)(8) + (8)^2$

$= (p^2+8)^2$

100. $b^4 - 14b^2 + 49 = (b^2)^2 - 2(b^2)(7) + (7)^2$

$= (b^2-7)^2$

101. $x^2 + 8x + 16 - y^2$

$= x + 4^2 - (y)^2$

$= [(x+4)+y][(x+4)-y]$

$= (x+4+y)(x+4-y)$

102. $a^2 + 6ab + 9b^2 - 4c^2$

$= (a+3b)^2 - (2c)^2$

$= [(a+3b)+2c][(a+3b)-2c]$

$= (a+3b+2c)(a+3b-2c)$

103. $9x^2 + 6xy + y^2 = (3x)^2 + 2(3y)(y) + (y)^2$

$$= (3x + y)^2$$

104. $36b^2 - 60bc + 25c^2 = (6b)^2 - 2(6b)(5c) + (5c)^2$

$$= (6b - 5c)^2$$

105. $x^3 - 27 = x^3 - 3^3$

$$= (x - 3)\left[x^2 + x(3) + 3^2\right]$$

$$= (x - 3)\left(x^2 + 3x + 9\right)$$

106. $y^3 + 64 = (y)^3 + 4^3$

$$= (y + 4)\left[(y)^2 - (y)(4) + (4)^2\right]$$

$$= (y + 4)\left(y^2 - 4y + 16\right)$$

107. $125x^3 - 1 = (5x)^3 - 1^3$

$$= (5x - 1)\left[(5x)^2 + (5x)(1) + 1^2\right]$$

$$= (5x - 1)\left(25x^2 + 5x + 1\right)$$

108. $8a^3 - 27b^3 = (2a)^3 - (3b)^3$

$$= (2a - 3b)\left[(2a)^2 + (2a)(3b) + (3b)^2\right]$$

$$= (2a - 3b)\left(4a^2 + 6ab + 9b^2\right)$$

109. $(x + 1)^3 - 8$

$$= (x + 1)^3 - 2^3$$

$$= \left[(x + 1) - 2\right]\left[(x + 1)^2 + (x + 1)(2) + (2)^2\right]$$

$$= (x - 1)\left[x^2 + 2x + 1 + 2x + 2 + 4\right]$$

$$= (x - 1)\left(x^2 + 4x + 7\right)$$

110. $(x - 2)^3 - 27$

$$= (x - 2)^3 - 3^3$$

$$= \left[(x - 2) - 3\right]\left[(x - 2)^2 + (x - 2)(3) + (3)^2\right]$$

$$= (x - 5)\left[x^2 - 4x + 4 + 3x - 6 + 9\right]$$

$$= (x - 5)\left(x^2 - x + 7\right)$$

111. $y^3 - 64z^3 = (y)^3 - (4z)^3$

$$= (y - 4z)\left[(y)^2 + (y)(4z) + (4z)^2\right]$$

$$= (y - 4z)\left(y^2 + 4yz + 16z^2\right)$$

112. $(a + 3)^3 + 1$

$$= (a + 3)^3 + 1^3$$

$$= \left[(a + 3) + 1\right]\left[(a + 3)^2 - (a + 3)(1) + (1)^2\right]$$

$$= (x + 4)\left[a^2 + 6a + 9 + -a - 3 + 1\right]$$

$$= (x + 4)\left(a^2 + 5a + 7\right)$$

113. The area of the large square is x^2. The area of the smaller square is $(3)(3) = 9$. The area of the shaded region is $x^2 - 9$. In factored form, the area is $x^2 - 9 = (x + 3)(x - 3)$.

114. The area of the large square is a^2. The sum of the areas of the four small squares is $4b^2$. The area of the shaded region is $a^2 - 4b^2$. In factored form, the area is $a^2 - 4b^2 = (a + 2b)(a - 2b)$.

115. The volume of the large cube is $(2x)^3$. The volume of the small cube is y^3. The difference in the volumes is $(2x)^3 - y^3$ In factored form, the difference in the volumes is

$$(2x)^3 - y^3 = (2x - y)\left((2x)^2 + (2x)(y) + y^2\right)$$

$$= (2x - y)\left(4x^2 + 2xy + y^2\right)$$

116. The volume of the full figure is $(a)(a)(4a) = 4a^3$. The volume of the cut out space is $(c)(c)(4a) = 4ac^2$. The volume of the shaded region is $4a^3 - 4ac^2$ In factored form, the region is given by

$$4a^3 - 4ac^2 = 4a\left(a^2 - c^2\right)$$

$$= 4a(a + c)(a - c)$$

117. $x^2y^2 - 2xy^2 - 15y^2 = y^2\left(x^2 - 2x - 15\right)$
$$= y^2(x+3)(x-5) \quad \leftarrow \text{Use 3 and 5: } (3)(-5) = -15, 3+(-5) = -2$$

118. $3x^3 - 18x^2 + 24x = 3x\left(x^2 - 6x + 8\right)$
$$= 3x(x-4)(x-2) \quad \leftarrow \text{Use } -4 \text{ and } -2: (-4)(-2) = 8, -4+(-2) = -6$$

119. $3x^3y^4 + 18x^2y^4 - 6x^2y^4 - 36xy^4 = 3xy^4\left(x^2 + 6x - 2x - 12\right)$
$$= 3xy^4\left[x(x+6) - 2(x+6)\right]$$
$$= 3xy^4(x-2)(x+6)$$

120. $3y^5 - 27y = 3y\left(y^4 - 9\right)$
$$= 3y\left[\left(y^2\right)^2 - 3^2\right]$$
$$= 3y\left(y^2 + 3\right)\left(y^2 - 3\right)$$

121. $2x^3y + 16y = 2y\left(x^3 + 8\right)$
$$= 2y\left(x^3 + 2^3\right)$$
$$= 2y(x+2)\left[x^2 - x(2) + 2^2\right]$$
$$= 2y(x+2)\left(x^2 - 2x + 4\right)$$

122. $5x^4y + 20x^3y + 20x^2y = 5x^2y\left(x^2 + 4x + 4\right)$
$$= 5x^2y\left[x^2 + 2(x)(2) + 2^2\right]$$
$$= 5x^2y(x+2)^2$$

123. $6x^3 - 21x^2 - 12x = 3x\left(2x^2 - 7x - 4\right)$
$$= 3x\left(2x^2 + x - 8x - 4\right) \quad \leftarrow \text{Use } x - 8x \text{ for } -7x$$
$$= 3x\left[x(2x+1) - 4(2x+1)\right]$$
$$= 3x(x-4)(2x+1)$$

124. $x^2 + 10x + 25 - y^2 = (x+5)^2 - y^2$
$$= \left[(x+5) + y\right]\left[(x+5) - y\right]$$
$$= (x+5+y)(x+5-y)$$

125. $3x^3 + 24y^3 = 3\left(x^3 + 8y^3\right)$
$$= 3\left[x^3 + (2y)^3\right]$$
$$= 3(x+2y)\left[x^2 - x(2y) + (2y)^2\right]$$
$$= 3(x+2y)\left(x^2 - 2xy + 4y^2\right)$$

126.
$$x^2(x+4) - 3x(x+4) - 4(x+4) = (x+4)\left(x^2 + 3x - 4\right)$$
$$= (x+4)(x+4)(x-1)$$
$$= (x+4)^2(x-1)$$

127.
$$4(2x+3)^2 - 12(2x+3) + 5 = 4w^2 - 12w + 5 \qquad \leftarrow \text{Replace } 2x+3 \text{ by } w$$
$$= 4w^2 - 10w - 2w + 5 \qquad \leftarrow \text{Use } -10w - 2w \text{ for } -12w$$
$$= 2(2w-5) - 1(2w-5)$$
$$= (2w-1)(2w-5)$$
$$= \left[2(2x+3) - 1\right]\left[2(2x+3) - 5\right] \quad \leftarrow \text{Replace } w \text{ by } 2x+3$$
$$= (4x+6-1)(4x+6-5)$$
$$= (4x+5)(4x+1)$$

128.
$$4x^4 + 4x^2 - 3 = 4\left(x^2\right)^2 + 4x^2 - 3$$
$$= 4w^2 + 4w - 3 \qquad \leftarrow \text{Replace } x^2 \text{ by } w$$
$$= 4w^2 + 6w - 2w - 3 \qquad \leftarrow \text{Use } 6w - 2w \text{ for } 4w$$
$$= 2w(2w+3) - 1(2w+3)$$
$$= (2w-1)(2w+3)$$
$$= \left(2x^2 - 1\right)\left(2x^2 + 3\right) \qquad \leftarrow \text{Replace } w \text{ by } x^2$$

129.
$$(x-1)x^2 - (x-1)x - 2(x-1) = (x-1)\left(x^2 - x - 2\right)$$
$$= (x-1)(x-2)(x+1) \quad \leftarrow \text{Use } -2 \text{ and } 1: (-2)(1) = -2, -2 + (1) = -1$$

130
$$9ax - 3bx + 12ay - 4by = 3x(3a-b) + 4y(3a-b)$$
$$= (3x+4y)(3a-b)$$

131.
$$6p^2q^2 - 5pq - 6 = 6p^2q^2 - 9pq + 4pq - 6 \qquad \leftarrow \text{Use } -9pq + 4pq \text{ for } -5pq$$
$$= 3pq(2pq-3) + 2(2pq-3)$$
$$= (3pq+2)(2pq-3)$$

132.
$$9x^4 - 12x^2 + 4 = \left(3x^2\right)^2 - 2\left(3x^2\right)(2) + (2)^2$$
$$= \left(3x^2 - 2\right)^2$$

133.
$$4y^2 - \left(x^2 + 4x + 4\right) = (2y)^2 - (x+2)^2$$
$$= \left[2y + (x+2)\right]\left[2y - (x+2)\right]$$
$$= (2y + x + 2)(2y - x - 2)$$

134. $6(2a+3)^2 - 7(2a+3) - 3 = 6x^2 - 7x - 3$ ← Replace $2a+3$ by x

$\qquad = 6x^2 - 9x + 2x - 3$ ← Use $-9x + 2x$ for $-7x$
$\qquad = 3x(2x-3) + 1(2x-3)$
$\qquad = (3x+1)(2x-3)$
$\qquad = [3(2a+3)+1][2(2a+3)-3]$ ← Replace x by $2a+3$
$\qquad = (6a+9+1)(4a+6-3)$
$\qquad = (6a+10)(4a+3)$
$\qquad = 2(3a+5)(4a+3)$

135. $6x^4y^4 + 9x^3y^4 - 27x^2y^4$

$\qquad = 3x^2y^4(2x^2 + 3x - 9)$
$\qquad = 3x^2y^4(2x^2 + 6x - 3x - 9)$
$\qquad = 3x^2y^4[2x(x+3) - 3(x+3)]$
$\qquad = 3x^2y^4(2x-3)(x+3)$

136. $x^3 - \dfrac{8}{27}y^6$

$\qquad = x^3 - \left(\dfrac{2}{3}y^2\right)^3$

$\qquad = \left(x - \dfrac{2}{3}y^2\right)\left[x^2 + x\left(\dfrac{2}{3}y^2\right) + \left(\dfrac{2}{3}y^2\right)^2\right]$

$\qquad = \left(x - \dfrac{2}{3}y^2\right)\left(x^2 + \dfrac{2}{3}xy^2 + \dfrac{4}{9}y^4\right)$

137. The area of the large rectangle is $(x+6)(x+5)$. The area of the small cut out rectangle is $(6)(2) = 12$. The area of the shaded region in factored form is

$A = (x+6)(x+5) - 12$

$\qquad = x^2 + 5x + 6x + 30 - 12$
$\qquad = x^2 + 11x + 18$
$\qquad = (x+9)(x+2)$

138. The area of the large rectangle is $(y+8)(y+7)$. The area of the small cut out rectangle is $(3)(2) = 6$. The area of the shaded region in factored form is

$A = (y+8)(y+7) - 6$

$\qquad = y^2 + 7y + 8y + 56 - 6$
$\qquad = y^2 + 15y + 50$
$\qquad = (y+10)(y+5)$

139. The area of the large square is a^2. The area of the 4 small cut out squares is $4b^2$. The area of the shaded region in factored form is

$A = a^2 - 4b^2$

$\qquad = (a+2b)(a-2b)$

140. The sum of the areas of the two large rectangles is $ab + ab = 2ab$. The sum of the areas of the two small squares is $b^2 + b^2 = 2b^2$. The area of the shaded region is $2ab + 2b^2$. In factored form, the area is $2ab + 2b^2 = 2b(a+b)$.

141. The sum of the areas of the three rectangles is $a(a+3b) + a(a+3b) + b(a+3b)$ $= 2a(a+3b) + b(a+3b)$. In factored form, the area is $2a(a+3b) + b(a+3b) = (2a+b)(a+3b)$

142. The area of the large square is a^2. The area of the small square is b^2. The sum of the area of the two rectangles is $ab + ab = 2ab$. The area of the shaded region is $a^2 + 2ab + b^2$. In factored form, the area is $a^2 + 2ab + b^2 = (a+b)^2$.

143. $(x-3)(4x+1) = 0$

$x-3=0 \quad$ or $\quad 4x+1=0$
$\quad x=3 \qquad\qquad 4x=-1$
$\qquad\qquad\qquad\qquad x=-\dfrac{1}{4}$

The solutions are $3, -\dfrac{1}{4}$.

144. $(2x+5)(3x+7) = 0$

$2x+5=0 \quad$ or $\quad 3x+7=0$
$\quad 2x=-5 \qquad\qquad 3x=-7$
$\quad x=-\dfrac{5}{2} \qquad\qquad x=-\dfrac{7}{3}$

The solutions are $-\dfrac{5}{2}, -\dfrac{7}{3}$.

145.
$2x^2 = 4x$
$2x^2 - 4x = 0$
$2x(x-2) = 0$
$2x = 0 \quad$ or $\quad x-2 = 0$
$x = 0 \qquad\qquad x = 2$

The solutions are 0, 2.

146.
$15x^2 + 20x = 0$
$5x(3x+4) = 0$
$5x = 0 \quad$ or $\quad 3x+4 = 0$
$x = 0 \qquad\qquad 3x = -4$
$\qquad\qquad\qquad x = -\dfrac{4}{3}$

The solutions are $-\dfrac{4}{3}, 0$.

147.
$x^2 + 7x + 12 = 0$
$(x+4)(x+3) = 0$
$x+4 = 0 \quad$ or $\quad x+3 = 0$
$x = -4 \qquad\qquad x = -3$
The solutions are –4, –3.

148.
$a^2 + a - 30 = 0$
$(a+6)(a-5) = 0$
$a+6 = 0 \quad$ or $\quad a-5 = 0$
$a = -6 \qquad\qquad a = 5$
The solutions are –6, 5.

149.
$x^2 = 8x - 7$
$x^2 - 8x + 7 = 0$
$(x-7)(x-1) = 0$
$x-7 = 0 \quad$ or $\quad x-1 = 0$
$x = 7 \qquad\qquad x = 1$
The solutions are 7, 1.

150.
$c^3 - 6c^2 + 8c = 0$
$c(c^2 - 6c + 8) = 0$
$c(c-2)(c-4) = 0$
$c = 0 \quad$ or $\quad c-2 = 0 \quad$ or $\quad c-4 = 0$
$\qquad\qquad\qquad c = 2 \qquad\qquad c = 4$
The solutions are 0, 2, 4.

151.
$12d^2 = 13d + 4 = 0$
$12d^2 - 13d - 4 = 0$
$(3d-4)(4d+1) = 0$

$3d-4 = 0 \quad$ or $\quad 4d+1 = 0$
$3d = 4 \qquad\qquad 4d = -1$
$d = \dfrac{4}{3} \qquad\qquad d = -\dfrac{1}{4}$
The solutions are $-\dfrac{1}{4}, \dfrac{4}{3}$.

152.
$20p^2 - 6 = 7p$

$4x-3 = 0 \quad$ or $\quad 5x+2 = 0$
$4x = 3 \qquad\qquad 5x = -2$
$x = \dfrac{3}{4} \qquad\qquad x = -\dfrac{2}{5}$
The solutions are $\dfrac{3}{4}, -\dfrac{2}{5}$.

153.
$5x^2 = 20$
$5x^2 - 20 = 0$
$5(x^2 - 4) = 0$
$5(x+2)(x-2) = 0$
$x+2 = 0 \quad$ or $\quad x-2 = 0$
$x = -2 \qquad\qquad x = 2$
The solutions are –2, 2.

154.
$x(x+3) = 2(x+4) - 2$
$x^2 + 3x = 2x + 8 - 2$
$x^2 + 3x = 2x + 6$
$x^2 + x - 6 = 0$
$(x+3)(x-2) = 0$
$x+3 = 0 \quad$ or $\quad x-2 = 0$
$x = -3 \qquad\qquad x = 2$
The solutions are –3, 2.

155.
$y = 2x^2 - 2x - 60$
Set $y = 0$ and solve for x.
$2x^2 - 2x - 60 = 0$
$x^2 - x - 30 = 0$
$(x-6)(x+5) = 0$
$x-6 = 0 \quad$ or $\quad x+5 = 0$
$x = 6 \qquad\qquad x = -5$
The x-intercepts are 6 and –5.

156.
$y = 20x^2 - 49x + 30$
Set $y = 0$ and solve for x.
$20x^2 - 49x + 30 = 0$
$(5x-6)(4x-5) = 0$

$5x - 6 = 0$ or $4x - 5 = 0$

$5x = 6$ $4x = 5$

$x = \dfrac{6}{5}$ $x = \dfrac{5}{4}$

The x-intercepts are $\dfrac{6}{5}$ and $\dfrac{5}{4}$.

157. $y = (x + 3)(x - 6)$

$= x^2 - 6x + 3x - 18$

$= x^2 - 3x - 18$

158. $y = (2x + 3)(6x + 5)$

$= 12x^2 + 10x + 18x + 15$

$= 12x^2 + 28x + 15$

159. Let x be the width of the carpet. Then, the length is $x + 2$.

$x(x + 2) = 99$

$x^2 + 2x = 99$

$x^2 + 2x - 99 = 0$

$(x - 9)(x + 11) = 0$

$x - 9 = 0$ or $x + 11 = 0$

$x = 9$ $x = -11$

Reject -11 for x since width cannot be negative. Thus, the width is 9 feet and the length is
$9 + 2 = 11$ feet.

160. Let x be the height. Then $2x + 3$ is the base

$\dfrac{1}{2}bh = A$

$\dfrac{1}{2}(2x + 3)x = 22$

$(2x + 3)x = 44$

$2x^2 + 3x = 44$

$2x^2 + 3x - 44 = 0$

$(x - 4)(2x + 11) = 0$

$x - 4 = 0$ or $2x + 11 = 0$

$x = 4$ $2x = -11$

                   $x = -\dfrac{11}{2}$

Reject $-\dfrac{11}{2}$ for x. Thus, the height is 4 feet and the base is $2(4) + 3 = 8 + 3 = 11$ feet.

161. Let x be the length of a side of the smaller square. Then $x + 4$ is the length of a side of the larger square.

$(x + 4)^2 = 49$

$(x + 4)^2 - 49 = 0$

$(x + 4)^2 - 7^2 = 0$

$(x + 4 - 7)(x + 4 + 7) = 0$

$(x - 3)(x + 11) = 0$

$x - 3 = 0$ or $x + 11 = 0$

$x = 3$ $x = -11$

Reject -11 for x. Thus, $x = 3$ inches for the smaller square and $x + 4 = 3 + 4 = 7$ inches for the larger square.

162. $s(t) = -16t^2 + 128t + 144$

Set $s(t) = 0$

$0 = -16t^2 + 128t + 144$

$0 = -16(t^2 - 8t - 9)$

$0 = -16(t - 9)(t + 1)$

$t - 9 = 0$ or $t + 1 = 0$

$t = 9$ $t = -1$

Reject $t = -1$. Thus, $t = 9$ seconds.

163. $c^2 = a^2 + b^2$

$(x + 32)^2 = x^2 + (x + 31)^2$

$x^2 + 64x + 1024 = x^2 + x^2 + 62x + 961$

$0 = x^2 - 2x - 63$

$0 = (x - 9)(x + 7)$

$x - 9 = 0$ or $x + 7 = 0$

$x = 9$ $x = -7$

Disregard a negative length. x is 9.

Practice Test

1. a. Trinomial since it has three terms

   b. $-6x^4 - 4x^2 + 2x$

   c. Degree is 4

   d. The leading coefficient of the polynomial is -6.

2. $(7x^2y - 5y^2 + 2x) - (3x^2y + 9y^2 - 6y)$

$= 7x^2y - 5y^2 + 2x - 3x^2y - 9y^2 + 6y$

$= 4x^2y - 14y^2 + 2x + 6y$

3. $2x^3 y^2 \left(-4x^5 y + 10x^3 y^2 - 6x\right)$

    $= 2x^3 y^2 \left(-4x^5 y\right) + 2x^3 y^2 \left(10x^3 y^2\right) + 2x^3 y^2 (-6x)$

    $= -8x^8 y^3 + 20x^6 y^4 - 12x^4 y^2$

4. $(2a - 3b)(5a + b)$

    $= (2a)(5a) + (2a)(b) + (-3b)(5a) + (-3b)(b)$

    $= 10a^2 + 2ab - 15ab - 3b^2$

    $= 10a^2 - 13ab - 3b^2$

5. $$\begin{array}{r} 2x^2 + 3xy - 6y^2 \\ 2x + y \\ \hline 2x^2 y + 3xy^2 - 6y^3 \\ 4x^3 + 6x^2 y - 12xy^2 \\ \hline 4x^3 + 8x^2 y - 9xy^2 - 6y^3 \end{array}$$

6. $\dfrac{12x^6 - 15x^2 y + 21}{3x^2} = \dfrac{12x^6}{3x^2} - \dfrac{15x^2 y}{3x^2} + \dfrac{21}{3x^2}$

    $= 4x^4 - 5y + \dfrac{7}{x^2}$

7. $$\begin{array}{r} x - 5 \\ 2x+3{\overline{\smash{\big)}\,2x^2 - 7x + 10}} \\ \underline{2x^2 + 3x} \\ -10x + 10 \\ \underline{-10x - 15} \\ 25 \end{array}$$

    Thus, $\dfrac{2x^2 - 7x + 10}{2x + 3} = x - 5 + \dfrac{25}{2x + 3}$

8. $$\begin{array}{r|rrrrr} 5 & 3 & -12 & 0 & -60 & 4 \\ & & 15 & 15 & 75 & 75 \\ \hline & 3 & 3 & 15 & 15 & 79 \end{array}$$

    Thus, $\dfrac{3x^4 - 12x^3 - 60x + 4}{x - 5} = 3x^3 + 3x^2 + 15x + 15 + \dfrac{79}{x - 5}$

9. $$\begin{array}{r|rrrr} -3 & 2 & -6 & -5 & 4 \\ & & -6 & 36 & -93 \\ \hline & 2 & -12 & 31 & -89 \end{array}$$

    Thus, the remainder is -89.

10. $12x^3 y + 10x^2 y^4 - 8xy^3 = 2xy\left(6x^2 + 5xy^3 - 4y^2\right)$ ← $2xy$ is a common factor

11. $x^3 - 2x^2 - 3x = x\left(x^2 - 2x - 3\right)$ ← x is a common factor

    $= x(x - 3)(x + 1)$ ← Use -3 and 1: $(-3)(1) = -3, -3 + 1 = -2$

12. $2a^2 + 4ab + 3ab + 6b^2 = 2a(a + 2b) + 3b(x + 2b)$ ← Factor by grouping

    $= (2a + 3b)(a + 2b)$

13.
$$2b^4 + 5b^2 - 18 = 2b^2 + 5b - 18$$
$$= 2b^2 - 4b + 9b - 18$$
$$= 2b(b-2) + 9(b-2)$$
$$= (2b+9)(b-2)$$
$$= (2b^2+9)(b^2-2)$$

14.
$$4(x-3)^2 + 20(x-3) = 4(x-3)\cdot(x-3) + 20(x-3)$$
$$= 4(x-3)[(x-3)+5] \qquad \leftarrow 4(x-3) \text{ is a common factor}$$
$$= 4(x-3)(x+2) \qquad\quad \leftarrow \text{ Simplify}$$

15.
$$(x+5)^2 + 2(x+5) - 3 = w^2 + 2w - 3$$
$$= (w+3)(w-1)$$
$$= [(x+5)+3][(x+5)-1]$$
$$= (x+8)(x+4)$$

16.
$$27p^3q^6 - 8q^6 = q^6(27p^3 - 8) \qquad\qquad \leftarrow q^6 \text{ is a common factor}$$
$$= q^6\left[(3p)^3 - 2^3\right] \qquad\qquad \leftarrow \text{ Difference of two cubes}$$
$$= q^6(3p-2)\left[(3p)^2 + (3p)(2) + (2)^2\right]$$
$$= q^6(3p-2)(9p^2 + 6p + 4)$$

17. $f(x) = 3x - 4,\ g(x) = x - 5$

    a. $(f \cdot g)(x) = f(x) \cdot g(x)$
$$= (3x-4)(x-5)$$
$$= 3x^2 - 19x + 20$$

    b. $(f \cdot g)(2) = 3(2)^2 - 19(2) + 20$
$$= 12 - 38 + 20$$
$$= -6$$

18. $A = (2x)(2x) - 4y^2$
$$= 4x^2 - 4y^2$$
$$= 4(x^2 - y^2)$$
$$= 4(x+y)(x-y)$$

19. $A = (x+8)(x+7) - (4)(3)$
$$= x^2 + 7x + 8x + 56 - 12$$
$$= x^2 + 15x + 44$$
$$= (x+11)(x+4)$$

20.
$$7x^2 + 25x - 12 = 0$$
$$(7x - 3)(x + 4) = 0$$
$$7x - 3 = 0 \quad \text{or} \quad x + 4 = 0$$
$$7x = 3 \qquad\qquad\quad x = -4$$
$$x = \frac{3}{7}$$

The solutions are $\frac{3}{7}, -4$.

21. $x^3 + 3x^2 - 4x = 0$

$x(x^2 + 3x - 4) = 0$

$x(x+4)(x-1) = 0$

$x = 0$ or $x + 4 = 0$ or $x - 1 = 0$

$\qquad\qquad x = -4 \qquad\qquad x = 1$

The solutions are 0, –4, 1.

22. $y = 8x^2 + 10x - 3$

Set $y = 0$ and solve for x

$8x^2 + 10x - 3 = 0$

$(4x - 1)(2x + 3) = 0$

$4x - 1 = 0$ or $2x + 3 = 0$

$4x = 1 \qquad\qquad 2x = -3$

$x = \dfrac{1}{4} \qquad\qquad x = -\dfrac{3}{2}$

The x-intercepts are $\dfrac{1}{4}$ and $-\dfrac{3}{2}$.

23. $y = (x - 2)(x - 6)$

$y = x^2 - 6x - 2x + 12$

$y = x^2 - 8x + 12$

24. Let x be the height of the triangle. Then, $3x + 2$ is the base.

$\dfrac{1}{2}$(base)(height) $= A$

$\dfrac{1}{2}(3x + 2)(x) = 28$

$(3x + 2)(x) = 56$

$3x^2 + 2x = 56$

$3x^2 + 2x - 56 = 0$

$(x - 4)(3x + 14) = 0$

$x - 4 = 0$ or $3x + 14 = 0$

$x = 4 \qquad\qquad 3x = -14$

$\qquad\qquad\qquad x = -\dfrac{14}{3}$

Reject $-\dfrac{14}{3}$. Thus, the height is 4 meters and the base is $3 \cdot 4 + 2 = 12 + 2 = 14$ meters.

25. $s(t) = -16t^2 + 48t + 448$

Set $s(t) = 0$ and solve for t

$0 = -16t^2 + 48t + 448$

$0 = -16(t^2 - 3t - 28)$

$0 = -16(t - 7)(t + 4)$

$t - 7 = 0$ or $t + 4 = 0$

$t = 7 \qquad\qquad t = -4$

Reject $t = -4$. The baseball strikes the ground in 7 seconds.

Cumulative Review Test

1. $A \cup B = \{2, 3, 4, 5, 6, 8\}$

2.

-5

3. $\left|\dfrac{3}{8}\right| \div (-2) = \dfrac{3}{8} \div \left(-\dfrac{2}{1}\right) = \dfrac{3}{8} \cdot \left(-\dfrac{1}{2}\right) = -\dfrac{3}{16}$

4. $(-3)^3 - 2^2 - (-2)^2 + (7 - 7)^2$

$(-3)^3 - 2^2 - (-2)^2 + (0)^2$

$-27 - 4 - 4 + (0)^2$

-35

5. $\left(\dfrac{2r^4 s^5}{r^2}\right)^3 = \left(2r^2 s^5\right)^3$

$= 2^3 r^{2\cdot3} s^{5\cdot3}$

$= 8 r^6 s^{15}$

6. $4(2x - 2) - 3(x + 7) = -4$

$8x - 8 - 3x - 21 = -4$

$5x - 29 = -4$

$5x = 25$

$x = 5$

7. $k = 2(d + e)$

$k = 2d + 2e$

$k - 2d = 2e$

$\dfrac{k - 2d}{2} = e$ or $e = \dfrac{k - 2d}{2}$

8. Let x = the length of a side either square in meters. The total amount to be fenced is $7x$.

$7x = 91$

$x = 13$

Each square is 13 meters by 13 meters.

9. Let x be the number of pages.
$$0.15x + 0.05(6x) = 279$$
$$0.15x + 0.3x = 279$$
$$0.45x = 279$$
$$x = \frac{279}{0.45} = 620$$
The manuscript is 620 pages long.

10. $70 \leq \dfrac{68 + 72 + 90 + 86 + x}{5} < 80$
$$350 \leq 316 + x < 400$$
$$34 \leq x < 84$$
If Santo scores at least 34 points but less than 84 points, his average
is in the 70's (and he will receive a grade of C).

11. Substitute 4 for x and 1 for y to see if these
$$3x + 2y = 9$$
satisfy the equation.
$$3(4) + 2(1) \overset{?}{=} 9$$
$$12 + 2 \overset{?}{=} 9$$
$$14 \neq 9$$
(4, 1) is not a solution.

12. $2 = 6x - 3y \implies 6x - 3y = 2$

13. Let $(x_1, y_1) = (8, -4)$ and $(x_2, y_2) = (-1, -2)$
$$m = \frac{y_2 - y_1}{x_2 - x_1} = \frac{-2 - (-4)}{-1 - 8} = \frac{2}{-9} = -\frac{2}{9}$$

14. $f(x) = 2x^3 - 4x^2 + x - 16$
$$f(-4) = 2(-4)^3 - 4(-4)^2 + (-4) - 16$$
$$= 2(-64) - 4(16) + (-4) - 16$$
$$= -128 - 64 - 4 - 16$$
$$= -212$$

15. $2x - y \leq 6$
Graph the line $2x - y = 6$ using a solid line.
$$-y = -2x + 6$$
$$y = 2x - 6$$
For the test point, select $(0, 0)$:
$$2x - y \leq 6$$
$$2(0) - 0 \leq 6$$
$$0 - 0 \leq 6$$
$$0 \leq 6$$
Since this is a true statement, shade the region
which contains $(0, 0)$.

16.
$$\frac{1}{5}x + \frac{1}{2}y = 4$$
$$\frac{2}{3}x - y = \frac{8}{3}$$
To clear out the fractions, multiply the first
equation by 10 and the second equation by 3.
$$10\left[\frac{1}{5}x + \frac{1}{2}y = 4\right] \implies 2x + 5y = 40 \quad (1)$$
$$3\left[\frac{2}{3}x - y = \frac{8}{3}\right] \implies 2x - 3y = 8 \quad (2)$$
To eliminate x, multiply the first equation by -1
and then add.
$$-1(2x + 5y = 40)$$
$$2x - 3y = 8$$
gives
$$-2x - 5y = -40$$
$$\underline{2x - 3y = 8}$$
Add: $\qquad -8y = -32$
$$y = 4$$
To find x, substitute 4 for y into equation (1).
$$2x + 5(4) = 40$$
$$2x + 20 = 40$$
$$2x = 20$$
$$x = 10$$
The solution is $(10, 4)$.

17.
$$x - 2y = 2 \quad (1)$$
$$2x + 3y = 11 \quad (2)$$
$$-y + 4z = 7 \quad (3)$$
Notice that equations (1) and (2) form a system
of equations in two variables. To eliminate x
between these equations, multiply equation (1)
by -2 and add to equation (2).
$$-2[x - 2y = 2]$$
$$2x + 3y = 11$$
gives

$$-2x + 4y = -4 \quad (4)$$
$$\underline{2x + 3y = 11} \quad (5)$$
$$7y = 7$$
$$y = 1$$

Substitute 1 for y in equation (4).
$$-2x + 4(1) = -4$$
$$-2x + 4 = -4$$
$$-2x = -8$$
$$x = 4$$

Substitute 1 for y in equation (3).
$$-(1) + 4z = 7$$
$$4z = 8$$
$$z = 2$$

The solution is (4, 1, 2).

18.

$$\begin{vmatrix} 7 & 3 \\ -2 & 1 \end{vmatrix} = (7)(1) - (-2)(3) = 7 + 6 = 13$$

19.

$$\begin{array}{r} 2x^2 + 12x + 63 \\ x-6 \overline{\smash{\big)}\, 2x^3 + 0x^2 - 9x + 15} \\ \underline{2x^3 - 12x^2} \\ 12x^2 - 9x \\ \underline{12x^2 - 72x} \\ 63x + 15 \\ \underline{63x - 378} \\ 393 \end{array}$$

Thus, $\dfrac{2x^3 - 9x + 15}{x - 6} = 2x^2 + 12x + 63 + \dfrac{393}{x - 6}$

20.

$$64x^3 - 27y^3 = (4x)^3 - (3y)^3$$
$$= (4x - 3y)\left((4x)^2 + (4x)(3y) + (3y)^2\right)$$
$$= (4x - 3y)\left(16x^2 + 12xy + 9y^2\right)$$

Chapter 6

1. a. A rational expression is an expression of the form $\frac{p}{q}$, p and q polynomials, $q \neq 0$.

b. Answers will vary.

3. a. a rational function is a function of the form $f(x) = \frac{p}{q}$, p and q polynomials, $q \neq 0$.

b. Answers will vary.

5. a. The domain of a rational function is the set of values that can replace the variable.

b. $\frac{3}{x^2 - 9} = \frac{3}{(x+3)(x-3)}$

The domain is $\{x | x$ is a real number, $x \neq -4, x \neq 4\}$.

7. a. Answers will vary. One possible answer is: Factor out (-1) from the numerator and then cancel the remaining factor with the denominator.

b. $\frac{3x^2 - 2x - 8}{-3x^2 + 2x + 8} = \frac{-(-3x^2 + 2x + 8)}{-3x^2 + 2x + 8} = -1$

9. a. Answers will vary. One possible answer is: Invert the second fraction and then multiply by factoring and canceling common factors between the numerator and denominator.

b. $\dfrac{r+2}{r^2 + 9r + 18} \div \dfrac{(r+2)^2}{r^2 + 5r + 6}$

$= \dfrac{r+2}{r^2 + 9r + 18} \cdot \dfrac{r^2 + 5r + 6}{(r+2)^2}$

$= \dfrac{r+2}{(r+6)(r+3)} \cdot \dfrac{(r+3)(r+2)}{(r+2)(r+2)}$

$= \dfrac{1}{r+6}$

11. $\dfrac{4x}{3x - 12} = \dfrac{4x}{4(x-4)}$

The excluded value is 4.

13. $\dfrac{4}{2x^2 - 15x + 25} = \dfrac{4}{(x-5)(2x-5)}$

The excluded values are 5 and $\frac{5}{2}$.

15. $\dfrac{x-3}{x^2 + 4}$

There are no values for which $x^2 + 4 = 0$. Thus, there are no excluded values.

17. $\dfrac{x^2 + 36}{x^2 - 36} = \dfrac{x^2 + 36}{(x+6)(x-6)}$ The excluded values are –6 and 6.

19. $f(p) = \dfrac{p+1}{p-2}$

The domain is $\{p | p$ is a real number and $p \neq 2\}$

21. $y = \dfrac{5}{x^2 + x - 6}$

$y = \dfrac{5}{(x+3)(x-2)}$

The domain is $\{x | x$ is a real number and $x \neq -3, x \neq 2\}$

23. $f(a) = \dfrac{3a^2 - 6a + 4}{2a^2 + 3a - 2}$

$2a^2 + 3a - 2 = 0$

$(2a - 1)(a + 2) = 0$

$2a - 1 = 0$ or $a + 2 = 0$

$2a = 1$ or $a = -2$

$a = \dfrac{1}{2}$

The domain is $\left\{ a \middle| a \text{ is a real number and } a \neq \dfrac{1}{2},\ a \neq -2 \right\}$

25. $g(x) = \dfrac{x^2 - x + 2}{x^2 + 1}$

There are no values for which $x^2 + 1 = 0$. Thus, there are no excluded values. The domain is $\{x | x$ is a real number$\}$

27. $m(a) = \dfrac{a^2 + 49}{a^2 - 49}$

$= \dfrac{a^2 + 49}{(a+7)(a-7)}$

The domain is $\{x | x$ is a real number and $x \neq -7, x \neq 7\}$

29. $\dfrac{x - xy}{x} = \dfrac{x(1-y)}{x} = 1 - y$

31. $\dfrac{5x^2 - 10xy}{15x} = \dfrac{5x(x-2y)}{5x \cdot 3} = \dfrac{x-2y}{3}$

33. $\dfrac{x^3 - x}{x^2 - 1} = \dfrac{x\left(x^2-1\right)}{x^2-1} = x$

35. $\dfrac{5r-4}{4-5r} = \dfrac{-1(4-5r)}{4-5r} = -1$

37. $\dfrac{p^2 - 2p - 24}{6-p} = \dfrac{(p-6)(p+4)}{-1(p-6)}$

$\qquad = \dfrac{p+4}{-1}$

$\qquad = -(p+4) \text{ or } -p-4$

39. $\dfrac{a^2 - 3a - 10}{a^2 + 5a + 6} = \dfrac{(a-5)(a+2)}{(a+3)(a+2)} = \dfrac{a-5}{a+3}$

41. $\dfrac{8x^3 - 125y^3}{2x - 5y} = \dfrac{(2x-5y)(4x^2 + 10xy + 25y^2)}{2x - 5y}$

$\qquad = 4x^2 + 10xy + 25y^2$

43. $\dfrac{(x+5)(x-3) + (x+5)(x-2)}{2(x+5)}$

$\qquad = \dfrac{(x+5)[(x-3) + (x-2)]}{2(x+5)}$

$\qquad = \dfrac{(x+5)(2x-5)}{2(x+5)}$

$\qquad = \dfrac{2x-5}{2}$

45. $\dfrac{a^2 + 3a - ab - 3b}{a^2 - ab + 5a - 5b} = \dfrac{a(a+3) - b(a+3)}{a(a-b) + 5(a-b)}$

$\qquad = \dfrac{(a-b)(a+3)}{(a+5)(a-b)}$

$\qquad = \dfrac{a+3}{a+5}$

47. $\dfrac{a^3 - b^3}{a^2 - b^2} = \dfrac{(a-b)(a^2 + ab + b^2)}{(a-b)(a+b)}$

$\qquad = \dfrac{a^2 + ab + b^2}{a+b}$

49. $\dfrac{2x}{3y} \cdot \dfrac{y^3}{6} = \dfrac{x \cdot y^2}{3 \cdot 3} = \dfrac{xy^2}{9}$

51. $\dfrac{9x^3}{4} \div \dfrac{3}{16y^2} = \dfrac{9x^3}{4} \cdot \dfrac{16y^2}{3}$

$\qquad = \dfrac{3x^3 \cdot 4y^2}{1}$

$\qquad = \dfrac{12x^3 y^2}{1}$

$\qquad = 12x^3 y^2$

53. $\dfrac{3-r}{r-3} \cdot \dfrac{r-6}{6-r} = \dfrac{-1(r-3)}{r-3} \cdot \dfrac{-1(6-r)}{6-r}$

$\qquad = (-1)(-1)$

$\qquad = 1$

55. $\dfrac{p^2 + 7p + 10}{p+5} \cdot \dfrac{1}{p+2} = \dfrac{(p+5)(p+2)}{p+5} \cdot \dfrac{1}{p+2}$

$\qquad = 1$

57. $\dfrac{r^2 + 10r + 21}{r+7} \div (r^2 - 5r - 24)$

$\qquad = \dfrac{r^2 + 10r + 21}{r+7} \cdot \dfrac{1}{r^2 - 5r - 24}$

$\qquad = \dfrac{(r+3)(r+7)}{r+7} \cdot \dfrac{1}{(r+3)(r-8)}$

$\qquad = \dfrac{1}{r-8}$

59. $\dfrac{x^2 + 12x + 35}{x^2 + 4x - 5} \div \dfrac{x^2 + 3x - 28}{x-1}$

$\qquad = \dfrac{x^2 + 12x + 35}{x^2 + 4x - 5} \cdot \dfrac{x-1}{x^2 + 3x - 28}$

$\qquad = \dfrac{(x+7)(x+5)}{(x+5)(x-1)} \cdot \dfrac{x-1}{(x+7)(x-4)}$

$\qquad = \dfrac{1}{x-4}$

61. $\dfrac{a-b}{9a+9b} \div \dfrac{a^2 - b^2}{a^2 + 2a + 1}$

$\qquad = \dfrac{a-b}{9a+9b} \cdot \dfrac{a^2 + 2a + 1}{a^2 - b^2}$

$\qquad = \dfrac{a-b}{9(a+b)} \cdot \dfrac{(a+1)(a+1)}{(a+b)(a-b)}$

$\qquad = \dfrac{(a+1)^2}{9(a+b)^2}$

63. $\dfrac{3x^2 - x - 4}{4x^2 + 5x + 1} \cdot \dfrac{2x^2 - 5x - 12}{6x^2 + x - 12}$

$= \dfrac{(3x - 4)(x + 1)}{(4x + 1)(x + 1)} \cdot \dfrac{(2x + 3)(x - 4)}{(2x + 3)(3x - 4)}$

$= \dfrac{x - 4}{4x + 1}$

65. $\dfrac{x + 2}{x^3 - 8} \cdot \dfrac{(x - 2)^2}{x^2 + 4}$

$= \dfrac{x + 2}{(x - 2)(x^2 + 2x + 4)} \cdot \dfrac{(x - 2)(x - 2)}{x^2 + 4}$

$= \dfrac{(x + 2)(x - 2)}{(x^2 + 2x + 4)(x^2 + 4)}$

67. $\dfrac{x^4 - y^8}{x^2 + y^4} \div \dfrac{x^2 - y^4}{x^4}$

$= \dfrac{x^4 - y^8}{x^2 + y^4} \cdot \dfrac{x^4}{x^2 - y^4}$

$= \dfrac{(x^2 + y^4)(x + y^2)(x - y^2)}{x^2 + y^4} \cdot \dfrac{x^4}{(x + y^2)(x - y^2)}$

$= x^4$

69. $\dfrac{2x^4 + 4x^2}{6x^2 + 14x + 4} \div \dfrac{x^2 + 2}{3x^2 + x}$

$= \dfrac{2x^4 + 4x^2}{6x^2 + 14x + 4} \cdot \dfrac{3x^2 + x}{x^2 + 2}$

$= \dfrac{2x^2(x^2 + 2)}{2(3x + 1)(x + 2)} \cdot \dfrac{x(3x + 1)}{x^2 + 2}$

$= \dfrac{x^3}{x + 2}$

71. $\dfrac{(a - b)^3}{a^3 - b^3} \cdot \dfrac{a^2 - b^2}{(a - b)^2}$

$= \dfrac{(a - b)^3}{(a - b)(a^2 + ab + b^2)} \cdot \dfrac{(a - b)(a + b)}{(a - b)^2}$

$= \dfrac{(a - b)(a + b)}{a^2 + ab + b^2}$

73. $\dfrac{4x + y}{5x + 2y} \cdot \dfrac{10x^2 - xy - 2y^2}{8x^2 - 2xy - y^2}$

$= \dfrac{4x + y}{5x + 2y} \cdot \dfrac{(5x + 2y)(2x - y)}{(4x + y)(2x - y)}$

$= 1$

75. $\dfrac{ac - ad + bc - bd}{ac + ad + bc + bd} \cdot \dfrac{pc + pd - qc - qd}{pc - pd + qc - qd}$

$= \dfrac{a(c - d) + b(c - d)}{a(c + d) + b(c + d)} \cdot \dfrac{p(c + d) - q(c + d)}{p(c - d) + q(c - d)}$

$= \dfrac{(a + b)(c - d)}{(a + b)(c + d)} \cdot \dfrac{(p - q)(c + d)}{(p + q)(c - d)}$

$= \dfrac{p - q}{p + q}$

77. $\dfrac{x^3 - 4x^2 + x - 4}{x^4 - x^3 + x^2 - x} \cdot \dfrac{2x^3 + 2x^2 + x + 1}{2x^3 - 8x^2 + x - 4}$

$= \dfrac{x^2(x - 4) + 1(x - 4)}{x[x^2(x - 1) + 1(x - 1)]} \cdot \dfrac{2x^2(x + 1) + 1(x + 1)}{2x^2(x - 4) + 1(x - 4)}$

$= \dfrac{(x^2 + 1)(x - 4)}{x(x^2 + 1)(x - 1)} \cdot \dfrac{(2x^2 + 1)(x + 1)}{(2x^2 + 1)(x - 4)}$

$= \dfrac{x + 1}{x(x - 1)}$

79. One possible answer is
$\dfrac{1}{(x - 2)(x + 3)}$ or $\dfrac{1}{x^2 + x - 6}$.

81. The numerator is never 0.

83. a. It is zero when the numerator is zero. That is, when $x - 4 = 0$, or $x = 4$.

    b. It is undefined when the denominator is zero. That is, when

$$x^2 - 4 = 0$$
$$(x + 2)(x - 2) = 0$$
$$x + 2 = 0 \quad \text{or} \quad x - 2 = 0$$
$$x = -2 \qquad\qquad x = 2$$

85. One possible answer is
$f(x) = \dfrac{x - 2}{(x - 3)(x + 1)}$.

87. $x^2 + 2x - 15 = (x - 3)(x + 5)$
$x + 5$ is the factor missing from the denominator of the fraction on the right side.
$\dfrac{1}{x - 3} \cdot \dfrac{x + 5}{x + 5} = \dfrac{x + 5}{(x - 3)(x + 5)} = \dfrac{x + 5}{x^2 + 2x - 15}$.
The desired numerator is $x + 5$.

89. $y^2 - y - 20 = (y - 5)(y + 4)$

$y - 5$ is the factor missing from the numerator of the fraction on the right side.

$$\frac{y+4}{y+1} \cdot \frac{y-5}{y-5} = \frac{(y+4)(y-5)}{(y+1)(y-5)} = \frac{y^2-y-20}{y^2-4y-5}.$$

The desired denominator is $y^2 - 4y - 5$.

91.
$$\frac{x^2-x-12}{x^2+2x-3} \cdot \frac{?}{x^2-2x-8} = 1$$
$$\frac{(x-4)(x+3)}{(x+3)(x-1)} \cdot \frac{?}{(x-4)(x+2)} = 1$$
$$\frac{?}{(x-1)(x+2)} = 1$$

The only way the left side can simplify to 1 is if the numerator is $(x - 1)(x + 2)$.
The corresponding polynomial is $x^2 + x - 2$.

93.
$$\frac{x^2-9}{2x^2+3x-2} \div \frac{2x^2-9x+9}{?} = \frac{x+3}{2x-1}$$
$$\frac{x^2-9}{2x^2+3x-2} \cdot \frac{?}{2x^2-9x+9} = \frac{x+3}{2x-1}$$
$$\frac{(x+3)(x-3)}{(2x-1)(x+2)} \cdot \frac{?}{(2x-3)(x-3)} = \frac{x+3}{2x-1}$$
$$\frac{x+3}{(2x-1)(x+2)} \cdot \frac{?}{(2x-3)} = \frac{x+3}{2x-1}$$

The only way the left side can simplify to the right side is if the missing numerator is $(2x - 3)(x + 2)$.
The corresponding polynomial is $2x^2 + x - 6$.

95. Area = (length)(width)
$$3a^2 + 7ab + 2b^2 = (2a + 4b)w$$
$$\frac{3a^2+7ab+2b^2}{2a+4b} = w$$
$$\frac{(3a+b)(a+2b)}{2(a+2b)} = w$$
$$w = \frac{3a+b}{2}$$

97. Area = $\dfrac{1}{2}$(base)(height)
$$a^2 + 4ab + 3b^2 = \frac{1}{2}(a+3b)h$$
$$2(a^2+4ab+3b^2) = 2\left[\frac{1}{2}(a+3b)h\right]$$
$$2(a^2+4ab+3b^2) = (a+3b)h$$
$$\frac{2(a^2+4ab+3b^2)}{a+3b} = h$$
$$\frac{2(a+3b)(a+b)}{a+3b} = h$$
$$h = 2(a+b)$$

99.
$$\left(\frac{2x^2-3x-14}{2x^2-9x+7} \div \frac{6x^2+x-15}{3x^2+2x-5}\right) \cdot \frac{6x^2-7x-3}{2x^2-x-3} = \left(\frac{2x^2-3x-14}{2x^2-9x+7} \cdot \frac{3x^2+2x-5}{6x^2+x-15}\right) \cdot \frac{6x^2-7x-3}{2x^2-x-3}$$
$$= \frac{(x+2)(2x-7)}{(x-1)(2x-7)} \cdot \frac{(x-1)(3x+5)}{(3x+5)(2x-3)} \cdot \frac{(3x+1)(2x-3)}{(x+1)(2x-3)}$$
$$= \frac{(x+2)(3x+1)}{(2x-3)(x+1)}$$

101.
$$\frac{5x^2(x-1)-3x(x-1)-2(x-1)}{10x^2(x-1)+9x(x-1)+2(x-1)} \cdot \frac{2x+1}{x+3}$$
$$= \frac{(x-1)(5x^2-3x-2)}{(x-1)(10x^2+9x+2)} \cdot \frac{2x+1}{x+3}$$
$$= \frac{(x-1)(5x+2)(x-1)}{(x-1)(5x+2)(2x+1)} \cdot \frac{2x+1}{x+3}$$
$$= \frac{x-1}{x+3}$$

103.
$$\frac{(x-p)^n}{x^{-2}} \div \frac{(x-p)^{2n}}{x^{-4}}$$
$$= x^2(x-p)^n \div x^4(x-p)^{2n}$$
$$= \frac{x^2(x-p)^n}{1} \cdot \frac{1}{x^4(x-p)^{2n}}$$
$$= \frac{x^2(x-p)^n}{1} \cdot \frac{1}{x^4(x-p)^n(x-p)^n}$$
$$= \frac{1}{x^2(x-p)^n}$$

105.
$$\frac{x^{5y}+3x^{4y}}{3x^{3y}+x^{4y}} = \frac{x^y(x^{4y}+3x^{3y})}{3x^{3y}+x^{4y}} = x^y$$

107. a. $f(x) = \dfrac{1}{x-2}$. The denominator cannot equal zero. Therefore, $x \neq 2$. The domain is $\{x | x$ is a real number, $x \neq 2\}$.

b.

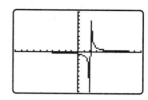

$$-10,\ 10,\ 1,\ -10,\ 1($$

c. The function is decreasing as x gets closer to 2, approaching 2 from the left side.

d. The function is increasing as x gets closer to 2, approaching 2 from the right side.

109. a. $f(x) = \dfrac{x^2}{x-2}$. The denominator cannot equal zero. Therefore, $x \neq 2$. The domain is $\{x | x$ is a real number, $x \neq 2\}$.

b.

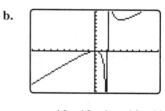

$$-10,\ 10,\ 1,\ -10,\ 1($$

c. The function is decreasing as x gets closer to 2, approaching 2 from the left side.

d. The function is increasing as x gets closer to 2, approaching 2 from the right side.

111. a. $\{x | x \neq 0\}$

b.

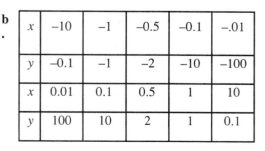

x	-10	-1	-0.5	-0.1	$-.01$
y	-0.1	-1	-2	-10	-100
x	0.01	0.1	0.5	1	10
y	100	10	2	1	0.1

c.

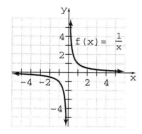

d. No, the numerator can never be 0.

113. $3(x-2) + 3y = 6x$

$3x - 6 + 3y = 6x$

$3y = 3x + 6$

$\dfrac{3y}{3} = \dfrac{3x+6}{3}$

$y = x + 2$

115. $\left| \dfrac{2x-4}{5} \right| = 12$

$\dfrac{2x-4}{5} = -12$ or $\dfrac{2x-4}{5} = 12$

$2x - 4 = -60$ $2x - 4 = 60$

$2x = -56$ $2x = 64$

$x = -28$ $x = 32$

The solution is $\{-28, 32\}$.

117. $3x + 4y = 2$

$2x + 5y = -1$

To eliminate x, multiply the first equation by -2 and the second equation by 3 then add.

$-2[3x + 4y = 2]$

$3[2x + 5y = -1]$

gives

$-6x - 8y = -4$

$\underline{6x + 15y = -3}$

Add: $7y = -7$

$y = -1$

To find x, substitute -1 for y into the first equation.

$3x + 4(-1) = 2$

$3x - 4 = 2$

$3x = 6$

$x = 2$

The solution is $(2, -1)$.

Exercise Set 6.2

1. a. Answers will vary. One possible answer is: The LCD is the 'smallest' denominator into which the individual denominators divide.

   b. Answers will vary. One possible answer is: Factor each denominator completely. Any factors that occur more than once should be expressed as powers. When the same factor appears in more than one denominator, write the factor with the highest power that appears. The LCD is the product of all of those factors found.

   c. $\dfrac{5}{64x^2-121}, \dfrac{1}{8x^2-27x+22}$
   Factor denominators:
   $$64x^2-121=(8x+11)(8x-11)$$
   $$8x^2-27x+22=(8x-11)(x-2)$$
   LCD is $(8x+11)(8x-11)(x-2)$.

3. a. The entire numerator was not subtracted.

   b. $\dfrac{x^2-4x}{(x+3)(x-2)}-\dfrac{x^2+x-2}{(x+3)(x-2)}$
   $$=\dfrac{x^2-4x-(x^2+x-2)}{(x+3)(x-2)}$$
   $$=\dfrac{x^2-4x-x^2-x+2}{(x+3)(x-2)}$$

5. $\dfrac{3x}{x+2}+\dfrac{5}{x+2}=\dfrac{3x+5}{x+2}$

7. $\dfrac{7x}{x-5}-\dfrac{2}{x-5}=\dfrac{7x-2}{x-5}$

9. $\dfrac{x}{x+3}+\dfrac{9}{x+3}-\dfrac{2}{x+3}=\dfrac{x+9-2}{x+3}$
$$=\dfrac{x+7}{x+3}$$

11. $\dfrac{5x-6}{x-2}+\dfrac{2x-5}{x-2}=\dfrac{5x-6+2x-5}{x-2}=\dfrac{7x-11}{x-2}$

13. $\dfrac{x^2-2}{x^2+6x-7}-\dfrac{-4x+19}{x^2+6x-7}=\dfrac{x^2-2-(-4x+19)}{x^2+6x-7}$
$$=\dfrac{x^2-2+4x-19}{x^2+6x-7}$$
$$=\dfrac{x^2+4x-21}{x^2+6x-7}$$
$$=\dfrac{(x-3)(x+7)}{(x-1)(x+7)}$$
$$=\dfrac{x-3}{x-1}$$

15. $\dfrac{3r^2+15r}{r^3+2r^2-8r}+\dfrac{2r^2+5r}{r^3+2r^2-8r}$
$$=\dfrac{3r^2+15r+2r^2+5r}{r^3+2r^2-8r}$$
$$=\dfrac{5r^2+20r}{r^3+2r^2-8r}$$
$$=\dfrac{5r(r+4)}{r(r+4)(r-2)}$$
$$=\dfrac{5}{r-2}$$

17. $\dfrac{3x^2-x}{2x^2-x-21}+\dfrac{3x-8}{2x^2-x-21}-\dfrac{x^2-x+27}{2x^2-x-21}$
$$=\dfrac{3x^2-x+(3x-8)-(x^2-x+27)}{2x^2-x-21}$$
$$=\dfrac{3x^2-x+3x-8-x^2+x-27}{2x^2-x-21}$$
$$=\dfrac{2x^2+3x-35}{2x^2-x-21}$$
$$=\dfrac{(2x-7)(x+5)}{(2x-7)(x+3)}$$
$$=\dfrac{x+5}{x+3}$$

19. $\dfrac{7}{2a^2}+\dfrac{9}{3a^3}$
Factor denominators: $2a^2=2\cdot a^2$
$$3a^3=3\cdot a^3$$
The LCD is $2\cdot3\cdot a^3=6a^3$.

21. $\dfrac{-4}{8x^2y^2}+\dfrac{7}{5x^4y^5}$
Factor denominators: $8x^2y^2=2^3\cdot x^2\cdot y^2$
$$5x^4y^5=5\cdot x^4\cdot y^5$$
The LCD is $2^3\cdot5\cdot x^4\cdot y^5=40x^4y^5$

23. $\dfrac{2}{3a^4b^2}+\dfrac{7}{2a^3b^5}$

Factor denominators: $3a^4b^2=3\cdot a^4\cdot b^2$

$$2a^3b^5=2\cdot a^3\cdot b^5$$

The LCD is $2\cdot 3\cdot a^4\cdot b^5=6a^4b^5$

25. $\dfrac{4x}{x+3}+\dfrac{6}{x+2}$

The LCD is $(x+3)(x+2)$

27. $\dfrac{5z^2}{1}+\dfrac{9z}{z-4}$

The LCD is $1(z-4)=z-4$.

29. $\dfrac{x}{x^4(x-2)}-\dfrac{x+9}{x^2(x-2)^3}$

The LCD is $x^4\cdot(x-2)^3=x^4(x-2)^3$.

31. $\dfrac{a-2}{a^2-5a-24}+\dfrac{3}{a^2+11a+24}$

Factor denominators:

$$a^2-5a-24=(a-8)(a+3)$$

$$a^2+11a+24=(a+3)(a+8)$$

The LCD is $(a-8)(a+3)(a+8)$

33. $\dfrac{3}{x^2+3x-4}-\dfrac{4}{4x^2+5x-9}+\dfrac{x+2}{4x^2+25x+36}$

Factor denominators:

$$x^2+3x-4=(x+4)(x-1)$$

$$4x^2+5x-9=(4x+9)(x-1)$$

$$4x^2+25x+36=(4x+9)(x+4)$$

The LCD is $(x+4)(x-1)(4x+9)$

35. $\dfrac{2}{3r}+\dfrac{5}{r}=\dfrac{2}{3r}+\dfrac{5}{r}\cdot\dfrac{3}{3}$ ← The LCD is $3r$

$$=\dfrac{2}{3r}+\dfrac{15}{3r}$$

$$=\dfrac{2+15}{3r}$$

$$=\dfrac{17}{3r}$$

37. $\dfrac{7}{12x}-\dfrac{1}{4x^2}=\dfrac{7}{12x}\cdot\dfrac{x}{x}-\dfrac{1}{4x^2}\cdot\dfrac{3}{3}$ ← The LCD is $3\cdot 2^2\cdot x^2=12x^2$

$$=\dfrac{7x}{12x^2}-\dfrac{3}{12x^2}$$

$$=\dfrac{7x-3}{12x^2}$$

39. $\dfrac{5}{8x^4y}+\dfrac{1}{5x^2y^3}=\dfrac{5}{8x^4y}\cdot\dfrac{5y^2}{5y^2}+\dfrac{1}{5x^2y^3}\cdot\dfrac{8x^2}{8x^2}$ ← The LCD is $40x^4y^3$

$$=\dfrac{25y^2}{40x^4y^3}+\dfrac{8x^2}{40x^4y^3}$$

$$=\dfrac{25y^2+8x^2}{40x^4y^3}$$

41. $\dfrac{8}{b-2}+\dfrac{3x}{2-b}=\dfrac{8}{b-2}+\dfrac{3x}{2-b}\cdot\dfrac{(-1)}{(-1)}$ ← The LCD is $b-2$

$$=\dfrac{8}{b-2}+\dfrac{-3x}{b-2}$$

$$=\dfrac{8-3x}{b-2}$$

43.

$$\frac{a}{a-b} - \frac{a}{b-a} = \frac{a}{a-b} - \frac{a}{b-a} \cdot \frac{(-1)}{(-1)} \quad \leftarrow \text{The LCD is } a-b$$

$$= \frac{a}{a-b} - \frac{-a}{a-b}$$

$$= \frac{2a}{a-b}$$

45.

$$\frac{4x}{x-4} + \frac{x+3}{x+1} = \frac{4x}{x-4} \cdot \frac{x+1}{x+1} + \frac{x+3}{x+1} \cdot \frac{x-4}{x-4} \quad \leftarrow \text{The LCD is } (x-4)(x+1)$$

$$= \frac{4x(x+1)}{(x-4)(x+1)} + \frac{(x+3)(x-4)}{(x-4)(x+1)}$$

$$= \frac{4x^2+4x}{(x-4)(x+1)} + \frac{x^2-x-12}{(x-4)(x+1)}$$

$$= \frac{4x^2+4x+x^2-x-12}{(x-4)(x+1)}$$

$$= \frac{5x^2+3x-12}{(x-4)(x+1)}$$

47.

$$\frac{3}{a+2} + \frac{a+1}{a^2+4a+4} = \frac{3}{a+2} + \frac{a+1}{(a+2)(a+2)}$$

$$= \frac{3}{a+2} \cdot \frac{a+2}{a+2} + \frac{a+1}{(a+2)(a+2)}$$

$$= \frac{3(a+2)}{(a+2)(a+2)} + \frac{a+1}{(a+2)(a+2)}$$

$$= \frac{3a+6}{(a+2)(a+2)} + \frac{a+1}{(a+2)(a+2)}$$

$$= \frac{3a+6+a+1}{(a+2)(a+2)}$$

$$= \frac{4a+7}{(a+2)^2}$$

49.

$$\frac{x}{x^2+2x-8} + \frac{x+3}{x^2-3x+2} = \frac{x}{(x+4)(x-2)} + \frac{x+3}{(x-2)(x-1)}$$

$$= \frac{x}{(x+4)(x-2)} \cdot \frac{x-1}{x-1} + \frac{x+3}{(x-2)(x-1)} \cdot \frac{x+4}{x+4}$$

$$= \frac{x(x-1)}{(x+4)(x-2)(x-1)} + \frac{(x+3)(x+4)}{(x-2)(x-1)(x+4)}$$

$$= \frac{x(x-1)+(x+3)(x+4)}{(x+4)(x-2)(x-1)}$$

$$= \frac{x^2-x+x^2+4x+3x+12}{(x+4)(x-2)(x-1)}$$

$$= \frac{2x^2+6x+12}{(x+4)(x-2)(x-1)}$$

51. Factor denominators and simplify second fraction

$$\frac{5x}{x^2-9x+8}-\frac{3(x+2)}{x^2-6x-16}=\frac{5x}{(x-8)(x-1)}-\frac{3(x+2)}{(x-8)(x+2)}$$

$$=\frac{5x}{(x-8)(x-1)}-\frac{3}{x-8}\cdot\frac{x-1}{x-1} \qquad \leftarrow \text{The LCD is } (x-8)(x-1)$$

$$=\frac{5x-(3x-3)}{(x-8)(x-1)}$$

$$=\frac{5x-3x+3}{(x-8)(x-1)}$$

$$=\frac{2x+3}{(x-8)(x-1)}$$

53.

$$5-\frac{x-1}{x^2+3x-10}=\frac{5}{1}\cdot\frac{x^2+3x-10}{x^2+3x-10}-\frac{x-1}{x^2+3x-10} \qquad \leftarrow \text{The LCD is } x^2+3x-10 \text{ or } (x+5)(x-2)$$

$$=\frac{5x^2+15x-50}{x^2+3x-10}-\frac{x-1}{x^2+3x-10}$$

$$=\frac{5x^2+15x-50-(x-1)}{x^2+3x-10}$$

$$=\frac{5x^2+14x-49}{x^2+3x-10}$$

$$=\frac{5x^2+14x-49}{(x+5)(x-2)}$$

55.

$$\frac{3a-4}{4a+1}+\frac{3a+6}{4a^2+9a+2}=\frac{3a-4}{4a+1}+\frac{3(a+2)}{(4a+1)(a+2)} \qquad \leftarrow \text{Factor the second fraction and simplify.}$$

$$=\frac{3a-4}{4a+1}+\frac{3}{4a+1}$$

$$=\frac{3a-4+3}{4a+1}$$

$$=\frac{3a-1}{4a+1}$$

57.

$$\frac{x-y}{x^2-4xy+4y^2}+\frac{x-3y}{x^2-4y^2}$$

$$=\frac{x-y}{(x-2y)(x-2y)}+\frac{x-3y}{(x-2y)(x+2y)} \qquad \leftarrow \text{Factor denominators}$$

$$=\frac{x-y}{(x-2y)(x-2y)}\cdot\frac{x+2y}{x+2y}+\frac{x-3y}{(x-2y)(x+2y)}\cdot\frac{x-2y}{x-2y} \leftarrow \text{The LCD is } (x-2y)(x-2y)(x+2y)$$

$$=\frac{(x-y)(x+2y)}{(x-2y)^2(x+2y)}+\frac{(x-3y)(x-2y)}{(x-2y)^2(x+2y)}$$

$$=\frac{x^2+xy-2y^2}{(x-2y)^2(x+2y)}+\frac{x^2-5xy+6y^2}{(x-2y)^2(x+2y)}$$

$$=\frac{x^2+xy-2y^2+x^2-5xy+6y^2}{(x-2y)^2(x+2y)}$$

$$=\frac{2x^2-4xy+4y^2}{(x-2y)^2(x+2y)}$$

59.
$$\frac{2r}{r-4}-\frac{2r}{r+4}+\frac{64}{r^2-16}=\frac{2r}{r-4}-\frac{2r}{r+4}+\frac{64}{(r+4)(r-4)}$$
← Factor third denominator

$$=\frac{2r}{r-4}\cdot\frac{r+4}{r+4}-\frac{2r}{r+4}\cdot\frac{r-4}{r-4}+\frac{64}{(r+4)(r-4)}$$
← The LCD is $(r+4)(r-4)$

$$=\frac{2r(r+4)}{(r+4)(r-4)}-\frac{2r(r-4)}{(r+4)(r-4)}+\frac{64}{(r+4)(r-4)}$$

$$=\frac{2r^2+8r}{(r+4)(r-4)}-\frac{2r^2-8r}{(r+4)(r-4)}+\frac{64}{(r+4)(r-4)}$$

$$=\frac{2r^2+8r-(2r^2-8r)+64}{(r+4)(r-4)}$$

$$=\frac{16r+64}{(r+4)(r-4)}$$

$$=\frac{16(r+4)}{(r+4)(r-4)}$$

$$=\frac{16}{r-4}$$

61.
$$\frac{-4}{x^2+2x-3}-\frac{1}{x+3}+\frac{1}{x-1}=\frac{-4}{(x+3)(x-1)}-\frac{1}{x+3}+\frac{1}{x-1}$$

$$=\frac{-4}{(x+3)(x-1)}-\frac{1}{x+3}\cdot\frac{x-1}{x-1}+\frac{1}{x-1}\cdot\frac{x+3}{x+3}$$

$$=\frac{-4}{(x+3)(x-1)}-\frac{x-1}{(x+3)(x-1)}+\frac{x+3}{(x+3)(x-1)}$$

$$=\frac{-4-(x-1)+x+3}{(x+3)(x-1)}$$

$$=\frac{-4-x+1+x+3}{(x+3)(x-1)}$$

$$=\frac{0}{(x+3)(x-1)}$$

$$=0$$

63.
$$\frac{3}{3x-2}-\frac{1}{x-4}+5=\frac{3}{3x-2}\cdot\frac{x-4}{x-4}-\frac{1}{x-4}\cdot\frac{3x-2}{3x-2}+\frac{5}{1}\cdot\frac{(x-4)(3x-2)}{(x-4)(3x-2)}$$
← The LCD is $(3x-2)(x-4)$

$$=\frac{3(x-4)}{(3x-2)(x-4)}-\frac{3x-2}{(3x-2)(x-4)}+\frac{5(x-4)(3x-2)}{(3x-2)(x-4)}$$

$$=\frac{3x-12}{(3x-2)(x-4)}-\frac{3x-2}{(3x-2)(x-4)}+\frac{15x^2-70x+40}{(3x-2)(x-4)}$$

$$=\frac{3x-12-(3x-2)+15x^2-70x+40}{(3x-2)(x-4)}$$

$$=\frac{15x^2-70x+30}{(3x-2)(x-4)}$$

65.
$$3-\frac{1}{8r^2+2r-15}+\frac{r+2}{4r-5}$$

$$=\frac{3}{1}-\frac{1}{(4r-5)(2r+3)}+\frac{r+2}{4r-5}$$
← Factor second denominator

$$=\frac{3}{1}\cdot\frac{(4r-5)(2r+3)}{(4r-5)(2r+3)}-\frac{1}{(4r-5)(2r+3)}+\frac{r+2}{4r-5}\cdot\frac{2r+3}{2r+3}$$
← The LCD is $(4r-5)(2r+3)$

$$=\frac{3(4r-5)(2r+3)}{(4r-5)(2r+3)}-\frac{1}{(4r-5)(2r+3)}+\frac{(r+2)(2r+3)}{(4r-5)(2r+3)}$$

$$= \frac{24r^2 + 6r - 45}{(4r-5)(2r+3)} - \frac{1}{(4r-5)(2r+3)} + \frac{2r^2 + 7r + 6}{(4r-5)(2r+3)}$$

$$= \frac{24r^2 + 6r - 45 - 1 + 2r^2 + 7r + 6}{(4r-5)(2r+3)}$$

$$= \frac{26r^2 + 13r - 40}{(4r-5)(2r+3)}$$

67. $\dfrac{3}{5x+6} + \dfrac{x^2 - x}{5x^2 - 4x - 12} - \dfrac{4}{x-2}$

$$= \frac{3}{5x+6} + \frac{x^2 - x}{(5x+6)(x-2)} - \frac{4}{x-2} \qquad \leftarrow \text{Factor second denominator}$$

$$= \frac{3}{5x+6} \cdot \frac{x-2}{x-2} + \frac{x^2 - x}{(5x+6)(x-2)} - \frac{4}{x-2} \cdot \frac{5x+6}{5x+6} \qquad \leftarrow \text{The LCD is } (5x+6)(x-2)$$

$$= \frac{3(x-2)}{(5x+6)(x-2)} + \frac{x^2 - x}{(5x+6)(x-2)} - \frac{4(5x+6)}{(5x+6)(x-2)}$$

$$= \frac{3x-6}{(5x+6)(x-2)} + \frac{x^2 - x}{(5x+6)(x-2)} - \frac{20x+24}{(5x+6)(x-2)}$$

$$= \frac{3x-6 + x^2 - x - (20x+24)}{(5x+6)(x-2)}$$

$$= \frac{3x-6 + x^2 - x - 20x - 24}{(5x+6)(x-2)}$$

$$= \frac{x^2 - 18x - 30}{(5x+6)(x-2)}$$

69. $\dfrac{m}{6m^2 + 13mn + 6n^2} + \dfrac{2m}{4m^2 + 8mn + 3n^2}$

$$= \frac{m}{(2m+3n)(3m+2n)} + \frac{2m}{(2m+3n)(2m+n)} \qquad \leftarrow \text{Factor denominators}$$

$$= \frac{m}{(2m+3n)(3m+2n)} \cdot \frac{2m+n}{2m+n} + \frac{2m}{(2m+3n)(2m+n)} \cdot \frac{3m+2n}{3m+2n} \qquad \leftarrow \text{The LCD is } (2m+3n)(3m+2n)(2m+n)$$

$$= \frac{m(2m+n)}{(2m+3n)(3m+2n)(2m+n)} + \frac{2m(3m+2n)}{(2m+3n)(3m+2n)(2m+n)}$$

$$= \frac{2m^2 + mn}{(2m+3n)(3m+2n)(2m+n)} + \frac{6m^2 + 4mn}{(2m+3n)(3m+2n)(2m+n)}$$

$$= \frac{2m^2 + mn + 6m^2 + 4mn}{(2m+3n)(3m+2n)(2m+n)}$$

$$= \frac{8m^2 + 5mn}{(2m+3n)(3m+2n)(2m+n)}$$

71. $\dfrac{5r-2s}{25r^2-4s^2}-\dfrac{2r-s}{10r^2-rs-2s^2}=\dfrac{5r-2s}{(5r+2s)(5r-2s)}-\dfrac{2r-s}{(5r+2s)(2r-s)}$ ← Factor denominators and simplify

$$=\dfrac{1}{5r+2s}-\dfrac{1}{5r+2s}$$

$$=\dfrac{1-1}{5r+2s}$$

$$=\dfrac{0}{5r+2s}$$

$$=0$$

73. $\dfrac{2}{2x+3y}-\dfrac{4x^2-6xy+9y^2}{8x^3+27y^3}$ ← Factor second denominator and simplify

$$=\dfrac{2}{2x+3y}-\dfrac{4x^2-6xy+9y^2}{(2x+3y)(4x^2-6xy+9y^2)}$$

$$=\dfrac{2}{2x+3y}-\dfrac{1}{2x+3y}$$

$$=\dfrac{2-1}{2x+3y}$$

$$=\dfrac{1}{2x+3y}$$

75. No; they should be added first, then factored.

77. Yes, factor −1 from the numerator and the denominator.

79. a. $f(x)=\dfrac{x+2}{x-3}$

The denominator cannot equal zero. Therefore, $x\neq 3$. The domain is $\{x|x$ is a real number, $x\neq 3\}$

b. $g(x)=\dfrac{x}{x+4}$

The denominator cannot equal zero. Therefore, $x\neq -4$. The domain is $\{x|x$ is a real number, $x\neq -4\}$

c. $(f+g)(x)=f(x)+g(x)$

$$=\dfrac{x+2}{x-3}+\dfrac{x}{x+4}$$

$$=\dfrac{x+2}{x-3}\cdot\dfrac{x+4}{x+4}+\dfrac{x}{x+4}\cdot\dfrac{x-3}{x-3}$$

$$=\dfrac{(x+2)(x+4)+x(x-3)}{(x-3)(x+4)}$$

$$=\dfrac{x^2+6x+8+x^2-3x}{(x-3)(x+4)}$$

$$=\dfrac{2x^2+3x+8}{(x-3)(x+4)}$$

d. The denominator cannot equal zero. Therefore, $x\neq 3$ and $x\neq -4$. The domain is $\{x|x$ is a real number, $x\neq 3, x\neq -4\}$

81. $P(x) = R(x) - C(x)$

$P(x) = \dfrac{4x-5}{x+1} - \dfrac{2x-7}{x+2}$

$= \dfrac{4x-5}{x+1} \cdot \dfrac{x+2}{x+2} - \dfrac{2x-7}{x+2} \cdot \dfrac{x+1}{x+1}$

$= \dfrac{(4x-5)(x+2) - (2x-7)(x+1)}{(x+1)(x+2)}$

$= \dfrac{4x^2 + 3x - 10 - (2x^2 - 5x - 7)}{(x+1)(x+2)}$

$= \dfrac{4x^2 + 3x - 10 - 2x^2 + 5x + 7}{(x+1)(x+2)}$

$= \dfrac{2x^2 + 8x - 3}{(x+1)(x+2)}$

83. $P(x) = R(x) - C(x)$

$P(x) = \dfrac{8x-3}{x+2} - \dfrac{5x-8}{x+3}$

$= \dfrac{8x-3}{x+2} \cdot \dfrac{x+3}{x+3} - \dfrac{5x-8}{x+3} \cdot \dfrac{x+2}{x+2}$

$= \dfrac{(8x-3)(x+3) - (5x-8)(x+2)}{(x+2)(x+3)}$

$= \dfrac{8x^2 + 21x - 9 - (5x^2 + 2x - 16)}{(x+2)(x+3)}$

$= \dfrac{8x^2 + 21x - 9 - 5x^2 - 2x + 16}{(x+2)(x+3)}$

$= \dfrac{3x^2 + 19x + 7}{(x+2)(x+3)}$

85. The domain is $\{x | x \text{ is a real number}, x \neq 2\}$
The range is $\{y | y \text{ is a real number}, y \neq 1\}$

87. $(f+g)(x) = f(x) + g(x)$

$= \dfrac{x}{x^2-4} + \dfrac{2}{x^2+x-6}$

$= \dfrac{x}{(x-2)(x+2)} + \dfrac{2}{(x-2)(x+3)}$

$= \dfrac{x}{(x-2)(x+2)} \cdot \dfrac{(x+3)}{(x+3)} + \dfrac{2}{(x-2)(x+3)} \cdot \dfrac{(x+2)}{(x+2)}$

$= \dfrac{x^2 + 3x + 2x + 4}{(x-2)(x+2)(x+3)}$

$= \dfrac{x^2 + 5x + 4}{(x-2)(x+2)(x+3)}$

89. $(f \cdot g)(x) = f(x) \cdot g(x)$

$= \dfrac{x}{x^2-4} \cdot \dfrac{2}{x^2+x-6}$

$= \dfrac{x}{x^2-4} \cdot \dfrac{2}{x^2+x-6}$

$= \dfrac{2x}{x^4 + x^3 - 6x^2 - 4x^2 - 4x + 24}$

$= \dfrac{2x}{x^4 + x^3 - 10x^2 - 4x + 24}$

91. $\dfrac{a}{b} + \dfrac{c}{d} = \dfrac{a}{b} \cdot \dfrac{d}{d} + \dfrac{c}{d} \cdot \dfrac{b}{b}$

$= \dfrac{ad}{bd} + \dfrac{cb}{db}$

$= \dfrac{ad + cb}{bd} \text{ or } \dfrac{ad + bc}{bd}$

93. a. Perimeter is

$\dfrac{a+b}{a} + \dfrac{a+b}{a} + \dfrac{a-b}{a} + \dfrac{a-b}{a}$

$= \dfrac{a+b+a+b+a-b+a-b}{a}$

$= \dfrac{4a}{a}$

$= 4$

b. Area is

$\left(\dfrac{a+b}{a}\right)\left(\dfrac{a-b}{a}\right) = \dfrac{(a+b)(a-b)}{a \cdot a} = \dfrac{a^2 - b^2}{a^2}$

95. Let $ax^2 + bx + c$ denote the missing numerator.

$\dfrac{5x^2 - 6}{x^2 - x - 1} - \dfrac{ax^2 + bx + c}{x^2 - x - 1} = \dfrac{-2x^2 + 6x - 12}{x^2 - x - 1}$

Since the denominators are the same, the fractions on the left side can be subtracted.

$\dfrac{5x^2 - 6 - (ax^2 + bx + c)}{x^2 - x - 1} = \dfrac{-2x^2 + 6x - 12}{x^2 - x - 1}$

Since the denominators are equal, the numerators must be equal for the fractions to be the same.

$5x^2 - 6 - ax^2 - bx - c = -2x^2 + 6x - 12$

$(5-a)x^2 + (-b)x + (-6-c) = -2x^2 + 6x - 12$

Thus,

$\begin{array}{lll} 5 - a = -2 & -b = 6 & -6 - c = -12 \\ -a = -7 & b = -6 & -c = -6 \\ a = 7 & & c = 6 \end{array}$

The missing numerator is $7x^2 - 6x + 6$.

97.

$$\left(3+\frac{1}{x+3}\right)\left(\frac{x+3}{x-2}\right)$$

$$=\left(\frac{3}{1}\cdot\frac{x+3}{x+3}+\frac{1}{x+3}\right)\left(\frac{x+3}{x-2}\right)$$

$$=\left(\frac{3x+9+1}{x+3}\right)\left(\frac{x+3}{x-2}\right)$$

$$=\left(\frac{3x+10}{x+3}\right)\left(\frac{x+3}{x-2}\right)$$

$$=\frac{3x+10}{x-2}$$

99.

$$\left(\frac{5}{a-5}-\frac{2}{a+3}\right)\div(3a+25)$$

$$=\left(\frac{5}{a-5}-\frac{2}{a+3}\right)\cdot\frac{1}{3a+25}$$

$$=\left(\frac{5}{a-5}\cdot\frac{a+3}{a+3}-\frac{2}{a+3}\cdot\frac{a-5}{a-5}\right)\cdot\frac{1}{3a+25}$$

$$=\left(\frac{5a+15}{(a-5)(a+3)}-\frac{2a-10}{(a-5)(a+3)}\right)\cdot\frac{1}{3a+25}$$

$$=\left(\frac{5a+15-2a+10}{(a-5)(a+3)}\right)\cdot\frac{1}{3a+25}$$

$$=\frac{3a+25}{(a-5)(a+3)}\cdot\frac{1}{3a+25}$$

$$=\frac{1}{(a-5)(a+3)}$$

101.

$$\left(\frac{x+5}{x-3}-x\right)\div\frac{1}{x-3}=\left(\frac{x+5}{x-3}-x\right)(x-3)$$

$$=\frac{x+5}{x-3}\cdot(x-3)-x(x-3)$$

$$=x+5-x^2+3x$$

$$=-x^2+4x+5$$

103. **a.**

$$a\left(\frac{x}{n}\right)+b\left(\frac{n-x}{n}\right)=\frac{ax}{n}+\frac{bn-bx}{n}$$

$$=\frac{ax+bn-bx}{n}$$

b.

$$60\left(\frac{2}{5}\right)+92\left(\frac{3}{5}\right)=\frac{120}{5}+\frac{276}{5}=\frac{396}{5}=79.2$$

105.

$$(a-b)^{-1}+(a-b)^{-2}=\frac{1}{a-b}+\frac{1}{(a-b)^2}$$

$$=\frac{1}{a-b}\cdot\frac{a-b}{a-b}+\frac{1}{(a-b)^2}$$

$$=\frac{a-b}{(a-b)^2}+\frac{1}{(a-b)^2}$$

$$=\frac{a-b+1}{(a-b)^2}$$

107.

$$y_1=\frac{x-3}{x+4}+\frac{x}{x^2-2x-24}$$

$$y_2=\frac{x^2-10x+18}{(x+4)(x-6)}$$

-10, 10, 1, -10, 1(

No, the addition is not correct because the graphs are not the same.

109. **a.**

$$1+\frac{1}{x}=\frac{x}{x}+\frac{1}{x}=\frac{x+1}{x}$$

b.

$$1+\frac{1}{x}+\frac{1}{x^2}=1\cdot\frac{x^2}{x^2}+\frac{1}{x}\cdot\frac{x}{x}+\frac{1}{x^2}$$

$$=\frac{x^2}{x^2}+\frac{x}{x^2}+\frac{1}{x^2}$$

$$=\frac{x^2+x+1}{x^2}$$

c.

$$1+\frac{1}{x}+\frac{1}{x^2}+\frac{1}{x^3}+\frac{1}{x^4}+\frac{1}{x^5}$$

$$=\frac{x^5+x^4+x^3+x^2+x+1}{x^5}$$

d.

$$1+\frac{1}{x}+\frac{1}{x^2}+\cdots+\frac{1}{x^n}$$

$$=\frac{x^n+x^{n-1}+x^{n-2}+\cdots+1}{x^n}$$

111.
$$f(x) = \frac{1}{x+1}$$

$$f(a+b) - f(a) = \frac{1}{a+b+1} - \frac{1}{a+1}$$

$$= \frac{1}{a+b+1} \cdot \frac{a+1}{a+1} - \frac{1}{a+1} \cdot \frac{a+b+1}{a+b+1}$$

$$= \frac{a+1 - (a+b+1)}{(a+1)(a+b+1)}$$

$$= \frac{a+1-a-b-1}{(a+1)(a+b+1)}$$

$$= \frac{-b}{(a+1)(a+b+1)}$$

113.
$$|x-3| - 2 < 3$$

$$|x-3| < 5$$

$$-5 < x - 3 < 5$$

$$-5 + 3 < x - 3 + 3 < 5 + 3$$

$$-2 < x < 8$$

$$\{x \mid -2 < x < 8\}$$

115.
$$\begin{vmatrix} -1 & 3 \\ 5 & 6 \end{vmatrix} = (-1)(6) - (5)(3) = -6 - 15 = -21$$

117.
$$3p^2 = 22p - 7$$

$$3p^2 - 22p + 7 = 0$$

$$(3p-1)(p-7) = 0$$

$$3p - 1 = 0 \quad \text{or} \quad p - 7 = 0$$

$$p = \frac{1}{3} \qquad\qquad p = 7$$

Exercise Set 6.3

1. A complex fraction is one that has a fractional expression in the numerator or the denominator or both the numerator and the denominator.

3.
$$\frac{\frac{15a}{b^2}}{\frac{b^3}{5}} = \frac{5b^2\left(\frac{15a}{b^2}\right)}{5b^2\left(\frac{b^3}{5}\right)} = \frac{75a}{b^5} \quad \text{or}$$

$$\frac{\frac{15a}{b^2}}{\frac{b^3}{5}} = \frac{15a}{b^2} \div \frac{b^3}{5} = \frac{15a}{b^2} \cdot \frac{5}{b^3} = \frac{75a}{b^5}$$

5.
$$\frac{1 - \frac{x}{y}}{3x} = \frac{y\left(1 - \frac{x}{y}\right)}{y(3x)} = \frac{y(1) - y\left(\frac{x}{y}\right)}{3xy} = \frac{y-x}{3xy}$$

7.
$$\frac{\frac{36x^4}{5y^4z^5}}{\frac{9xy^2}{15z^5}} = \frac{15y^4z^5\left(\frac{36x^4}{5y^4z^5}\right)}{15y^4z^5\left(\frac{9xy^2}{15z^5}\right)} = \frac{108x^4}{9xy^6} = \frac{12x^3}{y^6}$$

or

$$\frac{\frac{36x^4}{5y^4z^5}}{\frac{9xy^2}{15z^5}} = \frac{36x^4}{5y^4z^5} \div \frac{9xy^2}{15z^5} = \frac{36x^4}{5y^4z^5} \cdot \frac{15z^5}{9xy^2} = \frac{12x^3}{y^6}$$

9.
$$\frac{x - \frac{x}{y}}{\frac{3+x}{y}} = \frac{y\left(x - \frac{x}{y}\right)}{y\left(\frac{3+x}{y}\right)}$$

$$= \frac{y(x) - y\left(\frac{x}{y}\right)}{y\left(\frac{3+x}{y}\right)}$$

$$= \frac{xy - x}{3+x} \quad \text{or} \quad \frac{x(y-1)}{3+x}$$

11.
$$\frac{\frac{2}{a} + \frac{1}{2a}}{a + \frac{a}{2}} = \frac{2a\left(\frac{2}{a} + \frac{1}{2a}\right)}{2a\left(a + \frac{a}{2}\right)}$$

$$= \frac{2a\left(\frac{2}{a}\right) + 2a\left(\frac{1}{2a}\right)}{2a(a) + 2a\left(\frac{a}{2}\right)}$$

$$= \frac{4+1}{2a^2 + a^2}$$

$$= \frac{5}{3a^2}$$

13.
$$\frac{\frac{x}{y} - \frac{y}{x}}{\frac{x+y}{x}} = \frac{xy\left(\frac{x}{y} - \frac{y}{x}\right)}{xy\left(\frac{x+y}{x}\right)}$$

$$= \frac{xy\left(\frac{x}{y}\right) - xy\left(\frac{y}{x}\right)}{xy\left(\frac{x+y}{x}\right)}$$

$$= \frac{x^2 - y^2}{y(x+y)}$$

$$= \frac{(x+y)(x-y)}{y(x+y)}$$

$$= \frac{x-y}{y}$$

15.

$$\frac{\frac{1}{m}+\frac{2}{m^2}}{2+\frac{1}{m^2}} = \frac{m^2\left(\frac{1}{m}+\frac{2}{m^2}\right)}{m^2\left(2+\frac{1}{m^2}\right)}$$

$$= \frac{m^2\left(\frac{1}{m}\right)+m^2\left(\frac{2}{m^2}\right)}{m^2(2)+m^2\left(\frac{1}{m^2}\right)}$$

$$= \frac{m+2}{2m^2+1}$$

17.

$$\frac{\frac{4x+8}{3x^2}}{\frac{4x^3}{6}} = \frac{6x^2\left(\frac{4x+8}{3x^2}\right)}{6x^2\left(\frac{4x^3}{6}\right)}$$

$$= \frac{2(4x+8)}{4x^5}$$

$$= \frac{2\cdot4(x+2)}{4x^5}$$

$$= \frac{2(x+2)}{x^5} \text{ or } \frac{2x+4}{x^5}$$

19.

$$\frac{\frac{a}{a+1}-1}{\frac{2a+1}{a-1}} = \frac{(a-1)(a+1)\left(\frac{a}{a+1}-1\right)}{(a-1)(a+1)\left(\frac{2a+1}{a-1}\right)}$$

$$= \frac{(a-1)(a+1)\left(\frac{a}{a+1}\right)-(a-1)(a+1)(1)}{(a-1)(a+1)\left(\frac{2a+1}{a-1}\right)}$$

$$= \frac{a(a-1)-(a-1)(a+1)}{(a+1)(2a+1)}$$

$$= \frac{(a-1)[a-(a+1)]}{(a+1)(2a+1)}$$

$$= \frac{(a-1)(-1)}{(a+1)(2a+1)}$$

$$= \frac{-a+1}{(a+1)(2a+1)}$$

21.

$$\frac{1+\frac{x}{x+1}}{\frac{2x+1}{x-1}} = \frac{(x-1)(x+1)\left(1+\frac{x}{x+1}\right)}{(x-1)(x+1)\left(\frac{2x+1}{x-1}\right)}$$

$$= \frac{(x-1)(x+1)(1)+(x-1)(x+1)\left(\frac{x}{x+1}\right)}{(x-1)(x+1)\left(\frac{2x+1}{x-1}\right)}$$

$$= \frac{(x-1)(x+1)+(x-1)(x)}{(x+1)(2x+1)}$$

$$= \frac{(x-1)(x+1+x)}{(x+1)(2x+1)}$$

$$= \frac{(x-1)(2x+1)}{(x+1)(2x+1)}$$

$$= \frac{x-1}{x+1}$$

23.

$$\frac{\frac{a+1}{a-1}+\frac{a-1}{a+1}}{\frac{a+1}{a-1}-\frac{a-1}{a+1}}$$

$$= \frac{(a-1)(a+1)\left(\frac{a+1}{a-1}+\frac{a-1}{a+1}\right)}{(a-1)(a+1)\left(\frac{a+1}{a-1}-\frac{a-1}{a+1}\right)}$$

$$= \frac{(a-1)(a+1)\left(\frac{a+1}{a-1}\right)+(a-1)(a+1)\left(\frac{a-1}{a+1}\right)}{(a-1)(a+1)\left(\frac{a+1}{a-1}\right)-(a-1)(a+1)\left(\frac{a-1}{a+1}\right)}$$

$$= \frac{(a+1)^2+(a-1)^2}{(a+1)^2-(a-1)^2}$$

$$= \frac{a^2+2a+1+a^2-2a+1}{a^2+2a+1-(a^2-2a+1)}$$

$$= \frac{2a^2+2}{4a}$$

$$= \frac{a^2+1}{2a}$$

25.

$$\frac{\frac{5}{5-x}+\frac{6}{x-5}}{\frac{3}{x}+\frac{2}{x-5}} = \frac{x(x-5)\left(\frac{5}{5-x}+\frac{6}{x-5}\right)}{x(x-5)\left(\frac{3}{x}+\frac{2}{x-5}\right)}$$

$$= \frac{x(x-5)\left(\frac{5}{5-x}\right)+x(x-5)\left(\frac{6}{x-5}\right)}{x(x-5)\left(\frac{3}{x}\right)+x(x-5)\left(\frac{2}{x-5}\right)}$$

$$= \frac{-5x+6x}{3(x-5)+2x}$$

$$= \frac{x}{3x-15+2x}$$

$$= \frac{x}{5x-15} \text{ or } \frac{x}{5(x-3)}$$

27.

$$\frac{\frac{3}{x^2}-\frac{1}{x}+\frac{2}{x-2}}{\frac{1}{x}}$$

$$= \frac{x^2(x-2)\left(\frac{3}{x^2}-\frac{1}{x}+\frac{2}{x-2}\right)}{x^2(x-2)\left(\frac{1}{x}\right)}$$

$$= \frac{x^2(x-2)\left(\frac{3}{x^2}\right)-x^2(x-2)\left(\frac{1}{x}\right)+x^2(x-2)\left(\frac{2}{x-2}\right)}{x^2(x-2)\left(\frac{1}{x}\right)}$$

$$= \frac{3(x-2)-x(x-2)+2x^2}{x(x-2)}$$

$$= \frac{3x-6-x^2+2x+2x^2}{x(x-2)}$$

$$= \frac{x^2+5x-6}{x(x-2)}$$

29.

$$\frac{\dfrac{2}{x^2+x-20}+\dfrac{3}{x^2-6x+8}}{\dfrac{2}{x^2+3x-10}+\dfrac{3}{x^2+2x-24}}$$

$$=\frac{\dfrac{2}{(x+5)(x-4)}+\dfrac{3}{(x-4)(x-2)}}{\dfrac{2}{(x+5)(x-2)}+\dfrac{3}{(x+6)(x-4)}}$$

$$=\frac{\dfrac{2(x-2)+3(x+5)}{(x+5)(x-4)(x-2)}}{\dfrac{2(x-4)(x+6)+3(x-2)(x+5)}{(x+5)(x-2)(x+6)(x-4)}}$$

$$=\frac{2x-4+3x+15}{(x+5)(x-4)(x-2)}\cdot\frac{(x+5)(x-2)(x+6)(x-4)}{2x^2+4x-48+3x^2+9x-30}$$

$$=\frac{(5x+11)(x+6)}{5x^2+13x-78}$$

31.

$$3a^{-2}+b=\frac{3}{a^2}+\frac{b}{1}=\frac{3}{a^2}+\frac{b}{1}\cdot\frac{a^2}{a^2}=\frac{3+a^2b}{a^2}$$

33.

$$(a^{-1}+b^{-1})^{-1}=\left(\frac{1}{a}+\frac{1}{b}\right)^{-1}$$

$$=\left(\frac{1}{a}\cdot\frac{b}{b}+\frac{1}{b}\cdot\frac{a}{a}\right)^{-1}$$

$$=\left(\frac{b}{ab}+\frac{a}{ab}\right)^{-1}$$

$$=\left(\frac{b+a}{ab}\right)^{-1}$$

$$=\frac{ab}{b+a}$$

35.

$$\frac{a^{-1}+1}{b^{-1}-1}=\frac{\frac{1}{a}+1}{\frac{1}{b}-1}$$

$$=\frac{ab\left(\frac{1}{a}+1\right)}{ab\left(\frac{1}{b}-1\right)}$$

$$=\frac{ab\left(\frac{1}{a}\right)+ab(1)}{ab\left(\frac{1}{b}\right)-ab(1)}$$

$$=\frac{b+ab}{a-ab}\ \text{or}\ \frac{b(1+a)}{a(1-b)}$$

37.

$$\frac{x^{-1}-y^{-1}}{x^{-1}+y^{-1}}=\frac{\frac{1}{x}-\frac{1}{y}}{\frac{1}{x}+\frac{1}{y}}$$

$$=\frac{xy\left(\frac{1}{x}-\frac{1}{y}\right)}{xy\left(\frac{1}{x}+\frac{1}{y}\right)}$$

$$=\frac{xy\left(\frac{1}{x}\right)-xy\left(\frac{1}{y}\right)}{xy\left(\frac{1}{x}\right)+xy\left(\frac{1}{y}\right)}$$

$$=\frac{y-x}{y+x}$$

39.

$$\frac{a^{-1}+b^{-1}}{(a+b)^{-1}}=\frac{\frac{1}{a}+\frac{1}{b}}{\frac{1}{a+b}}=\frac{ab(a+b)\left(\frac{1}{a}+\frac{1}{b}\right)}{ab(a+b)\left(\frac{1}{a+b}\right)}$$

$$=\frac{ab(a+b)\left(\frac{1}{a}\right)+ab(a+b)\left(\frac{1}{b}\right)}{ab(a+b)\left(\frac{1}{a+b}\right)}$$

$$=\frac{b(a+b)+a(a+b)}{ab}$$

$$=\frac{(a+b)(a+b)}{ab}$$

$$=\frac{(a+b)^2}{ab}$$

41.

$$2x^{-1}-(3y)^{-1}=\frac{2}{x}-\frac{1}{3y}$$

$$=\frac{2}{x}\cdot\frac{3y}{3y}-\frac{1}{3y}\cdot\frac{x}{x}$$

$$=\frac{6y}{3xy}-\frac{x}{3xy}$$

$$=\frac{6y-x}{3xy}$$

43.

$$\frac{\frac{2}{xy}-\frac{3}{y}+\frac{5}{x}}{3x^{-1}-4y^{-2}}=\frac{\frac{2}{xy}-\frac{3}{y}+\frac{5}{x}}{\frac{3}{x}-\frac{4}{y^2}}$$

$$=\frac{xy^2\left(\frac{2}{xy}-\frac{3}{y}+\frac{5}{x}\right)}{xy^2\left(\frac{3}{x}-\frac{4}{y^2}\right)}$$

$$=\frac{xy^2\left(\frac{2}{xy}\right)-xy^2\left(\frac{3}{y}\right)+xy^2\left(\frac{5}{x}\right)}{xy^2\left(\frac{3}{x}\right)-xy^2\left(\frac{4}{y^2}\right)}$$

$$=\frac{2y-3xy+5y^2}{3y^2-4x}$$

45.

$$A = lw \ \Rightarrow \ l = \frac{A}{w} = A \div w$$

$$l = \frac{x^2 + 12x + 35}{x+3} \div \frac{x^2 + 6x + 5}{x^2 + 5x + 6}$$

$$l = \frac{x^2 + 12x + 35}{x+3} \cdot \frac{x^2 + 5x + 6}{x^2 + 6x + 5}$$

$$l = \frac{(x+7)(x+5)}{x+3} \cdot \frac{(x+3)(x+2)}{(x+1)(x+5)}$$

$$l = \frac{(x+7)(x+2)}{x+1} \quad \text{or} \quad \frac{x^2 + 9x + 14}{x+1}$$

47.

$$A = lw \ \Rightarrow \ l = \frac{A}{w} = A \div w$$

$$l = \frac{x^2 + 11x + 28}{x+5} \div \frac{x^2 + 8x + 7}{x^2 + 4x - 5}$$

$$l = \frac{x^2 + 11x + 28}{x+5} \cdot \frac{x^2 + 4x - 5}{x^2 + 8x + 7}$$

$$l = \frac{(x+7)(x+4)}{x+5} \cdot \frac{(x+5)(x-1)}{(x+7)(x+1)}$$

$$l = \frac{(x+4)(x-1)}{x+1} \quad \text{or} \quad \frac{x^2 + 3x - 4}{x+1}$$

49 a. Substitute $\frac{2}{3}$ for h.

$$E = \frac{\frac{1}{2}h}{h + \frac{1}{2}}$$

$$= \frac{\frac{1}{2}\left(\frac{2}{3}\right)}{\frac{2}{3} + \frac{1}{2}}$$

$$= \frac{\frac{1}{3}}{\frac{2}{3} + \frac{1}{2}}$$

$$= \frac{6\left(\frac{1}{3}\right)}{6\left(\frac{2}{3} + \frac{1}{2}\right)} \quad \leftarrow \text{Multiply by LCD of 6}$$

$$= \frac{6\left(\frac{1}{3}\right)}{6\left(\frac{2}{3}\right) + 6\left(\frac{1}{2}\right)}$$

$$= \frac{2}{4+3}$$

$$= \frac{2}{7}$$

b. Substitute $\frac{4}{5}$ for h.

$$E = \frac{\frac{1}{2}h}{}$$

$$E = \frac{\frac{1}{2}h}{h + \frac{1}{2}}$$

$$= \frac{\frac{1}{2}\left(\frac{4}{5}\right)}{\frac{4}{5} + \frac{1}{2}}$$

$$= \frac{\frac{2}{5}}{\frac{4}{5} + \frac{1}{2}}$$

$$= \frac{10\left(\frac{2}{5}\right)}{10\left(\frac{4}{5} + \frac{1}{2}\right)} \quad \leftarrow \text{Multiply by LCD of 10}$$

$$= \frac{10\left(\frac{2}{5}\right)}{10\left(\frac{4}{5}\right) + 10\left(\frac{1}{2}\right)}$$

$$= \frac{4}{8+5}$$

$$= \frac{4}{13}$$

51.

$$R_T = \frac{R_1 R_2 R_3 (1)}{R_1 R_2 R_3 \left(\frac{1}{R_1} + \frac{1}{R_2} + \frac{1}{R_3}\right)}$$

$$= \frac{R_1 R_2 R_3}{R_1 R_2 R_3 \left(\frac{1}{R_1}\right) + R_1 R_2 R_3 \left(\frac{1}{R_2}\right) + R_1 R_2 R_3 \left(\frac{1}{R_3}\right)}$$

$$= \frac{R_1 R_2 R_3}{R_2 R_3 + R_1 R_3 + R_1 R_2}$$

53.

$$f(x) = \frac{1}{x}$$

$$f(a) = \frac{1}{a}$$

$$f(f(a)) = \frac{1}{\left(\frac{1}{a}\right)} = a$$

55.

$$f(x) = \frac{1}{x}$$

$$\frac{f(a+h) - f(a)}{h} = \frac{\frac{1}{a+h} - \frac{1}{a}}{h}$$

$$= \frac{\frac{a - (a+h)}{a(a+h)}}{h}$$

$$= \frac{\frac{-h}{a(a+h)}}{h}$$

$$= \frac{-1}{a(a+h)}$$

57.

$$f(x) = \frac{1}{x+1}$$

$$\frac{f(a+h) - f(a)}{h} = \frac{\dfrac{1}{a+h+1} - \dfrac{1}{a+1}}{h}$$

$$= \frac{\dfrac{a+1-(a+h+1)}{(a+1)(a+h+1)}}{h}$$

$$= \frac{\dfrac{-h}{(a+1)(a+h+1)}}{h}$$

$$= \frac{-1}{(a+1)(a+h+1)}$$

59.

$$f(x) = \frac{1}{x^2}$$

$$\frac{f(a+h) - f(a)}{h} = \frac{\dfrac{1}{(a+h)^2} - \dfrac{1}{a^2}}{h}$$

$$= \frac{\dfrac{a^2 - (a+h)^2}{(a+h)^2 a^2}}{h}$$

$$= \frac{\dfrac{a^2 - \left(a^2 + 2ah + h^2\right)}{(a+h)^2 a^2}}{h}$$

$$= \frac{\dfrac{-2ah - h^2}{(a+h)^2 a^2}}{h}$$

$$= \frac{\dfrac{h(-2a - h)}{(a+h)^2 a^2}}{h}$$

$$= \frac{-2a - h}{(a+h)^2 a^2}$$

61.

$$\frac{1}{2a + \dfrac{1}{2a + \frac{1}{2a}}} = \frac{1}{2a + \dfrac{1}{\frac{(2a)(2a)+1}{2a}}}$$

$$= \frac{1}{2a + \dfrac{1}{\frac{4a^2+1}{2a}}}$$

$$= \frac{1}{2a + \dfrac{2a}{4a^2+1}}$$

$$= \frac{1}{\dfrac{2a(4a^2+1) + 2a}{4a^2+1}}$$

$$= \frac{1}{\dfrac{8a^3 + 2a + 2a}{4a^2+1}}$$

$$= \frac{1}{\dfrac{8a^3 + 4a}{4a^2+1}}$$

$$= \frac{4a^2 + 1}{8a^3 + 4a}$$

$$= \frac{4a^2 + 1}{4a(2a^2 + 1)}$$

63.

$$\frac{1}{2 + \dfrac{1}{1 + \frac{1}{2}}} = \frac{1}{2 + \dfrac{1}{\frac{3}{2}}} = \frac{1}{2 + \frac{2}{3}} = \frac{1}{\frac{12}{5}} = \frac{5}{12}$$

65.

$$\frac{3}{5} < \frac{-x-5}{3} < 6$$

$$15\left(\frac{3}{5}\right) < 15\left(\frac{-x-5}{3}\right) < 15(6)$$

$$9 < -5x - 25 < 90$$

$$9 + 25 < -5x - 25 + 25 < 90 + 25$$

$$34 < -5x < 115$$

$$\frac{34}{-5} > \frac{-5x}{-5} > \frac{115}{-5}$$

$$\frac{34}{-5} > \frac{-5x}{-5} > \frac{115}{-5}$$

$$-\frac{34}{5} > x > -23 \quad \Rightarrow \quad -23 < x < -\frac{34}{5}$$

In interval notation: $\left(-23, -\dfrac{34}{5}\right)$

67.

$$6x + 2y = 8 \;\Rightarrow\; y = -3x + 4 \;\Rightarrow\; m_1 = -3$$

$$4x - 9 = -y \;\Rightarrow\; y = -4x + 9 \;\Rightarrow\; m_2 = -4$$

Since the slopes are neither the same nor opposite reciprocals, the line are neither parallel nor perpendicular.

Exercise Set 6.4

1. An extraneous root is a number obtained when solving an equation that is not a true solution to the original equation.

3. **a.** Multiply both sides of the equation by the LCD of 12. This removes fractions.

   b. $12\left(\dfrac{x}{4}\right) - 12\left(\dfrac{x}{3}\right) = 12(2)$

   $$3x - 4x = 24$$
   $$-x = 24$$
   $$x = \dfrac{24}{-1} = -24$$

   c. Write each term with the common denominator of 12. This allows the fractions to be added or subtracted.

   d. $\dfrac{x}{4} - \dfrac{x}{3} + 2 = \dfrac{x}{4} \cdot \dfrac{3}{3} - \dfrac{x}{3} \cdot \dfrac{4}{4} + \dfrac{2}{1} \cdot \dfrac{12}{12}$

   $\qquad = \dfrac{3x}{12} - \dfrac{4x}{12} + \dfrac{24}{12}$

   $\qquad = \dfrac{3x - 4x + 24}{12} = \dfrac{-x + 24}{12}$

5. Similar figures are figures whose corresponding angles are the same and whose corresponding sides are in proportion.

7. Tom's solution of $x = 3$ is incorrect since this causes the denominator to be zero. The correct answer is that the equation has no solution.

9. $\qquad \dfrac{7}{x} = 1$

   $\qquad \dfrac{7}{x} = \dfrac{1}{1}$

   $(7)(1) = (x)(1) \qquad \leftarrow$ Cross multiply

   $\qquad 7 = x$

   This solution checks. The solution is 7.

This solution checks. The solution is 7.

11. $\qquad \dfrac{10}{b} = 2$

   $\qquad \dfrac{10}{b} = \dfrac{2}{1}$

   $(10)(1) = (b)(2) \qquad \leftarrow$ Cross multiply

   $\qquad 10 = 2b$

   $\qquad b = 5$

   This solution checks. The solution is 5.

13. $\qquad \dfrac{1}{4} = \dfrac{z+2}{12}$

   $4(z+2) = 12 \qquad \leftarrow$ Cross multiply

   $\qquad 4z + 8 = 12$

   $\qquad 4z = 4$

   $\qquad z = \dfrac{4}{4} = 1$

   This solution checks. The solution is 1.

15. $\qquad \dfrac{6x+7}{5} = \dfrac{2x+9}{3}$

   $3(6x+7) = 5(2x+9) \qquad \leftarrow$ Cross multiply

   $\qquad 18x + 21 = 10x + 45$

   $\qquad 8x + 21 = 45$

   $\qquad 8x = 24$

   $\qquad x = 3$

   This solution checks. The solution is 3.

17. $\qquad \dfrac{z}{3} - \dfrac{3z}{4} = -\dfrac{5z}{12}$

   $12\left(\dfrac{z}{3}\right) - 12\left(\dfrac{3z}{4}\right) = 12\left(-\dfrac{5z}{12}\right) \quad \leftarrow$ Multiply each term by the LCD of 12

   $\qquad 4z - 9z = -5z$

   $\qquad -5z = -5z$

   Since this statement is true for all values of z, the solution is all real numbers.

19. $\dfrac{3}{4} - x = 2x$

$$\dfrac{3}{4} = 3x$$

$$\dfrac{3}{4} = \dfrac{3x}{1}$$

$$3(1) = 4(3x) \quad \leftarrow \text{ Cross multiply}$$

$$3 = 12x$$

$$\dfrac{3}{12} = x$$

$$\dfrac{1}{4} = x$$

This solution checks. The solution is $\dfrac{1}{4}$.

21. $\dfrac{3}{r} + \dfrac{5}{3r} = 1$

$$3r\left(\dfrac{3}{r}\right) + 3r\left(\dfrac{5}{3r}\right) = 3r(1) \quad \leftarrow \text{ Multiply each term by the LCD of } 3x$$

$$9 + 5 = 3r$$

$$14 = 3r$$

$$\dfrac{14}{3} = r$$

This solution checks. The solution is $\dfrac{14}{3}$.

23. $\dfrac{x-1}{x-5} = \dfrac{4}{x-5}$

Since the denominators are the same, the numerators must be equal.

$$X - 1 = 4$$

$$x = 5$$

This does not check, since both denominators are 0 when $x = 5$. There is no solution.

25. $\dfrac{5y-2}{7} = \dfrac{15y-2}{28}$

$$28(5y-2) = 7(15y-2) \quad \leftarrow \text{ Cross multiply}$$

$$140y - 56 = 105y - 14$$

$$35y = 42$$

$$y = \dfrac{42}{35} = \dfrac{6}{5}$$

This solution checks. The solution is $\dfrac{6}{5}$.

27. $\dfrac{5.6}{-p-6.2} = \dfrac{2}{p}$

$$5.6(p) = 2(-p-6.2) \quad \leftarrow \text{ Cross multiply}$$

$$5.6p = -2p - 12.4$$

$$7.6p = -12.4$$

$$p = \dfrac{-12.4}{7.6} \approx -1.63$$

This solution checks. The solution is ≈ -1.63.

29.
$$\frac{m+1}{m+10} = \frac{m-2}{m+4}$$
$$(m+4)(m+1) = (m-2)(m+10) \quad \leftarrow \text{ Cross multiply}$$
$$m^2 + 5m + 4 = m^2 + 8m - 20$$
$$5m + 4 = 8m - 20$$
$$4 = 3m - 20$$
$$24 = 3m$$
$$\frac{24}{3} = m$$
$$8 = m$$

This solution checks. The solution is 8.

31.
$$x - \frac{4}{3x} = -\frac{1}{3}$$
$$3x(x) - 3x\left(\frac{4}{3x}\right) = 3x\left(-\frac{1}{3}\right)$$
$$3x^2 - 4 = -x$$
$$3x^2 + x - 4 = 0$$
$$(3x+4)(x-1) = 0$$
$$3x+4 = 0 \quad \text{or} \quad x-1 = 0$$
$$3x = -4 \qquad\qquad x = 1$$
$$x = -\frac{4}{3}$$

These solutions check. The solutions are $-\frac{4}{3}$ and 1.

33.
$$\frac{2x-1}{3} - \frac{x}{4} = \frac{7.4}{6}$$
$$12\left(\frac{2x-1}{3}\right) - 12\left(\frac{x}{4}\right) = 12\left(\frac{7.4}{6}\right) \quad \leftarrow \text{ Multiply each term by the LCD of 12.}$$
$$4(2x-1) - 3x = 2(7.4)$$
$$8x - 4 - 3x = 14.8$$
$$5x - 4 = 14.8$$
$$5x = 18.8$$
$$x = \frac{18.8}{5} = 3.76$$

This solution checks. The solution is 3.76.

35.
$$x + \frac{6}{x} = -5$$
$$x(x) + x\left(\frac{6}{x}\right) = x(-5) \quad \leftarrow \text{ Multiply each term by the LCD of } x$$
$$x^2 + 6 = -5x$$
$$x^2 + 5x + 6 = 0$$
$$(x+3)(x+2) = 0$$
$$x+3 = 0 \quad \text{or} \quad x+2 = 0$$
$$x = -3 \qquad\qquad x = -2$$

These solutions check. The solutions are −3 and −2.

37.

$$2 - \frac{5}{2b} = \frac{2b}{b+1}$$

$$2[2b(b+1)] - 2b(b+1)\left(\frac{5}{2b}\right) = 2b(b+1)\left(\frac{2b}{b+1}\right) \quad \leftarrow \text{ Multiply each term by the LCD of } 2b(b+1)$$

$$4b(b+1) - 5(b+1) = 2b(2b)$$

$$4b^2 + 4b - 5b - 5 = 4b^2$$

$$4b^2 - b - 5 = 4b^2$$

$$-b - 5 = 0$$

$$b = -5$$

This solution checks. The solution is –5.

39.

$$\frac{1}{w-3} + \frac{1}{w+3} = \frac{-5}{(w+3)(w-3)}$$

$$(w+3)(w-3)\left(\frac{1}{w-3}\right) + (w+3)(w-3)\left(\frac{1}{w+3}\right) = (w+3)(w-3)\left(\frac{-5}{(w+3)(w-3)}\right)$$

$$w + 3 + w - 3 = -5$$

$$2w = -5$$

$$w = \frac{-5}{2} = -\frac{5}{2}$$

This solution checks. The solution is $-\dfrac{5}{2}$.

41.

$$\frac{8}{x^2 - 9} = \frac{2}{x-3} - \frac{4}{x+3}$$

$$\frac{8}{(x-3)(x+3)} = \frac{2}{x-3} - \frac{4}{x+3}$$

$$(x-3)(x+3)\left(\frac{8}{(x-3)(x+3)}\right) = (x-3)(x+3)\left(\frac{2}{x-3}\right) - (x-3)(x+3)\left(\frac{4}{x+3}\right)$$

$$8 = 2(x+3) - 4(x-3)$$

$$8 = 2x + 6 - 4x + 12$$

$$8 = -2x + 18$$

$$-10 = -2x$$

$$x = \frac{-10}{-2} = 5$$

This solution checks. The solution is 5.

43.
$$\frac{y}{2y+2}+\frac{2y-16}{4y+4}=\frac{2y-3}{y+1}$$
$$\frac{y}{2y+2}+\frac{2(y-8)}{4(y+1)}=\frac{2y-3}{y+1}$$
$$\frac{y}{2(y+1)}+\frac{y-8}{2(y+1)}=\frac{2y-3}{y+1}$$
$$\frac{y+y-8}{2(y+1)}=\frac{2y-3}{y+1}$$
$$\frac{2y-8}{2(y+1)}=\frac{2y-3}{y+1}$$
$$\frac{2(y-4)}{2(y+1)}=\frac{2y-3}{y+1}$$
$$\frac{y-4}{y+1}=\frac{2y-3}{y+1}$$

Since the denominators are the same, the numerators must be equal.
$$y-4=2y-3$$
$$-4=y-3$$
$$-1=y$$

This does not check since all the original denominators are 0 when $y=-1$. There is no solution.

45.
$$\frac{1}{x+2}+\frac{1}{x-2}=\frac{4}{x^2-4}$$
$$\frac{1}{x+2}+\frac{1}{x-2}=\frac{4}{(x+2)(x-2)}$$
$$(x+2)(x-2)\left(\frac{1}{x+2}\right)+(x+2)(x-2)\left(\frac{1}{x-2}\right)=(x+2)(x-2)\left(\frac{4}{(x+2)(x-2)}\right)$$
$$(x-2)+(x+2)=4$$
$$2x=4$$
$$x=\frac{4}{2}=2$$

This does not check since the denominators $x-2$ and x^2-4 are both 0 when $x=2$. There is no solution.

47.
$$\frac{5}{x^2+4x+3}+\frac{2}{x^2+x-6}=\frac{3}{x^2-x-2}$$
$$\frac{5}{(x+3)(x+1)}+\frac{2}{(x+3)(x-2)}=\frac{3}{(x-2)(x+1)}$$
$$(x+3)(x+1)(x-2)\left(\frac{5}{(x+3)(x+1)}\right)+(x+3)(x+1)(x-2)\left(\frac{2}{(x+3)(x-2)}\right)=(x+3)(x+1)(x-2)\left(\frac{3}{(x-2)(x+1)}\right)$$
$$5(x-2)+2(x+1)=3(x+3)$$
$$5x-10+2x+2=3x+9$$
$$7x-8=3x+9$$
$$7x=3x+17$$
$$4x=17$$
$$x=\frac{17}{4}$$

This solution checks. The solution is $\frac{17}{4}$.

49.
$$\frac{6x}{4} = \frac{6}{x}$$
$$x(6x) = 4(6)$$
$$6x^2 = 24$$
$$6x^2 - 24 = 0$$
$$6(x^2 - 4) = 0$$
$$6(x + 2)(x - 2) = 0$$
$$x + 2 = 0 \text{ or } x - 2 = 0$$
$$x = -2 \qquad x = 2$$
Reject $x = -2$ since x cannot be a negative number. Thus, $x = 2$ and $6x$ is $6(2) = 12$. The unknown lengths are 2 and 12.

51.
$$\frac{8}{2x + 10} = \frac{x + 3}{6}$$
$$(2x + 10)(x + 3) = 8(6)$$
$$2x^2 + 16x + 30 = 48$$
$$2x^2 + 16x - 18 = 0$$
$$2(x^2 + 8x - 9) = 0$$
$$2(x + 9)(x - 1) = 0$$
$$x + 9 = 0 \quad \text{ or } \quad x - 1 = 0$$
$$x = -9 \qquad x = 1$$
Reject $x = -9$ since x cannot be a negative number. Thus, $x = 1$ so that $x + 3$ is $1 + 3 = 4$ and $2x + 10$ is $2 \cdot 1 + 10 = 2 + 10 = 12$. The unknown lengths are 4 and 12.

53.
$$f(x) = 2x - \frac{4}{x}$$
$$f(a) = 2a - \frac{4}{a}$$
$$-2 = 2a - \frac{4}{a}$$
$$a(-2) = a(2a) - a\left(\frac{4}{a}\right)$$
$$-2a = 2a^2 - 4$$
$$0 = 2a^2 + 2a - 4$$
$$0 = 2(a + 2)(a - 1)$$
$$a + 2 = 0 \quad \text{ or } \quad a - 1 = 0$$
$$a = -2 \qquad a = 1$$
$f(a) = -2$ when $a = -2$ and $a = 1$.

55.
$$f(x) = 3x - \frac{5}{x}$$
$$f(a) = 3a - \frac{5}{a}$$
$$-14 = 3a - \frac{5}{a}$$
$$a(-14) = a(3a) - a\left(\frac{5}{a}\right)$$
$$-14a = 3a^2 - 5$$
$$0 = 3a^2 + 14a - 5$$
$$0 = (3a - 1)(a + 5)$$
$$3a - 1 = 0 \quad \text{ or } \quad a + 5 = 0$$
$$a = \frac{1}{3} \qquad \qquad a = -5$$
$f(a) = -14$ when $a = -5$ and $a = \frac{1}{3}$.

57.
$$f(x) = \frac{x + 3}{x + 5}$$
$$f(a) = \frac{a + 3}{a + 5}$$
$$\frac{5}{7} = \frac{a + 3}{a + 5}$$
$$5(a + 5) = 7(a + 3)$$
$$5a + 25 = 7a + 21$$
$$4 = 2a$$
$$a = 2$$
$f(a) = \frac{5}{7}$ when $a = 2$.

59.
$$\frac{V_1}{V_2} = \frac{P_2}{P_1}$$
$$P_2 V_2 = V_1 P_1$$
$$P_2 = \frac{V_1 P_1}{V_2}$$

61.
$$\frac{V_1}{V_2} = \frac{P_2}{P_1}$$
$$P_2 V_2 = V_1 P_1$$
$$V_2 = \frac{V_1 P_1}{P_2}$$

63.
$$m = \frac{y - y_1}{x - x_1}$$
$$m(x - x_1) = y - y_1$$
$$y = y_1 + m(x - x_1)$$

65.
$$z = \frac{x - \bar{x}}{s}$$
$$zs = x - \bar{x}$$
$$zs + \bar{x} = x \text{ or } x = zs + \bar{x}$$

67.
$$d = \frac{fl}{f+w}$$
$$d(f+w) = fl$$
$$df + dw = fl$$
$$dw = fl - df$$
$$w = \frac{fl - df}{d}$$

69.
$$\frac{1}{p} + \frac{1}{q} = \frac{1}{f}$$
$$pqf\left(\frac{1}{p}\right) + pqf\left(\frac{1}{q}\right) = pqf\left(\frac{1}{f}\right)$$
$$qf + pf = pq$$
$$pf = pq - qf$$
$$pf = q(p-f)$$
$$\frac{pf}{p-f} = q \text{ or } q = \frac{pf}{p-f}$$

71.
$$at_2 - at_1 + v_1 = v_2$$
$$at_2 - at_1 = v_2 - v_1$$
$$a(t_2 - t_1) = v_2 - v_1$$
$$a = \frac{v_2 - v_1}{t_2 - t_1}$$

73.
$$a_n = a_1 + nd - d$$
$$a_n - a_1 = nd - d$$
$$a_n - a_1 = d(n-1)$$
$$\frac{a_n - a_1}{n-1} = d \text{ or } d = \frac{a_n - a_1}{n-1}$$

75.
$$F = \frac{Gm_1 m_2}{d^2}$$
$$d^2(F) = d^2\left(\frac{Gm_1 m_2}{d^2}\right)$$
$$d^2 F = Gm_1 m_2$$
$$\frac{d^2 F}{m_1 m_2} = G \text{ or } G = \frac{d^2 F}{m_1 m_2}$$

77.
$$\frac{P_1 V_1}{T_1} = \frac{P_2 V_2}{T_2}$$
$$T_1(P_2 V_2) = T_2(P_1 V_1)$$
$$T_1 = \frac{T_2 P_1 V_1}{P_2 V_2}$$

79.
$$\frac{s - s_0}{v_0 + gt} = t$$
$$s - s_0 = t(v_0 + gt)$$
$$s - s_0 = tv_0 + gt^2$$
$$s - s_0 - gt^2 = tv_0$$
$$\frac{s - s_0 - gt^2}{t} = v_0$$

81.a.
$$\frac{2}{x-2} + \frac{3}{x^2 - 4} = \frac{2}{x-2} + \frac{3}{(x-2)(x+2)}$$
$$= \frac{2}{x-2} \cdot \frac{x+2}{x+2} + \frac{3}{(x-2)(x+2)}$$
$$= \frac{2(x+2)}{(x-2)(x+2)} + \frac{3}{(x-2)(x+2)}$$
$$= \frac{2x+4}{(x-2)(x+2)} + \frac{3}{(x-2)(x+2)}$$
$$= \frac{2x+7}{(x-2)(x+2)}$$

b.
$$\frac{2}{x-2} + \frac{3}{x^2 - 4} = 0$$
$$\frac{2x+7}{(x-2)(x+2)} = 0$$
$$2x + 7 = 0$$
$$2x = -7$$
$$x = -\frac{7}{2}$$

83. a.
$$\frac{b+3}{b} - \frac{b+4}{b+5} - \frac{15}{b^2 + 5b}$$
$$= \frac{b+3}{b} - \frac{b+4}{b+5} - \frac{15}{b(b+5)}$$
$$= \frac{b+3}{b} \cdot \frac{b+5}{b+5} - \frac{b+4}{b+5} \cdot \frac{b}{b} - \frac{15}{b(b+5)}$$
$$= \frac{(b+3)(b+5)}{b(b+5)} - \frac{b(b+4)}{b(b+5)} - \frac{15}{b(b+5)}$$
$$= \frac{b^2 + 8b + 15}{b(b+5)} - \frac{b^2 + 4b}{b(b+5)} - \frac{15}{b(b+5)}$$
$$= \frac{b^2 + 8b + 15 - (b^2 + 4b) - 15}{b(b+5)}$$
$$= \frac{4b}{b(b+5)}$$
$$= \frac{4}{b+5}$$

b.
$$\frac{b+3}{b} - \frac{b+4}{b+5} = \frac{15}{b(b+5)}$$

$$b(b+5)\left(\frac{b+3}{b}\right) - b(b+5)\left(\frac{b+4}{b+5}\right) = b(b+5)\left(\frac{15}{b(b+5)}\right)$$

$$(b+5)(b+3) - b(b+4) = 15$$

$$b^2 + 8b + 15 - b^2 - 4b = 15$$

$$4b + 15 = 15$$

$$4b = 0$$

$$b = 0$$

This does not check since the denominators b and $b(b+5)$ are 0 when $b = 0$.
There is no solution.

85. $c \neq 0$, since division by 0 is not defined.

87. $f(x)$ is graph **b)** and $g(x)$ is graph **a)**;
$f(x)$ is not defined for $x = 3$.

89. a. $I = \dfrac{AC}{0.80R}$

$$I = \frac{50,000(10,000)}{0.80(100,000)}$$

$$I = 6250$$

The insurance company will pay \$6250.

b. $I = \dfrac{AC}{0.80R}$

$$I(0.80R) = AC$$

$$R = \frac{AC}{0.80\,I}$$

91. a. $a = \dfrac{v_2 - v_1}{t_2 - t_1}$

$$a = \frac{60 - 20}{22 - 20}$$

$$a = 20$$

The average acceleration is 20 ft / min^2.

b. $a = \dfrac{v_2 - v_1}{t_2 - t_1}$

$$a(t_2 - t_1) = v_2 - v_1$$

$$at_2 - at_1 = v_2 - v_1$$

$$-at_1 = -at_2 + v_2 - v_1$$

$$at_1 = at_2 + v_1 - v_2$$

$$t_1 = \frac{at_2 + v_1 - v_2}{a}$$

$$t_1 = t_2 + \frac{v_1 - v_2}{a}$$

93. $Q = \dfrac{F + D}{R - V}$

$$Q = \frac{2500 + 8000}{500 - 200}$$

$$= 35$$

35 apartment units must be rented.

95. $\dfrac{1}{R_T} = \dfrac{1}{R_1} + \dfrac{1}{R_2} + \dfrac{1}{R_3}$

$$\frac{1}{R_T} = \frac{1}{300} + \frac{1}{500} + \frac{1}{3000}$$

$$\frac{3000R_T}{R_T} = \frac{3000R_T}{300} + \frac{3000R_T}{500} + \frac{3000R_T}{3000}$$

$$3000 = 10R_T + 6R_T + R_T$$

$$3000 = 17R_T$$

$$\frac{3000}{17} = R_T \text{ or } R_T \approx 176.47$$

The total resistance is about 176.47 ohms

97. $\dfrac{1}{p} + \dfrac{1}{q} = \dfrac{1}{f}$

Solve for p.

$$pqf\left(\frac{1}{p} + \frac{1}{q}\right) = pqf\left(\frac{1}{f}\right)$$

$$qf + pf = pq$$

$$pq - pf = qf$$

$$p(q - f) = qf$$

$$p = \frac{qf}{q - f}$$

$$p = \frac{7.5(0.1)}{7.5 - 0.1}$$

$$p \approx 0.101$$

The lens should be about 0.101 m from the film.

99. a. $T_a = \dfrac{T_f}{1 - [f + (s + c)(1 - f)]}$

$$= \frac{0.0601}{1 - [0.33 + (0.046 + 0.03)(1 - 0.33)]}$$

$$= \frac{0.0601}{1 - [0.33 + (0.076)(0.67)]}$$

$$= \frac{0.0601}{1 - (0.33 + 0.05092)}$$

$$= \frac{0.0601}{1 - 0.38092}$$

$$= \frac{0.0601}{0.61908}$$

$$\approx 0.0970795$$

Thus, the taxable equivalent is $T_a \approx 9.71\%$.

b. Howard Levy should choose the Tax Free Money Market since $9.71\% > 7.68\%$.

101. Several answers are possible. One such equation is $\dfrac{1}{x-4} + \dfrac{1}{x+2} = 0$. Another one might be $\dfrac{1}{(x-4)(x+2)} = 0$.

103. Several answers are possible. One possible answer is $\frac{1}{x}+\frac{1}{x}=\frac{2}{x}$.

105.
$$-2 \le 4-2x < 6$$
$$-2-4 \le 4-2x-4 < 6-4$$
$$-6 \le -2x < 2$$
$$\frac{-6}{-2} \ge \frac{-2x}{-2} > \frac{2}{-2}$$
$$3 \ge x > -1$$
$$-1 < x \le 3$$

107.
$$3x^2y-4xy+2y^2-\left(3xy+6y^2+2x\right)$$
$$3x^2y-4xy+2y^2-3xy-6y^2-2x$$
$$3x^2y-4xy-3xy+2y^2-6y^2-2x$$
$$3x^2y-7xy-4y^2-2x$$

Exercise Set 6.5

1. The total time needed will be equal to $\frac{1}{2}$ the time of each painting separately. In $\frac{1}{2}$ the time, each will complete $\frac{1}{2}$ the job.

3. Let x be the time to do the task together.

a.

worker	Rate of Work	Time Worked	Part of Task Completed
Bill	$\frac{1}{7}$	x	$\frac{x}{7}$
Bob	$\frac{1}{8}$	x	$\frac{x}{8}$

b. $\frac{x}{7}+\frac{x}{8}=1$

c. It will take less than 7 hours working together since Bill working alone can do the job in 7 hours.

5. Let x be the time for both working together.

worker	Rate of Work	Time Worked	Part of Task Completed
Margerie	$\frac{1}{2}$	x	$\frac{x}{2}$
Matthew	$\frac{1}{6}$	x	$\frac{x}{6}$

$$\frac{x}{2}+\frac{x}{6}=1$$
$$6\left(\frac{x}{2}+\frac{x}{6}\right)=6(1)$$
$$3x+x=6$$
$$4x=6$$
$$x=1.5$$

It will take them 1.5 months to carve the totem pole working together.

7. Let x be the time for both working together.

worker	Rate of Work	Time Worked	Part of Task Completed
Jason	$\frac{1}{3}$	x	$\frac{x}{3}$
Tom	$\frac{1}{6}$	x	$\frac{x}{6}$

$$\frac{x}{3}+\frac{x}{6}=1$$
$$6\left(\frac{x}{3}\right)+6\left(\frac{x}{6}\right)=6(1)$$
$$2x+x=6$$
$$3x=6$$
$$x=2$$

Working together, they can shampoo the carpet in 2 hours.

9. Let x be the time for both working together.

worker	Rate of Work	Time Worked	Part of Task Completed
Richard	$\frac{1}{30}$	x	$\frac{x}{30}$
Duane	$\frac{1}{50}$	x	$\frac{x}{50}$

$$\frac{x}{30} + \frac{x}{50} = 1$$

$$150 \cdot \frac{x}{30} + 150 \cdot \frac{x}{50} = 150 \cdot 1$$

$$5x + 3x = 150$$

$$8x = 150$$

$$x = \frac{150}{8} = 18.75$$

Working together, the task can be completed in 18.75 minutes.

11. Let x be the time for both working together.

worker	Rate of Work	Time Worked	Part of Task Completed
Wanda	$\frac{1}{4}$	x	$\frac{x}{4}$
Shawn	$\frac{1}{6}$	x	$\frac{x}{6}$

$$\frac{x}{4} + \frac{x}{6} = 1$$

$$12 \cdot \frac{x}{4} + 12 \cdot \frac{x}{6} = 12 \cdot 1$$

$$3x + 2x = 12$$

$$5x = 12$$

$$x = \frac{12}{5} = 2.4$$

Working together, the task can be completed in about 2.4 hours.

13. Let x be the time for both working together.

	Rate of Work	Time Worked	Part of Task Completed
$\frac{1}{2}''$ hose	$\frac{1}{8}$	x	$\frac{x}{8}$
$\frac{4}{5}''$ hose	$\frac{1}{5}$	x	$\frac{x}{5}$

$$\frac{x}{8} + \frac{x}{5} = 1$$

$$40 \cdot \frac{x}{8} + 40 \cdot \frac{x}{5} = 40 \cdot 1$$

$$5x + 8x = 40$$

$$13x = 40$$

$$x = \frac{40}{13} \approx 3.08$$

Working together, the task can be completed in about 3.08 hours

15. Let x be the time for both working together.

	Rate of Work	Time Worked	Part of Task Completed
In-valve	$\frac{1}{20}$	x	$\frac{x}{20}$
Out-valve	$-\frac{1}{25}$	x	$-\frac{x}{25}$

$$\frac{x}{20} - \frac{x}{25} = 1$$

$$100 \cdot \frac{x}{20} - 100 \cdot \frac{x}{25} = 100 \cdot 1$$

$$5x - 4x = 100$$

$$x = 100$$

With both valves open, the tank will fill in 100 hours.

17. Let x be the time for Henry to complete the job working by himself.

worker	Rate of Work	Time Worked	Part of Task Completed
Indiana	$\frac{1}{3.9}$	2.6	$\frac{2.6}{3.9}$
Henry	$\frac{1}{x}$	2.6	$\frac{2.6}{x}$

$$\frac{2.6}{3.9} + \frac{2.6}{x} = 1$$

$$3.9x \cdot \frac{2.6}{3.9} + 3.9x \cdot \frac{2.6}{x} = 3.9x \cdot 1$$

$$2.6x + 10.14 = 3.9x$$

$$1.3x = 10.14$$

$$x = \frac{10.14}{1.3} = 7.8$$

Henry can complete the task by himself in 7.8 months.

19. Let x be the time for Shane to complete the job working by himself.

worker	Rate of Work	Time Worked	Part of Task Completed
John	$\frac{1}{50}$	30	$\frac{30}{50} = \frac{3}{5}$
Shane	$\frac{1}{x}$	30	$\frac{30}{x}$

$$\frac{3}{5} + \frac{30}{x} = 1$$
$$5x \cdot \frac{3}{5} + 5x \cdot \frac{30}{x} = 5x \cdot 1$$
$$3x + 150 = 5x$$
$$2x = 150$$
$$x = 75$$

Shane can complete the task by himself in 75 minutes.

21. Let x be the time to fill the tub with both valves open and the drain open.

	Rate of Work	Time Worked	Part of Task Completed
Hot	$\frac{1}{8}$	x	$\frac{x}{8}$
Cold	$\frac{1}{12}$	x	$\frac{x}{12}$
Drain	$-\frac{1}{7}$	x	$-\frac{x}{7}$

$$\frac{x}{8} + \frac{x}{12} - \frac{x}{7} = 1$$
$$168 \cdot \frac{x}{8} + 168 \cdot \frac{x}{12} - 168 \cdot \frac{x}{7} = 168 \cdot 1$$
$$21x + 14x - 24x = 168$$
$$11x = 168$$
$$x = \frac{168}{11} \approx 15.27$$

With both valves open and the drain open, the tub will fill in about 15.27 minutes.

23. Let x be the time to empty the basement if the pumps work together.

	Rate of Work	Time Worked	Part of Task Completed
Pump 1	$\frac{1}{6}$	x	$\frac{x}{6}$
Pump 2	$\frac{1}{5}$	x	$\frac{x}{5}$
Pump 3	$\frac{1}{4}$	x	$\frac{x}{4}$

$$\frac{x}{6} + \frac{x}{5} + \frac{x}{4} = 1$$
$$60 \cdot \frac{x}{6} + 60 \cdot \frac{x}{5} + 60 \cdot \frac{x}{4} = 60 \cdot 1$$
$$10x + 12x + 15x = 60$$
$$37x = 60$$
$$x = \frac{60}{37} \approx 1.62$$

With all three pumps, the basement can be emptied in about 1.62 hours.

25. Let x be the time for Anna to complete the job.

worker	Rate of Work	Time Worked	Part of Task Completed
Justin	$\frac{1}{15}$	6	$\frac{6}{15}$
Anna	$\frac{1}{20}$	x	$\frac{x}{20}$

$$\frac{6}{15} + \frac{x}{15} = 1$$
$$60 \cdot \frac{6}{15} + 60 \cdot \frac{x}{20} = 60 \cdot 1$$
$$24 + 3x = 60$$
$$3x = 36$$
$$x = 12$$

Anna can finish the job in 12 hours.

27. Let x be the unknown number.
$$\frac{4x}{3+x} = \frac{5}{2}$$
$$5(3+x) = 4x(2)$$
$$15 + 5x = 8x$$
$$15 = 3x$$
$$\frac{15}{3} = x$$
$$5 = x$$

29. Let x and $2x$ be the two numbers. Their reciprocals are $\frac{1}{x}$ and $\frac{1}{2x}$.
$$\frac{1}{x} + \frac{1}{2x} = \frac{3}{4}$$
$$4x\left(\frac{1}{x}\right) + 4x\left(\frac{1}{2x}\right) = 4x\left(\frac{3}{4}\right)$$
$$4 + 2 = 3x$$
$$6 = 3x$$
$$\frac{6}{3} = x$$
$$2 = x$$
Thus, $x = 2$ and $2x = 2 \cdot 2 = 4$. The two numbers are 2 and 4.

31. Let x and $x + 2$ be the two consecutive even integers. Their reciprocals are $\frac{1}{x}$ and $\frac{1}{x+2}$.
$$\frac{1}{x} + \frac{1}{x+2} = \frac{5}{12}$$
$$12x(x+2)\left(\frac{1}{x}\right) + 12x(x+2)\left(\frac{1}{x+2}\right) = 12x(x+2)\left(\frac{5}{12}\right)$$
$$12(x+2) + 12x(1) = 5x(x+2)$$
$$12x + 24 + 12x = 5x^2 + 10x$$
$$24x + 24 = 5x^2 + 10x$$
$$0 = 5x^2 - 14x - 24$$
$$0 = (5x+6)(x-4)$$
$$5x + 6 = 0 \quad \text{or} \quad x - 4 = 0$$
$$5x = -6 \quad \text{or} \quad x = 4$$
$$x = -\frac{6}{5}$$
Reject $x = -\frac{6}{5}$ since x must be an integer. Thus, $x = 4$ and $x + 2 = 4 + 2 = 6$. The two integers are 4 and 6.

33. Let x be the unknown number.
$$\frac{2}{x} + 3 = \frac{31}{10}$$
$$10x\left(\frac{2}{x}\right) + 10x(3) = 10x\left(\frac{31}{10}\right)$$
$$20 + 30x = 31x$$
$$20 = x$$

35. Let x be the unknown number.
$$3x + \frac{2}{x} = 5$$
$$x(3x) + x\left(\frac{2}{x}\right) = 5(x)$$
$$3x^2 + 2 = 5x$$
$$3x^2 - 5x + 2 = 0$$
$$(3x - 2)(x - 1) = 0$$
$$3x - 2 = 0 \quad \text{or} \quad x - 1 = 0$$
$$3x = 2 \qquad\qquad x = 1$$
$$x = \frac{2}{3}$$
The two numbers that work are $\frac{2}{3}$ and 1.

37. Let x be the rate of the current.

	d	r	$t = \frac{d}{r}$
upstream	3.5	$4 - x$	$\frac{3.5}{4-x}$
downstream	4.2	$4 + x$	$\frac{4.2}{4+x}$

$$\frac{4.2}{4+x} = \frac{3.5}{4-x}$$
$$4.2(4-x) = 3.5(4+x)$$
$$16.8 - 4.2x = 14 + 3.5x$$
$$2.8 = 7.7x$$
$$x = \frac{2.8}{7.7} \approx 0.36$$
The rate of the current is about 0.36 mph.

39. Let r be the rate of Nancy walking. Then $r + 2$ is the rate of Nancy walking on the moving sidewalk.

	d	r	$t = \dfrac{d}{r}$
On sidewalk	120	$r + 2$	$\dfrac{120}{r+2}$
Off sidewalk	52	r	$\dfrac{52}{r}$

The time is the same for both.

$$\frac{120}{r+2} = \frac{52}{r}$$
$$120(r) = 52(r+2)$$
$$120r = 52r + 104$$
$$68r = 104$$
$$r \approx 1.53$$

Nancy walks at a rate of about 1.53 ft / sec.

41. Let x be the length of the trail.

	d	r	$t = \dfrac{d}{r}$
Bonnie	x	6	$\dfrac{x}{6}$
Clide	x	10	$\dfrac{x}{10}$

Bonnie's time is a half hour more than Clide's time.

$$\frac{x}{10} + \frac{1}{2} = \frac{x}{6}$$
$$30\left(\frac{x}{10} + \frac{1}{2}\right) = 30\left(\frac{x}{6}\right)$$
$$3x + 15 = 5x$$
$$2x = 15$$
$$x = 7.5$$

The trail is 7.5 miles long.

43. Let x be Allen Angel's average speed (in mph) driving to Yosemite National Park.

	d	r	$t = \dfrac{d}{r}$
driving	60	x	$\dfrac{60}{x}$

He spent twice as much time visiting as he did driving. So he spent $2\left(\dfrac{60}{x}\right)$ hours visiting. The

total time was 5 hours.

$$\frac{60}{x} + 2\left(\frac{60}{x}\right) = 5$$
$$\frac{60}{x} + \frac{120}{x} = 5$$
$$\frac{180}{x} = 5$$
$$5x = 180$$
$$x = 36$$

Allen's average speed was 36 mph.

45. Let x be the distance the ball traveled at 14.7 yards per second. Then $80 - x$ is the distance Terry traveled at 5.8 yards per second.

	d	r	$t = \dfrac{d}{r}$
Ball	x	14.7	$\dfrac{x}{14.7}$
Terry	$80 - x$	5.8	$\dfrac{80-x}{5.8}$

The total time of the play is 10.6 seconds.

$$\frac{x}{14.7} + \frac{80-x}{5.8} = 10.6$$
$$85.26\left(\frac{x}{14.7}\right) + 85.26\left(\frac{80-x}{5.8}\right) = 85.26(10.6)$$
$$5.8x + 14.7(80-x) = 903.756$$
$$5.8x + 1176 - 14.7x = 903.756$$
$$-8.9x = -272.244$$
$$x \approx 30.59$$

The ball traveled about 30.59 yards before Terry caught it.

47. Let x be the speed of the local train.

	d	r	$t = \dfrac{d}{r}$
local	$24.2 - 7.8$ $= 16.4$	x	$\dfrac{16.4}{x}$
express	24.2	$x + 5.2$	$\dfrac{24.2}{x+5.2}$

The time is the same.

$$\frac{16.4}{x} = \frac{24.2}{x+5.2}$$

$$16.4(x+5.2) = 24.2x$$

$$16.4x + 85.25 = 24.2x$$

$$85.28 = 7.8x$$

$$10.93 \approx x$$

$$16.13 \approx x + 5.2$$

The local train's speed is about 10.93 mph and the express train's speed is about 16.13 mph.

49. Let x be the distance to the State Fair.

	d	r	$t = \dfrac{d}{r}$
train	x	70	$\dfrac{x}{70}$
car	x	50	$\dfrac{x}{50}$

The train arrives 2 hours ahead of the car.

$$\frac{x}{70} + 2 = \frac{x}{50}$$

$$350\left(\frac{x}{70}\right) + 350(2) = 350\left(\frac{x}{50}\right)$$

$$5x + 700 = 7x$$

$$700 = 2x$$

$$\frac{700}{2} = x$$

$$350 = x$$

The distance is 350 miles.

51. Let r be the speed of Mary Ann's car.

	d	r	$t = \dfrac{d}{r}$
Mary Ann	600	r	$\dfrac{600}{r}$
Carla	600	$r - 10$	$\dfrac{600}{r-10}$

$$\frac{600}{r} + 2 = \frac{600}{r-10}$$

$$r(r-10)\left(\frac{600}{r}\right) + 2r(r-10) = r(r-10)\left(\frac{600}{r-10}\right)$$

$$600(r-10) + 2r(r-10) = 600r$$

$$600r - 6000 + 2r^2 - 20r = 600r$$

$$2r^2 - 20r - 6000 = 0$$

$$2(r-60)(r+50) = 0$$

$$r - 60 = 0 \quad \text{or} \quad r + 50 = 0$$

$$r = 60 \qquad\qquad r = -50$$

Since a speed cannot be negative, $r = 60$.
Mary Ann's car travels at 60 mph.

53. Let x be the speed of the helicopter going to the glacier.

	d	r	$t = \dfrac{d}{r}$
to glacier	60	x	$\dfrac{60}{x}$
to TeAnu	140	$x + 20$	$\dfrac{140}{x+20}$

The entire trip took 2 hours.

$$\frac{60}{x} + \frac{1}{2} + \frac{140}{x+20} = 2$$

$$2x(x+20)\left(\frac{60}{x}+\frac{1}{2}+\frac{140}{x+20}\right)=2x(x+20)(2)$$
$$120(x+20)+x(x+20)+2x(140)=4x(x+20)$$
$$120x+2400+x^2+20x+280x=4x^2+80x$$
$$0=3x^2-340x-2400$$
$$0=(3x+20)(x-120)$$
$$3x+20=0 \quad\text{or}\quad x-120=0$$
$$x=-\frac{20}{3}\qquad x=120$$

Since a speed cannot be negative, $x=120$. The average speed of the helicopter going to the glacier is 120 kph.

55. Let x be Phil's average speed.

	d	r	$t=\dfrac{d}{r}$
Phil	450	x	$\dfrac{450}{x}$
Heim	450	$x+2$	$\dfrac{450}{x+2}$

The Heim's time plus 2.5 minutes is the Phil's time.
$$\frac{450}{x+2}+\frac{5}{2}=\frac{450}{x}$$
$$2x(x+2)\left(\frac{450}{x+2}\right)+2x(x+2)\left(\frac{5}{2}\right)=2x(x+2)\left(\frac{450}{x}\right)$$
$$900x+5x(x+2)=900(x+2)$$
$$900x+5x^2+10x=900x+1800$$
$$5x^2+10x-1800=0$$
$$(5x+100)(x-18)=0$$
$$5x+100=0 \quad\text{or}\quad x-18=0$$
$$x=-20 \quad\text{or}\quad x=18$$

Since a speed cannot be negative, $x=18$.
Phil's speed is at 18 feet per minute.

57. Let x be the distance between the space station and NASA headquarters.

	d	r	$t=\dfrac{d}{r}$
First rocket	x	20,000	$\dfrac{x}{20,000}$
Second rocket	x	18,000	$\dfrac{x}{18,000}$

$$\frac{x}{20,000}+0.6=\frac{x}{18,000}$$
$$180,000\left(\frac{x}{20,000}+0.6\right)=180,000\left(\frac{x}{18,000}\right)$$
$$9x+108,000=10x$$
$$108,000=x$$
The space station is 108,000 miles from NASA headquarters.

59. Answers will vary.

61. a. Let x be the distance the car will travel.

	d	r	$t=\dfrac{d}{r}$
Car	x	90	$\dfrac{x}{90}$
Aircraft	$x+10$	450	$\dfrac{x+10}{450}$

$$\frac{x}{90}=\frac{x+10}{450}$$
$$450x=90(x+10)$$
$$450x=90x+900$$
$$360x=900$$
$$x=\frac{900}{360}=\frac{5}{2}=2.5$$
The car will have traveled 2.5 miles.

b. $\text{time}=\dfrac{\text{distance}}{\text{rate}}$
$$=\frac{2.5}{90}$$
$$=0.02\overline{7}\text{ hours}$$
$$=0.02\overline{7}(60)$$
$$=1.\overline{6}\text{ minutes}$$
The aircraft will reach the car in about 1.7 minutes.

c. In one minute or $\dfrac{1}{60}$ hour, the car has

traveled $\dfrac{90}{60} = 1.5$ miles. The total distance

the plane must travel is
$10 + 1.5 = 11.5$ miles.

$$\text{rate} = \dfrac{\text{distance}}{\text{time}}$$
$$= \dfrac{11.5}{\frac{1}{60}}$$
$$= 11.5(60)$$
$$= 690$$

The speed of the plane must be 690 mph.

63. $5,260,000,000 = 5.26 \times 10^9$

65. Make a table of values to graph the equation.
$y = |x| - 2$

$x = -3 \Rightarrow y = |-3| - 2 = 3 - 2 = 1$
$x = -2 \Rightarrow y = |-2| - 2 = 2 - 2 = 0$
$x = -1 \Rightarrow y = |-1| - 2 = 1 - 2 = -1$
$x = 0 \Rightarrow y = |0| - 2 = 0 - 2 = -2$
$x = 1 \Rightarrow y = |1| - 2 = 1 - 2 = -1$
$x = 2 \Rightarrow y = |2| - 2 = 2 - 2 = 0$
$x = 3 \Rightarrow y = |3| - 2 = 3 - 2 = 1$

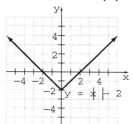

Exercise Set 6.6

1. a. As one quantity increases, the other increases.

   b. Answers will vary.

   c. Answers will vary.

3. One quantity varies as a product of two or more quantities.

5. a. y decreases

   b. inverse variation

7. Direct

9. Inverse

11. Direct

13. Direct

15. Direct

17. Inverse

19. Direct

21. Inverse

23. Inverse

25. a. $x = ky$

   b. Substitute 12 for y and 6 for k.
$x = 6(12)$
$x = 72$

27. a. $y = kR$

   b. Substitute 180 for R and 1.7 for k.
$y = 1.7(180)$
$y = 306$

29. a. $R = \dfrac{k}{W}$

   b. Substitute 160 for W and 8 for k.
$R = \dfrac{8}{160}$
$R = \dfrac{1}{20} = 0.05$

31. a. $A = \dfrac{kB}{C}$

   b. Substitute 12 for B, 4 for C, and 3 for k.
$A = \dfrac{3(12)}{4} = \dfrac{36}{4} = 9$

33. a. $x = ky$

   b. To find k, substitute 12 for x and 3 for y.
$12 = k(3)$
$\dfrac{12}{3} = k$
$4 = k$
Thus, $x = 4y$
Now substitute 5 for y.
$x = 4(5) = 20$

35. a. $y = kR^2$

b.   To find k, substitute 5 for y and 5 for R.

$$5 = k(5)^2$$
$$5 = k(25)$$
$$\frac{5}{25} = k$$
$$\frac{1}{5} = k$$

Thus $y = \frac{1}{5}R^2$.

Now substitute 10 for R.

$$y = \frac{1}{5}(10)^2 = \frac{1}{5}(100) = 20$$

37. a. $C = \dfrac{k}{J}$

b.   To find k, substitute 7 for C and 0.7 for J.

$$7 = \frac{k}{0.7}$$
$$7(0.7) = k$$
$$4.9 = k$$

Thus $C = \dfrac{4.9}{J}$.

Now substitute 12 for J.

$$C = \frac{4.9}{12} \approx 0.41$$

39. a. $F = \dfrac{kM_1 M_2}{d}$

b.   To find k, substitute 5 for M_1, 10 for M_2, 0.2 for d, and 20 for F.

$$20 = \frac{k(5)(10)}{0.2}$$
$$20 = k(250)$$
$$\frac{20}{250} = k$$
$$0.08 = k$$

Thus $F = \dfrac{0.08 M_1 M_2}{d}$.

Now substitute 10 for M_1, 20 for M_2, and 0.4 for d.

$$F = \frac{0.08(10)(20)}{0.4} = \frac{16}{0.4} = 40$$

41. $a = kb$
$k(2b) = 2(kb) = 2a$
If b is doubled, a is doubled.

43. $y = \dfrac{k}{x}$

$$\frac{k}{2x} = \frac{1}{2}\left(\frac{k}{x}\right) = \frac{1}{2}y$$

If x is doubled, y is halved.

45. $F = \dfrac{km_1 m_2}{d^2}$

$$\frac{k(2m_1)m_2}{d^2} = \frac{2km_1 m_2}{d^2} = 2 \cdot \frac{km_1 m_2}{d^2} = 2F$$

If m_1 is doubled, F is doubled.

47. $F = \dfrac{km_1 m_2}{d^2}$

$$\frac{k(2m_1)\left(\frac{1}{2}m_2\right)}{d^2} = \frac{2 \cdot \frac{1}{2}km_1 m_2}{d^2} = \frac{1 \cdot km_1 m_2}{d^2} = F$$

If m_1 is doubled and m_2 is halved, F is unchanged.

49. $F = \dfrac{km_1 m_2}{d^2}$

$$\frac{k\left(\frac{1}{2}m_1\right)(4m_2)}{d^2} = \frac{\frac{1}{2} \cdot 4\, km_1 m_2}{d^2} =$$

$$\frac{2 \cdot km_1 m_2}{d^2} = 2 \cdot \frac{km_1 m_2}{d^2} = 2F$$

If m_1 is halved and m_2 is quadrupled, F is doubled.

51.   Notice that as x gets bigger, y gets smaller. This suggests that the variation is inverse rather than direct. Therefore use the equation $y = \frac{k}{x}$. To determine the value of k, choose one of the ordered pairs and substitute the values into the equation $y = \frac{k}{x}$ and solve for k. We'll use the ordered pair $(5, 1)$.

$$y = \frac{k}{x}$$
$$1 = \frac{k}{5} \Rightarrow k = 5$$

53. The equation is $p = kl$ To find k substitute 150 for l and 2542.50 for p.

$$2542.50 = k(150)$$

$$k = \frac{2542.50}{150}$$

$$k = 16.95$$

Thus $p = 16.95l$.

Now substitute 520 for l.

$$p = 16.95(520)$$

$$p = 8814$$

The profit would be $8814.

55. The equation is $d = kw$. To find k, substitute 2376 for d and 132 for w.

$$2376 = k132$$

$$k = \frac{2376}{132}$$

$$k = 18$$

Thus $d = 18w$. Now substitute 172 for w.

$$d = 18(172)$$

$$d = 3096$$

The recommended dosage for Bill is 3096 mg.

57. The equation is $t = \frac{k}{n}$. To find k, substitute 8 for t and 5 for n.

$$8 = \frac{k}{5}$$

$$k = 8(5)$$

$$k = 40$$

Thus $t = \frac{40}{n}$.

Now substitute 4 for n.

$$t = \frac{40}{4}$$

$$t = 10$$

It will take 4 bricklayers 10 hours.

59. The equation is $V = \frac{k}{P}$. To find k, substitute 800 for V and 200 for P.

$$800 = \frac{k}{200}$$

$$800(200) = k$$

$$160{,}000 = k$$

Thus $V = \frac{160{,}000}{P}$.

Now substitute 25 for P.

$$V = \frac{160{,}000}{25} = 6400$$

The volume is 6400 cc.

61. The equation is $t = \frac{k}{s}$. To find k, substitute 6 for s and 2.6 for t.

$$2.6 = \frac{k}{6}$$

$$k = 6(2.6)$$

$$k = 15.6$$

Thus $t = \frac{15.6}{s}$.

Now substitute 5 for s.

$$t = \frac{15.6}{5}$$

$$t = 3.12$$

Leif will take 3.12 hours.

63. The equation is $t = \frac{k}{s}$. To find k, substitute 122 for s and 0.21 for t.

$$0.21 = \frac{k}{122}$$

$$k = 0.21(122)$$

$$k = 25.62$$

Thus $t = \frac{25.62}{s}$.

Now substitute 80 for s.

$$t = \frac{25.62}{80} \approx 0.32$$

It takes about 0.32 seconds for the ball to hit the ground in the service box.

65. The equation is $d = ks^2$. To find k, substitute 40 for s and 60 for d.

$d = ks^2$

$60 = k(40)^2$

$60 = 1600k$

$k = \dfrac{60}{1600} = 0.0375$

Thus $d = 0.0375s^2$. Now substitute 56 for s.

$d = 0.0375s^2$

$d = 0.0375(56)^2$

$d = 117.6$

The stopping distance is 117.6 feet.

67. The equation is $P = krm$. To find k, substitute 50,000 for m and 0.07 for r and 332.5 for P.

$332.5 = k(0.07)(50,000)$

$332.5 = 3500k$

$k = \dfrac{332.5}{3500} = 0.095$

Thus $P = 0.095rm$.

Now substitute 66,000 for m and 0.07 for r.

$P = 0.095(0.07)(66,000)$

$P = 438.9$

The payment is $438.90.

69. The equation is $R = \dfrac{kA}{P}$. To find k, substitute 400 for A, 2 for P, and 4600 for R.

$4600 = \dfrac{k(400)}{2}$

$4600 = 200k$

$k = \dfrac{4600}{200} = 23$

Thus $R = \dfrac{23A}{P}$. Now substitute 500 for A and 2.50 for P.

$R = \dfrac{23(500)}{2.50}$

$R = \dfrac{11,500}{2.50}$

$R = 4600$ tapes

They would rent 4600 tapes per week.

71. The equation is $R = \dfrac{kL}{A}$. To find k, substitute 0.2 for R, 200 for L, and 0.05 for A.

$0.02 = \dfrac{k(200)}{0.05}$

$0.2 = k(4000)$

$\dfrac{0.2}{4000} = k$

$0.00005 = k$

Thus $R = \dfrac{0.00005L}{A}$. Now substitute 5000 for L and 0.01 for A.

$R = \dfrac{0.00005(5000)}{0.01}$

$R = \dfrac{0.25}{0.01}$

$R = 25$

The resistance is 25 ohms.

73. The equation is $W = \dfrac{kTA\sqrt{F}}{R}$

To find k, substitute 78 for T, 5.6 for R, 4 for F, 1000 for A, and 68 for W.

$68 = \dfrac{k(78)(1000)\sqrt{4}}{5.6}$

$68 = \dfrac{156,000k}{5.6}$

$\dfrac{(68)(5.6)}{156,000} = k$

$0.002441 \approx k$

Thus $W = \dfrac{0.002441TA\sqrt{E}}{R}$

Now, substitute 78 for T, 5.6 for R, 6 for E, and 1500 for A.

$W = \dfrac{0.002441(78)(1500)\sqrt{6}}{5.6} \approx 124.92$

The water bill is about $124.92.

75. a. The equation is $F = \dfrac{km_1 m_2}{d^2}$.

    b. If m_1 becomes $2m_1$, m_2 becomes $3m_2$ and d becomes $\dfrac{d}{2}$, then

$$F = \dfrac{k(2m_1)(3m_2)}{\left(\dfrac{d}{2}\right)^2}$$

$$= \dfrac{6km_1 m_2}{\dfrac{d^2}{4}}$$

$$= 24\dfrac{km_1 m_2}{d^2}$$

The new force is 24 times the original force.

77. $V = \frac{4}{3}\pi r^2 h$

$3(V) = 3\left(\frac{4}{3}\pi r^2 h\right)$

$3V = 4\pi r^2 h$

$\frac{3V}{4\pi r^2} = \frac{4\pi r^2 h}{4\pi r^2}$

$\frac{3V}{4\pi r^2} = h \implies h = \frac{3V}{4\pi r^2}$

79.

$$
\begin{array}{r}
-2x^2 - 4x + 1 \\
7x - 3 \\
\hline
6x^2 + 12x - 3 \\
-14x^3 - 28x^2 + 7x \\
\hline
-14x^3 - 22x^2 + 19x - 3
\end{array}
$$

Review Exercises

1. $\frac{3}{x-5}$

The excluded value is 5.

2. $\frac{x}{x+2}$

The excluded value is –2.

3. $\frac{-2x}{x^2+9}$

There are no values for which $x^2 + 9 = 0$
Thus, there are no excluded values.

4. $y = \frac{5}{(x+1)^2}$

$x + 1 = 0$

$x = -1$

The domain is $\{x | x \text{ is a real number and } x \neq -1\}$.

5. $f(x) = \frac{x+6}{x^2}$

$x^2 = 0$

$x = 0$

The domain is $\{x | x \text{ is a real number and } x \neq 0\}$.

6. $f(x) = \frac{x^2 - 2}{x^2 + 3x - 10}$

$x^2 + 3x - 10 = 0$

$(x+5)(x-2) = 0$

$x + 5 = 0$ or $x - 2 = 0$

$x = -5 \qquad x = 2$

The domain is
$\{x | x \text{ is a real number and } x \neq -5 \text{ and } x \neq 2\}$.

7. $\frac{x^2 + xy}{x+y} = \frac{x(x+y)}{x+y} = \frac{x}{1} = x$

8. $\frac{x^2 - 49}{x+7} = \frac{(x+7)(x-7)}{x+7} = x - 7$

9. $\frac{6 - 5x}{5x - 6} = \frac{-(5x-6)}{5x-6} = -1$

10. $\frac{x^2 + 3x - 4}{x^2 + 2x - 8} = \frac{(x+4)(x-1)}{(x+4)(x-2)} = \frac{x-1}{x-2}$

11. $\frac{2x^2 - 6x + 5x - 15}{2x^2 + 7x + 5} = \frac{2x(x-3) + 5(x-3)}{(2x+5)(x+1)}$

$= \frac{(2x+5)(x-3)}{(2x+5)(x+1)}$

$= \frac{x-3}{x+1}$

12. $\frac{a^3 - 8b^3}{a^2 - 4b^2}$

$= \frac{(a-2b)(a^2 + 2ab + 4b^2)}{(a-2b)(a+2b)}$

$= \frac{a^2 + 2ab + 4b^2}{a + 2b}$

13. $\frac{27x^3 - y^3}{9x^2 - y^2} = \frac{(3x)^3 - (y)^3}{(3x)^2 - (y)^2}$

$= \frac{(3x - y)\left((3x)^2 + (3x)(y) + (y)^2\right)}{(3x + y)(3x - y)}$

$= \frac{(3x - y)\left(9x^2 + 3xy + y^2\right)}{(3x + y)(3x - y)}$

$= \frac{\left(9x^2 + 3xy + y^2\right)}{(3x + y)}$

14.
$$\frac{2x^2+x-6}{x^3+8}=\frac{(2x-3)(x+2)}{(x+2)(x^2-2x+4)}$$
$$=\frac{(2x-3)}{(x^2-2x+4)}$$

15. Factor denominators: $x+1$ is $x+1$
$$x \text{ is } x.$$
The LCD is $x(x+1)$.

16. Factor denominators: $x+2y$ is $x+2y$

$$x^2-4y^2=(x+2y)(x-2y)$$
The LCD is $(x+2y)(x-2y)$.

17. Factor denominators:
$$x^2+2x-35=(x+7)(x-5)$$
$$x^2+9x+14=(x+7)(x+2)$$
The LCD is $(x+7)(x-5)(x+2)$.

18. Factor denominators: $(x+2)^2=(x+2)(x+2)$

The LCD is $(x+2)^2(x-2)(x+1)$.

19.
$$\frac{15x^2y^3}{3z}\cdot\frac{6z^3}{5xy^3}=\frac{6xz^2}{1}=6xz^2$$

20.
$$\frac{x}{x-7}\cdot\frac{7-x}{4}=\frac{x}{x-7}\cdot\frac{-(x-7)}{4}=\frac{-x}{4} \text{ or } -\frac{x}{4}$$

21.
$$\frac{16x^2y^4}{xz^5}\div\frac{2x^2y^4}{x^4z^{10}}=\frac{16x^2y^4}{xz^5}\cdot\frac{x^4z^{10}}{2x^2y^4}=8x^3z^5$$

22.
$$\frac{7}{3x}+\frac{2}{x^2}=\frac{7\cdot x}{3x\cdot x}+\frac{2\cdot3}{x^2\cdot3}$$
$$=\frac{7x}{3x^2}+\frac{6}{3x^2}$$
$$=\frac{7x+6}{3x^2}$$

23.
$$\frac{4x-4y}{x^2y}\cdot\frac{y^3}{8x}=\frac{4(x-y)}{x^2y}\cdot\frac{y^3}{8x}=\frac{(x-y)y^2}{2x^3}$$

24.
$$\frac{4x^2-11x+4}{x-3}-\frac{x^2-4x+10}{x-3}$$
$$=\frac{4x^2-11x+4-(x^2-4x+10)}{x-3}$$
$$=\frac{4x^2-11x+4-x^2+4x-10}{x-3}$$
$$=\frac{3x^2-7x-6}{x-3}$$
$$=\frac{(3x+2)(x-3)}{x-3}$$
$$=3x+2$$

25.
$$\frac{2}{xy}+\frac{3y}{5x^2}=\frac{2\cdot5x}{xy\cdot5x}+\frac{3y\cdot y}{5x^2\cdot y}$$
$$=\frac{10x}{5x^2y}+\frac{3y^2}{5x^2y}$$
$$=\frac{10x+3y^2}{5x^2y}$$

26.
$$\frac{x+2}{x-1}\cdot\frac{x^2+3x-4}{x^2+6x+8}=\frac{x+2}{x-1}\cdot\frac{(x+4)(x-1)}{(x+4)(x+2)}$$
$$=1$$

27.
$$\frac{3x^2-7x+4}{3x^2-14x-5}-\frac{x^2+2x+9}{3x^2-14x-5}$$
$$=\frac{(3x^2-7x+4)-(x^2+2x+9)}{3x^2-14x-5}$$
$$=\frac{3x^2-7x+4-x^2-2x-9}{3x^2-14x-5}$$
$$=\frac{2x^2-9x-5}{3x^2-14x-5}$$
$$=\frac{(2x+1)(x-5)}{(3x+1)(x-5)}$$
$$=\frac{2x+1}{3x+1}$$

28.
$$3+\frac{a+2}{a+1}=\frac{3}{1}\cdot\frac{a+1}{a+1}+\frac{a+2}{a+1}$$
$$=\frac{3(a+1)}{a+1}+\frac{a+2}{a+1}$$
$$=\frac{3a+3}{a+1}+\frac{a+2}{a+1}$$
$$=\frac{3a+3+a+2}{a+1}$$
$$=\frac{4a+5}{a+1}$$

29.
$$7 - \frac{b+1}{b-1} = \frac{7}{1} \cdot \frac{b-1}{b-1} - \frac{b+1}{b-1}$$
$$= \frac{7(b-1)}{b-1} - \frac{b+1}{b-1}$$
$$= \frac{7b-7}{b-1} - \frac{b+1}{b-1}$$
$$= \frac{7b-7-b-1}{b-1}$$
$$= \frac{6b-8}{b-1}$$

30.
$$\frac{a^2-b^2}{a+b} \cdot \frac{a^2+2ab+b^2}{a^3+a^2b}$$
$$= \frac{(a+b)(a-b)}{a+b} \cdot \frac{(a+b)^2}{a^2(a+b)}$$
$$= \frac{(a-b)(a+b)}{a^2}$$
$$= \frac{a^2-b^2}{a^2}$$

31.
$$\frac{1}{a^2+8a+15} \div \frac{3}{a+5} = \frac{1}{a^2+8a+15} \cdot \frac{a+5}{3}$$
$$= \frac{1}{(a+5)(a+3)} \cdot \frac{a+5}{3}$$
$$= \frac{1}{3(a+3)}$$

32.
$$\frac{a+c}{c} - \frac{a-c}{a} = \frac{a+c}{c} \cdot \frac{a}{a} - \frac{a-c}{a} \cdot \frac{c}{c}$$
$$= \frac{a(a+c)}{ac} - \frac{c(a-c)}{ac}$$
$$= \frac{a^2+ac}{ac} - \frac{ac-c^2}{ac}$$
$$= \frac{a^2+ac-(ac-c^2)}{ac}$$
$$= \frac{a^2+ac-ac+c^2}{ac}$$
$$= \frac{a^2+c^2}{ac}$$

33.
$$\frac{4x^2+8x-5}{2x+5} \cdot \frac{x+1}{4x^2-4x+1}$$
$$= \frac{(2x-1)(2x+5)}{2x+5} \cdot \frac{x+1}{(2x-1)(2x-1)}$$
$$= \frac{x+1}{2x-1}$$

34.
$$(a+b) \div \frac{a^2-2ab-3b^2}{a-3b}$$
$$= \frac{a+b}{1} \cdot \frac{a-3b}{a^2-2ab-3b^2}$$
$$= \frac{a+b}{1} \cdot \frac{a-3b}{(a-3b)(a+b)}$$
$$= 1$$

35.
$$\frac{x^2-3xy-10y^2}{6x} \div \frac{x+2y}{12x^2}$$
$$= \frac{x^2-3xy-10y^2}{6x} \cdot \frac{12x^2}{x+2y}$$
$$= \frac{(x+2y)(x-5y)}{6x} \cdot \frac{12x^2}{x+2y}$$
$$= 2x(x-5y)$$

36.
$$\frac{a+1}{2a} + \frac{3}{4a+8} = \frac{a+1}{2a} + \frac{3}{4(a+2)}$$
$$= \frac{a+1}{2a} \cdot \frac{2(a+2)}{2(a+2)} + \frac{3}{4(a+2)} \cdot \frac{a}{a}$$
$$= \frac{2(a+1)(a+2)}{4a(a+2)} + \frac{3a}{4a(a+2)}$$
$$= \frac{2a^2+6a+4}{4a(a+2)} + \frac{3a}{4a(a+2)}$$
$$= \frac{2a^2+6a+4+3a}{4a(a+2)}$$
$$= \frac{2a^2+9a+4}{4a(a+2)}$$

37.
$$\frac{x-4}{x-5} - \frac{3}{x+5} = \frac{x-4}{x-5} \cdot \frac{x+5}{x+5} - \frac{3}{x+5} \cdot \frac{x-5}{x-5}$$
$$= \frac{(x-4)(x+5)}{(x-5)(x+5)} - \frac{3(x-5)}{(x-5)(x+5)}$$
$$= \frac{x^2+x-20}{(x-5)(x+5)} - \frac{3x-15}{(x-5)(x+5)}$$
$$= \frac{x^2+x-20-(3x-15)}{(x-5)(x+5)}$$
$$= \frac{x^2-2x-5}{(x-5)(x+5)}$$

38.
$$\frac{x+4}{x^2-4} - \frac{3}{x-2} = \frac{x+4}{(x+2)(x-2)} - \frac{3}{x-2}$$
$$= \frac{x+4}{(x+2)(x-2)} - \frac{3}{x-2} \cdot \frac{x+2}{x+2}$$
$$= \frac{x+4}{(x+2)(x-2)} - \frac{3(x+2)}{(x-2)(x+2)}$$
$$= \frac{x+4}{(x+2)(x-2)} - \frac{3x+6}{(x-2)(x+2)}$$
$$= \frac{x+4-3x-6}{(x+2)(x-2)}$$
$$= \frac{-2x-2}{(x+2)(x-2)} \text{ or } -\frac{2(x+1)}{x^2-4}$$

39.
$$\frac{x+1}{x-3} \cdot \frac{x^2+2x-15}{x^2+7x+6} = \frac{x+1}{x-3} \cdot \frac{(x+5)(x-3)}{(x+6)(x+1)}$$
$$= \frac{x+5}{x+6}$$

40.
$$\frac{1}{x^2-x-6} - \frac{1}{x^2-4}$$
$$= \frac{1}{(x+2)(x-3)} - \frac{1}{(x-2)(x+2)}$$
$$= \frac{1}{(x+2)(x-3)} \cdot \frac{x-2}{x-2} - \frac{1}{(x+2)(x-2)} \cdot \frac{x-3}{x-3}$$
$$= \frac{x-2}{(x+2)(x-3)(x-2)} - \frac{x-3}{(x+2)(x-3)(x-2)}$$
$$= \frac{x-2-x+3}{(x+2)(x-3)(x-2)}$$
$$= \frac{1}{(x+2)(x-3)(x-2)}$$

41.
$$\frac{4x^2-16y^2}{9} \div \frac{(x+2y)^2}{12}$$
$$= \frac{4x^2-16y^2}{9} \cdot \frac{12}{(x+2y)^2}$$
$$= \frac{4(x+2y)(x-2y)}{9} \cdot \frac{12}{(x+2y)(x+2y)}$$
$$= \frac{16(x-2y)}{3(x+2y)}$$

42.
$$\frac{a^2+5a+6}{a^2+4a+4} \cdot \frac{3a+6}{a^4+3a^3}$$
$$= \frac{(a+3)(a+2)}{(a+2)^2} \cdot \frac{3(a+2)}{a^3(a+3)}$$
$$= \frac{3}{a^3}$$

43.
$$\frac{x+5}{x^2-15x+50} - \frac{x-2}{x^2-25}$$
$$= \frac{x+5}{(x-5)(x-10)} - \frac{x-2}{(x-5)(x+5)}$$

$$= \frac{x+5}{(x-5)(x-10)} \cdot \frac{x+5}{x+5} - \frac{x-2}{(x-5)(x+5)} \cdot \frac{x-10}{x-10}$$
$$= \frac{(x+5)(x+5)}{(x-5)(x-10)(x+5)} - \frac{(x-2)(x-10)}{(x-5)(x-10)(x+5)}$$
$$= \frac{x^2+10x+25}{(x-5)(x-10)(x+5)} - \frac{x^2-12x+20}{(x-5)(x-10)(x+5)}$$
$$= \frac{x^2+10x+25-(x^2-12x+20)}{(x-5)(x-10)(x+5)}$$
$$= \frac{x^2+10x+25-x^2+12x-20}{(x-5)(x-10)(x+5)}$$
$$= \frac{22x+5}{(x-5)(x-10)(x+5)}$$

44.
$$\frac{x+2}{x^2-x-6} + \frac{x-3}{x^2-8x+15}$$
$$= \frac{x+2}{(x+2)(x-3)} + \frac{x-3}{(x-3)(x-5)}$$
$$= \frac{1}{x-3} + \frac{1}{x-5}$$
$$= \frac{1}{x-3} \cdot \frac{x-5}{x-5} + \frac{1}{x-5} \cdot \frac{x-3}{x-3}$$
$$= \frac{x-5}{(x-3)(x-5)} + \frac{x-3}{(x-3)(x-5)}$$
$$= \frac{x-5+x-3}{(x-3)(x-5)}$$
$$= \frac{2x-8}{(x-3)(x-5)} \text{ or } \frac{2(x-4)}{(x-3)(x-5)}$$

45.
$$\frac{1}{x+3} - \frac{2}{x-3} + \frac{6}{x^2-9}$$
$$= \frac{1}{x+3} - \frac{2}{x-3} + \frac{6}{(x+3)(x-3)}$$
$$= \frac{1}{x+3} \cdot \frac{x-3}{x-3} - \frac{2}{x-3} \cdot \frac{x+3}{x+3} + \frac{6}{(x+3)(x-3)}$$
$$= \frac{x-3}{(x+3)(x-3)} - \frac{2(x+3)}{(x+3)(x-3)} + \frac{6}{(x+3)(x-3)}$$
$$= \frac{x-3}{(x+3)(x-3)} - \frac{2x+6}{(x+3)(x-3)} + \frac{6}{(x+3)(x-3)}$$
$$= \frac{x-3-(2x+6)+6}{(x+3)(x-3)}$$
$$= \frac{x-3-2x-6+6}{(x+3)(x-3)}$$
$$= \frac{-x-3}{(x+3)(x-3)}$$
$$= \frac{-(x+3)}{(x+3)(x-3)}$$
$$= \frac{-1}{x-3} \text{ or } -\frac{1}{x-3}$$

46. $\dfrac{a-4}{a-5} - \dfrac{3}{a+5} - \dfrac{10}{a^2-25}$

$= \dfrac{a-4}{a-5} - \dfrac{3}{a+5} - \dfrac{10}{(a+5)(a-5)}$

$= \dfrac{a-4}{a-5} \cdot \dfrac{a+5}{a+5} - \dfrac{3}{a+5} \cdot \dfrac{a-5}{a-5} - \dfrac{10}{(a+5)(a-5)}$

$= \dfrac{(a-4)(a+5)}{(a+5)(a-5)} - \dfrac{3(a-5)}{(a+5)(a-5)} - \dfrac{10}{(a+5)(a-5)}$

$= \dfrac{a^2+a-20}{(a+5)(a-5)} - \dfrac{3a-15}{(a+5)(a-5)} - \dfrac{10}{(a+5)(a-5)}$

$= \dfrac{a^2+a-20-(3a-15)-10}{(a+5)(a-5)}$

$= \dfrac{a^2+a-20-3a+15-10}{(a+5)(a-5)}$

$= \dfrac{a^2-2a-15}{(a+5)(a-5)}$

$= \dfrac{(a+3)(a-5)}{(a+5)(a-5)}$

$= \dfrac{a+3}{a+5}$

47. $\dfrac{x^3+64}{2x^2-32} \div \dfrac{x^2-4x+16}{2x+12}$

$= \dfrac{x^3+64}{2x^2-32} \cdot \dfrac{2x+12}{x^2-4x+16}$

$= \dfrac{(x+4)(x^2-4x+16)}{2(x-4)(x+4)} \cdot \dfrac{2(x+6)}{x^2-4x+16}$

$= \dfrac{x+6}{x-4}$

48. $\dfrac{a^2-b^4}{a^2+2ab+b^4} \div \dfrac{3a-3b^2}{a^2+3ab^2+2b^4}$

$= \dfrac{\left(a+b^2\right)\left(a-b^2\right)}{\left(a+b^2\right)^2} \cdot \dfrac{\left(a+2b^2\right)\left(a+b^2\right)}{3\left(a-b^2\right)}$

$= \dfrac{a+2b^2}{3}$

49. $\left(\dfrac{x^2-x-56}{x^2+14x+49} \cdot \dfrac{x^2+4x-21}{x^2-9x+8}\right) + \dfrac{3}{x^2+8x-9}$

$= \left(\dfrac{(x-8)(x+7)}{(x+7)(x+7)} \cdot \dfrac{(x+7)(x-3)}{(x-8)(x-1)}\right) + \dfrac{3}{(x-1)(x+9)}$

$= \dfrac{x-3}{x-1} + \dfrac{3}{(x-1)(x+9)}$

$= \dfrac{x-3}{x-1} \cdot \dfrac{x+9}{x+9} + \dfrac{3}{(x-1)(x+9)}$

$= \dfrac{(x-3)(x+9)}{(x-1)(x+9)} + \dfrac{3}{(x-1)(x+9)}$

$= \dfrac{x^2+6x-27}{(x-1)(x+9)} + \dfrac{3}{(x-1)(x+9)}$

$= \dfrac{x^2+6x-27+3}{(x-1)(x+9)}$

$= \dfrac{x^2+6x-24}{(x-1)(x+9)}$

50. $\left(\dfrac{x^2-8x+16}{2x^2-x-6} \cdot \dfrac{2x^2-7x-15}{x^2-2x-24}\right) \div \dfrac{x^2-9x+20}{x^2+2x-8}$

$= \left(\dfrac{x^2-8x+16}{2x^2-x-6} \cdot \dfrac{2x^2-7x-15}{x^2-2x-24}\right) \cdot \dfrac{x^2+2x-8}{x^2-9x+20}$

$= \dfrac{(x-4)(x-4)}{(2x+3)(x-2)} \cdot \dfrac{(2x+3)(x-5)}{(x-6)(x+4)} \cdot \dfrac{(x+4)(x-2)}{(x-5)(x-4)}$

$= \dfrac{x-4}{x-6}$

51. a. $f(x) = \dfrac{x+1}{x+2}$

The denominator cannot equal zero.
Therefore $x \neq -2$.
The domain is
$\{x | x \text{ is a real number, } x \neq -2\}$

b. $g(x) = \dfrac{x}{x+4}$

The denominator cannot equal zero.
Therefore, $x \neq -4$.
The domain is
$\{x | x \text{ is a real number, } x \neq -4\}$

c. $(f+g)(x) = f(x) + g(x)$

$= \dfrac{x+1}{x+2} + \dfrac{x}{x+4}$

$= \dfrac{x+1}{x+2} \cdot \dfrac{x+4}{x+4} + \dfrac{x}{x+4} \cdot \dfrac{x+2}{x+2}$

$= \dfrac{(x+1)(x+4) + x(x+2)}{(x+2)(x+4)}$

$= \dfrac{x^2+5x+4+x^2+2x}{(x+2)(x+4)}$

$= \dfrac{2x^2+7x+4}{(x+2)(x+4)}$

d. The denominator cannot equal zero.
Therefore, $x \neq -2$, $x \neq -4$.
The domain is
$\{x | x \text{ is a real number, } x \neq -2, x \neq -4\}$

52. a. $f(x) = \dfrac{x}{x^2 - 9}$ or $f(x) = \dfrac{x}{(x+3)(x-3)}$

The denominator cannot equal zero.
Therefore, $x \neq -3$, $x \neq 3$.
The domain is
$\{x | x$ is a real number, $x \neq -3, x \neq 3\}$

b. $g(x) = \dfrac{x+4}{x-3}$

The denominator cannot equal zero.
Therefore, $x \neq 3$.
The domain is $\{x | x$ is a real number, $x \neq 3\}$

c. $(f + g)(x) = f(x) + g(x)$

$= \dfrac{x}{x^2 - 9} + \dfrac{x+4}{x-3}$

$= \dfrac{x}{(x-3)(x+3)} + \dfrac{(x+4)}{(x-3)} \cdot \dfrac{(x+3)}{(x+3)}$

$= \dfrac{x + (x+4)(x+3)}{(x-3)(x+3)}$

$= \dfrac{x + x^2 + 7x + 12}{(x-3)(x+3)}$

$= \dfrac{x^2 + 8x + 12}{(x-3)(x+3)}$

d. The denominator cannot equal zero.
Therefore, $x \neq -3$ and $x \neq 3$.
The domain is
$\{x | x$ is a real number, $x \neq -3, x \neq 3\}$

53. $\dfrac{\frac{9a^2 b}{2c}}{\frac{6ab^4}{4c^3}} = \dfrac{9a^2 b}{2c} \cdot \dfrac{4c^3}{6ab^4} = \dfrac{3ac^2}{b^3}$

54. $\dfrac{\frac{1}{x} + \frac{1}{y}}{\frac{x}{y} + y^2} = \dfrac{xy\left(\frac{1}{x} + \frac{1}{y}\right)}{xy\left(\frac{x}{y} + y^2\right)} = \dfrac{x+y}{x^2 + xy^3}$

55. $\dfrac{\frac{3}{y} - \frac{1}{y^2}}{5 + \frac{1}{y^2}} = \dfrac{y^2\left(\frac{3}{y} - \frac{1}{y^2}\right)}{y^2\left(5 + \frac{1}{y^2}\right)}$

$= \dfrac{y^2\left(\frac{3}{y}\right) - y^2\left(\frac{1}{y^2}\right)}{y^2(5) + y^2\left(\frac{1}{y^2}\right)}$

$= \dfrac{3y - 1}{5y^2 + 1}$

56. $\dfrac{a^{-1} + 2}{a^{-1} + \frac{1}{a}} = \dfrac{\frac{1}{a} + 2}{\frac{1}{a} + \frac{1}{a}}$

$= \dfrac{\frac{1}{a} + 2}{\frac{2}{a}}$

$= \left(\dfrac{1}{a} + 2\right)\left(\dfrac{a}{2}\right)$

$= \dfrac{\left(\frac{1}{a} + 2\right)a}{2}$

$= \dfrac{1 + 2a}{2}$

57. $\dfrac{x^{-2} + \frac{1}{x}}{\frac{1}{x^2} - \frac{1}{x}} = \dfrac{\frac{1}{x^2} + \frac{1}{x}}{\frac{1}{x^2} - \frac{1}{x}}$

$= \dfrac{x^2\left(\frac{1}{x^2} + \frac{1}{x}\right)}{x^2\left(\frac{1}{x^2} - \frac{1}{x}\right)}$

$= \dfrac{x^2\left(\frac{1}{x^2}\right) + x^2\left(\frac{1}{x}\right)}{x^2\left(\frac{1}{x^2}\right) - x^2\left(\frac{1}{x}\right)}$

$= \dfrac{1+x}{1-x}$ or $\dfrac{x+1}{-x+1}$

58. $\dfrac{\frac{1}{x^2 - 3x - 18} + \frac{2}{x^2 - 2x - 15}}{\frac{3}{x^2 - 11x + 30} + \frac{1}{x^2 - 9x + 20}}$

$= \dfrac{\frac{1}{(x-6)(x+3)} + \frac{2}{(x+3)(x-5)}}{\frac{3}{(x-5)(x-6)} + \frac{1}{(x-5)(x-4)}}$

$= \dfrac{\frac{(x-5) + 2(x-6)}{(x-6)(x+3)(x-5)}}{\frac{3(x-4) + 1(x-6)}{(x-5)(x-6)(x-4)}}$

$= \dfrac{x - 5 + 2x - 12}{(x-6)(x+3)(x-5)} \cdot \dfrac{(x-5)(x-6)(x-4)}{3x - 12 + x - 6}$

$= \dfrac{(3x - 17)(x - 4)}{(4x - 18)(x + 3)}$

$= \dfrac{3x^2 - 29x + 68}{4x^2 - 6x - 54}$

59. $l = A \div w$

$$l = \frac{x^2 + 5x + 6}{x+4} \div \frac{x^2 + 8x + 15}{x^2 + 5x + 4}$$

$$= \frac{x^2 + 5x + 6}{x+4} \cdot \frac{x^2 + 5x + 4}{x^2 + 8x + 15}$$

$$= \frac{(x+3)(x+2)}{x+4} \cdot \frac{(x+4)(x+1)}{(x+5)(x+3)}$$

$$= \frac{(x+2)(x+1)}{x+5}$$

$$= \frac{x^2 + 3x + 2}{x+5}$$

60. $l = A \div w$

$$l = \frac{x^2 + 10x + 24}{x+5} \div \frac{x^2 + 9x + 18}{x^2 + 7x + 10}$$

$$= \frac{x^2 + 10x + 24}{x+5} \cdot \frac{x^2 + 7x + 10}{x^2 + 9x + 18}$$

$$= \frac{(x+6)(x+4)}{x+5} \cdot \frac{(x+5)(x+2)}{(x+6)(x+3)}$$

$$= \frac{(x+4)(x+2)}{x+3}$$

$$= \frac{x^2 + 6x + 8}{x+3}$$

61. $\dfrac{2}{x} = \dfrac{5}{9}$

$$5x = 2 \cdot 9$$

$$5x = 18$$

$$x = \frac{18}{5} \text{ or } 3\frac{3}{5}$$

This solution checks. The solution is $\frac{18}{5}$ or $3\frac{3}{5}$.

62. $\dfrac{x}{1.5} = \dfrac{x-4}{4.5}$

$$4.5x = 1.5(x-4)$$

$$4.5x = 1.5x - 6$$

$$3x = -6$$

$$x = -2$$

This solution checks. The solution is –2.

63. $\dfrac{3x+4}{5} = \dfrac{2x-8}{3}$

$$3(3x+4) = 5(2x-8)$$

$$9x + 12 = 10x - 40$$

$$9x + 52 = 10x$$

$$52 = x$$

This solution checks. The solution is 52.

64. $\dfrac{x}{4.8} + \dfrac{x}{2} = 1.7$

$$9.6\left(\frac{x}{4.8}\right) + 9.6\left(\frac{x}{2}\right) = 9.6(1.7)$$

$$2x + 4.8x = 16.32$$

$$6.8x = 16.32$$

$$x = \frac{16.32}{6.8} = 2.4$$

This solution checks. The solution is 2.4.

65. $\dfrac{2}{y} + \dfrac{1}{5} = \dfrac{3}{y}$

$$5y\left(\frac{2}{y}\right) + 5y\left(\frac{1}{5}\right) = 5y\left(\frac{3}{y}\right)$$

$$10 + y = 15$$

$$y = 5$$

This solution checks. The solution is 5.

66.
$$\frac{2}{x+4} - \frac{3}{x-4} = \frac{-11}{x^2 - 16}$$

$$\frac{2}{x+4} - \frac{3}{x-4} = \frac{-11}{(x+4)(x-4)}$$

$$(x+4)(x-4)\left(\frac{2}{x+4}\right) - (x+4)(x-4)\left(\frac{3}{x-4}\right) = (x+4)(x-4)\left(\frac{-11}{(x+4)(x-4)}\right)$$

$$2(x-4) - 3(x+4) = -11$$

$$2x - 8 - 3x - 12 = -11$$

$$-x - 20 = -11$$

$$-x = 9$$

$$x = -9$$

This solution checks. The solution is –9.

67.

$$\frac{x}{x^2-9}+\frac{2}{x+3}=\frac{4}{x-3}$$

$$\frac{x}{(x+3)(x-3)}+\frac{2}{x+3}=\frac{4}{x-3}$$

$$(x+3)(x-3)\left(\frac{x}{(x+3)(x-3)}\right)+(x+3)(x-3)\left(\frac{2}{x+3}\right)=(x+3)(x-3)\left(\frac{4}{x-3}\right)$$

$$x+2(x-3)=4(x+3)$$
$$x+2x-6=4x+12$$
$$3x-6=4x+12$$
$$-6=x+12$$
$$-18=x$$

This solution checks. The solution is −18.

68.

$$\frac{7}{x^2-25}+\frac{3}{x+5}=\frac{4}{x-5}$$

$$\frac{7}{(x+5)(x-5)}+\frac{3}{x+5}=\frac{4}{x-5}$$

$$(x+5)(x-5)\left(\frac{7}{(x+5)(x-5)}\right)+(x+5)(x-5)\left(\frac{3}{x+5}\right)=(x+5)(x-5)\left(\frac{4}{x-5}\right)$$

$$7+3(x-5)=4(x+5)$$
$$7+3x-15=4x+20$$
$$3x-8=4x+20$$
$$-8=x+20$$
$$-28=x$$

This solution checks. The solution is −28.

69.

$$\frac{x-3}{x-2}+\frac{x+1}{x+3}=\frac{2x^2+x+1}{x^2+x-6}$$

$$\frac{x-3}{x-2}+\frac{x+1}{x+3}=\frac{2x^2+x+1}{(x+3)(x-2)}$$

$$(x+3)(x-2)\left(\frac{x-3}{x-2}\right)+(x+3)(x-2)\left(\frac{x+1}{x+3}\right)=(x+3)(x-2)\left(\frac{2x^2+x+1}{(x+3)(x-2)}\right)$$

$$(x+3)(x-3)+(x-2)(x+1)=2x^2+x+1$$
$$x^2-9+x^2-x-2=2x^2+x+1$$
$$2x^2-x-11=2x^2+x+1$$
$$-x-11=x+1$$
$$-11=2x+1$$
$$-12=2x$$
$$-6=x$$

This solution checks. The solution is −6.

70.

$$\frac{x+1}{x+3}+\frac{x+2}{x-4}=\frac{2x^2-18}{x^2-x-12}$$

$$\frac{x+1}{x+3}+\frac{x+2}{x-4}=\frac{2x^2-18}{(x+3)(x-4)}$$

$$(x+3)(x-4)\left(\frac{x+1}{x+3}\right)+(x+3)(x-4)\left(\frac{x+2}{x-4}\right)=(x+3)(x-4)\left(\frac{2x^2-18}{(x+3)(x-4)}\right)$$

$$(x-4)(x+1)+(x+3)(x+2)=2x^2-18$$

$$x^2-3x-4+x^2+5x+6=2x^2-18$$

$$2x^2+2x+2=2x^2-18$$

$$2x+2=-18$$

$$2x=-20$$

$$x=-10$$

This solution checks. The solution is -10.

71.

$$\frac{1}{a}+\frac{1}{b}=\frac{1}{c}$$

$$abc\cdot\frac{1}{a}+abc\cdot\frac{1}{b}=abc\cdot\frac{1}{c}$$

$$bc+ac=ab$$

$$ac=ab-bc$$

$$ac=b(a-c)$$

$$\frac{ac}{a-c}=\frac{b(a-c)}{a-c}$$

$$\frac{ac}{a-c}=b \text{ or } b=\frac{ac}{a-c}$$

72.

$$z=\frac{x-\bar{x}}{s}$$

$$zs=x-\bar{x}$$

$$zs-x=-\bar{x}$$

$$-zs+x=\bar{x} \text{ or } \bar{x}=x-sz$$

73.

$$\frac{1}{R_T}=\frac{1}{R_1}+\frac{1}{R_2}+\frac{1}{R_3}$$

Substitute 100 for R_1, 200 for R_2, and 600 for R_3.

$$\frac{1}{R_T}=\frac{1}{100}+\frac{1}{200}+\frac{1}{600}$$

$$600R_T\left(\frac{1}{R_T}\right)=600R_T\left(\frac{1}{100}\right)+600R_T\left(\frac{1}{200}\right)+600R_T\left(\frac{1}{600}\right)$$

$$600=6R_T+3R_T+R_T$$

$$600=10R_T$$

$$\frac{600}{10}=R_T$$

$$R_T=60$$

The total resistance is 60 ohms.

74. $\dfrac{1}{p}+\dfrac{1}{q}=\dfrac{1}{f}$

$\dfrac{1}{6}+\dfrac{1}{2}=\dfrac{1}{f}$

$\dfrac{1}{6}+\dfrac{3}{6}=\dfrac{1}{f}$

$\dfrac{4}{6}=\dfrac{1}{f}$

$\dfrac{2}{3}=\dfrac{1}{f}$

$2f=3$

$f=\dfrac{3}{2}$ or 1.5

The focal length is 1.5 centimeters.

75. $\dfrac{2x}{5}=\dfrac{4}{x-3}$

$(2x)(x-3)=(5)(4)$

$2x^2-6x=20$

$2x^2-6x-20=0$

$2\left(x^2-3x-10\right)=0$

$2(x-5)(x+2)=0$

$x-5=0$ or $x+2=0$

$x=5 \qquad x=-2$

The negative value of x produces negative lengths so we may disregard this value of x. Therefore, the values for the missing sides using $x=5$ are $2(5)=10$ and $(5)-3=2$.

76. $\dfrac{2x+1}{9}=\dfrac{7}{\dfrac{x}{2}-2}$

$(2x+1)\left(\dfrac{x}{2}-2\right)=(9)(7)$

$x^2-4x+\dfrac{1}{2}x-2=63 \ \leftarrow$ multiply by 2

$2x^2-8x+x-4=126$

$2x^2-7x-130=0$

$(2x+13)(x-10)=0$

$2x+13=0$ or $x-10=0$

$x=-\dfrac{13}{2} \qquad x=10$

The negative value of x produces negative lengths so we may disregard this value of x. Therefore, the values for the missing sides using $x=10$ are $2(10)+1=21$ and $\dfrac{10}{2}-2=5-2=3$.

77. Let x be time needed for both of them to pick the string beans.

	Rate	Time Worked	Part of job completed
Jerome	$\dfrac{1}{30}$	x	$\dfrac{x}{30}$
Sanford	$\dfrac{1}{40}$	x	$\dfrac{x}{40}$

$\dfrac{x}{30}+\dfrac{x}{40}=1$

$120\left(\dfrac{x}{30}\right)+12\left(\dfrac{x}{40}\right)=120(1)$

$4x+3x=120$

$7x=120$

$x=\dfrac{120}{7}\approx 17.14$

Working together, they can pick a basket of string beans in about 17.14 minutes.

78. Let x be the time needed for Fran to plant the garden by herself.

	Rate	Time Worked	Part of job completed
Fran	$\dfrac{1}{x}$	4.2	$\dfrac{4.2}{x}$
Sam	$\dfrac{1}{6}$	4.2	$\dfrac{4.2}{6}$

$\dfrac{4.2}{6}+\dfrac{4.2}{x}=1$

$6x\left(\dfrac{4.2}{6}\right)+6x\left(\dfrac{4.2}{x}\right)=6x(1)$

$4.2x+25.2=6x$

$25.2=1.8x$

$\dfrac{25.2}{1.8}=x$

$14=x$

Working alone, it takes Fran 14 hours to plant the garden.

79. Let x be the unknown number.

$\dfrac{1+x}{11-x}=\dfrac{1}{2}$

$2(1+x)=1(11-x)$

$2+2x=11-x$

$3x=9$

$x=3$

The desired number is 3.

80. Let x be the number.

$$1 - \frac{1}{2x} = \frac{1}{3x}$$

$$6x(1) - 6x\left(\frac{1}{2x}\right) = 6x\left(\frac{1}{3x}\right)$$

$$6x - 3 = 2$$

$$6x = 5$$

$$x = \frac{5}{6}$$

The desired number is $\frac{5}{6}$.

81. Let x be the speed of the current.

	d	r	$t = \dfrac{d}{r}$
With current	20	$15 + x$	$\dfrac{20}{15 + x}$
Against current	10	$15 - x$	$\dfrac{10}{15 - x}$

The times are the same.

$$\frac{20}{15 + x} = \frac{10}{15 - x}$$

$$20(15 - x) = 10(15 + x)$$

$$300 - 20x = 150 + 10x$$

$$300 = 150 + 30x$$

$$150 = 30x$$

$$5 = x$$

The speed of the current is 5 mph.

82. Let x be the speed of the car.

	d	r	$t = \dfrac{d}{r}$
Car	450	x	$\dfrac{450}{x}$
Plane	450	$3x$	$\dfrac{450}{3x}$

$$\frac{450}{3x} + 6 = \frac{450}{x}$$

$$\frac{150}{x} + 6 = \frac{450}{x}$$

$$x\left(\frac{150}{x}\right) + x(6) = x\left(\frac{450}{x}\right)$$

$$150 + 6x = 450$$

$$6x = 300$$

$$x = \frac{300}{6} = 50$$

The speed of the car is 50 mph and the speed of the plane is $3(50) = 150$ mph.

83. The equation is $x = ky^2$. To find k, substitute 45 for x and 3 for y.

$$45 = k(3)^2$$

$$45 = 9k$$

$$\frac{45}{9} = k$$

$$5 = k$$

Thus $x = 5y^2$. Now substitute 2 for y.

$$A = 5(2)^2 = 5(4) = 20$$

84. The equation is $W = \dfrac{kL^2}{A}$. To find k, substitute 4 for W, 2 for L, and 10 for A.

$$4 = \frac{k(2)^2}{10}$$

$$4 = \frac{4k}{10}$$

$$40 = 4k$$

$$10 = k$$

Thus $W = \dfrac{10L^2}{A}$. Now substitute 5 for L and 20 for A.

$$W = \frac{10 \cdot (5)^2}{20} = \frac{250}{20} = \frac{25}{2}$$

85. The equation is $z = \dfrac{kxy}{r^2}$. To find k, substitute 12 for z, 20 for x, 8 for y, and 8 for r.

$$12 = \frac{k(20)(8)}{(8)^2}$$

$$12 = \frac{160k}{64}$$

$$12(64) = 160k$$

$$768 = 160k$$

$$\frac{768}{160} = k$$

$$k = 4.8$$

Thus $z = \dfrac{4.8xy}{r^2}$. Now substitute 10 for x, 80 for y, and 3 for r.

$$! = \frac{4.8(10)(80)}{3^2} \approx 426.7$$

Practice Test

86. Let s represent the surcharge and let E represent the energy used in kilowatt-hours. The equation is $s = kE$.

To find k, substitute 7.20 for s and 3600 for E.

$s = kE$

$7.20 = k(3600) \Rightarrow k = \dfrac{7.20}{3600} = 0.002$

Thus $s = 0.002E$. Now substitute 4200 for E.

$s = 0.002E$

$s = 0.002(4200)$

$s = 8.40$

The surcharge is $8.40.

87. The equation is $d = kt^2$. To find k, substitute 16 for d and 1 for t.

$16 = k(1)^2$

$16 = k(1)$

$16 = k$

Thus $d = 16t^2$. Now substitute 10 for t.

$d = 16(10)^2 = 16(100) = 1600$

An object will fall 1600 feet.

88. The equation is $A = kr^2$. To find k, substitute 78.5 for A and 5 for r.

$78.5 = k(5)^2$

$78.5 = k(25)$

$\dfrac{78.5}{25} = k$

$3.14 = k$

Thus $A = 3.14r^2$. Now substitute 8 for r.

$A = 3.14(8)^2$

$A = 3.14(64)$

$A = 200.96$

The area is 200.96 square units.

89. The equation is $t = \dfrac{k}{w}$ where t is time and w is water temperature. To find k, substitute 1.7 for t and 70 for w.

$1.7 = \dfrac{k}{70}$

$(1.7)(70) = k$

$119 = k$

Thus $t = \dfrac{119}{w}$. Now substitute 50 for w.

$t = \dfrac{119}{50} = 2.38$

It takes the ice cube 2.38 minutes to melt.

1. $\dfrac{x+4}{x^2+3x-28} = \dfrac{x+4}{(x-4)(x+7)}$

The denominator cannot equal zero. Therefore, the excluded values are 4 and -7.

2. $f(x) = \dfrac{x^2+7}{2x^2+7x-4} = \dfrac{x^2+7}{(2x-1)(x+4)}$

The denominator cannot equal zero. Therefore,

$2x-1 \neq 0 \qquad$ or $\qquad x+4 \neq 0$

$x \neq \dfrac{1}{2} \qquad\qquad\qquad x \neq -4$

The domain is

$\left\{ x \middle| x \text{ is a real number and } x \neq \dfrac{1}{2}, x \neq -4 \right\}$

3. $\dfrac{8x^7y^2 + 16x^2y + 18x^3y^3}{2x^2y}$

$= \dfrac{8x^7y^2}{2x^2y} + \dfrac{16x^2y}{2x^2y} + \dfrac{18x^3y^3}{2x^2y}$

$= 4x^5y + 8 + 9xy^2$

4. $\dfrac{x^2-3xy-10y^2}{x^2+3xy+2y^2} = \dfrac{(x-5y)(x+2y)}{(x+2y)(x+y)}$

$= \dfrac{x-5y}{x+y}$

5. $\dfrac{3xy^4}{6x^2y^3} \cdot \dfrac{2x^2y^4}{x^5y^7} = \dfrac{3 \cdot 2x^{1+2}y^{4+4}}{6 \cdot 1x^{2+5}y^{7+3}}$

$= \dfrac{6x^3y^8}{6x^7y^{10}}$

$= \dfrac{1}{x^4y^2}$

6. $\dfrac{x+1}{x^2-7x-8} \cdot \dfrac{x^2-x-56}{x^2+9x+14}$

$= \dfrac{x+1}{(x-8)(x+1)} \cdot \dfrac{(x-8)(x+7)}{(x+7)(x+2)}$

$= \dfrac{1}{x+2}$

7.

$$\frac{5a+10b}{a^2-4b^2} \div \frac{a^3+a^2b}{a^2-2ab}$$

$$= \frac{5a+10b}{a^2-4b^2} \cdot \frac{a^2-2ab}{a^3+a^2b}$$

$$= \frac{5(a+2b)}{(a+2b)(a-2b)} \cdot \frac{a(a-2b)}{a^2(a+b)}$$

$$= \frac{5}{a(a+b)}$$

8.

$$\frac{x^3+y^3}{x+y} \div \frac{x^2-xy+y^2}{x^2+y^2}$$

$$= \frac{x^3+y^3}{x+y} \cdot \frac{x^2+y^2}{x^2-xy+y^2}$$

$$= \frac{(x+y)(x^2-xy+y^2)}{x+y} \cdot \frac{x^2+y^2}{x^2-xy+y^2}$$

$$= x^2+y^2$$

9.

$$\frac{3}{x+1} + \frac{2}{x^2} = \frac{3}{x+1} \cdot \frac{x^2}{x^2} + \frac{2}{x^2} \cdot \frac{(x+1)}{(x+1)}$$

$$= \frac{3x^2}{x^2(x+1)} + \frac{2x+2}{x^2(x+1)}$$

$$= \frac{3x^2+2x+2}{x^2(x+1)}$$

10.

$$\frac{x-1}{x^2-9} - \frac{x}{x^2-2x-3}$$

$$= \frac{x-1}{(x+3)(x-3)} - \frac{x}{(x-3)(x+1)}$$

$$= \frac{x-1}{(x+3)(x-3)} \cdot \frac{x+1}{x+1} - \frac{x}{(x-3)(x+1)} \cdot \frac{x+3}{x+3}$$

$$= \frac{x^2-1}{(x+3)(x-3)(x+1)} - \frac{x^2+3x}{(x+3)(x-3)(x+1)}$$

$$= \frac{x^2-1-x^2-3x}{(x+3)(x-3)(x+1)}$$

$$= \frac{-3x-1}{(x+3)(x-3)(x+1)}$$

11.

$$\frac{m}{12m^2+4mn-5n^2} + \frac{2m}{12m^2+28mn+15n^2} = \frac{m}{(6m+5n)(2m-n)} + \frac{2m}{(6m+5n)(2m+3n)}$$

$$= \frac{m}{(6m+5n)(2m-n)} \cdot \frac{2m+3n}{2m+3n} + \frac{2m}{(6m+5n)(2m+3n)} \cdot \frac{2m-n}{2m-n}$$

$$= \frac{m(2m+3n)+2m(2m-n)}{(6m+5n)(2m-n)(2m+3n)}$$

$$= \frac{2m^2+3mn+4m^2-2mn}{(6m+5n)(2m-n)(2m+3n)}$$

$$= \frac{6m^2+mn}{(6m+5n)(2m-n)(2m+3n)} \text{ or } \frac{m(6m+n)}{(6m+5n)(2m-n)(2m+3n)}$$

12.

$$\frac{x+1}{4x^2-4x+1} + \frac{3}{2x^2+5x-3} = \frac{x+1}{(2x-1)(2x-1)} + \frac{3}{(2x-1)(x+3)}$$

$$= \frac{x+1}{(2x-1)(2x-1)} \cdot \frac{x+3}{x+3} + \frac{3}{(2x-1)(x+3)} \cdot \frac{2x-1}{2x-1}$$

$$= \frac{(x+1)(x+3)}{(2x-1)(2x-1)(x+3)} + \frac{3(2x-1)}{(2x-1)(2x-1)(x+3)}$$

$$= \frac{x^2+4x+3}{(2x-1)(2x-1)(x+3)} + \frac{6x-3}{(2x-1)(2x-1)(x+3)}$$

$$= \frac{x^2+4x+3+6x-3}{(2x-1)(2x-1)(x+3)}$$

$$= \frac{x^2+10x}{(2x-1)(2x-1)(x+3)} \text{ or } \frac{x(x+10)}{(2x-1)^2(x+3)}$$

13.

$$\dfrac{x^3-8}{x^2+5x-14} \div \dfrac{x^2+2x+4}{x^2+10x+21}$$

$$= \dfrac{x^3-8}{x^2+5x-14} \cdot \dfrac{x^2+10x+21}{x^2+2x+4}$$

$$= \dfrac{(x-2)(x^2+2x+4)}{(x+7)(x-2)} \cdot \dfrac{(x+7)(x+3)}{x^2+2x+4}$$

$$= x+3$$

14. a. $(f+g)(x) = f(x) + g(x)$

$$= \dfrac{x-3}{x+5} + \dfrac{x}{2x+3}$$

$$= \dfrac{x-3}{x+5} \cdot \dfrac{2x+3}{2x+3} + \dfrac{x}{2x+3} \cdot \dfrac{x+5}{x+5}$$

$$= \dfrac{(x-3)(2x+3) + x(x+5)}{(x+5)(2x+3)}$$

$$= \dfrac{2x^2-3x-9+x^2+5x}{(x+5)(2x+3)}$$

$$= \dfrac{3x^2+2x-9}{(x+5)(2x+3)}$$

b. The denominator of $(f+g)(x)$ cannot be zero.

Therefore $x+5 \neq 0$ or $2x+3 \neq 0$

$$x \neq -5 \qquad\qquad x \neq -\dfrac{3}{2}$$

The domain is

$$\left\{ x \middle| x \text{ is a real number}, x \neq -5, x \neq -\dfrac{3}{2} \right\}$$

15.   area = length × width

width = area ÷ length

$$\text{width} = \dfrac{x^2+11x+30}{x+2} \div \dfrac{x^2+9x+18}{x+3}$$

$$= \dfrac{x^2+11x+30}{x+2} \cdot \dfrac{x+3}{x^2+9x+18}$$

$$= \dfrac{(x+6)(x+5)}{x+2} \cdot \dfrac{x+3}{(x+6)(x+3)}$$

$$= \dfrac{x+5}{x+2}$$

16.

$$\dfrac{\dfrac{1}{x}+\dfrac{1}{y}}{\dfrac{1}{x}-\dfrac{1}{y}} = \dfrac{xy\left(\dfrac{1}{x}+\dfrac{1}{y}\right)}{xy\left(\dfrac{1}{x}-\dfrac{1}{y}\right)} = \dfrac{xy\left(\dfrac{1}{x}\right)+xy\left(\dfrac{1}{y}\right)}{xy\left(\dfrac{1}{x}\right)-xy\left(\dfrac{1}{y}\right)} = \dfrac{y+x}{y-x}$$

17.

$$\dfrac{\dfrac{a^2-b^2}{ab}}{\dfrac{a+b}{b^2}} = \dfrac{\dfrac{a^2}{ab}-\dfrac{b^2}{ab}}{\dfrac{a}{b^2}+\dfrac{b}{b^2}}$$

$$= \dfrac{ab^2\left(\dfrac{a^2}{ab}-\dfrac{b^2}{ab}\right)}{ab^2\left(\dfrac{a}{b^2}+\dfrac{b}{b^2}\right)}$$

$$= \dfrac{a^2b-b^3}{a^2+ab}$$

$$= \dfrac{b\left(a^2-b^2\right)}{a(a+b)}$$

$$= \dfrac{b(a+b)(a-b)}{a(a+b)}$$

$$= \dfrac{b(a-b)}{a}$$

18.

$$\dfrac{\dfrac{3}{x}-\dfrac{4}{x^2}}{5-\dfrac{1}{x}} = \dfrac{x^2\left(\dfrac{3}{x}-\dfrac{4}{x^2}\right)}{x^2\left(5-\dfrac{1}{x}\right)}$$

$$= \dfrac{3x-4}{5x^2-x}$$

19.

$$\dfrac{x}{6}-\dfrac{x}{5} = -1$$

$$30\left(\dfrac{x}{6}\right)-30\left(\dfrac{x}{5}\right) = 30(-1)$$

$$5x-6x = -30$$

$$-x = -30$$

$$x = 30$$

20.

$$\frac{x}{x-8} + \frac{6}{x-2} = \frac{x^2}{x^2 - 10x + 16}$$

$$\frac{x}{x-8} + \frac{6}{x-2} = \frac{x^2}{(x-8)(x-2)}$$

$$(x-8)(x-2)\left(\frac{x}{x-8}\right) + (x-8)(x-2)\left(\frac{6}{x-2}\right) = (x-8)(x-2)\left(\frac{x^2}{(x-8)(x-2)}\right)$$

$$x(x-2) + 6(x-8) = x^2$$
$$x^2 - 2x + 6x - 48 = x^2$$
$$x^2 + 4x - 48 = x^2$$
$$4x - 48 = 0$$
$$4x = 48$$
$$x = 12$$

This solution checks. The solution is 12.

21.

$$A = \frac{2b}{c-d}$$
$$A(c-d) = 2b$$
$$Ac - Ad = 2b$$
$$Ac = 2b + Ad$$
$$\frac{Ac}{A} = \frac{2b + Ad}{A}$$
$$c = \frac{2b + Ad}{A}$$

22. The equation is $W = kI^2 R$.
To find k, substitute 10 for W, 1 for I, and 1000 for R.
$$10 = k \cdot 1^2 \cdot 1000$$
$$10 = 1000k$$
$$0.01 = k$$
Thus $W = 0.01I^2 R$. Now substitute 0.5 for I and 300 for R.
$$W = 0.01(0.5)^2(300)$$
$$W = 0.75$$
The wattage is 0.75 watt.

23. The equation is $R = \frac{kP}{T^2}$.
To find k, substitute 30 for R, 40 for P, and 2 for T.
$$30 = \frac{k(40)}{2^2}$$
$$30 = \frac{40k}{4}$$
$$30 = 10k$$
$$3 = k$$

Thus $R = \frac{3P}{T^2}$. Now substitute 50 for P, and 5 for T.
$$R = \frac{3(50)}{5^2} = \frac{150}{25} = 6$$

24. Let x be the amount of time needed for both of them to wash the windows.

	Rate	Time worked	Part of job
Paul	$\frac{1}{10}$	x	$\frac{x}{10}$
Nancy	$\frac{1}{7}$	x	$\frac{x}{7}$

$$\frac{x}{10} + \frac{x}{7} = 1$$
$$70\left(\frac{x}{10}\right) + 70\left(\frac{x}{7}\right) = 70(1)$$
$$7x + 10x = 70$$
$$17x = 70$$
$$x = \frac{70}{17} \approx 4.12$$

Working together, they can wash the windows in about 4.12 hrs.

25. Let x be the length of the trail.

	d	r	$t = \dfrac{d}{r}$
Cameron	x	8	$\dfrac{x}{8}$
Ashley	x	5	$\dfrac{x}{5}$

$$\frac{x}{8} = \frac{x}{5} - \frac{1}{2}$$
$$40\left(\frac{x}{8}\right) = 40\left(\frac{x}{5}\right) - 40\left(\frac{1}{2}\right)$$
$$5x = 8x - 20$$
$$20 = 3x$$
$$\frac{20}{3} = x$$
$$x = 6\frac{2}{3}$$

The trail is $6\frac{2}{3}$ miles long.

Cumulative Review Test

1. $\left\{x \middle| -\dfrac{5}{3} < x \le \dfrac{19}{4}\right\}$

2. $-3x^3 - 2x^2y + \dfrac{1}{2}xy^2$

$= -3(2)^3 - 2(2)^2\left(\frac{1}{2}\right) + \frac{1}{2}(2)\left(\frac{1}{2}\right)^2$

$= -3(8) - 2(4)\left(\frac{1}{2}\right) + \frac{1}{2}(2)\left(\frac{1}{4}\right)$

$= -24 - 4 + \dfrac{1}{4}$

$= -28 + \dfrac{1}{4}$

$= -27\dfrac{3}{4}$

3. $2(x+3) = \dfrac{1}{2}(x-5)$

$2x + 6 = \dfrac{1}{2}x - \dfrac{5}{2}$

$2(2x+6) = 2\left(\dfrac{1}{2}x - \dfrac{5}{2}\right)$

$4x + 12 = x - 5$

$3x = -17$

$x = -\dfrac{17}{3}$

4. a.

other $= 100\% - (20\% + 15\% + 10\% + 7\% + 7\% + 13\%)$

$= 100\% - (72\%)$

$= 28\%$

The "other" category makes up 28%.

b. 20% of $220,000 = (0.20)(220,000)$

$= 44,000$

About 44,000 business degrees were awarded.

5. $4x^2 - 3y - 5$

$4(4)^2 - 3(-2) - 5$

$4(16) - 3(-2) - 5$

$64 - 3(-2) - 5$

$64 + 6 - 5$

65

6. $\left(\dfrac{3x^5 y^6}{6x^4 y^7}\right)^3 = \left(\dfrac{x}{2y}\right)^3 = \dfrac{x^3}{8y^3}$

7. $F = \dfrac{mv^2}{r}$

$rF = r\left(\dfrac{mv^2}{r}\right)$

$rF = mv^2$

$\dfrac{rF}{v^2} = \dfrac{mv^2}{v^2}$

$\dfrac{rF}{v^2} = m$ or $m = \dfrac{rF}{v^2}$

8. Let r be the intersest rate as a decimal.

$$5300 = 5000 + 5000r$$

$$300 = 5000r$$

$$r = \frac{300}{5000} = 0.06$$

The simple interest rate was 6%.

9. Let x be the time, in hours, until they meet.

	distance	rate	Time
Dawn	$60t$	60	t
Paula	$50t$	50	t

The total distance is 330 miles.

$$60t + 50t = 330$$

$$110t = 330$$

$$t = 3$$

It will take them 3 hours to meet. Since they started at 8 am, they will meet at 11am.

10.

$$\left|\frac{3x+5}{3}\right| - 3 = 6$$

$$\left|\frac{3x+5}{3}\right| = 9$$ The

$$\frac{3x+5}{3} = 9 \quad \text{or} \quad \frac{3x+5}{3} = -9$$

$$3x+5 = 27 \qquad\qquad 3x+5 = -27$$

$$3x = 22 \qquad\qquad\quad 3x = -32$$

$$x = \frac{22}{3} \qquad\qquad\quad x = -\frac{32}{3}$$

solution is $\left\{\frac{22}{3}, -\frac{32}{3}\right\}$.

11. $y = x^2 - 2$

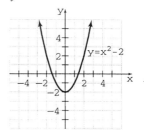

12. $f(x) = \sqrt{2x+7}$

$$f(9) = \sqrt{2(9)+7}$$

$$= \sqrt{18+7}$$

$$= \sqrt{25}$$

$$= 5$$

13.

$$m = \frac{y_2 - y_1}{x_2 - x_1}$$

$$= \frac{-3 - (-4)}{-5 - 2}$$

$$= \frac{-3 + 4}{-7}$$

$$= \frac{1}{-7} \quad \text{or} \quad -\frac{1}{7}$$

14. First find the slope of the given line.

$$2x + 3y - 9 = 0$$

$$3y = -2x + 9$$

$$y = -\frac{2}{3}x + 3 \implies m = -\frac{2}{3}$$

Now use the point-slope equation using the slope $-\frac{2}{3}$ and the given point $\left(\frac{1}{2}, 3\right)$ to find the equation.

$$y - y_1 = m(x - x_1)$$

$$y - 3 = -\frac{2}{3}\left(x - \frac{1}{2}\right)$$

$$y - 3 = -\frac{2}{3}x + \frac{1}{3}$$

$$3(y-3) = 3\left(-\frac{2}{3}x + \frac{1}{3}\right)$$

$$3y - 9 = -2x + 1$$

$$2x + 3y = 10$$

15.

$$2x - y = -2$$

$$4x + 3y = 11$$

To eliminate y, multiply the first equation by 3 then add.

$$3[2x - y = -2]$$

$$4x + 3y = 11$$ gives

$$6x - 3y = -6$$

$$\underline{4x + 3y = 11}$$

Add: $10x \quad = 5$ $x = \frac{5}{10} = \frac{1}{2}$

Substitute $\frac{1}{2}$ for x in the second equation.

$$4\left(\frac{1}{2}\right) + 3y = 11$$

$$2 + 3y = 11$$

$$3y = 9 \implies y = 3$$

The solution is $\left(\frac{1}{2}, 3\right)$.

16. $\left(3x^2 - 4y\right)\left(3x^2 + 4y\right)$

$\qquad = 9x^4 + 12x^2 y - 12x^2 y - 16y^2$

$\qquad = 9x^4 - 16y^2$

17. $3x^2 - 30x + 75 = 3\left(x^2 - 10x + 25\right)$

$\qquad\qquad\qquad = 3(x-5)(x-5)$

$\qquad\qquad\qquad = x(x-5)^2$

18. $y = |x| + 2$

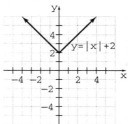

19. $\dfrac{7}{3x^2 + x - 4} + \dfrac{9x+2}{3x^2 - 2x - 8}$

$\quad = \dfrac{7}{(3x+4)(x-1)} + \dfrac{9x+2}{(3x+4)(x-2)}$

$\quad = \dfrac{7}{(3x+4)(x-1)} \cdot \dfrac{x-2}{x-2} + \dfrac{9x+2}{(3x+4)(x-2)} \cdot \dfrac{x-1}{x-1}$

$\quad = \dfrac{7(x-2)}{(3x+4)(x-1)(x-2)} + \dfrac{(9x+2)(x-1)}{(3x+4)(x-2)(x-1)}$

$\quad = \dfrac{7(x-2) + (9x+2)(x-1)}{(3x+4)(x-1)(x-2)}$

$\quad = \dfrac{7x - 14 + 9x^2 - 9x + 2x - 2}{(3x+4)(x-1)(x-2)}$

$\quad = \dfrac{9x^2 - 16}{(3x+4)(x-1)(x-2)}$

$\quad = \dfrac{(3x+4)(3x-4)}{(3x+4)(x-1)(x-2)}$

$\quad = \dfrac{3x-4}{(x-1)(x-2)}$

20. $\qquad\qquad \dfrac{3y-2}{y+1} = 4 - \dfrac{y+2}{y-1}$

$(y+1)(y-1)\left(\dfrac{3y-2}{y+1} = 4 - \dfrac{y+2}{y-1}\right)$

$(y-1)(3y-2) = 4(y+1)(y-1) - (y+1)(y+2)$

$3y^2 - 5y + 2 = 4\left(y^2 - 1\right) - \left(y^2 + 3y + 2\right)$

$3y^2 - 5y + 2 = 4y^2 - 4 - y^2 - 3y - 2$

$\qquad\qquad -2y = -8$

$\qquad\qquad\quad y = 4$

Chapter 7

Exercise Set 7.1

1. a. Every real number has two square roots; a positive or principal square root and a negative square root.

b. The square roots of 49 are 7 and –7.

c. When we say square root, we are referring to the principal square root.

d. $\sqrt{49} = 7$

3. There is no real number which, when squared, results in –81.

5. No. If the number under the radical is negative, the answer is not a real number.

7. a. $\sqrt{(1.3)^2} = \sqrt{1.69} = 1.3$

b. $\sqrt{(-1.3)^2} = \sqrt{1.69} = 1.3$

9. a. $\sqrt[3]{27} = 3$ since $3^3 = 27$

b. $-\sqrt[3]{27} = -3$

c. $\sqrt[3]{-27} = -3$ since $(-3)^3 = -27$

11. $\sqrt{64} = 8$ since $8^2 = 64$

13. $\sqrt[3]{-64} = -4$ since $(-4)^3 = -64$

15. $\sqrt[3]{-125} = -5$ since $(-5)^3 = -125$

17. $\sqrt[5]{1} = 1$ since $1^5 = 1$

19. $-\sqrt[5]{-1} = 1$

21. $\sqrt[6]{-64} = 2$ is not a real number.

23. $\sqrt[3]{-343} = -7$ since $(-7)^3 = -343$

25. $\sqrt{-36}$ is not a real number.

27. $\sqrt{-45.3}$ is not a real number.

29. $\sqrt{\dfrac{1}{25}} = \dfrac{1}{5}$ since $\left(\dfrac{1}{5}\right)^2 = \dfrac{1}{25}$

31. $\sqrt[3]{\dfrac{1}{8}} = \dfrac{1}{2}$ since $\left(\dfrac{1}{2}\right)^3 = \dfrac{1}{8}$

33. $\sqrt{\dfrac{4}{9}} = \dfrac{2}{3}$ since $\left(\dfrac{2}{3}\right)^2 = \dfrac{4}{9}$

35. $\sqrt[3]{-\dfrac{8}{27}} = -\dfrac{2}{3}$ since $\left(-\dfrac{2}{3}\right)^3 = -\dfrac{8}{27}$

37. $-\sqrt[4]{18.2} \approx -2.07$

39. $\sqrt{9^2} = |9| = 9$

41. $\sqrt{(-19)^2} = |-19| = 19$

43. $\sqrt{152^2} = |152| = 152$

45. $\sqrt{(235.23)^2} = |235.23| = 235.23$

47. $\sqrt{(0.06)^2} = |0.06| = 0.06$

49. $\sqrt{\left(\dfrac{11}{13}\right)^2} = \left|\dfrac{11}{13}\right| = \dfrac{11}{13}$

51. $\sqrt{(x-9)^2} = |x-9|$

53. $\sqrt{(x-3)^2} = |x-3|$

55. $\sqrt{(3x^2-2)^2} = |3x^2-2|$

57. $\sqrt{(6a^3-5b^4)^2} = |6a^3-5b^4|$

59. $\sqrt{a^{10}} = \sqrt{(a^5)^2} = |a^5|$

61. $\sqrt{z^{30}} = \sqrt{(z^{15})^2} = |z^{15}|$

63. $\sqrt{a^2-8a+16} = \sqrt{(a-4)^2} = |a-4|$

65. $\sqrt{9a^2+12ab+4b^2} = \sqrt{(3a+2b)^2} = |3a+2b|$

67. $f(x) = \sqrt{5x - 6}$
$f(2) = \sqrt{5 \cdot 2 - 6}$
$\quad = \sqrt{10 - 6}$
$\quad = \sqrt{4}$
$\quad = 2$

69. $g(x) = \sqrt{64 - 8x}$
$g(-3) = \sqrt{64 - 8(-3)}$
$\quad = \sqrt{64 + 24}$
$\quad = \sqrt{88}$
$\quad \approx 9.381$

71. $h(x) = \sqrt[3]{9x^2 + 4}$
$h(4) = \sqrt[3]{9(4)^2 + 4}$
$\quad = \sqrt[3]{144 + 4}$
$\quad = \sqrt[3]{148}$
$\quad \approx 5.290$

73. $f(a) = \sqrt[3]{-2a^2 + a - 6}$
$f(-3) = \sqrt[3]{-2(-3)^2 + (-3) - 6}$
$\quad = \sqrt[3]{-18 - 3 - 6}$
$\quad = \sqrt[3]{-27}$
$\quad = -3$

75. $f(x) = x + \sqrt{x} + 5$
$f(81) = 81 + \sqrt{81} + 5$
$\quad = 81 + 9 + 5$
$\quad = 95$

77. $t(x) = \frac{x}{2} + \sqrt{2x} - 1$
$t(18) = \frac{18}{2} + \sqrt{2(18)} - 1$
$\quad = 9 + \sqrt{36} - 1$
$\quad = 9 + 6 - 1$
$\quad = 14$

79. $k(x) = x^2 + \sqrt{\frac{x}{2}} - 11$
$k(8) = (8)^2 + \sqrt{\frac{8}{2}} - 11$
$\quad = 64 + \sqrt{4} - 11$
$\quad = 64 + 2 - 11$
$\quad = 55$

81. Select $x = 0$.
$\sqrt{(2(0) - 1)^2} \neq 2(0) - 1$
$\sqrt{(-1)^2} \neq -1$
$\sqrt{1} \neq -1$
$1 \neq -1$
This is true for all $x < \frac{1}{2}$.

83. $\sqrt{(x - 1)^2} = x - 1$ for all $x \geq 1$. The expression
$\sqrt{(x - 1)^2} = x - 1$, when $(x - 1)$ is equal to
zero or positive. Therefore, $x - 1 \geq 0$ and
$x \geq 1$.

85. $\sqrt{(2x - 6)^2} = 2x - 6$ for all $x \geq 3$. The
expression $\sqrt{(2x - 6)^2} = 2x - 6$, when $(2x - 6)$ is positive or equal to 0. Therefore,
$2x - 6 \geq 0$
$x \geq 3$

87.
a. $\sqrt{a^2} = |a|$ for all real values

b. $\sqrt{a^2} = a$ when $a \geq 0$

c. $\sqrt[3]{a^3} = a$ for all real values

89. If n is even, we are finding the even root of a
positive number. If n is odd, the expression is
also real.

91. $\dfrac{\sqrt{x + 5}}{\sqrt[3]{x + 5}}$ The denominator cannot equal zero.
$\sqrt[3]{x + 5} \neq 0$
$\qquad x \neq -5$
The numerator must be greater than or equal
to zero.
$\sqrt{x + 5} \geq 0$
$\qquad x \geq -5$
Therefore the domain is
$\{x | x$ is a real number $x > -5\}$

93. $f(x) = \sqrt{x}$ matches graph d).
The x-intercept is 0 and the domain is $x \geq 0$.

95. $f(x) = \sqrt{x - 5}$ matches graph a). The x-intercept
is 5.

97. One answer is $f(x) = \sqrt{x - 6}$

99. $f(x) = -\sqrt{x}$

   a. No

   b. Yes

   c. Yes

   Explanations will vary.

101. $V = \sqrt{64.4h}$

   a. $V = \sqrt{64.4(20)}$
   $= \sqrt{1288}$
   ≈ 35.89
   The velocity will be about 35.89 ft/sec.

   b. $V = \sqrt{64.4(40)}$
   $= \sqrt{2576}$
   ≈ 50.75
   The velocity will be about 50.75 ft/sec.

103. $f(x) = \sqrt{x+1}$

x	$f(x)$
−1	0
0	1
3	2
8	3

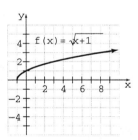

105. $g(x) = \sqrt{x} + 1$

x	$g(x)$
0	1
4	3
9	4

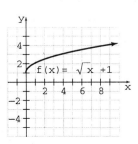

107. $y_1 = \sqrt{x+1}$

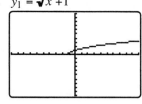

−10, 10, 1, −10, 10

109. $y_1 = \dfrac{\sqrt{x+5}}{\sqrt[3]{x+5}}$
Yes, $x > -5$.

111. $y = \sqrt[3]{x} + 4$

−10, 10, 1, −10, 10

115. $9ax - 3bx + 12ay - 4by = 3x(3a-b) + 4y(3a-b)$
$= (3a-b)(3x+4y)$

117. $4x^4 + 4x^2 - 3$
$= 4(x^2)^2 + 4(x^2) - 3 \leftarrow$ use y for x^2
$= 4y^2 + 4y - 3$
$= (2y-1)(2y+3) \quad \leftarrow$ use x^2 for y
$= (2x^2-1)(2x^2+3)$

Exercise Set 7.2

1. a. $\sqrt[n]{a}$ is a real number when n is even and $a \geq 0$, or n is odd.

   b. $\sqrt[n]{a}$ can be expressed with rational exponents as $a^{1/n}$.

3. a. $\sqrt[n]{a^n}$ is always real

   b. $\sqrt[n]{a^n} = a$ when $a \geq 0$ and n is even

   c. $\sqrt[n]{a^n} = a$ when n is odd

d. $\sqrt[n]{a^n} = |a|$ when n is even and a is any real number

5. a. No, $(xy)^{1/2} = x^{1/2}y^{1/2} \neq xy^{1/2}$

b No, since $(xy)^{-1/2} = \dfrac{1}{(xy)^{1/2}} = \dfrac{1}{x^{1/2}y^{1/2}}$

but $\dfrac{x^{1/2}}{y^{-1/2}} = x^{1/2}y^{1/2}$

7. $\sqrt{a^3} = a^{3/2}$

9. $\sqrt{9^5} = 9^{5/2}$

11. $\sqrt[3]{z^5} = z^{5/3}$

13. $\sqrt[3]{7^{10}} = 7^{10/3}$

15. $\sqrt[4]{9^7} = 7^{7/4}$

17. $\left(\sqrt[3]{y}\right)^{13} = y^{13/3}$

19. $\sqrt[4]{a^3 b} = (a^3 b)^{1/4}$

21. $\sqrt[4]{x^9 y^5} = (x^9 y^5)^{1/4}$

23. $\sqrt[3]{5x^6 y^7} = (5x^6 y^7)^{1/3}$

25. $\sqrt[6]{3a+5b} = (3a+5b)^{1/6}$

27. $a^{1/2} = \sqrt{a}$

29. $c^{5/2} = \sqrt{c^5}$

31. $17^{5/3} = \sqrt[3]{17^5}$

33. $(24x^3)^{1/2} = \sqrt{24x^3}$

35. $(7b^2 c)^{3/5} = \left(\sqrt[5]{7b^2 c}\right)^3$

37. $(6a+5b)^{1/5} = \sqrt[5]{6a+5b}$

39. $(b^3 - c)^{-1/3} = \dfrac{1}{\sqrt[3]{b^3 - c}}$

41. $\sqrt{a^4} = a^{4/2} = a^2$

43. $\sqrt[3]{x^9} = x^{9/3} = x^3$

45. $\sqrt[6]{y^2} = y^{2/6} = y^{1/3} = \sqrt[3]{y}$

47. $\sqrt[8]{b^4} = b^{4/8} = b^{1/2} = \sqrt{b}$

49. $\left(\sqrt{18.1}\right)^2 = (18.1)^{2/2} = (18.1)^1 = 18.1$

51. $(\sqrt[5]{xy^2})^{15} = (xy^2)^{15/5}$
$= (xy^2)^3$
$= x^3 y^6$

53. $(\sqrt[8]{xyz})^4 = (xyz)^{4/8}$
$= (xyz)^{1/2}$
$= \sqrt{xyz}$

55. $\sqrt{\sqrt{x}} = (\sqrt{x})^{1/2}$
$= (x^{1/2})^{1/2}$
$= x^{1/4}$
$= \sqrt[4]{x}$

57. $\sqrt{\sqrt[4]{y}} = \left(\sqrt[4]{y}\right)^{1/2}$
$= \left(y^{1/4}\right)^{1/2}$
$= y^{1/8}$
$= \sqrt[8]{y}$

59. $\sqrt[3]{\sqrt[3]{x^2 y}} = (\sqrt[3]{x^2 y})^{1/3}$
$= (x^2 y)^{1/3 \cdot 1/3}$
$= (x^2 y)^{1/9}$
$= \sqrt[9]{x^2 y}$

61. $\sqrt{\sqrt[5]{a^7}} = \left(\sqrt[5]{a^7}\right)^{1/2}$
$= \left(a^{7/5}\right)^{1/2}$
$= a^{7/10}$
$= \sqrt[10]{a^7}$

63. $9^{1/2} = \sqrt{9} = 3$

65. $\quad 64^{1/3} = \sqrt[3]{64} = 4$

67. $\quad 16^{3/2} = \left(\sqrt{16}\right)^3 = 4^3 = 64$

69. $\quad (-25)^{1/2} = \sqrt{-25}$
Not a real number

71. $\quad \left(\dfrac{16}{9}\right)^{1/2} = \sqrt{\dfrac{16}{9}} = \dfrac{4}{3}$

73. $\quad \left(\dfrac{1}{8}\right)^{1/3} = \sqrt[3]{\dfrac{1}{8}} = \dfrac{1}{2}$

75. $\quad -36^{1/2} = -\sqrt{36} = -6$

77. $\quad -64^{1/3} = -\sqrt[3]{64} = -4$

79. $\quad 64^{-1/3} = \dfrac{1}{64^{1/3}} = \dfrac{1}{\sqrt[3]{64}} = \dfrac{1}{4}$

81. $\quad 64^{-2/3} = \dfrac{1}{64^{2/3}} = \dfrac{1}{\left(\sqrt[3]{64}\right)^2} = \dfrac{1}{4^2} = \dfrac{1}{16}$

83. $\quad \left(\dfrac{64}{27}\right)^{-1/3} = \left(\dfrac{27}{64}\right)^{1/3} = \sqrt[3]{\dfrac{27}{64}} = \dfrac{3}{4}$

85. $\quad (-100)^{3/2} = \left(\sqrt{-100}\right)^3$ Not a real number.

87. $\quad 81^{1/2} + 169^{1/2} = \sqrt{81} + \sqrt{169} = 9 + 13 = 22$

89. $\quad 343^{-1/3} + 4^{-1/2} = \dfrac{1}{343^{1/3}} + \dfrac{1}{4^{1/2}}$
$\qquad = \dfrac{1}{\sqrt[3]{343}} + \dfrac{1}{\sqrt{4}}$
$\qquad = \dfrac{1}{7} + \dfrac{1}{2}$
$\qquad = \dfrac{2}{14} + \dfrac{7}{14}$
$\qquad = \dfrac{9}{14}$

91. $\quad x^4 \cdot x^{1/2} = x^{4+1/2} = x^{9/2}$

93. $\quad \dfrac{x^{1/2}}{x^{1/3}} = x^{1/2 - 1/3} = x^{3/6 - 2/6} = x^{1/6}$

95. $\quad \left(x^{1/2}\right)^{-2} = x^{1/2(-2)} = x^{-1} = \dfrac{1}{x}$

97. $\quad \left(7^{-1/3}\right)^0 = 7^{-1/3(0)} = 7^0 = 1$

99. $\quad \dfrac{5y^{-1/3}}{60y^{-2}} = \dfrac{1}{12}y^{-1/3-(-2)} = \dfrac{1}{12}y^{5/3} = \dfrac{y^{5/3}}{12}$

101. $\quad 4x^{5/3} \cdot 2x^{-7/2} = 4 \cdot 2 \cdot x^{5/3} \cdot x^{-7/2} = 8x^{5/3-7/2}$
$\qquad = 8x^{10/6-21/6} = 8x^{-11/6} = \dfrac{8}{x^{11/6}}$

103. $\quad \left(\dfrac{8}{64x}\right)^{1/3} = \dfrac{8^{1/3}}{64^{1/3}x^{1/3}} = \dfrac{2}{4x^{1/3}} = \dfrac{1}{2x^{1/3}}$
$\qquad$ or $\left(\dfrac{8}{64x}\right)^{1/3} = \left(\dfrac{1}{8x}\right)^{1/3} = \dfrac{1}{8^{1/3}x^{1/3}} = \dfrac{1}{2x^{1/3}}$

105. $\quad \left(\dfrac{22x^{3/7}}{2x^{1/2}}\right)^2 = (11x^{3/7-1/2})^2 = (11x^{6/14-7/14})^2$
$\qquad = (11x^{-1/14})^2 = (11)^2(x^{-1/14})^2 = 121x^{-1/7}$
$\qquad = \dfrac{121}{x^{1/7}}$

107. $\quad \left(\dfrac{a^4}{5a^{-2/5}}\right)^{-3} = \dfrac{a^{-12}}{5^{-3}a^{6/5}}$
$\qquad\qquad = 5^3 a^{-12-6/5}$
$\qquad\qquad = 125a^{-66/5}$
$\qquad\qquad \dfrac{125}{a^{66/5}}$

109. $\quad \left(\dfrac{x^{3/4}y^{-2}}{x^{1/2}y^2}\right)^4 = \left(x^{3/4-1/2}y^{-2-2}\right)^4$
$\qquad\qquad = (x^{1/4}y^{-4})^4$
$\qquad\qquad = (x^{1/4})^4(y^{-4})^4$
$\qquad\qquad = xy^{-16}$
$\qquad\qquad = \dfrac{x}{y^{16}}$

111. $\quad 3z^{-1/2}(2z^4 - z^{1/2}) = 3z^{-1/2} \cdot 2z^4 - 3z^{-1/2}z^{1/2}$
$\qquad\qquad = 6z^{-1/2+4} - 3z^{-1/2+1/2}$
$\qquad\qquad = 6z^{7/2} - 3z^0$
$\qquad\qquad = 6z^{7/2} - 3$

113. $\quad 5x^{-1}(x^{-4} + 4x^{-1/2}) = 5x^{-1} \cdot x^{-4} + 5x^{-1} \cdot 4x^{-1/2}$
$\qquad\qquad = 5x^{-1-4} + 20x^{-1-1/2}$
$\qquad\qquad = 5x^{-5} + 20x^{-3/2}$
$\qquad\qquad = \dfrac{5}{x^5} + \dfrac{20}{x^{3/2}}$

115. $-4x^{5/3}(-2x^{1/2}+7x^{1/3})$

$= (-4x^{5/3})(-2x^{1/2})+(-4x^{5/3})(7x^{1/3})$

$= 8x^{5/3+1/2}-28x^{5/3+1/3}$

$= 8x^{13/6}-28x^{6/3}$

$= 8x^{13/6}-28x^{2}$

117. $\sqrt{140}\approx 11.83$

119. $\sqrt[5]{402.83}\approx 3.32$

121. $45^{2/3}\approx 12.65$

123. $1000^{-1/2}\approx 0.03$

125. $\sqrt[n]{a^{n}}=\left(\sqrt[n]{a}\right)^{n}=a$ when n is odd, or n is even with $a\geq 0$.

127. To show $(a^{1/2}+b^{1/2})^{2}\neq a+b$, use $a=9$ and $b=16$. Then $(a^{1/2}+b^{1/2})^{2}$ becomes $(9^{1/2}+16^{1/2})^{2}=(3+4)^{2}=7^{2}=49$ whereas $a+b$ becomes $9+16=25$. Since $49\neq 25$, then $(a^{1/2}+b^{1/2})^{2}\neq a+b$. Answers will vary.

129. To show $(a^{1/3}+b^{1/3})^{3}\neq a+b$, use $a=1$ and $b=1$. Then $(a^{1/3}+b^{1/3})^{3}$ becomes $(1^{1/3}+1^{1/3})^{3}=(\sqrt[3]{1}+\sqrt[3]{1})^{3}=(1+1)^{3}=2^{3}=8$ whereas $a+b$ becomes $1+1=2$. Since $8\neq 2$, then $(a^{1/3}+b^{1/3})^{3}\neq a+b$. Answers will vary.

131. $x^{5/2}+x^{1/2}=x^{1/2}\cdot x^{2}+x^{1/2}$

$= x^{1/2}(x^{2}+1)$

133. $y^{1/3}-y^{7/3}=y^{1/3}-y^{1/3}y^{2}$

$= y^{1/3}(1-y^{2})$

$= y^{1/3}(1-y)(1+y)$

135. $y^{-2/5}+y^{8/5}=y^{-2/5}+y^{-2/5}y^{2}$

$= y^{-2/5}(1+y^{2})$

$= \dfrac{1+y^{2}}{y^{2/5}}$

137. a. $E(t)=2^{10}\cdot 2^{t}$

$E(0)=2^{10}\cdot 2^{0}$

$= 2^{10}\cdot 1$

$= 2^{10}$

Initially, there are 2^{10} or 1024 bacteria.

b. $E\left(\dfrac{1}{2}\right)=2^{10}\cdot 2^{1/2}$

$= 2^{10}\sqrt{2}$

≈ 1448.15

After $\dfrac{1}{2}$ hour there are about 1448 bacteria.

139. $A(t)=2.69t^{3/2}$

a. $t=200-1993=7$

$A(7)=2.69(7)^{3/2}$

≈ 49.82

In 2000, there was about $49.82 billion in total assets in the U.S. in 401(k) plans.

b. $t=2007-1993=14$

$A(14)=2.69(14)^{3/2}$

≈ 140.91

In 2007, there will be about $140.91 billion in total assets in the U.S. in 401(k) plans.

141. $(3^{\sqrt{2}})^{\sqrt{2}}=3^{\sqrt{2}\cdot\sqrt{2}}=3^{2}=9$

143. $f(x)=(x-5)^{1/2}(x+3)^{-1/2}$

$= \dfrac{(x-5)^{1/2}}{(x+3)^{1/2}}$

$= \dfrac{\sqrt{x-5}}{\sqrt{x+3}}$

The denominator must be greater than zero.

$\sqrt{x+3}>0$

$x>-3$

The numerator must be greater than or equal to zero.

$\sqrt{x-5}\geq 0$

$x\geq 5$

Therefore, the domain is $\{x|x$ is a real number $x\geq 5\}$

145. a. If n is even: $\sqrt[n]{(x-4)^{2n}}=(x-4)^{2}$

b. If n is odd: $\sqrt[n]{(x-4)^{2n}}=(x-4)^{2}$

147. Let a be the unknown index in the shaded area.

$$\sqrt[4]{\sqrt[5]{a\sqrt[3]{z}}} = z^{1/120}$$

$$\left(\left(\left(z^{1/3}\right)^{1/a}\right)^{1/5}\right)^{1/4} = z^{1/120}$$

$$z^{1/60a} = z^{1/120}$$

$$\frac{1}{60a} = \frac{1}{120} \leftarrow \text{Equate exponents}$$

$$60a = 120$$

$$a = 2$$

149. a. The graph is a relation but not a function.

   b. The graph is a relation but not a function.

   c. The graph is both a relation and a function.

151.
$$\frac{3x-2}{x+4} = \frac{2x+1}{3x-2}$$
$$(3x-2)(3x-2) = (2x+1)(x+4)$$
$$9x^2 - 12x + 4 = 2x^2 + 9x + 4$$
$$7x^2 - 21x = 0$$
$$7x(x-3) = 0$$
$$7x = 0 \quad \text{or} \quad x - 3 = 0$$
$$x = 0 \qquad\qquad x = 3$$
The solution is 0 or 3.

Exercise Set 7.3

1. a. Square the natural numbers.

   b. $1^2 = 1,\ 2^2 = 4,\ 3^2 = 9,$
   $4^2 = 16,\ 5^2 = 25,\ 6^2 = 36$

3. a. Raise natural numbers to the fifth power.

   b. $1^5 = 1,\ 2^5 = 32,\ 3^5 = 243,$
   $4^5 = 1024,\ 5^5 = 3125$

5. If n is even and a or b is negative, the numbers are not real numbers and the rule does not apply.

7. If n is even and a or b is negative, the numbers are not real numbers and the rule does not apply.

9. $\sqrt{8} = \sqrt{4\cdot 3} = \sqrt{4}\sqrt{3} = 2\sqrt{3}$

11. $\sqrt{28} = \sqrt{4\cdot 7} = \sqrt{4}\sqrt{7} = 2\sqrt{7}$

13. $\sqrt{12} = \sqrt{4\cdot 3} = \sqrt{4}\sqrt{3} = 2\sqrt{3}$

15. $\sqrt{50} = \sqrt{25\cdot 2} = \sqrt{25}\sqrt{2} = 5\sqrt{2}$

17. $\sqrt{75} = \sqrt{25\cdot 3} = \sqrt{25}\sqrt{3} = 5\sqrt{3}$

19. $\sqrt{40} = \sqrt{4\cdot 10} = \sqrt{4}\sqrt{10} = 2\sqrt{10}$

21. $\sqrt[3]{16} = \sqrt[3]{8\cdot 2} = \sqrt[3]{8}\sqrt[3]{2} = 2\sqrt[3]{2}$

23. $\sqrt[3]{54} = \sqrt[3]{27\cdot 2} = \sqrt[3]{27}\sqrt[3]{2} = 3\sqrt[3]{2}$

25. $\sqrt[3]{32} = \sqrt[3]{8\cdot 4} = \sqrt[3]{8}\sqrt[3]{4} = 2\sqrt[3]{4}$

27. $\sqrt[3]{108} = \sqrt[3]{27\cdot 4} = \sqrt[3]{27}\sqrt[3]{4} = 3\sqrt[3]{4}$

29. $\sqrt[4]{162} = \sqrt[4]{81\cdot 2} = \sqrt[4]{81}\sqrt[4]{2} = 3\sqrt[4]{2}$

31. $-\sqrt[5]{64} = -\sqrt[5]{32\cdot 2} = -\sqrt[5]{32}\sqrt[5]{2} = -2\sqrt[5]{2}$

33. $\sqrt{x^3} = \sqrt{x^2\cdot x} = \sqrt{x^2}\sqrt{x} = x\sqrt{x}$

35. $\sqrt{a^{11}} = \sqrt{a^{10}\cdot a} = \sqrt{a^{10}}\sqrt{a} = a^5\sqrt{a}$

37. $-\sqrt{z^{21}} = -\sqrt{z^{20}\cdot z} = -\sqrt{z^{20}}\sqrt{z} = -z^{10}\sqrt{z}$

39. $\sqrt[3]{a^7} = \sqrt[3]{a^6\cdot a} = \sqrt[3]{a^6}\sqrt[3]{a} = a^2\sqrt[3]{a}$

41. $\sqrt[3]{b^{13}} = \sqrt[3]{b^{12}\cdot b} = \sqrt[3]{b^{12}}\sqrt[3]{b} = b^4\sqrt[3]{b}$

43. $\sqrt[4]{x^5} = \sqrt[4]{x^4\cdot x} = \sqrt[4]{x^4}\sqrt[4]{x} = x\sqrt[4]{x}$

45. $\sqrt[5]{z^7} = \sqrt[5]{z^5\cdot z^2} = \sqrt[5]{z^5}\sqrt[5]{z^2} = z\sqrt[5]{z^2}$

47. $3\sqrt[5]{y^{23}} = 3\sqrt[5]{y^{20}\cdot y^3} = 3\sqrt[5]{y^{20}}\sqrt[5]{y^3} = 3y^4\sqrt[5]{y^3}$

49.
$$\sqrt{24x^3} = \sqrt{4\cdot 6\cdot x^2\cdot x}$$
$$= \sqrt{4x^2\cdot 6x}$$
$$= \sqrt{4x^2}\sqrt{6x}$$
$$= 2x\sqrt{6x}$$

51.
$$\sqrt{8x^4y^7} = \sqrt{4\cdot 2\cdot x^4\cdot y^6\cdot y} = \sqrt{4x^4y^6\cdot 2y}$$
$$= \sqrt{4x^4y^6}\sqrt{2y} = 2x^2y^3\sqrt{2y}$$

53.
$$-\sqrt{20x^6y^7z^{12}} = -\sqrt{4\cdot 5\cdot x^6\cdot y^6\cdot y\cdot z^{12}}$$
$$= -\sqrt{4x^6y^6z^{12}\cdot 5y}$$
$$= -\sqrt{4x^6y^6z^{12}}\sqrt{5y}$$
$$= -2x^3y^3z^6\sqrt{5y}$$

55. $\sqrt[3]{x^3 y^7} = \sqrt[3]{x^3 \cdot y^6 \cdot y}$

$\phantom{\sqrt[3]{x^3 y^7}} = \sqrt[3]{x^3 y^6 \cdot y}$

$\phantom{\sqrt[3]{x^3 y^7}} = \sqrt[3]{x^3 y^6} \sqrt[3]{y}$

$\phantom{\sqrt[3]{x^3 y^7}} = xy^2 \sqrt[3]{y}$

57. $\sqrt[3]{81a^6 b^8} = \sqrt[3]{27 \cdot 3 \cdot a^6 \cdot b^6 \cdot b^2}$

$\phantom{\sqrt[3]{81a^6 b^8}} = \sqrt[3]{27a^6 b^6 \cdot 3b^2}$

$\phantom{\sqrt[3]{81a^6 b^8}} = \sqrt[3]{27a^6 b^6} \sqrt[3]{3b^2}$

$\phantom{\sqrt[3]{81a^6 b^8}} = 3a^2 b^2 \sqrt[3]{3b^2}$

59. $\sqrt[4]{32x^8 y^9 z^{19}} = \sqrt[4]{16 \cdot 2 \cdot x^8 \cdot y^8 \cdot y \cdot z^{16} \cdot z^3}$

$\phantom{\sqrt[4]{32x^8 y^9 z^{19}}} = \sqrt[4]{16x^8 y^8 z^{16} \cdot 2yz^3}$

$\phantom{\sqrt[4]{32x^8 y^9 z^{19}}} = \sqrt[4]{16x^8 y^8 z^{16}} \sqrt[4]{2yz^3}$

$\phantom{\sqrt[4]{32x^8 y^9 z^{19}}} = 2x^2 y^2 z^4 \sqrt[4]{2yz^3}$

61. $\sqrt[4]{81a^8 b^9} = \sqrt[4]{81 \cdot a^8 \cdot b^8 \cdot b}$

$\phantom{\sqrt[4]{81a^8 b^9}} = \sqrt[4]{81a^8 b^8 \cdot b}$

$\phantom{\sqrt[4]{81a^8 b^9}} = \sqrt[4]{81a^8 b^8} \sqrt[4]{b}$

$\phantom{\sqrt[4]{81a^8 b^9}} = 3a^2 b^2 \sqrt[4]{b}$

63. $\sqrt[5]{32a^{10}b^{12}} = \sqrt[5]{32 \cdot a^{10} \cdot b^{10} \cdot b^2}$

$\phantom{\sqrt[5]{32a^{10}b^{12}}} = \sqrt[5]{32a^{10}b^{10} \cdot b^2}$

$\phantom{\sqrt[5]{32a^{10}b^{12}}} = \sqrt[5]{32a^{10}b^{10}} \sqrt[5]{b^2}$

$\phantom{\sqrt[5]{32a^{10}b^{12}}} = 2a^2 b^2 \sqrt[5]{b^2}$

65. $\sqrt{\dfrac{36}{4}} = \sqrt{9} = 3$

67. $\sqrt{\dfrac{4}{25}} = \dfrac{\sqrt{4}}{\sqrt{25}} = \dfrac{2}{5}$

69. $\dfrac{\sqrt{27}}{\sqrt{3}} = \sqrt{\dfrac{27}{3}} = \sqrt{9} = 3$

71. $\dfrac{\sqrt{3}}{\sqrt{48}} = \sqrt{\dfrac{3}{48}} = \sqrt{\dfrac{1}{16}} = \dfrac{1}{4}$

73. $\sqrt[3]{\dfrac{2}{16}} = \sqrt[3]{\dfrac{1}{8}} = \dfrac{\sqrt[3]{1}}{\sqrt[3]{8}} = \dfrac{1}{2}$

75. $\dfrac{\sqrt[3]{3}}{\sqrt[3]{81}} = \sqrt[3]{\dfrac{3}{81}} = \sqrt[3]{\dfrac{1}{27}} = \dfrac{1}{3}$

77. $\sqrt[4]{\dfrac{3}{48}} = \sqrt[4]{\dfrac{1}{16}} = \dfrac{1}{2}$

79. $\sqrt[5]{\dfrac{96}{3}} = \sqrt[5]{32} = 2$

81. $\sqrt{\dfrac{r^4}{25}} = \dfrac{\sqrt{r^4}}{\sqrt{25}} = \dfrac{r^2}{5}$

83. $\sqrt{\dfrac{36x^4}{25y^{10}}} = \dfrac{\sqrt{36x^4}}{\sqrt{25y^{10}}} = \dfrac{6x^2}{5y^5}$

85. $\sqrt[3]{\dfrac{c^6}{27}} = \dfrac{\sqrt[3]{c^6}}{\sqrt[3]{27}} = \dfrac{c^2}{3}$

87. $\sqrt[4]{\dfrac{a^8 b^{12}}{b^{-4}}} = \sqrt[4]{a^8 b^{12+4}}$

$\phantom{\sqrt[4]{\dfrac{a^8 b^{12}}{b^{-4}}}} = \sqrt[4]{a^8 b^{16}}$

$\phantom{\sqrt[4]{\dfrac{a^8 b^{12}}{b^{-4}}}} = a^2 b^4$

89. $\dfrac{-\sqrt{24}}{\sqrt{3}} = -\sqrt{\dfrac{24}{3}} = -\sqrt{8} = -\sqrt{4 \cdot 2} = -2\sqrt{2}$

91. $\dfrac{\sqrt{27x^6}}{\sqrt{3x^2}} = \sqrt{\dfrac{27x^6}{3x^2}} = \sqrt{9x^4} = 3x^2$

93. $\dfrac{\sqrt{40x^6 y^9}}{\sqrt{5x^2 y^4}} = \sqrt{\dfrac{40x^6 y^9}{5x^2 y^4}}$

$\phantom{\dfrac{\sqrt{40x^6 y^9}}{\sqrt{5x^2 y^4}}} = \sqrt{8x^4 y^5}$

$\phantom{\dfrac{\sqrt{40x^6 y^9}}{\sqrt{5x^2 y^4}}} = \sqrt{4x^4 y^4 \cdot 2y}$

$\phantom{\dfrac{\sqrt{40x^6 y^9}}{\sqrt{5x^2 y^4}}} = 2x^2 y^2 \sqrt{2y}$

95. $\sqrt[3]{\dfrac{7xy}{8x^{13}}} = \sqrt[3]{\dfrac{7y}{8x^{12}}} = \dfrac{\sqrt[3]{7y}}{\sqrt[3]{8x^{12}}} = \dfrac{\sqrt[3]{7y}}{2x^4}$

97.
$$\sqrt[3]{\frac{25x^2y^9}{5x^8y^2}}=\sqrt[3]{\frac{5y^7}{x^6}}$$
$$=\frac{\sqrt[3]{5y^7}}{\sqrt[3]{x^6}}$$
$$=\frac{\sqrt[3]{y^6\cdot 5y}}{x^2}$$
$$=\frac{y^2\sqrt[3]{5y}}{x^2}$$

99.
$$\sqrt[4]{\frac{20x^4y}{81x^{-8}}}=\sqrt[4]{\frac{20x^{12}y}{81}}$$
$$=\frac{\sqrt[4]{20x^{12}y}}{\sqrt[4]{81}}$$
$$=\frac{\sqrt[4]{x^{12}}\sqrt[4]{20y}}{\sqrt[4]{81}}$$
$$=\frac{x^3\sqrt[4]{20y}}{3}$$

101. $\sqrt{a\cdot b}=(a\cdot b)^{1/2}=a^{1/2}\cdot b^{1/2}=\sqrt{a}\cdot\sqrt{b}$

103. No, for example $\frac{\sqrt{18}}{\sqrt{2}}=\sqrt{\frac{18}{2}}=\sqrt{9}=3$.

105. **a.** no

b. $\frac{\sqrt[n]{x}}{\sqrt[n]{x}}$ is equal to 1 when $\sqrt[n]{x}$ is a real number and not equal to 0.

107.
$$\left|\frac{2x-4}{5}\right|=12$$
$$\frac{2x-4}{5}=-12 \quad\text{or}\quad \frac{2x-4}{5}=12$$
$$2x-4=-60 \qquad 2x-4=60$$
$$2x=-56 \qquad 2x=64$$
$$x=-28 \qquad x=32$$
The solution is {−28, 32}.

109.
$$(x-3)^3+8=(x-3)^3+(2)^3$$
$$=\left((x-3)+2\right)\left((x-3)^2-(x-3)(2)+(2)^2\right)$$
$$=(x-1)\left(x^2-6x+9-2x+6+4\right)$$
$$=(x-1)\left(x^2-8x+19\right)$$

Exercise Set 7.4

1. Like radicals are radicals with the same radicands and index.

3. $\sqrt{3}+3\sqrt{2}\approx 1.732+3(1.414)$
$\approx 1.732+4.242$
≈ 5.974 or 5.97

5. No. To see this, let $a=16$ and $b=9$. Then, the left side is $\sqrt{a}+\sqrt{b}=\sqrt{16}+\sqrt{9}=4+3=7$ whereas the right side is
$\sqrt{a+b}=\sqrt{16+9}=\sqrt{25}=5$.

7. $\sqrt{5}-\sqrt{5}=0$

9. $6\sqrt{3}-2\sqrt{3}=4\sqrt{3}$

11. $2\sqrt{3}-2\sqrt{3}-4\sqrt{3}+5=-4\sqrt{3}+5$

13. $3\sqrt[4]{y}-9\sqrt[4]{y}=-6\sqrt[4]{y}$

15. $3\sqrt{5}-\sqrt[3]{x}+4\sqrt{5}+3\sqrt[3]{x}=7\sqrt{5}+2\sqrt[3]{x}$

17. $5\sqrt{x}-4\sqrt{y}+3\sqrt{x}+2\sqrt{y}-\sqrt{x}=7\sqrt{x}-2\sqrt{y}$

19. $\sqrt{8}-\sqrt{12}=\sqrt{4}\cdot\sqrt{2}-\sqrt{4}\cdot\sqrt{3}$
$=2\sqrt{2}-2\sqrt{3}$
$=2\left(\sqrt{2}-\sqrt{3}\right)$

21. $-6\sqrt{75}+4\sqrt{125}=-6\sqrt{25}\cdot\sqrt{3}+4\sqrt{25}\cdot\sqrt{5}$
$=-6\left(5\sqrt{3}\right)+4\left(5\sqrt{5}\right)$
$=-30\sqrt{3}+20\sqrt{5}$

23. $-4\sqrt{90}+3\sqrt{40}+2\sqrt{10}$
$=-4\sqrt{9}\cdot\sqrt{10}+3\sqrt{4}\cdot\sqrt{10}+2\sqrt{10}$
$=-4\left(3\sqrt{10}\right)+3\left(2\sqrt{10}\right)+2\left(\sqrt{10}\right)$
$=-12\sqrt{10}+6\sqrt{10}+2\sqrt{10}$
$=-4\sqrt{10}$

25. $\sqrt{500xy^2}+y\sqrt{320x}$
$=\sqrt{100y^2}\cdot\sqrt{5x}+y\sqrt{64}\sqrt{5x}$
$=10y\sqrt{5x}+8y\sqrt{5x}$
$=18y\sqrt{5x}$

27. $2\sqrt{5x} - 3\sqrt{20x} - 4\sqrt{45x}$

$= 2\sqrt{5x} - 3\sqrt{4}\cdot\sqrt{5x} - 4\sqrt{9}\cdot\sqrt{5x}$

$= 2\sqrt{5x} - 3\left(2\sqrt{5x}\right) - 4\left(3\sqrt{5x}\right)$

$= 2\sqrt{5x} - 6\sqrt{5x} - 12\sqrt{5x}$

$= -16\sqrt{5x}$

29. $3\sqrt{50a^2} - 3\sqrt{72a^2} - 8a\sqrt{18}$

$= 3\sqrt{25a^2}\cdot\sqrt{2} - 3\sqrt{36a^2}\cdot\sqrt{2} - 8a\sqrt{9}\cdot\sqrt{2}$

$= 3\left(5a\sqrt{2}\right) - 3\left(6a\sqrt{2}\right) - 8a\left(3\sqrt{2}\right)$

$= 15a\sqrt{2} - 18a\sqrt{2} - 24a\sqrt{2}$

$= -27a\sqrt{2}$

31. $\sqrt[3]{108} + 2\sqrt[3]{32} = \sqrt[3]{27}\cdot\sqrt[3]{4} + 2\sqrt[3]{8}\cdot\sqrt[3]{4}$

$= 3\sqrt[3]{4} + 2(2\sqrt[3]{4})$

$= 3\sqrt[3]{4} + 4\sqrt[3]{4}$

$= 7\sqrt[3]{4}$

33. $\sqrt[3]{27} - 5\sqrt[3]{8} = 3 - 5\cdot 2 = 3 - 10 = -7$

35. $2\sqrt[3]{a^4 b^2} + 3a\,\sqrt[3]{ab^2} = 2\sqrt[3]{a^3}\cdot\sqrt[3]{ab^2} + 3a\sqrt[3]{ab^2}$

$= 2a\sqrt[3]{ab^2} + 3a\sqrt[3]{ab^2}$

$= 5a\sqrt[3]{ab^2}$

37. $\sqrt{4r^7 s^5} + 3r^2\sqrt{r^3 s^5} - 2rs\sqrt{r^5 s^3}$

$= \sqrt{4r^6 s^4}\cdot\sqrt{rs} + 3r^2\sqrt{r^2 s^4}\cdot\sqrt{rs} - 2rs\sqrt{r^4 s^2}\cdot\sqrt{rs}$

$= 2r^3 s^2\sqrt{rs} + 3r^2(rs^2\sqrt{rs}) - 2rs(r^2 s\sqrt{rs})$

$= 2r^3 s^2\sqrt{rs} + 3r^3 s^2\sqrt{rs} - 2r^3 s^2\sqrt{rs}$

$= 3r^3 s^2\sqrt{rs}$

39. $\sqrt[3]{128x^9 y^{10}} - 2x^2 y^3\sqrt[3]{16x^3 y^7}$

$= \sqrt[3]{64x^9 y^9}\sqrt[3]{2y} - 2x^2 y^3\sqrt[3]{8x^3 y^6}\sqrt[3]{2y}$

$= 4x^3 y^3\sqrt[3]{2y} - 2x^2 y\left(2xy^2\sqrt[3]{2y}\right)$

$= 4x^3 y^3\sqrt[3]{2y} - 4x^3 y^3\sqrt[3]{2y}$

$= 0$

41. $\sqrt{50}\sqrt{2} = \sqrt{50\cdot 2} = \sqrt{100} = 10$

43. $\sqrt[3]{2}\,\sqrt[3]{28} = \sqrt[3]{56} = \sqrt[3]{8\cdot 7} = 2\sqrt[3]{7}$

45. $\sqrt{9m^3 n^7}\,\sqrt{3mn^4} = \sqrt{9m^3 n^7 \cdot 3mn^4}$

$= \sqrt{27m^4 n^{11}}$

$= \sqrt{9\cdot 3\cdot m^4\cdot n^{10}\cdot n}$

$= \sqrt{9m^4 n^{10}\cdot 3n}$

$= \sqrt{9m^4 n^{10}}\,\sqrt{3n}$

$= 3m^2 n^5\sqrt{3n}$

47. $\sqrt[3]{9x^7 y^{12}}\,\sqrt[3]{6x^4 y} = \sqrt[3]{9x^7 y^{12}\cdot 6x^4 y}$

$= \sqrt[3]{54x^{11} y^{13}}$

$= \sqrt[3]{27\cdot 2\cdot x^9\cdot x^2\cdot y^{12}\cdot y}$

$= \sqrt[3]{27x^9 y^{12}\cdot 2x^2 y}$

$= \sqrt[3]{27x^9 y^{12}}\,\sqrt[3]{2x^2 y}$

$= 3x^3 y^4\sqrt[3]{2x^2 y}$

49. $\sqrt[4]{3x^9 y^{12}}\,\sqrt[4]{54x^4 y^7} = \sqrt[4]{3x^9 y^{12}\cdot 54x^4 y^7}$

$= \sqrt[4]{162x^{13} y^{19}}$

$= \sqrt[4]{81\cdot 2\cdot x^{12}\cdot x\cdot y^{16}\cdot y^3}$

$= \sqrt[4]{81x^{12} y^{16}\cdot 2xy^3}$

$= \sqrt[4]{81x^{12} y^{16}}\,\sqrt[4]{2xy^3}$

$= 3x^3 y^4\sqrt[4]{2xy^3}$

51. $\sqrt[4]{8x^4 yz^3}\,\sqrt[4]{2x^2 y^3 z^7}$

$= \sqrt[4]{8x^4 yz^3\cdot 2x^2 y^3 z^7}$

$= \sqrt[4]{16x^6 y^4 z^{10}}$

$= \sqrt[4]{16\cdot x^4\cdot x^2\cdot y^4\cdot z^8\cdot z^2}$

$= \sqrt[4]{16x^4 y^4 z^8\cdot x^2 z^2}$

$= \sqrt[4]{16x^4 y^4 z^8}\cdot\sqrt[4]{x^2 z^2}$

$= 2xyz^2\sqrt[4]{x^2 z^2}$

53. $\sqrt{5}\left(\sqrt{5} - \sqrt{3}\right) = \left(\sqrt{5}\right)\left(\sqrt{5}\right) - \left(\sqrt{5}\right)\left(\sqrt{3}\right)$

$= \sqrt{25} - \sqrt{15}$

$= 5 - \sqrt{15}$

55. $\sqrt[3]{y}\left(2\sqrt[3]{y} - \sqrt[3]{y^8}\right)$

$= \left(\sqrt[3]{y}\right)\left(2\sqrt[3]{y}\right) - \left(\sqrt[3]{y}\right)\left(\sqrt[3]{y^8}\right)$

$= 2\sqrt[3]{y^2} - \sqrt[3]{y^9}$

$= 2\sqrt[3]{y^2} - y^3$

57.

$$2\sqrt[3]{x^4 y^5}\left(\sqrt[3]{8x^{12}y^4} + \sqrt[3]{16xy^9}\right)$$

$$= \left(2\sqrt[3]{x^4 y^5}\right)\left(\sqrt[3]{8x^{12}y^4}\right) + \left(2\sqrt[3]{x^4 y^5}\right)\left(\sqrt[3]{16xy^9}\right)$$

$$= 2\sqrt[3]{8x^{16}y^9} + 2\sqrt[3]{16x^5 y^{14}}$$

$$= 2\sqrt[3]{8x^{15}y^9}\sqrt[3]{x} + 2\sqrt[3]{8x^3 y^{12}}\sqrt[3]{2x^2 y^2}$$

$$= 2\cdot 2x^5 y^3 \sqrt[3]{x} + 2\cdot 2xy^4 \sqrt[3]{2x^2 y^2}$$

$$= 4x^5 y^3 \sqrt[3]{x} + 4xy^4 \sqrt[3]{2x^2 y^2}$$

59.

$$(5+\sqrt5)(5-\sqrt5) = 5^2 - (\sqrt5)^2$$

$$= 25 - 5$$

$$= 20$$

61.

$$\left(\sqrt6 + x\right)\left(\sqrt6 - x\right) = \left(\sqrt6\right)^2 - x^2$$

$$= 6 - x^2$$

63.

$$\left(\sqrt5 + \sqrt z\right)\left(\sqrt5 - \sqrt z\right) = \left(\sqrt5\right)^2 - \left(\sqrt z\right)^2$$

$$= 5 - z$$

65.

$$\left(\sqrt3 + 4\right)\left(\sqrt3 + 5\right)$$

$$= \sqrt9 + 5\sqrt3 + 4\sqrt3 + 20$$

$$= 3 + 9\sqrt3 + 20$$

$$= 23 + 9\sqrt3$$

67.

$$\left(3 - \sqrt2\right)\left(4 - \sqrt8\right)$$

$$= 12 - 3\sqrt8 - 4\sqrt2 + \sqrt{16}$$

$$= 12 - 3\cdot 2\sqrt2 - 4\sqrt2 + 4$$

$$= 12 - 6\sqrt2 - 4\sqrt2 + 4$$

$$= 16 - 10\sqrt2$$

69.

$$\left(4\sqrt3 + \sqrt2\right)\left(\sqrt3 - \sqrt2\right)$$

$$= 4\sqrt9 - 4\sqrt6 + \sqrt6 - \sqrt4$$

$$= 4\cdot 3 - 3\sqrt6 - 2$$

$$= 12 - 3\sqrt6 - 2$$

$$= 10 - 3\sqrt6$$

71.

$$\left(2\sqrt5 - 3\right)^2$$

$$= \left(2\sqrt5 - 3\right)\left(2\sqrt5 - 3\right)$$

$$= 4\sqrt{25} - 6\sqrt5 - 6\sqrt5 + 9$$

$$= 4\cdot 5 - 12\sqrt5 + 9$$

$$= 20 + 9 - 12\sqrt5$$

$$= 29 - 12\sqrt5$$

73.

$$\left(2\sqrt{3x} - \sqrt y\right)\left(3\sqrt{3x} + \sqrt y\right)$$

$$= 6\left(\sqrt{3x}\right)^2 + 2\sqrt{3x}\sqrt y - 3\sqrt{3x}\sqrt y - \left(\sqrt y\right)^2$$

$$= 6(3x) + 2\sqrt{3xy} - 3\sqrt{3xy} - y$$

$$= 18x - \sqrt{3xy} - y$$

75.

$$\left(\sqrt[3]{4} - \sqrt[3]{6}\right)\left(\sqrt[3]{2} - \sqrt[3]{36}\right)$$

$$= \sqrt[3]{4}\sqrt[3]{2} - \sqrt[3]{4}\sqrt[3]{36} - \sqrt[3]{6}\sqrt[3]{2} + \sqrt[3]{6}\sqrt[3]{36}$$

$$= \sqrt[3]{8} - \sqrt[3]{144} - \sqrt[3]{12} + \sqrt[3]{216}$$

$$= 2 - 2\sqrt[3]{18} - \sqrt[3]{12} + 6$$

$$= 8 - 2\sqrt[3]{18} - \sqrt[3]{12}$$

77.

$$(f\cdot g)(x) = f(x)\cdot g(x)$$

$$= \sqrt{2x}\left(\sqrt{8x} - \sqrt{32}\right)$$

$$= \sqrt{2x}\cdot\sqrt{8x} - \sqrt{2x}\cdot\sqrt{32}$$

$$= \sqrt{16x^2} - \sqrt{64x}$$

$$= 4x - 8\sqrt x$$

79.

$$(f\cdot g)(x) = f(x)\cdot g(x)$$

$$= \sqrt[3]{x}\left(\sqrt[3]{x^5} + \sqrt[3]{x^4}\right)$$

$$= \sqrt[3]{x}\sqrt[3]{x^5} + \sqrt[3]{x}\sqrt[3]{x^4}$$

$$= \sqrt[3]{x^6} + \sqrt[3]{x^5}$$

$$= \sqrt[3]{x^6} + \sqrt[3]{x^3\cdot x^2}$$

$$= x^2 + x\sqrt[3]{x^2}$$

81.

$$(f\cdot g)(x) = f(x)\cdot g(x)$$

$$= \sqrt[4]{3x^2}\left(\sqrt[4]{9x^4} - \sqrt[4]{x^7}\right)$$

$$= \sqrt[4]{3x^2}\sqrt[4]{9x^4} - \sqrt[4]{3x^2}\sqrt[4]{x^7}$$

$$= \sqrt[4]{27x^6} - \sqrt[4]{3x^9}$$

$$= \sqrt[4]{x^4}\sqrt[4]{27x^2} - \sqrt[4]{x^8}\sqrt[4]{3x}$$

$$= x\sqrt[4]{27x^2} - x^2\sqrt[4]{3x}$$

83. $\sqrt{24} = \sqrt{4 \cdot 6} = 2\sqrt{6}$

85. $\sqrt{125} + \sqrt{20} = \sqrt{25 \cdot 5} + \sqrt{4 \cdot 5}$
$$= 5\sqrt{5} + 2\sqrt{5}$$
$$= 7\sqrt{5}$$

87. $\left(3\sqrt{2} - 4\right)\left(\sqrt{2} + 5\right)$
$$= 3\left(\sqrt{2}\right)^2 + 15\sqrt{2} - 4\sqrt{2} - 20$$
$$= 6 + 11\sqrt{2} - 20$$
$$= -14 + 11\sqrt{2}$$

89. $\sqrt{6}\left(4 - \sqrt{2}\right) = \sqrt{6} \cdot 4 - \sqrt{6} \cdot \sqrt{2}$
$$= 4\sqrt{6} - \sqrt{12}$$
$$= 4\sqrt{6} - 2\sqrt{3}$$

91. $\sqrt{75}\sqrt{6} = \sqrt{450} = \sqrt{225 \cdot 2} = 15\sqrt{2}$

93. $\sqrt[3]{80x^{11}} = \sqrt[3]{8x^9 \cdot 10x^2} = 2x^3\sqrt[3]{10x^2}$

95. $\sqrt[6]{128ab^{17}c^9} = \sqrt[6]{64b^{12}c^6 \cdot 2ab^5c^3}$
$$= 2b^2c\sqrt[6]{2ab^5c^3}$$

97. $2b\sqrt[4]{a^4 b} + ab\sqrt[4]{16b}$
$$= 2b\sqrt[4]{a^4} \cdot \sqrt[4]{b} + ab\sqrt[4]{16} \cdot \sqrt[4]{b}$$
$$= 2b\left(a\sqrt[4]{b}\right) + ab\left(2\sqrt[4]{b}\right)$$
$$= 2ab\sqrt[4]{b} + 2ab\sqrt[4]{b}$$
$$= 4ab\sqrt[4]{b}$$

99. $\left(\sqrt[3]{x^2} - \sqrt[3]{y}\right)\left(\sqrt[3]{x} - 2\sqrt[3]{y^2}\right)$
$$= \sqrt[3]{x^2}\sqrt[3]{x} - 2\sqrt[3]{x^2}\sqrt[3]{y^2} - \sqrt[3]{y}\sqrt[3]{x} + 2\sqrt[3]{y}\sqrt[3]{y^2}$$
$$= \sqrt[3]{x^3} - 2\sqrt[3]{x^2y^2} - \sqrt[3]{xy} + 2\sqrt[3]{y^3}$$
$$= x - 2\sqrt[3]{x^2y^2} - \sqrt[3]{xy} + 2y$$

101. $\sqrt[3]{3ab^2}\left(\sqrt[3]{4a^4b^3} - \sqrt[3]{8a^5b^4}\right)$
$$= \left(\sqrt[3]{3ab^2}\right)\left(\sqrt[3]{4a^4b^3}\right) - \left(\sqrt[3]{3ab^2}\right)\left(\sqrt[3]{8a^5b^4}\right)$$
$$= \sqrt[3]{12a^5b^5} - \sqrt[3]{24a^6b^6}$$
$$= \sqrt[3]{a^3b^3 \cdot 12a^2b^2} - \sqrt[3]{8a^6b^6 \cdot 3}$$
$$= ab\sqrt[3]{12a^2b^2} - 2a^2b^2\sqrt[3]{3}$$

103. $f(x) = \sqrt{2x+5}\sqrt{2x+5} = 2x+5$

No absolute value needed since $x \geq -\dfrac{5}{2}$.

105. $h(r) = \sqrt{4r^2 - 32r + 64}$
$$= \sqrt{4\left(r^2 - 8r + 16\right)}$$
$$= \sqrt{4(r-4)^2}$$
$$= 2|r-4|$$

107. Perimeter $= \sqrt{45} + \sqrt{45} + \sqrt{80} + \sqrt{80}$
$$= 2\sqrt{45} + 2\sqrt{80}$$
$$= 2\sqrt{9}\sqrt{5} + 2\sqrt{16}\sqrt{5}$$
$$= 2\left(3\sqrt{5}\right) + 2\left(4\sqrt{5}\right)$$
$$= 6\sqrt{5} + 8\sqrt{5}$$
$$= 14\sqrt{5}$$

Area $= \sqrt{45}\sqrt{80}$
$$= 3\sqrt{5} \cdot 4\sqrt{5}$$
$$= 12\left(\sqrt{5}\right)^2$$
$$= 12 \cdot 5$$
$$= 60$$

109. Perimeter $= \sqrt{245} + \sqrt{180} + \sqrt{80}$
$$= \sqrt{49}\sqrt{5} + \sqrt{36}\sqrt{5} + \sqrt{16}\sqrt{5}$$
$$= 7\sqrt{5} + 6\sqrt{5} + 4\sqrt{5}$$
$$= 17\sqrt{5}$$

Area $= \dfrac{1}{2}\sqrt{245}\sqrt{45}$
$$= \dfrac{1}{2}\sqrt{49}\sqrt{5}\sqrt{9}\sqrt{5}$$
$$= \dfrac{1}{2} \cdot 7 \cdot 3\left(\sqrt{5}\right)^2$$
$$= \dfrac{21}{2} \cdot 5$$
$$= 52.5$$

111. No, for example $-\sqrt{2} + \sqrt{2} = 0$

113.

a. $s = \sqrt{30FB}$
$$s = \sqrt{30(0.85)(80)} \approx 45.17$$
The car's speed was about 45.17 mph.

b. $s = \sqrt{30FB}$
$$s = \sqrt{30(0.52)(80)} \approx 35.33$$
The car's speed was about 35.33 mph.

115. $f(t) = 3\sqrt{t} + 19$

   a. $t = 36$
$$f(36) = 3\sqrt{36} + 19$$
$$= 3(6) + 19$$
$$= 18 + 19$$
$$= 37$$
The length at 36 months is 37 inches.

   b. $t = 40$
$$f(40) = 3\sqrt{40} + 19$$
$$= 3\sqrt{4}\sqrt{10} + 19$$
$$= 3 \cdot 2\sqrt{10} + 19$$
$$= 6\sqrt{10} + 19$$
$$\approx 37.97$$
The length at 40 months is about 37.97 inches.

117. **a.**
$$f(x) = \sqrt{x}$$
$$g(x) = 2$$
$$(f + g)(x) = f(x) + g(x)$$
$$= \sqrt{x} + 2$$

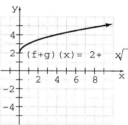

   b. It raises the graph 2 units.

119. **a.** $(f - g)(x) = f(x) - g(x)$
$$= \sqrt{x} - \left(\sqrt{x} - 2\right)$$
$$= \sqrt{x} - \sqrt{x} + 2$$
$$= 2$$

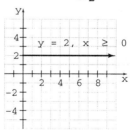

   b. $\sqrt{x} \geq 0$, so $x \geq 0$
The domain is $\{x | x \text{ is a real number, } x \geq 0\}$.

121. $f(x) = \sqrt{x^2}$

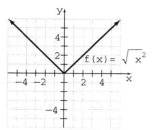

123. A rational number is a number that can be expressed as the quotient of two integers with nonzero denominator.

125. An irrational number is any real number that cannot be expressed as the quotient of two integers.

127. $E = \dfrac{1}{2}mv^2$
$$2E = 2\left(\dfrac{1}{2}mv^2\right)$$
$$2E = mv^2$$
$$\dfrac{2E}{v^2} = \dfrac{mv^2}{v^2}$$
$$\dfrac{2E}{v^2} = m \text{ or } m = \dfrac{2E}{v^2}$$

Exercise Set 7.5

1. a. The conjugate of a binomial is a binomial with the same two terms as the original but the sign of the second term is changed. The conjugate of $a + b$ is $a - b$. Also, the conjugate of $a - b$ is $a + b$.

   b. The conjugate of $x - \sqrt{3}$ is $x + \sqrt{3}$.

3. a. Answers will vary. Possible answer: Multiply the numerator and denominator by a quantity that will result in no radicals in the denominator.

   b. $\dfrac{4}{\sqrt{3y}} = \dfrac{4}{\sqrt{3y}} \cdot \dfrac{\sqrt{3y}}{\sqrt{3y}} = \dfrac{4\sqrt{3y}}{\sqrt{9y^2}} = \dfrac{4\sqrt{3y}}{3y}$

5. (1) No perfect powers are factors of any radicand.

   (2) No radicand contains fractions.

   (3) No radicals are in any denominator.

7. $\dfrac{1}{\sqrt{3}} = \dfrac{1}{\sqrt{3}} \cdot \dfrac{\sqrt{3}}{\sqrt{3}} = \dfrac{\sqrt{3}}{3}$

9. $\dfrac{3}{\sqrt{7}} = \dfrac{3}{\sqrt{7}} \cdot \dfrac{\sqrt{7}}{\sqrt{7}} = \dfrac{3\sqrt{7}}{7}$

11. $\dfrac{1}{\sqrt{17}} = \dfrac{1}{\sqrt{17}} \cdot \dfrac{\sqrt{17}}{\sqrt{17}} = \dfrac{\sqrt{17}}{17}$

13. $\dfrac{7}{\sqrt{7}} = \dfrac{7}{\sqrt{7}} \cdot \dfrac{\sqrt{7}}{\sqrt{7}} = \dfrac{7\sqrt{7}}{7} = \sqrt{7}$

15. $\dfrac{p}{\sqrt{2}} = \dfrac{p}{\sqrt{2}} \cdot \dfrac{\sqrt{2}}{\sqrt{2}} = \dfrac{p\sqrt{2}}{2}$

17. $\dfrac{\sqrt{y}}{\sqrt{5}} = \dfrac{\sqrt{y}}{\sqrt{5}} \cdot \dfrac{\sqrt{5}}{\sqrt{5}} = \dfrac{\sqrt{5y}}{5}$

19. $\dfrac{5\sqrt{3}}{\sqrt{5}} = \dfrac{5\sqrt{3}}{\sqrt{5}} \cdot \dfrac{\sqrt{5}}{\sqrt{5}} = \dfrac{5\sqrt{15}}{5} = \sqrt{15}$

21. $\dfrac{\sqrt{x}}{\sqrt{y}} = \dfrac{\sqrt{x}}{\sqrt{y}} \cdot \dfrac{\sqrt{y}}{\sqrt{y}} = \dfrac{\sqrt{xy}}{y}$

23. $\sqrt{\dfrac{5m}{8}} = \dfrac{\sqrt{5m}}{\sqrt{8}}$

$= \dfrac{\sqrt{5m}}{2\sqrt{2}}$

$= \dfrac{\sqrt{5m}}{2\sqrt{2}} \cdot \dfrac{\sqrt{2}}{\sqrt{2}}$

$= \dfrac{\sqrt{10m}}{2 \cdot 2} = \dfrac{\sqrt{10m}}{4}$

25. $\dfrac{2n}{\sqrt{18n}} = \dfrac{2n}{\sqrt{9}\sqrt{2n}}$

$= \dfrac{2n}{3\sqrt{2n}}$

$= \dfrac{2n}{3\sqrt{2n}} \cdot \dfrac{\sqrt{2n}}{\sqrt{2n}}$

$= \dfrac{2n\sqrt{2n}}{3 \cdot 2n} = \dfrac{\sqrt{2n}}{3}$

27. $\sqrt{\dfrac{18x^4 y^3}{2z^3}} = \sqrt{\dfrac{9x^4 y^3}{z^3}} = \dfrac{\sqrt{9x^4 y^3}}{\sqrt{z^2 \cdot z}}$

$= \dfrac{\sqrt{9x^4 y^2}\sqrt{y}}{\sqrt{z^2}\sqrt{z}}$

$= \dfrac{3x^2 y\sqrt{y}}{z\sqrt{z}}$

$= \dfrac{3x^2 y\sqrt{y}}{z\sqrt{z}} \cdot \dfrac{\sqrt{z}}{\sqrt{z}}$

$= \dfrac{3x^2 y\sqrt{yz}}{z^2}$

29. $\sqrt{\dfrac{20y^4 z^3}{3xy^{-2}}} = \sqrt{\dfrac{20y^6 z^3}{3x}}$

$= \dfrac{\sqrt{20y^6 z^3}}{\sqrt{3x}}$

$= \dfrac{\sqrt{4y^6 z^2}\sqrt{5z}}{\sqrt{3x}}$

$= \dfrac{2y^3 z\sqrt{5z}}{\sqrt{3x}}$

$= \dfrac{2y^3 z\sqrt{5z}}{\sqrt{3x}} \cdot \dfrac{\sqrt{3x}}{\sqrt{3x}}$

$= \dfrac{2y^3 z\sqrt{15xz}}{3x}$

31. $\sqrt{\dfrac{75x^6 y^5}{3z^3}} = \sqrt{\dfrac{25x^6 y^5}{z^3}} = \dfrac{\sqrt{25x^6 y^5}}{\sqrt{z^2 \cdot z}}$

$= \dfrac{\sqrt{25x^6 y^4}\sqrt{y}}{\sqrt{z^2}\sqrt{z}}$

$= \dfrac{5x^3 y^2\sqrt{y}}{z\sqrt{z}}$

$= \dfrac{5x^3 y^2\sqrt{y}}{z\sqrt{z}} \cdot \dfrac{\sqrt{z}}{\sqrt{z}}$

$= \dfrac{5x^3 y^2\sqrt{yz}}{z^2}$

33. $\dfrac{1}{\sqrt[3]{2}} = \dfrac{1}{\sqrt[3]{2}} \cdot \dfrac{\sqrt[3]{4}}{\sqrt[3]{4}} = \dfrac{\sqrt[3]{4}}{\sqrt[3]{8}} = \dfrac{\sqrt[3]{4}}{2}$

35. $\dfrac{3}{\sqrt[3]{x}} = \dfrac{3}{\sqrt[3]{x}} \cdot \dfrac{\sqrt[3]{x^2}}{\sqrt[3]{x^2}} = \dfrac{3\sqrt[3]{x^2}}{x}$

37. $\dfrac{1}{\sqrt[4]{2}} = \dfrac{1}{\sqrt[4]{2}} \cdot \dfrac{\sqrt[4]{8}}{\sqrt[4]{8}} = \dfrac{\sqrt[4]{8}}{\sqrt[4]{16}} = \dfrac{\sqrt[4]{8}}{2}$

39. $\dfrac{z}{\sqrt[4]{8}} = \dfrac{z}{\sqrt[4]{8}} \cdot \dfrac{\sqrt[4]{2}}{\sqrt[4]{2}} = \dfrac{z\sqrt[4]{2}}{\sqrt[4]{16}} = \dfrac{z\sqrt[4]{2}}{2}$

41. $\dfrac{x}{\sqrt[4]{z^2}} = \dfrac{x}{\sqrt[4]{z^2}} \cdot \dfrac{\sqrt[4]{z^2}}{\sqrt[4]{z^2}} = \dfrac{x\sqrt[4]{z^2}}{\sqrt[4]{z^4}} = \dfrac{x\sqrt[4]{z^2}}{z}$

43. $\dfrac{13}{\sqrt[5]{y^2}} = \dfrac{13}{\sqrt[5]{y^2}} \cdot \dfrac{\sqrt[5]{y^3}}{\sqrt[5]{y^3}} = \dfrac{13\sqrt[5]{y^3}}{\sqrt[5]{y^5}} = \dfrac{13\sqrt[5]{y^3}}{y}$

45. $\dfrac{3}{\sqrt[7]{a^3}} = \dfrac{3}{\sqrt[7]{a^3}} \cdot \dfrac{\sqrt[7]{a^4}}{\sqrt[7]{a^4}} = \dfrac{3\sqrt[7]{a^4}}{\sqrt[7]{a^7}} = \dfrac{3\sqrt[7]{a^4}}{a}$

47. $\sqrt[3]{\dfrac{1}{4x}} = \dfrac{\sqrt[3]{1}}{\sqrt[3]{4x}} = \dfrac{1}{\sqrt[3]{4x}} \cdot \dfrac{\sqrt[3]{2x^2}}{\sqrt[3]{2x^2}} = \dfrac{\sqrt[3]{2x^2}}{2x}$

49. $\dfrac{5m}{\sqrt[4]{2}} = \dfrac{5m}{\sqrt[4]{2}} \cdot \dfrac{\sqrt[4]{2^3}}{\sqrt[4]{2^3}} = \dfrac{5m\sqrt[4]{8}}{2}$

51. $\sqrt[4]{\dfrac{5}{3x^3}} = \dfrac{\sqrt[4]{5}}{\sqrt[4]{3x^3}} \cdot \dfrac{\sqrt[4]{3^3x}}{\sqrt[4]{3^3x}} = \dfrac{\sqrt[4]{135x}}{3x}$

53. $\sqrt[3]{\dfrac{3x^2}{2y^2}} = \dfrac{\sqrt[3]{3x^2}}{\sqrt[3]{2y^2}} \cdot \dfrac{\sqrt[3]{4y}}{\sqrt[3]{4y}}$

$\qquad = \dfrac{\sqrt[3]{12x^2y}}{2y}$

55. $\sqrt[3]{\dfrac{8xy^2}{2z^2}} = \sqrt[3]{\dfrac{4xy^2}{z^2}}$

$\qquad = \dfrac{\sqrt[3]{4xy^2}}{\sqrt[3]{z^2}}$

$\qquad = \dfrac{\sqrt[3]{4xy^2}}{\sqrt[3]{z^2}} \cdot \dfrac{\sqrt[3]{z}}{\sqrt[3]{z}}$

$\qquad = \dfrac{\sqrt[3]{4xy^2z}}{z}$

57. $\dfrac{1}{\sqrt{3}+1} = \dfrac{1}{\sqrt{3}+1} \cdot \dfrac{\left(\sqrt{3}-1\right)}{\left(\sqrt{3}-1\right)}$

$\qquad = \dfrac{\sqrt{3}-1}{\left(\sqrt{3}\right)^2 - 1^2}$

$\qquad = \dfrac{\sqrt{3}-1}{3-1}$

$\qquad = \dfrac{\sqrt{3}-1}{2}$

59. $\dfrac{1}{2+\sqrt{3}} = \dfrac{1}{2+\sqrt{3}} \cdot \dfrac{\left(2-\sqrt{3}\right)}{\left(2-\sqrt{3}\right)}$

$\qquad = \dfrac{2-\sqrt{3}}{2^2 - (\sqrt{3})^2}$

$\qquad = \dfrac{2-\sqrt{3}}{4-3}$

$\qquad = \dfrac{2-\sqrt{3}}{1}$

$\qquad = 2-\sqrt{3}$

61. $\dfrac{4}{\sqrt{2}-7} = \dfrac{4}{\sqrt{2}-7} \cdot \dfrac{\left(\sqrt{2}+7\right)}{\left(\sqrt{2}+7\right)}$

$\qquad = \dfrac{4\sqrt{2}+28}{2-49}$

$\qquad = \dfrac{4\sqrt{2}+28}{-47}$

$\qquad = \dfrac{-4\sqrt{2}-28}{47}$

63. $\dfrac{\sqrt{5}}{2\sqrt{5}-\sqrt{6}} = \dfrac{\sqrt{5}}{2\sqrt{5}-\sqrt{6}} \cdot \dfrac{\left(2\sqrt{5}+\sqrt{6}\right)}{\left(2\sqrt{5}+\sqrt{6}\right)}$

$\qquad = \dfrac{10+\sqrt{30}}{20-6} = \dfrac{10+\sqrt{30}}{14}$

65. $\dfrac{2}{6+\sqrt{x}} = \dfrac{2}{6+\sqrt{x}} \cdot \dfrac{\left(6-\sqrt{x}\right)}{\left(6-\sqrt{x}\right)}$

$\qquad = \dfrac{12-2\sqrt{x}}{36-x}$

67.
$$\frac{4\sqrt{x}}{\sqrt{x}-y} = \frac{4\sqrt{x}}{\sqrt{x}-y} \cdot \frac{\left(\sqrt{x}+y\right)}{\left(\sqrt{x}+y\right)}$$
$$= \frac{4x+4y\sqrt{x}}{x-y^2}$$

69.
$$\frac{\sqrt{2}-2\sqrt{3}}{\sqrt{2}+4\sqrt{3}} = \frac{\sqrt{2}-2\sqrt{3}}{\sqrt{2}+4\sqrt{3}} \cdot \frac{\left(\sqrt{2}-4\sqrt{3}\right)}{\left(\sqrt{2}-4\sqrt{3}\right)}$$
$$= \frac{2-4\sqrt{6}-2\sqrt{6}+8\cdot3}{2-16\cdot3}$$
$$= \frac{26-6\sqrt{6}}{-46} = \frac{-13+3\sqrt{6}}{23}$$

71.
$$\frac{\sqrt{a^3}+\sqrt{a^7}}{\sqrt{a}} = \frac{\sqrt{a^3}+\sqrt{a^7}}{\sqrt{a}} \cdot \frac{\left(\sqrt{a}\right)}{\left(\sqrt{a}\right)}$$
$$= \frac{\sqrt{a^4}+\sqrt{a^8}}{a}$$
$$= \frac{a^2+a^4}{a} = a+a^3$$

73.
$$\frac{2}{\sqrt{x+2}-3} = \frac{2}{\sqrt{x+2}-3} \cdot \frac{\left(\sqrt{x+2}+3\right)}{\left(\sqrt{x+2}+3\right)}$$
$$= \frac{2\sqrt{x+2}+6}{\left(\sqrt{x+2}\right)^2 - 3^2}$$
$$= \frac{2\sqrt{x+2}+6}{x+2-9} = \frac{2\sqrt{x+2}+6}{x-7}$$

75. $\sqrt{\dfrac{x}{9}} = \dfrac{\sqrt{x}}{\sqrt{9}} = \dfrac{\sqrt{x}}{3}$

77. $\sqrt{\dfrac{2}{5}} = \dfrac{\sqrt{2}}{\sqrt{5}} = \dfrac{\sqrt{2}}{\sqrt{5}} \cdot \dfrac{\sqrt{5}}{\sqrt{5}} = \dfrac{\sqrt{10}}{5}$

79. $\left(\sqrt{5}+\sqrt{6}\right)\left(\sqrt{5}-\sqrt{6}\right) = \left(\sqrt{5}\right)^2 - \left(\sqrt{6}\right)^2$
$$= 5 - 6 = -1$$

81.
$$\sqrt{\frac{24x^3y^6}{5z}} = \frac{\sqrt{24x^3y^6}}{\sqrt{5z}}$$
$$= \frac{\sqrt{4x^2y^6}\,\sqrt{6x}}{\sqrt{5z}}$$
$$= \frac{2xy^3\sqrt{6x}}{\sqrt{5z}} \cdot \frac{\sqrt{5z}}{\sqrt{5z}} = \frac{2xy^3\sqrt{30xz}}{5z}$$

83.
$$\sqrt{\frac{12xy^4}{2x^3y^4}} = \sqrt{\frac{6}{x^2}} = \frac{\sqrt{6}}{\sqrt{x^2}} = \frac{\sqrt{6}}{x}$$

85.
$$\frac{1}{\sqrt{a}+3} = \frac{1}{\sqrt{a}+3} \cdot \frac{\sqrt{a}-3}{\sqrt{a}-3}$$
$$= \frac{\sqrt{a}-3}{\left(\sqrt{a}+3\right)\left(\sqrt{a}-3\right)}$$
$$= \frac{\sqrt{a}-3}{\left(\sqrt{a}\right)^2 - (3)^2}$$
$$= \frac{\sqrt{a}-3}{a-9}$$

87.
$$-\frac{7\sqrt{x}}{\sqrt{98}} = -\frac{7\sqrt{x}}{7\sqrt{2}}$$
$$= -\frac{\sqrt{x}}{\sqrt{2}} \cdot \frac{\sqrt{2}}{\sqrt{2}}$$
$$= -\frac{\sqrt{2x}}{\sqrt{4}} = -\frac{\sqrt{2x}}{2}$$

89.
$$\sqrt[4]{\frac{3y^2}{2x}} = \frac{\sqrt[4]{3y^2}}{\sqrt[4]{2x}} \cdot \frac{\sqrt[4]{8x^3}}{\sqrt[4]{8x^3}}$$
$$= \frac{\sqrt[4]{24x^3y^2}}{\sqrt[4]{16x^4}} = \frac{\sqrt[4]{24x^3y^2}}{2x}$$

91.
$$\sqrt[3]{\frac{32y^{12}z^{10}}{2x}} = \sqrt[3]{\frac{16y^{12}z^{10}}{x}}$$
$$= \frac{\sqrt[3]{16y^{12}z^{10}}}{\sqrt[3]{x}}$$
$$= \frac{\sqrt[3]{8y^{12}z^9}\,\sqrt[3]{2z}}{\sqrt[3]{x}}$$
$$= \frac{2y^4z^3\sqrt[3]{2z}}{\sqrt[3]{x}} \cdot \frac{\sqrt[3]{x^2}}{\sqrt[3]{x^2}}$$
$$= \frac{2y^4z^3\sqrt[3]{2x^2z}}{\sqrt[3]{x^3}}$$
$$= \frac{2y^4z^3\sqrt[3]{2x^2z}}{x}$$

93.
$$\frac{\sqrt{ar}}{\sqrt{a}-2\sqrt{r}} \cdot \frac{\left(\sqrt{a}+2\sqrt{r}\right)}{\left(\sqrt{a}+2\sqrt{r}\right)} = \frac{\sqrt{ar}\left(\sqrt{a}+2\sqrt{r}\right)}{\left(\sqrt{a}\right)^2 - \left(2\sqrt{r}\right)^2}$$
$$= \frac{a\sqrt{r}+2r\sqrt{a}}{a-4r}$$

95.
$$\frac{\sqrt[3]{6x}}{\sqrt[3]{5xy}} = \sqrt[3]{\frac{6x}{5xy}}$$
$$= \sqrt[3]{\frac{6}{5y}}$$
$$= \frac{\sqrt[3]{6}}{\sqrt[3]{5y}} \cdot \frac{\sqrt[3]{25y^2}}{\sqrt[3]{25y^2}} = \frac{\sqrt[3]{150y^2}}{5y}$$

97.
$$\sqrt[4]{\frac{2x^7 y^{12} z^4}{3x^9}} = \sqrt[4]{\frac{2y^{12} z^4}{3x^2}}$$
$$= \frac{\sqrt[4]{2y^{12} z^4}}{\sqrt[4]{3x^2}}$$
$$= \frac{\sqrt[4]{y^{12} z^4} \sqrt[4]{2}}{\sqrt[4]{3x^2}}$$
$$= \frac{y^3 z \sqrt[4]{2}}{\sqrt[4]{3x^2}} \cdot \frac{\sqrt[4]{27x^2}}{\sqrt[4]{27x^2}}$$
$$= \frac{y^3 z \sqrt[4]{54x^2}}{\sqrt[4]{81x^4}}$$
$$= \frac{y^3 z \sqrt[4]{54x^2}}{3x}$$

99.
$$\frac{1}{\sqrt{2}} + \frac{\sqrt{2}}{2} = \frac{1}{\sqrt{2}} \cdot \frac{\sqrt{2}}{\sqrt{2}} + \frac{\sqrt{2}}{2}$$
$$= \frac{\sqrt{2}}{\sqrt{4}} + \frac{\sqrt{2}}{2}$$
$$= \frac{\sqrt{2}}{2} + \frac{\sqrt{2}}{2}$$
$$= \frac{2\sqrt{2}}{2}$$
$$= \sqrt{2}$$

101.
$$\sqrt{5} - \frac{1}{\sqrt{5}} = \sqrt{5} - \frac{1}{\sqrt{5}} \cdot \frac{\sqrt{5}}{\sqrt{5}}$$
$$= \sqrt{5} - \frac{\sqrt{5}}{5}$$
$$= \frac{5\sqrt{5} - \sqrt{5}}{5}$$
$$= \frac{4\sqrt{5}}{5}$$

103.
$$\sqrt{\frac{1}{6}} + \sqrt{24} = \frac{1}{\sqrt{6}} + 2\sqrt{6}$$
$$= \frac{1}{\sqrt{6}} \cdot \frac{\sqrt{6}}{\sqrt{6}} + 2\sqrt{6}$$
$$= \frac{\sqrt{6}}{6} + 2\sqrt{6}$$

$$= \frac{\sqrt{6}}{6} + \frac{(2\sqrt{6})6}{6}$$
$$= \frac{\sqrt{6}}{6} + \frac{12\sqrt{6}}{6}$$
$$= \frac{13\sqrt{6}}{6}$$

105.
$$3\sqrt{2} - \frac{2}{\sqrt{8}} + \sqrt{50}$$
$$= 3\sqrt{2} - \frac{2}{\sqrt{8}} \cdot \frac{\sqrt{8}}{\sqrt{8}} + \sqrt{25}\sqrt{2}$$
$$= 3\sqrt{2} - \frac{2\sqrt{4}\sqrt{2}}{\sqrt{64}} + 5\sqrt{2}$$
$$= \frac{3\sqrt{2}}{1} - \frac{4\sqrt{2}}{8} + \frac{5\sqrt{2}}{1}$$
$$= \frac{6\sqrt{2}}{2} - \frac{\sqrt{2}}{2} + \frac{10\sqrt{2}}{2}$$
$$= \frac{(6 - 1 + 10)\sqrt{2}}{2}$$
$$= \frac{15\sqrt{2}}{2}$$

107.
$$\sqrt{\frac{1}{2}} + 3\sqrt{2} + \sqrt{18}$$
$$= \frac{\sqrt{1}}{\sqrt{2}} \cdot \frac{\sqrt{2}}{\sqrt{2}} + 3\sqrt{2} + \sqrt{9} \cdot \sqrt{2}$$
$$= \frac{\sqrt{2}}{\sqrt{4}} + 3\sqrt{2} + 3\sqrt{2}$$
$$= \frac{\sqrt{2}}{2} + 6\sqrt{2}$$
$$= \frac{\sqrt{2}}{2} + \frac{12\sqrt{2}}{2}$$
$$= \frac{13\sqrt{2}}{2}$$

109.
$$\frac{2}{\sqrt{50}} - 3\sqrt{50} - \frac{1}{\sqrt{8}}$$
$$= \frac{2}{5\sqrt{2}} - 3\left(5\sqrt{2}\right) - \frac{1}{2\sqrt{2}}$$
$$= \frac{2}{5\sqrt{2}} \cdot \frac{\sqrt{2}}{\sqrt{2}} - 15\sqrt{2} - \frac{1}{2\sqrt{2}} \cdot \frac{\sqrt{2}}{\sqrt{2}}$$
$$= \frac{2\sqrt{2}}{10} - 15\sqrt{2} - \frac{\sqrt{2}}{4}$$
$$= \frac{\sqrt{2}}{5} - 15\sqrt{2} - \frac{\sqrt{2}}{4}$$
$$= \frac{4\sqrt{2}}{20} - \frac{300\sqrt{2}}{20} - \frac{5\sqrt{2}}{20}$$
$$= \frac{-301\sqrt{2}}{20}$$

111.
$$\sqrt{\frac{3}{8}} + \sqrt{\frac{3}{2}} = \frac{\sqrt{3}}{\sqrt{8}} + \frac{\sqrt{3}}{\sqrt{2}}$$
$$= \frac{\sqrt{3}}{2\sqrt{2}} + \frac{\sqrt{3}}{\sqrt{2}}$$
$$= \frac{\sqrt{3}}{2\sqrt{2}} \cdot \frac{\sqrt{2}}{\sqrt{2}} + \frac{\sqrt{3}}{\sqrt{2}} \cdot \frac{2\sqrt{2}}{2\sqrt{2}}$$
$$= \frac{\sqrt{6}}{4} + \frac{2\sqrt{6}}{4}$$
$$= \frac{3\sqrt{6}}{4}$$

113.
$$-2\sqrt{\frac{x}{y}} + 3\sqrt{\frac{y}{x}} = -2\frac{\sqrt{x}}{\sqrt{y}} + 3\frac{\sqrt{y}}{\sqrt{x}}$$
$$= -2\frac{\sqrt{x}}{\sqrt{y}} \cdot \frac{\sqrt{y}}{\sqrt{y}} + 3\frac{\sqrt{y}}{\sqrt{x}} \cdot \frac{\sqrt{x}}{\sqrt{x}}$$
$$= -2\frac{\sqrt{xy}}{y} + 3\frac{\sqrt{xy}}{x}$$
$$= \left(-\frac{2}{y} + \frac{3}{x}\right)\sqrt{xy}$$

115.
$$\frac{3}{\sqrt{a}} - \sqrt{\frac{9}{a}} + \sqrt{a} = \frac{3}{\sqrt{a}} - \frac{\sqrt{9}}{\sqrt{a}} + \sqrt{a}$$
$$= \frac{3}{\sqrt{a}}\left(\frac{\sqrt{a}}{\sqrt{a}}\right) - \frac{\sqrt{9}}{\sqrt{a}}\left(\frac{\sqrt{a}}{\sqrt{a}}\right) + \sqrt{a}$$
$$= \frac{3\sqrt{a}}{a} - \frac{3\sqrt{a}}{a} + \sqrt{a}$$
$$= \sqrt{a}$$

117.
$$\frac{\sqrt{(a+b)^4}}{\sqrt[3]{a+b}} = \frac{(a+b)^{4/2}}{(a+b)^{1/3}}$$
$$= (a+b)^{6/3 - 1/3}$$
$$= (a+b)^{5/3} = \sqrt[3]{(a+b)^5}$$

119.
$$\frac{\sqrt[5]{(a+2b)^4}}{\sqrt[3]{(a+2b)^2}} = \frac{(a+2b)^{4/5}}{(a+2b)^{2/3}}$$
$$= (a+2b)^{4/5 - 2/3}$$
$$= (a+2b)^{2/15} = \sqrt[15]{(a+2b)^2}$$

121.
$$\frac{\sqrt[3]{r^2 s^4}}{\sqrt{rs}} = \frac{(r^2 s^4)^{1/3}}{(rs)^{1/2}}$$
$$= \frac{r^{2/3} s^{4/3}}{r^{1/2} s^{1/2}}$$
$$= r^{2/3 - 1/2} s^{4/3 - 1/2}$$
$$= r^{1/6} s^{5/6}$$
$$= (rs^5)^{1/6}$$
$$= \sqrt[6]{rs^5}$$

123.
$$\frac{\sqrt[5]{x^4 y^6}}{\sqrt[3]{(xy)^2}} = \frac{(x^4 y^6)^{1/5}}{(xy)^{2/3}}$$
$$= \frac{x^{4/5} y^{6/5}}{x^{2/3} y^{2/3}}$$
$$= x^{4/5 - 2/3} y^{6/5 - 2/3}$$
$$= x^{2/15} y^{8/15}$$
$$= (x^2 y^8)^{1/15}$$
$$= \sqrt[15]{x^2 y^8}$$

125.
$$d = \sqrt{\frac{72}{I}}$$
$$d = \sqrt{\frac{72}{5.3}} \approx 3.69$$
The person is about 3.69 m from the light source.

127.
$$r = \sqrt[3]{\frac{3V}{4\pi}}$$
$$r = \sqrt[3]{\frac{3(7238.23)}{4\pi}} = 12$$
The radius of the tank is 12 inches.

129.
$$N(t) = \frac{6.21}{\sqrt[4]{t}}$$

a. $t = 1960 - 1959 = 1$
$$N(1) = \frac{6.21}{\sqrt[4]{1}} = 6.21$$
The number of farms in 1960 was 6.21 million.

b. $t = 2007 - 1959 = 48$
$$N(48) = \frac{6.21}{\sqrt[4]{48}} \approx 2.36$$
The number of farms in 2007 will be about 2.36 million.

131.

$$\frac{2}{\sqrt{2}} = \frac{2}{\sqrt{2}} \cdot \frac{\sqrt{2}}{\sqrt{2}} = \frac{2\sqrt{2}}{\sqrt{4}} = \frac{2\sqrt{2}}{2} = \sqrt{2}$$

$$\frac{3}{\sqrt{3}} = \frac{3}{\sqrt{3}} \cdot \frac{\sqrt{3}}{\sqrt{3}} = \frac{3\sqrt{3}}{\sqrt{9}} = \frac{3\sqrt{3}}{3} = \sqrt{3}$$

Since $3 > 2$, then $\sqrt{3} > \sqrt{2}$ and we conclude that $\frac{3}{\sqrt{3}} > \frac{2}{\sqrt{2}}$.

133.

$$\frac{1}{\sqrt{3}+2} = \frac{1}{\sqrt{3}+2} \cdot \frac{\sqrt{3}-2}{\sqrt{3}-2}$$

$$= \frac{\sqrt{3}-2}{\left(\sqrt{3}\right)^2 - 2^2}$$

$$= \frac{\sqrt{3}-2}{3-4}$$

$$= \frac{\sqrt{3}-2}{-1}$$

$$= -\sqrt{3}+2$$

$$= 2 - \sqrt{3}$$

$$2 + \sqrt{3} > 2 - \sqrt{3}$$

Therefore, $2 + \sqrt{3} > \dfrac{1}{\sqrt{3}+2}$.

135. $f(x) = x^{a/2}$, $g(x) = x^{b/3}$

a. $x^{4/2} = x^2$

$x^{12/2} = x^6$

$x^{8/2} = x^4$

Therefore $x^{a/2}$ is a perfect square when $a = 4, 8, 12$.

b. $x^{9/3} = x^3$

$x^{18/3} = x^6$

$x^{27/3} = x^9$

Therefore, $x^{b/3}$ is a perfect cube when $b = 9, 18, 27$.

c. $(f \cdot g)(x) = f(x) \cdot g(x)$

$$= x^{a/2} \cdot x^{b/3}$$

$$= x^{a/2+b/3}$$

$$= x^{3a/6+2b/6}$$

$$= x^{(3a+2b)/6}$$

d. $\left(\dfrac{f}{g}\right)(x) = \dfrac{f(x)}{g(x)}$

$$= \frac{x^{a/2}}{x^{b/3}}$$

$$= x^{a/2-b/3}$$

$$= x^{3a/6-2b/6}$$

$$= x^{(3a-2b)/6}$$

137.

$$\frac{3}{\sqrt{2a-3b}} = \frac{3}{\sqrt{2a-3b}} \cdot \frac{\sqrt{2a-3b}}{\sqrt{2a-3b}}$$

$$= \frac{3\sqrt{2a-3b}}{2a-3b}$$

139.

$$\frac{5-\sqrt{5}}{6} = \frac{5-\sqrt{5}}{6} \cdot \frac{5+\sqrt{5}}{5+\sqrt{5}}$$

$$= \frac{25-5}{30+6\sqrt{5}}$$

$$= \frac{20}{2(15+3\sqrt{5})}$$

$$= \frac{10}{15+3\sqrt{5}}$$

141.

$$\frac{\sqrt{x+h}-\sqrt{x}}{h} = \frac{\sqrt{x+h}-\sqrt{x}}{h} \cdot \frac{\sqrt{x+h}+\sqrt{x}}{\sqrt{x+h}+\sqrt{x}}$$

$$= \frac{x+h-x}{h\left(\sqrt{x+h}+\sqrt{x}\right)}$$

$$= \frac{h}{h\left(\sqrt{x+h}+\sqrt{x}\right)}$$

$$= \frac{1}{\sqrt{x+h}+\sqrt{x}}$$

145. Let r be the rate of the slower car and $r + 10$ be the rate of the faster.

Distance the first traveled plus distance the second traveled is 270 miles.

$$3r + 3(r+10) = 270$$

$$3r + 3r + 30 = 270$$

$$6r + 30 = 270$$

$$6r = 240$$

$$r = 40$$

The rate of the slower car is 40 mph and the rate of the faster car is $r + 10 = 50$ mph.

147.
$$\frac{x}{2} - \frac{4}{x} = -\frac{7}{2}$$
$$2x\left(\frac{x}{2} - \frac{4}{x}\right) = 2x\left(-\frac{7}{2}\right)$$
$$x^2 - 8 = -7x$$
$$x^2 + 7x - 8 = 0$$
$$(x+8)(x-1) = 0$$
$$x = -8 \text{ or } 1$$

Exercise Set 7.6

1. a. Answers will vary.

b.
$$\sqrt{2x + 26} - 2 = 4$$
$$\sqrt{2x + 26} - 2 + 2 = 4 + 2$$
$$\sqrt{2x + 26} = 6$$
$$\left(\sqrt{2x + 26}\right)^2 = 6^2$$
$$2x + 26 = 36$$
$$2x = 10$$
$$x = \frac{10}{2}$$
$$x = 5$$

3. 0 is the only solution to the equation. For all other values, the left side of the equation is negative and the right side is positive.

5. Answers will vary. Possible answer:
The equation has no solution since the left side is a positive number whereas the right side is 0. A positive number is never equal to 0.
Also, the equation can be written as $\sqrt{x-3} = -3$ for which the left side is positive and the right side is negative. It is impossible for $\sqrt{x-3}$ to equal a negative number.

7. One solution, $x = 9$.

9.
$$\sqrt{x} = 4$$
$$\left(\sqrt{x}\right)^2 = 4^2$$
$$x = 16$$

11. $\sqrt{x} = -9$ No solution.

13.
$$\sqrt[3]{x} = -4$$
$$\left(\sqrt[3]{x}\right)^3 = (-4)^3$$
$$x = -64$$

15.
$$-\sqrt{2x+4} = -6$$
$$\left(-\sqrt{2x+4}\right)^2 = (-6)^2$$
$$2x + 4 = 36$$
$$2x = 32$$
$$x = 16$$
Check:
$$-\sqrt{2x+4} = -6$$
$$-\sqrt{2(16)+4} = -6$$
$$-\sqrt{32+4} = -6$$
$$-\sqrt{36} = -6$$
$$-6 = -6 \quad \text{True}$$

17.
$$\sqrt[3]{3x} + 4 = 7$$
$$\sqrt[3]{3x} = 3$$
$$\left(\sqrt[3]{3x}\right)^3 = (3)^3$$
$$3x = 27$$
$$x = 9$$

19.
$$\sqrt[3]{2x+29} = 3$$
$$\left(\sqrt[3]{2x+29}\right)^3 = 3^3$$
$$2x + 29 = 27$$
$$2x = -2$$
$$x = -1$$

21.
$$\sqrt[4]{x} = 2$$
$$\left(\sqrt[4]{x}\right)^4 = 2^4$$
$$x = 16$$

23.
$$\sqrt[4]{x+5} = 3$$
$$\left(\sqrt[4]{x+5}\right)^4 = 3^4$$
$$x + 5 = 81$$
$$x = 76$$

25. $\sqrt[4]{2x+1}+5=1$

   $\sqrt[4]{2x+1}=-4 \Rightarrow$ no solution

27. $\sqrt{x+8}=\sqrt{x-8}$

   $\left(\sqrt{x+8}\right)^2=\left(\sqrt{x-8}\right)^2$

   $x+8=x-8$

   $8=-8 \Rightarrow$ no solution

29. $\sqrt[3]{6t+1}=\sqrt[3]{2t+5}$

   $\left(\sqrt[3]{6t+1}\right)^3=\left(\sqrt[3]{2t+5}\right)^3$

   $6t+1=2t+5$

   $4t=4$

   $t=1$

31.

33. $\sqrt[4]{3x+1}-4=0$

   $\sqrt[4]{3x+1}=4$

   $\left(\sqrt[4]{3x+1}\right)^4=(4)^4$

   $3x+1=16$

   $3x=15$

   $x=5$

35. $\sqrt{m^2+6m-4}=m$

   $\left(\sqrt{m^2+6m-4}\right)^2=(m)^2$

   $m^2+6m-4=m^2$

   $6m-4=0$

   $6m=4$

   $m=\dfrac{2}{3}$

37. $\sqrt{6c+1}-11=0$

   $\sqrt{6c+1}=11$

   $\left(\sqrt{6c+1}\right)^2=11^2$

   $6c+1=121$

   $6c=120$

   $c=20$

39. $\sqrt{z^2+3}=z+1$

   $\left(\sqrt{z^2+3}\right)^2=(z+1)^2$

   $z^2+3=z^2+2z+1$

   $3=2z+1$

   $2=2z$

   $1=z$

41. $\sqrt{2y+5}=y-5$

   $\left(\sqrt{2y+5}\right)^2=(y-5)^2$

   $2y+5=y^2-10y+25$

   $0=y^2-12y+20$

   $0=(y-10)(y-2)$

   $y=10$ or $y=2$

   Check:

   $\sqrt{2y+5}=y-5$

   $\sqrt{2(10)+5}=(10)-5$

   $\sqrt{25}=5$

   $5=5$ True

   Check:

   $\sqrt{2y+5}=y-5$

   $\sqrt{2(2)+5}=(2)-5$

   $\sqrt{9}=-3$

   $3=-3$ False

   This check shows that 10 is the only solution to this equation.

43. $\sqrt{5x+6}=2x-6$

   $\left(\sqrt{5x+6}\right)^2=(2x-6)^2$

   $5x+6=4x^2-24x+36$

   $0=4x^2-29x+30$

   $0=(4x-5)(x-6)$

   $x=\dfrac{5}{4}$ or $y=6$

   Check:

   $\sqrt{5x+6}=2x-6$

   $\sqrt{5\left(\frac{5}{4}\right)+6}=2\left(\frac{5}{4}\right)-6$

   $\sqrt{\dfrac{49}{4}}=-\dfrac{14}{4}$

   $\dfrac{7}{2}=-\dfrac{7}{2}$ False

Check:
$$\sqrt{5x+6} = 2x-6$$
$$\sqrt{5(6)+6} = 2(6)-6$$
$$\sqrt{36} = 12-6$$
$$6 = 6 \quad \text{True}$$
This check shows that 6 is the only solution to this equation.

45. $(2a+9)^{1/2} - a + 3 = 0$
$$(2a+9)^{1/2} = a-3$$
$$[(2a+9)^{1/2}]^2 = (a-3)^2$$
$$2a+9 = a^2 - 6a + 9$$
$$0 = a^2 - 8a$$
$$0 = a(a-8)$$
$$a = 0 \quad \text{or} \quad a = 8$$
Check:
$$(2a+9)^{1/2} - a + 3 = 0$$
$$(2 \cdot 0 + 9)^{1/2} - 0 + 3 = 0$$
$$3 + 3 = 0$$
$$6 = 0 \quad \text{False}$$
Check: $(2a+9)^{1/2} - a + 3 = 0$
$$(2 \cdot 8 + 9)^{1/2} - 8 + 3 = 0$$
$$5 - 8 + 3 = 0$$
$$0 = 0 \quad \text{True}$$
Only 8 is a solution. 0 is an extraneous solution.

47. $(2x^2 + 4x + 6)^{1/2} = \sqrt{2x^2 + 6}$
$$[(2x^2 + 4x + 6)^{1/2}]^2 = \left(\sqrt{2x^2 + 6}\right)^2$$
$$2x^2 + 4x + 6 = 2x^2 + 6$$
$$4x = 0$$
$$x = 0$$

49. $(r+2)^{1/3} = (3r+8)^{1/3}$
$$[(r+2)^{1/3}]^3 = [(3r+8)^{1/3}]^3$$
$$r + 2 = 3r + 8$$
$$2 = 2r + 8$$
$$-6 = 2r$$
$$-3 = r$$
Check: $(r+2)^{1/3} = (3r+8)^{1/3}$
$$(-3+2)^{1/3} = [3(-3)+8]^{1/3}$$
$$(-1)^{1/3} = (-1)^{1/3}$$
$$-1 = -1 \quad \text{True}$$

51. $(5x+8)^{1/4} = (9x+2)^{1/4}$
$$[(5x+8)^{1/4}]^4 = [(9x+2)^{1/4}]^4$$
$$5x + 8 = 9x + 2$$
$$8 = 4x + 2$$
$$6 = 4x$$
$$\frac{3}{2} = x$$
Check:
$$(5x+8)^{1/4} = (9x+2)^{1/4}$$
$$(5 \cdot \tfrac{3}{2} + 8)^{1/4} = (9 \cdot \tfrac{3}{2} + 2)^{1/4}$$
$$(\tfrac{15}{2} + 8)^{1/4} = (\tfrac{27}{2} + 2)^{1/4}$$
$$(\tfrac{31}{2})^{1/4} = (\tfrac{31}{2})^{1/4} \quad \text{True}$$

53. $\sqrt[4]{x+5} = -3$
$$\left(\sqrt[4]{x+5}\right)^4 = (-3)^4$$
$$x + 5 = 81$$
$$x = 76$$
Check: $\sqrt[4]{x+5} = -3$
$$\sqrt[4]{76+5} = -3$$
$$\sqrt[4]{81} = -3$$
$$3 = -3 \quad \text{False}$$
Thus, 76 is not a solution to this equation and we conclude that there is no solution.

55. $\sqrt{3x-5} = \sqrt{2x}-1$
$$\left(\sqrt{3x-5}\right)^2 = \left(\sqrt{2x}-1\right)^2$$
$$3x - 5 = 2x - 2\sqrt{2x} + 1$$
$$x - 6 = -2\sqrt{2x}$$
$$(x-6)^2 = \left(-2\sqrt{2x}\right)^2$$
$$x^2 - 12x + 36 = 4(2x)$$
$$x^2 - 20x + 36 = 0$$
$$(x-18)(x-2) = 0$$
$$x = 18 \quad \text{or} \quad x = 2$$
Upon checking these values, only $x = 2$ satisfies the equation. The solution is $x = 2$.

57.
$$2\sqrt{b} - 1 = \sqrt{b+16}$$
$$\left(2\sqrt{b}-1\right)^2 = \left(\sqrt{b+16}\right)^2$$
$$\left(2\sqrt{b}\right)^2 - 2\cdot1\cdot2\sqrt{b} + 1^2 = b+16$$
$$4b - 4\sqrt{b} + 1 = b + 16$$
$$3b - 15 = 4\sqrt{b}$$
$$\left(3b-15\right)^2 = \left(4\sqrt{b}\right)^2$$
$$9b^2 - 90b + 225 = 16b$$
$$9b^2 - 106b + 225 = 0$$
$$\left(9b-25\right)\left(b-9\right) = 0$$
$$b = \frac{25}{9} \quad \text{or} \quad b = 9$$

Upon checking these values, only $x = 9$ satisfies the equation. The solution is $x = 9$.

59.
$$\sqrt{x+3} = \sqrt{x} - 3$$
$$\left(\sqrt{x+3}\right)^2 = \left(\sqrt{x}-3\right)^2$$
$$x + 3 = x - 6\sqrt{x} + 9$$
$$-6 = -6\sqrt{x}$$
$$1 = \sqrt{x}$$
$$(1)^2 = \left(\sqrt{x}\right)^2$$
$$1 = x$$

Check:
$$\sqrt{x+3} = \sqrt{x} - 3$$
$$\sqrt{1+3} = \sqrt{1} - 3$$
$$\sqrt{4} = 1 - 3$$
$$2 = -2 \quad \text{False}$$

Thus, 1 is not a solution to this equation and we conclude that there is no solution.

61.
$$\sqrt{x+7} = 6 - \sqrt{x-5}$$
$$\left(\sqrt{x+7}\right)^2 = \left(6 - \sqrt{x-5}\right)^2$$
$$x + 7 = 36 - 12\sqrt{x-5} + x - 5$$
$$12\sqrt{x-5} = 24$$
$$\sqrt{x-5} = 2$$
$$x - 5 = 4 \quad \Rightarrow \quad x = 9$$

Check:
$$\sqrt{x+7} = 6 - \sqrt{x-5}$$
$$\sqrt{9+7} = 6 - \sqrt{9-5}$$
$$\sqrt{16} = 6 - \sqrt{4}$$
$$4 = 6 - 2$$
$$4 = 4 \quad \text{True}$$

63.
$$\sqrt{4x-3} = 2 + \sqrt{2x-5}$$
$$\left(\sqrt{4x-3}\right)^2 = \left(2 + \sqrt{2x-5}\right)^2$$
$$4x - 3 = 4 + 4\sqrt{2x-5} + 2x - 5$$
$$2x - 2 = 4\sqrt{2x-5}$$
$$x - 1 = 2\sqrt{2x-5}$$
$$(x-1)^2 = \left(2\sqrt{2x-5}\right)^2$$
$$x^2 - 2x + 1 = 4(2x-5)$$
$$x^2 - 2x + 1 = 8x - 20$$
$$x^2 - 10x + 21 = 0$$
$$(x-7)(x-3) = 0$$
$$x - 7 = 0 \quad \text{or} \quad x - 3 = 0$$
$$x = 7 \qquad\qquad x = 3$$

Check:
$$\sqrt{4x-3} = 2 + \sqrt{2x-5}$$
$$\sqrt{4(7)-3} = 2 + \sqrt{2(7)-5}$$
$$\sqrt{25} = 2 + \sqrt{9}$$
$$5 = 2 + 3$$
$$5 = 5 \quad \text{True}$$

Check:
$$\sqrt{4x-3} = 2 + \sqrt{2x-5}$$
$$\sqrt{4(3)-3} = 2 + \sqrt{2(3)-5}$$
$$\sqrt{9} = 2 + \sqrt{1}$$
$$3 = 3 \quad \text{True}$$

Both 7 and 3 are solutions.

65.
$$\sqrt{y+1} = \sqrt{y+5} - 2$$
$$\left(\sqrt{y+1}\right)^2 = \left(\sqrt{y+5} - 2\right)^2$$
$$y + 1 = \left(\sqrt{y+5}\right)^2 - 4\sqrt{y+5} + 4$$
$$y + 1 = y + 5 - 4\sqrt{y+5} + 4$$
$$4\sqrt{y+5} = 8$$
$$\sqrt{y+5} = 2$$
$$\left(\sqrt{y+5}\right)^2 = 2^2$$
$$y + 5 = 4 \quad \Rightarrow \quad y = -1$$

67.
$$f(x) = g(x)$$
$$\sqrt{x+5} = \sqrt{2x-2}$$
$$\left(\sqrt{x+5}\right)^2 = \left(\sqrt{2x-2}\right)^2$$
$$x + 5 = 2x - 2$$
$$7 = x$$

69.
$$f(x) = g(x)$$
$$\sqrt[3]{5x-17} = \sqrt[3]{6x-21}$$
$$\left(\sqrt[3]{5x-17}\right)^3 = \left(\sqrt[3]{6x-21}\right)^3$$
$$5x - 17 = 6x - 21$$
$$x = 4$$

71.
$$f(x) = g(x)$$
$$2(8x+24)^{1/3} = 4(2x-2)^{1/3}$$
$$[2(8x+24)^{1/3}]^3 = [4(2x-2)^{1/3}]^3$$
$$8(8x+24) = 64(2x-2)$$
$$64x + 192 = 128x - 128$$
$$64x = 320$$
$$x = 5$$

73.
$$p = \sqrt{2v}$$
$$p^2 = \left(\sqrt{2v}\right)^2$$
$$p^2 = 2v$$
$$\frac{p^2}{2} = v$$

75.
$$v = \sqrt{2gh}$$
$$v^2 = \left(\sqrt{2gh}\right)^2$$
$$v^2 = 2gh$$
$$g = \frac{v^2}{2h}$$

77.
$$v = \sqrt{\frac{FR}{M}}$$
$$v^2 = \left(\sqrt{\frac{FR}{M}}\right)^2$$
$$v^2 = \frac{FR}{M}$$
$$Mv^2 = FR$$
$$F = \frac{Mv^2}{R}$$

79.
$$x = \sqrt{\frac{m}{k}} V_0$$
$$x^2 = \left(\sqrt{\frac{m}{k}} V_0\right)^2$$
$$x^2 = \frac{mV_0^2}{k}$$
$$x^2 k = mV_0^2$$
$$m = \frac{x^2 k}{V_0^2}$$

81.
$$r = \sqrt{\frac{A}{\pi}}$$
$$r^2 = \left(\sqrt{\frac{A}{\pi}}\right)^2$$
$$r^2 = \frac{A}{\pi}$$
$$\pi r^2 = A \text{ or } A = \pi r^2$$

83.
$$a^2 + b^2 = c^2$$
$$\left(\sqrt{6}\right)^2 + 9^2 = x^2$$
$$6 + 81 = x^2$$
$$87 = x^2 \Rightarrow x = \sqrt{87}$$

85.
$$a^2 + b^2 = c^2$$
$$x^2 + 5^2 = \left(\sqrt{57}\right)^2$$
$$x^2 + 25 = 57$$
$$x^2 = 32$$
$$x = \sqrt{32} \Rightarrow x = 4\sqrt{2}$$

87.
$$\sqrt{x+5} - \sqrt{x} = \sqrt{x-3}$$
$$\left(\sqrt{x+5} - \sqrt{x}\right)^2 = \left(\sqrt{x-3}\right)^2$$
$$x + 5 - 2\sqrt{x(x+5)} + x = x - 3$$
$$x + 8 = 2\sqrt{x^2 + 5x}$$
$$(x+8)^2 = \left(2\sqrt{x^2+5x}\right)^2$$
$$x^2 + 16x + 64 = 4\left(x^2 + 5x\right)$$
$$x^2 + 16x + 64 = 4x^2 + 20x$$
$$3x^2 + 4x - 64 = 0$$
$$(3x+16)(x-4) = 0 \Rightarrow x = -\frac{16}{3} \text{ or } x = 4$$

Upon checking, only $x = 4$ satisfies the equation.

89.
$$\sqrt{4y+6}+\sqrt{y+5}=\sqrt{y+1}$$
$$\left(\sqrt{4y+6}+\sqrt{y+5}\right)^2=\left(\sqrt{y+1}\right)^2$$
$$4y+6+2\sqrt{(4y+6)(y+5)}+y+5=y+1$$
$$2\sqrt{(4y+6)(y+5)}=-4y-10$$
$$\left(2\sqrt{4y^2+26y+30}\right)^2=(-4y-10)^2$$
$$4\left(4y^2+26y+30\right)=16y^2+80y+100$$
$$16y^2+104y+120=16y^2+80y+100$$
$$24y=-20 \implies y=-\frac{5}{6}$$
Upon checking, this value does not satisfy the equation. There is no solution.

91.
$$\sqrt{a+2}-\sqrt{a-3}=\sqrt{a-6}$$
$$\left(\sqrt{a+2}-\sqrt{a-3}\right)^2=\left(\sqrt{a-6}\right)^2$$
$$a+2-2\sqrt{(a+2)(a-3)}+a-3=a-6$$
$$a+5=2\sqrt{(a+2)(a-3)}$$
$$(a+5)^2=\left(2\sqrt{a^2-a-6}\right)^2$$
$$a^2+10a+25=4\left(a^2-a-6\right)$$
$$a^2+10a+25=4a^2-4a-24$$
$$3a^2-14a-49=0$$
$$(3a+7)(a-7)=0 \implies a=-\frac{7}{3} \text{ or } a=7$$
Upon checking, only $a=7$ satisfies the equation.

93.
$$\sqrt{2t-1}+\sqrt{t-4}=\sqrt{3t+1}$$
$$\left(\sqrt{2t-1}+\sqrt{t-4}\right)^2=\left(\sqrt{3t+1}\right)^2$$
$$2t-1+2\sqrt{(2t-1)(t-4)}+t-4=3t+1$$
$$2\sqrt{(2t-1)(t-4)}=6$$
$$\left(2\sqrt{2t^2-9t+4}\right)^2=(6)^2$$
$$4\left(2t^2-9t+4\right)=36$$
$$8t^2-36t+16=36$$
$$8t^2-36t-20=0$$
$$4(2t+1)(t-5)=0 \implies t=-\frac{1}{2} \text{ or } t=5$$
Upon checking, only $t=5$ satisfies the equation.

95.
$$\sqrt{2-\sqrt{x}}=\sqrt{x}$$
$$\left(\sqrt{2-\sqrt{x}}\right)^2=\left(\sqrt{x}\right)^2$$
$$2-\sqrt{x}=x$$
$$2-x=\sqrt{x}$$
$$(2-x)^2=\left(\sqrt{x}\right)^2$$
$$4-4x+x^2=x$$
$$x^2-5x+4=0$$
$$(x-4)(x-1)=0 \implies x=4 \text{ or } x=1$$
Upon checking, only $x=1$ satisfies the equation.

97.
$$\sqrt{2+\sqrt{x+1}}=\sqrt{7-x}$$
$$\left(\sqrt{2+\sqrt{x+1}}\right)^2=\left(\sqrt{7-x}\right)^2$$
$$2+\sqrt{x+1}=7-x$$
$$\sqrt{x+1}=5-x$$
$$\left(\sqrt{x+1}\right)^2=(5-x)^2$$
$$x+1=25-10x+x^2$$
$$x^2-11x+24=0$$
$$(x-8)(x-3)=0 \implies x=8 \text{ or } x=3$$
Upon checking, only $x=3$ satisfies the equation.

99.
$$l = \sqrt{20^2 + 40^2}$$
$$l = \sqrt{400 + 1600}$$
$$= \sqrt{2000}$$
$$\approx 44.7 \text{ ft}$$

101.
$$s = \sqrt{A}$$
$$s = \sqrt{144}$$
$$= 12 \text{ feet}$$

103.
$$T = 2\pi\sqrt{\frac{l}{32}}$$

c.   Let $l = 10$
$$T = 2\pi\sqrt{\frac{l}{32}}$$
$$= 2\pi\sqrt{\frac{10}{32}}$$
$$= 2\pi\sqrt{0.3125}$$
$$\approx 2\pi(0.55901)$$
$$\approx 3.51 \text{ seconds}$$

d.   Replace l with $2l$:
$$T_D = 2\pi\sqrt{\frac{2l}{32}}$$
$$= 2\pi\sqrt{2}\sqrt{\frac{l}{32}}$$
$$= \sqrt{2}\left(2\pi\sqrt{\frac{l}{32}}\right)$$
$$= \sqrt{2}T$$

c. This part must be solved in two phases. First, we need to find the length of the pendulum:
$$T = 2\pi\sqrt{\frac{l}{g}}$$
$$2 = 2\pi\sqrt{\frac{l}{32}}$$
$$\frac{1}{\pi} = \sqrt{\frac{l}{32}}$$
$$\left(\frac{1}{\pi}\right)^2 = \frac{l}{32}$$
$$l = \frac{32}{\pi^2}$$

Now, find T using $g = \dfrac{32}{6}$ and $l = \dfrac{32}{\pi^2}$

$$T = 2\pi\sqrt{\frac{l}{g}}$$
$$= 2\pi\sqrt{\frac{\frac{32}{\pi^2}}{\frac{32}{6}}}$$
$$= 2\pi\sqrt{\frac{6}{\pi^2}}$$
$$= 2\pi\frac{\sqrt{6}}{\sqrt{\pi^2}}$$
$$= 2\pi\frac{\sqrt{6}}{\pi}$$
$$= 2\sqrt{6}$$
$$\approx 4.90 \text{ seconds}$$

105.
$$r = \sqrt[4]{\frac{8\mu l}{\pi R}}$$
$$r^4 = \left(\sqrt[4]{\frac{8\mu l}{\pi R}}\right)^4$$
$$r^4 = \frac{8\mu l}{\pi R^4}$$
$$\pi R r^4 = 8\mu l$$
$$R = \frac{8\mu l}{\pi r^4}$$

107.
$$N = 0.2\left(\sqrt{R}\right)^3$$
$$N = 0.2\left(\sqrt{149.4}\right)^3$$
$$= 0.2(12.223)^3$$
$$= 0.2(1826.106)$$
$$\approx 365.2 \text{ days}$$

109.
$$R = \sqrt{F_1^2 + F_2^2}$$
$$R = \sqrt{60^2 + 80^2}$$
$$= \sqrt{10,000}$$
$$= 100 \text{ lb}$$

111. $c = \sqrt{gH} = \sqrt{32 \cdot 10} = \sqrt{320} \approx 17.89 \text{ ft / sec}$

113. The diagonal and the two given sides form a right triangle. Use the Pythagorean formula to solve for the diagonal.

$$a^2 + b^2 = c^2$$

$$25^2 + 32^2 = c^2$$

$$625 + 1024 = c^2$$

$$1649 = c^2 \implies c = \sqrt{1649} \approx 40.6$$

The diagonal is about 37.7 inches in length.

115.

$$x = \frac{-b \pm \sqrt{b^2 - 4ac}}{2a}$$

$$x = \frac{-0 \pm \sqrt{0^2 - 4(1)(-4)}}{2(1)} = \frac{\pm\sqrt{16}}{2}$$

Now, $x = \dfrac{\sqrt{16}}{2} = \dfrac{4}{2} = 2$ or

$$x = -\frac{\sqrt{16}}{2} = -\frac{4}{2} = -2$$

117.

$$x = \frac{-b \pm \sqrt{b^2 - 4ac}}{2a}$$

$$x = \frac{-5 \pm \sqrt{5^2 - 4(2)(-12)}}{2(2)}$$

$$= \frac{-5 \pm \sqrt{121}}{4}$$

$$= \frac{-5 \pm 11}{4}$$

Now, $x = \dfrac{-5 + 11}{4} = \dfrac{6}{4} = \dfrac{3}{2}$ or

$$x = \frac{-5 - 11}{4} = \frac{-16}{4} = -4$$

119.

$$f(x) = \sqrt{x - 5}$$

$$4 = \sqrt{x - 5}$$

$$4^2 = \left(\sqrt{x - 5}\right)^2$$

$$16 = x - 5$$

$$21 = x$$

121.

$$f(x) = \sqrt{3x^2 - 11} + 4$$

$$12 = \sqrt{3x^2 - 11} + 4$$

$$8 = \sqrt{3x^2 - 11}$$

$$8^2 = \left(\sqrt{3x^2 - 11}\right)^2$$

$$64 = 3x^2 - 11$$

$$75 = 3x^2$$

$$25 = x^2$$

$$\pm 5 = x$$

123. **a.** $y = \sqrt{4x - 12}$, $y = x - 3$

The points of intersection are $(3, 0)$ and $(7, 4)$. The x-values are 3 and 7.

b. $\sqrt{4x - 12} = x - 3$

For $x = 3$:	For $x = 7$:
$\sqrt{4 \cdot 3 - 12} = 3 - 3$	$\sqrt{4x - 12} = x - 3$
$\sqrt{12 - 12} = 0$	$\sqrt{4 \cdot 7 - 12} = 7 - 3$
$\sqrt{0} = 0$	$\sqrt{16} = 4$
$0 = 0$ True	$4 = 4$ True

c. $\sqrt{4x - 12} = x - 3$

$$\left(\sqrt{4x - 12}\right)^2 = (x - 3)^2$$

$$4x - 12 = x^2 - 6x + 9$$

$$0 = x^2 - 10x + 21$$

$$0 = (x - 3)(x - 7)$$

$$x - 3 = 0 \quad \text{or} \quad x - 7 = 0$$

$$x = 3 \qquad\qquad x = 7$$

125. At $x = 4$, $g(x) = 0$ or $y = 0$.

Therefore, the graph must have an x-intercept at 4.

127.

$$L_1 = p - 1.96\sqrt{\frac{p(1 - p)}{n}}$$

$$L_1 = 0.60 - 1.96\sqrt{\frac{0.60(1 - 0.60)}{36}}$$

$$\approx 0.60 - 0.16$$

$$\approx 0.44$$

$$L_2 = p + 1.96\sqrt{\frac{p(1 - p)}{n}}$$

$$L_2 = 0.60 + 1.96\sqrt{\frac{0.60(1 - 0.60)}{36}}$$

$$= 0.60 + 0.16$$

$$\approx 0.76$$

129.

$$\sqrt{x^2 + 9} = (x^2 + 9)^{1/2}$$

$$\left(\sqrt{x^2 + 9}\right)^2 = [(x^2 + 9)^{1/2}]^2$$

$$x^2 + 9 = x^2 + 9$$

$$9 = 9$$

All real numbers, x, satisfy this equation.

131. Graph:

$$y_1 = \sqrt{x+8}$$
$$y_2 = \sqrt{3x+5}$$

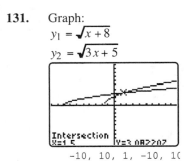

−10, 10, 1, −10, 10

The graphs of the equations intersect when
$x = 1.5$.

133. Graph:

$$y = \sqrt[3]{5x^2 - 6} - 4$$

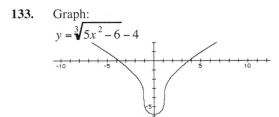

The graph of the equation crosses the x-axis
at
$x \approx -3.74$ and $x \approx 3.74$.

135.

$$\sqrt{\sqrt{x+25} - \sqrt{x}} = 5$$
$$\left(\sqrt{\sqrt{x+25} - \sqrt{x}}\right)^2 = 5^2$$
$$\sqrt{x+25} - \sqrt{x} = 25$$
$$\sqrt{x+25} = 25 + \sqrt{x}$$
$$\left(\sqrt{x+25}\right)^2 = \left(25 + \sqrt{x}\right)^2$$
$$x + 25 = 625 + 50\sqrt{x} + x$$
$$-600 = 50\sqrt{x}$$
$$-12 = \sqrt{x}$$
$$(-12)^2 = \left(\sqrt{x}\right)^2$$
$$144 = x$$

Check:
$$\sqrt{\sqrt{x+25} - \sqrt{x}} = 5$$
$$\sqrt{\sqrt{144+25} - \sqrt{144}} = 5$$
$$\sqrt{\sqrt{169} - \sqrt{144}} = 5$$
$$\sqrt{13 - 12} = 5$$
$$\sqrt{1} = 5$$
$$1 = 5 \text{ False}$$

Thus, 144 is not a solution and we conclude
that there is no solution.

137.

$$z = \frac{\bar{x} - \mu}{\frac{\sigma}{\sqrt{n}}}$$

$$z\left(\frac{\sigma}{\sqrt{n}}\right) = \bar{x} - \mu$$

$$\left(z\frac{\sigma}{\sqrt{n}}\right)^2 = (\bar{x} - \mu)^2$$

$$\frac{z^2\sigma^2}{n} = (\bar{x} - \mu)^2$$

$$z^2\sigma^2 = n(\bar{x} - \mu)^2$$

$$\frac{z^2\sigma^2}{(\bar{x} - \mu)^2} = n \text{ or } n = \frac{z^2\sigma^2}{(\bar{x} - \mu)^2}$$

141.

$$\frac{x(x-3) + x(x-4)}{2x-7} = \frac{x^2 - 3x + x^2 - 4x}{2x-7}$$

$$= \frac{2x^2 - 7x}{2x-7}$$

$$= \frac{x(2x-7)}{2x-7}$$

$$= x$$

143.

$$(t^2 - t - 12) \div \frac{t^2 - 9}{t^2 - 3t}$$

$$= (t^2 - t - 12) \cdot \frac{t^2 - 3t}{t^2 - 9}$$

$$= (t-4)(t+3) \cdot \frac{t(t-3)}{(t+3)(t-3)}$$

$$= t(t-4)$$

145.

$$2 + \frac{3x}{x-1} = \frac{8}{x-1}$$

$$(x-1)(2) + (x-1)\left(\frac{3x}{x-1}\right) = (x-1)\left(\frac{8}{x-1}\right)$$

$$2(x-1) + 3x = 8$$

$$2x - 2 + 3x = 8$$

$$5x - 2 = 8$$

$$5x = 10$$

$$x = 2$$

Exercise Set 7.7

1. $i = \sqrt{-1}$

3. Yes

5. Yes

7. The conjugate of $a + bi$ is $a - bi$.

9. Answers will vary. Possible answers:
   a. $\sqrt{2}$
   b. 2
   c. $\sqrt{-3}$
   d. 6
   e. Every number we have studied is a complex

11. $5 = 5 + 0i$

13. $\sqrt{49} = 7 = 7 + 0i$

15. $21 - \sqrt{-36} = 21 - \sqrt{36}\sqrt{-1}$
    $= 21 - 6i$

17. $\sqrt{-24} = \sqrt{4}\sqrt{-1}\sqrt{6} = 2i\sqrt{6} = 0 + 2i\sqrt{6}$

19. $8 - \sqrt{-12} = 8 - \sqrt{12}\sqrt{-1}$
    $= 8 - \sqrt{4}\sqrt{3}\sqrt{-1}$
    $= 8 - 2i\sqrt{3}$

21. $1 + \sqrt{-98} = 1 + \sqrt{98}\sqrt{-1}$
    $= 1 + \sqrt{49}\sqrt{2}\sqrt{-1}$
    $= 1 + 7i\sqrt{2}$

23. $9 - \sqrt{-25} = 9 - \sqrt{25}\sqrt{-1}$
    $= 9 - 5i$

25. $2i - \sqrt{-45} = 0 + 2i - \sqrt{9}\sqrt{5}\sqrt{-1}$
    $= 0 + 2i - 3i\sqrt{5}$
    $= 0 + \left(2 - 3\sqrt{5}\right)i$

27. $(19 - i) + (2 + 6i) = 19 - i + 2 + 6i$
    $= 21 + 5i$

29. $(8 - 3i) + (-8 + 3i) = 8 - 3i - 8 + 3i$
    $= 0$

31. $\left(1 + \sqrt{-1}\right) + \left(-13 - \sqrt{-169}\right) = 1 + \sqrt{-1} - 13 - \sqrt{-169}$
    $= 1 + i - 13 - 13i$
    $= -12 - 12i$

33. $\left(\sqrt{3} + \sqrt{2}\right) + \left(3\sqrt{2} - \sqrt{-8}\right)$
    $= \sqrt{3} + \sqrt{2} + 3\sqrt{2} - \sqrt{-8}$
    $= \sqrt{3} + \sqrt{2} + 3\sqrt{2} - \sqrt{-4 \cdot 2}$
    $= \sqrt{3} + \sqrt{2} + 3\sqrt{2} - 2i\sqrt{2}$
    $= \sqrt{3} + 4\sqrt{2} - 2i\sqrt{2}$
    $= \left(\sqrt{3} + 4\sqrt{2}\right) - 2i\sqrt{2}$

35. $\left(3 - \sqrt{-72}\right) + \left(6 + \sqrt{-8}\right)$
    $= 3 - \sqrt{-72} + 6 + \sqrt{-8}$
    $= 3 - \sqrt{36}\sqrt{2}\sqrt{-1} + 6 + \sqrt{4}\sqrt{2}\sqrt{-1}$
    $= 3 - 6i\sqrt{2} + 6 + 2i\sqrt{2}$
    $= 9 - 4i\sqrt{2}$

37. $\left(\sqrt{4} - \sqrt{-45}\right) + \left(-\sqrt{81} + \sqrt{-5}\right)$
    $= \sqrt{4} - \sqrt{-45} - \sqrt{81} + \sqrt{-5}$
    $= \sqrt{4} - \sqrt{9}\sqrt{5}\sqrt{-1} - \sqrt{81} + \sqrt{-1}\sqrt{5}$
    $= 2 - 3i\sqrt{5} - 9 + i\sqrt{5}$
    $= -7 - 2i\sqrt{5}$

39. $2(5 - i) = 10 - 2i$

41. $i(2 + 9i) = 2i + 9i^2 = 2i + 9(-1) = -9 + 2i$

43. $\sqrt{-9}(7 + 11i) = 3i(7 + 11i)$
    $= 21i + 33i^2$
    $= 21i + 33(-1)$
    $= -33 + 21i$

45. $\sqrt{-16}\left(\sqrt{3} - 5i\right) = 4i\left(\sqrt{3} - 5i\right)$
    $= 4i\sqrt{3} - 20i^2$
    $= 4i\sqrt{3} - 20(-1)$
    $= 4i\sqrt{3} + 20$
    $= 20 + 4i\sqrt{3}$

47. $\sqrt{-32}\left(\sqrt{2}+\sqrt{-8}\right)$

$=\sqrt{-16}\sqrt{2}\left(\sqrt{2}+\sqrt{-4}\sqrt{2}\right)$

$=4i\sqrt{2}\left(\sqrt{2}+2i\sqrt{2}\right)$

$=4i\cdot 2+8i^2\cdot 2$

$=8i+16i^2$

$=8i+16(-1)$

$=8i-16 \ \text{ or } \ -16+8i$

49. $(3+2i)(1+i)$

$=3(1)+3(i)+2i(1)+2i(i)$

$=3+3i+2i+2i^2$

$=3+3i+2i+2(-1)$

$=3+3i+2i-2$

$=1+5I$

51. $(20-3i)(20+3i)=400+60i-60i-9i^2$

$=400+60i-60i-9(-1)$

$=400+9$

$=409$

53. $\left(7+\sqrt{-2}\right)\left(5-\sqrt{-8}\right)$

$=\left(7+i\sqrt{2}\right)\left(5-2i\sqrt{2}\right)$

$=35-14i\sqrt{2}+5i\sqrt{2}-2i^2\cdot 2$

$=35-14i\sqrt{2}+5i\sqrt{2}-2(-1)\cdot 2$

$=35-14i\sqrt{2}+5i\sqrt{2}+4$

$=39-9i\sqrt{2}$

55. $\left(\dfrac{1}{2}-\dfrac{1}{3}i\right)\left(\dfrac{1}{4}+\dfrac{2}{3}i\right)$

$=\dfrac{1}{8}+\dfrac{1}{3}i-\dfrac{1}{12}i-\dfrac{2}{9}i^2$

$=\dfrac{1}{8}+\dfrac{1}{3}i-\dfrac{1}{12}i-\dfrac{2}{9}(-1)$

$=\dfrac{1}{8}+\dfrac{1}{3}i-\dfrac{1}{12}i+\dfrac{2}{9}$

$=\dfrac{1}{8}+\dfrac{2}{9}+\left(\dfrac{1}{3}-\dfrac{1}{12}\right)i$

$=\dfrac{25}{72}+\dfrac{1}{4}i$

57. $\dfrac{2}{3i}=\dfrac{2}{3i}\cdot\dfrac{-i}{-i}=\dfrac{-2i}{-3i^2}=\dfrac{-2i}{-3(-1)}=-\dfrac{2i}{3}$

59. $\dfrac{2+3i}{2i}=\dfrac{2+3i}{2i}\cdot\dfrac{-i}{-i}$

$=\dfrac{(2+3i)(-i)}{-2i^2}$

$=\dfrac{-2i-3i^2}{-2i^2}$

$=\dfrac{-2i-3(-1)}{-2(-1)}$

$=\dfrac{-2i+3}{2} \ \text{ or } \ \dfrac{3-2i}{2}$

61. $\dfrac{4}{2-i}=\dfrac{4}{2-i}\cdot\dfrac{2+i}{2+i}$

$=\dfrac{4(2+i)}{(2-i)(2+i)}$

$=\dfrac{8+4i}{4+2i-2i-i^2}$

$=\dfrac{8+4i}{4+2i-2i-(-1)}$

$=\dfrac{8+4i}{5}$

63. $\dfrac{9}{1-2i}=\dfrac{9}{1-2i}\cdot\dfrac{1+2i}{1+2i}$

$=\dfrac{9(1+2i)}{(1-2i)(1+2i)}$

$=\dfrac{9+18i}{1+2i-2i-4i^2}$

$=\dfrac{9+18i}{1+2i-2i-4(-1)}$

$=\dfrac{9+18i}{5}$

65. $\dfrac{6-3i}{4+2i}=\dfrac{6-3i}{4+2i}\cdot\dfrac{4-2i}{4-2i}$

$=\dfrac{(6-3i)(4-2i)}{16-4i^2}$

$=\dfrac{24-12i-12i+6i^2}{16-4i^2}$

$=\dfrac{24-12i-12i-6}{16+4}$

$=\dfrac{18-24i}{20}$

$=\dfrac{2(9-12i)}{20}$

$=\dfrac{9-12i}{10}$

67. $\dfrac{4}{6-\sqrt{-4}} = \dfrac{4}{6-\sqrt{4}\sqrt{-1}}$

$= \dfrac{4}{6-2i} \cdot \dfrac{6+2i}{6+2i}$

$= \dfrac{4(6+2i)}{36-4i^2}$

$= \dfrac{24+8i}{36-4(-1)}$

$= \dfrac{24+8i}{36+4}$

$= \dfrac{8(3+i)}{40}$

$= \dfrac{3+i}{5}$

69. $\dfrac{\sqrt{2}}{5+\sqrt{-12}} = \dfrac{\sqrt{2}}{5+\sqrt{4}\sqrt{3}\sqrt{-1}}$

$= \dfrac{\sqrt{2}}{5+2i\sqrt{3}} \cdot \dfrac{5-2i\sqrt{3}}{5-2i\sqrt{3}}$

$= \dfrac{\sqrt{2}\left(5-2i\sqrt{3}\right)}{25-4i^2\sqrt{3}^2}$

$= \dfrac{5\sqrt{2}-2i\sqrt{6}}{25-4(-1)(3)}$

$= \dfrac{5\sqrt{2}-2i\sqrt{6}}{25+12}$

$= \dfrac{5\sqrt{2}-2i\sqrt{6}}{37}$

71. $\dfrac{\sqrt{10}+\sqrt{-3}}{5-\sqrt{-20}}$

$= \dfrac{\sqrt{10}+\sqrt{3}\sqrt{-1}}{5-\sqrt{4}\sqrt{5}\sqrt{-1}}$

$= \dfrac{\sqrt{10}+i\sqrt{3}}{5-2i\sqrt{5}} \cdot \dfrac{5+2i\sqrt{5}}{5+2i\sqrt{5}}$

$= \dfrac{(\sqrt{10}+i\sqrt{3})(5+2i\sqrt{5})}{5^2-4i^2\sqrt{5}^2}$

$= \dfrac{5\sqrt{10}+2i\sqrt{50}+5i\sqrt{3}+2i^2\sqrt{15}}{5^2-4(-1)(5)}$

$= \dfrac{5\sqrt{10}+2i\sqrt{25}\sqrt{2}+5i\sqrt{3}+2(-1)\sqrt{15}}{25+20}$

$= \dfrac{(5\sqrt{10}-2\sqrt{15})+(10\sqrt{2}+5\sqrt{3})i}{45}$

73. $\dfrac{\sqrt{-75}}{\sqrt{-3}} = \dfrac{\sqrt{25}\sqrt{3}\sqrt{-1}}{\sqrt{3}\sqrt{-1}} = \dfrac{5i\sqrt{3}}{i\sqrt{3}} = 5$

75. $\dfrac{\sqrt{-32}}{\sqrt{-18}\sqrt{2}} = \dfrac{\sqrt{16}\sqrt{2}\sqrt{-1}}{\sqrt{9}\sqrt{2}\sqrt{-1}\sqrt{2}}$

$= \dfrac{4i\sqrt{2}}{3\cdot 2i} = \dfrac{2\sqrt{2}}{3}$

77. $(4-2i)+(3-5i) = 4+3-2i-5i = 7-7i$

79. $\left(\sqrt{8}-\sqrt{2}\right)-\left(\sqrt{-12}-\sqrt{-48}\right)$

$= \left(2\sqrt{2}-\sqrt{2}\right)-\left(2i\sqrt{3}-4i\sqrt{3}\right)$

$= \sqrt{2}-\left(-2i\sqrt{3}\right)$

$= \sqrt{2}+2i\sqrt{3}$

81. $5.2(4-3.2i)$

$= 5.2(4)-5.2(3.2i)$

$= 20.8-16.64i$

83. $(9+2i)(3-5i)$

$= 27-45i+6i-10i^2$

$= 27-39i-10(-1)$

$= 27+10-39i$

$= 37-39i$

85. $\dfrac{5+4i}{2i} = \dfrac{5+4i}{2i} \cdot \dfrac{-2i}{-2i}$

$= \dfrac{(5+4i)(-2i)}{-4i^2}$

$= \dfrac{-10i-8i^2}{-4i^2}$

$= \dfrac{-10i-8(-1)}{-4(-1)}$

$= \dfrac{8-10i}{4}$ or $\dfrac{4-5i}{2}$

87. $\dfrac{5}{\sqrt{3}-\sqrt{-4}} = \dfrac{5}{\sqrt{3}-2i}$

$= \dfrac{5}{\sqrt{3}-2i} \cdot \dfrac{\sqrt{3}+2i}{\sqrt{3}+2i}$

$= \dfrac{5(\sqrt{3}+2i)}{(\sqrt{3})^2-(2i)^2}$

$= \dfrac{5\sqrt{3}+10i}{3-4i^2}$

$= \dfrac{5\sqrt{3}+10i}{3-4(-1)}$

$= \dfrac{5\sqrt{3}+10i}{7}$

89.

$$\left(5-\frac{5}{9}i\right)-\left(4-\frac{3}{5}i\right)=5-\frac{5}{9}i-4+\frac{3}{5}i$$

$$=1-\frac{5}{9}i+\frac{3}{5}i$$

$$=1-\frac{25}{45}i+\frac{27}{45}i$$

$$=1+\frac{2}{45}i$$

91.

$$\left(\frac{2}{3}-\frac{1}{5}i\right)\left(\frac{3}{5}-\frac{3}{4}i\right)$$

$$=\left(\frac{2}{3}\right)\left(\frac{3}{5}\right)-\frac{2}{3}\left(\frac{3}{4}i\right)-\left(\frac{1}{5}i\right)\left(\frac{3}{5}\right)+\left(\frac{1}{5}i\right)\left(\frac{3}{4}i\right)$$

$$=\frac{2}{5}-\frac{1}{2}i-\frac{3}{25}i+\frac{3}{20}i^2$$

$$=\frac{2}{5}-\frac{1}{2}i-\frac{3}{25}i+\frac{3}{20}(-1)$$

$$=\left(\frac{2}{5}-\frac{3}{20}\right)+\left(-\frac{1}{2}-\frac{3}{25}\right)i$$

$$=\left(\frac{8}{20}-\frac{3}{20}\right)+\left(-\frac{25}{50}-\frac{6}{50}\right)i$$

$$=\frac{5}{20}-\frac{31}{50}i$$

$$=\frac{1}{4}-\frac{31}{50}i$$

93.

$$\frac{\sqrt{-96}}{\sqrt{-24}}=\frac{\sqrt{96}\sqrt{-1}}{\sqrt{24}\sqrt{-1}}$$

$$=\frac{i\sqrt{96}}{i\sqrt{24}}$$

$$=\frac{\sqrt{96}}{\sqrt{24}}$$

$$=\sqrt{\frac{96}{24}}$$

$$=\sqrt{4}$$

$$=2$$

95. $(5.23-6.41i)-(9.56+4.5i)$
$=5.23-6.41i-9.56-4.5i$
$=-4.33-10.91i$

97. $i^{10}=i^8 \cdot i^2$

$\phantom{i^{10}}=(i^4)^2 i^2=1^2 \cdot i^2=1(i^2)=i^2=-1$

99. $i^{200}=(i^4)^{50}=1^{50}=1$

101. $i^{93}=i^{92}\cdot i^1$

$\phantom{i^{93}}=(i^4)^{23}i=1^{23}\cdot i=1(i)=i$

103. $i^{807}=i^{804}\cdot i^3$

$\phantom{i^{807}}=(i^4)^{201}\cdot i^3$

$\phantom{i^{807}}=1^{201}\cdot i^3$

$\phantom{i^{807}}=1\cdot(i^3)$

$\phantom{i^{807}}=i^3$

$\phantom{i^{807}}=-i$

105. **a.** The additive inverse of $2+3i$ is its opposite, $-2-3i$. Note that $(2+3i)+(-2-3i)=0$.

b. The multiplicative inverse of $2+3i$ is its reciprocal, $\dfrac{1}{2+3i}$. To simplify this, multiply the numerator and denominator by the conjugate of the denominator.

$$\frac{1}{2+3i}=\frac{1}{2+3i}\cdot\frac{2-3i}{2-3i}$$

$$=\frac{2-3i}{(2+3i)(2-3i)}$$

$$=\frac{2-3i}{4-6i+6i-9i^2}$$

$$=\frac{2-3i}{4+9} \text{ or } \frac{2-3i}{13}$$

107. True. The product of two pure imaginary numbers is always a real number. Consider two pure imaginary numbers bi and di where b, d are non-zero real numbers whose product
$(bi)(di)=bdi^2$
$=bd(-1)$
$=-bd$
which is a real number.

109. False. The product of two complex numbers is not always a real number. For example,
$(1+i)(1+i)=1+i+i+i^2$
$=1+2i+(-1)$
$=0+2i$
which is not a real number.

111. Even values of n will result in i^n being a real number. $i^2=-1$, $i^{2n}=(i^2)^n=(-1)^n$

113.
$$f(x)=x^2$$
$$f(i)=i^2=-1$$

115.
$$f(x) = x^4 - 2x$$
$$f(2i) = (2i)^4 - 2(2i)$$
$$= 2^4 i^4 - 4i$$
$$= 16(1) - 4i$$
$$= 16 - 4i$$

117.
$$f(x) = x^2 + x$$
$$f(3+i) = (3+i)^2 + (3+i)$$
$$= 9 + 6i + i^2 + 3 + i$$
$$= 9 + 6i - 1 + 3 + i$$
$$= 11 + 7i$$

119. $x^2 - 2x + 5$
$$= (1 - 2i)^2 - 2(1 - 2i) + 5$$
$$= 1^2 - 2(1)(2i) + (2i)^2 - 2 + 4i + 5$$
$$= 1 - 4i - 4 - 2 + 4i + 5$$
$$= 0 + 0i$$
$$= 0$$

121. $x^2 + 2x + 7$
$$= (-1 + i\sqrt{5})^2 + 2(-1 + i\sqrt{5}) + 7$$
$$= (-1)^2 - 2(1)(i\sqrt{5}) + (i\sqrt{5})^2 - 2 + 2i\sqrt{5} + 7$$
$$= 1 - 2i\sqrt{5} - 5 - 2 + 2i\sqrt{5} + 7$$
$$= 1 + 0i$$
$$= 1$$

123.
$$x^2 - 4x + 5 = 0$$
$$(2-i)^2 - 4(2-i) + 5 = 0$$
$$2^2 - 2(2)(i) + (i)^2 - 8 + 4i + 5 = 0$$
$$4 - 4i - 1 - 8 + 4i + 5 = 0$$
$$0 + 0i = 0$$
$$0 = 0 \quad \text{True}$$

$2 - i$ is a solution.

125.
$$x^2 - 6x + 11 = 0$$
$$(-3 + i\sqrt{3})^2 - 6(-3 + i\sqrt{3}) + 11 = 0$$
$$(-3)^2 - 2(3)(i\sqrt{3}) + (i\sqrt{3})^2 + 18 - 6i\sqrt{3} + 11 = 0$$
$$9 - 6i\sqrt{3} - 3 + 18 - 6i\sqrt{3} + 11 = 0$$
$$35 - 12i\sqrt{3} = 0 \quad \text{False}$$

$-3 + i\sqrt{3}$ is not a solution.

127.
$$Z = \frac{V}{I}$$
$$Z = \frac{1.8 + 0.5i}{0.6i}$$
$$= \frac{1.8 + 0.5i}{0.6i} \cdot \frac{-0.6i}{-0.6i}$$

$$= \frac{-1.08i - 0.3i^2}{-0.36i^2}$$
$$= \frac{-1.08i - 0.3(-1)}{-0.36(-1)}$$
$$= \frac{0.3 - 1.08i}{0.36}$$
$$\approx 0.83 - 3i$$

129.
$$Z_T = \frac{Z_1 Z_2}{Z_1 + Z_2}$$
$$= \frac{(2-i)(4+i)}{(2-i) + (4+i)}$$
$$= \frac{8 + 2i - 4i - i^2}{6}$$
$$= \frac{8 - 2i - (-1)}{6}$$
$$= \frac{9 - 2i}{6}$$
$$\approx 1.5 - 0.33i$$

131. $i^{-1} = \dfrac{1}{i} = \dfrac{1}{i} \cdot \dfrac{i}{i} = \dfrac{i}{i^2} = \dfrac{i}{-1} = -i$

133.
$$x^2 - 4x + 6 = 0$$
$$a = 1, \, b = -4, \, c = 6$$
$$x = \frac{-(-4) \pm \sqrt{(-4)^2 - 4(1)(6)}}{2(1)}$$
$$= \frac{4 \pm \sqrt{16 - 24}}{2}$$
$$= \frac{4 \pm \sqrt{-8}}{2}$$
$$= \frac{4 \pm 2i\sqrt{2}}{2}$$
$$= \frac{2(2 \pm i\sqrt{2})}{2}$$
$$= 2 \pm i\sqrt{2}$$

135.
$$a + b = 5 + 2i\sqrt{3} + 1 + i\sqrt{3}$$
$$= 5 + 1 + 2i\sqrt{3} + i\sqrt{3}$$
$$= 6 + 3i\sqrt{3}$$

137.
$$ab = (5 + 2i\sqrt{3})(1 + i\sqrt{3})$$
$$= 5(1) + (5)(i\sqrt{3}) + (2i\sqrt{3})(1) + (2i\sqrt{3})(i\sqrt{3})$$
$$= 5 + 5i\sqrt{3} + 2i\sqrt{3} + 2i^2(\sqrt{3})^2$$
$$= 5 + 5i\sqrt{3} + 2i\sqrt{3} - 6$$
$$= -1 + 7i\sqrt{3}$$

139. This problem can be solved using a single variable. To do this, let x be the amount that is $5.50 per pound. Then $40 - x$ is the amount that is $6.30 per pound and the equation is

$$5.50(x) + 6.30(40 - x) = 6(40)$$
$$5.5x + 252 - 6.3x = 240$$
$$252 - 0.8x = 240$$
$$-0.8x = -12$$
$$x = 15$$

Thus, combine 15 lb of the $5.50 per pound coffee with $40 - 15 = 25$ lb of the $6.30 per pound coffee to obtain 40 lb of $6.00 per pound coffee.

141.
$$\frac{b}{a-b} + \frac{a+b}{b} = \frac{b}{a-b} \cdot \frac{b}{b} + \frac{a+b}{b} \cdot \frac{a-b}{a-b}$$

$$= \frac{b^2}{b(a-b)} + \frac{(a+b)(a-b)}{b(a-b)}$$

$$= \frac{b^2 + (a+b)(a-b)}{b(a-b)}$$

$$= \frac{b^2 + a^2 - b^2}{b(a-b)}$$

$$= \frac{a^2}{b(a-b)}$$

Review Exercises

1. $\sqrt{49} = 7$

2. $\sqrt[3]{-27} = -3$

3. $\sqrt[4]{256} = 4$

4. $\sqrt[3]{-125} = -5$

5. $\sqrt{(-7)^2} = |-7| = 7$

6. $\sqrt{(-93.4)^2} = |-93.4| = 93.4$

7. $\sqrt{x^2} = |x|$

8. $\sqrt{(x-2)^2} = |x-2|$

9. $\sqrt{(x-y)^2} = |x-y|$

10. $\sqrt{(x^2 - 4x + 12)^2} = |x^2 - 4x + 12|$

11. $f(x) = \sqrt{10x + 9}$

$$f(4) = \sqrt{10(4) + 9}$$
$$= \sqrt{40 + 9}$$
$$= \sqrt{49}$$
$$= 7$$

12.
$$k(x) = 2x + \sqrt{\frac{x}{3}}$$

$$k(27) = 2(27) + \sqrt{\frac{27}{3}}$$

$$= 54 + \sqrt{9}$$

$$= 54 + 3$$

$$= 57$$

13. $g(x) = \sqrt[3]{2x + 3}$

$$g(4) = \sqrt[3]{2(4) + 3}$$
$$= \sqrt[3]{11}$$
$$\approx 2.2$$

14. $\text{Area} = (\text{side})^2$

$$121 = s^2$$
$$\pm 11 = s$$

Disregard the negative value since lengths must be positive. The length of each side is 11 m.

15. $\sqrt{x^5} = x^{5/2}$

16. $\sqrt[3]{x^5} = x^{5/3}$

17. $\left(\sqrt[4]{y}\right)^{15} = y^{15/4}$

18. $\sqrt[7]{5^2} = 5^{2/7}$

19. $x^{1/2} = \sqrt{x}$

20. $a^{4/5} = \sqrt[5]{a^4}$

21. $(3m^2 n)^{7/4} = \left(\sqrt[4]{3m^2 n}\right)^7$

22. $(x + 3y)^{-5/3} = \dfrac{1}{\left(\sqrt[3]{x + 3y}\right)^5}$

23. $\sqrt[3]{3^6} = 3^{6/3} = 3^2 = 9$

24. $\sqrt{x^{10}} = x^{10/2} = x^5$

25. $\left(\sqrt[4]{7}\right)^8 = 7^{8/4} = 7^2 = 49$

26. $\sqrt[20]{a^5} = a^{5/20} = a^{1/4} = \sqrt[4]{a}$

27. $-25^{1/2} = -\sqrt{25} = -5$

28. $(-25)^{1/2}$ is not a real number.

29. $\left(\dfrac{64}{27}\right)^{-1/3} = \left(\dfrac{27}{64}\right)^{1/3} = \sqrt[3]{\dfrac{27}{64}} = \dfrac{\sqrt[3]{27}}{\sqrt[3]{64}} = \dfrac{3}{4}$

30. $64^{-1/2} + 8^{-2/3} = \dfrac{1}{64^{1/2}} + \dfrac{1}{8^{2/3}}$

$= \dfrac{1}{\sqrt{64}} + \dfrac{1}{\left(\sqrt[3]{8}\right)^2}$

$= \dfrac{1}{8} + \dfrac{1}{2^2}$

$= \dfrac{1}{8} + \dfrac{1}{4}$

$= \dfrac{1}{8} + \dfrac{2}{8}$

$= \dfrac{3}{8}$

31. $x^{3/5} x^{-1/3} = x^{3/5 - 1/3} = x^{9/15 - 5/15} = x^{4/15}$

32. $\left(\dfrac{64}{y^6}\right)^{1/3} = \sqrt[3]{\dfrac{64}{y^6}} = \dfrac{\sqrt[3]{64}}{\sqrt[3]{y^6}} = \dfrac{4}{y^2}$

33. $\left(\dfrac{a^{-6/5}}{a^{1/5}}\right)^{2/3} = \dfrac{a^{-6/5 \cdot 2/3}}{a^{1/5 \cdot 2/3}}$

$= \dfrac{a^{-12/15}}{a^{2/15}}$

$= a^{-12/15 - (2/15)}$

$= a^{-14/15}$

$= \dfrac{1}{a^{14/15}}$

34. $\left(\dfrac{28x^5 y^{-3}}{4y^{1/2}}\right)^2 = \left(\dfrac{7x^5}{y^{7/2}}\right)^2$

$= \dfrac{7^2 x^{5 \cdot 2}}{y^{(7/2) \cdot 2}}$

$= \dfrac{49 x^{10}}{y^7}$

35. $a^{1/2}\left(5a^{3/2} - 2a^2\right) = a^{1/2}\left(5a^{3/2}\right) - a^{1/2}\left(2a^2\right)$

$= 5a^{1/2 + 3/2} - 2a^{1/2 + 2}$

$= 5a^{4/2} - 2a^{1/2 + 4/2}$

$= 5a^2 - 2a^{5/2}$

36. $4x^{-2/3}\left(x^{-1/2} + \dfrac{9}{4} x^{2/3}\right)$

$= 4x^{-2/3}\left(x^{-1/2}\right) + 4x^{-2/3}\left(\dfrac{9}{4} x^{2/3}\right)$

$= 4x^{-2/3 + (-1/2)} + 9x^{-2/3 + (2/3)}$

$= 4x^{-4/6 + (-3/6)} + 9x^{0/3}$

$= 4x^{-7/6} + 9x^0$

$= \dfrac{4}{x^{7/6}} + 9$

37. $x^{2/5} + x^{7/5} = x^{2/5} + x^{2/5} \cdot x^1$

$= x^{2/5}(1 + x)$

38. $a^{-1/2} + a^{5/2} = a^{-1/2} + a^{-1/2} \cdot a^{6/2}$

$= a^{-1/2}(1 + a^3)$

$= \dfrac{1 + a^3}{a^{1/2}}$

39. $f(x) = \sqrt{7x - 17}$

$f(6) = \sqrt{7(6) - 17}$

$= \sqrt{42 - 17}$

$= \sqrt{25}$

$= 5$

40. $g(x) = \sqrt[3]{9r - 17}$

$g(4) = \sqrt[3]{9(4) - 17}$

$= \sqrt[3]{36 - 17}$

$= \sqrt[3]{19}$

≈ 2.668

41. $f(x) = \sqrt{x}$

x	$f(x)$
0	0
1	1
4	2
9	3

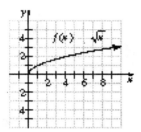

42. $f(x) = \sqrt{x} - 4$

x	$f(x)$
0	-4
1	-3
4	-2
9	-1
16	0

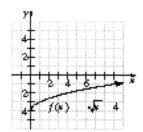

43. $\sqrt{75} = \sqrt{25}\sqrt{3} = 5\sqrt{3}$

44. $\sqrt[3]{128} = \sqrt[3]{64}\sqrt[3]{2} = 4\sqrt[3]{2}$

45. $\sqrt{\dfrac{49}{4}} = \dfrac{\sqrt{49}}{\sqrt{4}} = \dfrac{7}{2}$

46. $\sqrt[3]{\dfrac{27}{125}} = \dfrac{\sqrt[3]{27}}{\sqrt[3]{125}} = \dfrac{3}{5}$

47. $-\sqrt{\dfrac{81}{64}} = -\dfrac{\sqrt{81}}{\sqrt{64}} = -\dfrac{9}{8}$

48. $\sqrt[3]{-\dfrac{8}{125}} = \dfrac{\sqrt[3]{-8}}{\sqrt[3]{125}} = \dfrac{-2}{5} = -\dfrac{2}{5}$

49. $\sqrt{20}\sqrt{5} = \sqrt{20 \cdot 5} = \sqrt{100} = 10$

50. $\sqrt[3]{16} \cdot \sqrt[3]{4} = \sqrt[3]{16 \cdot 4} = \sqrt[3]{64} = 4$

51. $\sqrt{8x^2 y^3 z^4} = \sqrt{4x^2 y^2 z^4}\sqrt{2y}$

$= 2xyz^2\sqrt{2y}$

52. $\sqrt{50x^3 y^7} = \sqrt{25x^2 y^6}\sqrt{2xy}$

$= 5xy^3\sqrt{2xy}$

53. $\sqrt[3]{54a^7 b^{10}} = \sqrt[3]{27a^6 b^9}\sqrt[3]{2ab}$

$= 3a^2 b^3\sqrt[3]{2ab}$

54. $\sqrt[3]{125x^8 y^9 z^{16}} = \sqrt[3]{125x^6 y^9 z^{15}}\sqrt[3]{x^2 z}$

$= 5x^2 y^3 z^5\sqrt[3]{x^2 z}$

55. $\left(\sqrt[6]{x^2 y^3 z^5}\right)^{42} = (x^2 y^3 z^5)^{42/6}$

$= (x^2 y^3 z^5)^7$

$= x^{14} y^{21} z^{35}$

56. $\left(\sqrt[5]{2ab^4 c^6}\right)^{15} = \left(2ab^4 c^6\right)^{15/5}$

$= \left(2ab^4 c^6\right)^3$

$= 8a^3 b^{12} c^{18}$

57. $\sqrt{5x}\sqrt{8x^5} = \sqrt{40x^6}$

$= \sqrt{4x^6}\sqrt{10}$

$= 2x^3\sqrt{10}$

58. $\sqrt[3]{2x^2 y}\sqrt[3]{4x^9 y^4} = \sqrt[3]{8x^{11} y^5}$

$= 2x^3 y\sqrt[3]{x^2 y^2}$

59.
$$\sqrt[3]{2x^4y^5}\sqrt[3]{16x^4y^4} = \sqrt[3]{32x^8y^9}$$
$$= \sqrt[3]{8x^6y^9}\sqrt[3]{4x^2}$$
$$= 2x^2y^3\sqrt[3]{4x^2}$$

60.
$$\sqrt[4]{8x^4y^7}\sqrt[4]{2x^5y^9} = \sqrt[4]{16x^9y^{16}}$$
$$= \sqrt[4]{16x^8y^{16}}\sqrt[4]{x}$$
$$= 2x^2y^4\sqrt[4]{x}$$

61.
$$\sqrt{3x}(\sqrt{12x} - \sqrt{20}) = \sqrt{36x^2} - \sqrt{60x}$$
$$= \sqrt{36x^2} - \sqrt{4}\sqrt{15x}$$
$$= 6x - 2\sqrt{15x}$$

62.
$$\sqrt[3]{2x^2y}\left(\sqrt[3]{4x^4y^7} + \sqrt[3]{9x}\right)$$
$$= \sqrt[3]{8x^6y^8} + \sqrt[3]{18x^3y}$$
$$= \sqrt[3]{8x^6y^6}\sqrt[3]{y^2} + \sqrt[3]{x^3}\sqrt[3]{18y}$$
$$= 2x^2y^2\sqrt[3]{y^2} + x\sqrt[3]{18y}$$

63.
$$\sqrt{\sqrt{a^3b^2}} = \left(\sqrt{a^3b^2}\right)^{1/2}$$
$$= \left[\left(a^3b^2\right)^{1/2}\right]^{1/2}$$
$$= \left(a^3b^2\right)^{1/4}$$
$$= \sqrt[4]{a^3b^2}$$

64.
$$\sqrt{\sqrt[3]{x^5y^2}} = \left(\sqrt[3]{x^5y^2}\right)^{1/2}$$
$$= \left[\left(x^5y^2\right)^{1/3}\right]^{1/2}$$
$$= \left(x^5y^2\right)^{1/6}$$
$$= \sqrt[6]{\left(x^5y^2\right)}$$

65.
$$\left(\frac{3r^2p^{1/3}}{r^{1/2}p^{4/3}}\right)^3 = (3r^{2-1/2}p^{1/3-4/3})^3$$
$$= (3r^{3/2}p^{-1})^3$$
$$= 3^3(r^{3/2})^3(p^{-1})^3$$
$$= 27r^{9/2}p^{-3}$$
$$= \frac{27r^{9/2}}{p^3}$$

66.
$$\left(\frac{4y^{2/5}z^{1/3}}{x^{-1}y^{3/5}}\right)^{-1} = \left(\frac{4y^{2/5-3/5}z^{1/3}}{x^{-1}}\right)^{-1}$$
$$= \left(\frac{4y^{-1/5}z^{1/3}}{x^{-1}}\right)^{-1}$$
$$= \left(\frac{4xz^{1/3}}{y^{1/5}}\right)^{-1}$$
$$= \frac{y^{1/5}}{4xz^{1/3}}$$

67.
$$\sqrt{\frac{3}{5}} = \frac{\sqrt{3}}{\sqrt{5}}\cdot\frac{\sqrt{5}}{\sqrt{5}} = \frac{\sqrt{15}}{5}$$

68.
$$\sqrt[3]{\frac{7}{4}} = \frac{\sqrt[3]{7}}{\sqrt[3]{4}} = \frac{\sqrt[3]{7}}{\sqrt[3]{4}}\cdot\frac{\sqrt[3]{2}}{\sqrt[3]{2}} = \frac{\sqrt[3]{14}}{\sqrt[3]{8}} = \frac{\sqrt[3]{14}}{2}$$

69.
$$\sqrt[4]{\frac{2}{3}} = \frac{\sqrt[4]{2}}{\sqrt[4]{3}} = \frac{\sqrt[4]{2}}{\sqrt[4]{3}}\cdot\frac{\sqrt[4]{3^3}}{\sqrt[4]{3^3}} = \frac{\sqrt[4]{54}}{\sqrt[4]{3^4}} = \frac{\sqrt[4]{54}}{3}$$

70.
$$\frac{x}{\sqrt{11}} = \frac{x}{\sqrt{11}}\cdot\frac{\sqrt{11}}{\sqrt{11}} = \frac{x\sqrt{11}}{11}$$

71.
$$\frac{6}{\sqrt{x}} = \frac{6}{\sqrt{x}}\cdot\frac{\sqrt{x}}{\sqrt{x}} = \frac{6\sqrt{x}}{x}$$

72.
$$\frac{a}{\sqrt[3]{25}} = \frac{a}{\sqrt[3]{5^2}}\cdot\frac{\sqrt[3]{5}}{\sqrt[3]{5}} = \frac{a\sqrt[3]{5}}{\sqrt[3]{5^3}} = \frac{a\sqrt[3]{5}}{5}$$

73.
$$\frac{9}{\sqrt[3]{y^2}} = \frac{9}{\sqrt[3]{y^2}}\cdot\frac{\sqrt[3]{y}}{\sqrt[3]{y}} = \frac{9\sqrt[3]{y}}{\sqrt[3]{y^3}} = \frac{9\sqrt[3]{y}}{y}$$

74.
$$\frac{7}{\sqrt[4]{z}} = \frac{7}{\sqrt[4]{z}}\cdot\frac{\sqrt[4]{z^3}}{\sqrt[4]{z^3}} = \frac{7\sqrt[4]{z^3}}{\sqrt[4]{z^4}} = \frac{7\sqrt[4]{z^3}}{z}$$

75.
$$\sqrt[3]{\frac{x^3}{8}} = \frac{\sqrt[3]{x^3}}{\sqrt[3]{8}} = \frac{x}{2}$$

76.
$$\frac{\sqrt[3]{2x^9}}{\sqrt[3]{16x^6}} = \sqrt[3]{\frac{2x^9}{16x^6}} = \sqrt[3]{\frac{x^3}{8}} = \frac{\sqrt[3]{x^3}}{\sqrt[3]{8}} = \frac{x}{2}$$

77.
$$\sqrt{\frac{32x^2y^5}{2x^4y}} = \sqrt{\frac{16y^4}{x^2}} = \frac{\sqrt{16y^4}}{\sqrt{x^2}} = \frac{4y^2}{x}$$

78.
$$\sqrt[4]{\frac{32x^9y^{15}}{2xy^3}} = \sqrt[4]{16x^8y^{12}} = 2x^2y^3$$

79.
$$\sqrt{\frac{5x^4}{y}} = \frac{\sqrt{5x^4}}{\sqrt{y}}$$
$$= \frac{\sqrt{x^4}\sqrt{5}}{\sqrt{y}}$$
$$= \frac{x^2\sqrt{5}}{\sqrt{y}} \cdot \frac{\sqrt{y}}{\sqrt{y}}$$
$$= \frac{x^2\sqrt{5y}}{y}$$

80.
$$\sqrt{\frac{12a}{7b}} = \frac{\sqrt{12a}}{\sqrt{7b}}$$
$$= \frac{2\sqrt{3a}}{\sqrt{7b}}$$
$$= \frac{2\sqrt{3a}}{\sqrt{7b}} \cdot \frac{\sqrt{7b}}{\sqrt{7b}}$$
$$= \frac{2\sqrt{21ab}}{7b}$$

81.
$$\sqrt{\frac{18x^4y^5}{3z}} = \frac{\sqrt{18x^4y^5}}{\sqrt{3z}}$$
$$= \frac{\sqrt{9x^4y^4}\sqrt{2y}}{\sqrt{3z}}$$
$$= \frac{3x^2y^2\sqrt{2y}}{\sqrt{3z}}$$
$$= \frac{3x^2y^2\sqrt{2y}}{\sqrt{3z}} \cdot \frac{\sqrt{3z}}{\sqrt{3z}}$$
$$= \frac{3x^2y^2\sqrt{6yz}}{3z}$$
$$= \frac{x^2y^2\sqrt{6yz}}{z}$$

82.
$$\sqrt{\frac{125x^2y^5}{3z}} = \frac{\sqrt{125x^2y^5}}{\sqrt{3z}}$$
$$= \frac{\sqrt{25x^2y^4}\sqrt{5y}}{\sqrt{3z}}$$
$$= \frac{5xy^2\sqrt{5y}}{\sqrt{3z}} \cdot \frac{\sqrt{3z}}{\sqrt{3z}}$$
$$= \frac{5xy^2\sqrt{15yz}}{3z}$$

83.
$$\sqrt[3]{\frac{108x^3y^7}{2y^3}} = \sqrt[3]{54x^3y^4} = 3xy\sqrt[3]{2y}$$

84.
$$\sqrt[3]{\frac{3x}{5y}} = \frac{\sqrt[3]{3x}}{\sqrt[3]{5y}} \cdot \frac{\sqrt[3]{25y^2}}{\sqrt[3]{25y^2}} = \frac{\sqrt[3]{75xy^2}}{5y}$$

85.
$$\sqrt[3]{\frac{4x^5y^3}{x^6}} = \sqrt[3]{\frac{4y^3}{x}}$$
$$= \frac{\sqrt[3]{4y^3}}{\sqrt[3]{x}}$$
$$= \frac{\sqrt[3]{y^3}\sqrt[3]{4}}{\sqrt[3]{x}}$$
$$= \frac{y\sqrt[3]{4}}{\sqrt[3]{x}} \cdot \frac{\sqrt[3]{x^2}}{\sqrt[3]{x^2}}$$
$$= \frac{y\sqrt[3]{4x^2}}{x}$$

86.
$$\sqrt[3]{\frac{y^6}{2x^2}} = \frac{\sqrt[3]{y^6}}{\sqrt[3]{2x^2}}$$
$$= \frac{y^2}{\sqrt[3]{2x^2}} \cdot \frac{\sqrt[3]{4x}}{\sqrt[3]{4x}}$$
$$= \frac{y^2\sqrt[3]{4x}}{2x}$$

87.
$$\sqrt[4]{\frac{3a^2b^{11}}{a^5b}} = \sqrt[4]{\frac{3b^{10}}{a^3}}$$
$$= \frac{\sqrt[4]{3b^{10}}}{\sqrt[4]{a^3}} \cdot \frac{\sqrt[4]{a}}{\sqrt[4]{a}}$$
$$= \frac{\sqrt[4]{3ab^{10}}}{\sqrt[4]{a^4}}$$
$$= \frac{b^2\sqrt[4]{3ab^2}}{a}$$

88.
$$\sqrt[4]{\frac{2x^2y^6}{8x^3}} = \sqrt[4]{\frac{y^6}{4x}}$$
$$= \frac{\sqrt[4]{y^6}}{\sqrt[4]{4x}}$$
$$= \frac{y\sqrt[4]{y^2}}{\sqrt[4]{4x}}$$
$$= \frac{y\sqrt[4]{y^2}}{\sqrt[4]{4x}} \cdot \frac{\sqrt[4]{4x^3}}{\sqrt[4]{4x^3}}$$
$$= \frac{y\sqrt[4]{4x^3y^2}}{2x}$$

89. $\left(3-\sqrt{2}\right)\left(3+\sqrt{2}\right) = 3^2 - \left(\sqrt{2}\right)^2 = 9 - 2 = 7$

90. $\left(\sqrt{x}+y\right)\left(\sqrt{x}-y\right) = \left(\sqrt{x}\right)^2 - y^2 = x - y^2$

91. $\left(x-\sqrt{y}\right)\left(x+\sqrt{y}\right) = x^2 - \left(\sqrt{y}\right)^2 = x^2 - y$

92. $\left(\sqrt{3}+5\right)^2 = \left(\sqrt{3}\right)^2 + 2(5)\left(\sqrt{3}\right) + 5^2$
$$= 3 + 10\sqrt{3} + 25$$
$$= 28 + 10\sqrt{3}$$

93. $\left(\sqrt{x}-\sqrt{3y}\right)\left(\sqrt{x}+\sqrt{5y}\right)$
$$= \left(\sqrt{x}\right)^2 + \sqrt{x}\sqrt{5y} - \sqrt{x}\sqrt{3y} - \sqrt{3y}\sqrt{5y}$$
$$= x + \sqrt{5xy} - \sqrt{3xy} - \sqrt{15y^2}$$
$$= x + \sqrt{5xy} - \sqrt{3xy} - y\sqrt{15}$$

94. $\left(\sqrt[3]{2x}-\sqrt[3]{3y}\right)\left(\sqrt[3]{3x}-\sqrt[3]{2y}\right)$
$$= \sqrt[3]{2x}\left(\sqrt[3]{3x}\right) - \left(\sqrt[3]{2x}\right)\left(\sqrt[3]{2y}\right)$$
$$\quad - \sqrt[3]{3y}\left(\sqrt[3]{3x}\right) + \sqrt[3]{3y}\sqrt[3]{2y}$$
$$= \sqrt[3]{6x^2} - \sqrt[3]{4xy} - \sqrt[3]{9xy} + \sqrt[3]{6y^2}$$

95.
$$\frac{5}{2+\sqrt{5}} = \frac{5}{2+\sqrt{5}} \cdot \frac{2-\sqrt{5}}{2-\sqrt{5}}$$
$$= \frac{5\left(2-\sqrt{5}\right)}{2^2 - \left(\sqrt{5}\right)^2}$$
$$= \frac{10-5\sqrt{5}}{4-5}$$
$$= \frac{10-5\sqrt{5}}{-1}$$
$$= -10 + 5\sqrt{5}$$

96.
$$\frac{x}{3+\sqrt{x}} = \frac{x}{3+\sqrt{x}} \cdot \frac{3-\sqrt{x}}{3-\sqrt{x}}$$
$$= \frac{x\left(3-\sqrt{x}\right)}{3^2 - \left(\sqrt{x}\right)^2}$$
$$= \frac{3x - x\sqrt{x}}{9-x}$$

97.
$$\frac{a}{7-\sqrt{b}} = \frac{a}{7-\sqrt{b}} \cdot \frac{7+\sqrt{b}}{7+\sqrt{b}}$$
$$= \frac{a\left(7+\sqrt{b}\right)}{\left(7-\sqrt{b}\right)\left(7+\sqrt{b}\right)}$$
$$= \frac{7a + a\sqrt{b}}{49 + 7\sqrt{b} - 7\sqrt{b} - b}$$
$$= \frac{7a + a\sqrt{b}}{49-b}$$

98.

$$\frac{x}{\sqrt{y}-8} = \frac{x}{\sqrt{y}-8}\cdot\frac{\sqrt{y}+8}{\sqrt{y}+8}$$

$$= \frac{x\left(\sqrt{y}+8\right)}{\left(\sqrt{y}-8\right)\left(\sqrt{y}+8\right)}$$

$$= \frac{x\sqrt{y}+8x}{y+8\sqrt{y}-8\sqrt{y}-64}$$

$$= \frac{x\sqrt{y}+8x}{y-64}$$

99.

$$\frac{\sqrt{x}}{\sqrt{x}+\sqrt{y}} = \frac{\sqrt{x}}{\sqrt{x}+\sqrt{y}}\cdot\frac{\sqrt{x}-\sqrt{y}}{\sqrt{x}-\sqrt{y}}$$

$$= \frac{\sqrt{x}\left(\sqrt{x}-\sqrt{y}\right)}{\left(\sqrt{x}\right)^2-\left(\sqrt{y}\right)^2}$$

$$= \frac{\sqrt{x^2}-\sqrt{xy}}{x-y}$$

$$= \frac{x-\sqrt{xy}}{x-y}$$

100.

$$\frac{\sqrt{x}-2\sqrt{y}}{\sqrt{x}-\sqrt{y}} = \frac{\sqrt{x}-2\sqrt{y}}{\sqrt{x}-\sqrt{y}}\cdot\frac{\sqrt{x}+\sqrt{y}}{\sqrt{x}+\sqrt{y}}$$

$$= \frac{x+\sqrt{xy}-2\sqrt{xy}-2y}{\left(\sqrt{x}\right)^2-\left(\sqrt{y}\right)^2}$$

$$= \frac{x-\sqrt{xy}-2y}{x-y}$$

101.

$$\frac{3}{\sqrt{a-1}-2} = \frac{3}{\sqrt{a-1}-2}\cdot\frac{\sqrt{a-1}+2}{\sqrt{a-1}+2}$$

$$= \frac{3\left(\sqrt{a-1}+2\right)}{\left(\sqrt{a-1}-2\right)\left(\sqrt{a-1}+2\right)}$$

$$= \frac{3\sqrt{a-1}+6}{a-1+2\sqrt{a-1}-2\sqrt{a-1}-4}$$

$$= \frac{3\sqrt{a-1}+6}{a-5}$$

102.

$$\frac{4}{\sqrt{y+2}-3} = \frac{4}{\sqrt{y+2}-3}\cdot\frac{\sqrt{y+2}+3}{\sqrt{y+2}+3}$$

$$= \frac{4\sqrt{y+2}+12}{\left(\sqrt{y+2}\right)^2-3^2}$$

$$= \frac{4\sqrt{y+2}+12}{y+2-9}$$

$$= \frac{4\sqrt{y+2}+12}{y-7}$$

103. $\sqrt[3]{x}+3\sqrt[3]{x}-2\sqrt[3]{x}=2\sqrt[3]{x}$

104. $\sqrt{3}+\sqrt{27}-\sqrt{192}=\sqrt{3}+3\sqrt{3}-\sqrt{64}\sqrt{3}$

$$= \sqrt{3}+3\sqrt{3}-8\sqrt{3}$$

$$= -4\sqrt{3}$$

105. $\sqrt[3]{16}-5\sqrt[3]{54}+2\sqrt[3]{64}$

$$= \sqrt[3]{8}\sqrt[3]{2}-5\sqrt[3]{27}\sqrt[3]{2}+2\sqrt[3]{64}$$

$$= 2\sqrt[3]{2}-5\left(3\sqrt[3]{2}\right)+2(4)$$

$$= 2\sqrt[3]{2}-15\sqrt[3]{2}+8$$

$$= 8-13\sqrt[3]{2}$$

106. $4\sqrt{2}-\frac{3}{\sqrt{32}}+\sqrt{50}$

$$= 4\sqrt{2}-\frac{3}{4\sqrt{2}}+5\sqrt{2}$$

$$= 4\sqrt{2}-\frac{3}{4\sqrt{2}}\cdot\frac{\sqrt{2}}{\sqrt{2}}+5\sqrt{2}$$

$$= 4\sqrt{2}-\frac{3\sqrt{2}}{8}+5\sqrt{2}$$

$$= \frac{8}{8}\left(4\sqrt{2}\right)-\frac{3\sqrt{2}}{8}+\left(\frac{8}{8}\right)5\sqrt{2}$$

$$= \frac{32\sqrt{2}}{8}-\frac{3\sqrt{2}}{8}+\frac{40\sqrt{2}}{8}$$

$$= \frac{69\sqrt{2}}{8}$$

107. $3\sqrt{x^5y^6}-\sqrt{16x^7y^8}$

$$= 3\sqrt{x^4y^6}\sqrt{x}-\sqrt{16x^6y^8}\sqrt{x}$$

$$= 3x^2y^3\sqrt{x}-4x^3y^4\sqrt{x}$$

$$= \left(3x^2y^3-4x^3y^4\right)\sqrt{x}$$

108.
$$2\sqrt[3]{x^7 y^8} - \sqrt[3]{x^4 y^2} + 3\sqrt[3]{x^{10} y^2}$$
$$= 2\sqrt[3]{x^6 y^6}\sqrt[3]{xy^2} - \sqrt[3]{x^3}\sqrt[3]{xy^2} + 3\sqrt[3]{x^9}\sqrt[3]{xy^2}$$
$$= 2x^2 y^2\sqrt[3]{xy^2} - x\sqrt[3]{xy^2} + 3x^3\sqrt[3]{xy^2}$$
$$= (2x^2 y^2 - x + 3x^3)\sqrt[3]{xy^2}$$

109.
$$(f \cdot g)(x) = f(x) \cdot g(x)$$
$$= \sqrt{3x} \cdot \left(\sqrt{6x} - \sqrt{10}\right)$$
$$= \sqrt{3x}\sqrt{6x} - \sqrt{3x}\sqrt{10}$$
$$= \sqrt{18x^2} - \sqrt{30x}$$
$$= \sqrt{9x^2}\sqrt{2} - \sqrt{30x}$$
$$= 3x\sqrt{2} - \sqrt{30x}$$

110.
$$(f \cdot g)(x) = f(x) \cdot g(x)$$
$$= \sqrt[3]{2x^2}\left(\sqrt[3]{4x^4} + \sqrt[3]{8x^5}\right)$$
$$= \sqrt[3]{2x^2}\sqrt[3]{4x^4} + \sqrt[3]{2x^2}\sqrt[3]{8x^5}$$
$$= \sqrt[3]{8x^6} + \sqrt[3]{16x^7}$$
$$= \sqrt[3]{8x^6} + \sqrt[3]{8x^6}\sqrt[3]{2x}$$
$$= 2x^2 + 2x^2\sqrt[3]{2x}$$

111.
$$f(x) = \sqrt{2x+4}\sqrt{2x+4}, \quad x \ge -2$$
$$= \sqrt{(2x+4)^2}$$
$$= |2x+4|$$
$$= 2x+4 \quad \text{since } x \ge -2$$

112.
$$g(a) = \sqrt{20a^2 + 50a + 125}$$
$$= \sqrt{5(4a^2 + 10a + 25)}$$
$$= \sqrt{5(2a+5)^2}$$
$$= \sqrt{5}|2a+5|$$

113.
$$\frac{\sqrt[3]{(x+5)^5}}{\sqrt{(x+5)^3}} = \frac{(x+5)^{5/3}}{(x+5)^{3/2}}$$
$$= (x+5)^{5/3 - 3/2}$$
$$= (x+5)^{1/6}$$
$$= \sqrt[6]{x+5}$$

114.
$$\frac{\sqrt[3]{a^3 b^2}}{\sqrt[4]{a^4 b}} = \frac{a\sqrt[3]{b^2}}{a\sqrt[4]{b}}$$
$$= \frac{\sqrt[3]{b^2}}{\sqrt[4]{b}}$$
$$= \frac{b^{2/3}}{b^{1/4}}$$
$$= b^{2/3 - 1/4}$$
$$= b^{5/12}$$
$$= \sqrt[12]{b^5}$$

115. **a.**
$$P = 2l + 2w$$
$$P = 2\sqrt{48} + 2\sqrt{12}$$
$$= 2\sqrt{16 \cdot 3} + 2\sqrt{4 \cdot 3}$$
$$= 8\sqrt{3} + 4\sqrt{3}$$
$$= 12\sqrt{3}$$

b.
$$A = lw$$
$$A = \left(\sqrt{48}\right)\left(\sqrt{12}\right)$$
$$= \sqrt{576}$$
$$= 24$$

116. **a.**
$$P = s_1 + s_2 + s_3$$
$$P = \sqrt{125} + \sqrt{45} + \sqrt{130}$$
$$= 5\sqrt{5} + 3\sqrt{5} + \sqrt{130}$$
$$= 8\sqrt{5} + \sqrt{130}$$

b.
$$A = \frac{1}{2}bh$$
$$A = \frac{1}{2}\left(\sqrt{130}\right)\left(\sqrt{20}\right)$$
$$= \frac{1}{2}\sqrt{2600}$$
$$= \frac{1}{2}\sqrt{100 \cdot 26}$$
$$= \frac{10}{2}\sqrt{26}$$
$$= 5\sqrt{26}$$

117. a. $f(x) = \sqrt{x} + 2$

$g(x) = -3$

$(f + g)(x) = f(x) + g(x)$

$= \sqrt{x} + 2 - 3$

$= \sqrt{x} - 1$

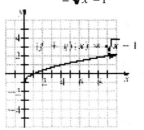

b. $\sqrt{x} \geq 0, \; x \geq 0$

The domain is $\{x \mid x \geq 0\}$.

118. a. $f(x) = -\sqrt{x}$

$g(x) = \sqrt{x} + 2$

$(f + g)(x) = f(x) + g(x)$

$= -\sqrt{x} + \sqrt{x} + 2$

$= 2$

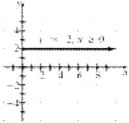

b. $\sqrt{x} \geq 0, \; x \geq 0$

The domain is $\{x \mid x \geq 0\}$.

119. $\sqrt{x} = 8$

$\left(\sqrt{x}\right)^2 = 8^2$

$x = 64$

Check: $\sqrt{64} = 8$ True

64 is the solution.

120. $\sqrt{x} = -8$

$\left(\sqrt{x}\right)^2 = (-8)^2$

$x = 64$

Check: $\sqrt{64} \neq -8$ False

no solution

121. $\sqrt[3]{x} = 5$

$\left(\sqrt[3]{x}\right)^3 = 5^3$

$x = 125$

Check: $\sqrt[3]{x} = 5$

$\sqrt[3]{125} = 5$

$5 = 5$ True

125 is a solution.

122. $\sqrt[3]{x} = -5$

$\left(\sqrt[3]{x}\right)^3 = (-5)^3$

$x = -125$

Check: $\sqrt[3]{x} = -5$

$\sqrt[3]{-125} = -5$

$-5 = -5$ True

-125 is a solution.

123. $3 + \sqrt{x} = 10$

$\sqrt{x} = 7$

$\left(\sqrt{x}\right)^2 = 7^2$

$x = 49$

Check: $3 + \sqrt{x} = 10$

$3 + \sqrt{49} = 10$

$3 + 7 = 10$

$10 = 10$ True

49 is a solution.

124. $8 + \sqrt[3]{x} = 12$

$\sqrt[3]{x} = 4$

$\left(\sqrt[3]{x}\right)^3 = 4^3$

$x = 64$

Check: $8 + \sqrt[3]{x} = 12$

$8 + \sqrt[3]{64} = 12$

$8 + 4 = 12$

$12 = 12$ True

64 is a solution.

125 $\sqrt{3x + 4} = \sqrt{5x + 12}$

$\left(\sqrt{3x + 4}\right)^2 = \left(\sqrt{5x + 12}\right)^2$

$3x + 4 = 5x + 12$

$-8 = 2x$

$-4 = x$

Check: $\sqrt{3x + 4}$ becomes

$\sqrt{3(-4) + 4} = \sqrt{-12 + 4} = \sqrt{-8}$

which is not a real number. −4 is not a solution and there is no real solution.

126. $\sqrt{x^2 + 2x - 4} = x$

$\left(\sqrt{x^2 + 2x - 4}\right)^2 = (x)^2$

$x^2 + 2x - 4 = x^2$

$2x - 4 = 0$

$x = 2$

Check: $\sqrt{2^2 + 2 \cdot 2 - 4} = 2$

$\sqrt{4 + 4 - 4} = 2$

$\sqrt{4} = 2$

$2 = 2$ True

2 is a solution.

127. $\sqrt[3]{x - 9} = \sqrt[3]{5x + 3}$

$\left(\sqrt[3]{x - 9}\right)^3 = \left(\sqrt[3]{5x + 3}\right)^3$

$x - 9 = 5x + 3$

$-4x = 12$

$x = -3$

Check: $\sqrt[3]{-3 - 9} = \sqrt[3]{5(-3) + 3}$

$\sqrt[3]{-12} = \sqrt[3]{-15 + 3}$

$\sqrt[3]{-12} = \sqrt[3]{-12}$ True

−3 is a solution.

128. $(x^2 + 5)^{1/2} = x + 1$

$\left[(x^2 + 5)^{1/2}\right]^2 = (x + 1)^2$

$x^2 + 5 = x^2 + 2x + 1$

$5 = 2x + 1$

$4 = 2x$

$x = 2$

Check: $(2^2 + 5)^{1/2} = 2 + 1$

$(4 + 5)^{1/2} = 3$

$9^{1/2} = 3$

$3 = 3$ True

2 is a solution.

129. $\sqrt{x} + 3 = \sqrt{3x + 9}$

$\left(\sqrt{x} + 3\right)^2 = \left(\sqrt{3x + 9}\right)^2$

$\left(\sqrt{x} + 3\right)\left(\sqrt{x} + 3\right) = 3x + 9$

$x + 6\sqrt{x} + 9 = 3x + 9$

$6\sqrt{x} = 2x$

$\left(6\sqrt{x}\right)^2 = (2x)^2$

$36x = 4x^2$

$4x^2 - 36x = 0$

$4x(x - 9) = 0$

$4x = 0$ or $x - 9 = 0$

$x = 0$ $x = 9$

A check shows that 0 and 9 are solutions.

130.
$$\sqrt{6x-5} - \sqrt{2x+6} - 1 = 0$$
$$\sqrt{6x-5} = \sqrt{2x+6} + 1$$
$$\left(\sqrt{6x-5}\right)^2 = \left(\sqrt{2x+6}+1\right)^2$$
$$6x-5 = 2x+6+2\sqrt{2x+6}+1$$
$$6x-5 = 2x+7+2\sqrt{2x+6}$$
$$4x-12 = 2\sqrt{2x+6}$$
$$\frac{4x}{2} - \frac{12}{2} = \frac{2}{2}\sqrt{2x+6}$$
$$2x-6 = \sqrt{2x+6}$$
$$(2x-6)^2 = \left(\sqrt{2x+6}\right)^2$$
$$4x^2 - 24x + 36 = 2x+6$$
$$4x^2 - 26x + 30 = 0$$
$$2x^2 - 13x + 15 = 0$$
Express the middle term, $-13x$, as $-10x - 3x$.
$$2x^2 - 10x - 3x + 15 = 0$$
$$2x(x-5) - 3(x-5) = 0$$
$$(2x-3)(x-5) = 0$$
$$2x-3 = 0 \quad \text{or} \quad x-5 = 0$$
$$x = \frac{3}{2} \qquad\qquad x = 5$$

The solution $x = 5$ checks in the original equation but $x = \frac{3}{2}$ does not check.
Therefore the only solution is $x = 5$.

131.
$$f(x) = g(x)$$
$$\sqrt{3x+4} = 2\sqrt{2x-4}$$
$$\left(\sqrt{3x+4}\right)^2 = \left(2\sqrt{2x-4}\right)^2$$
$$3x+4 = 4(2x-4)$$
$$3x+4 = 8x-16$$
$$20 = 5x$$
$$4 = x$$

132.
$$f(x) = g(x)$$
$$(4x+3)^{1/3} = (6x-9)^{1/3}$$
$$[(4x+3)^{1/3}]^3 = [(6x-9)^{1/3}]^3$$
$$4x+3 = 6x-9$$
$$12 = 2x$$
$$6 = x$$

133.
$$V = \sqrt{\frac{2L}{w}} \quad \text{Solve for } L.$$
$$V^2 = \frac{2L}{w}$$
$$V^2 w = 2L$$
$$\frac{V^2 w}{2} = L \text{ or } L = \frac{V^2 w}{2}$$

134.
$$r = \sqrt{\frac{A}{\pi}} \quad \text{Solve for } A.$$
$$r^2 = \left(\sqrt{\frac{A}{\pi}}\right)^2$$
$$r^2 = \frac{A}{\pi}$$
$$\pi r^2 = A \text{ or } A = \pi r^2$$

135. Pythagorean Theorem: $a^2 + b^2 = c^2$
$$\left(\sqrt{20}\right)^2 + 6^2 = x^2$$
$$20 + 36 = x^2$$
$$56 = x^2$$
$$\sqrt{56} = x \text{ or } x = 2\sqrt{14}$$

136. Pythagorean Theorem: $a^2 + b^2 = c^2$
$$\left(\sqrt{26}\right)^2 + x^2 = \left(\sqrt{101}\right)^2$$
$$26 + x^2 = 101$$
$$x^2 = 75$$
$$x = \sqrt{75} \text{ or } x = 5\sqrt{3}$$

137.
$$l = \sqrt{a^2 + b^2}$$
$$= \sqrt{5^2 + 2^2}$$
$$= \sqrt{29}$$
$$\approx 5.39 \text{ m}$$

138.
$$v = \sqrt{2gh}$$
$$= \sqrt{2(32)(20)}$$
$$= \sqrt{1280} \approx 35.78 \text{ ft/sec}$$

139.
$$T = 2\pi\sqrt{\frac{L}{32}}$$
$$= 2\pi\sqrt{\frac{64}{32}}$$
$$= 2\pi\sqrt{2}$$
$$\approx 8.89 \text{ sec}$$

140.
$$V = \sqrt{\frac{2K}{m}}$$
$$= \sqrt{\frac{2(45)}{0.145}}$$
$$\approx 25 \text{ meters per second}$$

141.
$$m = \frac{m_0}{\sqrt{1 - \frac{v^2}{c^2}}}$$
$$= \frac{m_0}{\sqrt{1 - \frac{(0.98c)^2}{c^2}}}$$
$$= \frac{m_0}{\sqrt{1 - \frac{0.9604 c^2}{c^2}}}$$
$$= \frac{m_0}{\sqrt{1 - 0.9604}}$$
$$= \frac{m_0}{\sqrt{0.0396}}$$
$$\approx 5m_0$$

It is about 5 times its original mass.

142. $5 = 5 + 0i$

143. $-6 = -6 + 0i$

144. $2 - \sqrt{-256} = 2 - \sqrt{-1}\sqrt{256}$
$$= 2 - 16i$$

145. $3 + \sqrt{-16} = 3 + \sqrt{16}\sqrt{-1}$
$$= 3 + 4i$$

146. $(3 + 2i) + (4 - i) = 7 + i$

147. $(4 - 6i) - (3 - 4i) = 4 - 6i - 3 + 4i$
$$= 1 - 2i$$

148. $\left(\sqrt{3} + \sqrt{-5}\right) + \left(2\sqrt{3} - \sqrt{-7}\right)$
$$= \sqrt{3} + \sqrt{5}\sqrt{-1} + 2\sqrt{3} - \sqrt{7}\sqrt{-1}$$
$$= \sqrt{3} + i\sqrt{5} + 2\sqrt{3} - i\sqrt{7}$$
$$= 3\sqrt{3} + \left(\sqrt{5} - \sqrt{7}\right)i$$

149. $\sqrt{-6}\left(\sqrt{6} + \sqrt{-6}\right) = \sqrt{6}\sqrt{-1}\left(\sqrt{6} + \sqrt{6}\sqrt{-1}\right)$
$$= i\sqrt{6}\left(\sqrt{6} + i\sqrt{6}\right)$$
$$= i\sqrt{36} + i^2\sqrt{36}$$
$$= 6i + 6(-1) = -6 + 6i$$

150. $(4 + 3i)(2 - 3i) = 8 - 12i + 6i - 9i^2$
$$= 8 - 6i - 9(-1)$$
$$= 8 - 6i + 9$$
$$= 17 - 6i$$

151. $\left(6 + \sqrt{-3}\right)\left(4 - \sqrt{-15}\right)$
$$= \left(6 + \sqrt{3}\sqrt{-1}\right)\left(4 - \sqrt{15}\sqrt{-1}\right)$$
$$= \left(6 + i\sqrt{3}\right)\left(4 - i\sqrt{15}\right)$$
$$= 24 - 6i\sqrt{15} + 4i\sqrt{3} - i^2\sqrt{45}$$
$$= 24 - 6i\sqrt{15} + 4i\sqrt{3} - (-1)\sqrt{9}\sqrt{5}$$
$$= \left(24 + 3\sqrt{5}\right) + \left(4\sqrt{3} - 6\sqrt{15}\right)i$$

152. $\frac{2}{3i} = \frac{2}{3i} \cdot \frac{-3i}{-3i}$
$$= \frac{-6i}{-9i^2}$$
$$= \frac{-6i}{-9(-1)}$$
$$= \frac{-6i}{9}$$
$$= \frac{-2i}{3}$$

153. $\frac{2 + \sqrt{3}}{2i} = \frac{2 + \sqrt{3}}{2i} \cdot \frac{-2i}{-2i}$
$$= \frac{-4i - 2i\sqrt{3}}{-4i^2}$$
$$= \frac{-4i - 2i\sqrt{3}}{-4(-1)}$$
$$= \frac{2\left(-2i - i\sqrt{3}\right)}{4}$$
$$= \frac{-2i - i\sqrt{3}}{2}$$
$$= \frac{\left(-2 - \sqrt{3}\right)i}{2}$$

154. $\frac{5}{3 + 2i} = \frac{5}{3 + 2i} \cdot \frac{3 - 2i}{3 - 2i}$
$$= \frac{5(3 - 2i)}{9 - 4i^2}$$
$$= \frac{15 - 10i}{9 - 4(-1)}$$
$$= \frac{15 - 10i}{9 + 4}$$
$$= \frac{15 - 10i}{13}$$

155.
$$\frac{\sqrt{3}}{5-\sqrt{-6}} = \frac{\sqrt{3}}{5-i\sqrt{6}}$$
$$= \frac{\sqrt{3}}{\left(5-i\sqrt{6}\right)} \cdot \frac{5+i\sqrt{6}}{5+i\sqrt{6}}$$
$$= \frac{5\sqrt{3}+i\sqrt{18}}{(5)^2 - \left(i\sqrt{6}\right)^2}$$
$$= \frac{5\sqrt{3}+3i\sqrt{2}}{(5)^2 + \left(\sqrt{6}\right)^2}$$
$$= \frac{5\sqrt{3}+3i\sqrt{2}}{25+6}$$
$$= \frac{5\sqrt{3}+3i\sqrt{2}}{31}$$

156. $x^2 - 2x + 9$
$$= \left(1+2i\sqrt{2}\right)^2 - 2\left(1+2i\sqrt{2}\right)+9$$
$$= 1^2 + 2(1)\left(2i\sqrt{2}\right) + \left(2i\sqrt{2}\right)^2 - 2 - 4i\sqrt{2} + 9$$
$$= 1 + 4i\sqrt{2} - 8 - 2 - 4i\sqrt{2} + 9$$
$$= 0 + 0i$$
$$= 0$$

157. $x^2 - 2x + 12$
$$= (1-2i)^2 - 2(1-2i) + 12$$
$$= 1^2 - 2(1)(2i) + (2i)^2 - 2 + 4i + 12$$
$$= 1 - 4i - 4 - 2 + 4i + 12$$
$$= 7 + 0i$$
$$= 7$$

158. $i^{53} = i^{52}i = (i^4)^{13} = 1^{13} \cdot i = i$

159. $i^{19} = i^{16}i^3 = (i^4)^4 i^3 = 1^4 \, ?i^3 = 1(i^3) = i^3 = -i$

160. $i^{404} = (i^4)^{101} = 1^{101} = 1$

161. $i^{5326} = i^{5324}i^2$
$$= (i^4)^{1331}i^2$$
$$= 1^{1331} \cdot i^2$$
$$= 1(i^2)$$
$$= i^2$$
$$= -1$$

2.
$$\left(\frac{x^{2/5} \cdot x^{-1}}{x^{3/5}}\right)^2 = \left(x^{2/5-3/5-1}\right)^2$$
$$= \left(x^{2/5-3/5-5/5}\right)^2$$
$$= \left(x^{-6/5}\right)^2$$
$$= x^{-12/5}$$
$$= \frac{1}{x^{12/5}}$$

3. $x^{-2/3} + x^{4/3} = x^{-2/3}(1) + x^{-2/3}\left(x^{6/3}\right)$
$$= x^{-2/3}\left(1 + x^{6/3}\right)$$
$$= x^{-2/3}\left(1 + x^2\right)$$
$$= \frac{1+x^2}{x^{2/3}}$$

4. $g(x) = \sqrt{x}$

5. $\sqrt{48x^7y^{10}} = \sqrt{16x^6y^{10}}\sqrt{3x}$
$$= 4x^3y^5\sqrt{3x}$$

6. $\sqrt[3]{4x^5y^2}\sqrt[3]{10x^6y^8} = \sqrt[3]{40x^{11}y^{10}}$
$$= \sqrt[3]{8x^9y^9} \cdot \sqrt[3]{5x^2y}$$
$$= 2x^3y^3\sqrt[3]{5x^2y}$$

Practice Test

1. $\sqrt{(5x-1)^2} = |5x-1|$

7.

$$\sqrt{\frac{3x^6 y^3}{8z}} = \frac{\sqrt{3x^6 y^3}}{\sqrt{8z}}$$

$$= \frac{\sqrt{x^6 y^2}\sqrt{3y}}{\sqrt{4}\sqrt{2z}}$$

$$= \frac{x^3 y\sqrt{3y}}{2\sqrt{2z}} \cdot \frac{\sqrt{2z}}{\sqrt{2z}}$$

$$= \frac{x^3 y\sqrt{6yz}}{2(2z)}$$

$$= \frac{x^3 y\sqrt{6yz}}{4z}$$

8.

$$\frac{4}{\sqrt[3]{x}} = \frac{4}{\sqrt[3]{x}} \cdot \frac{\sqrt[3]{x^2}}{\sqrt[3]{x^2}} = \frac{4\sqrt[3]{x^2}}{x}$$

9.

$$\frac{\sqrt{3}}{3+\sqrt{27}} = \frac{\sqrt{3}}{3+\sqrt{27}} \cdot \frac{3-\sqrt{27}}{3-\sqrt{27}}$$

$$= \frac{\sqrt{3}\left(3-\sqrt{27}\right)}{\left(3+\sqrt{27}\right)\left(3-\sqrt{27}\right)}$$

$$= \frac{3\sqrt{3}-\sqrt{81}}{9-3\sqrt{27}+3\sqrt{27}-27}$$

$$= \frac{3\sqrt{3}-9}{-18}$$

$$= \frac{\sqrt{3}-3}{-6} \quad \text{or} \quad \frac{3-\sqrt{3}}{6}$$

10.

$$2\sqrt{24} - 5\sqrt{6} + 3\sqrt{54}$$

$$= 2\sqrt{4}\sqrt{6} - 5\sqrt{6} + 3\sqrt{9}\sqrt{6}$$

$$= 4\sqrt{6} - 5\sqrt{6} + 9\sqrt{6}$$

$$= 8\sqrt{6}$$

11.

$$\sqrt[3]{8x^3 y^5} + 2\sqrt[3]{x^6 y^8}$$

$$= \sqrt[3]{8x^3 y^3}\sqrt[3]{y^2} + 2\sqrt[3]{x^6 y^6}\sqrt[3]{y^2}$$

$$= 2xy\sqrt[3]{y^2} + 2x^2 y^2\sqrt[3]{y^2}$$

$$= (2xy + 2x^2 y^2)\sqrt[3]{y^2}$$

12.

$$\left(\sqrt{3} - 5\right)\left(6 - \sqrt{8}\right) = \sqrt{3}(6) - \sqrt{3}\sqrt{8} - 5(6) + 5\sqrt{8}$$

$$= 6\sqrt{3} - \sqrt{24} - 30 + 5\sqrt{8}$$

$$= 6\sqrt{3} - \sqrt{4 \cdot 6} - 30 + 5\sqrt{4 \cdot 2}$$

$$= 6\sqrt{3} - 2\sqrt{6} - 30 + 10\sqrt{2}$$

13.

$$\sqrt[4]{\sqrt{x^5 y^3}} = \sqrt[4]{\left(x^5 y^3\right)^{1/2}}$$

$$= \left[\left(x^5 y^3\right)^{1/2}\right]^{1/4}$$

$$= \left(x^5 y^3\right)^{1/8}$$

$$= \sqrt[8]{x^5 y^3}$$

14.

$$\frac{\sqrt[4]{(7x+2)^5}}{\sqrt[3]{(7x+2)^2}} = \frac{(7x+2)^{5/4}}{(7x+2)^{2/3}}$$

$$= (7x+2)^{5/4 - 2/3}$$

$$= (7x+2)^{7/12}$$

$$= \sqrt[12]{(7x+2)^7}$$

15.

$$\sqrt{3x+4} = 5$$

$$\left(\sqrt{3x+4}\right)^2 = 5^2$$

$$3x+4 = 25$$

$$3x = 21$$

$$x = 7$$

Check: $\sqrt{3x+4} = 5$

$$\sqrt{3 \cdot 7 + 4} = 5$$

$$\sqrt{25} = 5$$

$$5 = 5 \quad \text{True}$$

7 is the solution.

16.

$$\sqrt{x^2 - x - 12} = x + 3$$

$$\left(\sqrt{x^2 - x - 12}\right)^2 = (x+3)^2$$

$$x^2 - x - 12 = x^2 + 6x + 9$$

$$-x - 12 = 6x + 9$$

$$-12 = 7x + 9$$

$$-21 = 7x$$

$$x = -3$$

Check:

$$\sqrt{(-3)^2 - (-3) - 12} \quad 0 \quad -3 + 3$$

$$\sqrt{9 + 3 - 12} = -3 + 3$$

$$\sqrt{0} = 0$$

$$0 = 0$$

−3 is the solution.

17.

$$\sqrt{a-8} = \sqrt{a} - 2$$

$$\left(\sqrt{a-8}\right)^2 = \left(\sqrt{a}-2\right)^2$$

$$a - 8 = a - 4\sqrt{a} + 4$$

$$-12 = -4\sqrt{a}$$

$$\sqrt{a} = 3$$

$$a = 3^2 = 9$$

$$\sqrt{a-8} = \sqrt{a} - 2$$

Check: $\sqrt{9-8} = \sqrt{9} - 2$

$$\sqrt{1} = 3 - 2$$

$$1 = 1 \quad \text{True}$$

9 is the solution.

18.

$$f(x) = g(x)$$

$$(9x+37)^{1/3} = 2(2x+2)^{1/3}$$

$$[(9x+37)^{1/3}]^3 = [\,2(2x+2)^{1/3}\,]^3$$

$$9x + 37 = 8(2x+2)$$

$$9x + 37 = 16x + 16$$

$$21 = 7x$$

$$3 = x$$

19.

$$w = \frac{\sqrt{2gh}}{4} \quad \text{Solve for } g.$$

$$4w = \sqrt{2gh}$$

$$(4w)^2 = 2gh$$

$$\frac{16w^2}{2h} = \frac{2gh}{2h}$$

$$\frac{8w^2}{h} = g$$

20.

$$V = \sqrt{64.4h}$$

$$V = \sqrt{64.4(200)}$$

$$= \sqrt{12,880}$$

$$\approx 113.49 \ \text{ft / sec}$$

21. Let x be the length of the ladder.

$$x = \sqrt{12^2 + 5^2}$$

$$= 169$$

$$= 13 \text{ feet}$$

22.

$$T = 2\pi\sqrt{\frac{m}{k}}$$

$$T = 2\pi\sqrt{\frac{1400}{65,000}}$$

$$\approx 0.92 \text{ sec}$$

23.

$$\left(6 - \sqrt{-4}\right)\left(2 + \sqrt{-9}\right) = (6 - 2i)(2 + 3i)$$

$$= 12 + 18i - 4i - 6i^2$$

$$= 12 + 14i - 6(-1)$$

$$= 12 + 14i + 6$$

$$= 18 + 14i$$

24.

$$\frac{5-i}{7+2i} = \frac{5-i}{7+2i} \cdot \frac{7-2i}{7-2i}$$

$$= \frac{(5-i)(7-2i)}{(7+2i)(7-2i)}$$

$$= \frac{35 - 10i - 7i + 2i^2}{49 - 14i + 14i - 4i^2}$$

$$= \frac{35 - 17i + 2(-1)}{49 - 4(-1)}$$

$$= \frac{35 - 17i - 2}{49 + 4}$$

$$= \frac{33 - 17i}{53}$$

25.

$$x^2 + 6x + 12$$

$$= (-3+i)^2 + 6(-3+i) + 12$$

$$= (-3)^2 - 2(3)(i) + (i)^2 - 18 + 6i + 12$$

$$= 9 - 6i - 1 - 18 + 6i + 12$$

$$= 2 + 0i$$

$$= 2$$

Cumulative Review Test

1.

$$\frac{1}{5}(x-3) = \frac{3}{4}(x+3) - x$$

$$20\left[\frac{1}{5}(x-3)\right] = 20\left[\frac{3}{4}(x+3)\right] - 20x$$

$$4(x-3) = 5(3)(x+3) - 20x$$

$$4x - 12 = 15x + 45 - 20x$$

$$4x - 12 = -5x + 45$$

$$9x - 12 = 45$$

$$9x = 57$$

$$x = \frac{57}{9}$$

2. $3(x-4) = 6x - (4-5x)$

$3x - 12 = 6x - 4 + 5x$

$3x - 12 = 11x - 4$

$-8x = 8$

$x = -1$

3.   Let x be the original price of the sweater.
$x - 60\% x = 20$

$x - .60x = 20$

$.40x = 20$

$x = \dfrac{20}{.40}$

$x = 50$

The original price of the sweater is $50.

4. $|3 - 2x| < 7$

$-7 < 3 - 2x < 7$

$-7 - 3 < 3 - 2x - 3 < 7 - 3$

$-10 < -2x < 4$

$\dfrac{-10}{-2} > \dfrac{-2x}{-2} > \dfrac{4}{-2}$

$5 > x > -2$ or $-2 < x < 5$

The solution set is $\{x \mid -2 < x < 5\}$

5. $y = \dfrac{3}{2}x - 3$

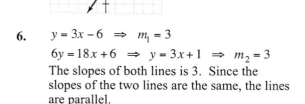

6. $y = 3x - 6 \implies m_1 = 3$

$6y = 18x + 6 \implies y = 3x + 1 \implies m_2 = 3$

The slopes of both lines is 3. Since the slopes of the two lines are the same, the lines are parallel.

7. $f(x) = x^2 - 3x + 4$ and $g(x) = 2x - 5$

$(g - f)(x) = (2x - 5) - (x^2 - 3x + 4)$

$= 2x - 5 - x^2 + 3x - 4$

$= -x^2 + 5x - 9$

8.   First find the slope of the given line.
$3x - 2y = 6$

$-2y = -3x + 6$

$y = \dfrac{3}{2}x - 3 \implies$ The slope is $\dfrac{3}{2}$.

The slope of any line parallel to this line must have an opposite reciprocal slope. Therefore, the slope of the line perpendicular to the given line is $-\dfrac{2}{3}$. Finally, use the point-slope formula to find the equation of the line.

$y - y_1 = m(x - x_1)$ with $m = -\dfrac{2}{3}$ an $(3, -4)$

$y - (-4) = -\dfrac{2}{3}(x - 3)$

$y + 4 = -\dfrac{2}{3}x + 2$

$y = -\dfrac{2}{3}x - 2$

9. $\begin{aligned} x + 2y &= 12 \quad (1) \\ 4x &= 8 \quad (2) \end{aligned}$

$3x - 4y + 5z = 20 \quad (3)$

Using equation (2), solve for x.

$4x = 8 \implies x = \dfrac{8}{4} \implies x = 2$

Substitute 2 for x in equation (1) in order to solve for y.
$2 + 2y = 12 \implies 2y = 10 \implies y = 5$
Substitute 2 for x and 5 for y in equation (3) in order to solve for z.

$3(2) - 4(5) + 5z = 20$

$6 - 20 + 5z = 20$

$-14 + 5z = 20$

$5z = -34$

$z = -\dfrac{34}{5}$

The solution is $\left(2, 5, -\dfrac{34}{5}\right)$.

10.

$$\begin{vmatrix} 3 & -6 & -1 \\ 2 & 1 & -2 \\ 1 & 3 & 1 \end{vmatrix}$$

$$= 3\begin{vmatrix} 1 & -2 \\ 3 & 1 \end{vmatrix} - (-6)\begin{vmatrix} 2 & -2 \\ 1 & 1 \end{vmatrix} + (-1)\begin{vmatrix} 2 & 1 \\ 1 & 3 \end{vmatrix}$$

$$= 3(1-(-6)) + 6(2-(-2)) - (6-1)$$

$$= 3(1+6) + 6(2+2) - (6-1)$$

$$= 3(7) + 6(4) - (5)$$

$$= 21 + 24 - 5$$

$$= 40$$

11. $V = lwh$

$$6r^3 + 5r^2 + r = (3r+1)(w)(r)$$

$$\frac{6r^3 + 5r^2 + r}{(3r+1)(r)} = \frac{(3r+1)(w)(r)}{(3r+1)(r)}$$

$$\frac{r(6r^2 + 5r + 1)}{r(3r+1)} = w$$

$$\frac{r(3r+1)(2r+1)}{r(3r+1)} = w \text{ or } w = 2r+1$$

12. $(5xy - 6)(5xy + 6)$

$$= 25x^2y^2 + 30xy - 30xy - 36$$

$$= 25x^2y^2 - 36$$

13. $\sqrt{2x^2 + 7} + 3 = 8$

$$\sqrt{2x^2 + 7} = 5$$

$$\left(\sqrt{2x^2 + 7}\right)^2 = 5^2$$

$$2x^2 + 7 = 25$$

$$2x^2 = 18$$

$$x^2 = 9$$

$$x = 3 \text{ or } -3$$

$$\sqrt{2(3)^2 + 7} + 3 = 8 \quad \text{or} \quad \sqrt{2(-3)^2 + 7} + 3 = 8$$

$$\sqrt{25} = 5 \qquad\qquad \sqrt{25} = 5$$

$$5 = 5 \qquad\qquad\qquad 5 = 5$$

Both values check. The solution is 3 and –3.

14. $4x^3 - 9x^2 + 5x = x(4x^2 - 9x + 5)$

$$= x(4x - 5)(x - 1)$$

15. $(x+1)^3 - 8$

$$= (x+1)^3 - 2^3$$

$$= (x+1-2)((x+1)^2 + 2(x+1) + 2^2)$$

$$= (x-1)(x^2 + 2x + 1 + 2x + 2 + 4)$$

$$= (x-1)(x^2 + 4x + 7)$$

16. $8x^2 - 3 = -10x$

$$8x^2 + 10x - 3 = 0$$

$$(4x - 1)(2x + 3) = 0$$

$$4x - 1 = 0 \quad \text{or} \quad 2x + 3 = 0$$

$$4x = 1 \qquad\qquad 2x = -3$$

$$x = \frac{1}{4} \qquad\qquad x = -\frac{3}{2}$$

17.

$$\frac{4x + 4y}{x^2 y} \cdot \frac{y^3}{8x} = \frac{4(x+y)}{x^2 y} \cdot \frac{y^3}{8x}$$

$$= \frac{x+y}{x^2} \cdot \frac{y^2}{2x}$$

$$= \frac{(x+y)y^2}{2x^3}$$

18.

$$\frac{x-4}{x-5} - \frac{3}{x+5} - \frac{10}{x^2 - 25}$$

$$= \frac{x-4}{x-5} - \frac{3}{x+5} - \frac{10}{(x+5)(x-5)}$$

$$= \frac{x-4}{x-5} \cdot \frac{x+5}{x+5} - \frac{3}{x+5} \cdot \frac{x-5}{x-5} - \frac{10}{(x+5)(x-5)}$$

$$= \frac{(x-4)(x+5)}{(x+5)(x-5)} - \frac{3(x-5)}{(x+5)(x-5)} - \frac{10}{(x+5)(x-5)}$$

$$= \frac{(x-4)(x+5) - 3(x-5) - 10}{(x+5)(x-5)}$$

$$= \frac{x^2 + x - 20 - 3x + 15 - 10}{(x+5)(x-5)}$$

$$= \frac{x^2 - 2x - 15}{(x+5)(x-5)}$$

$$= \frac{(x-5)(x+3)}{(x+5)(x-5)} \text{ or } \frac{x+3}{x+5}$$

19. $\dfrac{4}{x} - \dfrac{1}{6} = \dfrac{1}{x}$

$6x\left(\dfrac{4}{x} - \dfrac{1}{6} = \dfrac{1}{x}\right)$

$24 - x = 6$

$-x = -18$

$x = 18$

Upon checking, this value satisfies the equation. The solution is 18.

20. $d = kt^2$

$16 = k(1)^2 \quad \Rightarrow \quad k = 16$

$d = 16(5)^2$

$\quad = 16 \cdot 25$

$\quad = 400$

The object will fall 400 feet in 5 seconds.

Chapter 8

Exercise Set 8.1

1. The two square roots of 36 are $\pm\sqrt{36} = \pm6$.

3. The square root property is: If $x^2 = a$, where a is a real number, then $x = \pm\sqrt{a}$.

5. A trinomial, $x^2 + bx + c$, is a perfect square trinomial if $\left(\dfrac{b}{2}\right)^2 = c$.

7. **a.** Yes, $x = 9$ is the solution to the equation. It is the only real number that satisfies the equation.

   b. No, $x = 3$ is not the solution. Both -3 and 3 satisfy the equation.

9. Multiply the equation by 1/2.

11. You should add the square of half the coefficient of the first degree term: $\left(\dfrac{-6}{2}\right)^2 = (-3)^2 = 9$.

13. $x^2 = 49$

$\qquad x = \pm\sqrt{49} = \pm7$

15. $x^2 + 49 = 0$

$\qquad x^2 = -49$

$\qquad x = \pm\sqrt{-49} = \pm7i$

17. $y^2 + 48 = 0$

$\qquad y^2 = -48$

$\qquad y = \pm\sqrt{-48} = \pm4i\sqrt{3}$

19. $y^2 + 11 = -50$

$\qquad y^2 = -61$

$\qquad y = \pm\sqrt{-61} = \pm i\sqrt{61}$

21. $(p-4)^2 = 16$

$\qquad p - 4 = \pm\sqrt{16}$

$\qquad p - 4 = \pm4$

$\qquad p = 4 \pm 4$

$\qquad p = 4 + 4 \quad$ or $\quad P = 4 - 4$
$\qquad P = 8 \qquad\qquad\quad P = 0$

23. $(x+3)^2 + 49 = 0$

$\qquad (x+3)^2 = -49$

$\qquad x + 3 = \pm\sqrt{-49}$

$\qquad x + 3 = \pm\sqrt{-49}$

$\qquad x = -3 \pm 7i$

25. $(a-4)^2 + 45 = 0$

$\qquad (a-4)^2 = -45$

$\qquad a - 4 = \pm\sqrt{-45}$

$\qquad a - 4 = \pm3i\sqrt{5}$

$\qquad a = 4 \pm 3i\sqrt{5}$

27. $\left(b+\dfrac{1}{3}\right)^2 = \dfrac{4}{9}$

$\qquad b + \dfrac{1}{3} = \pm\sqrt{\dfrac{4}{9}}$

$\qquad b + \dfrac{1}{3} = \pm\dfrac{2}{3}$

$\qquad b = -\dfrac{1}{3} \pm \dfrac{2}{3}$

$\qquad b = -\dfrac{1}{3} + \dfrac{2}{3} \quad$ or $\quad b = -\dfrac{1}{3} - \dfrac{2}{3}$

$\qquad b = \dfrac{1}{3} \qquad\qquad\quad b = -\dfrac{3}{3}$

$\qquad\qquad\qquad\qquad\qquad b = -1$

29.
$$\left(b-\frac{1}{3}\right)^2+\frac{4}{9}=0$$
$$\left(b-\frac{1}{3}\right)^2=-\frac{4}{9}$$
$$b-\frac{1}{3}=\pm\sqrt{-\frac{4}{9}}$$
$$b-\frac{1}{3}=\pm\frac{2}{3}i$$
$$b=\frac{1}{3}\pm\frac{2}{3}i \text{ or } b=\frac{1\pm2i}{3}$$

31.
$$(x+1.8)^2=0.81$$
$$x+1.8=\pm\sqrt{0.81}$$
$$x+1.8=\pm0.9$$
$$x=-1.8\pm0.9$$
$$x=-1.8+0.9 \text{ or } x=-1.8-0.9$$
$$x=-0.9 \qquad x=-2.7$$

33.
$$(2a-5)^2=12$$
$$2a-5=\pm\sqrt{12}$$
$$2a-5=\pm2\sqrt{3}$$
$$2a=5\pm2\sqrt{3}$$
$$a=\frac{5\pm2\sqrt{3}}{2}$$

35.
$$\left(2y+\frac{1}{2}\right)^2=\frac{4}{25}$$
$$2y+\frac{1}{2}=\pm\sqrt{\frac{4}{25}}$$
$$2y+\frac{1}{2}=\pm\frac{2}{5}$$
$$2y+\frac{1}{2}=\frac{2}{5} \text{ or } 2y+\frac{1}{2}=-\frac{2}{5}$$
$$2y=-\frac{1}{2}+\frac{2}{5} \qquad 2y=-\frac{1}{2}-\frac{2}{5}$$
$$2y=-\frac{1}{10} \qquad 2y=-\frac{9}{10}$$
$$y=-\frac{1}{20} \qquad y=-\frac{9}{20}$$

37.
$$x^2+3x-4=0$$
$$x^2+3x=4$$
$$x^2+3x+\frac{9}{4}=4+\frac{9}{4}$$
$$\left(x+\frac{3}{2}\right)^2=\frac{25}{4}$$
$$x+\frac{3}{2}=\pm\sqrt{\frac{25}{4}}$$
$$x+\frac{3}{2}=\pm\frac{5}{2}$$
$$x=-\frac{3}{2}\pm\frac{5}{2}$$
$$x=-\frac{3}{2}+\frac{5}{2} \text{ or } x=-\frac{3}{2}-\frac{5}{2}$$
$$x=\frac{2}{2} \qquad x=\frac{-8}{2}$$
$$x=1 \qquad x=-4$$

39.
$$x^2+2x-15=0$$
$$x^2+2x=15$$
$$x^2+2x+1=15+1$$
$$(x+1)^2=16$$
$$x+1=\pm4$$
$$x=\pm4-1$$
$$x=4-1 \text{ or } x=-4-1$$
$$x=3 \qquad x=-5$$

41.
$$x^2-6x+8=0$$
$$x^2-6x=-8$$
$$x^2-6x+9=-8+9$$
$$x^2-6x+9=1$$
$$(x-3)^2=1$$
$$x-3=\pm1$$
$$x=\pm1+3$$
$$x=1+3 \text{ or } x=-1+3$$
$$x=4 \qquad x=2$$

43.
$$x^2-6x+5=0$$
$$x^2-6x=-5$$
$$x^2-6x+9=-5+9$$
$$x^2-6x+9=4$$
$$(x-3)^2=4$$
$$x-3=\pm2$$
$$x=\pm2+3$$
$$x=2+3 \text{ or } x=-2+3$$
$$x=5 \qquad x=1$$

45.
$$2x^2 + x - 1 = 0$$
$$\tfrac{1}{2}(2x^2 + x - 1) = \tfrac{1}{2}(0)$$
$$x^2 + \tfrac{1}{2}x - \tfrac{1}{2} = 0$$
$$x^2 + \tfrac{1}{2}x = \tfrac{1}{2}$$
$$x^2 + \tfrac{1}{2}x + \tfrac{1}{16} = \tfrac{1}{2} + \tfrac{1}{16}$$
$$\left(x + \tfrac{1}{4}\right)^2 = \tfrac{9}{16}$$
$$x + \tfrac{1}{4} = \pm\sqrt{\tfrac{9}{16}}$$
$$x + \tfrac{1}{4} = \pm\tfrac{3}{4}$$
$$x = \pm\tfrac{3}{4} - \tfrac{1}{4}$$
$$x = \tfrac{3}{4} - \tfrac{1}{4} \quad \text{or} \quad x = -\tfrac{3}{4} - \tfrac{1}{4}$$
$$x = \tfrac{2}{4} \qquad\qquad x = -\tfrac{4}{4}$$
$$x = \tfrac{1}{2} \qquad\qquad x = -1$$

47.
$$2z^2 - 7z - 4 = 0$$
$$\tfrac{1}{2}(2z^2 - 7z - 4) = \tfrac{1}{2}(0)$$
$$z^2 - \tfrac{7}{2}z - 2 = 0$$
$$z^2 - \tfrac{7}{2}z = 2$$
$$z^2 - \tfrac{7}{2}z + \tfrac{49}{16} = 2 + \tfrac{49}{16}$$
$$\left(z - \tfrac{7}{4}\right)^2 = \tfrac{81}{16}$$
$$z - \tfrac{7}{4} = \pm\sqrt{\tfrac{81}{16}}$$
$$z - \tfrac{7}{4} = \pm\tfrac{9}{4}$$
$$z = \pm\tfrac{9}{4} + \tfrac{7}{4}$$
$$z = \tfrac{9}{4} + \tfrac{7}{4} \quad \text{or} \quad z = -\tfrac{9}{4} + \tfrac{7}{4}$$
$$z = \tfrac{16}{4} \qquad\qquad z = -\tfrac{2}{4}$$
$$z = 4 \qquad\qquad z = -\tfrac{1}{2}$$

49.
$$x^2 - 11x + 28 = 0$$
$$x^2 - 11x = -28$$
$$x^2 - 11x + \tfrac{121}{4} = -28 + \tfrac{121}{4}$$
$$\left(x - \tfrac{11}{2}\right)^2 = \tfrac{9}{4}$$
$$x - \tfrac{11}{2} = \pm\sqrt{\tfrac{9}{4}}$$
$$x - \tfrac{11}{2} = \pm\tfrac{3}{2}$$
$$x = \pm\tfrac{3}{2} + \tfrac{11}{2}$$
$$x = \tfrac{3}{2} + \tfrac{11}{2} \quad \text{or} \quad x = -\tfrac{3}{2} + \tfrac{11}{2}$$
$$x = \tfrac{14}{2} \qquad\qquad x = \tfrac{8}{2}$$
$$x = 7 \qquad\qquad x = 4$$

51.
$$-x^2 + 3x + 4 = 0 \quad \Leftarrow \text{ multiply by } -1$$
$$x^2 - 3x - 4 = 0$$
$$x^2 - 3x = 4$$
$$x^2 - 3x + \tfrac{9}{4} = 4 + \tfrac{9}{4}$$
$$\left(x - \tfrac{3}{2}\right)^2 = \tfrac{25}{4}$$
$$x - \tfrac{3}{2} = \pm\sqrt{\tfrac{25}{4}}$$
$$x - \tfrac{3}{2} = \pm\tfrac{5}{2}$$
$$x = \tfrac{3}{2} \pm \tfrac{5}{2}$$
$$x = \tfrac{3}{2} + \tfrac{5}{2} \quad \text{or} \quad x = \tfrac{3}{2} - \tfrac{5}{2}$$
$$x = \tfrac{8}{2} \qquad\qquad x = \tfrac{-2}{2}$$
$$x = 4 \qquad\qquad x = -1$$

53.
$$-z^2 + 9z - 20 = 0 \quad \Leftarrow \text{ multiply by } -1$$
$$z^2 - 9z + 20 = 0$$
$$z^2 - 9z = -20$$
$$z^2 - 9z + \tfrac{81}{4} = -20 + \tfrac{81}{4}$$
$$\left(z - \tfrac{9}{2}\right)^2 = \tfrac{1}{4}$$
$$z - \tfrac{9}{2} = \pm\tfrac{1}{2}$$
$$z = \pm\tfrac{1}{2} + \tfrac{9}{2}$$

$$z = \frac{1}{2} + \frac{9}{2} \quad \text{or} \quad z = -\frac{1}{2} + \frac{9}{2}$$
$$z = \frac{10}{2} \qquad\qquad z = \frac{8}{2}$$
$$z = 5 \qquad\qquad z = 4$$

55.
$$b^2 = 3b + 28$$
$$b^2 - 3b = 28$$
$$b^2 - 3b + \frac{9}{4} = \frac{112}{4} + \frac{9}{4}$$
$$\left(b - \frac{3}{2}\right)^2 = \frac{121}{4}$$
$$b - \frac{3}{2} = \pm\frac{11}{2}$$
$$b = \pm\frac{11}{2} + \frac{3}{2}$$
$$b = -\frac{11}{2} + \frac{3}{2} \quad \text{or} \quad b = \frac{11}{2} + \frac{3}{2}$$
$$b = -\frac{8}{2} \qquad\qquad b = \frac{14}{2}$$
$$b = -4 \qquad\qquad b = 7$$

57.
$$x^2 + 9x = 10$$
$$x^2 + 9x + \frac{81}{4} = 10 + \frac{81}{4}$$
$$\left(x + \frac{9}{2}\right)^2 = \frac{40}{4} + \frac{81}{4}$$
$$\left(x + \frac{9}{2}\right)^2 = \frac{121}{4}$$
$$x + \frac{9}{2} = \pm\frac{11}{2}$$
$$x = \pm\frac{11}{2} - \frac{9}{2}$$
$$x = \frac{11}{2} - \frac{9}{2} \quad \text{or} \quad x = -\frac{11}{2} - \frac{9}{2}$$
$$x = \frac{2}{2} \qquad\qquad x = -\frac{20}{2}$$
$$x = 1 \qquad\qquad x = -10$$

59. $x^2 - 4x - 10 = 0$
$$x^2 - 4x = 10$$
$$x^2 - 4x + 4 = 10 + 4$$
$$(x - 2)^2 = 14$$
$$x - 2 = \pm\sqrt{14}$$
$$x = 2 \pm \sqrt{14}$$

61. $r^2 + 8r + 5 = 0$
$$r^2 + 8r = -5$$
$$r^2 + 8r + 16 = -5 + 16$$
$$(r + 4)^2 = 11$$
$$r + 4 = \pm\sqrt{11}$$
$$r = -4 \pm \sqrt{11}$$

63. $c^2 - c - 3 = 0$
$$c^2 - c = 3$$
$$c^2 - c + \frac{1}{4} = 3 + \frac{1}{4}$$
$$\left(c - \frac{1}{2}\right)^2 = \frac{13}{4}$$
$$c - \frac{1}{2} = \pm\sqrt{\frac{13}{4}}$$
$$c = \frac{1}{2} \pm \frac{\sqrt{13}}{2}$$
$$c = \frac{1 \pm \sqrt{13}}{2}$$

65. $x^2 + 3x + 6 = 0$
$$x^2 + 3x = -6$$
$$x^2 + 3x + \frac{9}{4} = -\frac{24}{4} + \frac{9}{4}$$
$$\left(x + \frac{3}{2}\right)^2 = \frac{-15}{4}$$
$$x + \frac{3}{2} = \pm\sqrt{\frac{-15}{4}}$$
$$x + \frac{3}{2} = \pm\frac{i\sqrt{15}}{2}$$
$$x = -\frac{3}{2} \pm \frac{i\sqrt{15}}{2}$$
$$x = \frac{-3 \pm i\sqrt{15}}{2}$$

67.
$$2x^2 - 2x = 0$$
$$x^2 - x = 0$$
$$x^2 - x + \frac{1}{4} = \frac{1}{4}$$
$$\left(x - \frac{1}{2}\right)^2 = \frac{1}{4}$$
$$x - \frac{1}{2} = \pm\frac{1}{2}$$
$$x = \pm\frac{1}{2} + \frac{1}{2}$$
$$x = \frac{1}{2} + \frac{1}{2} \quad \text{or} \quad x = -\frac{1}{2} + \frac{1}{2}$$
$$x = \frac{2}{2} \qquad\qquad x = 0$$
$$x = 1 \qquad\qquad x = 0$$

69.
$$-\frac{1}{4}b^2 - \frac{1}{2}b = 0$$
$$-4\left(-\frac{1}{4}b^2 - \frac{1}{2}b = 0\right)$$
$$b^2 + 2b = 0$$
$$b^2 + 2b + 1 = 0 + 1$$
$$\left(b+1\right)^2 = 1$$
$$b + 1 = \pm 1$$
$$b + 1 = 1 \quad \text{or} \quad b + 1 = -1$$
$$b = 0 \qquad\qquad b = -2$$

71.
$$18z^2 - 6z = 0$$
$$z^2 - \frac{1}{3}z = 0$$
$$z^2 - \frac{1}{3}z + \frac{1}{36} = 0 + \frac{1}{36}$$
$$\left(z - \frac{1}{6}\right)^2 = \frac{1}{36}$$
$$z - \frac{1}{6} = \pm\frac{1}{6}$$
$$z = \pm\frac{1}{6} + \frac{1}{6}$$
$$z = \frac{1}{6} + \frac{1}{6} \quad \text{or} \quad z = -\frac{1}{6} + \frac{1}{6}$$
$$z = \frac{2}{6} \qquad\qquad z = 0$$
$$z = \frac{1}{3} \qquad\qquad z = 0$$

73.
$$-\frac{1}{2}p^2 - p + \frac{3}{2} = 0$$
$$p^2 + 2p - 3 = 0$$
$$p^2 + 2p = 3$$
$$p^2 + 2p + 1 = 3 + 1$$
$$\left(p+1\right)^2 = 4$$
$$p + 1 = \pm 2$$
$$p = \pm 2 - 1$$
$$p = 2 - 1 \quad \text{or} \quad p = -2 - 1$$
$$p = 1 \qquad\qquad p = -3$$

75.
$$2x^2 = 8x + 90$$
$$x^2 = 4x + 45$$
$$x^2 - 4x = 45$$
$$x^2 - 4x + 4 = 45 + 4$$
$$\left(x - 2\right)^2 = 49$$
$$x - 2 = \pm 7$$
$$x = \pm 7 + 2$$
$$x = 7 + 2 \quad \text{or} \quad x = -7 + 2$$
$$x = 9 \qquad \text{or} \quad x = -5$$

77.
$$3x^2 + 33x + 72 = 0$$
$$x^2 + 11x + 24 = 0$$
$$x^2 + 11x = -24$$
$$x^2 + 11x + \frac{121}{4} = -24 + \frac{121}{4}$$
$$\left(x + \frac{11}{2}\right)^2 = -\frac{96}{4} + \frac{121}{4}$$
$$\left(x - \frac{11}{2}\right)^2 = \frac{25}{4}$$
$$x + \frac{11}{2} = \pm\frac{5}{2}$$
$$x = \pm\frac{5}{2} - \frac{11}{2}$$
$$x = -\frac{5}{2} - \frac{11}{2} \quad \text{or} \quad x = \frac{5}{2} - \frac{11}{2}$$
$$x = -\frac{16}{2} \qquad \text{or} \quad x = -\frac{6}{2}$$
$$x = -8 \qquad \text{or} \quad x = -3$$

79.
$$3w^2 + 2w - 1 = 0$$
$$3w^2 + 2w = 1$$
$$w^2 + \frac{2}{3}w = \frac{1}{3}$$
$$w^2 + \frac{2}{3}w + \frac{1}{9} = \frac{1}{3} + \frac{1}{9}$$
$$\left(w + \frac{1}{3}\right)^2 = \frac{4}{9}$$
$$w + \frac{1}{3} = \pm\frac{2}{3}$$
$$w = \pm\frac{2}{3} - \frac{1}{3}$$
$$w = -\frac{2}{3} - \frac{1}{3} \quad \text{or} \quad w = \frac{2}{3} - \frac{1}{3}$$
$$w = -\frac{3}{3} \qquad\qquad w = \frac{1}{3}$$
$$w = -1$$

81.
$$2x^2 - x = -5$$
$$x^2 - \frac{1}{2}x = -\frac{5}{2}$$
$$x^2 - \frac{1}{2}x + \frac{1}{16} = -\frac{40}{16} + \frac{1}{16}$$
$$\left(x - \frac{1}{4}\right)^2 = -\frac{39}{16}$$
$$x - \frac{1}{4} = \pm\frac{i\sqrt{39}}{4}$$
$$x = \frac{1}{4} \pm \frac{i\sqrt{39}}{4}$$
$$x = \frac{1 \pm i\sqrt{39}}{4}$$

83.
$$\frac{5}{2}x^2 + \frac{3}{2}x - \frac{5}{4} = 0$$
$$\frac{2}{5}\left[\frac{5}{2}x^2 + \frac{3}{2}x - \frac{5}{4} = 0\right]$$

$$x^2 + \frac{3}{5}x - \frac{1}{2} = 0$$
$$x^2 + \frac{3}{5}x = \frac{1}{2}$$
$$x^2 + \frac{3}{5}x + \frac{9}{100} = \frac{1}{2} + \frac{9}{100}$$
$$\left(x + \frac{3}{10}\right)^2 = \frac{59}{100}$$
$$x + \frac{3}{10} = \pm\frac{\sqrt{59}}{10}$$
$$x = -\frac{3}{10} \pm \frac{\sqrt{59}}{10}$$
$$x = \frac{-3 \pm \sqrt{59}}{10}$$

85. **a.** $21 = (x+2)(x-2)$

    b. $21 = (x+2)(x-2)$
$$21 = x^2 - 2x + 2x - 4$$
$$0 = x^2 - 25$$
$$0 = (x+5)(x-5)$$
$$x + 5 = 0 \quad \text{or} \quad x - 5 = 0$$
$$x = -5 \qquad\qquad x = 5$$
Disregard the negative answer since x represents a distance. $x = 5$.

87. **a.** $18 = (x+4)(x+2)$

    b. $18 = (x+4)(x+2)$
$$18 = x^2 + 2x + 4x + 8$$
$$0 = x^2 + 6x - 10$$
Using the quadratic formula:
$$x = \frac{-(6) \pm \sqrt{6^2 - 4(1)(-10)}}{2(1)}$$
$$x = \frac{-6 \pm \sqrt{76}}{2}$$
$$x = \frac{-6 \pm 2\sqrt{19}}{2}$$
$$x = -3 \pm \sqrt{19}$$
Disregard the negative answer since x represents a distance. $x = -3 + \sqrt{19}$.

89. $d = \frac{1}{6}x^2$

$24 = \frac{1}{6}x^2$

$6 \cdot 24 = x^2$

$144 = x^2$

$x = 12$

The car's speed was about 12 mph.

91. Let x be the first integer. Then $x + 2$ is the next consecutive odd integer.

$x(x + 2) = 63$

$x^2 + 2x = 63$

$x^2 + 2x + 1 = 63 + 1$

$(x + 1)^2 = 64$

$x + 1 = \pm 8$

$x = -1 \pm 8$

$x = -1 + 8$ or $x = -1 - 8$

$x = 7$ $x = -9$

Since it was given that the integers are positive, one integer is 7 and the other is $7 + 2 = 9$.

93. Let x be the width of the rectangle. Then $2x + 2$ is the length. Use length $\cdot$ width = area.

$(2x + 2)x = 60$

$2x^2 + 2x = 60$

$x^2 + x = 30$

$x^2 + x + \frac{1}{4} = 30 + \frac{1}{4}$

$\left(x + \frac{1}{2}\right)^2 = \frac{120}{4} + \frac{1}{4}$

$\left(x + \frac{1}{2}\right)^2 = \frac{121}{4}$

$x + \frac{1}{2} = \pm \frac{11}{2}$

$x = -\frac{1}{2} \pm \frac{11}{2}$

$x = -\frac{1}{2} + \frac{11}{2}$ or $x = -\frac{1}{2} - \frac{11}{2}$

$x = \frac{10}{2} = 5$ $x = -\frac{12}{2} = 6$

Since the width cannot be negative, the width is 5 ft.
Length = $2(5) + 2 = 10 + 2 = 12$ ft.
The rectangle is 5 ft by 12 ft.

95. Let s be the length of the side. Then $s + 6$ is the length of the diagonal (d). Use $s^2 + s^2 = d^2$.

$2s^2 = (s + 6)^2$

$2s^2 = s^2 + 12s + 36$

$s^2 = 12s + 36$

$s^2 - 12s = 36$

$s^2 - 12s + 36 = 36 + 36$

$(s - 6)^2 = 72$

$s - 6 = \pm 6\sqrt{2}$

$s = 6 \pm 6\sqrt{2}$

Length is never negative. Thus,
$s = 6 + 6\sqrt{2} \approx 14.49$.
The room is about 14.49 ft by 14.49 ft.

97. Since the radius is 10 inches, the diameter (d) is 20 inches. Use the formula $s^2 + s^2 = d^2$ to find the length (s) of the other two sides.

$s^2 + s^2 = d^2$

$2s^2 = 20^2$

$2s^2 = 400$

$s^2 = 200$

$s = \pm\sqrt{200} = \pm 10\sqrt{2}$

Length is never negative.
Thus $s = 10\sqrt{2} \approx 14.14$ inches.

99. $A = \pi r^2$

$24\pi = \pi r^2$

$24 = r^2$

$\pm\sqrt{24} = r$

$\pm 2\sqrt{6} = r$

Length is never negative.
Thus $r = 2\sqrt{6} \approx 4.90$ feet.

101. $A = P\left(1 + \frac{r}{n}\right)^{nt}$

$540.80 = 500\left(1 + \frac{r}{1}\right)^{1(2)}$

$540.80 = 500(1 + r)^2$

$1.0816 = (1 + r)^2$

$\pm 1.04 = 1 + r$

$-1 \pm 1.04 = r$

An interest rate is never negative. Thus
$r = -1 + 1.04 = 0.04 = 4\%$.

103.
$$A = P\left(1 + \frac{r}{n}\right)^{nt}$$
$$1432.86 = 1200\left(1 + \frac{r}{2}\right)^{2(3)}$$
$$1432.86 = 1200\left(1 + \frac{r}{2}\right)^{6}$$
$$1.19405 = \left(1 + \frac{r}{2}\right)^{6}$$
$$\pm 1.03 \approx 1 + \frac{r}{2}$$
$$-1 \pm 1.03 \approx \frac{r}{2}$$
$$-2 \pm 2.06 \approx r$$
An interest rate is never negative.
Thus Steve Rodi's annual interest rate is about
$-2 + 2.06 = 0.06 = 6\%.$

105. **a.** To find the surface area, we must first
determine the radius. Use $V = \pi r^2 h$ with
$V = 160$ and $h = 10$ to get
$$160 = \pi r^2 (10)$$
$$16 = \pi r^2$$
$$\frac{16}{\pi} = r^2$$
$$\frac{4}{\sqrt{\pi}} = r$$

Since the radius equals $\frac{4}{\sqrt{\pi}}$, use the formula

$S = 2\pi r^2 + 2\pi rh$ to calculate the surface
$$S = 2\pi\left(\frac{4}{\sqrt{\pi}}\right)^2 + 2\pi\left(\frac{4}{\sqrt{\pi}}\right)(10)$$
area. $\quad = 2\pi\left(\frac{16}{\pi}\right) + \frac{80\pi}{\sqrt{\pi}}$
$$= 32 + 80\sqrt{\pi}$$
$$\approx 173.80$$
The surface area is about
173.80 square inches.

b. Use $V = \pi r^2 h$ with $V = 160$ and $h = 10$ to
obtain $160 = \pi r^2 (10)$. In part (a) this was
solved for r to get
$$r = \frac{4}{\sqrt{\pi}} = \frac{4}{\sqrt{\pi}} \cdot \frac{\sqrt{\pi}}{\sqrt{\pi}} = \frac{4\sqrt{\pi}}{\pi} \approx 2.26$$
The radius is about 2.26 inches.

c. Use $S = 2\pi r^2 + 2\pi rh$ with $S = 160$ and $h = 10.$

$$160 = 2\pi r^2 + 2\pi r(10)$$
$$160 = 2\pi r^2 + 20\pi r$$
$$\frac{160}{2\pi} = \frac{2\pi r^2}{2\pi} + \frac{20\pi r}{2\pi}$$
$$\frac{80}{\pi} = r^2 + 10r$$
$$\frac{80}{\pi} + 25 = r^2 + 10r + 25$$
$$\frac{80 + 25\pi}{\pi} = (r + 5)^2$$
$$\pm\sqrt{\frac{80 + 25\pi}{\pi}} = r + 5$$
$$\pm\sqrt{\frac{80 + 25\pi}{\pi}} - 5 = r$$
The radius is never negative.
Thus $r \approx 2.1$ inches.

107. $-4(2z - 6) = -3(z - 4) + z$
$$-8z + 24 = -3z + 12 + z$$
$$-8z + 24 = -2z + 12$$
$$-6z = -12$$
$$z = 2$$

109. $|x + 3| = |2x - 7|$
$x + 3 = 2x - 7 \quad$ or $\quad x + 3 = -(2x - 7)$
$-x = -10 \qquad\qquad x + 3 = -2x + 7$
$x = 10 \qquad\qquad\quad 3x = 4$
$$x = \frac{4}{3}$$

111.
$$\begin{array}{r} 4x^2 + 9x - 2 \\ \underline{x - 2} \\ -8x^2 - 18x + 4 \\ \underline{4x^3 + 9x^2\ - 2x} \\ 4x^3 + \ x^2 - 20x + 4 \end{array}$$

Exercise Set 8.2

1. The quadratic formula is $x = \dfrac{-b \pm \sqrt{b^2 - 4ac}}{2a}$

which gives the values of x where $ax^2 + bx + c = 0$.

3. $a = -3$, $b = 6$, and $c = 5$

5. Yes, multiply both sides of the equation $-6x^2 + \dfrac{1}{2}x - 5 = 0$ by -1 to obtain

$6x^2 - \dfrac{1}{2}x + 5 = 0$. The equations are equivalent so they will have the same solutions.

7. a. For a quadratic equation in standard form, $ax^2 + bx + c = 0$, the discriminant is the expression under the square root symbol in the quadratic formula, $b^2 - 4ac$.

b. $3x^2 - 6x + 20 = 0$, $a = 3$, $b = -6$, and $c = 20$.

$$b^2 - 4ac = (-6)^2 - 4(3)(20)$$
$$= 36 - 240$$
$$= -204$$

c. If $b^2 - 4ac > 0$, then the quadratic equation will have two distinct real solutions. Since there is a positive number under the radical sign in the quadratic formula, the value of the radical will be real and there will be two real solutions. If $b^2 - 4ac = 0$, then the equation has the single real solution $\dfrac{-b}{2a}$. If $b^2 - 4ac < 0$, the expression under the radical sign in the quadratic formula is negative. Thus the equation has no real solution.

9. $x^2 + 3x + 2 = 0$

$$b^2 - 4ac = (3)^2 - 4(1)(2)$$
$$= 9 - 8$$
$$= 1$$

Since $1 > 0$, there are two real solutions.

11. $3z^2 + 4z + 5 = 0$

$$b^2 - 4ac = 4^2 - 4(3)(5)$$
$$= 16 - 60$$
$$= -44$$

Since $-44 < 0$, there is no real solution.

13. $5p^2 + 3p - 7 = 0$

$$b^2 - 4ac = 3^2 - 4(5)(-7)$$
$$= 9 + 140$$
$$= 149$$

Since $149 > 0$ there are two real solutions.

15. $-5x^2 + 5x - 6 = 0$

$$b^2 - 4ac = 5^2 - 4(-5)(-6)$$
$$= 25 - 120$$
$$= -95$$

Since $-95 < 0$, there is no real solution.

17. $x^2 + 10.2x + 26.01 = 0$

$$b^2 - 4ac = (10.2)^2 - 4(1)(26.01)$$
$$= 104.04 - 104.04$$
$$= 0$$

There is one real solution.

19. $b^2 = -3b - \dfrac{9}{4}$

$$b^2 + 3b + \dfrac{9}{4} = 0$$

$$b^2 - 4ac = 3^2 - 4(1)\left(\dfrac{9}{4}\right)$$
$$= 9 - 9$$
$$= 0$$

There is one real solution.

21. $x^2 - 9x + 18 = 0$

$$x = \dfrac{9 \pm \sqrt{9^2 - 4(1)(18)}}{2(1)}$$

$$= \dfrac{9 \pm \sqrt{81 - 72}}{2}$$

$$= \dfrac{9 \pm \sqrt{9}}{2}$$

$$= \dfrac{9 \pm 3}{2}$$

$$x = \dfrac{9+3}{2} \quad \text{or} \quad x = \dfrac{9-3}{2}$$
$$= \dfrac{12}{2} \qquad\qquad = \dfrac{6}{2}$$
$$= 6 \qquad\qquad\quad = 3$$

The solutions are 6 and 3.

23. $a^2 - 6a + 8 = 0$

$$a = \frac{-b \pm \sqrt{b^2 - 4ac}}{2a}$$

$$= \frac{6 \pm \sqrt{(-6)^2 - 4(1)(8)}}{2(1)}$$

$$= \frac{6 \pm \sqrt{36 - 32}}{2}$$

$$= \frac{6 \pm \sqrt{4}}{2}$$

$$= \frac{6 \pm 2}{2}$$

$a = \dfrac{6-2}{2}$ or $a = \dfrac{6+2}{2}$

$\quad = \dfrac{4}{2} \qquad\qquad = \dfrac{8}{2}$

$\quad = 2 \qquad\qquad\;\; = 4$

The solutions are 2 and 4.

25. $x^2 = -2x + 3$

$$x^2 + 2x - 3 = 0$$

$$x = \frac{-2 \pm \sqrt{2^2 - 4(1)(-3)}}{2(1)}$$

$$= \frac{-2 \pm \sqrt{4 + 12}}{2}$$

$$= \frac{-2 \pm \sqrt{16}}{2}$$

$$= \frac{-2 \pm 4}{2}$$

$x = \dfrac{-2+4}{2}$ or $x = \dfrac{-2-4}{2}$

$\quad = \dfrac{2}{2} \qquad\qquad = \dfrac{-6}{2}$

$\quad = 1 \qquad\qquad\;\; = -3$

The solutions are 1 and −3.

27. $-b^2 = 4b - 20$

$$b^2 + 4b - 20 = 0$$

$$b = \frac{-4 \pm \sqrt{(4)^2 - 4(1)(-20)}}{2(1)}$$

$$= \frac{-4 \pm \sqrt{16 + 80}}{2}$$

$$= \frac{-4 \pm \sqrt{96}}{2}$$

$$= \frac{-4 \pm 4\sqrt{6}}{2}$$

$$= -2 \pm \sqrt{6}$$

The solutions are $-2 + 2\sqrt{6}$ and $-2 - 2\sqrt{6}$.

29. $b^2 - 49 = 0$

$$b = \frac{0 \pm \sqrt{0^2 - 4(1)(-49)}}{2(1)}$$

$$= \frac{\pm\sqrt{196}}{2}$$

$$= \frac{\pm 14}{2}$$

$b = \dfrac{14}{2}$ or $b = \dfrac{-14}{2}$

$\quad = 7 \qquad\qquad = -7$

The solutions are 7 and −7.

31. $3w^2 - 4w + 5 = 0$

$$w = \frac{-(-4) \pm \sqrt{(-4)^2 - 4(3)(5)}}{2(3)}$$

$$= \frac{4 \pm \sqrt{16 - 60}}{6}$$

$$= \frac{4 \pm \sqrt{-44}}{6}$$

$$= \frac{4 \pm 2i\sqrt{11}}{6}$$

$$= \frac{2(2 \pm i\sqrt{11})}{6}$$

$$= \frac{2 \pm i\sqrt{11}}{3}$$

The solutions are $\dfrac{2 - i\sqrt{11}}{3}$ and $\dfrac{2 + i\sqrt{11}}{3}$.

33. $c^2 - 3c = 0$

$$c = \frac{3 \pm \sqrt{(-3)^2 - 4(1)(0)}}{2(1)}$$

$$= \frac{3 \pm \sqrt{9}}{2}$$

$$= \frac{3 \pm 3}{2}$$

$c = \dfrac{3+3}{2}$ or $c = \dfrac{3-3}{2}$

$\quad = \dfrac{6}{2} \qquad\qquad = \dfrac{0}{2}$

$\quad = 3 \qquad\qquad\;\; = 0$

The solutions are 3 and 0.

35.
$$4s^2 - 8s + 6 = 0$$
$$\frac{1}{2}(4s^2 - 8s + 6 = 0)$$
$$2s^2 - 4s + 3 = 0$$
$$s = \frac{-(-4) \pm \sqrt{(-4)^2 - 4(2)(3)}}{2(2)}$$
$$= \frac{4 \pm \sqrt{16 - 24}}{4}$$
$$= \frac{4 \pm \sqrt{-8}}{4}$$
$$= \frac{4 \pm 2i\sqrt{2}}{4}$$
$$= \frac{2 \pm i\sqrt{2}}{2}$$

The solutions are $\dfrac{2 - i\sqrt{2}}{2}$ and $\dfrac{2 + i\sqrt{2}}{2}$.

37.
$$a^2 + 2a + 1 = 0$$
$$a = \frac{-(2) \pm \sqrt{(2)^2 - 4(1)(1)}}{2(1)}$$
$$= \frac{-2 \pm \sqrt{4 - 4}}{2}$$
$$= \frac{-2 \pm \sqrt{0}}{2}$$
$$= \frac{-2 \pm 0}{2}$$
$$= \frac{-2}{2}$$
$$= -1$$

The solution is –1.

39.
$$x^2 - 10x + 25 = 0$$
$$x = \frac{-(-10) \pm \sqrt{(-10)^2 - 4(1)(25)}}{2(1)}$$
$$= \frac{10 \pm \sqrt{100 - 100}}{2}$$
$$= \frac{10 \pm \sqrt{0}}{2}$$
$$= \frac{10 \pm 0}{2}$$
$$= \frac{10}{2}$$
$$= 5$$

The solution is 5.

41.
$$x^2 - 2x - 1 = 0$$
$$x = \frac{-(-2) \pm \sqrt{(-2)^2 - 4(1)(-1)}}{2(1)}$$
$$= \frac{2 \pm \sqrt{4 + 4}}{2}$$
$$= \frac{2 \pm \sqrt{8}}{2}$$
$$= \frac{2 \pm 2\sqrt{2}}{2}$$
$$= 1 \pm \sqrt{2}$$

The solutions are $1 - \sqrt{2}$ and $1 + \sqrt{2}$.

43.
$$2 - 3r^2 = -4r$$
$$3r^2 - 4r - 2 = 0$$
$$r = \frac{-(-4) \pm \sqrt{(-4)^2 - 4(3)(-2)}}{2(3)}$$
$$= \frac{4 \pm \sqrt{16 + 24}}{6}$$
$$= \frac{4 \pm \sqrt{40}}{6}$$
$$= \frac{4 \pm 2\sqrt{10}}{6}$$
$$= \frac{2 \pm \sqrt{10}}{3}$$

The solutions are $\dfrac{2 + \sqrt{10}}{3}$ and $\dfrac{2 - \sqrt{10}}{3}$.

45.
$$2x^2 + 5x - 3 = 0$$
$$x = \frac{-(5) \pm \sqrt{(5)^2 - 4(2)(-3)}}{2(2)}$$
$$= \frac{-5 \pm \sqrt{25 + 24}}{4}$$
$$= \frac{-5 \pm \sqrt{49}}{4}$$
$$= \frac{-5 \pm 7}{4}$$
$$x = \frac{-5 + 7}{4} \quad \text{or} \quad x = \frac{-5 - 7}{4}$$
$$= \frac{2}{4} \qquad\qquad = \frac{-12}{4}$$
$$= \frac{1}{2} \qquad\qquad = -3$$

The solutions are $\frac{1}{2}$ and –3.

47. $(2a + 3)(3a - 1) = 2$

$6a^2 + 7a - 3 = 2$

$6a^2 + 7a - 5 = 0$

$a = \dfrac{-(7) \pm \sqrt{(7)^2 - 4(6)(-5)}}{2(6)}$

$= \dfrac{-7 \pm \sqrt{49 + 120}}{12}$

$= \dfrac{-7 \pm \sqrt{169}}{12}$

$= \dfrac{-7 \pm 13}{12}$

$a = \dfrac{-7 - 13}{12}$ or $a = \dfrac{-7 + 13}{12}$

$= \dfrac{-20}{12}$ $\qquad = \dfrac{6}{12}$

$= -\dfrac{5}{3}$ $\qquad = \dfrac{1}{2}$

The solutions are $\dfrac{1}{2}$ and $-\dfrac{5}{3}$.

49. $\dfrac{1}{2}t^2 + t - 12 = 0$

$2\left(\dfrac{1}{2}t^2 + t - 12 = 0\right)$

$t^2 + 2t - 24 = 0$

$t = \dfrac{-(2) \pm \sqrt{(2)^2 - 4(1)(-24)}}{2(1)}$

$= \dfrac{-2 \pm \sqrt{4 + 96}}{2}$

$= \dfrac{-2 \pm \sqrt{100}}{2}$

$= \dfrac{-2 \pm 10}{2}$

$t = \dfrac{-2 + 10}{2}$ or $t = \dfrac{-2 - 10}{2}$

$= \dfrac{8}{2}$ $\qquad = \dfrac{-12}{2}$

$= 4$ $\qquad = -6$

The solutions are 4 and –6.

51. $9r^2 - 9r + 2 = 0$

$r = \dfrac{-(-9) \pm \sqrt{(-9)^2 - 4(9)(2)}}{2(9)}$

$= \dfrac{9 \pm \sqrt{81 - 72}}{18}$

$= \dfrac{9 \pm \sqrt{9}}{18}$

$= \dfrac{9 \pm 3}{18}$

$r = \dfrac{9 + 3}{18}$ or $r = \dfrac{9 - 3}{18}$

$= \dfrac{12}{18}$ $\qquad = \dfrac{6}{18}$

$= \dfrac{2}{3}$ $\qquad = \dfrac{1}{3}$

The solutions are $\dfrac{2}{3}$ and $\dfrac{1}{3}$..

53. $\dfrac{1}{2}x^2 + 2x + \dfrac{2}{3} = 0$

$6\left(\dfrac{1}{2}x^2 + 2x + \dfrac{2}{3} = 0\right)$

$3x^2 + 12x + 4 = 0$

$x = \dfrac{-12 \pm \sqrt{(12)^2 - 4(3)(4)}}{2(3)}$

$= \dfrac{-12 \pm \sqrt{144 - 48}}{6}$

$= \dfrac{-12 \pm \sqrt{96}}{6}$

$= \dfrac{-12 \pm 4\sqrt{6}}{6}$

$= \dfrac{2(-6 \pm 2\sqrt{6})}{2(3)}$

$= \dfrac{-6 \pm 2\sqrt{6}}{3}$

The solutions are $\dfrac{-6 + 2\sqrt{6}}{3}$ and $\dfrac{-6 - 2\sqrt{6}}{3}$.

55. $a^2 - \dfrac{a}{5} - \dfrac{1}{3} = 0$

$15\left(a^2 - \dfrac{a}{5} - \dfrac{1}{3} = 0\right)$

$15a^2 - 3a - 5 = 0$

$a = \dfrac{-(-3) \pm \sqrt{(-3)^2 - 4(15)(-5)}}{2(15)}$

$= \dfrac{3 \pm \sqrt{9 + 300}}{30}$

$= \dfrac{3 \pm \sqrt{309}}{30}$

The solutions are $\dfrac{3 - \sqrt{309}}{30}$ and $\dfrac{3 + \sqrt{309}}{30}$.

57.
$$c = \frac{6-c}{c-4}$$
$$c(c-4) = -c+6$$
$$c^2 - 4c = -c+6$$
$$c^2 - 3c - 6 = 0$$
$$c = \frac{-(-3) \pm \sqrt{(-3)^2 - 4(1)(-6)}}{2(1)}$$
$$= \frac{3 \pm \sqrt{9+24}}{2}$$
$$= \frac{3 \pm \sqrt{33}}{2}$$
The solutions are $\dfrac{3+\sqrt{33}}{2}$ and $\dfrac{3-\sqrt{33}}{2}$.

59.
$$2x^2 - 4x + 3 = 0$$
$$x = \frac{-(-4) \pm \sqrt{(-4)^2 - 4(2)(3)}}{2(2)}$$
$$= \frac{4 \pm \sqrt{16-24}}{4}$$
$$= \frac{4 \pm \sqrt{-8}}{4}$$
$$= \frac{4 \pm 2i\sqrt{2}}{4}$$
$$= \frac{2 \pm i\sqrt{2}}{2}$$
The solutions are
$\dfrac{2+i\sqrt{2}}{2}$ and $\dfrac{2-i\sqrt{2}}{2}$.

61.
$$2y^2 + y = -3$$
$$2y^2 + y + 3 = 0$$
$$y = \frac{-1 \pm \sqrt{(1)^2 - 4(2)(3)}}{2(2)}$$
$$= \frac{-1 \pm \sqrt{1-24}}{4}$$
$$= \frac{-1 \pm \sqrt{-23}}{4}$$
$$= \frac{-1 \pm i\sqrt{23}}{4}$$
The solutions are $\dfrac{-1+i\sqrt{23}}{4}$ and $\dfrac{-1-i\sqrt{23}}{4}$.

63.
$$0.1x^2 + 0.6x - 1.2 = 0$$
$$10(0.1x^2 + 0.6x - 1.2 = 0)$$
$$x^2 + 6x - 12 = 0$$

$$x = \frac{-6 \pm \sqrt{6^2 - 4(1)(-12)}}{2(1)}$$
$$= \frac{-6 \pm \sqrt{36+48}}{2}$$
$$= \frac{-6 \pm \sqrt{84}}{2}$$
$$= \frac{-6 \pm 2\sqrt{21}}{2}$$
$$= -3 \pm \sqrt{21}$$
The solutions are $-3 + \sqrt{21}$ or $-3 - \sqrt{21}$.

65.
$$f(x) = x^2 - 2x + 4, \ f(x) = 4$$
$$x^2 - 2x + 4 = 4$$
$$x^2 - 2x = 0$$
$$x = \frac{2 \pm \sqrt{(-2)^2 - 4(1)(0)}}{2(1)}$$
$$= \frac{2 \pm \sqrt{4}}{2}$$
$$= \frac{2 \pm 2}{2}$$
$$x = \frac{2+2}{2} \quad \text{or} \quad x = \frac{2-2}{2}$$
$$= \frac{4}{2} \qquad\qquad = \frac{0}{2}$$
$$= 2 \qquad\qquad = 0$$
The values of x are 2 and 0.

67.
$$k(x) = x^2 - x - 10, \ k(x) = 20$$
$$x^2 - x - 10 = 20$$
$$x^2 - x - 30 = 0$$
$$x = \frac{1 \pm \sqrt{(-1)^2 - 4(1)(-30)}}{2(1)}$$
$$= \frac{1 \pm \sqrt{1+120}}{2}$$
$$= \frac{1 \pm \sqrt{121}}{2}$$
$$= \frac{1 \pm 11}{2}$$
$$x = \frac{1+11}{2} \quad \text{or} \quad x = \frac{1-11}{2}$$
$$= \frac{12}{2} \qquad\qquad = \frac{-10}{2}$$
$$= 6 \qquad\qquad = -5$$
The values of x are 6 and −5.

69. $h(t) = 2t^2 - 7t + 1$, $h(t) = -3$

$2t^2 - 7t + 1 = -3$

$2t^2 - 7t + 4 = 0$

$t = \dfrac{7 \pm \sqrt{(-7)^2 - 4(2)(4)}}{2(2)}$

$= \dfrac{7 \pm \sqrt{49 - 32}}{4}$

$= \dfrac{7 \pm \sqrt{17}}{4}$

The values of t are $\dfrac{7 + \sqrt{17}}{4}$ and $\dfrac{7 - \sqrt{17}}{4}$.

71. $g(a) = 2a^2 - 3a + 16$, $g(a) = 14$

$2a^2 - 3a + 16 = 14$

$2a^2 - 3a + 2 = 0$

$a = \dfrac{3 \pm \sqrt{(-3)^2 - 4(2)(2)}}{2(2)}$

$= \dfrac{3 \pm \sqrt{9 - 16}}{4}$

$= \dfrac{3 \pm \sqrt{-7}}{4}$

There are no real values of a for which $g(a) = 14$.

73. If 2 and 5 are solutions, the factors must be $(x - 2)$ and $(x - 5)$.

$f(x) = (x - 2)(x - 5)$

$f(x) = x^2 - 5x - 2x + 10$

$f(x) = x^2 - 7x + 10$

75. If 4 and −6 are solutions, the factors must be $(x - 4)$ and $(x + 6)$.

$f(x) = (x - 4)(x + 6)$

$f(x) = x^2 + 6x - 4x - 24$

$f(x) = x^2 + 2x - 24$

77. If $-\dfrac{3}{5}$ and $\dfrac{2}{3}$ are solutions, the factors must be $(5x + 3)$ and $(3x - 2)$.

$f(x) = (5x + 3)(3x - 2)$

$f(x) = 15x^2 - 10x + 9x - 6$

$f(x) = 15x^2 - x - 6$

79. If $\sqrt{3}$ and $-\sqrt{3}$ are solutions, the factors must be $\left(x - \sqrt{3}\right)$ and $\left(x + \sqrt{3}\right)$.

must be $\left(x - \sqrt{3}\right)$ and $\left(x + \sqrt{3}\right)$.

$f(x) = \left(x - \sqrt{3}\right)\left(x + \sqrt{3}\right)$

$f(x) = x^2 - 3$

81. $2i$ and $-2i$ are solutions, the factors must be $(x - 2i)$ and $(x + 2i)$.

$f(x) = (x - 2i)(x + 2i)$

$f(x) = x^2 - 4i^2$

$f(x) = x^2 + 4$

83. If $3 + \sqrt{2}$ and $3 - \sqrt{2}$ are solutions, the factors must be $\left(x - \left(3 + \sqrt{2}\right)\right)$ and $\left(x - \left(3 - \sqrt{2}\right)\right)$.

$f(x) = \left(x - \left(3 + \sqrt{2}\right)\right)\left(x - \left(3 - \sqrt{2}\right)\right)$

$f(x) = \left(x - 3 - \sqrt{2}\right)\left(x - 3 + \sqrt{2}\right)$

$f(x) = (x - 3)^2 - \left(\sqrt{2}\right)^2$

$f(x) = x^2 - 6x + 9 - 2$

$f(x) = x^2 - 6x + 7$

85. If $2 + 3i$ and $2 - 3i$ are solutions, the factors must be $\left(x - (2 + 3i)\right)$ and $\left(x - (2 - 3i)\right)$.

$f(x) = \left(x - (2 + 3i)\right)\left(x - (2 - 3i)\right)$

$f(x) = (x - 2 - 3i)(x - 2 + 3i)$

$f(x) = (x - 2)^2 - 9i^2$

$f(x) = x^2 - 4x + 4 + 9$

$f(x) = x^2 - 4x + 13$

87. a. $n(10 - 0.02n) = 450$

b $n(10 - 0.02n) = 450$

$10n - 0.02n^2 = 450$

$0.02n^2 - 10n + 450 = 0$

$n = \dfrac{10 \pm \sqrt{(-10)^2 - 4(0.02)(450)}}{2(0.02)}$

$n = \dfrac{10 \pm \sqrt{100 - 36}}{0.04}$

$n = \dfrac{10 \pm \sqrt{64}}{0.04}$

$n = \dfrac{10 \pm 8}{0.04} \implies n = 450$ or $n = 50$

Since n ≤ 65, the number of lamps that must be sold is 50.

89. **a.** $n(50-0.2n)=1680$

  b $n(50-0.2n)=1680$

$50n-0.2n^2 = 1680$

$0.2n^2 - 50n + 1680 = 0$

$n = \dfrac{50 \pm \sqrt{(-50)^2 - 4(0.2)(1680)}}{2(0.2)}$

$n = \dfrac{50 \pm \sqrt{2500 - 1344}}{0.4}$

$n = \dfrac{50 \pm \sqrt{1156}}{0.4}$

$n = \dfrac{50 \pm 34}{0.4} \quad \Rightarrow \quad n = 210 \ \text{or} \ n = 40$

Since $n \le 50$, the number of chairs that must be sold is 40.

91. Any quadratic equation for which the discriminant is a non-negative perfect square can be solved by factoring. Any quadratic equation for which the discriminant is a positive number but not a perfect square can be solved by the quadratic formula but not by factoring over the set of integers.

93. Yes. If the discriminant is a perfect square, the simplified expression will not contain a radical and the quadratic equation can be solved by factoring.

95. Let x be the number.

$2x^2 + 3x = 14$

$2x^2 + 3x - 14 = 0$

$x = \dfrac{-3 \pm \sqrt{3^2 - 4(2)(-14)}}{2(2)}$

$= \dfrac{-3 \pm \sqrt{9 + 112}}{4}$

$= \dfrac{-3 \pm \sqrt{121}}{4}$

$= \dfrac{-3 \pm 11}{4}$

$x = \dfrac{-3 + 11}{4}$ since x is positive

$x = \dfrac{8}{4}$

$x = 2$

97. Let x be the width. Then $3x - 2$ is the length. Use $A = (\text{length})(\text{width})$.

$21 = (3x - 2)(x)$

$21 = (3x - 2)(x)$

$21 = 3x^2 - 2x$

$3x^2 - 2x - 21 = 0$

$x = \dfrac{-(-2) \pm \sqrt{(-2)^2 - 4(3)(-21)}}{2(3)}$

$= \dfrac{2 \pm \sqrt{4 + 252}}{6}$

$= \dfrac{2 \pm \sqrt{256}}{6}$

$= \dfrac{2 \pm 16}{6}$

Since width is positive, use

$x = \dfrac{2 + 16}{6} = \dfrac{18}{6} = 3$

$3x - 2 = 3(3) - 2 = 9 - 2 = 7$

The width is 3 feet and the length is 7 feet.

99. Let x be the amount by which each side is to be reduced.

Then $6 - x$ is the new width and $8 - x$ is the new length

new area $= \dfrac{1}{2}$ (old area)

$= \dfrac{1}{2}(6 \cdot 8)$

$= \dfrac{1}{2}(48)$

$= 24$

new area $= (\text{new width})(\text{new length})$

$24 = (6 - x)(8 - x)$

$0 = 48 - 14x + x^2 - 24$

$0 = x^2 - 14x + 24$

$x = \dfrac{-(-14) \pm \sqrt{(-14)^2 - 4(1)(24)}}{2(1)}$

$= \dfrac{14 \pm \sqrt{196 - 96}}{2}$

$= \dfrac{14 \pm \sqrt{100}}{2}$

$= \dfrac{14 \pm 10}{2}$

$x = \dfrac{14 + 10}{2} \quad \text{or} \quad x = \dfrac{14 - 10}{2}$

$= \dfrac{24}{2} \qquad\qquad = \dfrac{4}{2}$

$= 12 \qquad\qquad\quad = 2$

We reject $x = 12$, since this would give negative values for width and length. The only meaningful value is $x = 2$ inches since this gives positive values for the new width and length.

101.

a. $h = \frac{1}{2}at^2 + v_0t + h_0$

$20 = \frac{1}{2}(-32)t^2 + 60t + 80$

$20 = -16t^2 + 60t + 80$

$0 = -16t^2 + 60t + 60$

$0 = 16t^2 - 60t - 60$

$t = \dfrac{-(-60) \pm \sqrt{(-60)^2 - 4(16)(-60)}}{2(16)}$

$t = \dfrac{60 \pm \sqrt{7440}}{32}$

Since time must be positive, use

$t = \dfrac{60 + \sqrt{7440}}{32} \approx 4.57$

The horseshoe is 20 feet from the ground after about 4.57 seconds.

b. $0 = \frac{1}{2}(-32)t^2 + 60t + 80$

$0 = -16t^2 + 60t + 80$

$t = \dfrac{-60 \pm \sqrt{60^2 - 4(-16)(80)}}{2(-16)}$

$t = \dfrac{-60 \pm \sqrt{8720}}{-32}$

$t = \dfrac{60 \pm \sqrt{8720}}{32}$

Since time must be positive, use

$t = \dfrac{60 + \sqrt{8720}}{32} \approx 4.79$

The horseshoes strike the ground after about 4.79 seconds.

103. $x^2 - \sqrt{5}x - 10 = 0$, $a = 1$, $b = -\sqrt{5}$, $c = -10$

$x = \dfrac{-\left(-\sqrt{5}\right) \pm \sqrt{\left(-\sqrt{5}\right)^2 - 4(1)(-10)}}{2(1)}$

$= \dfrac{\sqrt{5} \pm \sqrt{5 + 40}}{2}$

$= \dfrac{\sqrt{5} \pm \sqrt{45}}{2}$

$= \dfrac{\sqrt{5} \pm 3\sqrt{5}}{2}$

$x = \dfrac{\sqrt{5} + 3\sqrt{5}}{2}$ or $x = \dfrac{\sqrt{5} - 3\sqrt{5}}{2}$

$= \dfrac{4\sqrt{5}}{2}$ $= \dfrac{-2\sqrt{5}}{2}$

$= 2\sqrt{5}$ $= -\sqrt{5}$

The solutions are $2\sqrt{5}$ and $-\sqrt{5}$.

105. Let s be the length of the side of the original cube. Then $s + 0.2$ is the length of the side of the expanded cube.

$(s + 0.2)^3 = s^3 + 6$

$s^3 + 0.6s^2 + 0.12s + 0.008 = s^3 + 6$

$0.6s^2 + 0.12s + 0.008 = 6$

$0.6s^2 + 0.12s - 5.992 = 0$

$s = \dfrac{-0.12 \pm \sqrt{(0.12)^2 - 4(0.6)(-5.992)}}{2(0.6)}$

$= \dfrac{-0.12 \pm \sqrt{0.0144 + 14.3803}}{1.2}$

$= \dfrac{-0.12 \pm \sqrt{14.3952}}{1.2}$

Use the positive value since a length cannot be negative.

$s = \dfrac{-0.12 + \sqrt{14.3952}}{1.2}$

$\approx \dfrac{-0.12 + 3.7941}{1.2}$

≈ 3.0618

The original side was about 3.0618 millimeters long.

107.

a. $h = \frac{1}{2}at^2 + v_0t + h_0$

$0 = \frac{1}{2}(-32)t^2 + 0t + 60$

$0 = -16t^2 + 0t + 60$

$t = \dfrac{-(0) \pm \sqrt{0^2 - 4(-16)(60)}}{2(-16)}$

$t = \dfrac{0 \pm \sqrt{3840}}{-32}$

$t \approx -1.94$ or $t \approx 1.94$

Since time must be positive, use 1.94 sec.

b. $h = \frac{1}{2}at^2 + v_0t + h_0$

$0 = \frac{1}{2}(-32)t^2 + 0t + 120$

$0 = -16t^2 + 0t + 120$

$t = \dfrac{-(0) \pm \sqrt{0^2 - 4(-16)(120)}}{2(-16)}$

$t = \dfrac{0 \pm \sqrt{7680}}{-32}$

$t \approx -2.74$ or $t \approx 2.74$

Since time must be positive, use 2.74 sec.

c. Courtney's rock will strike the ground first.

d. The height of Travis' rock is given by $h(t) = -16t^2 + 100t + 60$. The height of Courtney's rock is given by $h(t) = -16t^2 + 60t + 120$. We want to know when these will be equal.

$-16t^2 + 100t + 60 = -16t^2 + 60t + 120$

$100t + 60 = 60t + 120$

$40t = 60$

$t = \dfrac{60}{40} \implies t = 1.5$

The rocks will be the same distance above the ground after 1.5 seconds.

109. $f(x) = x^2 + 2x - 5$

$f(3) = (3)^2 + 2(3) - 5$

$ = 9 + 6 - 5$

$ = 10$

111. $2x^{-1} - (3y)^{-1} = \dfrac{2}{x} - \dfrac{1}{3y}$

$\phantom{2x^{-1} - (3y)^{-1}} = \dfrac{2}{x} \cdot \dfrac{3y}{3y} - \dfrac{1}{3y} \cdot \dfrac{x}{x}$

$\phantom{2x^{-1} - (3y)^{-1}} = \dfrac{6y - x}{3xy}$

Exercise Set 8.3

1. Answers will vary..

3. $A = s^2$, for s.

$\sqrt{A} = s$

5. $A = S^2 - s^2$, for S

$A + s^2 = S^2$

$\sqrt{A + s^2} = S \implies S = \sqrt{A + s^2}$

7. $E = i^2 r$, for i

$\dfrac{E}{r} = i^2$

$\sqrt{\dfrac{E}{r}} = i$

9. $d = 16t^2$, for t

$\dfrac{d}{16} = t^2$

$\sqrt{\dfrac{d}{16}} = t \implies t = \dfrac{\sqrt{d}}{4}$

11. $E = mc^2$, for c

$\dfrac{E}{m} = c^2$

$\sqrt{\dfrac{E}{m}} = c$

13. $V = \dfrac{1}{3} \pi r^2 h$, for r

$3V = \pi r^2 h$

$\dfrac{3V}{\pi h} = r^2$

$\sqrt{\dfrac{3V}{\pi h}} = r$

15. $d = \sqrt{L^2 + W^2}$, for W

$d^2 = L^2 + W^2$

$d^2 - L^2 = W^2$

$\sqrt{d^2 - L^2} = W$

17. $a^2 + b^2 = c^2$, for b

$b^2 = c^2 - a^2$

$b = \sqrt{c^2 - a^2}$

19. $d = \sqrt{L^2 + W^2 + H^2}$, for H

$d^2 = L^2 + W^2 + H^2$

$d^2 - L^2 - W^2 = H^2$

$\sqrt{d^2 - L^2 - W^2} = H$

21. $h = -16t^2 + s_0$, for t

$16t^2 = s_0 - h$

$t^2 = \dfrac{s_0 - h}{16}$

$t = \sqrt{\dfrac{s_0 - h}{16}}$

$t = \dfrac{\sqrt{s_0 - h}}{4}$

23. $E = \dfrac{1}{2} mv^2$, for v

$2E = mv^2$

$\dfrac{2E}{m} = v^2$

$\sqrt{\dfrac{2E}{m}} = v$

25.

$a = \dfrac{v_2^2 - v_1^2}{2d}$, for v_1

$2ad = v_2^2 - v_1^2$

$2ad + v_1^2 = v_2^2$

$v_1^2 = v_2^2 - 2ad$

$v_1 = \sqrt{v_2^2 - 2ad}$

27.

$v' = \sqrt{c^2 - v^2}$, for c

$(v')^2 = c^2 - v^2$

$(v')^2 + v^2 = c^2$

$c = \sqrt{(v')^2 + v^2}$

29. a.

$P(n) = 2.4\,n^2 + 9n - 3$

$P(6) = 2.4(6)^2 + 9(6) - 3$

$\qquad = 137.4 \;\Rightarrow\; \$13{,}740$

The profit would be $\$13{,}740$.

b.

$P(n) = 2.4n^2 + 9n - 3$

$200 = 2.4n^2 + 9n - 3$

$2.4n^2 + 9n - 203 = 0$

$x = \dfrac{-9 \pm \sqrt{9^2 - 4(2.4)(-203)}}{2(2.4)}$

$x = \dfrac{-9 \pm \sqrt{2029.8}}{4.8}$

$x \approx 8$ or $x \approx -11$

We disregard the negative answer. 8 tractors must be sold.

31. $T = 6.2t^2 + 12t + 32$

a. When the car is turned on, $t = 0$.

$T = 6.2(0)^2 + 12(0) + 32 = 32$

The temperature is $32°$F.

b. $T = 6.2(1)^2 + 12(1) + 32 = 50.2$

The temperature after 1 minute is $50.2°$F.

c. $120 = 6.2t^2 + 12t + 32$

$0 = 6.2t^2 + 12t - 88$

$t = \dfrac{-12 \pm \sqrt{12^2 - 4(6.2)(-88)}}{2(6.2)}$

$t \approx \dfrac{-12 \pm 48.23}{12.4}$

$t \approx 2.92$ or $t \approx -4.86$

The radiator temperature will reach $120°$F about 2.92 min. after the engine is started.

33. a. $C = -0.01(1500)^2 + 80(1500) + 20{,}000$

$\qquad = 117{,}500$

The cost is about $\$117{,}500$.

b. $150{,}000 = -0.01s^2 + 80s + 20{,}000$

$0 = -0.01s^2 + 80s - 130{,}000$

$s = \dfrac{-80 \pm \sqrt{80^2 - 4(-0.01)(-130{,}000)}}{2(-0.01)}$

$s \approx \dfrac{-80 \pm 34.64}{-0.02}$

$s \approx 2268$ or $s \approx 5732$

Notice that s must fall between 1200 and 4000. Therefore, Mr. Boyle can purchase a 2268 sq ft house for $\$150{,}000$.

35. a. $0 = -3.3t^2 - 2.3t + 62$

$$t = \frac{-(-2.3) \pm \sqrt{(-2.3)^2 - 4(-3.3)(62)}}{2(-3.3)}$$

$$t = \frac{2.3 \pm 28.7}{-6.6}$$

$t \approx -4.7$ or $t = 4$

Since time must be positive, the car takes 4 seconds for the drop.

b. $s = 6.74(4) + 2.3 = 29.26$

The speed is 29.26 feet per second.

37. a. $m(t) = 0.05t^2 - 0.32t + 3.15$

In 2003, $t = 21$.

$m(21) = 0.05(21^2) - 0.32(21) + 3.15$

$\qquad = 22.05 - 6.72 + 3.15$

$\qquad \approx 18.5$

Veterinary bills for dogs in 2003 amounted to about \$18.5 billion.

b. $m(t) = 0.05t^2 - 0.32t + 3.15$, $m(t) = 12$

$25 = 0.05t^2 - 0.32t + 3.15$

$0 = 0.05t^2 - 0.32t - 21.85$

$$t = \frac{0.32 \pm \sqrt{(0.32)^2 - 4(0.05)(-21.85)}}{2(0.05)}$$

$$= \frac{0.32 \pm \sqrt{0.1024 + 4.37}}{0.1}$$

$$= \frac{0.32 \pm \sqrt{4.4724}}{0.1}$$

$$\approx \frac{0.32 \pm 2.1148050}{0.1}$$

$$t \approx \frac{0.32 + 2.1148050}{0.1} = \frac{2.4348050}{0.1} \approx 24.3$$

or

$$t \approx \frac{0.32 - 2.1148050}{0.1} = \frac{-1.794805}{0.1} \approx -17.9$$

Since $1 \le t \le 28$, the only solution is $t \approx 24.3$. Thus \$25 billion will be spent on veterinary bills for dogs approximately 24.3 years after 1982 or in 2006.

39. Let x be the width of the playground. Then the length is given by $x + 5$.

Area = length × width

$500 = x(x + 5)$

$x^2 + 5x - 500 = 0$

$(x - 20)(x + 25) = 0$

$x = 20$ or $x = -25$

Disregard the negative value. The width of the playground is 20 meters and the length is $20 + 5 = 25$ meters.

41. Let r be the rate at which the present equipment drills.

	d	r	$t = \dfrac{d}{r}$
present equipment	64	r	$\dfrac{64}{r}$
new equipment	64	$r + 1$	$\dfrac{64}{r + 1}$

They would have hit water in 3.2 hours less time with the new equipment.

$$\frac{64}{r+1} = \frac{64}{r} - 3.2$$

$$r(r+1)\left(\frac{64}{r+1}\right) = r(r+1)\left(\frac{64}{r}\right) - r(r+1)(3.2)$$

$$64r = 64(r+1) - 3.2r(r+1)$$

$$64r = 64r + 64 - 3.2r^2 - 3.2r$$

$$0 = 64 - 3.2r^2 - 3.2r$$

$3.2r^2 + 3.2r - 64 = 0$

$r^2 + r - 20 = 0$

$(r + 5)(r - 4) = 0$

$r + 5 = 0$ or $r - 4 = 0$

$r = -5$ $\qquad\qquad$ $r = 4$

Use the positive value. The present equipment drills at a rate of 4 ft/hr.

43. Let x be Latoya's rate going uphill so $x + 2$ is her rating going downhill. Using $\dfrac{d}{r} = t$ gives

$t_{\text{uphill}} + t_{\text{downhill}} = 1.75$

$$\frac{6}{x} + \frac{6}{x+2} = 1.75$$

$$x(x+2)\left(\frac{6}{x}\right) + x(x+2)\left(\frac{6}{x+2}\right) = x(x+2)(1.75)$$

$$6(x+2) + 6x = 1.75x(x+2)$$

$$6x + 12 + 6x = 1.75x^2 + 3.5x$$

$$0 = 1.75x^2 - 8.5x - 12$$

$$x = \frac{-(-8.5) \pm \sqrt{(-8.5)^2 - 4(1.75)(-12)}}{2(1.75)}$$

$$= \frac{8 \pm \sqrt{156.25}}{3.5}$$

$$= \frac{8.5 \pm 12.5}{3.5}$$

$x = 6$ or $x \approx -1.14$

Since the time must be positive, Latoya's uphill rate is 6 mph and her downhill rate is $x + 2 = 8$ mph.

45. Let x be the time of the experienced mechanic then $x + 1$ is the time of the inexperienced mechanic.

$$\frac{6}{x} + \frac{6}{x+1} = 1$$

$$x(x+1)\left(\frac{6}{x}\right) + x(x+1)\left(\frac{6}{x+1}\right) = x(x+1)(1)$$

$$6(x+1) + 6x = x^2 + x$$

$$6x + 6 + 6x = x^2 + x$$

$$0 = x^2 - 11x - 6$$

$$x = \frac{-(-11) \pm \sqrt{(-11)^2 - 4(1)(-6)}}{2(1)}$$

$$= \frac{11 \pm \sqrt{121 + 24}}{2}$$

$$= \frac{11 \pm \sqrt{145}}{2}$$

$$x = \frac{11 + \sqrt{145}}{2} \quad \text{or} \quad x = \frac{11 - \sqrt{145}}{2}$$

$$\approx 11.52 \qquad\qquad \approx -0.52$$

Since the time must be positive, it takes Bonita about 11.52 hours and Pamela about 12.52 hours to rebuild the engine.

47. Let r be the speed of the plane in still air.

	d	r	$t = \dfrac{d}{r}$
With wind	80	$r + 30$	$\dfrac{80}{r+30}$
Against wind	80	$r - 30$	$\dfrac{80}{r-30}$

The total time is 1.3 hours

$$\frac{80}{r+30} + \frac{80}{r-30} = 1.3$$

$$(r+30)(r-30)\left(\frac{80}{r+30} + \frac{80}{r-30} = 1.3\right)$$

$$80(r-3) + 80(r+30) = 1.3\left(r^2 - 900\right)$$

$$80r - 240 + 80r + 240 = 1.3r^2 - 1170$$

$$160r = 1.3r^2 - 1170$$

$$0 = 1.3r^2 - 160r - 1170$$

$$r = \frac{-(-160) \pm \sqrt{(-160)^2 - 4(1.3)(-1170)}}{2(1.3)}$$

$$= \frac{160 \pm \sqrt{25,600 + 6084}}{2.6}$$

$$= \frac{160 \pm \sqrt{31,684}}{2.6}$$

$$= \frac{160 \pm 178}{2.6}$$

$$r = \frac{160 + 178}{2.6} \quad \text{or} \quad r = \frac{160 - 178}{2.6}$$

$$= \frac{338}{2.6} \qquad\qquad = \frac{-18}{2.6}$$

$$= 130 \qquad\qquad \approx -6.92$$

Since speed must be positive, the speed of the plane in still air is 130 mph.

49. Let t be the number of hours for Chris to clean alone. Then $t + 0.5$ is the number of hours for John to clean alone.

	Rate of work	Time worked	Part of Task completed
Chris	$\dfrac{1}{t}$	6	$\dfrac{6}{t}$
John	$\dfrac{1}{t+0.5}$	6	$\dfrac{6}{t+0.5}$

$$\frac{6}{t} + \frac{6}{t+0.5} = 1$$

$$t(t+0.5)\left(\frac{6}{t}\right) + t(t+0.5)\left(\frac{6}{t+0.5}\right) = t(t+0.5)(1)$$

$$6(t+0.5) + 6t = t(t+0.5)$$

$$6t + 3 + 6t = t^2 + 0.5t$$

$$12t + 3 = t^2 + 0.5t$$

$$0 = t^2 - 11.5t - 3$$

$$t = \frac{11.5 \pm \sqrt{(-11.5)^2 - 4(1)(-3)}}{2(1)}$$

$$= \frac{11.5 \pm \sqrt{132.25 + 12}}{2}$$

$$= \frac{11.5 \pm \sqrt{144.25}}{2}$$

$$t = \frac{11.5 + \sqrt{144.25}}{2} \quad \text{or} \quad t = \frac{11.5 - \sqrt{144.25}}{2}$$

$$\approx 11.76 \qquad\qquad \approx -0.26$$

Since the time must be positive, it takes Chris about 11.76 hours and John about $11.76 + 0.5 = 12.26$ hours to clean alone.

51. Let x be the speed of the trip from Lubbock to Plainview. Then $x - 10$ is the speed from Plainview to Amarillo.

	d	r	t
first part	60	x	$\dfrac{60}{x}$
second part	100	$x - 10$	$\dfrac{100}{x-10}$

Including the 2.5 hours she spent in Plainview, the entire trip took Lisa 5.5 hours.

$$\frac{60}{x} + 2.5 + \frac{100}{x-10} = 5.5$$

$$\frac{60}{x} + \frac{100}{x-10} = 3$$

$$x(x-10)\left(\frac{60}{x} + \frac{100}{x-10} = 3\right)$$

$$60(x-10) + 100x = 3(x^2 - 10x)$$

$$60x - 600 + 100x = 3x^2 - 30x$$

$$-600 + 160x = 3x^2 - 30x$$

$$0 = 3x^2 - 190x + 600$$

$$0 = (x-60)(3x-10)$$

$$x - 60 = 0 \quad \text{or} \quad 3x - 10 = 0$$

$$x = 60 \qquad\qquad x = \frac{10}{3}$$

$\dfrac{10}{3}$ miles per hour is too slow for a car, so the speed of the trip from Lubbock to Plainview was 60 mph.

53. Answers will vary.

55. Let l = original length and w = original width. A system of equations that describes this situation is

$$l \cdot w = 18$$

$$(l+2)(w+3) = 48$$

If you solve for l in the first equation you get $l = \dfrac{18}{w}$. Substitute $\dfrac{18}{w}$ into the l in the second equation. The result is an equation in only one variable which can be solved.

$$(l+2)(w+3) = 48$$

$$\left(\frac{18}{w} + 2\right)(w+3) = 48$$

$$18 + \frac{54}{w} + 2w + 6 = 48$$

$$2w - 24 + \frac{54}{w} = 0$$

$$w\left(2w - 24 + \frac{54}{w} = 0\right)$$

$$2w^2 - 24w + 54 = 0$$

$$2(w-3)(w-9) = 0$$

$$w = 3 \quad \text{or} \quad w = 9$$

If $w = 3$, then $l = \dfrac{18}{3} = 6$. One possible set of dimensions for the original rectangle is 6 m by 3 m.

If $w = 9$, then $l = \dfrac{18}{9} = 2$. Another possible set of dimensions for the original rectangle is 2 m by 9 m.

57.
$$-\left[4(5-3)^3\right] + 2^3$$
$$-\left[4(2)^3\right] + 2^3$$
$$-\left[4(8)\right] + 8$$
$$-32 + 8$$
$$-24$$

59.
$$\frac{2r}{r-4} - \frac{2r}{r+4} + \frac{64}{r^2 - 16}$$

$$= \frac{2r}{r-4} \cdot \frac{r+4}{r+4} - \frac{2r}{r+4} \cdot \frac{r-4}{r-4} + \frac{64}{(r+4)(r-4)}$$

$$= \frac{2r^2 + 8r}{(r+4)(r-4)} - \frac{2r^2 - 8r}{(r+4)(r-4)} + \frac{64}{(r+4)(r-4)}$$

$$= \frac{2r^2 + 8r - (2r^2 - 8r) + 64}{(r+4)(r-4)}$$

$$= \frac{16r + 64}{(r+4)(r-4)}$$

$$= \frac{16(r+4)}{(r+4)(r-4)} \quad \text{or} \quad \frac{16}{r-4}$$

61. $\sqrt{x^2 + 3x + 9} = x$

$x^2 + 3x + 9 = x^2$

$3x + 9 = 0$

$3x = -9 \implies x = -3$

Upon checking, this value does not satisfy the equation. There is no real solution.

Exercise Set 8.4

1. A given equation can be expressed as an equation in quadratic form if the equation can be written in the form $au^2 + bu + c = 0$.

3. Let $u = x^2$. Then $3x^4 - 5x^2 + 1 = 0 \implies 3\left(x^2\right)^2 - 5x^2 + 1 = 0 \implies 3u^2 - 5u + 1 = 0$

5. Let $u = z^{-1}$. Then $z^{-2} - z^{-1} = 56 \implies \left(z^{-1}\right)^2 - z^{-1} = 56 \implies u^2 - u = 56$

7. $x^4 - 10x^2 + 9 = 0$

$\left(x^2\right)^2 - 10x^2 + 9 = 0$

$u^2 - 10u + 9 = 0 \leftarrow$ Replace x^2 with u

$(u - 9)(u - 1) = 0$

$u - 9 = 0 \qquad$ or $\quad u - 1 = 0$

$\qquad u = 9 \qquad\qquad\qquad u = 1$

$\qquad x^2 = 9 \qquad\qquad\qquad x^2 = 1 \leftarrow$ Replace u with x^2

$\qquad x = \pm\sqrt{9} = \pm 3 \qquad x = \pm\sqrt{1} = \pm 1$

The solutions are 3, –3, 1, and –1.

9. $x^4 - 26x^2 + 25 = 0$

$\left(x^2\right)^2 - 26x^2 + 25 = 0$

$u^2 - 26u + 25 = 0 \leftarrow$ Replace x^2 with u

$(u - 25)(u - 1) = 0$

$u - 25 = 0 \qquad\qquad u - 1 = 0$

$\qquad u = 25 \qquad\qquad\qquad u = 1$

$\qquad x^2 = 25 \qquad\qquad\qquad x^2 = 1 \leftarrow$ Replace u with x^2

$\qquad x = \pm\sqrt{25} = \pm 5 \qquad x = \pm\sqrt{1} = \pm 1$

The solutions are 5, –5, 1, and –1.

11. $x^4 - 13x^2 + 36 = 0$

$\left(x^2\right)^2 - 13x^2 + 36 = 0$

$u^2 - 13u + 36 = 0$ ← Replace x^2 with u

$(u - 9)(u - 4) = 0$

$u - 9 = 0 \qquad\qquad u - 4 = 0$

$u = 9 \qquad\qquad\qquad u = 4$

$x^2 = 9 \qquad\qquad\qquad x^2 = 4$ ← Replace u with x^2

$x = \pm\sqrt{9} = \pm 3 \qquad x = \pm\sqrt{4} = \pm 2$

The solutions are 3, –3, 2, and –2.

13. $a^4 - 7a^2 + 12 = 0$

$\left(a^2\right)^2 - 7a^2 + 12 = 0$

$u^2 - 7u + 12 = 0$ ← Replace a^2 with u

$(u - 4)(u - 3) = 0$

$u - 4 = 0 \qquad$ or $\quad u - 3 = 0$

$u = 4 \qquad\qquad\qquad u = 3$

$a^2 = 4 \qquad\qquad\qquad a^2 = 3$ ← Replace u with a^2

$a = \pm\sqrt{4} = \pm 2 \qquad a = \pm\sqrt{3}$

The solutions are 2, –2, $\sqrt{3}$, and $-\sqrt{3}$.

15. $4x^4 - 5x^2 + 1 = 0$

$4\left(x^2\right)^2 - 5x^2 + 1 = 0$

$4u^2 - 5u + 1 = 0$ ← Replace x^2 with u

$(4u - 1)(u - 1) = 0$

$4u - 1 = 0 \qquad$ or $\quad u - 1 = 0$

$u = \dfrac{1}{4} \qquad\qquad\qquad u = 1$

$x^2 = \dfrac{1}{4} \qquad\qquad\qquad x^2 = 1$ ← Replace u with x^2

$x = \pm\sqrt{\dfrac{1}{4}} = \pm\dfrac{1}{2} \qquad x = \pm\sqrt{1} = \pm 1$

The solutions are $\dfrac{1}{2}$, $-\dfrac{1}{2}$, 1, and –1.

17. $r^4 - 8r^2 = -15$

$r^4 - 8r^2 + 15 = 0$

$\left(r^2\right)^2 - 8r^2 + 15 = 0$

$u^2 - 8u + 15 = 0$ ← Replace r^2 with u

$(u - 3)(u - 5) = 0$

$u - 3 = 0 \qquad\qquad u - 5 = 0$

$u = 3 \qquad\qquad\qquad u = 5$

$r^2 = 3 \qquad\qquad\qquad r^2 = 5$ ← Replace u with r^2

$r = \pm\sqrt{3} \qquad\qquad r = \pm\sqrt{5}$

The solutions are $\sqrt{3}$, $-\sqrt{3}$, $\sqrt{5}$, and $-\sqrt{5}$.

19. $z^4 - 7z^2 = 18$

$z^4 - 7z^2 - 18 = 0$

$\left(z^2\right)^2 - 7z^2 - 18 = 0$

$u^2 - 7u - 18 = 0$ ← Replace z^2 with u

$(u-9)(u+2) = 0$

$u - 9 = 0 \qquad u + 2 = 0$

$u = 9 \qquad\qquad u = -2$

$z^2 = 9 \qquad\qquad z^2 = -2$ ← Replace u with z^2

$z = \pm 3 \qquad\qquad z = \pm\sqrt{-2} = \pm i\sqrt{2}$

The solutions are $3, -3, i\sqrt{2},$ and $-i\sqrt{2}$.

21. $-c^4 = 4c^2 - 5$

$c^4 + 4c^2 - 5 = 0$

$\left(c^2\right)^2 + 4c^2 - 5 = 0$

$u^2 + 4u - 5 = 0$ ← Replace c^2 with u

$(u-1)(u+5) = 0$

$u - 1 = 0 \qquad u + 5 = 0$

$u = 1 \qquad\qquad u = -5$

$c^2 = 1 \qquad\qquad c^2 = -5$ ← Replace u with c^2

$c = \pm 1 \qquad\qquad c = \pm\sqrt{-5} = \pm i\sqrt{5}$

The solutions are $1, -1, i\sqrt{5},$ and $-i\sqrt{5}$.

23. $\sqrt{x} = 2x - 6$

$2x - \sqrt{x} - 6 = 0$

$2\left(x^{1/2}\right)^2 - x^{1/2} - 6 = 0$

$2u^2 - u - 6 = 0$ ← Replace $x^{1/2}$ with u

$(2u+3)(u-2) = 0$

$2u + 3 = 0 \qquad$ or $\quad u - 2 = 0$

$u = -\dfrac{3}{2} \quad$ or $\qquad u = 2$

$x^{1/2} = -\dfrac{3}{2} \quad$ or $\quad x^{1/2} = 2$ ← Replace u with $x^{1/2}$

$x = 2^2 = 4$

$x^{1/2} = -\dfrac{3}{2}$ has no solution since there is no value of x for which $x^{1/2} = -\dfrac{3}{2}$.

The solution is 4.

25. $x + \sqrt{x} = 6$

$$x + \sqrt{x} - 6 = 0$$

$$\left(x^{1/2}\right)^2 + x^{1/2} - 6 = 0$$

$$u^2 + u - 6 = 0 \quad \leftarrow \text{Replace } x^{1/2} \text{ with } u$$

$$(u + 3)(u - 2) = 0$$

$u + 3 = 0 \quad$ or $\quad u - 2 = 0$

$\quad u = -3 \quad$ or $\qquad u = 2$

$\quad x^{1/2} = -3 \quad$ or $\quad x^{1/2} = 2 \quad \leftarrow \text{Replace } u \text{ with } x^{1/2}$

$\quad x = 2^2 = 4$

$x^{1/2} = -3$ has no solution since there is no value of x for which $x^{1/2} = -3$.
The solution is 4.

27. $\qquad 9x + 3\sqrt{x} = 2$

$$9x + 3\sqrt{x} - 2 = 0$$

$$9\left(x^{1/2}\right)^2 + 3x^{1/2} - 2 = 0$$

$$9u^2 + 3u - 2 = 0 \quad \leftarrow \text{Replace } x^{1/2} \text{ with } u$$

$$(3u - 1)(3u + 2) = 0$$

$3u - 1 = 0 \quad$ or $\quad 3u + 2 = 0$

$\qquad u = \dfrac{1}{3} \qquad\qquad u = -\dfrac{2}{3}$

$\qquad x^{1/2} = \dfrac{1}{3} \qquad x^{1/2} = -\dfrac{2}{3} \quad \leftarrow \text{Replace } u \text{ with } x^{1/2}$

$\qquad x = \dfrac{1}{9}$

$x^{1/2} = -\dfrac{2}{3}$ has no solution since there is no value of x for which $x^{1/2} = -\dfrac{2}{3}$.

The solution is $\dfrac{1}{9}$.

29. $\quad (x + 3)^2 + 2(x + 3) = 24$

$$(x + 3)^2 + 2(x + 3) - 24 = 0$$

$$u^2 + 2u - 24 = 0 \quad \leftarrow \text{Replace } x + 3 \text{ with } u$$

$$(u - 4)(u + 6) = 0$$

$u - 4 = 0 \quad$ or $\quad u + 6 = 0$

$\quad u = 4 \qquad\qquad u = -6$

$x + 3 = 4 \qquad x + 3 = -6 \quad \leftarrow \text{Replace } u \text{ with } x + 3$

$\quad x = 1 \qquad\qquad x = -9$

The solutions are 1 and –9.

31.
$$6(a-2)^2 = -19(a-2)-10$$
$$6(a-2)^2 + 19(a-2) + 10 = 0$$
$$6u^2 + 19u + 10 = 0 \quad \leftarrow \text{Replace } a-2 \text{ with } u$$
$$(3u+2)(2u+5) = 0$$
$$3u+2 = 0 \qquad \text{or} \qquad 2u+5 = 0$$
$$u = -\frac{2}{3} \qquad\qquad u = -\frac{5}{2}$$
$$a-2 = -\frac{2}{3} \qquad a-2 = -\frac{5}{2} \quad \leftarrow \text{Replace } u \text{ with } a-2$$
$$a = \frac{4}{3} \qquad\qquad a = -\frac{1}{2}$$

The solutions are $\frac{4}{3}$ and $-\frac{1}{2}$.

33.
$$(x^2-1)^2 - (x^2-1) - 6 = 0$$
$$u^2 - u - 6 = 0 \quad \leftarrow \text{Replace } x^2-1 \text{ with } u$$
$$(u+2)(u-3) = 0$$
$$u+2 = 0 \qquad\qquad \text{or} \qquad u-3 = 0$$
$$u = -2 \qquad\qquad\qquad u = 3$$
$$x^2 - 1 = -2 \qquad\qquad x^2 - 1 = 3 \quad \leftarrow \text{Replace } u \text{ with } x^2-1$$
$$x^2 = -1 \qquad\qquad\qquad x^2 = 4$$
$$x = \sqrt{-1} = \pm i \qquad x = \pm\sqrt{4} = \pm 2$$

The solutions are i, $-i$, 2, and -2.

35.
$$2(b+2)^2 + 5(b+2) - 3 = 0$$
$$2u^2 + 5u - 3 = 0 \quad \leftarrow \text{Replace } b+2 \text{ with } u$$
$$(u+3)(2u-1) = 0$$
$$u+3 = 0 \qquad \text{or} \qquad 2u-1 = 0$$
$$u = -3 \qquad\qquad u = \frac{1}{2}$$
$$b+2 = -3 \qquad b+2 = \frac{1}{2} \quad \leftarrow \text{Replace } u \text{ with } b+2$$
$$b = -5 \qquad\qquad b = -\frac{3}{2}$$

The solutions are -5 and $-\frac{3}{2}$.

37. $18(x^2-5)^2+27(x^2-5)+10=0$

$\qquad 18u^2+27u+10=0 \leftarrow$ Replace x^2-5 with u

$\qquad (3u+2)(6u+5)=0$

$3u+2=0 \qquad\qquad$ or $\quad 6u+5=0$

$\qquad u=-\dfrac{2}{3} \qquad\qquad\qquad u=-\dfrac{5}{6}$

$x^2-5=-\dfrac{2}{3} \qquad\qquad x^2-5=-\dfrac{5}{6} \leftarrow$ Replace u with x^2-5

$\qquad x^2=\dfrac{13}{3} \qquad\qquad\qquad x^2=\dfrac{25}{6}$

$\qquad x=\pm\sqrt{\dfrac{13}{3}} \qquad\qquad x=\pm\sqrt{\dfrac{25}{6}}$

$\qquad =\pm\dfrac{\sqrt{13}}{\sqrt{3}}\cdot\dfrac{\sqrt{3}}{\sqrt{3}} \qquad\qquad =\pm\dfrac{5}{\sqrt{6}}\cdot\dfrac{\sqrt{6}}{\sqrt{6}}$

$\qquad =\pm\dfrac{\sqrt{39}}{3} \qquad\qquad\qquad =\pm\dfrac{5\sqrt{6}}{6}$

The solutions are $\dfrac{\sqrt{39}}{3}$, $-\dfrac{\sqrt{39}}{3}$, $\dfrac{5\sqrt{6}}{6}$, and $-\dfrac{5\sqrt{6}}{6}$.

39. $x^{-2}+10x^{-1}+25=0$

$(x^{-1})^2+10(x^{-1})+25=0$

$\qquad u^2+10u+25=0 \leftarrow$ Replace x^{-1} with u

$\qquad (u+5)(u+5)=0$

$\qquad u+5=0$

$\qquad u=-5$

$\qquad x^{-1}=-5 \qquad \leftarrow$ Replace u with x^{-1}

$\qquad x=-\dfrac{1}{5}$

The solution is $-\dfrac{1}{5}$.

41. $6b^{-2}-5b^{-1}+1=0$

$6(b^{-1})^2-5(b^{-1})+1=0$

$\qquad 6u^2-5u+1=0 \leftarrow$ Replace b^{-1} with u

$\qquad (2u-1)(3u-1)=0$

$\qquad 2u-1=0 \quad$ or $\quad 3u-1=0$

$\qquad u=\dfrac{1}{2} \qquad\qquad u=\dfrac{1}{3}$

$\qquad b^{-1}=\dfrac{1}{2} \qquad\qquad b^{-1}=\dfrac{1}{3} \leftarrow$ Replace u with b^{-1}

$\qquad b=2 \qquad\qquad\quad b=3$

The solutions are 2 and 3.

43.
$$2b^{-2} = 7b^{-1} - 3$$
$$2b^{-2} - 7b^{-1} + 3 = 0$$
$$2\left(b^{-1}\right)^2 - 7\left(b^{-1}\right) + 3 = 0$$
$$2u^2 - 7u + 3 = 0 \quad \leftarrow \text{ Replace } b^{-1} \text{ with } u$$
$$(2u - 1)(u - 3) = 0$$

$$2u - 1 = 0 \quad \text{or} \quad u - 3 = 0$$
$$u = \frac{1}{2} \qquad\qquad u = 3$$
$$b^{-1} = \frac{1}{2} \qquad\quad b^{-1} = 3 \leftarrow \text{ Replace } u \text{ with } b^{-1}$$
$$b = 2 \qquad\qquad b = \frac{1}{3}$$

The solutions are 2 and $\frac{1}{3}$.

45.
$$x^{-2} + 9x^{-1} = 10$$
$$x^{-2} + 9x^{-1} - 10 = 0$$
$$\left(x^{-1}\right)^2 + 9\left(x^{-1}\right) - 10 = 0$$
$$u^2 + 9u - 10 = 0 \quad \leftarrow \text{ Replace } x^{-1} \text{ with } u$$
$$(u + 10)(u - 1) = 0$$

$$u + 10 = 0 \qquad \text{or} \quad u - 1 = 0$$
$$u = -10 \qquad\qquad u = 1$$
$$x^{-1} = -10 \qquad\quad x^{-1} = 1 \leftarrow \text{ Replace } u \text{ with } x^{-1}$$
$$x = -\frac{1}{10} \qquad\qquad x = 1$$

The solutions are $-\dfrac{1}{10}$ and 1.

47.
$$x^{-2} = 4x^{-1} + 12$$
$$x^{-2} - 4x^{-1} - 12 = 0$$
$$\left(x^{-1}\right)^2 - 4\left(x^{-1}\right) - 12 = 0$$
$$u^2 - 4u - 12 = 0 \quad \leftarrow \text{ Replace } x^{-1} \text{ with } u$$
$$(u + 2)(u - 6) = 0$$

$$u + 2 = 0 \qquad \text{or} \quad u - 6 = 0$$
$$u = -2 \qquad\qquad u = 6$$
$$x^{-1} = -2 \qquad\quad x^{-1} = 6 \leftarrow \text{ Replace } u \text{ with } x^{-1}$$
$$x = -\frac{1}{2} \qquad\qquad x = \frac{1}{6}$$

The solutions are $-\dfrac{1}{2}$ and $\dfrac{1}{6}$.

49.
$$x^{2/3} - 3x^{1/3} = -2$$
$$\left(x^{1/3}\right)^2 - 3x^{1/3} + 2 = 0$$
$$u^2 - 3u + 2 = 0 \quad \leftarrow \text{ Replace } x^{1/3} \text{ with } u$$
$$(u-1)(u-2) = 0$$

$$u - 1 = 0 \quad \text{or} \quad u - 2 = 0$$
$$u = 1 \qquad\qquad u = 2$$
$$x^{1/3} = 1 \qquad\quad x^{1/3} = 2 \quad \leftarrow \text{ Replace } u \text{ with } x^{1/3}$$
$$x = 1^3 \qquad\qquad x = 2^3$$
$$= 1 \qquad\qquad\quad = 8$$

The solutions are 1 and 8.

51.
$$b^{2/3} + 11b^{1/3} + 28 = 0$$
$$\left(b^{1/3}\right)^2 + 11b^{1/3} + 28 = 0$$
$$u^2 + 11u + 28 = 0 \quad \leftarrow \text{ Replace } b^{1/3} \text{ with } u$$
$$(u+7)(u+4) = 0$$

$$u + 7 = 0 \qquad\quad \text{or} \quad u + 4 = 0$$
$$u = -7 \qquad \text{or} \qquad u = -4$$
$$b^{1/3} = -7 \qquad \text{or} \qquad b^{1/3} = -4 \quad \leftarrow \text{ Replace } u \text{ with } b^{1/3}$$
$$b = (-7)^3 \quad \text{or} \qquad b = (-4)^3$$
$$= -343 \qquad\qquad = -64$$

The solutions are −343 and −64.

53.
$$-2a - 5a^{1/2} + 3 = 0$$
$$-2\left(a^{1/2}\right)^2 - 5a^{1/2} + 3 = 0$$
$$-2u^2 - 5u + 3 = 0 \quad \leftarrow \text{ Replace } a^{1/2} \text{ with } u$$
$$2u^2 + 5u - 3 = 0$$
$$(2u - 1)(u + 3) = 0$$

$$2u - 1 = 0 \qquad\quad \text{or} \quad u + 3 = 0$$
$$u = \frac{1}{2} \qquad\qquad u = -3$$
$$a^{1/2} = 2 \qquad\qquad a^{1/2} = -3 \quad \leftarrow \text{ Replace } u \text{ with } a^{1/2}$$
$$a = \left(\frac{1}{2}\right)^2 = \frac{1}{4}$$

$a^{1/2} = -3$ has no solution since there is no value of a for which $a^{\frac{1}{2}} = -3$.
The solution is $\frac{1}{4}$.

55.
$$c^{2/5} - 3c^{1/5} + 2 = 0$$
$$\left(c^{1/5}\right)^2 - 3c^{1/5} + 2 = 0$$
$$u^2 - 3u + 2 = 0 \quad \leftarrow \text{ Replace } c^{1/5} \text{ with } u$$
$$(u-2)(u-1) = 0$$

$$u - 2 = 0 \qquad u - 1 = 0$$
$$u = 2 \qquad\qquad u = 1$$
$$c^{1/5} = 2 \qquad c^{1/5} = 1 \;\leftarrow\; \text{Replace } u \text{ with } c^{1/5}$$
$$c = 2^5 \qquad\quad c = 1^5$$
$$= 32 \qquad\qquad = 1$$

The solutions are 32 and 1.

57. $f(x) = x - 5\sqrt{x} + 4$, $f(x) = 0$

$$0 = \left(x^{1/2}\right)^2 - 5x^{1/2} + 4$$
$$0 = u^2 - 5u + 4 \;\leftarrow\; \text{Replace } x^{1/2} \text{ with } u$$
$$0 = (u - 1)(u - 4)$$
$$u - 1 = 0 \quad \text{or} \quad u - 4 = 0$$
$$u = 1 \qquad\qquad u = 4$$
$$x^{1/2} = 1 \qquad x^{1/2} = 4 \;\leftarrow\; \text{Replace } u \text{ with } x^{1/2}$$
$$x = 1 \qquad\qquad x = 16$$

The x-intercepts are $(1, 0)$ and $(16, 0)$.

59. $h(x) = x + 13\sqrt{x} + 36$, $h(x) = 0$

$$0 = \left(x^{1/2}\right)^2 + 13x^{1/2} + 36$$
$$0 = u^2 + 13u + 36 \;\leftarrow\; \text{Replace } x^{1/2} \text{ with } u$$
$$0 = (u + 9)(u + 4)$$
$$u + 9 = 0 \quad \text{or} \quad u + 4 = 0$$
$$u = -9 \qquad\qquad u = -4$$
$$x^{1/2} = -9 \qquad x^{1/2} = -4 \;\leftarrow\; \text{Replace } u \text{ with } x^{1/2}$$

There are no values of x for which $x^{1/2} = -9$ or $x^{1/2} = -4$. There are no x-intercepts.

61. $p(x) = 4x^{-2} - 19x^{-1} - 5$, $p(x) = 0$

$$0 = 4\left(x^{-1}\right)^2 - 19x^{-1} - 5$$
$$0 = 4u^2 - 19u - 5 \;\leftarrow\; \text{Replace } x^{-1} \text{ with } u$$
$$0 = (4u + 1)(u - 5)$$
$$4u + 1 = 0 \quad \text{or} \quad u - 5 = 0$$
$$u = -\frac{1}{4} \qquad\qquad u = 5$$
$$x^{-1} = -\frac{1}{4} \qquad x^{-1} = 5 \;\leftarrow\; \text{Replace } u \text{ with } x^{-1}$$
$$x = -4 \qquad\qquad x = \frac{1}{5}$$

The x-intercepts are $(-4, 0)$ and $\left(\frac{1}{5}, 0\right)$.

63. $f(x) = x^{2/3} + x^{1/3} - 6$, $f(x) = 0$

$0 = \left(x^{1/3}\right)^2 + x^{1/3} - 6$

$0 = u^2 + u - 6$ ← Replace $x^{1/3}$ with u

$0 = (u + 3)(u - 2)$

$u + 3 = 0$ or $u - 2 = 0$

       $u = -3$ $u = 2$

       $x^{1/3} = -3$ $x^{1/3} = 2$ ← Replace u with $x^{1/3}$

          $x = -27$ $x = 8$

The x-intercepts are $(-27, 0)$ and $(8, 0)$.

65. $g(x) = \left(x^2 - 3x\right)^2 + 2\left(x^2 - 3x\right) - 24$, $g(x) = 0$

$0 = u^2 + 2u - 24$ ← Replace $x^2 - 3x$ with u

$0 = (u + 6)(u - 4)$

       $u + 6 = 0$ or $u - 4 = 0$

$x^2 - 3x + 6 = 0$ $x^2 - 3x - 4 = 0$ ← Replace u with $x^2 - 3x$

                       $(x - 4)(x + 1) = 0$

                       $x - 4 = 0$ or $x + 1 = 0$

                          $x = 4$ $x = -1$

There are no x-intercepts for $x^2 - 3x + 6 = 0$ since $b^2 - 4ac = (-3)^2 - 4(1)(6) = 9 - 24 = -15$.
The x-intercepts are $(4, 0)$ or $(-1, 0)$.

67.

$f(x) = x^4 - 20x + 64$, $f(x) = 0$

$0 = \left(x^2\right)^2 - 20x^2 + 64$

$0 = u^2 - 20u + 64$ ← Replace x^2 with u

$0 = (u - 16)(u - 4)$

$u - 16 = 0$ or $u - 4 = 0$

    $u = 16$ $u = 4$

    $x^2 = 16$ $x^2 = 4$ ← Replace u with x^2

    $x = \pm\sqrt{16} = \pm 4$ $x = \pm\sqrt{4} = \pm 2$

The x-intercepts are $(4, 0)$, $(-4, 0)$, $(2, 0)$, and $(-2, 0)$.

69. When solving an equation of the form $ax^4 + bx^2 + c = 0$, let $u = x^2$.

71. When solving an equation of the form $ax^{-2} + bx^{-1} + c = 0$, let $u = x^{-1}$.

73. If the solutions are ± 2 and ± 4, the factors must be $(x - 2)$, $(x + 2)$, $(x - 4)$ and $(x + 4)$.

$0 = (x - 2)(x + 2)(x - 4)(x + 4)$

$0 = \left(x^2 - 4\right)\left(x^2 - 16\right)$

$0 = x^4 - 20x^2 + 64$

75. If the solutions are $\pm\sqrt{2}$ and $\pm\sqrt{3}$, the factors must be $\left(x+\sqrt{2}\right),\left(x-\sqrt{2}\right),\left(x+\sqrt{3}\right),\left(x-\sqrt{3}\right)$.

$$0 = \left(x+\sqrt{2}\right)\left(x-\sqrt{2}\right)\left(x+\sqrt{3}\right)\left(x-\sqrt{3}\right)$$

$$0 = \left(x^2-2\right)\left(x^2-3\right)$$

$$0 = x^4 - 5x^2 + 6$$

77. No. An equation of the form $ax^4 + bx^2 + c = 0$ can have no imaginary solutions, two imaginary solutions, or four imaginary solutions.

79. a.
$$\frac{3}{x^2} - \frac{3}{x} = 60 \qquad \text{The LCD is } x^2$$

$$x^2\left(\frac{3}{x^2}\right) - x^2\left(\frac{3}{x}\right) = x^2(60)$$

$$3 - 3x = 60x^2$$

$$0 = 60x^2 + 3x - 3$$

$$0 = 3\left(20x^2 + x - 1\right)$$

$$0 = 3(5x - 1)(4x + 1)$$

$$5x - 1 = 0 \quad \text{or} \quad 4x + 1 = 0$$

$$x = \frac{1}{5} \qquad\qquad x = -\frac{1}{4}$$

The solutions are $\frac{1}{5}$ and $-\frac{1}{4}$.

b.
$$\frac{3}{x^2} - \frac{3}{x} = 60$$

$$3x^{-2} - 3x^{-1} = 60$$

$$3\left(x^{-1}\right)^2 - 3x^{-1} - 60 = 0$$

$$3u^2 - 3u - 60 = 0 \quad \leftarrow \text{Replace } x^{-1} \text{ with } u$$

$$3\left(u^2 - u - 20\right) = 0$$

$$3(u - 5)(u + 4) = 0$$

$$u - 5 = 0 \quad \text{or} \quad u + 4 = 0$$

$$u = 5 \qquad\qquad u = -4$$

$$x^{-1} = 5 \qquad\quad x^{-1} = -4 \quad \leftarrow \text{Replace } u \text{ with } x^{-1}$$

$$x = \frac{1}{5} \qquad\qquad x = -\frac{1}{4}$$

The solutions are $\frac{1}{5}$ and $-\frac{1}{4}$.

81.
$$15(r + 2) + 22 = -\frac{8}{r+2}$$

$$15(r+2)(r+2) + 22(r+2) = -\frac{8}{r+2}(r+2)$$

$$15(r + 2)^2 + 22(r + 2) = -8$$

$$15(r + 2)^2 + 22(r + 2) + 8 = 0$$

$$15u^2 + 22u + 8 = 0 \quad \leftarrow \text{Replace } r + 2 \text{ with } u$$

$$(5u + 4)(3u + 2) = 0$$

$$5u + 4 = 0 \quad \text{or} \quad 3u + 2 = 0$$

$$u = -\frac{4}{5} \qquad\qquad u = -\frac{2}{3}$$

$$r + 2 = -\frac{4}{5} \qquad r + 2 = -\frac{2}{3} \quad \leftarrow \text{Replace } u \text{ with } r + 2$$

$$r = -\frac{14}{5} \qquad\qquad r = -\frac{8}{3}$$

The solutions are $-\frac{14}{5}$ and $-\frac{8}{3}$.

83. $4 - (x-2)^{-1} = 3(x-2)^{-2}$

$$4 - u^{-1} = 3u^{-2} \quad \leftarrow \text{Replace } x-2 \text{ by } u$$

$$4 - \frac{1}{u} = \frac{3}{u^2}$$

$$u^2\left(4 - \frac{1}{u}\right) = u^2\left(\frac{3}{u^2}\right)$$

$$4u^2 - u = 3$$

$$4u^2 - u - 3 = 0$$

$$(4u+3)(u-1) = 0$$

$4u + 3 = 0 \quad$ or $\quad u - 1 = 0$

$\quad u = -\dfrac{3}{4} \qquad\qquad u = 1$

$\quad x - 2 = -\dfrac{3}{4} \qquad x - 2 = 1 \quad \leftarrow \text{Replace } u \text{ by } x - 2$

$\quad x = \dfrac{5}{4} \qquad\qquad x = 3$

The solutions are $\dfrac{5}{4}$ and 3.

85. $x^6 - 9x^3 + 8 = 0$

$$\left(x^3\right)^2 - 9x^3 + 8 = 0$$

$$u^2 - 9u + 8 = 0 \quad \leftarrow \text{Replace } x^3 \text{ with } u$$

$$(u-8)(u-1) = 0$$

$u - 8 = 0 \quad$ or $\quad u - 1 = 0$

$\quad u = 8 \qquad\qquad u = 1$

$\quad x^3 = 8 \qquad\qquad x^3 = 1 \quad \leftarrow \text{Replace } u \text{ with } x^3$

$\quad x = 2 \qquad\qquad x = 1$

The solutions are 2 and 1.

87. $\left(x^2 + 2x - 2\right)^2 - 7\left(x^2 + 2x - 2\right) + 6 = 0$

$$u^2 - 7u + 6 = 0 \quad \leftarrow \text{Replace } x^2 + 2x - 2 \text{ with } u$$

$$(u-6)(u-1) = 0$$

$u - 6 = 0 \qquad$ or $\qquad u - 1 = 0$

$\quad u = 6 \qquad\qquad\qquad\qquad u = 1$

$\quad x^2 + 2x - 2 = 6 \qquad\qquad x^2 + 2x - 2 = 1 \quad \leftarrow \text{Replace } u \text{ with } x^2 + 2x - 2$

$\quad x^2 + 2x - 8 = 0 \qquad\qquad x^2 + 2x - 3 = 0$

$\quad (x+4)(x-2) = 0 \qquad\qquad (x+3)(x-1) = 0$

$x + 4 = 0 \quad$ or $\quad x - 2 = 0 \qquad x + 3 = 0 \quad$ or $\quad x - 1 = 0$

$\quad x = -4 \qquad\quad x = 2 \qquad\qquad x = -3 \qquad\quad x = 1$

The solutions are -4, 2, -3, and 1.

89. $2n^4 - 6n^2 - 3 = 0$

$2\left(n^2\right)^2 - 6n^2 - 3 = 0$

$2u^2 - 6u - 3 = 0 \quad \leftarrow$ Replace n^2 with u

$u = \dfrac{6 \pm \sqrt{(-6)^2 - 4(2)(-3)}}{2(2)}$

$= \dfrac{6 \pm \sqrt{60}}{4}$

$= \dfrac{6 \pm 2\sqrt{15}}{4}$

$= \dfrac{3 \pm \sqrt{15}}{2}$

$n^2 = \dfrac{3 \pm \sqrt{15}}{2} \quad \leftarrow$ Replace u with n^2

$n = \pm\sqrt{\dfrac{3 \pm \sqrt{15}}{2}}$

91. $\dfrac{4}{5} - \left(\dfrac{3}{4} - \dfrac{2}{3}\right) = \dfrac{4}{5} - \left(\dfrac{9}{12} - \dfrac{8}{12}\right)$

$= \dfrac{4}{5} - \left(\dfrac{1}{12}\right)$

$= \dfrac{48}{60} - \dfrac{5}{60}$

$= \dfrac{43}{60}$

93. $D:$ all real numbers

$R: \left\{y \mid y \geq 0\right\}$

95. $\sqrt{75} + \sqrt{108} = \sqrt{25 \cdot 3} + \sqrt{36 \cdot 3}$

$= 5\sqrt{3} + 6\sqrt{3}$

$= 11\sqrt{3}$

Exercise Set 8.5

1. The graph of a quadratic equation is called a parabola.

3. The axis of symmetry of a parabola is the line where, if the graph is folded, the two sides overlap.

5. For $f(x) = ax^2 + bx + c$, the vertex of the graph is $\left(-\dfrac{b}{2a}, \dfrac{4ac - b^2}{4}\right)$.

7. **a.** For $f(x) = ax^2 + bx + c$, $f(x)$ will have a minimum if $a > 0$ since the graph opens upward.

    b. For $f(x) = ax^2 + bx + c$, $f(x)$ will have a maximum if $a < 0$ since the graph opens downward.

9. To find the y-intercepts of the graph of a quadratic function, set $x = 0$ and solve for y.

11. **a.** For $f(x) = ax^2$, the general shape of $f(x)$ if $a > 0$ is

    b. For $f(x) = ax^2$, the general shape of $f(x)$ if $a < 0$ is

13. Since $a = 3$ is greater than 0, the graph opens upward, and therefore has a minimum value.

15. $f(x) = x^2 + 8x + 15$

    a. Since $a = 1$, the parabola opens upward.

    b. $y = 0^2 + 8(0) + 15 = 15$
         The y-intercept is $(0, 15)$.

    c. $x = -\dfrac{b}{2a} = -\dfrac{8}{2(1)} = -\dfrac{8}{2} = -4$

$$y = \dfrac{4ac - b^2}{4a}$$
$$= \dfrac{4(1)(15) - 8^2}{4(1)}$$
$$= \dfrac{60 - 64}{4}$$
$$= \dfrac{-4}{4}$$
$$= -1$$
The vertex is $(-4, -1)$.

d. $0 = x^2 + 8x + 15 = (x + 5)(x + 3)$
      $x + 5 = 0$ or $x + 3 = 0$
      $x = -5$ $x = -3$
      The x-intercepts are $(-5, 0)$ and $(-3, 0)$.

e.
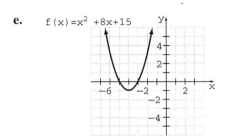

17. $g(x) = x^2 + 2x - 3$

    a. Since $a = 1$ the parabola opens upward.

    b. $y = 0^2 + 2(0) - 3 = -3$
         The y-intercept is $(0, -3)$.

    c. $x = -\dfrac{b}{2a} = -\dfrac{2}{2(1)} = -\dfrac{2}{2} = -1$

      $y = \dfrac{4ac - b^2}{4a} = \dfrac{4(1)(-3) - (2)^2}{4(1)} = -4$
      The vertex is $(-1, -4)$.

    d. $0 = x^2 + 2x - 3$
         $(x - 1)(x + 3) = 0$
         $x = 1$ or $x = -3$
         The x-intercepts are $(1, 0)$ and $(-3, 0)$.

e.

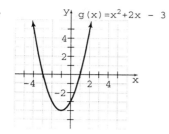

$g(x) = x^2 + 2x - 3$

19. $f(x) = -x^2 - 2x + 8$

a. Since $a = -1$, the parabola opens downward.

b. $y = -(0)^2 - 2(0) + 8 = 8$
The y-intercept is $(0, 8)$.

c. $x = -\dfrac{b}{2a} = -\dfrac{-2}{2(-1)} = -\dfrac{2}{2} = -1$

$y = \dfrac{4ac - b^2}{4a}$

$= \dfrac{4(-1)(8) - (-2)^2}{4(-1)}$

$= \dfrac{-32 - 4}{-4}$

$= \dfrac{-36}{-4}$

$= 9$
The vertex is $(1, 9)$.

d. $0 = -x^2 - 2x + 8 = -\left(x^2 + 2x - 8\right)$
$= -(x + 4)(x - 2)$

$x + 4 = 0$ or $x - 2 = 0$
$x = -4$ $\qquad$ $x = 2$
The x-intercepts are $(-4, 0)$ and $(2, 0)$.

e.

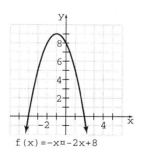

$f(x) = -x^2 - 2x + 8$

21. $p(x) = -x^2 + 8x - 15$

a. Since $a = -1$, the parabola opens downward.

b. $y = -(0)^2 + 8(0) - 15 = -15$
The y-intercept is $(0, -15)$.

c. $x = -\dfrac{b}{2a} = -\dfrac{8}{2(-1)} = \dfrac{8}{2} = 4$

$y = \dfrac{4ac - b^2}{4a}$

$= \dfrac{4(-1)(-15) - (8)^2}{4(-1)}$

$= \dfrac{60 - 64}{-4}$

$= \dfrac{-4}{-4}$

$= 1$
The vertex is $(4, 1)$.

d. $0 = -x^2 + 8x - 15 = -\left(x^2 - 8x + 15\right)$
$= -(x - 5)(x - 3)$

$x - 5 = 0$ or $x - 3 = 0$
$x = 5$ $\qquad$ $x = 3$
The x-intercepts are $(5, 0)$ and $(3, 0)$.

e.

$f(x) = -x^2 + 8x - 15$

23. $t(x) = -x^2 + 4x - 5$

a. Since $a = -1$, the parabola opens downward.

b. $y = -0^2 + 4(0) - 5 = -5$; The y-intercept is $(0, -5)$.

c. $x = -\dfrac{b}{2a} = -\dfrac{4}{2(-1)} = -\dfrac{4}{-2} = 2$

$y = \dfrac{4ac - b^2}{4a}$

$= \dfrac{4(-1)(-5) - (4)^2}{4(-1)}$

$= \dfrac{20 - 16}{-4}$

$= -1$
The vertex is $(2, -1)$

d. $0 = -x^2 + 4x - 5$
Since this is not factorable, check the discriminant.

$b^2 - 4ac = 4^2 - 4(-1)(-5)$
$= 16 - 20$
$= -4$
Since $-4 < 0$ there are no real roots. Thus, there are no x-intercepts.

e.

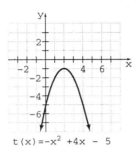
$t(x) = -x^2 + 4x - 5$

25. $f(x) = x^2 - 4x + 4$

a. Since $a = 1$, the parabola opens upward.

b. $y = 0^2 - 4(0) + 4 = 4$
The y-intercept is $(0, 4)$.

c. $x = -\dfrac{b}{2a} = -\dfrac{-4}{2(1)} = \dfrac{4}{2} = 2$

$y = \dfrac{4ac - b^2}{4a}$

$= \dfrac{4(1)(4) - (-4)^2}{4(1)}$

$= \dfrac{16 - 16}{4}$

$= \dfrac{0}{4}$

$= 0$
The vertex is $(2, 0)$.

d. $0 = x^2 - 4x + 4 = (x - 2)(x - 2)$
$x - 2 = 0$
$x = 2$
The x-intercept $(2, 0)$.

e.

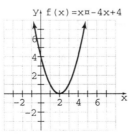
$f(x) = x^2 - 4x + 4$

27. $r(x) = x^2 + 2$

a. Since $a = 1$ the parabola opens upward.

b. $y = 0^2 + 2 = 2$
The y-intercept is $(0, 2)$.

c. $x = -\dfrac{b}{2a} = -\dfrac{0}{2(1)} = \dfrac{0}{2} = 0$

$y = \dfrac{4ac - b^2}{4a}$

$= \dfrac{4(1)(2) - 0^2}{4(1)}$

$= \dfrac{8}{4}$

$= 2$
The vertex is $(0, 2)$.

d. $0 = x^2 + 2$
Since this is not factorable, check the discriminant.
$b^2 - 4ac = 0 - 4(1)2 = -8$
There are no real roots. Thus, there are no x-intercepts.

e.

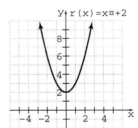
$r(x) = x^2 + 2$

29. $g(x) = -x^2 + 6x$

a. Since $a = -1$ the parabola opens downward.

b. $y = -0^2 + 6(0) = 0$
The y-intercept is $(0, 0)$.

c. $x = -\dfrac{b}{2a} = -\dfrac{6}{2(-1)} = -\dfrac{6}{-2} = 3$

$y = \dfrac{4ac - b^2}{4a}$

$= \dfrac{4(-1)(0) - 6^2}{4(-1)}$

$= \dfrac{0 - 36}{-4}$

$= \dfrac{-36}{-4}$

$= 9$
The vertex is $(3, 9)$.

d. $0 = -x^2 + 6x = -x(x-6)$

$-x = 0$ or $x - 6 = 0$

$x = 0$ $x = 6$

The *x*-intercepts are (0, 0) and (6, 0).

e.

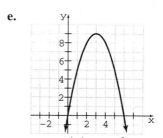

$g(x) = -x^2 + 6x$

31. $y = -2x^2 + 4x - 8$

a. Since $a = -2$ the parabola opens downward.

b. $y = -2(0)^2 + 4(0) - 8 = -8$

The *y*-intercept is (0, –8).

c. $x = -\dfrac{b}{2a} = -\dfrac{4}{2(-2)} = -\dfrac{4}{-4} = 1$

$y = \dfrac{4ac - b^2}{4a}$

$= \dfrac{4(-2)(-8) - (4)^2}{4(-2)}$

$= \dfrac{64 - 16}{-8}$

$= -6$

The vertex is (1, –6).

d. $0 = -2x^2 + 4x - 8 = -2\left(x^2 - 2x + 4\right)$

Since this is not factorable, check the discriminant.

$b^2 - 4ac = 4^2 - 4(-2)(-8)$

$= 16 - 64$

$= -48$

Since –48 < 0, there are no real roots. Thus, there are no *x*-intercepts.

e.

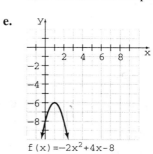

$f(x) = -2x^2 + 4x - 8$

33. $g(x) = -2x^2 - 6x + 4$

a. Since $a = -2$ the parabola opens downward.

b. $y = -2(0)^2 - 6(0) + 4 = 4$

The *y*-intercept is (0, 4).

c. $x = -\dfrac{b}{2a} = -\dfrac{(-6)}{2(-2)} = \dfrac{6}{-4} = -\dfrac{3}{2}$

$y = \dfrac{4ac - b^2}{4a}$

$= \dfrac{4(-2)(4) - (-6)^2}{4(-2)}$

$= \dfrac{-32 - 36}{-8}$

$= \dfrac{-68}{-8}$

$= \dfrac{17}{2}$

The vertex is $\left(-\dfrac{3}{2}, \dfrac{17}{2}\right)$.

d. $0 = -2x^2 - 6x + 4 = -2(x^2 + 3x - 2)$

Since this is not factorable, check the discriminant.

$b^2 - 4ac = (-6)^2 - 4(-2)(4)$

$= 36 + 32$

$= 68$

There are two real roots.

$x = \dfrac{-b \pm \sqrt{b^2 - 4ac}}{2a}$

$= \dfrac{-(-6) \pm \sqrt{68}}{2(-2)}$

$= \dfrac{6 \pm 2\sqrt{17}}{-4}$

$= \dfrac{3 \pm \sqrt{17}}{-2}$

$= \dfrac{-3 \pm \sqrt{17}}{2}$

The *x*-intercepts are

$\left(\dfrac{-3 + \sqrt{17}}{2},\ 0\right)$ and $\left(\dfrac{-3 - \sqrt{17}}{2}, 0\right)$.

e.

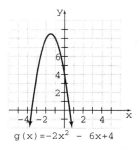

$g(x) = -2x^2 - 6x + 4$

35. $y = 3x^2 + 4x - 6$

   a. Since $a = 3$ the parabola opens upward.

   b. $y = 3(0)^2 + 4(0) - 6 = -6$
     The y-intercept is $(0, -6)$.

   c. $x = -\dfrac{b}{2a} = -\dfrac{4}{2(3)} = -\dfrac{4}{6} = -\dfrac{2}{3}$

$$y = \frac{4ac - b^2}{4a}$$
$$= \frac{4(3)(-6) - 4^2}{4(3)}$$
$$= \frac{-72 - 16}{12}$$
$$= \frac{-88}{12}$$
$$= -\frac{22}{3}$$

     The vertex is $\left(-\dfrac{2}{3}, -\dfrac{22}{3}\right)$.

   d. $0 = 3x^2 + 4x - 6$
     Since this is not factorable, check the discriminant.
$$b^2 - 4ac = 4^2 - 4(3)(-6)$$
$$= 16 + 72$$
$$= 88$$
     Since $88 > 0$ there are two real roots.
$$x = \frac{-b \pm \sqrt{b^2 - 4ac}}{2a}$$
$$= \frac{-4 \pm \sqrt{88}}{2(3)}$$
$$= \frac{-4 \pm 2\sqrt{22}}{6}$$
$$= \frac{-2 \pm \sqrt{22}}{3}$$
     The x-intercepts are
$$\left(\frac{-2 + \sqrt{22}}{3}, 0\right) \text{ and } \left(\frac{-2 - \sqrt{22}}{3}, 0\right).$$

e.

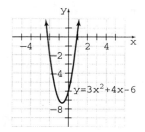

$y = 3x^2 + 4x - 6$

37. $y = 2x^2 - x - 6$

   a. Since $a = 2$ the parabola opens upward.

   b. $y = 2(0)^2 - 0 - 6 = -6$
     The y-intercept is $(0, -6)$.

   c. $x = -\dfrac{b}{2a} = -\dfrac{-1}{2(2)} = \dfrac{1}{4}$

$$y = \frac{4ac - b^2}{4a}$$
$$= \frac{4(2)(-6) - (-1)^2}{4(2)}$$
$$= \frac{-48 - 1}{8}$$
$$= -\frac{49}{8}$$

     The vertex is $\left(\dfrac{1}{4}, -\dfrac{49}{8}\right)$.

   d. $0 = 2x^2 - x - 6 = (2x + 3)(x - 2)$
     $2x + 3 = 0$ or $x - 2 = 0$
      $x = -\dfrac{3}{2}$ $x = 2$
     The x-intercepts are $\left(-\dfrac{3}{2}, 0\right)$ and $(2, 0)$.

e.

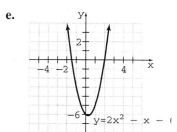

$y = 2x^2 - x - 6$

39. $f(x) = -x^2 + 3x - 5$

   a. Since $a = -1$ the parabola opens downward.

   b. $y = -0^2 + 3(0) - 5 = -5$
     The y-intercept is $(0, -5)$.

c. $x = -\dfrac{b}{2a} = -\dfrac{3}{2(-1)} = -\dfrac{3}{-2} = \dfrac{3}{2}$

$y = \dfrac{4ac - b^2}{4a} = \dfrac{4(-1)(-5) - 3^2}{4(-1)} = -\dfrac{11}{4}$

The vertex is $\left(\dfrac{3}{2}, -\dfrac{11}{4}\right)$.

d. $0 = -x^2 + 3x - 5$

Since this is not factorable, check the discriminant.

$b^2 - 4ac = 3^2 - 4(-1)(-5) = 9 - 20 = -11$

Since $-11 < 0$ there are no real roots. Thus, there are no x-intercepts.

e.

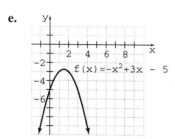

41. In the function $f(x) = (x - 3)^2$, h has a value of 3. The graph of $f(x)$ is the graph of $g(x) = x^2$ shifted 3 units to the right.

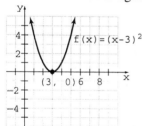

43. In the function $f(x) = (x + 1)^2$, h has a value of -1. The graph of $f(x)$ is the graph of $g(x) = x^2$ shifted 1 unit to the left.

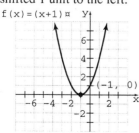

45. In the function $f(x) = x^2 + 3$, k has a value of 3. The graph $f(x)$ will be the graph of $g(x) = x^2$ shifted 3 units up.

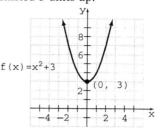

47. In the function $f(x) = x^2 - 1$, k has a value of -1. The graph $f(x)$ will be the graph of $g(x) = x^2$ shifted 1 units down.

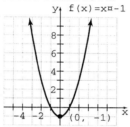

49. In the function $f(x) = (x - 2)^2 + 3$, h has a value of 2 and k has a value of 3. The graph of $f(x)$ will be the graph of $g(x) = x^2$ shifted 2 units to the right and 3 units up.

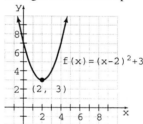

51. In the function $f(x) = (x + 4)^2 + 4$, h has a value of -4 and k has a value of 4. The graph of $f(x)$ will be the graph of $g(x) = x^2$ shifted 4 units to the left and 4 units up.

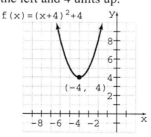

53. In the function $g(x) = -(x+3)^2 - 2$, a has the value -1, h has the value -3, and k has the value -2. Since $a < 0$, the parabola opens downward. The graph of $g(x)$ will be the graph of $f(x) = -x^2$ shifted 3 units to the left and 2 units down.

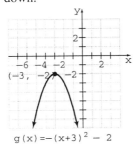

$g(x) = -(x+3)^2 - 2$

55. In the function $y = -2(x-2)^2 + 2$, a has a value of -2, h has a value of 2, and k has a value of 2. The graph of y will be the graph of $g(x) = -2x^2$ shifted 2 units to the right and 2 units up.

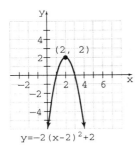

$y = -2(x-2)^2 + 2$

57. In the function $h(x) = -2(x+1)^2 - 3$, a has a value of -2, h has a value of -1, and k has a value of -3. Since $a < 0$, the parabola opens downward. The graph of $h(x)$ will be the graph of $f(x) = -2x^2$ shifted 1 unit left and 3 units down.

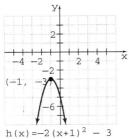

$h(x) = -2(x+1)^2 - 3$

59. a. $f(x) = x^2 - 6x + 8$
$$= \left(x^2 - 6x + 9\right) + 8 - 9$$
$$f(x) = (x-3)^2 - 1$$

b. Since $h = 3$ and $k = -1$, the vertex is $(3, -1)$

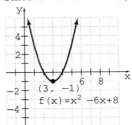

$f(x) = x^2 - 6x + 8$

61. a. $f(x) = x^2 - x + 1$
$$= \left(x^2 - x + \frac{1}{4}\right) + 1 - \frac{1}{4}$$
$$f(x) = \left(x - \frac{1}{2}\right)^2 + \frac{3}{4}$$

b. Since $h = \frac{1}{2}$ and $k = \frac{3}{4}$, the vertex is $\left(\frac{1}{2}, \frac{3}{4}\right)$.

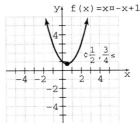

63. a. $f(x) = -x^2 - 4x - 6$
$$= -\left(x^2 + 4x\right) - 6$$
$$= -\left(x^2 + 4x + 4\right) - 6 - (-4)$$
$$= -\left(x^2 + 4x + 4\right) - 6 + 4$$
$$f(x) = -(x+2)^2 - 2$$

b. Since $h = -2$ and $k = -2$, the vertex is $(-2, -2)$. Since $a < 0$, the parabola opens downward.

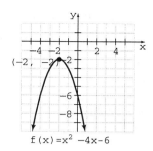

f(x) = x² −4x−6

65. a. $g(x) = x^2 - 4x - 5$

$$= \left(x^2 - 4x + 4\right) - 5 - 4$$

$$g(x) = (x - 2)^2 - 9$$

b. Since $h = 2$ and $k = -9$, the vertex is $(2, -9)$.

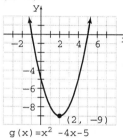

g(x) = x² −4x−5

67. a. $f(x) = 2x^2 + 5x - 3$

$$= 2\left(x^2 + \frac{5}{2}x\right) - 3$$

$$= 2\left(x^2 + \frac{5}{2}x + \frac{25}{16}\right) - 3 - 2\left(\frac{25}{16}\right)$$

$$= 2\left(x^2 + \frac{5}{2}x + \frac{25}{16}\right) - 3 - \frac{25}{8}$$

$$f(x) = 2\left(x + \frac{5}{4}\right)^2 - \frac{49}{8}$$

b. Since $h = -\dfrac{5}{4}$ and $k = -\dfrac{49}{8}$, the vertex is $\left(-\dfrac{5}{4}, -\dfrac{49}{8}\right)$. The graph of $f(x)$ will be the graph of $g(x) = 2x^2$ shifted $\dfrac{5}{4}$ units left and $\dfrac{49}{8}$ units down.

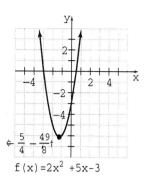

f(x) = 2x² +5x−3

69. $f(x) = 2(x + 3)^2 - 1$. The vertex is $(h, k) = (-3, -1)$. Since $a > 0$, the parabola opens up. The graph is d).

71. $f(x) = 2(x - 1)^2 + 3$ The vertex is $(h, k) = (1, 3)$. Since $a > 0$, the parabola opens up. The graph is b).

73. a. $f(x) = (x + 4)(18 - x)$

$$= 18x - x^2 + 72 - 4x$$

$$= -x^2 + 14x + 72$$

Since $a = -1$, the graph of this function is a parabola that opens downward and thus has a maximum value at its vertex.

$$x = -\frac{b}{2a} = -\frac{14}{2(-1)} = 7$$

b. $y = \dfrac{4ac - b^2}{4a}$

$$= \frac{4(-1)(72) - (14)^2}{4(-1)}$$

$$= \frac{-288 - 196}{-4}$$

$$= 121$$

The maximum area is 121 square units.

75. a. $f(x) = (x + 5)(26 - x)$

$$= 26x - x^2 + 130 - 5x$$

$$= -x^2 + 21x + 130$$

Since $a = -1$, the graph of this function is a parabola that opens downward and thus has a maximum value at its vertex.

$$x = -\frac{b}{2a} = -\frac{21}{2(-1)} = 10.5$$

b. $y = \dfrac{4ac - b^2}{4a}$

$= \dfrac{4(-1)(130) - (21)^2}{4(-1)}$

$= \dfrac{-520 - 441}{-4}$

$= 240.25$

The maximum area is 240.25 square units.

77.   **a.** $R(n) = -0.02n^2 + 10n$

Since $a = -0.02$, the graph of this function is a parabola that opens downward and thus has a maximum value at its vertex.

$x = -\dfrac{b}{2a} = -\dfrac{10}{2(-0.02)} = 250$

The maximum revenue will be achieved when 250 batteries are sold.

b. $y = \dfrac{4ac - b^2}{4a}$

$= \dfrac{4(-0.02)(0) - (10)^2}{4(-0.02)}$

$= \dfrac{0 - 100}{-0.08}$

$= 1250$

The maximum revenue is $1250.

79. $N(t) = -0.043t^2 + 1.22t + 46.0$

Since $a = -0.043$, the graph of this function is a parabola that opens downward and thus has a maximum value at its vertex.

$x = -\dfrac{b}{2a} = -\dfrac{1.22}{2(-0.043)} \approx 14.2$

The maximum enrollment will be obtained about 14 years after 1989 which is the year 2003.

81.
For $f(x) = (x - 2)^2 + \dfrac{5}{2}$, the vertex is $\left(2, \dfrac{5}{2}\right)$. For

$g(x) = (x - 2)^2 - \dfrac{3}{2}$, the vertex is $\left(2, -\dfrac{3}{2}\right)$. These

points are on the vertical line $x = 2$. The distance between the two points is

$\dfrac{5}{2} - \left(-\dfrac{3}{2}\right) = \dfrac{5}{2} + \dfrac{3}{2} = \dfrac{8}{2} = 4$ units.

83.   For $f(x) = 2(x + 4)^2 - 3$, the vertex is $(-4, -3)$.

For $g(x) = -(x + 1)^2 - 3$, the vertex is $(-1, -3)$.

These points are on the horizontal line $y = -3$. The distance between the two points is

$-1 - (-4) = -1 + 4 = 3$ units.

85.   A function that has the shape of $f(x) = 2x^2$ will have the form $f(x) = 2(x - h)^2 + k$. If $(h, k) = (3, -2)$, the function is $f(x) = 2(x - 3)^2 - 2$.

87.   A function that has the shape of $f(x) = -4x^2$ will have the form $f(x) = -4(x - h)^2 + k$. If $(h, k) = \left(-\dfrac{3}{5}, -\sqrt{2}\right)$, the function is

$f(x) = -4\left(x + \dfrac{3}{5}\right)^2 - \sqrt{2}$.

89.   **a.**   The graphs will have the same x-intercepts but $f(x) = x^2 - 8x + 12$ will open up and $g(x) = -x^2 + 8x - 12$ will open down.

b.   Yes, because the x-intercepts are located by setting $x^2 - 8x + 12$ and $-x^2 + 8x - 12$ equal to zero. They have the same solution set, therefore the x-intercepts are equal. The x-intercepts for both are $(6, 0)$, and $(2, 0)$.

c.
No. The vertex for $f(x) = x^2 - 8x + 12$ is $(4, -4)$ and the vertex for $g(x) = -x^2 + 8x - 12$ is $(4, 4)$.

d.
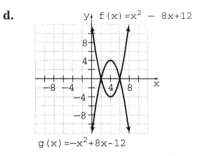

91. a. The vertex $x = -\dfrac{b}{2a} = -\dfrac{24}{2(-1)} = 12$

$I = -(12)^2 + 24(12) - 44$
$\quad = -144 + 288 - 44$
$\quad = 100$

The vertex is at (12, 100). To find the roots set $I = 0$.

$0 = -x^2 + 24x - 44$
$\quad = -1\left(x^2 - 24x + 44\right)$
$\quad = -1(x - 2)(x - 22)$
$x - 2 = 0 \quad$ or $\quad x - 22 = 0$
$\qquad x = 2 \qquad\qquad\qquad x = 22$

The roots are 2 and 22.

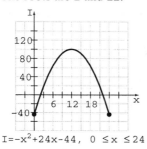

$I = -x^2 + 24x - 44, \quad 0 \le x \le 24$

b. The minimum cost will be \$2 since the smaller root is 2.

c. The maximum cost is \$22 since the larger root is 22.

d. The maximum value will occur at the vertex of the parabola, (12, 100). Therefore, they should charge \$12.

e. The maximum value will occur at the vertex of the parabola, (12, 100). Since I is in hundreds of dollars the maximum income is 100(\$100) = \$10,000.

92. a. $d = -16t^2 + 192t$
Let $t = 3$:
$d = -16t^2 + 192t$
$\quad = -16(3)^2 + 192(3)$
$\quad = -16(9) + 192(3)$
$\quad = -144 + 576$
$\quad = 432$

After 3 seconds, the object is 432 feet above the ground.

b. $t = -\dfrac{b}{2a} = -\dfrac{192}{-2(16)} = 6$

When $t = 6$,
$d = -16(6)^2 + 192(6)$
$\quad = -576 + 1152$
$\quad = 576$

The vertex is (6, 576). To find the roots, set $d = 0$.

$0 = -16t^2 + 192t$
$\quad = -16t(t - 12)$
$-16t = 0 \quad$ or $\quad t - 12 = 0$
$\qquad t = 0 \quad$ or $\qquad t = 12$

The roots are 0 and 12. These are the x-intercepts.

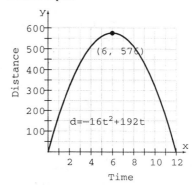

c. The object will reach a maximum height of 576 ft.

d. It will reach its maximum height after 6 seconds.

e. The object strikes after 12 seconds.

93. a. The number of bird feeders sold for the maximum profit will be the x-coordinate of the vertex.

$f(x) = -0.4x^2 + 80x - 200$

$x = -\dfrac{b}{2a} = -\dfrac{80}{2(-0.4)} = -\dfrac{80}{-0.8} = 100$

The company must sell 100 bird feeders for maximum profit.

b. The maximum profit will be the y-coordinate of the vertex, $y = f(100)$.

$f(100) = -0.4\left(100^2\right) + 80(100) - 200$
$\qquad\quad = -0.4(10,000) + 8000 - 200$
$\qquad\quad = -4000 + 8000 - 200$
$\qquad\quad = 3800$

The maximum profit will be \$3800.

95. **a.** The maximum height is h, the y-coordinate of the vertex.

$h(t) = -4.9t^2 + 24.5t + 9.8$

$h = \dfrac{4ac - b^2}{4a}$

$= \dfrac{4(-4.9)(9.8) - (24.5)^2}{4(-4.9)}$

$= \dfrac{-192.08 - 600.25}{-19.6}$

$= \dfrac{-792.33}{-19.6}$

$= 40.425$

The maximum height obtained by the cannonball is 40.425 meters.

b. The time the cannonball reaches the maximum height is t, the x-coordinate of the vertex,. $t = -\dfrac{b}{2a} = -\dfrac{24.5}{2(-4.9)} = 2.5$

The cannonball will reach the maximum height after 2.5 seconds.

c. $f(x) = 0$ when the cannonball hits the ground.

$h(t) = -4.9t^2 + 24.5t + 9.8$

$0 = -4.9t^2 + 24.5t + 9.8$

$t = \dfrac{-24.5 \pm \sqrt{(24.5)^2 - 4(-4.9)(9.8)}}{2(-4.9)}$

$t = \dfrac{-24.5 \pm \sqrt{792.33}}{-9.8}$

$t \approx \dfrac{-24.5 \pm 28.14836}{-9.8}$

$t \approx -0.37$ and $t \approx 5.37$
Disregard the negative value. The cannonball will hit the ground after about 5.37 seconds.

97. **a.** $2004 \Rightarrow x = 13$

$C(x) = 0.19x^2 - 0.657x + 16.6$

$C(13) = 0.19(13)^2 - 0.657(13) + 16.6$

≈ 40.17

The average annual rent per square foot in 2004 should be about $40.17.

b. The function will reach a minimum at it's vertex:

$x = -\dfrac{b}{2a} = -\dfrac{-0.657}{2(0.19)} \approx 1.7$

The annual rent per square foot reached a minimum about 1.7 years after 1991 which is in 1992.

c. $h = \dfrac{4ac - b^2}{4a}$

$= \dfrac{4(0.19)(16.6) - (-0.657)^2}{4(0.19)}$

$= \dfrac{12.616 - 0.431649}{.76}$

≈ 16.03

The minimum annual rent per square foot was about $16.

99. If the perimeter of the room is 60 ft., then $60 = 2l + 2w$, where l is the length and w is the width. Then $60 = 2(l + w)$ and $30 = l + w$. Therefore $l = 30 - w$. The area of the room is $A = lw = (30 - w)w = 30w - w^2 = -w^2 + 30w$. The maximum area is the y-coordinate of the vertex.

$A = \dfrac{4ac - b^2}{4a}$

$= \dfrac{4(-1)(0) - 30^2}{4(-1)}$

$= \dfrac{0 - 900}{-4}$

$= 225$

The maximum area is 225 ft^2.

101. If two numbers differ by 8 and x is one of the numbers, then $x + 8$ is the other number. The product is $f(x) = x(x + 8) = x^2 + 8x$. The maximum product is the y-coordinate of the vertex.

$x = -\dfrac{b}{2a} = -\dfrac{8}{2(1)} = -4$

$y = f(-4)$

$= (-4)^2 + 8(-4)$

$= 16 - 32$

$= -16$

The maximum product is -16. The numbers are -4 and $-4 + 8 = 4$.

103. If two numbers add to 40 and x is one of the numbers, then $40 - x$ is the other number. The product is

$f(x) = x(40 - x) = 40x - x^2 = -x^2 + 40x$.

The maximum product is the y-coordinate of the vertex.

$x = -\dfrac{b}{2a} = -\dfrac{40}{2(-1)} = -\dfrac{40}{-2} = 20$

$y = f(20) = -20^2 + 40(20) = -400 + 800 = 400$

The maximum product is 400. The numbers are 20 and $40 - 20 = 20$.

105. $C(x) = 2000 + 40x,\ R(x) = 800x - x^2$

$P(x) = R(x) - C(x)$

$P(x) = \left(800x - x^2\right) - (2000 + 40x)$

$\quad\quad = 800x - x^2 - 2000 - 40x$

$\quad\quad = -x^2 + 760x - 2000$

The maximum profit is $P(x)$, the y-coordinate of the vertex. The number of items that must be produced and sold to obtain maximum profit is the x coordinate of the vertex.

$x = -\dfrac{b}{2a} = -\dfrac{760}{2(-1)} = 380$

   a. $\ P(380) = -380^2 + 760(380) - 2000$

$\quad\quad\quad\quad\quad = -144{,}400 + 288800 - 2000$

$\quad\quad\quad\quad\quad = 142{,}400$

      The maximum profit is \$142,400.

   b. The number of items that must be produced and sold to obtain maximum profit is 380.

107.   **a.** $\ f(t) = -16t^2 + 52t + 3$

$\quad\quad = -16\left(t^2 - 3.25t\right) + 3$

$\quad\quad = -16\left(t^2 - 3.25t + \left(\dfrac{3.25}{2}\right)^2\right) + 3 + (16)\left(\left(\dfrac{3.25}{2}\right)^2\right)$

$\quad\quad = -16(t - 1.625)^2 + 3 + 42.25$

$\quad\quad = -16(t - 1.625)^2 + 45.25$

   b. The maximum height was 45.25 feet obtained at 1.625 seconds.

   c. It is the same answer.

109. The radius of the outer circle is $r = 15$ ft. The area $A = \pi r^2 = \pi\left(15^2\right) = 225\pi$ ft^2. The radius of the inner circle is $r = 5$ ft. The area is $A = \pi r^2 = \pi\left(5^2\right) = 25\pi$ ft^2. The blue shaded area is 225π ft$^2 - 25\pi$ ft$^2 = 200\pi$ ft^2.

111. $x - y \quad\quad = -5 \quad (1)$

$\quad\quad 2x + 2y - z = 0 \quad (2)$

$\quad\quad x + \ y + z = 3 \quad (3)$

First eliminate the variable z from equations (2) and (3) by adding these equations.

$\quad\quad 2x + 2y - z = 0$

$\quad\quad \underline{x + \ y + z = 3}$

$\quad\quad 3x + 3y \quad = 3 \quad (4)$

Equations (1) and (4) form a system of equations in two variables. Multiply equation (1) by 3 and add the result to equation (4) to eliminate the variable y.

$3(x - y = -5) \ \Rightarrow \ 3x - 3y = -15$

$3x + 3y = 3 \quad \Rightarrow \ \underline{3x + 3y = \quad 3}$

$\quad\quad\quad\quad\quad\quad\quad\quad 6x \quad\quad = -12$

$\quad\quad\quad\quad\quad\quad\quad\quad\quad x = -2$

Substitute -2 for x in equation (1) to find y.

$(-2) + y = -5$

$\quad\quad\quad y = 3$

Substitute -2 for x and 3 for y in equation (3) to find z.

$(-2) + (3) + z = 3$

$\quad\quad 1 + z = 3$

$\quad\quad\quad\quad z = 2$

The solution is $(-2, 3, 2)$.

113. $\ (x - 3) \div \dfrac{x^2 + 3x - 18}{x} = \dfrac{x - 3}{1} \cdot \dfrac{x}{x^2 + 3x - 18}$

$\quad\quad\quad\quad\quad\quad\quad\quad = \dfrac{x - 3}{1} \cdot \dfrac{x}{(x + 6)(x - 3)}$

$\quad\quad\quad\quad\quad\quad\quad\quad = \dfrac{x}{x + 6}$

Exercise Set 8.6

1. a. For $f(x) = x^2 - 7x + 10$, $f(x) > 0$ when the graph is above the *x*-axis. The solution is $x < 2$ or $x > 5$.

　b. For $f(x) = x^2 - 7x + 10$　$f(x) < 0$ when the graph is below the *x*-axis. The solution is $2 < x < 5$.

3. Yes. The boundary values 5 and –3 are included in the solution set since this is a greater than *or equal to* inequality. These values make the expression equal to zero.

5. The boundary values –2 and 1 are included in the solution set since this is a less than *or equal to* inequality. These values make the expression equal to zero. However, the boundary value –1 is not included in the solution set since it would result in a zero in the denominator, which is undefined.

7. $x^2 - 2x - 8 \geq 0$
$(x + 2)(x - 4) \geq 0$

9. $x^2 + 8x + 7 > 0$
$(x + 7)(x + 1) > 0$

11. $p^2 + 4p > 0$
$p(p + 4) > 0$

13. $x^2 - 16 < 0$
$(x + 4)(x - 4) < 0$

15. $2x^2 + 5x - 3 \geq 0$
$(2x - 1)(x + 3) \geq 0$

17. 　$5x^2 + 19x \leq 4$
$5x^2 + 19x - 4 \leq 0$
$(x + 4)(5x - 1) \leq 0$

19. $2x^2 - 12x + 9 \leq 0$
$2x^2 - 12x + 9 = 0$

$$x = \frac{-(-12) \pm \sqrt{(-12)^2 - 4(2)(9)}}{2(2)}$$

$$= \frac{12 \pm \sqrt{144 - 72}}{4}$$

$$= \frac{12 \pm \sqrt{72}}{4}$$

$$= \frac{12 \pm 6\sqrt{2}}{4}$$

$$= \frac{6 \pm 3\sqrt{2}}{2}$$

21. $(x - 2)(x + 1)(x + 3) \geq 0$
$x - 2 = 0$　$x + 1 = 0$　$x + 3 = 0$
　$x = 2$　　　$x = -1$　　　$x = -3$

$[-3, -1] \cup [2, \infty)$

23. $(a-3)(a+2)(a+4) < 0$

$a-3=0 \quad a+2=0 \quad a+4=0$

$a=3 \qquad a=-2 \qquad a=-4$

$a+4$
$a+2$
$a-3$

$(-\infty, -4) \cup (-2, 3)$

25. $(2c+5)(3c-6)(c+6) > 0$

$2c+5=0 \qquad 3c-6=0 \quad c+6=0$

$2c=-5 \qquad 3c=6 \qquad c=-6$

$c=-\dfrac{5}{2} \qquad c=2$

$c+6$
$3c+5$
$3c \quad 6$

$\left(-6, -\dfrac{5}{2}\right) \cup (2, \infty)$

27. $(3x+5)(x-3)(x+4) > 0$

$3x+5=0 \qquad x-3=0 \quad x+4=0$

$3x=-5 \qquad x=3 \qquad x=-4$

$x=-\dfrac{5}{3}$

$x+4$
$3x+5$
$x-3$

$\left(-4, -\dfrac{5}{3}\right) \cup (3, \infty)$

29. $(x+2)(x+2)(3x-8) \geq 0$

$x+2=0 \qquad 3x-8=0$

$x=-2 \qquad x=\dfrac{8}{3}$

$(x+2)^2$
$3x-8$

$\left[\dfrac{8}{3}, \infty\right)$

31. $x^3 - 4x^2 + 4x < 0$

$x(x^2 - 4x - 4) < 0$

$x(x-2)^2 < 0$

$x=0 \quad x-2=0$

$x=2$

x
$(x-2)^2$

$(-\infty, 0)$

33. $f(x) = x^2 - 3x, \; f(x) \geq 0$

$x^2 - 3x \geq 0$

$x(x-3) \geq 0$

$x=0 \quad x-3=0$

$x=3$

x

35. $f(x) = x^2 + 4x, \; f(x) > 0$

$x^2 + 4x > 0$

$x(x+4) > 0$

$x=0 \quad x+4=0$

$x=-4$

x
$x+4$

37. $f(x) = x^2 - 14x + 48, \; f(x) < 0$

$x^2 - 14x + 48 < 0$

$(x-6)(x-8) < 0$

$x-6=0 \quad x-8=0$

$x=6 \qquad x=8$

$x-6$
$x-8$

39. $f(x) = 2x^2 + 9x - 4,\ f(x) \le 2$

$2x^2 + 9x - 4 \le 2$

$2x^2 + 9x - 6 \le 0$

$x = \dfrac{-9 \pm \sqrt{9^2 - 4(2)(-6)}}{2(2)}$

$ = \dfrac{-9 \pm \sqrt{129}}{4}$

$x = \dfrac{-9 - \sqrt{129}}{4} \qquad x = \dfrac{-98 + \sqrt{129}}{4}$

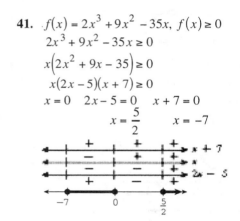

41. $f(x) = 2x^3 + 9x^2 - 35x,\ f(x) \ge 0$

$2x^3 + 9x^2 - 35x \ge 0$

$x(2x^2 + 9x - 35) \ge 0$

$x(2x - 5)(x + 7) \ge 0$

$x = 0 \quad 2x - 5 = 0 \quad x + 7 = 0$

$ x = \dfrac{5}{2} \qquad x = -7$

43. $\dfrac{x+2}{x-4} > 0$

$x \ne 4$

$\{x \mid x < -2 \text{ or } x > 4\}$

45. $\dfrac{x-3}{x+5} < 0$

$x \ne -5$

$\{x \mid -5 < x < 3\}$

47. $\dfrac{x+1}{x-1} \ge 0$

$x \ne 1$

$\{x \mid x \le -1 \text{ or } x > 1\}$

49. $\dfrac{a-4}{a+5} < 0$

$a \ne -5$

$\{a \mid -5 < a < 4\}$

51. $\dfrac{c-8}{c-4} > 0$

$c \ne 4$

$\{c \mid c < 4 \text{ or } c > 8\}$

53. $\dfrac{3y+6}{y+6} \le 0$

$y \ne -6,$

$3y + 6 = 0 \ \Rightarrow\ y = -2$

$\{y \mid -6 < y \le -2\}$

55. $\dfrac{3a+6}{2a-1} \ge 0$

$a \ne \dfrac{1}{2}$

$\left\{a \,\middle|\, a \le -2 \text{ or } a > \dfrac{1}{2}\right\}$

57. $\dfrac{3x+4}{2x-1} < 0$

$x \neq \dfrac{1}{2}$

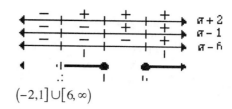

$\left\{ x \,\middle|\, -\dfrac{4}{3} < x < \dfrac{1}{2} \right\}$

59. $\dfrac{3x+5}{x-2} \leq 0$

$x \neq 2$

$\left\{ x \,\middle|\, \dfrac{-5}{3} \leq x < 2 \right\}$

61. $\dfrac{(x+1)(x-5)}{x+3} < 0$

$x \neq -3$

$(-\infty, -3) \cup (-1, 5)$

63. $\dfrac{(x-2)(x+3)}{x-4} > 0$

$x \neq 4$

$(-3, 2) \cup (4, \infty)$

65. $\dfrac{(a-1)(a-6)}{a+2} \geq 0$

$a \neq -2$

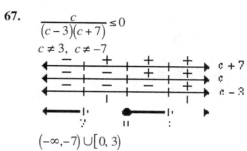

$(-2, 1] \cup [6, \infty)$

67. $\dfrac{c}{(c-3)(c+7)} \leq 0$

$c \neq 3, \ c \neq -7$

$(-\infty, -7) \cup [0, 3)$

69. $\dfrac{x-6}{(x+4)(x-1)} \leq 0$

$x \neq -4, \ x \neq 1$

$(-\infty, -4) \cup (1, 6]$

71. $\dfrac{(x-3)(2x+5)}{x-6} > 0$

$x \neq 6$

$\left(-\dfrac{5}{2}, 3 \right) \cup (6, \infty)$

73.
$$\frac{2}{x-4} \geq 1$$
$$\frac{2}{x-4} - 1 \geq 0$$
$$\frac{2}{x-4} + \frac{-1(x-4)}{x-4} \geq 0$$
$$\frac{2-x+4}{x-4} \geq 0$$
$$\frac{6-x}{x-4} \geq 0$$
$$x \neq 4$$

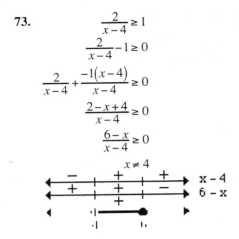

75.
$$\frac{3}{x-1} > -1$$
$$\frac{3}{x-1} + 1 > 0$$
$$\frac{3}{x-1} + \frac{1(x-1)}{x-1} > 0$$
$$\frac{3+x-1}{x-1} > 0$$
$$\frac{x+2}{x-1} > 0$$
$$x \neq 1$$

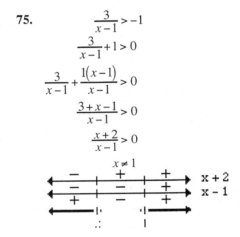

77.
$$\frac{4}{x+2} \leq 1$$
$$\frac{4}{x+2} - 1 \leq 0$$
$$\frac{4}{x+2} + \frac{-1(x+2)}{x+2} \leq 0$$
$$\frac{4-x-2}{x+2} \leq 0$$
$$\frac{2-x}{x+2} \leq 0$$
$$x \neq -2$$

79.
$$\frac{2p-5}{p-4} \leq 1$$
$$\frac{2p-5}{p-4} - 1 \leq 0$$
$$\frac{2p-5}{p-4} - \frac{1(p-4)}{p-4} \leq 0$$
$$\frac{2p-5-p+4}{p-4} \leq 0$$
$$\frac{p-1}{p-4} \leq 0$$
$$p \neq 4$$

81.
$$\frac{4}{x-2} \geq 2$$
$$\frac{4}{x-2} - 2 \geq 0$$
$$\frac{4}{x-2} - \frac{2(x-2)}{x-2} \geq 0$$
$$\frac{4-2x+4}{x-2} \geq 0$$
$$\frac{8-2x}{x-2} \geq 0$$
$$x \neq 2$$

83.
$$\frac{w}{3w-2} > -2$$
$$\frac{w}{3w-2} + 2 > 0$$
$$\frac{w}{3w-2} + \frac{2(3w-2)}{3w-2} > 0$$
$$\frac{w+6w-4}{3w-2} > 0$$
$$\frac{7w-4}{3w-2} > 0$$
$$w \neq \frac{2}{3}$$

85. a. $y = \dfrac{x^2 - 4x + 4}{x - 4} > 0$ where the graph of y is above the x-axis, on the interval $(4, \infty)$.

b. $y = \dfrac{x^2 - 4x + 4}{x - 4} < 0$ where the graph of y is below the x-axis, on the interval $(-\infty, 2) \cup (2, 4)$.

87. A quadratic inequality with the union of the two outer regions of the number line as its solution, not including the boundary values, will be of the form $ax^2 + bx + c > 0$ with $a > 0$. Since the boundary values are $x = -4$ and $x = 2$, the factors are $x + 4$ and $x - 2$. Therefore one quadratic inequality is $(x + 4)(x - 2) > 0$ or $x^2 + 2x - 8 > 0$.

89. Since the solution set is $x \le -3$ and $x > 4$, the factors are $x + 3$ and $x - 4$. Because -3 is included in the solution set, $x + 3$ is the numerator. Since 4 is not included in the solution set, $x - 4$ is the denominator. The inequality symbol will be $\ge$ because the union of the outer regions of number line is the solution set.
Therefore, the rational inequality is $\dfrac{x + 3}{x - 4} \ge 0$.

91. $(x + 3)^2 (x - 1)^2 \ge 0$
The solution is all real numbers since any nonzero number squared is positive and zero squared is zero.

93. $\dfrac{x^2}{(x + 1)^2} \ge 0$
This statement is true for all real numbers, except -1, since any nonzero number squared is negative. It is undefined when $x = -1$. Therefore, -1 is not a solution.

95. If $f(x) = ax^2 + bx + c$ and $a > 0$, the graph of $f(x)$ opens upward. If the discriminant is negative, the graph of $f(x)$ has no x-intercepts. Therefore, the graph lies above the x-axis and $f(x) < 0$ has no solution.

97. $(x + 1)(x - 3)(x + 5)(x + 9) \ge 0$

99. One possible answer is: Use a parabola that opens upward and has x-intercepts of $(0, 0)$ and $(3, 0)$. The x-values for which the parabola lies above the x-axis are $(-\infty, 0) \cup (3, \infty)$.

101. One possible answer is: Use a parabola that opens upward and has its vertex on or above the x-axis. Then there are no x-values for which the parabola lies below the x-axis.
$x^2 < 0$

103.
$$x^4 - 10x^2 + 9 > 0$$
$$\left(x^2\right)^2 - 10x^2 + 9 > 0$$
$$u^2 - 10u + 9 > 0$$
$$(u - 9)(u - 1) > 0$$
$$\left(x^2 - 9\right)\left(x^2 - 1\right) > 0$$
$$(x + 3)(x - 3)(x + 1)(x - 1) > 0$$

$(-\infty, -3) \cup (-1, 1) \cup (3, \infty)$

105.
$$x^3 + x^2 - 4x - 4 \ge 0$$
$$\left(x^3 + x^2\right) - (4x + 4) \ge 0$$
$$x^2(x + 1) - 4(x + 1) \ge 0$$
$$\left(x^2 - 4\right)(x + 1) \ge 0$$
$$(x + 2)(x - 2)(x + 1) \ge 0$$

$[-2, -1] \cup [2, \infty)$

109. Let $x =$ the number of quarts of 100% antifreeze added. The equation below describes the situation.
$$100\%(x) + 20\%(10) = 50\%(x + 10)$$
$$x + 0.2(10) = 0.5(x + 10)$$
$$x + 2 = 0.5x + 5$$
$$0.5x = 3$$
$$x = 6$$
Paul should add 6 quarts of 100% antifreeze.

111. $(6r+5s-t)+(-3r-2s-5t)$
$= 6r+5s-t-3r-2s-5t$
$= 3r+3s-6t$

113. $(3-4i)(6+5i) = 18+15i-24i-20i^2$
$= 18-9i-20(-1)$
$= 18-9i+20$
$= 38-9i$

Review Exercises

1. $(x-3)^2 = 24$
$x-3 = \pm\sqrt{24}$
$x-3 = \pm2\sqrt{6}$
$x = 3\pm2\sqrt{6}$
$x = 3+2\sqrt{6}$ or $x = 3-2\sqrt{6}$

2. $(2x+5)^2 = 60$
$2x+5 = \pm\sqrt{60}$
$2x+5 = \pm2\sqrt{15}$
$2x = -5\pm2\sqrt{15}$
$x = \dfrac{-5\pm2\sqrt{15}}{2}$
$x = \dfrac{-5+2\sqrt{15}}{2}$ or $x = \dfrac{-5-2\sqrt{15}}{2}$

3. $\left(x-\dfrac{1}{3}\right)^2 = \dfrac{4}{9}$
$x-\dfrac{1}{3} = \pm\sqrt{\dfrac{4}{9}}$
$x-\dfrac{1}{3} = \pm\dfrac{2}{3}$
$x = \dfrac{1}{3}\pm\dfrac{2}{3}$
$x = \dfrac{1}{3}+\dfrac{2}{3}$ or $x = \dfrac{1}{3}-\dfrac{2}{3}$
$= \dfrac{3}{3}$ $\quad = -\dfrac{1}{3}$
$= 1$
$x = 1$ or $x = -\dfrac{1}{3}$

4. $\left(2x-\dfrac{1}{2}\right)^2 = 4$
$2x-\dfrac{1}{2} = \pm\sqrt{4}$
$2x-\dfrac{1}{2} = \pm2$
$2x = \dfrac{1}{2}\pm2$
$2x = \dfrac{1\pm4}{2}$
$x = \dfrac{1\pm4}{4}$
$x = \dfrac{1+4}{4}$ or $x = \dfrac{1-4}{4}$
$= \dfrac{5}{4}$ $\quad = -\dfrac{3}{4}$
$x = \dfrac{5}{4}$ or $x = -\dfrac{3}{4}$

5. $x^2-7x+12 = 0$
$x^2-7x = -12$
$x^2-7x+\dfrac{49}{4} = -\dfrac{48}{4}+\dfrac{49}{4}$
$x^2-7x+\dfrac{49}{4} = \dfrac{1}{4}$
$\left(x-\dfrac{7}{2}\right)^2 = \dfrac{1}{4}$
$x-\dfrac{7}{2} = \pm\dfrac{1}{2}$
$x = \dfrac{7}{2}\pm\dfrac{1}{2}$
$x = \dfrac{7}{2}+\dfrac{1}{2}$ or $x = \dfrac{7}{2}-\dfrac{1}{2}$
$= 4$ $\quad = 3$
$x = 4$ or $x = 3$

6. $x^2-4x-21 = 0$
$x^2-4x = 21$
$x^2-4x+4 = 21+4$
$(x-2)^2 = 25$
$x-2 = \pm5$
$x = 2\pm5$
$x = 7$ or $x = -3$

7. $a^2+2a-5 = 0$
$a^2+2a = 5$

$$a^2 + 2a = 5$$
$$a^2 + 2a + 1 = 5 + 1$$
$$(a+1)^2 = 6$$
$$a + 1 = \pm\sqrt{6}$$
$$a = -1 \pm \sqrt{6}$$
$$a = -1 + \sqrt{6} \quad \text{or} \quad a = -1 - \sqrt{6}$$

8.
$$z^2 + 6z = 10$$
$$z^2 + 6z + 9 = 10 + 9$$
$$(z+3)^2 = 19$$
$$z + 3 = \pm\sqrt{19}$$
$$z = -3 \pm \sqrt{19}$$
$$z = -3 + \sqrt{19} \quad \text{or} \quad z = -3 - \sqrt{19}$$

9.
$$x^2 - 2x + 10 = 0$$
$$x^2 - 2x = -10$$
$$x^2 - 2x + 1 = -10 + 1$$
$$(x-1)^2 = -9$$
$$(x-1)^2 = \sqrt{-9}$$
$$x - 1 = \pm 3i$$
$$x = 1 \pm 3i$$
$$x = 1 + 3i \quad \text{or} \quad x = 1 - 3i$$

10.
$$2r^2 - 8r = -64$$
$$r^2 - 4r = -32$$
$$r^2 - 4r + 4 = -32 + 4$$
$$(r-2)^2 = -28$$
$$r - 2 = \pm\sqrt{-28}$$
$$r = 2 \pm \sqrt{4}\sqrt{7}\sqrt{-1}$$
$$r = 2 \pm 2i\sqrt{7}$$
$$r = 2 + 2i\sqrt{7} \quad \text{or} \quad r = 2 - 2i\sqrt{7}$$

11. Area = length × width
$$32 = (x+5)(x+1)$$
$$32 = x^2 + x + 5x + 5$$
$$0 = x^2 + 6x - 27$$
$$0 = (x-3)(x+9)$$
$$x - 3 = 0 \quad \text{or} \quad x + 9 = 0$$
$$x = 3 \qquad x = -9$$
Disregard the negative value. $x = 3$.

12. Area = length × width
$$63 = (x+2)(x+4)$$
$$63 = x^2 + 4x + 2x + 8$$
$$0 = x^2 + 6x - 55$$
$$0 = (x-5)(x+11)$$
$$x - 5 = 0 \quad \text{or} \quad x + 11 = 0$$
$$x = 5 \qquad x = -11$$
Disregard the negative value. $x = 5$.

13. Let x = the smaller integer. The larger will then be $x + 1$. Their product is 72.
$$x(x+1) = 72$$
$$x^2 + x = 72$$
$$x^2 + x - 72 = 0$$
$$(x+9)(x-8) = 0$$
$$x + 9 = 0 \qquad x - 8 = 0$$
$$x = -9 \qquad x = 8$$
Since the integers must be positive, disregard the negative value. The smaller integer is 8 and the larger is 9.

14. Let x = the length of side of the square room. The diagonal can then be described by $x + 7$. Two of the adjacent sides and the diagonal make up a right triangle. Use the Pythagorean theorem to solve the problem.
$$a^2 + b^2 = c^2$$
$$x^2 + x^2 = (x+7)^2$$
$$2x^2 = x^2 + 14x + 49$$
$$x^2 - 14x - 49 = 0$$
$$x = \frac{-(-14) \pm \sqrt{(-14)^2 - 4(1)(-49)}}{2(1)}$$
$$x = \frac{14 \pm \sqrt{392}}{2}$$
$$x \approx 16.90 \quad \text{or} \quad x \approx -2.90$$
Disregard the negative value. The room is about 16.90 feet by 16.90 feet.

15.
$$2x^2 - 5x - 7 = 0$$
$$a = 2, b = -5, c = -7$$
$$b^2 - 4ac = (-5)^2 - 4(2)(-7)$$
$$= 25 + 56$$
$$= 81$$
Since the discriminant is positive, this equation has two distinct real solutions.

16. $3x^2 + 2x = -4$

$3x^2 + 2x + 4 = 0$
$a = 3, b = 2, c = 4$
$b^2 - 4ac = (2)^2 - 4(3)(4)$
$\quad = 4 - 48$
$\quad = -44$
Since the discriminant is negative, this equation has no real solutions.

17. $r^2 + 12n = -36$

$r^2 + 12n + 36 = 0$
$a = 1, b = 12, c = 36$
$b^2 - 4ac = (12)^2 - 4(1)(36)$
$\quad = 144 - 144$
$\quad = 0$
Since the discriminant is 0, the equation has one real solution.

18. $5x^2 - x + 1 = 0$
$a = 5, b = -1, c = 1$
$b^2 - 4ac = (-1)^2 - 4(5)(1)$
$\quad = 1 - 20$
$\quad = -19$
Since the discriminant is negative, this equation has no real solutions.

19. $a^2 - 14n = -49$

$a^2 - 14n + 49 = 0$
$a = 1, b = -14, c = 49$
$b^2 - 4ac = (-14)^2 - 4(1)(49)$
$\quad = 196 - 196$
$\quad = 0$
Since the discriminant is 0, the equation has one real solution.

20.

$a = \frac{1}{2}, b = -3, c = -10$
$b^2 - 4ac = (-3)^2 - 4\left(\frac{1}{2}\right)(-10)$
$\quad = 9 + 20$
$\quad = 29$
Since the discriminant is positive, this equation has two real solutions.

21. $3x^2 + 7x = 0 \quad a = 3, b = 7, c = 0$

$x = \dfrac{-b \pm \sqrt{b^2 - 4ac}}{2a}$

$x = \dfrac{-(7) \pm \sqrt{(7)^2 - 4(3)(0)}}{2(3)}$

$= \dfrac{-7 \pm \sqrt{49 - 0}}{6}$

$= \dfrac{-7 \pm \sqrt{49}}{6}$

$= \dfrac{-7 \pm 7}{6}$

$x = \dfrac{-7 + 7}{6}$ or $x = \dfrac{-7 - 7}{6}$
$x = \dfrac{0}{6}$ $\qquad x = \dfrac{-14}{6}$
$x = 0$ $\qquad x = -\dfrac{7}{3}$

22. $x^2 - 11x = -30$

$x^2 - 11x + 30 = 0$
$a = 1, b = -11, c = 30$
$x = \dfrac{-b \pm \sqrt{b^2 - 4ac}}{2a}$

$x = \dfrac{-(-11) \pm \sqrt{(-11)^2 - 4(1)(30)}}{2(1)}$

$= \dfrac{11 \pm \sqrt{121 - 120}}{2}$

$= \dfrac{11 \pm \sqrt{1}}{2}$

$= \dfrac{11 \pm 1}{2}$

$x = \dfrac{11 + 1}{2}$ or $x = \dfrac{11 - 1}{2}$
$= \dfrac{12}{2}$ $\qquad = \dfrac{10}{2}$
$= 6$ $\qquad = 5$

23. $r^2 = 7r + 8$

$r^2 - 7r - 8 = 0$
$a = 1, b = -7, c = -8$
$r = \dfrac{-b \pm \sqrt{b^2 - 4ac}}{2a}$

$r = \dfrac{-(-7) \pm \sqrt{(-7)^2 - 4(1)(-8)}}{2(1)}$

$= \dfrac{7 \pm \sqrt{49 + 32}}{2}$

$= \dfrac{7 \pm \sqrt{81}}{2}$

$= \dfrac{7 \pm 9}{2}$

$$r = \frac{7+9}{2} \quad \text{or} \quad r = \frac{7-9}{2}$$
$$= \frac{16}{2} \qquad\qquad = \frac{-2}{2}$$
$$= 8 \qquad\qquad = -1$$

24. $\quad 4x^2 = 9x$

$$4x^2 - 9x = 0$$
$$a = 4,\, b = -9,\, c = 0$$
$$x = \frac{-b \pm \sqrt{b^2 - 4ac}}{2a}$$
$$x = \frac{-(-9) \pm \sqrt{(-9)^2 - 4(4)(0)}}{2(4)}$$
$$= \frac{9 \pm \sqrt{81 - 0}}{8}$$
$$= \frac{9 \pm \sqrt{81}}{8}$$
$$= \frac{9 \pm 9}{8}$$
$$x = \frac{9-9}{8} \quad \text{or} \quad x = \frac{9+9}{8}$$
$$= \frac{0}{8} \qquad\qquad = \frac{18}{8}$$
$$= 0 \qquad\qquad = \frac{9}{4}$$

25. $\quad 6a^2 + a - 15 = 0$

$$a = 6,\, b = 1,\, c = -15$$
$$a = \frac{-b \pm \sqrt{b^2 - 4ac}}{2a}$$
$$a = \frac{-1 \pm \sqrt{1^2 - 4(6)(-15)}}{2(6)}$$
$$= \frac{-1 \pm \sqrt{1 + 360}}{12}$$
$$= \frac{-1 \pm \sqrt{361}}{12}$$
$$= \frac{-1 \pm 19}{12}$$
$$a = \frac{-1+19}{12} \quad \text{or} \quad a = \frac{-1-19}{12}$$
$$= \frac{18}{12} \qquad\qquad = \frac{-20}{12}$$
$$= \frac{3}{2} \qquad\qquad = -\frac{5}{3}$$

26. $\quad 4x^2 + 11x = 3$

$$4x^2 + 11x - 3 = 0$$
$$a = 4,\, b = 11,\, c = -3$$
$$x = \frac{-b \pm \sqrt{b^2 - 4ac}}{2a}$$
$$x = \frac{-(11) \pm \sqrt{(11)^2 - 4(4)(-3)}}{2(4)}$$
$$= \frac{-11 \pm \sqrt{121 + 48}}{8}$$
$$= \frac{-11 \pm \sqrt{169}}{8}$$
$$= \frac{-11 \pm 13}{8}$$
$$x = \frac{-11+13}{8} \quad \text{or} \quad x = \frac{-11-13}{8}$$
$$= \frac{2}{8} \qquad\qquad = \frac{-24}{8}$$
$$= \frac{1}{4} \qquad\qquad = -3$$

27. $\quad x^2 - 6x + 7 = 0$

$$a = 1,\, b = -6,\, c = 7$$
$$x = \frac{-b \pm \sqrt{b^2 - 4ac}}{2a}$$
$$x = \frac{-(-6) \pm \sqrt{(-6)^2 - 4(1)(7)}}{2(1)}$$
$$= \frac{6 \pm \sqrt{36 - 28}}{2}$$
$$= \frac{6 \pm \sqrt{8}}{2}$$
$$= \frac{6 \pm \sqrt{4}\sqrt{2}}{2}$$
$$= \frac{6 \pm 2\sqrt{2}}{2}$$
$$= \frac{2(3 \pm \sqrt{2})}{2}$$
$$x = 3 + \sqrt{2} \quad \text{or} \quad x = 3 - \sqrt{2}$$

28. $b^2 + 4b = 8$

$b^2 + 4b - 8 = 0$
$a = 1, b = 4, c = -8$

$b = \dfrac{-b \pm \sqrt{b^2 - 4ac}}{2a}$

$b = \dfrac{-(4) \pm \sqrt{(4)^2 - 4(1)(-8)}}{2(1)}$

$= \dfrac{-4 \pm \sqrt{16 + 32}}{2}$

$= \dfrac{-4 \pm \sqrt{48}}{2}$

$= \dfrac{-4 \pm \sqrt{16}\sqrt{3}}{2}$

$= \dfrac{-4 \pm 4\sqrt{3}}{2}$

$= \dfrac{2(-2 \pm 2\sqrt{3})}{2}$

$= -2 \pm 2\sqrt{3}$

$x = -2 + 2\sqrt{3}$ or $x = -2 - 2\sqrt{3}$

29. $2x^2 + 4x - 3 = 0$
$a = 2, b = 4, c = -3$

$x = \dfrac{-b \pm \sqrt{b^2 - 4ac}}{2a}$

$x = \dfrac{-4 \pm \sqrt{4^2 - 4(2)(-3)}}{2(2)}$

$= \dfrac{-4 \pm \sqrt{16 + 24}}{4}$

$= \dfrac{-4 \pm \sqrt{40}}{4}$

$= \dfrac{-4 \pm \sqrt{4}\sqrt{10}}{4}$

$= \dfrac{-4 \pm 2\sqrt{10}}{4}$

$= \dfrac{2(-2 \pm \sqrt{10})}{2(2)}$

$x = \dfrac{-2 + \sqrt{10}}{2}$ or $x = \dfrac{-2 - \sqrt{10}}{2}$

30. $3x^2 - 6x - 8 = 0$
$a = 3, b = -6, c = -8$

$x = \dfrac{-b \pm \sqrt{b^2 - 4ac}}{2a}$

$x = \dfrac{-(-6) \pm \sqrt{(-6)^2 - 4(3)(-8)}}{2(3)}$

$= \dfrac{6 \pm \sqrt{36 + 96}}{6}$

$= \dfrac{6 \pm \sqrt{132}}{6}$

$= \dfrac{6 \pm \sqrt{4}\sqrt{33}}{6}$

$= \dfrac{6 \pm 2\sqrt{33}}{6}$

$= \dfrac{2(3 \pm \sqrt{33})}{6}$

$x = \dfrac{3 + \sqrt{33}}{3}$ or $x = \dfrac{3 - \sqrt{33}}{3}$

31. $x^2 - x + 30 = 0$
$a = 1, b = -1, c = 30$

$x = \dfrac{-b \pm \sqrt{b^2 - 4ac}}{2a}$

$x = \dfrac{-(-1) \pm \sqrt{(-1)^2 - 4(1)(30)}}{2(1)}$

$= \dfrac{1 \pm \sqrt{1 - 120}}{2}$

$= \dfrac{1 \pm \sqrt{-119}}{2}$

$= \dfrac{1 \pm \sqrt{119}\sqrt{-1}}{2}$

$= \dfrac{1 \pm i\sqrt{119}}{2}$

$x = \dfrac{1 + i\sqrt{119}}{2}$ or $x = \dfrac{1 - i\sqrt{119}}{2}$

32. $1.2r^2 + 5.7r = 2.3$
$1.2r^2 + 5.7r - 2.3 = 0$
$a = 1.2, b = 5.7, c = -2.3$

$r = \dfrac{-b \pm \sqrt{b^2 - 4ac}}{2a}$

$r = \dfrac{-5.7 \pm \sqrt{(5.7)^2 - 4(1.2)(-2.3)}}{2(1.2)}$

$= \dfrac{-5.7 \pm \sqrt{32.49 + 11.04}}{2.4}$

$= \dfrac{-5.7 \pm \sqrt{43.53}}{2.4}$

$x = \dfrac{-5.7 + \sqrt{43.53}}{2.4}$ or $x = \dfrac{-5.7 - \sqrt{43.53}}{2.4}$

33.
$$x^2 - \frac{5}{6}x = \frac{25}{6}$$
$$6x^2 - 5x = 25$$
$$6x^2 - 5x - 25 = 0$$
$$a = 6,\ b = -5,\ c = -25$$
$$x = \frac{-b \pm \sqrt{b^2 - 4ac}}{2a}$$
$$x = \frac{-(-5) \pm \sqrt{(-5)^2 - 4(6)(-25)}}{2(6)}$$
$$x = \frac{5 \pm \sqrt{25 + 600}}{12}$$
$$= \frac{5 \pm \sqrt{625}}{12}$$
$$= \frac{5 \pm 25}{12}$$

$$x = \frac{5 + 25}{12} \quad \text{or} \quad x = \frac{5 - 25}{12}$$
$$= \frac{30}{12} \qquad\qquad = \frac{-20}{12}$$
$$= \frac{5}{2} \qquad\qquad = -\frac{5}{3}$$

34.
$$2x^2 + \frac{5x}{2} - \frac{3}{4} = 0$$
$$8x^2 + 10x - 3 = 0$$
$$a = 8,\ b = 10,\ c = -3$$
$$x = \frac{-b \pm \sqrt{b^2 - 4ac}}{2a}$$
$$= \frac{-10 \pm \sqrt{10^2 - 4(8)(-3)}}{2(8)}$$
$$= \frac{-10 \pm \sqrt{100 + 96}}{16}$$
$$= \frac{-10 \pm \sqrt{196}}{16}$$
$$= \frac{-10 \pm 14}{16}$$
$$x = \frac{-10 + 14}{16} \quad \text{or} \quad x = \frac{-10 - 14}{16}$$
$$= \frac{4}{16} \qquad\qquad = \frac{-24}{16}$$
$$= \frac{1}{4} \qquad\qquad = -\frac{3}{2}$$

35.
$$f(x) = x^2 - 4x - 45,\ f(x) = 15$$
$$x^2 - 4x - 45 = 15$$
$$x^2 - 4x - 60 = 0$$
$$(x - 10)(x + 6) = 0$$

$$x - 10 = 0 \quad \text{or} \quad x + 6 = 0$$
$$x = 10 \qquad\qquad x = -6$$
The solutions are 10 and –6.

36.
$$g(x) = 6x^2 + 5x,\ g(x) = 6$$
$$6x^2 + 5x = 6$$
$$6x^2 + 5x - 6 = 0$$
$$(2x + 3)(3x - 2) = 0$$
$$2x + 3 = 0 \quad \text{or} \quad 3x - 2 = 0$$
$$x = -\frac{3}{2} \qquad\qquad x = \frac{2}{3}$$
The solutions are $-\frac{3}{2}$ and $\frac{2}{3}$.

37.
$$h(r) = 5r^2 - 7r - 6,\ h(r) = -4$$
$$5r^2 - 7r - 6 = -4$$
$$5r^2 - 7r - 2 = 0$$
$$r = \frac{7 \pm \sqrt{(-7)^2 - 4(5)(-2)}}{2(5)}$$
$$= \frac{7 \pm \sqrt{49 + 40}}{10}$$
$$= \frac{7 \pm \sqrt{89}}{10}$$
The solutions are $\frac{7 + \sqrt{89}}{10}$ and $\frac{7 - \sqrt{89}}{10}$.

38.
$$f(x) = -2x^2 + 6x + 5,\ f(x) = -4$$
$$-2x^2 + 6x + 5 = -4$$
$$-2x^2 + 6x + 9 = 0$$
$$x = \frac{-6 \pm \sqrt{6^2 - 4(-2)(9)}}{2(-2)}$$
$$= \frac{-6 \pm \sqrt{36 + 72}}{-4}$$
$$= \frac{-6 \pm \sqrt{108}}{-4}$$
$$= \frac{-6 \pm 6\sqrt{3}}{-4}$$
$$= \frac{3 \pm 3\sqrt{3}}{2}$$
The solutions are $\frac{3 + 3\sqrt{3}}{2}$ and $\frac{3 - 3\sqrt{3}}{2}$.

39. Solutions are 4 and –1.
Factors are $(x - 4)$ and $(x + 1)$.
$$f(x) = (x - 4)(x + 1)$$
$$f(x) = x^2 - 3x - 4$$

40.   Solutions are $\dfrac{2}{3}$ and -2.

Factors are $(3x - 2)$ and $(x + 2)$.

$f(x) = (3x - 2)(x + 2)$

$f(x) = 3x^2 + 4x - 4$

41.   Solutions are $x = -\sqrt{7}$ and $x = \sqrt{7}$. Factors are $\left(x + \sqrt{7}\right)$ and $\left(x - \sqrt{7}\right)$.

$f(x) = \left(x + \sqrt{7}\right)\left(x - \sqrt{7}\right)$

$f(x) = x^2 - 7$

42.   Solutions are $x = 3 - 2i$ and $x = 3 + 2i$.
Factors are $x - (3 - 2i) = x - 3 + 2i$ and
$x - (3 + 2i) = x - 3 - 2i$.

$\begin{aligned} f(x) &= (x - 3 + 2i)(x - 3 - 2i) \\ &= (x - 3)^2 - (2i)^2 \\ &= x^2 - 6x + 9 - 4i^2 \\ &= x^2 - 6x + 9 + 4 \\ f(x) &= x^2 - 6x + 13 \end{aligned}$

43.   Let x = the width of the garden. Then the length is $x + 3$.

Area = length × width

$88 = (x + 3)x$

$88 = x^2 + 3x$

$x^2 + 3x - 88 = 0$

$(x + 11)(x - 8) = 0$

$x + 11 = 0$ or $x - 8 = 0$

$x = -11$ $x = 8$

Disregard the negative value. The width is 8 feet and the length is $8 + 3 = 11$ feet.

44.   Using the Pythagorean Theorem,

$a^2 + b^2 = c^2$

$8^2 + 8^2 = x^2$

$64 + 64 = x^2$

$128 = x^2$

$\sqrt{128} = x$

$x = 8\sqrt{2} \approx 11.31$

45.

$A = P\left(1 + \dfrac{r}{n}\right)^{nt}$

$882 = 800\left(1 + \dfrac{r}{1}\right)^{1(2)}$

$1323 = 1200(1 + r)^2$

$1.1025 = (1 + r)^2$

$\pm 1.05 = 1 + r$

$r = -1 \pm 1.05$

Since the rate must be positive,
$r = -1 + 1.05 = 0.05$.
The annual interest is 5%.

46.   Let x be the smaller positive number. Then $x + 2$ is the larger positive number.

$x(x + 2) = 63$

$x^2 + 2x - 63 = 0$

$(x + 9)(x - 7) = 0$

$x = -9$ or $x = 7$

Since x must be positive, $x = 7$ and
$7 + 2 = 9$.

47.   Let x be the width. Then $2x - 4$ is the length and the equation is $A = lw$.

$96 = (2x - 4)(x)$

$96 = 2x^2 - 4x$

$0 = 2x^2 - 4x - 96$

$0 = (2x + 12)(x - 8)$

$0 = 2x + 12$ or $0 = x - 8$

$-12 = 2x$ $8 = x$

$-6 = x$

Since the width must be positive, $x = 8$.
The width is 8 inches and the length $2x - 4$
is $2(8) - 4 = 16 - 4 = 12$ inches.

48.

$V = 12d - 0.05d^2$, $d = 50$

$V = 12(50) - 0.05(50)^2$

$V = 12(50) - 0.05(2500)$

$V = 600 - 125$

$V = 475$

The value is $475.

49. $d = -16t^2 + 784$

a. $d = -16(3)^2 + 784$

$d = -16(9) + 784$

$d = -144 + 784$

$d = 640$

The object is 640 feet from the ground 3 seconds after being dropped.

b. $0 = -16t^2 + 784$

$16t^2 = 784$

$t^2 = 49$

$t = \pm\sqrt{49}$

$t \approx \pm 7$

Since the time must be positive, $t = 7$ seconds.

50. $h = -16t^2 + 16t + 100$

a. $h = -16(2)^2 + 16(2) + 100$

$= -16(4) + 32 + 100$

$= -64 + 32 + 100$

$= 68$

The height is 68 feet.

b. $0 = -16t^2 + 16t + 100$

$0 = 4t^2 - 4t - 25$

$t = \dfrac{-(-4) \pm \sqrt{(-4)^2 - 4(4)(-25)}}{2(4)}$

$= \dfrac{4 \pm \sqrt{16 + 400}}{8}$

$= \dfrac{4 \pm \sqrt{416}}{8}$

Since the time must be positive,

$t = \dfrac{4 + \sqrt{416}}{8}$

≈ 3.05 seconds

The object hits the ground in about 3.05 seconds.

51. **a.** $L = 0.0004t^2 + 0.16t + 20$

$L = 0.0004(100)^2 + 0.16(100) + 20$

$= 40$

40 milliliters will leak out at 100°C.

b. $53 = 0.0004t^2 + 0.16t + 20$

$0 = 0.0004t^2 + 0.16t - 33$

$t = \dfrac{-0.16 \pm \sqrt{(0.16)^2 - 4(0.0004)(-33)}}{2(0.0004)}$

$= \dfrac{-0.16 \pm \sqrt{0.0784}}{0.0008}$

$t = \dfrac{-0.16 + \sqrt{0.0784}}{0.0008} = 150$

or $t = \dfrac{-0.16 - \sqrt{0.0784}}{0.0008} = -550$

Since the temperature must be positive, $t = 150$. The operating temperature is 150°C.

52. Let x be the time in which the smaller machine can do the job then $x - 1$ is the time for the larger machine.

$\dfrac{12}{x} + \dfrac{12}{x-1} = 1$

$x(x-1)\left(\dfrac{12}{x}\right) + x(x-1)\left(\dfrac{12}{x-1}\right) = x(x-1)$

$12(x-1) + 12x = x^2 - x$

$12x - 12 + 12x = x^2 - x$

$-12 + 24x = x^2 - x$

$0 = x^2 - 25x + 12$

$x = \dfrac{-(-25) \pm \sqrt{(-25)^2 - 4(1)(12)}}{2(1)}$

$= \dfrac{25 \pm \sqrt{577}}{2}$

$x = \dfrac{25 + \sqrt{577}}{2} \approx 24.5$ or

$x = \dfrac{25 - \sqrt{577}}{2} \approx 0.49$

x cannot equal 0.49 since this would mean the smaller machine could do the work in 0.49 hours and the larger can do the work in $x - 1$ or −0.51 hours. Therefore the smaller machine does the work in 24.51 hours and the larger machine does the work in 23.51 hours.

53. Let x be the speed (in miles per hour) for the first 25 miles. Then, the speed for the next 65 miles is $x + 15$. The time for the first 20 miles is $\dfrac{d}{r} = \dfrac{25}{x}$ and the time for the next 30 miles is $\dfrac{d}{r} = \dfrac{65}{x+15}$. The total time is 1.5 hours.

$$\frac{25}{x} + \frac{65}{x+15} = 1.5$$

$$x(x+15)\left(\frac{25}{x} + \frac{65}{x+15}\right) = x(x+15)(1.5)$$

$$25(x+15) + x(65) = \left(x^2 + 15x\right)(1.5)$$

$$90x + 375 = 1.5x^2 + 22.5x$$

$$0 = 1.5x^2 - 67.5x - 375$$

$$0 = 3x^2 - 135x - 750$$

$$0 = 3(x - 50)(x + 5)$$

$$x - 50 = 0 \quad \text{or} \quad x + 5 = 0$$

$$x = 50 \quad \text{or} \quad x = -5$$

Since the speed must be positive, $x = 50$. Thus, the speed was 50 mph.

54. Let r be the speed (in miles per hour) of the canoe in still water. For the trip downstream, the rate is $r + 0.4$ and the distance 3 miles so that the time is $t = \dfrac{3}{r+0.4}$. For the trip upstream the rate is $r - 0.4$ and the distance is 3 miles so that the time is $t = \dfrac{3}{r-0.4}$. The total time is 4 hours.

$$\frac{3}{r+0.4} + \frac{3}{r-0.4} = 4$$

$$(r+0.4)(r-0.4)\left[\frac{3}{r+0.4} + \frac{3}{r-0.4} = 4\right]$$

$$3(r-0.4) + 3(r+0.4) = 4(r+0.4)(r-0.4)$$

$$3r - 1.2 + 3r + 1.2 = 4\left(r^2 - 0.16\right)$$

$$6r = 4r^2 - 0.64$$

$$0 = 4r^2 - 6r - 0.64$$

$$0 = 2r^2 - 3r - 0.32$$

$$r = \frac{-(-3) \pm \sqrt{(-3)^2 - 4(2)(-0.32)}}{2(2)}$$

$$= \frac{3 \pm \sqrt{9 + 2.56}}{4}$$

$$= \frac{3 \pm \sqrt{11.56}}{4}$$

$$= \frac{3 \pm 3.4}{4}$$

$$r = \frac{3 + 3.4}{4} \quad \text{or} \quad r = \frac{3 - 3.4}{4}$$

$$= \frac{6.4}{4} \qquad\qquad = \frac{-0.4}{4}$$

$$= 1.6 \qquad\qquad\quad = -0.1$$

Since the rate must be positive, $r = 1.6$. Rachel canoes 1.6 miles per hour in still water.

55. Let x be the length. The width is $x - 2$.
Area = length × width
$$73 = x(x-2)$$
$$73 = x^2 - 2x$$
$$0 = x^2 - 2x - 73$$
$$x = \frac{-(-2) \pm \sqrt{(-2)^2 - 4(1)(-73)}}{2(1)}$$
$$x = \frac{2 \pm \sqrt{296}}{2}$$
$$x \approx 9.6 \text{ or } x \approx -7.6$$

Since the width must be positive, $x = 9.6$.
The length is 9.6 inches and the width is
$9.6 - 2 = 7.6$ inches.

56. If the business sells n tables at a price of
$(60 - 0.3n)$ dollars per table, then the
revenue is given by $R(n) = n(60 - 0.3n)$
with n ≤ 40. Set this equal to 1530 and
solve for n.
$$R(n) = n(60 - 0.3n)$$
$$1530 = n(60 - 0.3n)$$
$$1530 = 60n - 0.3n^2$$
$$0.3n^2 - 60n + 1530 = 0 \iff \text{divide by } 0.3$$
$$n^2 - 200n + 5100 = 0$$
$$(n - 30)(n - 170) = 0$$
$$n = 30 \text{ or } n = 170$$

Disregard $n = 170$ since $n \le 40$. The
business must sell 30 tables.

57.
$$a^2 + b^2 = c^2$$
$$a^2 = c^2 - b^2$$
$$\sqrt{a^2} = \pm\sqrt{c^2 - b^2}$$
$$a = \pm\sqrt{c^2 - b^2}$$
Since a refers to a length, it cannot
be negative. Therefore disregard the
negative sign.
$$a = \sqrt{c^2 - b^2}$$

58.
$$h = -4.9t^2 + c$$
$$h - c = -4.9t^2$$
$$\frac{h - c}{-4.9} = \frac{-4.9t^2}{-4.9}$$
$$\frac{h - c}{-4.9} = t^2$$
$$\pm\sqrt{\frac{h - c}{-4.9}} = t \quad \text{or} \quad t = \pm\sqrt{\frac{c - h}{4.9}}$$
Disregard the negative value for time.
$$t = \sqrt{\frac{c - h}{4.9}}$$

59.
$$V_x^2 + V_y^2 = V^2 \text{ for } V_y$$
$$V_y^2 = V^2 - V_x^2$$
$$V_y = \sqrt{V^2 - V_x^2}$$

60.
$$a = \frac{v_2^2 - v_1^2}{2d} \text{ for } v_2$$
$$2ad = v_2^2 - v_1^2$$
$$2ad + v_1^2 = v_2^2$$
$$v_2 = \sqrt{v_1^2 + 2ad}$$

61.
$$x^4 - 13x^2 + 36 = 0$$
$$(x^2)^2 - 13x^2 + 36 = 0$$
$$u^2 - 13u + 36 = 0$$
$$(u - 9)(u - 4) = 0$$
$$u - 9 = 0 \quad \text{or} \quad u - 4 = 0$$

$u = 9$	$u = 4$
$x^2 = 9$	$x^2 = 4$
$x = \pm 3$	$x = \pm 2$

The solutions are ±3 and ±2.

62.
$$x^4 - 19x^2 + 48 = 0$$
$$(x^2)^2 - 19x^2 + 48 = 0$$
$$u^2 - 19u + 48 = 0$$
$$(u - 16)(u - 3) = 0$$
$$u - 16 = 0 \quad \text{or} \quad u - 3 = 0$$
$$u = 16 \qquad\qquad u = 3$$
$$x^2 = 16 \qquad\qquad x^2 = 3$$
$$x = \pm 4 \qquad\qquad x = \pm\sqrt{3}$$

The solutions are ± 4 and $\pm\sqrt{3}$.

63.
$$a^4 = 5a^2 + 24$$
$$a^4 - 5a^2 - 24 = 0$$
$$(a^2)^2 - 5a^2 - 24 = 0$$
$$u^2 - 5u - 24 = 0$$
$$(u - 8)(u + 3) = 0$$
$$u - 8 = 0 \quad \text{or} \quad u + 3 = 0$$
$$u = 8 \qquad\qquad u = -3$$
$$a^2 = 8 \qquad\qquad a^2 = -3$$
$$a = \pm\sqrt{8} \qquad\qquad a = \pm\sqrt{-3}$$
$$= \pm 2\sqrt{2} \qquad\qquad = \pm i\sqrt{3}$$

The solutions are $\pm 2\sqrt{2}$ and $\pm i\sqrt{3}$.

64.
$$6y^{-2} + 11y^{-1} - 10 = 0$$
$$\frac{6}{y^2} + \frac{11}{y} - 10 = 0$$
$$y^2\left(\frac{6}{y^2} + \frac{11}{y} - 10\right) = y^2(0)$$
$$6 + 11y - 10y^2 = 0$$
$$10y^2 - 11y - 6 = 0$$
$$(2y - 3)(5y + 2) = 0$$
$$2y - 3 = 0 \quad \text{or} \quad 5y + 2 = 0$$
$$2y = 3 \qquad\qquad 5y = -2$$
$$y = \frac{3}{2} \qquad\qquad y = -\frac{2}{5}$$

The solutions are $\frac{3}{2}$ and $-\frac{2}{5}$.

65.
$$4r + 23\sqrt{r} - 6 = 0$$
$$4\left(r^{1/2}\right)^2 + 23r^{1/2} - 6 = 0$$
$$4u^2 + 23u - 6 = 0$$
$$(4u - 1)(u + 6) = 0$$
$$4u - 1 = 0 \quad \text{or} \quad u + 6 = 0$$
$$4u = 1 \qquad\qquad u = -6$$
$$u = \frac{1}{4}$$
$$r^{1/2} = \frac{1}{4} \qquad\qquad r^{1/2} = -6$$
$$r = \left(\frac{1}{4}\right)^2$$
$$= \frac{1}{16}$$

There are no solutions for $r^{1/2} = -6$ since there is no real number x for which $r^{1/2} = -6$.

The solution is $\frac{1}{16}$.

66.
$$2p^{2/3} - 7p^{1/3} + 6 = 0$$
$$2\left(p^{1/3}\right)^2 - 7p^{1/3} + 6 = 0$$
$$2!^2 - 7! + 6 = 0$$
$$(2! - 3)(! - 2) = 0$$
$$2u - 3 = 0 \quad \text{or} \quad u - 2 = 0$$
$$u = \frac{3}{2} \qquad\qquad u = 2$$
$$p^{1/3} = \frac{3}{2} \qquad\qquad p^{1/3} = 2$$
$$p = \left(\frac{3}{2}\right)^3 \qquad\qquad p = 2^3$$
$$= \frac{27}{8} \qquad\qquad = 8$$

The solutions are $\frac{27}{8}$ and 8.

67.

$$6(x-2)^{-2} = -13(x-2)^{-1} + 8$$

$$6\left[(x-2)^{-1}\right]^2 = -13(x-2)^{-1} + 8$$

$$6u^2 = -13u + 8$$

$$6u^2 + 13u - 8 = 0$$

$$(2u-1)(3u+8) = 0$$

$$2u - 1 = 0 \quad \text{or} \quad 3u + 8 = 0$$

$$u = \frac{1}{2} \qquad\qquad u = -\frac{8}{3}$$

$$(x-2)^{-1} = \frac{1}{2} \quad (x-2)^{-1} = -\frac{8}{3}$$

$$x - 2 = 2 \qquad\quad x - 2 = -\frac{3}{8}$$

$$x = 4 \qquad\qquad\quad x = \frac{13}{8}$$

The solutions are 4 and $\frac{13}{8}$.

68.

$$10(r+2) = \frac{12}{r+2} - 7$$

$$10(r+2)^2 + 7(r+2) = 12$$

$$10(r+2)^2 + 7(r+2) - 12 = 0$$

$$10u^2 + 7u - 12 = 0$$

$$(5u-4)(2u+3) = 0$$

$$5u - 4 = 0 \quad \text{or} \quad 2u + 3 = 0$$

$$u = \frac{4}{5} \qquad\qquad u = -\frac{3}{2}$$

$$r + 2 = \frac{4}{5} \qquad r + 2 = -\frac{3}{2}$$

$$r = -\frac{6}{5} \qquad\quad r = -\frac{7}{2}$$

The solutions are $-\frac{6}{5}$ and $-\frac{7}{2}$.

69. $f(x) = x^4 - 29x^2 + 100$

To find the x-intercepts, set $f(x) = 0$.

$$0 = x^4 - 29x^2 + 100$$

$$0 = \left(x^2\right)^2 - 29x^2 + 100$$

$$0 = u^2 - 29u + 100$$

$$0 = (u-25)(u-4)$$

$$u - 25 = 0 \qquad u - 4 = 0$$

$$u = 25 \qquad\quad u = 4$$

$$x^2 = 25 \qquad x^2 = 4$$

$$x = \pm 5 \qquad\quad x = \pm 2$$

The x-intercepts are $(5, 0)$, $(-5, 0)$, $(2, 0)$, and $(-2, 0)$.

70. $f(x) = 30x + 13\sqrt{x} - 10$

To find the x-intercepts, set $f(x) = 0$.

$$0 = 30x + 13\sqrt{x} - 10$$

$$0 = 30\left(\sqrt{x}\right)^2 + 13\sqrt{x} - 10$$

$$0 = 30u^2 + 13u - 10$$

$$0 = (6u + 5)(5u - 2)$$

$$6u + 5 = 0 \qquad 5u - 2 = 0$$

$$u = -\frac{5}{6} \qquad\quad u = \frac{2}{5}$$

$$\sqrt{x} = -\frac{5}{6} \qquad \sqrt{x} = \frac{2}{5}$$

$$x = \frac{4}{25}$$

Since $\sqrt{x}$ cannot be negative, the solution is $\frac{4}{25}$. The only x-intercept is $\left(\frac{4}{25}, 0\right)$.

71. $f(x) = x - 6\sqrt{x} + 10$

To find the x-intercepts, set $f(x) = 0$.

$$0 = x - 6\sqrt{x} + 10$$

$$0 = \left(\sqrt{x}\right)^2 - 6\sqrt{x} + 10$$

$$0 = u^2 - 6u + 10$$

$$u = \frac{-(-6) \pm \sqrt{(-6)^2 - 4(1)(10)}}{2(1)}$$

$$u = \frac{6 \pm \sqrt{-4}}{2}$$

$$u = \frac{6 \pm 2i}{2} \quad \text{or} \quad u = 3 \pm i$$

$$\sqrt{x} = 3 \pm i \quad \Rightarrow \quad x = (3 \pm i)^2 = 8 \pm 6i$$

Since x-intercepts must be real numbers, this function has no x-intercepts.

72.
$$g(x) = \left(x^2 - 6x\right)^2 - 5\left(x^2 - 6x\right) - 24$$
To find the x-intercepts, set $g(x) = 0$.
$$0 = \left(x^2 - 6x\right)^2 - 5\left(x^2 - 6x\right) - 24$$
$$0 = u^2 - 5u - 24$$
$$0 = (u+3)(u-8)$$

$$u + 3 = 0 \qquad \text{or} \qquad u - 8 = 0$$
$$u = -3 \qquad\qquad\qquad u = 8$$
$$x^2 - 6x = -3 \qquad\qquad x^2 - 6x = 8$$
$$x^2 - 6x + 3 = 0 \qquad\quad x^2 - 6x - 8 = 0$$

$$\frac{6 \pm \sqrt{(-6)^2 - 4(1)(3)}}{2(1)} \qquad \frac{6 \pm \sqrt{(-6)^2 - 4(1)(-8)}}{2(1)}$$

$$\frac{6 \pm \sqrt{24}}{2} \qquad\qquad \frac{6 \pm \sqrt{68}}{2}$$

$$\frac{6 \pm 2\sqrt{6}}{2} \qquad\qquad \frac{6 \pm 2\sqrt{17}}{2}$$

$$3 \pm \sqrt{6} \qquad\qquad\quad 3 \pm \sqrt{17}$$

The x-intercepts are
$$\left(3 + \sqrt{6}, 0\right), \left(3 - \sqrt{6}, 0\right),$$
$$\left(3 + \sqrt{17}, 0\right) \text{ and } \left(3 - \sqrt{17}, 0\right).$$

73. $y = x^2 + 5x$

a. Since $a = 1$ the parabola opens upward.

b. $y = 0^2 + 5(0) = 0$
The y-intercept is $(0, 0)$.

c. $x = -\dfrac{b}{2a} = -\dfrac{5}{2(1)} = -\dfrac{5}{2}$

$y = \dfrac{4ac - b^2}{4a}$

$\quad = \dfrac{4(1)(0) - 5^2}{4(1)}$

$\quad = -\dfrac{25}{4}$

The vertex is $\left(-\dfrac{5}{2}, -\dfrac{25}{4}\right)$.

d.
$$0 = x^2 + 5x$$
$$0 = x(x + 5)$$
$$x = 0 \qquad x + 5 = 0$$
$$x = 0 \qquad\qquad x = -5$$
The x-intercepts are $(0, 0)$ and $(-5, 0)$.

e.
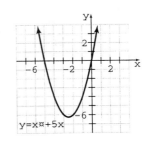

$y = x^2 + 5x$

74. $y = x^2 - 2x - 8$

a. Since $a = 1$ the parabola opens upward.

b. $y = (0)^2 - 2(0) - 8 = -8$
The y-intercept is $(0, -8)$.

c. $x = -\dfrac{b}{2a} = -\dfrac{-2}{2(1)} = \dfrac{2}{2} = 1$

$y = \dfrac{4ac - b^2}{4a}$

$\quad = \dfrac{4(1)(-8) - (-2)^2}{4(1)}$

$\quad = \dfrac{-32 - 4}{4}$

$\quad = \dfrac{-36}{4}$

$\quad = -9$

The vertex is $(1, -9)$.

d.
$$0 = x^2 - 2x - 8$$
$$0 = (x - 4)(x + 2)$$
$$x - 4 = 0 \qquad x + 2 = 0$$
$$x = 4 \qquad\qquad x = -2$$
The x-intercepts are $(4, 0)$ and $(-2, 0)$.

e.
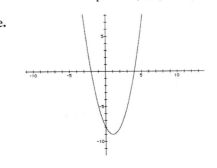

75. $y = -x^2 - 9$

a. Since $a = -1$ the parabola opens downward.

b. $y = -(0)^2 - 9 = -9$
The y-intercept is $(0, -9)$.

c. $x = -\dfrac{b}{2a} = -\dfrac{0}{2(-1)} = -\dfrac{0}{-2} = 0$

$y = \dfrac{4ac - b^2}{4a}$

$= \dfrac{4(-1)(-9) - 0^2}{4(-1)} = \dfrac{36}{-4} = -9$

The vertex is $(0, -9)$.

d. $0 = -x^2 - 9$
$x^2 = -9$
$x = \pm\sqrt{-9}$ or $\pm 3i$
There are no real roots. Thus, there are no x-intercepts.

e.

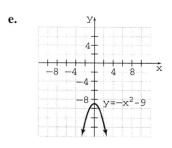
$y = -x^2 - 9$

76. $y = -2x^2 - x + 15$

a. Since $a = -2$ the parabola opens downward.

b. $y = -2(0)^2 - 0 + 15 = 15$
The y-intercept is $(0, 15)$.

c. $x = -\dfrac{b}{2a} = -\dfrac{-1}{2(-2)} = \dfrac{1}{-4} = -\dfrac{1}{4}$

$y = \dfrac{4ac - b^2}{4a}$

$= \dfrac{4(-2)(15) - (-1)^2}{4(-2)} = \dfrac{121}{8}$

The vertex is $\left(-\dfrac{1}{4}, \dfrac{121}{8}\right)$.

d. $0 = -1\left(2x^2 + x - 15\right)$
$= -1(2x - 5)(x + 3)$
$0 = (2x - 5)$ or $0 = x + 3$
$5 = 2x$
$\dfrac{5}{2} = x$ $\qquad -3 = x$
The x-intercepts are $(-3, 0)$ and $\left(\dfrac{5}{2}, 0\right)$.

e.

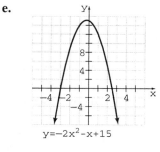
$y = -2x^2 - x + 15$

77. a. $I = -x^2 + 22x - 30$, $2 \le x \le 20$
The x-coordinate of the vertex will be the cost per ticket to maximize profit.
$x = -\dfrac{b}{2a} = -\dfrac{22}{2(-1)} = 11$
They should charge $11 per ticket.

b. The maximum profit in hundreds is the y-coordinate of the vertex.
$I(11) = -11^2 + 22(11) - 30$
$\qquad = -121 + 242 - 30$
$\qquad = 91$
The maximum profit is $91 hundred or $9100.

78. a. $s(t) = -16t^2 + 80t + 60$
The ball will attain maximum height at the x-coordinate of the vertex.
$t = -\dfrac{b}{2a} = -\dfrac{80}{2(-16)} = -\dfrac{80}{-32} = 2.5$
The ball will attain maximum height 2.5 seconds after being thrown.

b. The maximum height is the y-coordinate of the vertex.
$s(2.5) = -16(2.5)^2 + 80(2.5) + 60$
$\qquad = -100 + 200 + 60$
$\qquad = 160$
The maximum height is 160 feet.

79. The graph of $f(x) = (x-3)^2$ has vertex $(3, 0)$. The graph will be $g(x) = x^2$ shifted right 3 units.

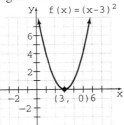

80. The graph of $f(x) = -(x+2)^2 - 3$ has vertex $(-2, -3)$. Since $a < 0$, the parabola opens downward. The graph will be $g(x) = -x^2$ shifted left 2 units and down 3 units.

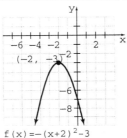

81. The graph of $g(x) = -2(x+4)^2 - 1$ has vertex $(-4, -1)$. Since $a < 0$, the parabola opens downward. The graph will be $f(x) = -2x^2$ shifted left 4 units and down 1 unit.

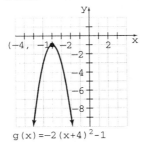

82. The graph of $h(x) = \frac{1}{2}(x-1)^2 + 3$ has vertex $(1, 3)$. The graph will be $f(x) = \frac{1}{2}x^2$ shifted right 1 unit and up 3 units.

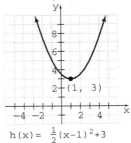

83. $x^2 + 7x + 6 \geq 0$
$(x+1)(x+6) \geq 0$

84. $x^2 + 3x - 10 \leq 0$
$(x+5)(x-2) \leq 0$

85. $x^2 \leq 11x - 20$
$x^2 - 11x + 20 \leq 0$
$x^2 - 11x + 20 = 0$

$$x = \frac{-(-11) \pm \sqrt{(-11)^2 - 4(1)(20)}}{2(1)}$$

$$= \frac{11 \pm \sqrt{121 - 80}}{2}$$

$$= \frac{11 \pm \sqrt{41}}{2}$$

86. $3x^2 + 8x > 16$

$3x^2 + 8x - 16 > 0$

$(3x - 4)(x + 4) > 0$

$3x - 4 = 0 \quad$ or $\quad x + 4 = 0$

$x = \dfrac{4}{3} \qquad\qquad x = -4$

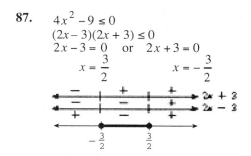

87. $4x^2 - 9 \le 0$

$(2x - 3)(2x + 3) \le 0$

$2x - 3 = 0 \quad$ or $\quad 2x + 3 = 0$

$x = \dfrac{3}{2} \qquad\qquad x = -\dfrac{3}{2}$

88. $5x^2 - 25 > 0$

$5(x^2 - 5) > 0$

$5(x + \sqrt{5})(x - \sqrt{5}) > 0$

$x + \sqrt{5} = 0 \quad$ or $\quad x - \sqrt{5} = 0$

$x = -\sqrt{5} \qquad\qquad x = \sqrt{5}$

89. $\dfrac{x+1}{x-3} > 0$

$x \ne 3$

$\left\{ x \mid x < -1 \text{ or } x > 3 \right\}$

90. $\dfrac{x-5}{x+2} \le 0$

$x = -2$

$\left\{ x \mid -2 < x \le 5 \right\}$

91. $\dfrac{2x-4}{x+3} \ge 0$

$\dfrac{2(x-2)}{x+3} \ge 0$

$x \ne -3$

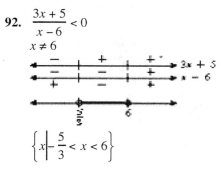

$\left\{ x \mid x < -3 \text{ or } x \ge 2 \right\}$

92. $\dfrac{3x+5}{x-6} < 0$

$x \ne 6$

$\left\{ x \mid -\dfrac{5}{3} < x < 6 \right\}$

93. $(x+3)(x+1)(x-2) > 0$

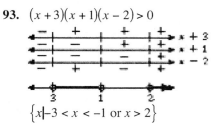

$\left\{ x \mid -3 < x < -1 \text{ or } x > 2 \right\}$

94. $x(x-3)(x-5) \le 0$

$\left\{ x \mid x \le 0 \text{ or } 3 \le x \le 5 \right\}$

95. $(3x+4)(x-1)(x-3) \ge 0$

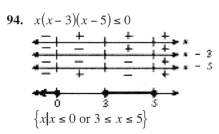

$\left[-\dfrac{4}{3}, 1 \right] \cup [3, \infty)$

96. $2x(x+2)(x+5) < 0$

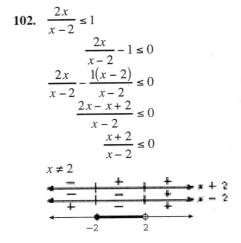

$(-\infty, -5) \cup (-2, 0)$

97. $\dfrac{x(x-4)}{x+2} > 0$

$x \ne -2$

$(-2, 0) \cup (4, \infty)$

98. $\dfrac{(x-2)(x-5)}{x+3} < 0$

$x \ne -3$

$(-\infty, -3) \cup (2, 5)$

99. $\dfrac{x-3}{(x+2)(x-5)} \ge 0$

$x \ne -2, x \ne 5$

$(-2, 3] \cup (5, \infty)$

100. $\dfrac{x(x-5)}{x+3} \le 0$

$x \ne -3$

$(-\infty, -3) \cup [0, 5]$

101. $\dfrac{3}{x+4} \ge -1$

$\dfrac{3}{x+4} + 1 \ge 0$

$\dfrac{3 + 1(x+4)}{x+4} \ge 0$

$\dfrac{3 + x + 4}{x+4} \ge 0$

$\dfrac{x+7}{x+4} \ge 0$

$x \ne -4$

102. $\dfrac{2x}{x-2} \le 1$

$\dfrac{2x}{x-2} - 1 \le 0$

$\dfrac{2x}{x-2} - \dfrac{1(x-2)}{x-2} \le 0$

$\dfrac{2x - x + 2}{x-2} \le 0$

$\dfrac{x+2}{x-2} \le 0$

$x \ne 2$

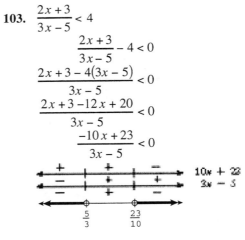

103. $\dfrac{2x+3}{3x-5} < 4$

$\dfrac{2x+3}{3x-5} - 4 < 0$

$\dfrac{2x+3 - 4(3x-5)}{3x-5} < 0$

$\dfrac{2x+3 - 12x + 20}{3x-5} < 0$

$\dfrac{-10x + 23}{3x-5} < 0$

Practice Test

1. $x^2 + 2x - 15 = 0$

$x^2 + 2x = 15$

$x^2 + 2x + 1 = 15 + 1$

$(x+1)^2 = 16$

$x + 1 = \pm 4$

$x = -1 \pm 4$

$x = 3$ or $x = -5$

2. $x^2 - 4x = -17$

$x^2 - 4x + 4 = -17 + 4$

$(x-2)^2 = -13$

$x - 2 = \pm\sqrt{-13}$

$x - 2 = \pm i\sqrt{13}$

$x = 2 \pm i\sqrt{13}$

$x = 2 + i\sqrt{13}$ or $x = 2 - i\sqrt{13}$

3. $x^2 - 5x - 14 = 0$ $a = 1, b = -5, c = -14$

$x = \dfrac{-b \pm \sqrt{b^2 - 4ac}}{2a}$

$x = \dfrac{-(-5) \pm \sqrt{(-5)^2 - 4(1)(-14)}}{2(1)}$

$= \dfrac{5 \pm \sqrt{25 + 56}}{2}$

$= \dfrac{5 \pm \sqrt{81}}{2}$

$= \dfrac{5 \pm 9}{2}$

$x = \dfrac{5+9}{2}$ or $x = \dfrac{5-9}{2}$

$= \dfrac{14}{2}$ $= \dfrac{-4}{2}$

$= 7$ $= -2$

4. $a^2 + 8a = -5$

$a^2 + 8a + 5 = 0$

$a = 1, b = 8, c = 5$

$a = \dfrac{-b \pm \sqrt{b^2 - 4ac}}{2a}$

$a = \dfrac{-8 \pm \sqrt{8^2 - 4(1)(5)}}{2(1)}$

$= \dfrac{-8 \pm \sqrt{64 - 20}}{2}$

$= \dfrac{-8 \pm \sqrt{44}}{2}$

$= \dfrac{-8 \pm 2\sqrt{11}}{2}$

$= \dfrac{2\left(-4 \pm \sqrt{11}\right)}{2}$

$= -4 \pm \sqrt{11}$

$a = -4 + \sqrt{11}$ or $a = -4 - \sqrt{11}$

5. $3r^2 + r = 2$

$3r^2 + r - 2 = 0$

$(3r - 2)(r + 1) = 0$

$3r - 2 = 0$ or $r + 1 = 0$

$3r = 2$ $r = -1$

$r = \dfrac{2}{3}$

6. $p^2 + 5 = -7p$

$p^2 + 7p + 5 = 0$

$p = \dfrac{-7 \pm \sqrt{(7)^2 - 4(1)(5)}}{2(1)}$

$p = \dfrac{-7 \pm \sqrt{29}}{2}$

$p = \dfrac{-7 + \sqrt{29}}{2}$ or $p = \dfrac{-7 - \sqrt{29}}{2}$

7. x-intercepts are 4 and $-\dfrac{2}{5}$

Factors are $(x - 4)$ and $(5x + 2)$

$f(x) = (x - 4)(5x + 2)$

$f(x) = 5x^2 - 18x - 8$

8. $K = \dfrac{1}{2}mv^2$ for v

$2K = mv^2$

$\dfrac{2K}{m} = v^2$

$v = \sqrt{\dfrac{2K}{m}}$

9. a. $c(s) = -0.01s^2 + 78s + 22,000$

$c(2000) = -0.01(2000)^2 + 78(2000) + 22,000$

$\qquad = -40,000 + 156,000 + 22,000$

$\qquad = 138,000$

The cost is $138,000.

b. $160,000 = -0.01s^2 + 78s + 22,000$

$0 = -0.01s^2 + 78s - 138,000$

$s = \dfrac{-78 \pm \sqrt{78^2 - 4(-0.01)(-138,000)}}{2(-0.01)}$

$= \dfrac{-78 \pm \sqrt{564}}{-0.02}$

$s = \dfrac{-78 + \sqrt{564}}{-0.02} \approx 2712.57$

$s = \dfrac{-78 - \sqrt{564}}{-0.02} \approx 5087.43$

Since $1300 \le s \le 3900$, the house should have about 2712.57 square feet.

10. The formula $d = rt$ can be written $t = \dfrac{d}{r}$.

Let r = his actual rate.

	distance	rate	time = $\dfrac{d}{r}$
actual trip	520	r	$\dfrac{520}{r}$
faster trip	520	$r + 15$	$\dfrac{520}{r+15}$

The faster trip would have taken 2.4 hours less time than the actual trip.

$\dfrac{520}{r+15} = \dfrac{520}{r} - 2.4$

$r(r+15)\left(\dfrac{520}{r+15}\right) = r(r+15)\left(\dfrac{520}{r} - 2.4\right)$

$520r = 520(r+15) - 2.4r(r+15)$

$520r = 520r + 7800 - 2.4r^2 - 36r$

$0 = -2.4r^2 - 36r + 7800$

$0 = r^2 + 15r - 3250$

$0 = (r + 65)(r - 50)$

$r + 65 = 0 \qquad r - 50 = 0$

$r = -65 \qquad\quad r = 50$

Since speed is never negative, Tom drove an average speed of 50 mph.

11. $2x^4 + 15x^2 - 50 = 0$

$2(x^2)^2 + 15x^2 - 50 = 0$

$2u^2 + 15u - 50 = 0$

$(u + 10)(2u - 5) = 0$

$u + 10 = 0 \qquad$ or $\qquad 2u - 5 = 0$

$u = -10 \qquad\qquad\qquad u = \dfrac{5}{2}$

$x^2 = -10 \qquad\quad x^2 = \dfrac{5}{2}$

$x = \pm\sqrt{-10} \qquad x = \pm\sqrt{\dfrac{5}{2}}$

$= \pm i\sqrt{10} \qquad\quad = \pm\dfrac{\sqrt{5}}{\sqrt{2}} \cdot \dfrac{\sqrt{2}}{\sqrt{2}}$

$\qquad\qquad\qquad\qquad = \pm\dfrac{\sqrt{10}}{2}$

12. $3r^{2/3} + 11r^{1/3} - 42 = 0$

$3(r^{1/3})^2 + 11r^{1/3} - 42 = 0$

$3u^2 + 11u - 42 = 0$

$(3u - 7)(u + 6) = 0$

$3u - 7 = 0 \qquad$ or $\qquad u + 6 = 0$

$u = \dfrac{7}{3} \qquad\qquad\qquad u = -6$

$r^{1/3} = \dfrac{7}{3} \qquad\qquad r^{1/3} = -6$

$r = \left(\dfrac{7}{3}\right)^3 \qquad\quad r = (-6)^3$

$= \dfrac{343}{27} \qquad\qquad r = -216$

13. $f(x) = 16x - 40\sqrt{x} + 25$

$0 = 16(\sqrt{x})^2 - 40\sqrt{x} + 25$

$0 = 16u^2 - 40u + 25$

$0 = (4u - 5)^2$

$4u - 5 = 0$

$u = \dfrac{5}{4}$

$\sqrt{x} = \dfrac{5}{4}$

$x = \dfrac{25}{16}$

The x-intercept is $\left(\dfrac{25}{16}, 0\right)$.

14. $f(x) = (x-3)^2 + 2$

The vertex is (3, –2). The graph will be the graph of $g(x) = x^2$ shifted 3 units right and 2 units down.

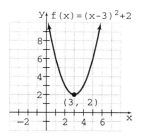

15. $h(x) = -\dfrac{1}{2}(x-2)^2 - 2$

The vertex is (2, –2). The graph will be the graph of $g(x) = -\dfrac{1}{2}x^2$ shifted 2 units right and 2 units down.

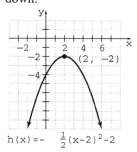

16. Begin by rewriting the equation in standard form.

$5x^2 - 4x - 3 = 0$ $a = 5, b = -4, c = -3$

The discriminant is

$b^2 - 4ac = (-4)^2 - 4(5)(-3)$

$= 76$

Since the discriminant is greater than 0, the quadratic equation has two distinct real solutions.

17. $y = x^2 + 2x - 8$

a. Since $a = 1$ the parabola opens upward.

b. $y = 0^2 + 2(0) - 8$

$y = -8$

The y-intercept is (0, –8).

c. $x = -\dfrac{b}{2a} = -\dfrac{2}{2(1)} = -1$

$y = (-1)^2 + 2(-1) - 8 = -9$

The vertex is (–1, –9).

d. The x-intercepts occur when $y = 0$.

$0 = x^2 + 2x - 8$

$0 = (x+4)(x-2)$

$x + 4 = 0$ or $x - 2 = 0$

$x = -4$ $x = 2$

The x-intercepts are (2, 0) and (–4, 0).

e.

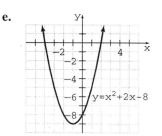

18. Since –6 and $\dfrac{1}{2}$ are the x-intercepts, the factors are $(x + 6)$ and $(2x - 1)$.

$f(x) = (x + 6)(2x - 1)$

$f(x) = 2x^2 + 11x - 6$

19. $x^2 - x \geq 42$

$x^2 - x - 42 \geq 0$

$(x - 7)(x + 6) \geq 0$

$x - 7 = 0$ or $x + 6 = 0$

$x = 7$ $x = -6$

20. $\dfrac{(x+3)(x-4)}{x+1} \geq 0$

$x \neq -1$

$x + 3 = 0$ or $x - 4 = 0$ or $x + 1 = 0$

$x = -3$ $x = 4$ $x = -1$

21.
$$\frac{x+3}{x+2} \le -1$$

$$\frac{x+3}{x+2} + 1 \le 0$$

$$\frac{x+3}{x+2} + \frac{x+2}{x+2} \le 0$$

$$\frac{2x+5}{x+2} \le 0$$

$$x \ne -2$$

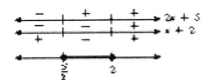

a. $\left[-\dfrac{5}{2}, -2\right)$

b. $\left\{x \middle| -\dfrac{5}{2} \le x < -2\right\}$

22. Let x be the width of the carpet. Then $2x + 4$ is the length $A = lw$.

$$48 = x(2x+4)$$
$$48 = 2x^2 + 4x$$
$$0 = 2x^2 + 4x - 48$$
$$0 = x^2 + 2x - 24$$
$$0 = (x-4)(x+6)$$
$$x - 4 = 0 \quad \text{or} \quad x + 6 = 0$$
$$x = 4 \qquad\qquad x = -6$$

The width is 4 feet and the length is $2 \cdot 4 + 4 = 8 + 4 = 12$ feet.

23. $d = -16t^2 + 64t + 80$
$d = 0$ when the ball strikes the ground.
$$0 = -16t^2 + 64t + 80$$
$$0 = -16\left(t^2 - 4t - 5\right)$$
$$0 = -16(t-5)(t+1)$$
$$t - 5 = 0 \quad \text{or} \quad t + 1 = 0$$
$$t = 5 \qquad\qquad t = -1$$

The time must be positive, so $t = 5$.
Thus, the ball strikes the ground in 5 seconds.

24. a. $f(x) = -1.4x^2 + 56x - 60$

$$x = -\frac{b}{2a} = -\frac{56}{2(-1.4)} = -\frac{56}{-2.8} = 20$$

The company must sell 20 carvings.

b. $f(20) = -1.4(20)^2 + 56(20) - 60$
$$= -560 + 1120 - 60$$
$$= 500$$
The maximum weekly profit is \$500.

25. If the business sells n brooms at a price of $(10 - 0.1n)$ dollars per broom, then the revenue is given by $R(n) = n(10 - 0.1n)$ with $n \le 32$. Set this equal to 160 and solve for n.

$$R(n) = n(10 - 0.1n)$$
$$160 = n(10 - 0.1n)$$
$$160 = 10n - 0.1n^2$$
$$0.1n^2 - 10n + 160 = 0 \quad \Leftarrow \text{ divide by } 0.1$$
$$n^2 - 100n + 1600 = 0$$
$$(n-20)(n-80) = 0$$
$$n = 20 \quad \text{or} \quad n = 80$$

Disregard $n = 80$ since $n \le 32$. The business must sell 20 brooms.

Cumulative Review Test

1. $-4 \div (-2) + 16 - \sqrt{49}$
$$-4 \div (-2) + 16 - 7$$
$$2 + 16 - 7$$
$$18 - 7$$
$$11$$

2. Evaluate $2x^2 + 3x + 1$ when $x = 2$.
$$2(2)^2 + 3(2) + 1 = 8 + 6 + 1 = 15$$

3. $183{,}000 = 1.83 \times 10^5$

4. $|4 - 2x| = 5$

$$4 - 2x = 5 \qquad\qquad 4 - 2x = -5$$
$$-2x = 1 \qquad\qquad -2x = -9$$
$$x = -\frac{1}{2} \qquad\qquad x = \frac{9}{2}$$

The solution set is $\left\{-\dfrac{1}{2}, \dfrac{9}{2}\right\}$

5. $4x - \{3 - [2(x-2) - 5x]\}$

$4x - \{3 - [2x - 4 - 5x]\}$

$4x - \{3 - [-4 - 3x]\}$

$4x - \{3 + 4 + 3x\}$

$4x - \{7 + 3x\}$

$4x - 7 - 3x$

$x - 7$

6. $-\frac{1}{2}(4x-6) = \frac{1}{3}(3-6x) + 2$

$-2x + 3 = 1 - 2x + 2$

$-2x + 3 = -2x + 3$

This is an identity. The solution is all real numbers.

7. $-4 < \frac{x+4}{2} < 8$

$-8 < x + 4 < 16$

$-12 < x < 12$

In interval notation the solution is $(-12, 12)$.

8. $9x + 7y = 15$

$7y = -9x + 15$

$y = \frac{-9x + 15}{7} \Rightarrow y = -\frac{9}{7}x + \frac{15}{7}$

slope $= -\frac{9}{7}$

y-intercept is $\left(0, \frac{15}{7}\right)$

9. $N(x) = -0.2x^2 + 40x$

$N(50) = -0.2(50)^2 + 40(50)$

$= 1500$

50 trees would produce about 1500 baskets of apples.

10. $m = \frac{y_2 - y_1}{x_2 - x_1} = \frac{1-3}{2-4} = \frac{-2}{-2} = 1$

$y - y_1 = m(x - x_1)$

$y - 3 = 1(x - 4)$

$y - 3 = x - 4 \Rightarrow y = x - 1$

11. a. No, the graph is not a function since each x-value does not have a unique y-value.

b. The domain is the set of x-values, Domain: $\{x | x \ge -2\}$. The range is the set of y-values, Range: R

12. a. $x = -4$ is a vertical line.

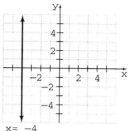

b. $y = 2$ is a horizontal line.

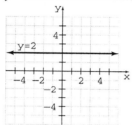

13. $\begin{vmatrix} 4 & 0 & -2 \\ 3 & 5 & 1 \\ 1 & -1 & 7 \end{vmatrix}$ (use row one)

$= 4 \begin{vmatrix} 5 & 1 \\ -1 & 7 \end{vmatrix} - 0 \begin{vmatrix} 3 & 1 \\ 1 & 7 \end{vmatrix} + (-2) \begin{vmatrix} 3 & 5 \\ 1 & -1 \end{vmatrix}$

$= 4(35 + 1) - 0(21 - 1) - 2(-3 - 5)$

$= 4(36) - 0(20) - 2(-8)$

$= 144 - 0 + 16$

$= 160$

14. $4x - 3y = 10$ (1)

$2x + y = 5$ (2)

In order to eliminate the y variable, multiply equation (2) by 3 and add the result to equation (1).

$4x - 3y = 10 \qquad\qquad 4x - 3y = 10$

$3(2x + y = 5) \Rightarrow \underline{6x + 3y = 15}$

$\qquad\qquad\qquad\qquad 10x \qquad = 25$

$\qquad\qquad\qquad\qquad x \qquad = \frac{5}{2}$

Substitute $\frac{5}{2}$ for x in equation (2) and solve for y.

$2\left(\dfrac{5}{2}\right) + y = 5$

$5 + y = 5 \implies y = 0$

The solution is $\left(\dfrac{5}{2}, 0\right)$.

15. $(x+5)^2 + 10(x+5) + 24$

$= \left((x+5)+4\right)\left((x+5)+6\right)$

$= (x+9)(x+11)$

16. **a.** $a^2 + 2ab + b^2$

b. $(a+b)^2$

17. $\dfrac{x+2}{x^2-x-6} + \dfrac{x-3}{x^2-8x+15}$

$= \dfrac{x+2}{(x-3)(x+2)} + \dfrac{x-3}{(x-5)(x-3)}$

$= \dfrac{1}{(x-3)} + \dfrac{1}{(x-5)}$

$= \dfrac{1}{x-3} \cdot \dfrac{x-5}{x-5} + \dfrac{1}{x-5} \cdot \dfrac{x-3}{x-3}$

$= \dfrac{x-5+x-3}{(x-3)(x-5)}$

$= \dfrac{2x-8}{(x-3)(x-5)}$ or $\dfrac{2(x-4)}{(x-3)(x-5)}$

18.

$\dfrac{1}{a-2} = \dfrac{4a-1}{a^2+5a-14} + \dfrac{2}{a+7}$

$\dfrac{1}{a-2} = \dfrac{4a-1}{(a+7)(a-2)} + \dfrac{2}{a+7}$

$(a+7)(a-2)\left[\dfrac{1}{a-2} = \dfrac{4a-1}{(a+7)(a-2)} + \dfrac{2}{a+7}\right]$

$a+7 = 4a-1+2(a-2)$

$a+7 = 4a-1+2a-4$

$a+7 = 6a-5$

$-5a+7 = -5$

$-5a = -12$

$a = \dfrac{12}{5}$

19. $w = kI^2 R, \ w = 12, \ I = 2, \ R = 100$

$12 = k\left(2^2\right)(100)$

$12 = 400k$

$\dfrac{12}{400} = k$

$k = \dfrac{3}{100}$

$w = \dfrac{3}{100}I^2 R, \ I = 0.8, R = 600$

$w = \dfrac{3}{100}(0.8)^2(600)$

$w = 11.52$

The wattage is 11.52 watts.

20. $\dfrac{3-4i}{2+3i} = \left(\dfrac{3-4i}{2+3i}\right)\left(\dfrac{2-3i}{2-3i}\right)$

$= \dfrac{6-17i+12i^2}{4-9i^2}$

$= \dfrac{6-17i-12}{4+9}$

$= \dfrac{-6-17i}{13}$

Chapter 9

Exercise Set 9.1

1. To find $(f \circ g)(x)$, substitute $g(x)$ for x in $f(x)$.

3. a. Each y has a unique x in a one-to-one function.

    b. Use the horizontal line test to determine whether a graph is one-to-one.

5. a. Yes; each first coordinate is paired with only one second coordinate.

    b. Yes; each second coordinate is paired with only one first coordinate.

    c. $\{(5, 3), (2, 4), (3, -1), (-2, 0)\}$ Reverse each ordered pair.

7. The domain of f is the range of f^{-1} and the range of f is the domain of f^{-1}.

9. $f(x) = x^2 + 1$, $g(x) = x + 5$

    a. $(f \circ g)(x) = (x+5)^2 + 1$
$$= x^2 + 10x + 25 + 1$$
$$= x^2 + 10x + 26$$

    b. $(f \circ g)(4) = 4^2 + 10(4) + 26 = 82w$

    c. $(g \circ f)(x) = (x^2 + 1) + 5 = x^2 + 6$

    d. $(g \circ f)(4) = 4^2 + 6 = 22$

11. $f(x) = x + 3$, $g(x) = x^2 + x - 4$

    a. $(f \circ g)(x) = (x^2 + x - 4) + 3 = x^2 + x - 1$

    b. $(f \circ g)(4) = 4^2 + 4 - 1 = 19$

    c. $(g \circ f)(x) = (x+3)^2 + (x+3) - 4$
$$= x^2 + 6x + 9 + x + 3 - 4$$
$$= x^2 + 7x + 8$$

    d. $(g \circ f)(4) = 4^2 + 7(4) + 8 = 52$

13. $f(x) = \frac{1}{x}$, $g(x) = 2x + 3$

    a. $(f \circ g)(x) = \frac{1}{2x + 3}$

    b. $(f \circ g)(4) = \frac{1}{2(4) + 3} = \frac{1}{11}$

    c. $(g \circ f)(x) = 2\left(\frac{1}{x}\right) + 3 = \frac{2}{x} + 3$

    d. $(g \circ f)(4) = \frac{2}{4} + 3 = 3\frac{1}{2}$

15. $f(x) = \frac{2}{x}$, $g(x) = x^2 + 1$

    a. $(f \circ g)(x) = \frac{2}{x^2 + 1}$

    b. $(f \circ g)(4) = \frac{2}{4^2 + 1} = \frac{2}{17}$

    c. $(g \circ f)(x) = \left(\frac{2}{x}\right)^2 + 1 = \frac{4}{x^2} + 1$

    d. $(g \circ f)(4) = \frac{4}{4^2} + 1 = 1\frac{1}{4}$

17. $f(x) = x^2 + 1$, $g(x) = x^2 + 5$

    a. $(f \circ g)(x) = (x^2 + 5)^2 + 1$
$$= x^4 + 10x^2 + 25 + 1$$
$$= x^4 + 10x^2 + 26$$

    b. $(f \circ g)(4) = 4^4 + 10(4)^2 + 26 = 442$

    c. $(g \circ f)(x) = (x^2 + 1)^2 + 5$
$$= x^4 + 2x^2 + 1 + 5$$
$$= x^4 + 2x^2 + 6$$

    d. $(g \circ f)(4) = 4^4 + 2(4)^2 + 6 = 294$

19. $f(x) = x - 4$, $g(x) = \sqrt{x + 5}$, $x \geq -5$

    a. $(f \circ g)(x) = \sqrt{x + 5} - 4$

    b. $(f \circ g)(4) = \sqrt{4 + 5} - 4$
$$= \sqrt{9} - 4$$
$$= 3 - 4$$
$$= -1$$

    c. $(g \circ f)(x) = \sqrt{(x - 4) + 5} = \sqrt{x + 1}$

    d. $(g \circ f)(4) = \sqrt{4 + 1} = \sqrt{5}$

21. This function is not a one-to-one function since it does not pass the horizontal line test.

23. This function is a one-to-one function since it passes both the vertical line test and the horizontal line test.

25. Yes, the ordered pairs represent a one-to-one function. For each value of x there is a unique value for y and each y-value has a unique x-value.

27. No, the ordered pairs do not represent a one-to-one function. For each value of x there is a unique y, but for each y-value there is not a unique x since $(-4, 2)$ and $(0, 2)$ are ordered pairs in the given set.

29. $y = 2x + 4$ is a line with a slope of 2 and having a y-intercept of 4. It is a one-to-one function since it passes both the vertical line test and the horizontal line test.

31. $y = x^2 - 4$ is a parabola with vertex at $(0, -4)$. It is not a one-to-one function since it does not pass the horizontal line test. Horizontal lines above $y = -4$ intersect the graph in 2 different points.

33. $y = x^2 - 2x + 6$ is a parabola with vertex at $(1, 5)$. It is not a one-to-one function since it does not pass the horizontal line test. Horizontal lines above $y = 5$ intersect the graph in two different points.

35. $y = x^2 - 4$, $x \geq 0$ is the right side of the parabola from Exercise 31. It is a one-to-one function since it passes both the vertical line test and the horizontal line test.

37. $y = |x|$. It is not a one-to-one function since it does not pass the vertical line test and the horizontal line test.

39. $y = -\sqrt{x}$ is a one-to-one function since it passes both the vertical line test and the horizontal line test.

41. $y = x^3$ is a one-to-one function since it passes both the vertical line test and the horizontal line test.

43. For $f(x)$: Domain: $\{-2, -1, 2, 4, 9\}$
Range: $\{0, 3, 4, 6, 7\}$
For $f^{-1}(x)$: Domain: $\{0, 3, 4, 6, 7\}$
Range: $\{-2, -1, 2, 4, 9\}$

45. For $f(x)$: Domain: $\{-1, 1, 2, 4\}$
Range: $\{-3, -1, 0, 2\}$
For $f^{-1}(x)$: Domain: $\{-3, -1, 0, 2\}$
Range: $\{-1, 1, 2, 4\}$

47. For $f(x)$: Domain: $\{x | x \geq 2\}$
Range: $\{y | y \geq 0\}$
For $f^{-1}(x)$: Domain: $\{x | x \geq 0\}$
Range: $\{y | y \geq 2\}$

49. **a.** Yes, $f(x) = x - 3$ is a one-to-one function.

    b.
$$y = x - 3$$
$$x = y - 3$$
$$x + 3 = y$$
$$y = x + 3$$
$$f^{-1}(x) = x + 3$$

51. **a.** Yes, $h(x) = 5x$ is a one-to-one function.

    b.
$$y = 5x$$
$$x = 5y$$
$$y = \frac{x}{5}$$
$$h^{-1}(x) = \frac{x}{5}$$

53. **a.** No, $p(x) = x^2$ is not a one-to-one function.

    b. Does not exist

55. **a.** No; $t(x) = x^2 + 3$ is not a one-to-one function.

    b. Does not exist

57. a. Yes; $g(x) = \dfrac{1}{x}$ is a one-to-one function.

b.
$$y = \frac{1}{x}$$
$$x = \frac{1}{y}$$
$$y = \frac{1}{x}$$
$$g^{-1}(x) = \frac{1}{x}$$

59`. a. No; $f(x) = x^2 + 4$ is not a one-to-one function.

b. Does not exist

61. a. Yes, $g(x) = x^3 - 5$ is a one-to-one function.

b.
$$y = x^3 - 5$$
$$x = y^3 - 5$$
$$x + 5 = y^3$$
$$\sqrt[3]{x + 5} = y$$
$$g^{-1}(x) = \sqrt[3]{x + 5}$$

63. a. Yes, $g(x) = \sqrt{x + 2}$, $x \geq -2$ is a one-to-one function.

b.
$$y = \sqrt{x + 2}$$
$$x = \sqrt{y + 2}$$
$$x^2 = y + 2$$
$$x^2 - 2 = y$$
$$g^{-1}(x) = x^2 - 2, \ x \geq 0$$

65. a. Yes, $h(x) = x^2 - 4, \ x \geq 0$ is a one-to-one function.

b.
$$y = x^2 - 4$$
$$x = y^2 - 4$$
$$x + 4 = y^2$$
$$y = \sqrt{x + 4}$$
$$h^{-1}(x) = \sqrt{x + 4}, \ x \geq -4$$

67. $f(x) = 2x + 8$

a.
$$y = 2x + 8$$
$$x = 2y + 8$$
$$x - 8 = 2y$$
$$\frac{x - 8}{2} = y$$
$$f^{-1}(x) = \frac{x - 8}{2}$$

b.

x	$f(x)$
0	8
−4	0

x	$f^{-1}(x)$
0	−4
8	0

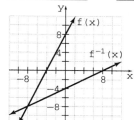

69. $f(x) = \sqrt{x}$, $x \geq 0$

a.
$$y = \sqrt{x}$$
$$x = \sqrt{y}$$
$$x^2 = \left(\sqrt{y}\right)^2$$
$$x^2 = y$$
$$f^{-1}(x) = x^2 \text{ for } x \geq 0$$

b.

x	$f(x)$
0	0
1	1
4	2

x	$f^{-1}(x)$
0	0
1	1
2	4

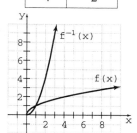

71. $f(x) = \sqrt{x+4}, \ x \geq -4$

   a. $y = \sqrt{x+4}$

           $x = \sqrt{y+4}$

           $x^2 = \left(\sqrt{y+4}\right)^2$

           $x^2 = y + 4$

         $x^2 - 4 = y$

         $f^{-1}(x) = x^2 - 4 \ \text{ for } x \geq 0$

   b.

x	$f(x)$
-4	0
-3	1
0	2

x	$f^{-1}(x)$
0	-4
1	-3
2	0

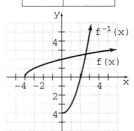

73. $f(x) = \sqrt[3]{x}$

   a. $y = \sqrt[3]{x}$

         $x = \sqrt[3]{y}$

         $x^3 = \left(\sqrt[3]{y}\right)^3$

         $x^3 = y$

         $f^{-1}(x) = x^3$

   b.

x	$f(x)$
-8	-2
-1	-1
0	0
1	1
8	2

x	$f^{-1}(x)$
-2	-8
-1	-1
0	0
1	1
2	8

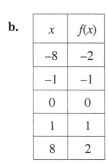

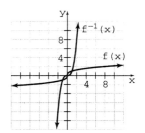

75. $f(x) = \dfrac{1}{x}, \ x > 0$

   a. $y = \dfrac{1}{x}$

         $x = \dfrac{1}{y}$

         $xy = 1$

         $y = \dfrac{1}{x}$

         $f^{-1}(x) = \dfrac{1}{x}, \ x > 0$

   b.

x	$f(x)$
$\dfrac{1}{2}$	2
1	1
3	$\dfrac{1}{3}$

x	$f^{-1}(x)$
2	$\dfrac{1}{2}$
1	1
$\dfrac{1}{3}$	3

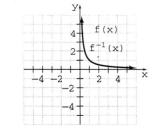

77. $(f \circ f^{-1})(x) = (x + 4) - 4 = x$

     $(f^{-1} \circ f)(x) = (x - 4) + 4 = x$

79.

$$(f \circ f^{-1})(x) = \frac{1}{2}(2x - 10) + 5$$

$$= x - 5 + 5$$

$$= x$$

$$(f^{-1} \circ f)(x) = 2\left(\frac{1}{2}x + 5\right) - 10$$

$$= x + 10 - 10$$

$$= x$$

81.
$$(f \circ f^{-1})(x) = \sqrt[3]{(x^3 + 2) - 2}$$
$$= \sqrt[3]{x^3}$$
$$= x$$
$$(f^{-1} \circ f)(x) = \left(\sqrt[3]{x - 2}\right)^3 + 2$$
$$= x - 2 + 2$$
$$= x$$

83.
$$(f \circ f^{-1})(x) = \frac{2}{\frac{2}{x}} = 2 \cdot \frac{x}{2} = x$$
$$(f^{-1} \circ f)(x) = \frac{2}{\frac{2}{x}} = 2 \cdot \frac{x}{2} = x$$

85. No, composition of functions is not commutative.
Let $f(x) = x^2$ and $g(x) = x + 1$.
Then $(f \circ g)(x) = (x + 1)^2 = x^2 + 2x + 1$ while $(g \circ f)(x) = x^2 + 1$.

87. a.
$$(f \circ g)(x) = f[g(x)]$$
$$= \left(\sqrt[3]{x - 2}\right)^3 + 2$$
$$= x - 2 + 2$$
$$= x$$
$$(g \circ f)(x) = g[f(x)]$$
$$= \sqrt[3]{\left(x^3 + 2\right) - 2}$$
$$= \sqrt[3]{x^3}$$
$$= x$$

b. The domain of f is all real numbers and the domain of g is all real numbers. The domains of $(f \circ g)(x)$ and $(g \circ f)(x)$ are also all real numbers.

89. The range of $f^{-1}(x)$ is the domain of $f(x)$.

91. $f(x) = 3x$ converts yards, x, into feet, y.
$$y = 3x$$
$$x = 3y$$
$$\frac{x}{3} = y$$
$$f^{-1}(x) = \frac{x}{3}$$
Here, x is feet and $f^{-1}(x)$ is yards. The inverse function converts feet to yards.

93. $f(x) = \frac{5}{9}(x - 32)$
$$y = \frac{5}{9}(x - 32)$$
$$x = \frac{5}{9}(y - 32)$$
$$\frac{9}{5}x = \frac{9}{5}\left[\frac{5}{9}(y - 32)\right]$$
$$\frac{9}{5}x = y - 32$$
$$\frac{9}{5}x + 32 = y$$
$$f^{-1}(x) = \frac{9}{5}x + 32$$

Here, x is degrees Celsius and $f^{-1}(x)$ is degrees Fahrenheit. The inverse function converts Celsius to Fahrenheit.

95.

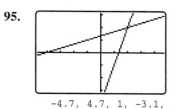

−4.7, 4.7, 1, −3.1,

Yes, the functions are inverses.

97.

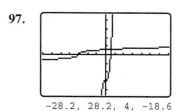

−28.2, 28.2, 4, −18.6

Yes, the functions are inverses.

99. a. $r(3) = 2(3) = 6$
The radius is 6 feet.

b. $A = \pi r^2$
$A = \pi(6)^2$
$A = 36\pi \approx 113.10$
The surface area is $36\pi \approx 113.10$ square feet.

c. $(A \circ r)(t) = \pi(2t)^2 = \pi(4t^2) = 4\pi t^2$

d. $4\pi(3)^2 = 4\pi(9) = 36\pi$

e. The answers agree.

103. First find the slope of the given line.
$$2x + 3y - 9 = 0$$
$$3y = -2x + 9$$
$$y = -\frac{2}{3}x + 3 \implies m = -\frac{2}{3}$$
Now use this slope together with the given point $\left(\frac{1}{2}, 3\right)$ to find the equation.

point - slope form:
$$y - y_1 = m(x - x_1)$$
$$y - 3 = -\frac{2}{3}\left(x - \frac{1}{2}\right)$$
$$y - 3 = -\frac{2}{3}x + \frac{1}{3}$$
$$3\left(y - 3 = -\frac{2}{3}x + \frac{1}{3}\right)$$
$$3y - 9 = -2x + 1$$
$$2x + 3y = 10$$

105. $\dfrac{1}{f} = \dfrac{1}{p} + \dfrac{1}{q}$ for p

$$fpq\left(\frac{1}{f} = \frac{1}{p} + \frac{1}{q}\right)$$
$$pq = fq + fp$$
$$pq - fp = fq$$
$$p(q - f) = fq$$
$$p = \frac{fq}{q - f}$$

Exercise Set 9.2

1. Exponential functions are functions of the form
$$f(x) = a^x, a > 0, \ a \neq 1.$$

3. a. $y = \left(\dfrac{1}{2}\right)^x$; as x increases, y decreases.

b. No, y can never be zero because $\left(\dfrac{1}{2}\right)^x$ can never be 0.

c. No, y can never be negative because $\left(\dfrac{1}{2}\right)^x$ is never negative.

5. $y = 2^x$ and $y = 3^x$

a. Let $x = 0$
$$\begin{array}{ll} y = 2^0 & y = 3^0 \\ y = 1 & y = 1 \end{array}$$
They have the same y-intercepts at $(0, 1)$.

b. $y = 3^x$ will be steeper than $y = 2^x$ for $x > 0$.

7. $y = 2^x$

x	-2	-1	0	1	2
y	$\frac{1}{4}$	$\frac{1}{2}$	1	2	4

Domain: R
R: $\{y | y > 0\}$

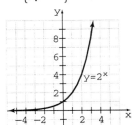

9. $y = \left(\dfrac{1}{2}\right)^x$

x	-2	-1	0	1	2
y	4	2	1	$\frac{1}{2}$	$\frac{1}{4}$

Domain: R
R: $\{y | y > 0\}$

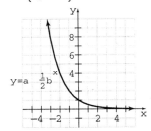

11. $y = 4^x$

x	-2	-1	0	1	2
y	$\frac{1}{16}$	$\frac{1}{4}$	1	4	16

Domain: R

R: $\left\{ y \mid y > 0 \right\}$

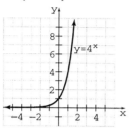

13. $y = \left(\frac{1}{4}\right)^x$

x	-2	-1	0	1	2
y	16	4	1	$\frac{1}{4}$	$\frac{1}{16}$

Domain: R

R: $\left\{ y \mid y > 0 \right\}$

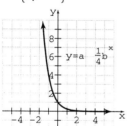

15. $y = 3^{-x} = \dfrac{1}{3^x} = \left(\dfrac{1}{3}\right)^x$

x	-2	-1	0	1	2
y	9	3	1	$\frac{1}{3}$	$\frac{1}{9}$

Domain: R

R: $\left\{ y \mid y > 0 \right\}$

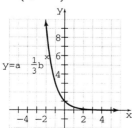

17. $y = \left(\dfrac{1}{3}\right)^{-x} = 3^x$

x	-2	-1	0	1	2
y	$\frac{1}{9}$	$\frac{1}{3}$	1	3	9

Domain: R

R: $\left\{ y \mid y > 0 \right\}$

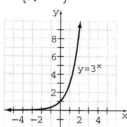

19. $y = 2^{x-1}$

x	-2	0	2	4	6
y	$\frac{1}{8}$	$\frac{1}{2}$	2	8	32

Domain: R

Range: $\left\{ y \mid y > 0 \right\}$

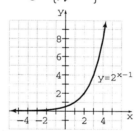

21. $y = \left(\dfrac{1}{3}\right)^{x+1}$

x	-3	-2	-1	0	1
y	9	3	1	$\frac{1}{3}$	$\frac{1}{9}$

Domain: R

R: $\left\{ y \mid y > 0 \right\}$

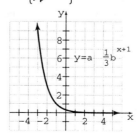

23. $y = 2^x - 1$

x	-2	-1	0	1	2	3
y	$-\frac{3}{4}$	$-\frac{1}{2}$	0	1	3	7

Domain: R

Range: $\left\{ y | y > -1 \right\}$

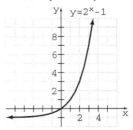

25. $y = 3^x - 1$

x	-2	-1	0	1	2
y	$-\frac{8}{9}$	$-\frac{2}{3}$	0	2	8

Domain: R

Range: $\left\{ y | y > -1 \right\}$

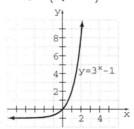

27. a. The graph is the horizontal line through $y = 1$.

b. Yes. A horizontal line will pass the vertical line test.

c. No. $f(x)$ is not one-to-one and therefore does not have an inverse function.

29. $y = a^x - k$ will have the same basic shape as the graph $y = a^x$. However, $y = a^x - k$ will be k units lower than $y = a^x$.

31. The graph of $y = a^{x+2}$ is the graph of $y = a^x$ shifted 2 units to the left.

33. a.

Cellular Phone Subscrib

b. 200 years

c. 40 years

35. $g = 2^n$, $n = 8$

$g = 2^8 = 256$

The plant has 256 gametes.

37. $N(t) = 4(3)^t$, $t = 2$

$N(2) = 4(3)^2 = 4 \cdot 9 = 36$

There will be 36 bacteria in the petri dish after two days.

39. $A = p\left(1 + \dfrac{r}{n}\right)^{nt}$

Use $p = 5000$,

$r = 6\% = 0.06$ and $n = 4$ and $t = 4$.

$A = 5000\left(1 + \dfrac{0.06}{4}\right)^{4 \cdot 4}$

$A = 5000(1 + 0.015)^{16}$

$A = 5000(1.015)^{16}$

$A \approx 5000(1.2689855)$

$A \approx 6344.93$

He has \$6344.93 after 4 years.

41. $A = A_0 2^{-t/5600}$

Use $A_0 = 12$ and $t = 1000$.

$A = 12(2^{-1000/5600})$

$A \approx 12(2^{-0.18})$

$A \approx 12(0.88)$

$A \approx 10.6$ grams

There are about 10.6 grams left.

43. $y = 80(2)^{-0.4t}$

a. $t = 10$

$y = 80(2)^{-0.4(10)}$

$y = 80(2)^{-4} = 80\left(\dfrac{1}{16}\right)$

$y = 5$

After 10 years, 5 grams remain.

b. $t = 100$

$y = 80(2)^{-0.4(100)}$

$y = 80(2)^{-40}$

$y \approx 80(9.094947 \times 10^{-13})$

$y \approx 7.28 \times 10^{-11}$

After 100 years, about 7.28×10^{-11} grams are left.

45. $y = 2000(1.2)^{0.1x}$

    a. $x = 10$

        $y = 2000(1.2)^{0.1(10)}$

        $y = 2000(1.2)^{1}$

        $y = 2400$

        In 10 years, the population is expected to be 2400.

    b. $x = 100$

        $y = 2000(1.2)^{0.1(100)}$

        $y = 2000(1.2)^{10}$

        $y \approx 2000(6.1917364)$

        $y \approx 12,383$

        In 100 years, the population is expected to be about 12,383.

47. $V(t) = 24,000(0.82)^{t}$, $t = 4$

$V(t) = 24,000(0.82)^{4} \approx 10,850.92$

The SUV will be worth about $10,850.92 in 4 years.

49. a. Answers will vary. One possible answer is: Since the amount is reduced by 5%, the consumption is 95% of the previous year, or 0.95. Thus, $A(t) = 116,000(0.95)^{t}$.

    b. $t = 2003 - 1998 = 5$

        $A(5) = 116,000(0.95)^{5}$

        $A \approx 116,000(0.7737809)$

        $\approx 89,758.6$

        The expected average use in 2003 is about 89,758.6 gallons.

51. $A = 41.97(0.996)^{x}$

$A(389) = 41.97(0.996)^{389}$

$A \approx 8.83$

The altitude at the top of Mt. Everest is about 8.83 kilometers.

53. a. $A = p\left(1 + \dfrac{r}{n}\right)^{nt}$

        $A = 100\left(1 + \dfrac{0.07}{365}\right)^{365 \cdot 10}$

        $A \approx 100(1.0001918)^{3650}$

        $A = 201.36$

        The amount is $201.36.

    b. For simple interest,

        $A = 100 + 100(0.07)t$

        $A = 100 + 100(0.07)(10)$

        $A = 100 + 70$

        $A = 170$

        $201.36 - $170 = $31.36

55. a. $y_1 = 3^{x-5}$

        $-10, 10, 1, -10, 1($

    b. $4 = 3^{x-5}$ when $x \approx 6.26$.

57. a. Day 15: $2^{15-1} = 2^{14} = $16,384$

    b. Day 20: $2^{20-1} = 2^{19} = $524,288$

    c. nth Day: 2^{n-1}

    d. Day 30: $2^{30-1} = $2^{29} = $536,870,912$

    e. $2^{0} + 2^{1} + 2^{2} + \cdots + 2^{29}$

59. a. $2.3x^{4}y - 6.2x^{6}y^{2} + 9.2x^{5}y^{2}$

        $= -6.2x^{6}y^{2} + 9.2x^{5}y^{2} + 2.3x^{4}y$

    b. $-6.2x^{6}y^{2}$ is the leading term.

        $6 + 2 = 8$ is the degree of the polynomial.

    c. $-6.2x^{6}y^{2}$ is the leading term, so -6.2 is the leading coefficient.

61. $\sqrt{a^{2} - 8a + 16} = \sqrt{(a-4)^{2}} = |a - 4|$

Exercise Set 9.3

1. $y = \log_a x$

   a. The base a must be positive and must not be equal to one.

   b. The argument x represents a number that is greater than 0. Thus, the domain is $\{x | x \text{ is a real number and } x > 0\}$.

   c. R

3. The functions $f(x) = a^x$ and $g(x) = \log_a x$ are inverse functions. Therefore, some of the points on the function are $g(x) = \log_a x$ are $\left(\frac{1}{27}, -3\right)\left(\frac{1}{9}, -2\right)$, $\left(\frac{1}{3}, -1\right)$(1, 0), (3, 1), (9, 2), and (27, 3).

5. The functions $y = a^x$ and $y = \log_a x$ for $a \neq 1$ are inverses of each other, thus the graphs are symmetric with respect to the line $y = x$. For each ordered pair (x, y) on the graph of $y = a^x$, the ordered pair (y, x) is on the graph of $y = \log_a x$.

7. $y = \log_2 x$
   Convert to exponential form.
   $2^y = x$

x	$\frac{1}{4}$	$\frac{1}{2}$	1	2	4
y	-2	-1	0	1	2

   Domain: $\{x | x > 0\}$
   Range: R

   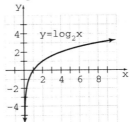

9. $y = \log_{1/2} x$
   Convert to exponential form.
   $x = \left(\frac{1}{2}\right)^y$

x	4	2	1	$\frac{1}{2}$	$\frac{1}{4}$
y	-2	-1	0	1	2

Domain: $\{x | x > 0\}$
Range: R

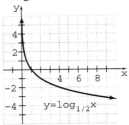

11. $y = \log_5 x$
    Convert to the exponential form.
    $x = 5^y$

x	$\frac{1}{25}$	$\frac{1}{5}$	1	5	25
y	-2	-1	0	1	2

Domain: $\{x | x > 0\}$
Range: R

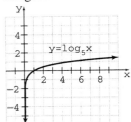

13. $y = \log_{1/5} x$ Convert to exponential form.
    $x = \left(\frac{1}{5}\right)^y$

x	25	5	1	$\frac{1}{5}$	$\frac{1}{25}$
y	-2	-1	0	1	2

Domain: $\{x | x > 0\}$
Range: R

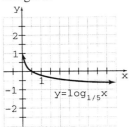

15. $y = 2^x$

x	-2	-1	0	1	2
y	$\frac{1}{4}$	$\frac{1}{2}$	1	2	4

$y = \log_{1/2} x$

Convert to exponential form.

$x = \left(\frac{1}{2}\right)^y$

x	4	2	1	$\frac{1}{2}$	$\frac{1}{4}$
y	-2	-1	0	1	2

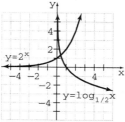

17. $y = 2^x$

x	-2	-1	0	1	2
y	$\frac{1}{4}$	$\frac{1}{2}$	1	2	4

$y = \log_2 x$

Convert to exponential form.

$x = 2^y$

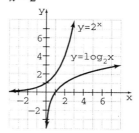

19. $\quad 2^3 = 8$

$\log_2 8 = 3$

21. $\quad 3^2 = 9$

$\log_3 9 = 2$

23. $\quad 16^{1/2} = 4$

$\log_{16} 4 = \frac{1}{2}$

25. $\quad 8^{1/3} = 2$

$\log_8 2 = \frac{1}{3}$

27. $\quad \left(\frac{1}{2}\right)^5 = \frac{1}{32}$

$\log_{1/2}\left(\frac{1}{32}\right) = 5$

29. $\quad 2^{-3} = \frac{1}{8}$

$\log_2 \frac{1}{8} = -3$

31. $\quad 4^{-3} = \frac{1}{64}$

$\log_4 \frac{1}{64} = -3$

33. $\quad 64^{1/3} = 4$

$\log_{64} 4 = \frac{1}{3}$

35. $\quad 16^{-1/2} = \frac{1}{4}$

$\log_{16} \frac{1}{4} = -\frac{1}{2}$

37. $\quad 32^{-1/5} = \frac{1}{2}$

$\log_{32} \frac{1}{2} = -\frac{1}{5}$

39. $10^{0.6990} = 5$

$\log_{10} 5 = 0.6990$

41. $\quad e^2 = 7.3891$

$\log_e 7.3891 = 2$

43. $\quad c^b = w$

$\log_c w = b$

45. $\log_2 8 = 3$

$\quad 2^3 = 8$

47. $\log_{1/3} \frac{1}{27} = 3$

$\left(\frac{1}{3}\right)^3 = \frac{1}{27}$

49. $\log_5 \dfrac{1}{625} = -4$

$$5^{-4} = \dfrac{1}{625}$$

51. $\log_{81} 9 = \dfrac{1}{2}$

$$81^{1/2} = 9$$

53. $\log_8 \dfrac{1}{64} = -2$

$$8^{-2} = \dfrac{1}{64}$$

55. $\log_{27} \dfrac{1}{3} = -\dfrac{1}{3}$

$$27^{-1/3} = \dfrac{1}{3}$$

57. $\log_6 216 = 3$

$$6^3 = 216$$

59. $\log_{10} 8 = 0.9031$
$10^{0.9031} = 8$

61. $\log_e 6.52 = 1.8749$
$$e^{1.8749} = 6.52$$

63. $\log_r c = -a$
$$r^{-a} = c$$

65. $\log_4 16 = y$
$$4^y = 16$$
$$4^y = 4^2$$
$$y = 2$$

67. $\log_a 81 = 4$
$$a^4 = 81$$
$$a^4 = 3^4$$
$$a = 3$$

69. $\log_2 x = 5$
$$2^5 = x$$
$$32 = x$$

71. $\log_2 \dfrac{1}{8} = y$

$$2^y = \dfrac{1}{8}$$
$$2^y = 2^{-3}$$
$$y = -3$$

73. $\log_{1/2} x = 2$

$$\left(\dfrac{1}{2}\right)^2 = x$$

$$\dfrac{1}{4} = x$$

75. $\log_a \dfrac{1}{27} = -3$

$$a^{-3} = \dfrac{1}{27}$$
$$a^{-3} = 3^{-3}$$
$$a = 3$$

77. $\log_{10} 100 = 2$ because $10^2 = 100$

79. $\log_{10} 10 = 1$ because $10^1 = 10$

81. $\log_{10} \dfrac{1}{10} = -1$ because $10^{-1} = \dfrac{1}{10^1} = \dfrac{1}{10}$

83. $\log_{10} 10,000 = 4$ because $10^4 = 10,000$

85. $\log_4 64 = 3$ because $4^3 = 64$

87. $\log_3 \dfrac{1}{81} = -4$ because $3^{-4} = \dfrac{1}{3^4} = \dfrac{1}{81}$

89. $\log_8 \dfrac{1}{64} = -2$ because $8^{-2} = \dfrac{1}{8^2} = \dfrac{1}{64}$

91. $\log_7 1 = 0$ because $7^0 = 1$

93. $\log_9 9 = 1$ because $9^1 = 9$

95. $\log_4 1024 = 5$ because $4^5 = 1024$

97. If $f(x) = 4^x$, then $f^{-1}(x) = \log_4 x$.

99. $\log_{10} 425$ lies between 2 and 3 since 425 lies between $10^2 = 100$ and $10^3 = 1000$.

101. $\log_3 62$ lies between 3 and 4 since 62 lies between $3^3 = 27$ and $3^4 = 81$.

103. For $x > 1$, 2^x will grow faster than $\log_{10} x$. Note that when $x = 10$, $2^x = 1024$ while $\log_{10} x = 1$.

105. $x = \log_{10} 10^5$
$$10^x = 10^5$$
$$x = 5$$

107. $x = \log_b b^3$
$b^x = b^3$
$x = 3$

109. $x = 10^{\log_{10} 8}$
$\log_{10} x = \log_{10} 8$
$x = 8$

111. $x = b^{\log_b 9}$
$\log_b x = \log_b 9$
$x = 9$

113. $R = \log_{10} I$
$7 = \log_{10} I$
$10^7 = I$
$I = 10,000,000$
The earthquake is 10,000,000 times more intense than the smallest measurable activity.

115.

$R = \log_{10} I$	$R = \log_{10} I$
$6 = \log_{10} I$	$2 = \log_{10} I$
$10^6 = I$	$10^2 = I$
$1,000,000 = I$	$100 = I$

$\dfrac{1,000,000}{100} = 10,000$

An earthquake that measures 6 is 10,000 times more intense than one that measures 2.

117. $y = \log_2 (x - 1)$ or $2^y = x - 1$

x	$1\frac{1}{4}$	$1\frac{1}{2}$	2	3	5
y	-2	-1	0	1	2

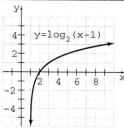

119. $3x^3 - 12x^2 - 36x = 3x\left(x^2 - 4x - 12\right)$
$= 3x(x - 6)(x + 2)$

121. $40x^2 + 52x - 12 = 4\left(10x^2 + 13x - 3\right)$
$= 4(5x - 1)(2x + 3)$

Exercise Set 9.4

1.   Answers will vary.

3.   Answers will vary.

5.   Yes. This is true because of the product rule for logarithms.

7. $\log_4 (3 \cdot 10) = \log_4 3 + \log_4 10$

9. $\log_8 7(x + 3) = \log_8 7 + \log_8 (x + 3)$

11. $\log_6 \dfrac{27}{5} = \log_6 27 - \log_6 5$

13. $\log_{10} \dfrac{\sqrt{x}}{x - 9} = \log_{10} \dfrac{x^{1/2}}{x - 9}$
$= \log_{10} x^{1/2} - \log_{10}(x - 9)$
$= \dfrac{1}{2} \log_{10} x - \log_{10}(x - 9)$

15. $\log_6 x^7 = 7 \log_6 x$

17. $\log_9 10(4^6) = \log_9 10 + \log_9 4^6$
$= \log_9 10 + 6 \log_9 4$

19. $\log_4 \sqrt{\dfrac{a^3}{a + 2}} = \log_4 \left(\dfrac{a^3}{a + 2}\right)^{1/2}$
$= \dfrac{1}{2} \log_4 \dfrac{a^3}{a + 2}$
$= \dfrac{1}{2}[\log_4 a^3 - \log_4 (a + 2)]$
$= \dfrac{1}{2}[3 \log_4 a - \log_4 (a + 2)]$
$= \dfrac{3}{2} \log_4 a - \dfrac{1}{2} \log_4 (a + 2)$

21. $\log_3 \dfrac{d^6}{(a - 5)^4} = \log_3 d^6 - \log_3 (a - 5)^4$
$= 6 \log_3 d - 4 \log_3 (a - 5)$

23. $\log_8 \dfrac{y(y + 2)}{y^3} = \log_8 y + \log_8 (y + 2) - \log_8 y^3$
$= \log_8 y + \log_8 (y + 2) - 3 \log_8 y$
$= -2 \log_8 y + \log_8 (y + 2)$

25.

$$\log_{10} \frac{2m}{3n} = \log_{10} 2m - \log_{10} 3n$$
$$= \log_{10} 2 + \log_{10} m - (\log_{10} 3 + \log_{10} n)$$
$$= \log_{10} 2 + \log_{10} m - \log_{10} 3 - \log_{10} n$$

27. $\log_5 2 + \log_5 3 = \log_5 6$

29. $\log_2 9 - \log_2 5 = \log_2 \dfrac{9}{5}$

31. $5\log_4 2 = \log_4 2^5 = \log_4 32$

33. $\log_{10} x + \log_{10}(x+3) = \log_{10} x(x+3)$

35.

$$2\log_9 z - \log_9(z-2) = \log_9 z^2 - \log_9(z-2)$$
$$= \log_9 \frac{z^2}{z-2}$$

37.

$$2(\log_5 p - \log_5 3) = 2\log_5 \frac{p}{3}$$
$$= \log_5 \left(\frac{p}{3}\right)^2$$

39.

$$\log_2 n + \log_2(n+4) - \log_2(n-3)$$
$$\log_2 n(n+4) - \log_2(n-3)$$
$$\log_2 \frac{n(n+4)}{n-3}$$

41.

$$\frac{1}{2}\big[\log_5(x-4) - \log_5 x\big] = \frac{1}{2}\log_5 \frac{x-4}{x}$$
$$= \log_5 \left[\frac{x-4}{x}\right]^{1/2}$$
$$= \log_5 \frac{\sqrt{x-4}}{x}$$

43.

$$2\log_9 5 + \frac{1}{3}\log_9(r-6) - \frac{1}{2}\log_9 r$$
$$= \log_9 5^2 + \log_9(r-6)^{1/3} - \log_9 r^{1/2}$$
$$= \log_9 25 + \log_9 \sqrt[3]{r-6} - \log_9 \sqrt{r}$$
$$= \log_9 25\sqrt[3]{r-6} - \log_9 \sqrt{r}$$
$$= \log_9 \frac{25\sqrt[3]{r-6}}{\sqrt{r}}$$

45.

$$4\log_6 3 - [2\log_6(x+3) + 4\log_6 x]$$
$$= \log_6 3^4 - [\log_6(x+3)^2 + \log_6 x^4]$$
$$= \log_6 3^4 - \log_6(x+3)^2 x^4$$
$$= \log_6 \frac{3^4}{(x+3)^2 x^4}$$

47.

$$\log_a 10 = \log_a (2)(5)$$
$$= \log_a 2 + \log_a(5)$$
$$= 0.3010 + 0.6990$$
$$= 1$$

49.

$$\log_a 2.5 = \log_a \frac{5}{2}$$
$$= \log_a 5 - \log_a 2$$
$$= 0.6990 - 0.3010$$
$$= 0.3980$$

51.

$$\log_a 25 = \log_a 5^2$$
$$= 2(\log_a 5)$$
$$= 2(0.6990)$$
$$= 1.3980$$

53. $5^{\log_5 10} = 10$

55. $\left(2^3\right)^{\log_8 5} = 8^{\log_8 5} = 5$

57. $\log_3 27 = \log_3 3^3 = 3$

59.

$$5\left(\sqrt[3]{27}\right)^{\log_3 5} = 5(3)^{\log_3 5}$$
$$= 5(5)$$
$$= 25$$

61. Yes

63.

$$\log_a \frac{x}{y} = \log_a xy^{-1}$$
$$= \log_a x + \log_a y^{-1}$$
$$= \log_a x + \log_a \frac{1}{y}$$

65.

$$\log_a(x^2 - 4) - \log_a(x+2) = \log_a \frac{x^2 - 4}{x+2}$$
$$= \log_a \frac{(x+2)(x-2)}{x+2}$$
$$= \log_a(x-2)$$

67. Yes; $\log_a(x^2+8x+16) = \log_a(x+4)^2$
$$= 2\log_a(x+4)$$

69. $\log_{10} x^2 = 2\log_{10} x$
$$= 2(0.4320)$$
$$= 0.8640$$

71. $\log_{10}\sqrt[4]{x} = \log_{10} x^{1/4}$
$$= \frac{1}{4}\log_{10} x$$
$$= \frac{1}{4}(0.4320) = 0.1080$$

73. $\log_{10} xy = \log_{10} x + \log_{10} y$
$$= 0.5000 + 0.2000$$
$$= 0.7000$$

75. No; answers will vary.

77. $\log_2 \dfrac{\sqrt[4]{xy}\,\sqrt[3]{a}}{\sqrt[5]{a-b}} = \log_2\sqrt[4]{xy}\,\sqrt[3]{a} - \log_2\sqrt[5]{a-b}$
$$= \log_2(xy)^{1/4} + \log_2 a^{1/3} - \log_2(a-b)^{1/5}$$
$$= \frac{1}{4}\log_2 xy + \frac{1}{3}\log_2 a - \frac{1}{5}\log_2(a-b)$$
$$= \frac{1}{4}\log_2 x + \frac{1}{4}\log_2 y + \frac{1}{3}\log_2 a - \frac{1}{5}\log_2(a-b)$$

79. Let $\log_a x = m$ and $\log_a y = n$. Then $a^m = x$ and $a^n = y$, so $\dfrac{x}{y} = \dfrac{a^m}{a^n} = a^{m-n}$.

Thus, $\log_a \dfrac{x}{y} = m - n = \log_a x - \log_a y$.

83.   **a.** $a^2 - 4c^2$

   b. $(a+2c)(a-2c)$

85. $(3i+4)(2i-3) = 6i^2 - 9i + 8i - 12$
$$= 6(-1) - i - 12$$
$$= -6 - i - 12$$
$$= -18 - i$$

Exercise Set 9.5

1. Common logarithms are logarithms with base 10.

3. Antilogarithms are numbers obtained by taking 10 to the power of the logarithm.

5. $\log 45 = 1.6532$

7. $\log 19{,}200 = 4.2833$

9. $\log 0.0613 = -1.2125$

11. $\log 100 = 2.0000$

13. $\log 3.75 = 0.5740$

15. $\log 0.000472 = -3.3261$

17. antilog 0.4193 = 2.63

19. antilog 4.6283 = 42,500

21. antilog(−1.7086) = 0.0196

23. antilog 0.0000 = 1.00

25. antilog 2.7625= 579

27. antilog(−0.1543) = 0.701

29. log N = 2.0000
  N = antilog 2.000
  N = 100

31. log N = −2.103
  N = antilog (−2.103)
  N = 0.00789

33. log$N$ = 4.1409
  N = antilog 4.1409
  N = 13,800

35. log N = −1.06
  N = antilog (−1.06)
  N = 0.0871

37. log$N$ = −0.6218
  N = antilog (−0.6218)
  N = 0.239

39. log N = −0.3936
  N = antilog (−0.3936)
  N = 0.404

41. log 3560 = 3.5514
  Therefore, $10^{3.5514} \approx 3560$.

43. log 0.0727 = −1.1385
  Therefore, $10^{-1.1385} \approx 0.0727$

45. log 102 = 2.0086
  Therefore, $10^{2.0086} \approx 102$.

47. log 0.00128 = −2.8928
  Therefore, $10^{-2.8928} \approx 0.00128$.

49. $10^{2.9153} = 823$

51. $10^{-0.158} = 0.695$

53. $10^{-1.4802} = 0.0331$

55. $10^{1.3503} = 22.4$

57. log 1 = x
  $10^x = 1$
  $10^x = 10^0$
  $x = 0$
  Therefore, log 1 = 0.

59. log 0.1 = x
  $10^x = 0.1$
  $10^x = \frac{1}{10}$
  $10^x = 10^{-1}$
  $x = -1$
  Therefore, log 0.1 = −1.

61. log 0.01 = x
  $10^x = 0.01$
  $10^x = \frac{1}{100}$
  $10^x = 10^{-2}$
  $x = -2$
  Therefore, log 0.01 = −2.

63. log 0.001 = x
  $10^x = 0.001$
  $10^x = \frac{1}{1000}$
  $10^x = 10^{-3}$
  $x = -3$
  Therefore, log 0.001 = −3.

65. $\log 10^7 = 7$

67. $10^{\log 7} = 7$

69. $6\log 10^{5.2} = 6(5.2) = 31.2$

71. $5(10^{\log 9.4}) = 5(9.4) = 47$

73. No; $10^2 = 100$ and since 462 > 100, log 462 must be greater than 2.

75. No; $10^0 = 1$ and $10^{-1} = 0.1$ and, since log 0.163 must be between 0 and −1.

77. No;
  $\log \frac{y}{3x} = \log y - \log 3x$
  $= \log y - (\log 3 + \log x)$
  $= \log y - \log 3 - \log x$

79. $\log 125 = \log 5^3$
$= 3 \log 5$
$= 3(0.6990)$
$= 2.0970$

81. $\log 30$ is not possible given this information.

83. $\log \dfrac{1}{25} = \log 25^{-1}$
$= -\log 25$
$= -1(1.3979)$
$= -1.3979$

85. $R = \log I, R = 3.41$
$3.41 = \log I$
$I = \text{anti}\log(3.41)$
$I \approx 2570$

This earthquake is about 2,570 times more intense than the smallest measurable activity.

87. $R = \log I, R = 6.37$
$6.37 = \log I$
$I = \text{anti}\log(6.37)$
$I \approx 2{,}340{,}000$

This earthquake is about 2,340,000 times more intense than the smallest measurable activity.

89. $\log d = 3.7 - 0.2g$

a. $g = 11$
$\log d = 3.7 - 0.2(11)$
$= 3.7 - 2.2$
$= 1.5$
$d = \text{antilog } 1.5 = 31.62$
A planet with absolute magnitude of 11 has a diameter of 31.62 kilometers.

b. $g = 20$
$\log d = 3.7 - 0.2(20)$
$= 3.7 - 4$
$= -0.3$
$d = \text{antilog } (-0.3) = 0.50$
A planet with absolute magnitude of 20 has a diameter of 0.50 kilometers.

c. $d = 5.8$
$\log 5.8 = 3.7 - 0.2g$
$\log 5.8 - 3.7 = -0.2g$
$0.76343 - 3.7 = -0.2g$
$-2.93657 = -0.2g$
$\dfrac{-2.93657}{-0.2} = g$
$14.68 = g$

A planet with diameter 5.8 kilometers has an absolute magnitude of 14.68.

91. $R(t) = 94 - 46.8 \log(t+1)$

a. $R(2) = 94 - 46.8 \log(2+1)$
$= 94 - 46.8 \log(3)$
≈ 72
After two months, Sammy will remember about 72% of the course material.

b. $R(48) = 94 - 46.8 \log(2+48)$
$= 94 - 46.8 \log(50)$
≈ 15
After forty-eight months, Sammy will remember about 15% of the course material.

93. $R = \log I, R = 4.6$
$4.6 = \log I$
$I = \text{anti}\log(4.6)$
$I \approx 39{,}800$

This earthquake is about 39,800 times more intense than the smallest measurable activity.

95. $\log E = 11.8 + 1.5 m_s$

a. $\log E = 11.8 + 1.5(6)$
$\log E = 20.8$
$10^{20.8} = E$
$E = 6.31 \times 10^{20}$
The energy released is 6.31×10^{20}.

b. $\log(1.2 \times 10^{15}) = 11.8 + 1.5 m_s$
$15.07918125 = 11.8 + 1.5 m_s$
$3.27918125 = 1.5 m_s$
$m_s \approx 2.19$
The surface wave has magnitude 2.19.

97. $M = \dfrac{\log E - 11.8}{1.5}$

$M = \dfrac{\log(1.259 \times 10^{21}) - 11.8}{1.5}$

$= \dfrac{\log 1.259 + \log 10^{21} - 11.8}{1.5}$

$= \dfrac{\log 1.259 + 21 - 11.8}{1.5}$

$= \dfrac{\log 1.259 + 9.2}{1.5}$

$\approx \dfrac{0.1000 + 9.2}{1.5}$

$\approx \dfrac{9.3}{1.5}$

≈ 6.2

The magnitude is about 6.2.

99. $R = \log I$

$\text{antilog}(R) = \text{antilog}(\log I)$

$\text{antilog}(R) = I$

101. $R = 85 - 41.9\log(t+1)$

$R - 85 = -41.9\log(t+1)$

$\dfrac{R-85}{-41.9} = \dfrac{-41.9\log(t+1)}{-41.9}$

$\dfrac{85-R}{41.9} = \log(t+1)$

$\text{antilog}\left(\dfrac{85-R}{41.9}\right) = \text{antilog}(\log(t+1))$

$\text{antilog}\left(\dfrac{85-R}{41.9}\right) = t+1$

$\text{antilog}\left(\dfrac{85-R}{41.9}\right) - 1 = t$

105. $3r = -4s - 6 \Rightarrow 3r + 4s = -6$ (1)

$3s = -5r + 1 \Rightarrow 5r + 3s = 1$ (2)

To eliminate the variable r, multiply equation (1) by -5 and equation (2) by 3 then add.

$-5(3r+4s=-6) \Rightarrow -15r - 20s = 30$

$3(5r+3s=1) \Rightarrow \underline{15r + 9s = 3}$

$-11s = 33$

$s = -3$

Substitute -3 for s in equation (1) and solve for r.

$3r + 4(-3) = -6$

$3r - 12 = -6$

$3r = 6$

$r = 2$

The solution is $(2, -3)$.

107. $\sqrt{(3x^2 - y)^2} = |3x^2 - y|$

Exercise Set 9.6

1. $c = d$

3. Check for extraneous roots.

5. $\log(-2)$ is not a real number

7. $5^x = 125$

$5^x = 5^3$

$x = 3$

9. $3^x = 243$

$3^x = 3^5$

$x = 5$

11. $49^x = 7$

$(7^2)^x = 7^1$

$7^{2x} = 7^1$

$2x = 1$

$x = \dfrac{1}{2}$

13. $5^{-x} = \dfrac{1}{25}$

$5^{-x} = 5^{-2}$

$-x = -2$

$x = 2$

15. $27^x = \dfrac{1}{3}$

$(3^3)^x = 3^{-1}$

$3^{3x} = 3^{-1}$

$3x = -1$

$x = -\dfrac{1}{3}$

17. $2^{x+1} = 64$
$2^{x+1} = 2^6$
$x + 1 = 6$
$x = 5$

19. $2^{3x-2} = 16$
$2^{3x-2} = 2^4$
$3x - 2 = 4$
$3x = 6$
$x = 2$

21. $27^x = 3^{2x+3}$
$3^{3x} = 3^{2x+3}$
$3x = 2x + 3$
$x = 3$

23. $7^x = 50$
$\log 7^x = \log 50$
$x \log 7 = \log 50$
$x = \dfrac{\log 50}{\log 7}$
$x \approx 2.01$

25. $4^{x-1} = 20$
$\log 4^{x-1} = \log 20$
$(x - 1) \log 4 = \log 20$
$x - 1 = \dfrac{\log 20}{\log 4}$
$x = \dfrac{\log 20}{\log 4} + 1$
$x \approx 3.16$

27. $1.63^{x+1} = 25$
$\log 1.63^{x+1} = \log 25$
$(x + 1) \log 1.63 = \log 25$
$x + 1 = \dfrac{\log 25}{\log 1.63}$
$x + 1 \approx 6.59$
$x \approx 5.59$

29. $3^{x+4} = 6^x$
$\log 3^{x+4} = \log 6^x$
$(x + 4) \log 3 = x \log 6$
$x \log 3 + 4 \log 3 = x \log 6$
$4 \log 3 = x \log 6 - x \log 3$
$4 \log 3 = x(\log 6 - \log 3)$
$\dfrac{4 \log 3}{\log 6 - \log 3} = x$
$6.34 \approx x$

31. $\log_{16} x = \dfrac{1}{2}$
$16^{1/2} = x$
$\sqrt{16} = x$
$4 = x$

33. $\log_{125} x = \dfrac{1}{3}$
$125^{1/3} = x$
$\sqrt[3]{125} = x$
$5 = x$

35. $\log_2 x = -3$
$2^{-3} = x$
$\dfrac{1}{2^3} = x$
$\dfrac{1}{8} = x$

37. $\log x = 1$
$\log_{10} x = 1$
$10^1 = x$
$10 = x$

39. $\log_2(5 - 3x) = 3$
$2^3 = 5 - 3x$
$8 = 5 - 3x$
$3x = -3$
$x = -1$

41. $\log_5(x + 2)^2 = 2$
$(x + 2)^2 = 5^2$
$x + 2 = \pm\sqrt{25}$
$x + 2 = \pm 5$
$x + 2 = 5 \quad \text{or} \quad x + 2 = -5$
$x = 3 \qquad\qquad x = -7$

Both values check. The solution is 3 and -7.

43. $\log_2(r + 4)^2 = 4$
$(r + 4)^2 = 2^4$
$r^2 + 8r + 16 = 16$
$r^2 + 8r = 0$
$r(r + 8) = 0$
$r = 0 \quad \text{or} \quad r + 8 = 0$
$r = -8$

45. $\log(x+3)=2$

$\log_{10}(x+3)=2$

$10^2=x+3$

$100=x+3$

$x=97$

47. $\log_2 x+\log_2 5=2$

$\log_2 5x=2$

$5x=2^2$

$x=\dfrac{4}{5}$

49. $\log(r+2)=\log(3r-1)$

$r+2=3r-1$

$3=2r$

$\dfrac{3}{2}=r$

51. $\log(2x+1)+\log 4=\log(7x+8)$

$\log(8x+4)=\log(7x+8)$

$8x+4=7x+8$

$x=4$

53. $\log n+\log(3n-5)=\log 2$

$\log(3n^2-5n)=\log 2$

$3n^2-5n=2$

$3n^2-5n-2=0$

$(3n+1)(n-2)=0$

$3n+1=0$ or $n-2=0$

$3n=-1$ $n=2$

$n=-\dfrac{1}{3}$

Check: $n=-\dfrac{1}{3}$

$\log n+\log(3n-5)=\log 2$

$\log\left(-\dfrac{1}{3}\right)+\log\left[3\left(\dfrac{-1}{3}\right)-5\right]=\log 2$

Logarithms of negative numbers are not real numbers.
Check: $n=2$

$\log n+\log(3n-5)=\log 2$

$\log 2+\log[3(2)-5]=\log 2$

$\log 2+\log 1=\log 2$

$\log(2\cdot1)=\log 2$

$\log 2=\log 2$

2 is the only solution.
$-\dfrac{1}{3}$ is an extraneous solution.

55. $\log 5+\log y=0.72$

$\log 5y=0.72$

$5y\approx5.2481$

$y\approx1.05$

57. $2\log x-\log 4=2$

$\log x^2-\log 4=2$

$\log\dfrac{x^2}{4}=2$

$\dfrac{x^2}{4}=\text{antilog }2$

$\dfrac{x^2}{4}=100$

$x^2=400$

$x^2-400=0$

$(x+20)(x-20)=0$

$x+20=0$ or $x-20=0$

$x=-20$ $x=20$

Check: $x=-20$

$2\log x-\log 4=2$

$2\log(-20)-\log 4=2$

Logarithms of negative numbers are not real numbers.
Check: $x=20$

$2\log x-\log 4=2$

$2\log 20-\log 4=2$

$\log\dfrac{400}{4}=2$

$\log 100=2$

$100=\text{antilog }2$

$100=100$

Thus, 20 is the only solution.
-20 is an extraneous solution.

59. $\log x+\log(x-3)=1$

$\log(x^2-3x)=1$

$x^2-3x=\text{antilog }1$

$x^2-3x=10$

$x^2-3x-10=0$

$(x-5)(x+2)=0$

$x-5=0$ or $x+2=0$

$x=5$ $x=-2$

A check shows that 5 is the only solution.
-2 is an extraneous solution.

61. $\log x = \dfrac{1}{3}\log 27$

$\log x = \log 27^{1/3}$

$\log x = \log 3$

$x = 3$

63. $\log_8 x = 3\log_8 2 - \log_8 4$

$\log_8 x = \log_8 2^3 - \log_8 4$

$\log_8 x = \log_8 \dfrac{8}{4}$

$\log_8 x = \log_8 2$

$x = 2$

65. $\log_5(x+3) + \log_5(x-2) = \log_5 6$

$\log_5(x+3)(x-2) = \log_5 6$

$\log_5(x^2 + x - 6) = \log_5 6$

$x^2 + x - 6 = 6$

$x^2 + x - 12 = 0$

$(x+4)(x-3) = 0$

$x = -4$ or $x = 3$

Disregard $x = -4$ since

$\log(-4+3) = \log(-1)$.

Therefore, $x = 3$ is the only solution.

67. $\log_2(x+3) - \log_2(x-6) = \log_2 4$

$\log_2 \dfrac{x+3}{x-6} = \log_2 4$

$\dfrac{x+3}{x-6} = 4$

$x+3 = 4x - 24$

$27 = 3x$

$9 = x$

69.

$50{,}000 = 4500(2^t)$

$\dfrac{50{,}000}{4500} = 2^t$

$\log \dfrac{50{,}000}{4500} = \log 2^t$

$\log \dfrac{50{,}000}{4500} = t\log 2$

$\log 50{,}000 - \log 4500 = t\log 2$

$\dfrac{\log 50{,}000 - \log 4500}{\log 2} = t$

$3.47 \approx t$

There are 50,000 bacteria after about 3.47 hours.

71.

$40 = 200(0.800)^t$

$0.2 = (0.800)^t$

$\log 0.2 = \log(0.800)^t$

$\log 0.2 = t\log 0.800$

$\dfrac{\log 0.2}{\log 0.800} = t$

$7.21 \approx t$

40 grams remain after about 7.21 years.

73.

$A = P\left(1 + \dfrac{r}{n}\right)^{nt}$

$4600 = 2000\left(1 + \dfrac{0.05}{1}\right)^{1 \cdot t}$

$4600 = 2000(1.05)^t$

$\dfrac{4600}{2000} = 1.05^t$

$2.3 = 1.05^t$

$\log 2.3 = \log 1.05^t$

$\log 2.3 = t\log 1.05$

$\dfrac{\log 2.3}{\log 1.05} = t \quad \Rightarrow \quad t \approx 17.07$ years

75. $f(t) = 26 - 12.1 \cdot \log(t+1)$

   a. $x = 1990 - 1960 = 30$

      $f(30) = 26 - 12.1\log(30+1) = 7.95$

      In 1990, the rate was 7.95 deaths per 1000 live births.

   b. $x = 2005 - 1960 = 45$

      $f(45) = 26 - 12.1\log(45+1) \approx 5.88$

      In 2005, the rate is expected to be 5.88 deaths per 1000 live births.

77. $c = 50{,}000, n = 12, r = 0.15.$

$S = c(1-r)^n$

$S = 50{,}000(1 - 0.15)^{12}$

$S = 50{,}000(0.85)^{12}$

$S \approx 7112.09$

The scrap value is about \$7112.09.

79. $P_{\text{out}} = 12.6$ and $P_{\text{in}} = 0.146$

$P = 10\log\left(\dfrac{12.6}{0.146}\right)$

$P \approx 10\log 86.30137$

$P \approx 10(1.936)$

$P \approx 19.36$

The power gain is about 19.36..

81. a.
$$d = 120$$
$$d = 10 \log I$$
$$120 = 10 \log I$$
$$12 = \log I$$
$$I = \text{antilog } 12$$
$$I = 10^{12}$$
$$I = 1,000,000,000,000$$

The intensity is 1,000,000,000,000 times the minimum intensity of audible sound.

b.
$$d = 70$$
$$d = 10 \log I$$
$$70 = 10 \log I$$
$$7 = \log I$$
$$I = \text{antilog } 7$$
$$I = 10^{7}$$
$$I = 10,000,000$$
$$\frac{1,000,000,000,000}{10,000,000} = 100,000$$

The sound of an airplane engine is 100,000 times more intense than the noise in a busy city street.

83. $8^x = 16^{x-2}$
$$2^{3x} = 2^{4(x-2)}$$
$$3x = 4(x-2)$$
$$3x = 4x - 8$$
$$8 = x$$

85. $2^{2x} - 6(2^x) + 8 = 0$
$$(2^x)^2 - 6(2^x) + 8 = 0$$
$$y^2 - 6y + 8 = 0 \leftarrow \text{Replace } 2^x \text{ with } y$$
$$(y - 4)(y - 2) = 0$$
$$y - 4 = 0 \quad \text{or} \quad y - 2 = 0$$
$$y = 4 \qquad\qquad y = 2$$
$$2^x = 4 \qquad 2^x = 2 \leftarrow \text{Replace } y \text{ with } 2^x$$
$$2^x = 2^2 \qquad 2^x = 2^1$$
$$x = 2 \qquad\quad x = 1$$
The solutions are $x = 2$ and $x = 1$.

87. $2^x = 8^y$
$$x + y = 4$$
The first equation simplifies to
$$2^x = (2^3)^y$$
$$2^x = 2^{3y}$$
$$x = 3y$$
The system becomes
$$x = 3y$$
$$x + y = 4$$
Substitute $3y$ for x in the second equation.

$$x + y = 4$$
$$3y + y = 4$$
$$4y = 4$$
$$y = 1$$
Now, substitute 1 for y in the first equation.
$$x = 3y$$
$$x = 3(1) = 3$$
The solution is (3, 1).

89. $\log(x + y) = 2$
$$x - y = 8$$
The first equation can be written as
$$x + y = 10^2$$
$$x + y = 100$$
The system becomes

$$x + y = 100$$
$$x - y = 8$$
Add: $2x = 108$
$$x = 54$$
Substitute 54 for x in the first equation.
$$54 + y = 100$$
$$y = 46$$
The solution is (54, 46).

91.

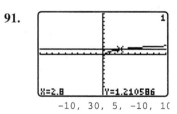

$$-10, 30, 5, -10, 1($$

The solution is $x \approx 2.8$.

93.

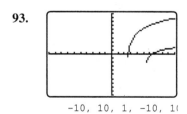

$$-10, 10, 1, -10, 1($$

There is no real-number solution.

95. Volume of cylinder:

$$V_1 = \pi r^2 h = \pi\left(\frac{3}{2}\right)^2 \cdot 4 \approx 28.2743 \text{ cubic feet}$$

Volume of box:

$$V_2 = l \cdot w \cdot h = (3)(3)(4) = 36 \text{ cubic feet}$$

The box has the greater volume.

Difference in volumes:

$$V_2 - V_1 \approx 7.73 \text{ cubic feet}$$

97. Graph both inequalities on the same coordinate plane. The solution to the system is the double-shaded region.

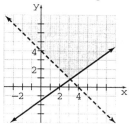

99. $E = mc^2$, for c

$$\frac{E}{m} = \frac{mc^2}{m}$$

$$\frac{E}{m} = c^2$$

$$\sqrt{\frac{E}{m}} = c$$

Exercise Set 9.7

1. a. The base in the natural exponential function is e.

   b. The approximate value of e is 2.7183.

3. The domain of $\ln x$ is $x > 0$.

5. $\log_a x = \dfrac{\log_b x}{\log_b a}$

7. $\ln e^x = x$

9. The inverse of $\ln x$ is e^x.

11. P decreases when t increases for $k < 0$.

13. $\ln 62 = 4.1271$

15. $\ln 0.813 = -0.2070$

17. $\ln N = 16$

$$e^{\ln N} = e^{1.6}$$

$$N = e^{1.6} \approx 4.95$$

19. $\ln N = -2.41$

$$e^{\ln N} = e^{-2.41}$$

$$N = e^{-2.41} \approx 0.0898$$

21. $\ln N = -0.0287$

$$e^{\ln N} = e^{-0.0287}$$

$$N = e^{-0.0287} \approx 0.972$$

23. $\log_3 56 = \dfrac{\log 56}{\log 3} \approx 3.6640$

25. $\log_2 21 = \dfrac{\log 21}{\log 2} \approx 4.3923$

27. $\log_4 11 = \dfrac{\log 11}{\log 4} \approx 1.7297$

29. $\log_5 63 = \dfrac{\log 63}{\log 5} \approx 2.5743$

31. $\log_6 123 = \dfrac{\log 123}{\log 6} \approx 2.6857$

33. $\log_7 51 = \dfrac{\log 51}{\log 7} \approx 2.0206$

35. $\log_5 0.463 = \dfrac{\log 0.463}{\log 5} \approx -0.4784$

37. $\ln x + \ln(x-1) = \ln 12$

$$\ln x(x-1) = \ln 12$$

$$e^{\ln[x(x-1)]} = e^{\ln 12}$$

$$x(x-1) = 12$$

$$x^2 - x - 12 = 0$$

$$(x-4)(x+3) = 0$$

$$x - 4 = 0 \qquad x + 3 = 0$$

$$x = 4 \qquad x = -3$$

Only $x = 4$ checks. $X = -3$ is an extraneous solution since $\ln x$ becomes $\ln(-3)$ which is not a real number.

39. $\ln x + \ln(x+4) = \ln 5$

$\ln x(x+4) = \ln 5$

$e^{\ln(x^2+4x)} = e^{\ln 5}$

$x^2 + 4x = 5$

$x^2 + 4x - 5 = 0$

$(x+5)(x-1) = 0$

$x+5 = 0 \quad$ or $\quad x-1 = 0$

$x = -5 \qquad\qquad x = 1$

Only $x = 1$ checks. $x = -5$ is an extraneous solution since $\ln x$ becomes $\ln(-5)$ which is not a real number.

41. $\ln x = 5\ln 2 - \ln 8$

$\ln x = \ln 2^5 - \ln 8$

$\ln x = \ln \dfrac{32}{8}$

$\ln x = \ln 4$

$e^{\ln x} = e^{\ln 4}$

$x = 4$

$x = 4$ checks.

43. $\ln(x^2-4) - \ln(x+2) = \ln 1$

$\ln(x^2-4) - \ln(x+2) = 0$

$\ln(x^2-4) = \ln(x+2)$

$e^{\ln(x^2-4)} = e^{\ln(x+2)}$

$x^2 - 4 = x + 2$

$x^2 - x - 6 = 0$

$(x-3)(x+2) = 0$

$x-3 = 0 \quad$ or $\quad x+2 = 0$

$x = 3 \qquad\qquad x = -2$

Only $x = 3$ checks. $X = -2$ is an extraneous solution since $\ln(x+2)$ becomes $\ln(-2+2) = \ln(0)$ which is not a real number.

45. $P = 120e^{(2.3)(1.6)}$

$P = 120e^{3.68}$

$P \approx 4757.5673$

47. $50 = P_0 e^{-0.5(3)}$

$50 = P_0 e^{-1.5}$

$\dfrac{50}{e^{-1.5}} = P_0$

$P_0 \approx 224.0845$

49. $90 = 30e^{1.4t}$

$3 = e^{1.4t}$

$\ln 3 = \ln e^{1.4t}$

$\ln 3 = 1.4t$

$t = \dfrac{\ln 3}{1.4}$

$t \approx 0.7847$

51. $80 = 40e^{k(3)}$

$2 = e^{3k}$

$\ln 2 = \ln e^{3k}$

$\ln 2 = 3k$

$k = \dfrac{\ln 2}{3}$

$k \approx 0.2310$

53. $20 = 40e^{k(2.4)}$

$0.5 = e^{2.4k}$

$\ln 0.5 = \ln e^{2.4k}$

$\ln 0.5 = 2.4k$

$k = \dfrac{\ln 0.5}{2.4}$

$k \approx -0.2888$

55. $A = 6000e^{-0.08(3)}$

$A = 6000e^{-0.24}$

$A \approx 4719.77$

57. $V = V_0 e^{kt}$

$\dfrac{V}{e^{kt}} = V_0$ or $V_0 = \dfrac{V}{e^{kt}}$

59. $P = 150e^{4t}$

$\dfrac{P}{150} = e^{4t}$

$\ln \dfrac{P}{150} = \ln e^{4t}$

$\ln \dfrac{P}{150} = 4t$

$\dfrac{\ln P - \ln 150}{4} = t$ or $t = \dfrac{\ln P - \ln 150}{4}$

61.
$$A = A_0 e^{kt}$$
$$\frac{A}{A_0} = e^{kt}$$
$$\ln\frac{A}{A_0} = \ln e^{kt}$$
$$\ln A - \ln A_0 = kt$$
$$\frac{\ln A - \ln A_0}{t} = k \text{ or } k = \frac{\ln A - \ln A_0}{t}$$

63. $\ln y - \ln x = 2.3$
$$\ln\frac{y}{x} = 2.3$$
$$e^{\ln(y/x)} = e^{2.3}$$
$$\frac{y}{x} = e^{2.3}$$
$$y = xe^{2.3}$$

65. $\ln y - \ln(x + 3) = 6$
$$\ln\frac{y}{x+3} = 6$$
$$e^{\ln\frac{y}{x+3}} = e^6$$
$$\frac{y}{x+3} = e^6$$
$$y = (x+3)e^6$$

67. $e^x = 12.183$
Take the natural logarithm of both sides of the equation.
$$\ln e^x = \ln 12.183$$
$$x = \ln 12.183 \approx 2.5000$$

69. $P = P_0 e^{kt}$

     a. $P = 5000 e^{0.08(2)}$
$$= 5000 e^{0.16}$$
$$\approx 5867.55$$
The amount will be $5867.55.

     b.   If the amount in the account is to double, then $P = 2(5000) = 10,000$.
$$10,000 = 5000 e^{0.08t}$$
$$2 = e^{0.08t}$$
$$\ln 2 = \ln e^{0.08t}$$
$$\ln 2 = 0.08t$$
$$\frac{\ln 2}{0.08} = t$$
$$8.66 \approx t$$

It would take about 8.66 years for the value to double.

71. $P = P_0 e^{-0.028t}$
$$P = 70 e^{-0.028(20)}$$
$$P = 70 e^{-0.56}$$
$$P \approx 39.98$$
After 20 years, about 39.98 grams remain.

73. $f(t) = 1 - e^{-0.04t}$

     a. $f(t) = 1 - e^{-0.04(50)} = 1 - e^{-2} \approx 0.8647$
About 86.47% of the target market buys the drink after 50 days of advertising.

     b. $0.75 = 1 - e^{-0.04t}$
$$-0.25 = -e^{-0.04t}$$
$$0.25 = e^{-0.04t}$$
$$\ln 0.25 = \ln e^{-0.04t}$$
$$\ln 0.25 = -0.04t$$

     b.
$$t = \frac{\ln 0.25}{-0.04}$$
$$t \approx 34.66$$

About 34.66 days of advertising are needed if 75% of the target market is to buy the soft drink.

75. $f(P) = 0.37 \ln P + 0.05$

     a. $f(972,000) = 0.37 \ln(972,000) + 0.05$
$$\approx 5.1012311 + 0.05$$
$$\approx 5.15$$
The average walking speed in Nashville, Tennessee is 5.15 feet per second.

     b $f(8,567,000) = 0.37 \ln(8,567,000) + 0.05$
$$\approx -5.906 + 0.05$$
$$\approx 5.96$$
The average walking speed in New York City is 5.96 feet per second.

c.
$$5 = 0.37 \ln P + 0.05$$
$$4.95 = 0.37 \ln P$$
$$13.378378 = \ln P$$
$$e^{13.378378} = e^{\ln P}$$
$$P = e^{13.378378}$$
$$P \approx 646,000$$
The population is about 646,000.

77. $V(t) = 24\,e^{0.08t}, \quad t = 2003 - 1626 = 377$

$V(377) = 24\,e^{0.08(377)}$

$\approx 300,977,000,000,000$

The value of Manhattan in 2003 is about $300,977,000,000,000.

79. $P(t) = 6.30e^{0.013t}$

a. $t = 2010 - 2003 = 7$

$P(7) = 6.30e^{0.013(7)}$The

$= 6.30e^{0.091}$

≈ 6.9

The world's population in 2010 is expected to be about 6.9 billion.

b $2(6.30 \text{ billion}) \Rightarrow 12.60 \text{ billion}$

$$12.60 = 6.30e^{0.013t}$$
$$\frac{12.60}{6.30} = \frac{6.30e^{0.013t}}{6.30}$$
$$2 = e^{0.013t}$$
$$\ln 2 = \ln e^{0.013t}$$
$$\ln 2 = 0.013t$$
$$t = \frac{\ln 2}{0.013} \approx 53$$

The world's population will double in about 53 years.

81. $y = 15.29 + 5.93 \ln x$

a. $y(18) = 15.29 + 5.93\ln(18) \approx 32.43$ in.

b $y(30) = 15.29 + 5.93\ln(30) \approx 35.46$ in.

83. $f(t) = v_0 e^{-0.0001205t}$

a.   Use $f(t) = 9$ and $v_0 = 20$.
$$9 = 20e^{-0.0001205t}$$
$$0.45 = e^{-0.0001205t}$$
$$\ln 0.45 = -0.0001205t$$
$$\frac{\ln 0.45}{-0.0001205} = t$$
$$t \approx 6626.62$$
The bone is about 6626.62 years old.

b   Let x equal the original amount of carbon 14 then $0.5x$ equals the remaining amount.
$$0.5x = xe^{-0.0001205t}$$
$$\frac{0.5x}{x} = \frac{xe^{-0.0001205t}}{x}$$
$$0.5 = e^{-0.0001205t}$$
$$\ln 0.5 = \ln e^{-0.0001205t}$$
$$\ln 0.5 = -0.0001205t$$
$$\frac{\ln 0.5}{-0.0001205} = t$$
$$t \approx 5752.26$$
If 50% of the carbon 14 remains, the item is about 5752.26 years old.

85.   Let P_0 be the initial investment, then $P = 20,000$, $k = 0.06$, and $t = 18$.
$$P = P_0 e^{kt}$$
$$20,000 = P_0 e^{0.06(18)}$$
$$20,000 = P_0 e^{1.08}$$
$$\frac{20,000}{e^{1.08}} = P_0$$
$$6791.91 \approx P_0$$
The initial investment should be $6791.91.

87.   a.   Strontium 90 has a higher decay rate so it will decompose more quickly.

b. $P = P_0 e^{-kt}$
$$P = P_0 e^{-0.023(50)}$$
$$= P_0 e^{-1.15}$$
$$\approx P_0 (0.3166)$$
About 31.66% of the original amount will remain.

89. Answers will vary.

90. Answers will vary.

91. $e^{x-4} = 12\ln(x+2)$

$y_1 = e^{x-4}$

$y_2 = 12\ln(x+2)$

Intersection
X=7.286251   Y=26.742419
-10,10,1,-10,50,5

The intersection is approximately
(7.286, 26.742). Therefore, $x \approx 7.286$.

93. $3x - 6 = 2e^{0.2x} - 12$

$y_1 = 3x - 6$

$y_2 = 2e^{0.2x} - 12$

Intersection
X=-1.506792 Y=-10.52037
-10,20,2,-50,50,10

The intersections are approximately
(−1.507, −10.520) and (16.659, 43.977).
Therefore, $x \approx -1.507$ and 16.659.

95. $x = \dfrac{1}{k}\ln(kv_0 t + 1)$

$xk = \ln(kv_0 t + 1)$

$e^{xk} = e^{\ln(kv_0 t + 1)}$

$e^{xk} = kv_0 t + 1$

$e^{xk} - 1 = kv_0 t$

$\dfrac{e^{xk} - 1}{kt} = v_0$ or $v_0 = \dfrac{e^{xk} - 1}{kt}$

97. $\ln i - \ln I = \dfrac{-t}{RC}$

$\ln \dfrac{i}{I} = \dfrac{-t}{RC}$

$e^{\ln(i/I)} = e^{-t/RC}$

$\dfrac{i}{I} = e^{-t/RC}$

$i = Ie^{-t/RC}$

99. Let x be the number of adult tickets sold and y be the number of children's tickets sold. The following system describes the situation.
$$x + y = 650$$
$$15x + 11y = 8790$$
Solve by elimination.
$$-11(x + y = 650) \quad \Rightarrow \quad -11x - 11y = -7150$$
$$15x + 11y = 8790 \quad \Rightarrow \quad \underline{15x + 11y = 8790}$$
$$4x \qquad\quad = 1640$$
$$x = 410$$
Substitute $x = 410$ into the first equation to find y.
$$410 + y = 650 \quad \Rightarrow \quad y = 240$$
410 adult tickets and 240 children's tickets must be sold.

101. $4x^2 + bx + 9 = (2x)^2 + bx + (3)^2$ will be a perfect square trinomial if
$$bx = \pm 2(2x)(3) \quad \Rightarrow \quad b = \pm 12$$

Review Exercises

1. $(f \circ g)(x) = (2x - 5)^2 - 3(2x - 5) + 4$
$$= 4x^2 - 20x + 25 - 6x + 15 + 4$$
$$= 4x^2 - 26x + 44$$

2. $(f \circ g)(x) = 4x^2 - 26x + 44$
$$(f \circ g)(2) = 4(2)^2 - 26(2) + 44$$
$$= 16 - 52 + 44$$
$$= 8$$

3. $(g \circ f)(x) = 2(x^2 - 3x + 4) - 5$
$$= 2x^2 - 6x + 8 - 5$$
$$= 2x^2 - 6x + 3$$

4. $(g \circ f)(x) = 2x^2 - 6x + 3$
$$(g \circ f)(-3) = 2(-3)^2 - 6(-3) + 3$$
$$= 18 + 18 + 3$$
$$= 39$$

5. $(f \circ g)(x) = 6\sqrt{x - 3} + 1,\ x \ge 3$

6. $(g \circ f)(x) = \sqrt{(6x+1)-3}$

$\qquad = \sqrt{6x-2}, \ x \geq \dfrac{1}{3}$

7. This function is one-to-one since it passes both the vertical line test and the horizontal line test.

8. The function is not one-to-one since the graph does not pass the horizontal line test.

9. Yes, the ordered pairs represent a one-to-one function. For each value of x, there is a unique value for y and each y-value has a unique x-value.

10. No, the ordered pairs do not represent a one-to-one function since the pairs $(0, -2)$ and $(3, -2)$ have different x-values but the same y-value.

11. Yes, $y = \sqrt{x+3}$, $x \geq -3$, is a one-to-one function since it passes both the vertical line test and the horizontal line test.

12. No, $y = x^2 - 4$ is a parabola with vertex at $(0, -4)$. It is not a one-to-one function since it does not pass the horizontal line test. Horizontal lines above $y = -4$ intersect the graph in two points.

13. $f(x)$: Domain: $\{-4, 0, 5, 6\}$
Range: $\{-3, 2, 3, 7\}$
$f^{-1}(x)$: Domain: $\{-3, 2, 3, 7\}$
Range: $\{-4, 0, 5, 6\}$

14. $f(x)$: Domain: $\{x \mid x \geq 0\}$
Range: $\{y \mid y \geq 2\}$
$f^{-1}(x)$: Domain: $\{x \mid x \geq 2\}$
Range: $\{y \mid y \geq 0\}$

15. $y = f(x) = 4x - 2$
$\qquad x = 4y - 2$
$\qquad x + 2 = 4y$
$\qquad \dfrac{x+2}{4} = y$
$\qquad f^{-1}(x) = \dfrac{x+2}{4}$

x	$f(x)$
0	-2
$\frac{1}{2}$	0

x	$f^{-1}(x)$
0	$\frac{1}{2}$
-2	0

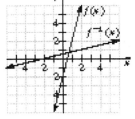

16. $y = f(x) = \sqrt[3]{x-1} = (x-1)^{1/3}$
$\qquad x = (y-1)^{1/3}$
$\qquad x^3 = [(y-1)^{1/3}]^3$
$\qquad x^3 = y - 1$
$\qquad x^3 + 1 = y$
$\qquad f^{-1}(x) = x^3 + 1$

x	$f(x)$
-7	-2
0	-1
1	0
2	1
9	2

x	$f^{-1}(x)$
-2	-7
-1	0
0	1
1	2
2	9

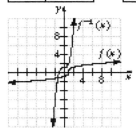

17. $f(x) = 36x \implies y = 36x \implies x = 36y \implies y = \dfrac{x}{36}$

$\qquad f^{-1}(x) = \dfrac{x}{36}$

$\qquad f^{-1}(x)$ represents yards and x represents inches.

18. $f(x) = 4x \Rightarrow y = 4x \Rightarrow x = 4y \Rightarrow y = \frac{x}{4}$

$f^{-1}(x) = \frac{x}{4}$

$f^{-1}(x)$ represents gallons and x represents quarts.

19. $y = 2^x$

x	-2	-1	0	1	2	3
y	$\frac{1}{4}$	$\frac{1}{2}$	1	2	4	8

Domain: R
Range: $\{y \mid y > 0\}$

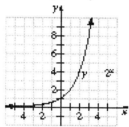

20. $y = \left(\frac{1}{2}\right)^x$

x	-2	-1	0	1	2
y	4	2	1	$\frac{1}{2}$	$\frac{1}{4}$

Domain: R
Range: $\{y \mid y > 0\}$

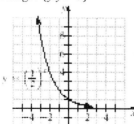

21. $f(t) = 7.02e^{0.365t}$

    a. $t = 2003 - 1999 = 4$

         $f(4) = 7.02e^{0.365(4)}$

           ≈ 30.23
The worldwide shipment in 2003 is about 30.23 million.

b. $t = 2005 - 1999 = 6$

     $f(4) = 7.02e^{0.365(6)}$

       ≈ 62.73
The worldwide shipment in 2005 will be about 62.73 million.

c. $t = 2007 - 1999 = 8$

     $f(8) = 7.02e^{0.365(8)}$

       ≈ 130.16
The worldwide shipment in 2007 will be about 130.16 million.

22. $7^2 = 49$

       $\log_7 49 = 2$

23. $81^{1/4} = 3$

       $\log_{81} 3 = \frac{1}{4}$

24. $5^{-2} = \frac{1}{25}$

       $\log_5 \frac{1}{25} = -2$

25. $\log_2 16 = 4$

       $2^4 = 16$

26. $\log_{1/3} \frac{1}{9} = 2$

       $\left(\frac{1}{3}\right)^2 = \frac{1}{9}$

27. $\log_6 \frac{1}{36} = -2$

       $6^{-2} = \frac{1}{36}$

28. $3 = \log_4 x$

       $x = 4^3$

       $x = 64$

29. $3 = \log_a 8$

       $a^3 = 8$

       $a^3 = 2^3$

        $a = 2$

30. $-3 = \log_{1/4} x$

$$x = \left(\frac{1}{4}\right)^{-3}$$

$$x = \frac{1}{\left(\frac{1}{4}\right)^3}$$

$$x = \frac{1}{\frac{1}{64}}$$

$$x = 64$$

31. $y = \log_3 x$

$x = 3^y$

x	$\frac{1}{9}$	$\frac{1}{3}$	1	3	9	27
y	-2	-1	0	1	2	3

Domain: $\{x | x > 0\}$

Range: R

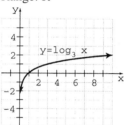

32. $y = \log_{1/2} x$

$$x = \left(\frac{1}{2}\right)^y$$

x	4	2	1	$\frac{1}{2}$	$\frac{1}{4}$
y	-2	-1	0	1	2

Domain: $\{x | x > 0\}$

Range: R

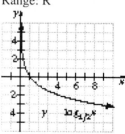

33. $\log_5 17^3 = 3\log_5 17$

34. $\log_3 \sqrt{x-5} = \log_3 (x-5)^{1/2} = \frac{1}{2}\log_3 (x-5)$

35. $\log\dfrac{6(a+1)}{b} = \log 6 + \log(a+1) - \log b$

36. $\log\dfrac{x^4}{9(2x+3)^5} = \log x^4 - \log 9(2x+3)^5$

$$= 4\log x - [\log 9 + \log(2x+3)^5]$$
$$= 4\log x - [\log 9 + 5\log(2x+3)]$$
$$= 4\log x - \log 9 - 5\log(2x+3)$$

37. $2\log x - 3\log(x+1)$

$$= \log x^2 - \log(x+1)^3$$
$$= \log\dfrac{x^2}{(x+1)^3}$$

38. $3(\log 2 + \log x) - \log y$

$$= 3(\log 2x) - \log y$$
$$= \log(2x)^3 - \log y$$
$$= \log\dfrac{(2x)^3}{y}$$

39. $\frac{1}{2}[\ln x - \ln(x+2)] - \ln 2$

$$= \frac{1}{2}\left(\ln\frac{x}{x+2}\right) - \ln 2$$
$$= \ln\left(\frac{x}{x+2}\right)^{1/2} - \ln 2$$
$$= \ln\left(\dfrac{\sqrt{\frac{x}{x+2}}}{2}\right)$$

40. $3\ln x + \frac{1}{2}\ln(x+1) - 3\ln(x+4)$

$$= \ln x^3 + \ln(x+1)^{1/2} - \ln(x+4)^3$$
$$= \ln\dfrac{x^3\sqrt{x+1}}{(x+4)^3}$$

41. $8^{\log_8 9} = 9$

42. $\log_4 4^5 = 5$

43. $7\log_9 81 = 7\log_9 9^2$

$$= 7 \cdot 2$$
$$= 14$$

44.
$$4^{\log_8 \sqrt{8}} = 4^{\log_8 8^{1/2}}$$
$$= 4^{1/2}$$
$$= \sqrt{4}$$
$$= 2$$

45. $\log 763 = 2.8825$

46. $\log 0.0281 = -3..5720$

47. antilog $3.159 = 1440$

48. antilog$(-2.645) = 0.00226$

49.
$$\log N = 2.3304$$
$$N = \text{antilog } 2.3304$$
$$N = 214$$

50.
$$\log N = -1.2262$$
$$N = \text{antilog } (-1.2262)$$
$$N = 0.0594$$

51. $\log 10^5 = 5$

52. $10^{\log 4} = 4$

53. $9\log 10^{3.2} = 9(3.2) = 28.8$

54. $2\left(10^{\log 4.7}\right) = 2(4.7) = 9.4$

55.
$$125 = 5^x$$
$$5^3 = 5^x$$
$$3 = x$$

56.
$$81^x = \frac{1}{9}$$
$$(9^2)^x = 9^{-1}$$
$$9^{2x} = 9^{-1}$$
$$2x = -1$$
$$x = -\frac{1}{2}$$

57.
$$2^{3x-1} = 32$$
$$2^{3x-1} = 2^5$$
$$3x - 1 = 5$$
$$3x = 6$$
$$x = 2$$

58.
$$27^x = 3^{2x+5}$$
$$(3^3)^x = 3^{2x+5}$$
$$3^{3x} = 3^{2x+5}$$
$$3x = 2x + 5$$
$$x = 5$$

59.
$$7^x = 89$$
$$\log 7^x = \log 89$$
$$x \log 7 = \log 89$$
$$x = \frac{\log 89}{\log 7}$$
$$x \approx 2.307$$

60.
$$2.6^x = 714$$
$$\log 2.6^x = \log 714$$
$$x \log 2.6 = \log 714$$
$$x = \frac{\log 714}{\log 2.6}$$
$$x \approx 6.877$$

61.
$$12.5^{x+1} = 381$$
$$\log 12.5^{x+1} = \log 381$$
$$(x+1)\log 12.5 = \log 381$$
$$x + 1 = \frac{\log 381}{\log 12.5}$$
$$x = \frac{\log 381}{\log 12.5} - 1$$
$$x \approx 1.353$$

62.
$$3^{x+2} = 8^x$$
$$\log 3^{x+2} = \log 8^x$$
$$(x+2)\log 3 = x\log 8$$
$$x\log 3 + 2\log 3 = x\log 8$$
$$2\log 3 = x\log 8 - x\log 3$$
$$2\log 3 = x(\log 8 - \log 3)$$
$$\frac{2\log 3}{\log 8 - \log 3} = x$$
$$2.240 \approx x$$

63.
$$\log_3 (5x+1) = 4$$
$$3^4 = 5x + 1$$
$$81 = 5x + 1$$
$$80 = 5x$$
$$x = 16$$

64.
$$\log x + \log(4x - 7) = \log 2$$
$$\log(x(4x - 7)) = \log 2$$
$$x(4x - 7) = 2$$
$$4x^2 - 7x - 2 = 0$$
$$(4x + 1)(x - 2) = 0$$
$$4x + 1 = 0 \quad \text{or} \quad x - 2 = 0$$
$$x = -\frac{1}{4} \qquad\qquad x = 2$$

Only $x = 2$ checks. $x = -\frac{1}{4}$ is an extraneous solution .

65.
$$\log_3 x + \log_3(2x + 1) = 1$$
$$\log_3 x(2x + 1) = 1$$
$$3^1 = x(2x + 1)$$
is an e
$$0 = 2x^2 + x - 3$$
$$0 = (2x + 3)(x - 1)$$
$$2x + 3 = 0 \quad \text{or} \quad x - 1 = 0$$
$$x = -\frac{3}{2} \qquad\qquad x = 1$$

Only $x = 1$ checks. $x = -\frac{3}{2}$ is an extraneous solution since $\log_3 x$ becomes $\log_3\left(-\frac{3}{2}\right)$ which is not a real number.

66.
$$\ln(x + 1) - \ln(x - 2) = \ln 4$$
$$\ln\frac{x + 1}{x - 2} = \ln 4$$
$$\frac{x + 1}{x - 2} = 4$$
$$x + 1 = 4(x - 2)$$
$$x + 1 = 4x - 8$$
$$1 = 3x - 8$$
$$9 = 3x$$
$$x = 3$$

67.
$$40 = 20e^{0.6t}$$
$$2 = e^{0.6t}$$
$$\ln 2 = \ln e^{0.6t}$$
$$\ln 2 = 0.6t$$
$$\frac{\ln 2}{0.6} = t$$
$$1.155 \approx t$$

68.
$$100 = A_0 e^{-0.42(3)}$$
$$100 = A_0 e^{-1.26}$$
$$\frac{100}{e^{-1.26}} = A_0$$
$$352.542 \approx A_0$$

69.
$$A = A_0 e^{kt}$$
$$\frac{A}{A_0} = e^{kt}$$
$$\ln\frac{A}{A_0} = \ln e^{kt}$$
$$\ln\frac{A}{A_0} = kt$$
$$\frac{\ln\frac{A}{A_0}}{k} = t$$
$$\frac{\ln A - \ln A_0}{k} = t \text{ or } t = \frac{\ln A - \ln A_0}{k}$$

70.
$$150 = 600e^{kt}$$
$$\frac{150}{600} = e^{kt}$$
$$0.25 = e^{kt}$$
$$\ln 0.25 = \ln e^{kt}$$
$$\ln 0.25 = kt$$
$$\frac{\ln 0.25}{t} = k \text{ or } k = \frac{\ln 0.25}{t}$$

71.
$$\ln y - \ln x = 4$$
$$\ln\frac{y}{x} = 4$$
$$e^{\ln\frac{y}{x}} = e^4$$
$$\frac{y}{x} = e^4$$
$$y = xe^4$$

72.
$$\ln(y + 1) - \ln(x + 5) = \ln 3$$
$$\ln\frac{y + 1}{x + 5} = \ln 3$$
$$\frac{y + 1}{x + 5} = 3$$
$$y + 1 = 3(x + 5)$$
$$y = 3(x + 5) - 1$$
$$y = 3x + 15 - 1$$
$$y = 3x + 14$$

73. $\log_2 196 = \frac{\log 196}{\log 2} \approx 7.6147$

74. $\log_3 74 = \frac{\log 74}{\log 3} \approx 3.9177$

75. $A = P(1+r)^n$

$\qquad = 12{,}000\,(1+0.1)^8$

$\qquad = 12{,}000\,(1.1)^8$

$\qquad \approx 25{,}723.07$

The amount is \$25,723.07.

76. $P = P_0 e^{kt}$

$P_0 = 10{,}000, \ k = 0.04, \text{ and } P = 20{,}000$

$20{,}000 = 10{,}000 e^{(0.04)t}$

$\qquad 2 = e^{0.04\,t}$

$\qquad \ln 2 = 0.04\,t$

$\qquad t = \dfrac{\ln 2}{0.04}$

$\qquad t \approx 17.3$

It will take about 17.3 years for the \$10,000 to double.

77. $N(t) = 2000(2)^{0.05t}$

a.   Let $N(t) = 50{,}000.$

$50{,}000 = 2000\,(2)^{0.05t}$

$\dfrac{50{,}000}{2000} = 2^{0.05t}$

$25 = 2^{0.05t}$

$\log 25 = \log 2^{0.05t}$

$\log 25 = 0.05t \log 2$

$\dfrac{\log 25}{0.05 \log 2} = t$

$92.88 \approx t$

The time is 92.88 minutes.

b.   Let $N(t) = 120{,}000.$

$120{,}000 = 2000(2)^{0.05t}$

$\dfrac{120{,}000}{2000} = 2^{0.05t}$

$60 = 2^{0.05t}$

$\log 60 = \log 2^{0.05t}$

$\log 60 = 0.05t \log 2$

$\dfrac{\log 60}{0.05 \log 2} = t$

$118.14 \cup t$

The time is 118.14 minutes.

78. $P = 14.7 e^{-0.00004x}$

$P = 14.7 e^{-0.00004(8842)}$

$P = 14.7 e^{-0.35368}$

$P \approx 14.7(0.7021)$

$P \approx 10.32$

The atmospheric pressure is 10.32 pounds per square inch at 8,842 feet above sea level.

79. $A(n) = 72 - 18\log(n+1)$

a. $A(0) = 72 - 18\log(0+1)$

$\qquad = 72 - 18\log(1)$

$\qquad = 72 - 18(0)$

$\qquad = 72$

The original class average was 72.

b. $A(2) = 72 - 18\log(2+1)$

$\qquad = 72 - 18\log(3)$

$\qquad \approx 72 - 8.6$

$\qquad = 63.4$

After 2 months, the class average was 63.4.

c.   Let $A(n) = 59.4.$

$59.4 = 72 - 18\log(n+1)$

$-12.6 = -18\log(n+1)$

$\dfrac{-12.6}{-18} = \log(n+1)$

$0.7 = \log(n+1)$

$10^{0.7} = 10^{\log(n+1)}$

$5.01 \approx n+1$

$4.01 \approx n$

It takes about 4 months.

Practice Test

1.   **a.**   Yes, $\{(4, 2), (-3, 8), (-1, 3), (5, 7)\}$ is one-to-one.

      b. $\{(2, 4), (8, -3), (3, -1), (7, 5)\}$ is the inverse function.

2.   **a.** $(f \circ g)(x) = f[\,g(x)]$

$\qquad = f(x+2)$

$\qquad = (x+2)^2 - 3$

$\qquad = x^2 + 4x + 4 - 3$

$\qquad = x^2 + 4x + 1$

      b. $(f \circ g)(5) = 5^2 + 4(5) + 1$

$\qquad = 25 + 20 + 1$

$\qquad = 46$

3.   **a.** $(g \circ f)(x) = g[\,f(x)]$

$\qquad = g(x^2 + 7)$

$\qquad = \sqrt{x^2 + 7 - 5}$

$\qquad = \sqrt{x^2 + 2}$

b. $(g \circ f)(4) = \sqrt{4^2 + 2}$

   $= \sqrt{16 + 2}$

   $= \sqrt{18}$

   $= 3\sqrt{2}$

4. a. $y = f(x) = -3x - 5$

   $x = -3y - 5$

   $x + 5 = -3y$

   $\dfrac{x+5}{-3} = y$

   $-\dfrac{1}{3}(x+5) = y$

   $f^{-1}(x) = -\dfrac{1}{3}(x+5)$

b.

x	$f(x)$
0	-5
$-\frac{5}{3}$	0

x	$f^{-1}(x)$
0	$-\frac{5}{3}$
-5	0

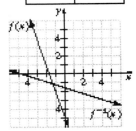

5. a. $y = f(x) = \sqrt{x-1}, \ x \geq 1$

   $x = (y-1)^{1/2}$

   $x^2 = [(y-1)^{1/2}]^2$

   $x^2 = y - 1$

   $x^2 + 1 = y$

   $f^{-1}(x) = x^2 + 1, \ x \geq 0$

b.

x	$f(x)$
1	0
2	1
5	2

x	$f^{-1}(x)$
0	1
1	2
2	5

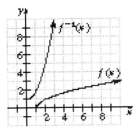

6. The domain of $y = \log_4(x)$ is $x > 0$.

7. $\log_3 \dfrac{1}{81} = \log_3 3^{-4} = -4$

8. $y = 3^x$

x	-2	-1	0	2	3
y	$\frac{1}{9}$	$\frac{1}{3}$	1	9	27

Domain: R

Range: $\{y | y > 0\}$

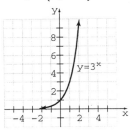

9. $y = \log_2 x$

   $x = 2^y$

x	$\frac{1}{4}$	$\frac{1}{2}$	1	2	4
y	-2	-1	0	1	2

Domain: $\{x | x > 0\}$

Range: R

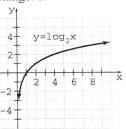

10. $2^{-5} = \dfrac{1}{32}$

   $\log_2 \dfrac{1}{32} = -5$

11. $\log_5 625 = 4$

$\quad 5^4 = 625$

12. $\quad 4 = \log_2(x+1)$

$\quad 2^4 = x+1$

$\quad 16 = x+1$

$\quad 15 = x$

13. $\quad y = \log_{64} 16$

$\quad 64^y = 16$

$\quad 4^{3y} = 4^2$

$\quad 3y = 2$

$\quad y = \dfrac{2}{3}$

14. $\log_2 \dfrac{x^3(x-4)}{x+2}$

$\quad = \log_2 x^3(x-4) - \log_2(x+2)$

$\quad = \log_2 x^3 + \log_2(x-4) - \log_2(x+2)$

$\quad = 3\log_2 x + \log_2(x-4) - \log_2(x+2)$

15. $5\log_6(x-4) + 2\log_6(x+3) - \dfrac{1}{2}\log_6 x$

$\quad = \log_6(x-4)^5 + \log_6(x+3)^2 - \log_6 x^{1/2}$

$\quad = \log_6 \dfrac{(x-4)^5(x+3)^2}{\sqrt{x}}$

16.

17. a. $\quad \log 4620 \approx 3.6646$

   b. $\quad \ln 0.0692 \approx -2.6708$

18. $\quad 3^x = 519$

$\quad \log 3^x = \log 519$

$\quad x\log 3 = \log 519$

$\quad x = \dfrac{\log 519}{\log 3}$

$\quad x \approx 5.69$

19. $\quad \log 4\, x = \log(x+3) + \log 2$

$\quad \log 4\, x = \log 2\,(x+3)$

$\quad 4x = 2(x+3)$

$\quad 4x = 2x+6$

$\quad 2x = 6$

$\quad x = 3$

20. $\quad \log(x+5) - \log(x-2) = \log 6$

$\quad \log \dfrac{x+5}{x-2} = \log 6$

$\quad \dfrac{x+5}{x-2} = 6$

$\quad x+5 = 6x-12$

$\quad 17 = 5x$

$\quad \dfrac{17}{5} = x$

21. $\quad \ln N = 3.52$

$\quad e^{3.52} = N$

$\quad 33.7844 \approx N$

22. $\quad \log_6 40 = \dfrac{\log 40}{\log 6} \approx 2.0588$

23. $\quad 200 = 500e^{-0.03t}$

$\quad \dfrac{200}{500} = e^{-0.03t}$

$\quad \ln\dfrac{200}{500} = -0.03t$

$\quad \dfrac{\ln\frac{200}{500}}{-0.03} = t$

$\quad t \approx 30.5430$

24. $\quad A = p\left(1 + \dfrac{r}{n}\right)^{nt}$

Use $p = 3500$, $r = 0.06$ and $n = 4$

$t = 10$

$\quad A = 3500\left(1 + \dfrac{0.06}{4}\right)^{4\cdot 10}$

$\quad\quad = 3500(1.015)^{40}$

$\quad\quad \approx 6349.06$

The amount in the account is \$6349.06.

25. $v = v_0 e^{-0.0001205t}$

Use $v = 40$, and $v_0 = 60$.

$$40 = 60e^{-0.0001205t}$$

$$\frac{40}{60} = e^{-0.0001205t}$$

$$\frac{2}{3} = e^{-0.0001205t}$$

$$\ln\frac{2}{3} = \ln e^{-0.0001205t}$$

$$\ln\frac{2}{3} = -0.0001205t$$

$$\frac{\ln\frac{2}{3}}{-0.0001205} = t$$

$$3364.86 \approx t$$

The fossil is approximately 3364.86 years old.

Cumulative Review Test

1. $\dfrac{\left(2xy^2 z^{-3}\right)^2}{\left(3x^{-1}yz^2\right)^{-1}} = \dfrac{2^2 x^2 y^4 z^{-6}}{3^{-1} x^1 y^{-1} z^{-2}}$

$$= \frac{2^2 \cdot 3 \, xy^5}{z^4}$$

$$\frac{12xy^5}{z^4}$$

2. $4^2 - \left(2 - 3^2\right)^2 + 4^3$

$$4^2 - \left(2 - 9\right)^2 + 4^3$$

$$4^2 - \left(-7\right)^2 + 4^3$$

$$16 - 49 + 64$$

$$31$$

3. Let r be the tax rate.

$$92 + 92r = 98.90$$

$$92r = 6.90$$

$$r = \frac{6.90}{92}$$

$$\approx 0.075$$

The tax rate is 7.5%.

4.
$$-3 \le 2x - 7 < 8$$
$$-3 + 7 \le 2x < 8 + 7$$
$$4 \le 2x < 15$$
$$2 \le x < \frac{15}{2}$$
$$\left\{x \,\middle|\, 2 \le x < \frac{15}{2}\right\}, \ \left[2, \frac{15}{2}\right)$$

5.
$$2x - 3y = 5$$
$$-3y = 5 - 2x$$
$$y = \frac{5 - 2x}{-3} \text{ or } y = \frac{2x - 5}{3}$$

6. $h(x) = \dfrac{x^2 + 4x}{x + 6}$

$$h(-3) = \frac{(-3)^2 + 4(-3)}{(-3) + 6}$$

$$= \frac{9 - 12}{3}$$

$$= \frac{-3}{3} \text{ or } -1$$

7. Two points on the line are (0, 3) and (−2,−1).

$$m = \frac{y_2 - y_1}{x_2 - x_1} = \frac{-1 - 3}{-2 - 0} = \frac{-4}{-2} = 2$$

Use point-slope form with $(0,3)$ and $m = 2$.

$$y - 3 = 2(x - 0)$$
$$y - 3 = 2x$$
$$y = 2x + 3$$

8. $4x = 3y - 3 \implies y = \frac{4}{3}x + 3$

Plot the y-intercept (0, 3) and use the slope to plot additional points.

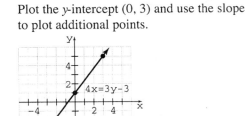

9. $y \le \frac{1}{3}x + 6$

Plot a dashed line at $y \le \frac{1}{3}x + 6$.

Use the point $(0, 0)$ as the check point.

$y \le \frac{1}{3}x + 6$

$0 \le \frac{1}{3}(0) + 6$

$0 \le 6$ True

Therefore, shade the half-plane containing $(0, 0)$

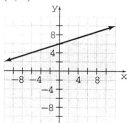

10. $\frac{1}{2}x + \frac{1}{3}y = 13$

$\frac{1}{5}x + \frac{1}{8}y = 5$

Clear out the fractions by multiplying through by its least common denominator.

$6\left(\frac{1}{2}x + \frac{1}{3}y = 13\right) \Rightarrow 3x + 2y = 78$ (1)

$40\left(\frac{1}{5}x + \frac{1}{8}y = 5\right) \Rightarrow 8x + 5y = 200$ (2)

Multiply equation (1) by -5, multiply equation (2) by 2 and add the results.

$-5(3x + 2y = 78) \Rightarrow -15x - 10y = -390$

$2(8x + 5y = 200) \Rightarrow \underline{16x + 10y = 400}$

$ x = 10$

Substitute 10 for x in equation (1).

$3(10) + 2y = 78$

$30 + 2y = 78$

$2y = 48$

$y = 24$

The solution is $(10, 24)$.

11. $\dfrac{x^3 + 3x^2 + 5x + 4}{x + 1}$

Using synthetic division:

$$
\begin{array}{r|rrrr}
-1 & 1 & 3 & 5 & 4 \\
   &   & -1 & -2 & -3 \\
\hline
   & 1 & 2 & 3 & 1
\end{array}
$$

$\dfrac{x^3 + 3x^2 + 5x + 4}{x + 1} = x^2 + 2x + 3 + \dfrac{1}{x + 1}$

12. $x^2 - 2xy + y^2 - 25$

$\left(x^2 - 2xy + y^2\right) - 25$

$(x - y)^2 - 25$

$(x - y + 5)(x - y - 5)$

13. $(2x + 5)^2 - 9 = 0$

$(2x + 5)^2 = 9$

$2x + 5 = \pm\sqrt{9}$

$2x + 5 = \pm 3$

$x = \dfrac{-5 \pm 3}{2}$

$x = \dfrac{-5 + 3}{2}$ or $x = \dfrac{-5 - 3}{2}$

$ = \dfrac{-2}{2}$ $= \dfrac{-8}{2}$

$ = -1$ $= -4$

14. $\dfrac{2x + 3}{x + 1} = \dfrac{3}{2}$

$(2)(2x + 3) = (3)(x + 1)$

$4x + 6 = 3x + 3$

$x = -3$

15. $a_n = a_1 + nd - d$, for d

$a_n - a_1 = nd - d$

$a_n - a_1 = d(n - 1)$

$\dfrac{a_n - a_1}{n - 1} = d$

16. The equation of variation is

$L = \dfrac{k}{P^2}$, with $P = 4$ and $k = 100$.

$L = \dfrac{100}{4^2} = \dfrac{100}{16} = 6.25$

17. $3\sqrt{45x^3} + \sqrt{5x}$

$3\sqrt{9x^2 \cdot 5x} + \sqrt{5x}$

$9x\sqrt{5x} + \sqrt{5x}$

$(9x+1)\sqrt{5x}$

18. $\sqrt{2a+9} - a + 3 = 0$

$\sqrt{2a+9} = a - 3$

$\left(\sqrt{2a+9}\right)^2 = (a-3)^2$

$2a + 9 = a^2 - 6a + 9$

$a^2 - 8a = 0$

$a(a-8) = 0$

$a = 0$ or $a - 8 = 0$

$a = 8$

Upon checking, $a = 0$ is an extraneous solution. The solution is $a = 8$.

19. $\left(x^2 - 5\right)^2 + 3\left(x^2 - 5\right) - 10 = 0$

$u^2 + 3u - 10 = 0$

$(u+5)(u-2) = 0$

$u + 5 = 0$ or $u - 2 = 0$

$x^2 - 5 + 5 = 0$ $x^2 - 5 - 2 = 0$

$x^2 = 0$ $x^2 = 7$

$x = 0$ $x = \pm\sqrt{7}$

20. $g(x) = x^2 - 4x - 5$

a. $g(x) = x^2 - 4x - 5$

$g(x) = \left(x^2 - 4x + 4\right) - 5 - 4$

$g(x) = (x-2)^2 - 9$

b.

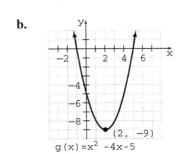

$g(x) = x^2 - 4x - 5$

Chapter 10

Exercise Set 10.1

1.

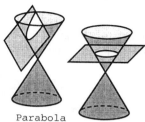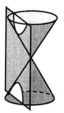

Parabola　　　Circle　　　Ellipse　　　Hyperbol

3. Yes, any parabola in the form $y = a(x - h)^2 + k$ is a function because each value of x corresponds to only one value of y. The domain is R, the set of all real numbers. Since the vertex is at (h, k) and $a > 0$, the range is $\{y | y \geq k\}$.

5. The graphs have the same vertex, (3, 4). The first graph opens upward, and the second one opens downward.

7. The distance is always a positive number because both distances are squared and we use the principal square root.

9. A circle is the set of all points in a plane that are the same distance from a fixed point.

11. No, the coefficients of the y^2- term and the x^2-term must both be the same.

13. No, the coefficients of the y^2- term and the x^2-term must both be the same.

15. No, equations of parabolas do not include both x^2 - and y^2- terms.

17. $y = (x - 2)^2 + 3$

This is a parabola in the form $y = a(x - h)^2 + k$ with $a = 1$, $h = 2$ and $k = 3$. Since $a > 0$, the parabola opens upward. The vertex is (2, 3). The y-intercept is (0, 7). There are no x-intercepts.

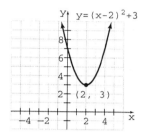

19. $y = (x + 3)^2 + 2$

This is a parabola in the form $y = a(x - h)^2 + k$ with $a = 1$, $h = -3$ and $k = 2$. Since $a > 0$, the parabola opens upward. The vertex is (−3, 2). The y-intercept is (0, 11). There are no x-intercepts.

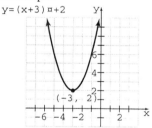

21. $y = (x - 2)^2 - 1$

This is a parabola in the form $y = a(x - h)^2 + k$ with $a = 1$, $h = 2$ and $k = -1$. Since $a > 0$, the parabola opens upward. The vertex is (2, −1). The y-intercept is (0, 3). The x-intercepts are (1, 0) and (3, 0).

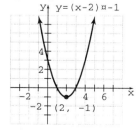

23. $y = -(x-1)^2 + 1$

This is a parabola in the form $y = a(x-h)^2 + k$ with $a = -1$, $h = 1$ and $k = 1$. Since $a < 0$, the parabola opens downward. The vertex is $(1, 1)$. The y-intercept is $(0, 0)$. The x-intercepts are $(0, 0)$ and $(2, 0)$.

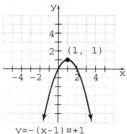

25. $y = -(x+3)^2 + 4$

This is a parabola in the form $y = a(x-h)^2 + k$ with $a = -1$, $h = -3$ and $k = 4$. Since $a < 0$, the parabola opens downward. The vertex is $(-3, 4)$. The y-intercept is $(0, -5)$. The x-intercepts are $(-5, 0)$ and $(-1, 0)$.

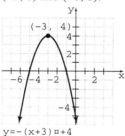

27. $y = -3(x-5)^2 + 3$

This is a parabola in the form $y = a(x-h)^2 + k$ with $a = -3$, $h = 5$ and $k = 3$. Since $a < 0$, the parabola opens downward. The vertex is $(5, 3)$. The y-intercept is $(0, -72)$. The x-intercepts are $(4, 0)$ and $(6, 0)$.

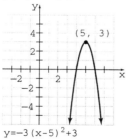

29. $x = (y-4)^2 - 3$

This is a parabola in the form $x = a(y-k)^2 + h$ with $a = 1$, $h = -3$ and $k = 4$. Since $a > 0$, the parabola opens to the right. The vertex is $(-3, 4)$. The y-intercepts are about $(0, 2.27)$ and $(0, 5.73)$. The x-intercept is $(13, 0)$.

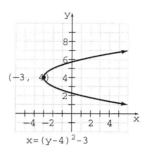

31. $x = -(y-5)^2 + 4$

This is a parabola in the form $x = a(y-k)^2 + h$ with $a = -1$, $h = 4$ and $k = 5$. Since $a < 0$, the parabola opens to the left. The vertex is $(4, 5)$. The y-intercepts are $(0, 3)$ and $(0, 7)$. The x-intercept is $(-21, 0)$.

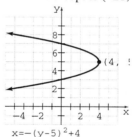

33. $x = -5(y+3)^2 - 6$

This is a parabola in the form $x = a(y-k)^2 + h$ with $a = -5$, $h = -6$ and $k = -3$. Since $a < 0$, the parabola opens to the left. The vertex is $(-6, -3)$. There are no y-intercepts. The x-intercept is $(-51, 0)$

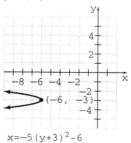

35.
$$y = -2\left(x + \frac{1}{2}\right)^2 + 6$$

This is a parabola in the form $y = a(x - h)^2 + k$ with $a = -2$, $h = -\frac{1}{2}$ and $k = 6$. Since $a < 0$, the parabola opens downward. The vertex is $\left(-\frac{1}{2},\ 6\right)$. The y-intercept is $\left(0,\ \frac{11}{2}\right)$. The x-intercepts are about $(-2.23, 0)$ and $(1.23, 0)$.

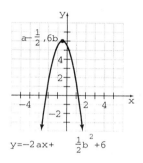

37. a.
$$y = x^2 + 2x$$
$$y = (x^2 + 2x + 1) - 1$$
$$y = (x + 1)^2 - 1$$

b. This is a parabola in the form $y = a(x - h)^2 + k$ with $a = 1$, $h = -1$ and $k = -1$. Since $a > 0$, the parabola opens upward. The vertex is $(-1, -1)$. The y-intercept is $(0, 0)$. The x-intercepts are $(-2, 0)$ and $(0, 0)$.

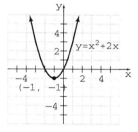

39. a.
$$y = x^2 + 6x$$
$$y = (x^2 + 6x + 9) - 9$$
$$y = (x + 3)^2 - 9$$

b. This is a parabola in the form $y = a(x - h)^2 + k$ with $a = 1$, $h = -3$ and $k = -9$. Since $a > 0$, the parabola opens upward. The vertex is $(-3, -9)$. The y-intercept is $(0, 0)$. The x-intercepts are $(-6, 0)$ and $(0, 0)$.

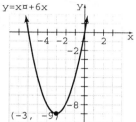

41. a.
$$x = y^2 + 4y$$
$$x = (y^2 + 4y + 4) - 4$$
$$x = (y + 2)^2 - 4$$

b. This is a parabola in the form $x = a(y - k)^2 + h$ with $a = 1$, $h = -4$ and $k = -2$. Since $a > 0$, the parabola opens to the right. The vertex is $(-4, -2)$. The y-intercepts are $(0, -4)$ and $(0, 0)$. The x-intercept is $(0, 0)$.

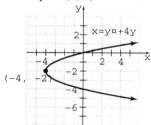

43. a.
$$y = x^2 + 7x + 10$$
$$y = \left(x^2 + 7x + \frac{49}{4}\right) - \frac{49}{4} + 10$$
$$y = \left(x + \frac{7}{2}\right)^2 - \frac{9}{4}$$

b. This is a parabola in the form
$y = a(x - h)^2 + k$ with $a = 1$, $h = -\dfrac{7}{2}$ and
$k = -\dfrac{9}{4}$. Since $a > 0$, the parabola opens
upward. The vertex is $\left(-\dfrac{7}{2}, -\dfrac{9}{4}\right)$. The
y-intercept is $(0, 10)$. The x-intercepts are
$(-5, 0)$ and $(-2, 0)$.

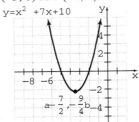

45.   **a.** $x = -y^2 + 6y - 9$
$x = -(y^2 - 6y) - 9$
$x = -(y^2 - 6y + 9) + 9 - 9$
$x = -(y - 3)^2$

b. This is a parabola in the form
$x = a(y - k)^2 + h$ with $a = -1$, $h = 0$ and
$k = 3$. Since $a < 0$, the parabola opens to
the left. The vertex is $(0, 3)$. The y-
intercept is $(0, 3)$. The x-intercept is
$(-9, 0)$.

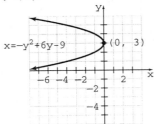

47.   **a.** $y = -x^2 + 4x - 4$
$y = -(x^2 - 4x) - 4$
$y = -(x^2 - 4x + 4) + 4 - 4$
$y = -(x - 2)^2$

b. This is a parabola in the form
$y = a(x - h)^2 + k$ with $a = -1$, $h = 2$ and
$k = 0$. Since $a < 0$, the parabola opens
downward. The vertex is $(2, 0)$. The
y-intercept is $(0, -4)$. The x-intercept is
$(2, 0)$.

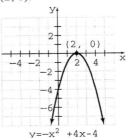

49.   **a.** $x = -y^2 + 3y - 4$
$x = -(y^2 - 3y) - 4$
$x = -\left(y^2 - 3y + \dfrac{9}{4}\right) + \dfrac{9}{4} - 4$
$x = -\left(y - \dfrac{3}{2}\right)^2 - \dfrac{7}{4}$

b. This is a parabola in the form
$x = a(y - k)^2 + h$ with $a = -1$, $h = -\dfrac{7}{4}$ and
$k = \dfrac{3}{2}$. Since $a < 0$, the parabola opens to
the left. The vertex is $\left(-\dfrac{7}{4}, \dfrac{3}{2}\right)$. There are
no y-intercepts. The x-intercept is $(-4, 0)$.

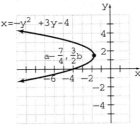

51. $d = \sqrt{(x_2 - x_1)^2 + (y_2 - y_1)^2}$
      $= \sqrt{(3 - 3)^2 + [-6 - (-1)]^2}$
      $= \sqrt{0^2 + (-5)^2}$
      $= \sqrt{0 + 25}$
      $= \sqrt{25}$
      $= 5$

53.
$$d = \sqrt{(x_2 - x_1)^2 + (y_2 - y_1)^2}$$
$$= \sqrt{[5-(-4)]^2 + (3-3)^2}$$
$$= \sqrt{9^2 + 0^2}$$
$$= \sqrt{81+0}$$
$$= \sqrt{81}$$
$$= 9$$

55.
$$d = \sqrt{(x_2 - x_1)^2 + (y_2 - y_1)^2}$$
$$= \sqrt{[4-(-1)]^2 + [9-(-3)]^2}$$
$$= \sqrt{5^2 + 12^2}$$
$$= \sqrt{25+144}$$
$$= \sqrt{169}$$
$$= 13$$

57.
$$d = \sqrt{(x_2 - x_1)^2 + (y_2 - y_1)^2}$$
$$= \sqrt{[5-(-4)]^2 + [-2-(-5)]^2}$$
$$= \sqrt{9^2 + 3^2}$$
$$= \sqrt{81+9}$$
$$= \sqrt{90}$$
$$\approx 9.49$$

59.
$$d = \sqrt{(x_2 - x_1)^2 + (y_2 - y_1)^2}$$
$$= \sqrt{\left(\frac{1}{2} - 3\right)^2 + [4-(-1)]^2}$$
$$= \sqrt{\left(-\frac{5}{2}\right)^2 + 5^2}$$
$$= \sqrt{\frac{25}{4} + 25}$$
$$= \sqrt{\frac{125}{4}}$$
$$\approx 5.59$$

61.
$$d = \sqrt{(x_2 - x_1)^2 + (y_2 - y_1)^2}$$
$$= \sqrt{[-4.3-(-1.6)]^2 + (-1.7-3.5)^2}$$
$$= \sqrt{(-2.7)^2 + (-5.2)^2}$$
$$= \sqrt{7.29+27.04}$$
$$= \sqrt{34.33}$$
$$\approx 5.86$$

63.
$$d = \sqrt{(x_2 - x_1)^2 + (y_2 - y_1)^2}$$
$$= \sqrt{\left(0-\sqrt{7}\right)^2 + \left[0-\sqrt{3}\right]^2}$$
$$= \sqrt{\left(-\sqrt{7}\right)^2 + \left(\sqrt{3}\right)^2}$$
$$= \sqrt{7+3}$$
$$= \sqrt{10}$$
$$\approx 3.16$$

65.
$$\text{Midpoint} = \left(\frac{x_1 + x_2}{2}, \frac{y_1 + y_2}{2}\right)$$
$$= \left(\frac{1+5}{2}, \frac{9+3}{2}\right)$$
$$= (3, 6)$$

67.
$$\text{Midpoint} = \left(\frac{x_1 + x_2}{2}, \frac{y_1 + y_2}{2}\right)$$
$$= \left(\frac{-7+7}{2}, \frac{2+(-2)}{2}\right)$$
$$= (0, 0)$$

69.
$$\text{Midpoint} = \left(\frac{x_1 + x_2}{2}, \frac{y_1 + y_2}{2}\right)$$
$$= \left(\frac{-1+4}{2}, \frac{4+6}{2}\right)$$
$$= \left(\frac{3}{2}, 5\right)$$

71.
$$\text{Midpoint} = \left(\frac{x_1 + x_2}{2}, \frac{y_1 + y_2}{2}\right)$$
$$= \left(\frac{3+2}{2}, \frac{\frac{1}{2}+(-4)}{2}\right)$$
$$= \left(\frac{5}{2}, -\frac{7}{4}\right)$$

73.
$$\text{Midpoint} = \left(\frac{x_1 + x_2}{2}, \frac{y_1 + y_2}{2} \right)$$
$$= \left(\frac{\sqrt{3} + \sqrt{2}}{2}, \frac{2 + 7}{2} \right)$$
$$= \left(\frac{\sqrt{3} + \sqrt{2}}{2}, \frac{9}{2} \right)$$

75.
$$(x - h)^2 + (y - k)^2 = r^2$$
$$(x - 0)^2 + (y - 0)^2 = 6^2$$
$$x^2 + y^2 = 36$$

77.
$$(x - h)^2 + (y - k)^2 = r^2$$
$$(x - 2)^2 + (y - 0)^2 = 5^2$$
$$(x - 2)^2 + y^2 = 25$$

79.
$$(x - h)^2 + (y - k)^2 = r^2$$
$$(x - 0)^2 + [y - 5]^2 = 2^2$$
$$x^2 + (y - 5)^2 = 4$$

81.
$$(x - h)^2 + (y - k)^2 = r^2$$
$$(x - 3)^2 + (y - 4)^2 = (9)^2$$
$$(x - 3)^2 + (y - 4)^2 = 81$$

83.
$$(x - h)^2 + (y - k)^2 = r^2$$
$$[x - 2]^2 + [y - (-6)]^2 = 10^2$$
$$(x - 2)^2 + (y + 6)^2 = 100$$

85.
$$(x - h)^2 + (y - k)^2 = r^2$$
$$(x - 1)^2 + (y - 2)^2 = \left(\sqrt{7} \right)^2$$
$$(x - 1)^2 + (y - 2)^2 = 7$$

87. The center is (0, 0) and the radius is 4.
$$(x - h)^2 + (y - k)^2 = r^2$$
$$(x - 0)^2 + (y - 0)^2 = 4^2$$
$$x^2 + y^2 = 16$$

89. The center is (3, –2) and the radius is 3.
$$(x - h)^2 + (y - k)^2 = r^2$$
$$(x - 3)^2 + [y - (-2)]^2 = 3^2$$
$$(x - 3)^2 + (y + 2)^2 = 9$$

91.
$$x^2 + y^2 = 16$$
$$x^2 + y^2 = 4^2$$
The graph is a circle with its center at the origin and radius 4.

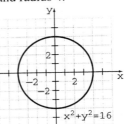

93.
$$x^2 + y^2 = 10$$
$$x^2 + y^2 = \left(\sqrt{10} \right)^2$$
The graph is a circle with its center at the origin and radius $\sqrt{10}$.

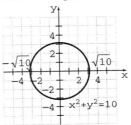

95.
$$(x + 4)^2 + y^2 = 25$$
$$(x + 4)^2 + (y - 0)^2 = 5^2$$
The graph is a circle with its center at (–4, 0) and radius 5.

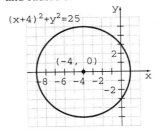

97.
$$x^2 + (y+1)^2 = 9$$
$$(x-0)^2 + (y+1)^2 = (3)^2$$
The graph is a circle with its center at $(0, -1)$ and radius 3.

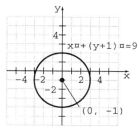

99.
$$(x+8)^2 + (y+2)^2 = 9$$
$$(x+8)^2 + (y+2)^2 = 3^2$$
The graph is a circle with its center at $(-8, -2)$ and radius 3.

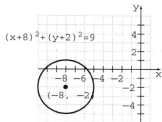

101.
$$y = \sqrt{25 - x^2}$$
If we solve $x^2 + y^2 = 25$ for y, we obtain
$y = \pm\sqrt{25 - x^2}$. Therefore, the graph of
$y = \sqrt{25 - x^2}$ is the upper half $(y \geq 0)$ of a circle with its center at the origin and radius 5.

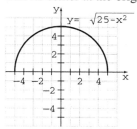

103.
$$y = -\sqrt{4 - x^2}$$
If we solve $x^2 + y^2 = 4$ for y, we obtain
$y = \pm\sqrt{4 - x^2}$. Therefore, the graph of
$y = -\sqrt{4 - x^2}$ is the lower half $(y \leq 0)$ of a circle with its center at the origin and radius 2.

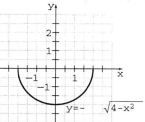

105. **a.**
$$x^2 + y^2 + 8x + 15 = 0$$
$$x^2 + 8x + y^2 = -15$$
$$(x^2 + 8x + 16) + y^2 = -15 + 16$$
$$(x+4)^2 + y^2 = 1$$
$$(x+4)^2 + y^2 = 1^2$$

b. The graph is a circle with center $(-4, 0)$ and radius 1.

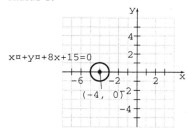

107. **a.**
$$x^2 + y^2 + 6x - 4y + 9 = 0$$
$$x^2 + 6x + y^2 - 4y = -9$$
$$(x^2 + 6x + 9) + (y^2 - 4y + 4) = -9 + 9 + 4$$
$$(x+3)^2 + (y-2)^2 = 4$$
$$(x+3)^2 + (y-2)^2 = 2^2$$

b. The graph is a circle with center (–3, 2) and radius 2.

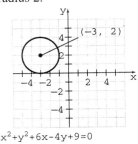

$x^2+y^2+6x-4y+9=0$

109. a.
$$x^2 + y^2 + 6x - 2y + 6 = 0$$
$$x^2 + 6x + y^2 - 2y = -6$$
$$(x^2 + 6x + 9) + (y^2 - 2y + 1) = -6 + 9 + 1$$
$$(x+3)^2 + (y-1)^2 = 4$$
$$(x+3)^2 + (y-1)^2 = 2^2$$

b. The graph is a circle with center (–3, 1) and radius 2.

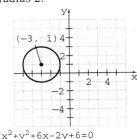

$x^2+y^2+6x-2y+6=0$

111. a.
$$x^2 + y^2 - 8x + 2y + 13 = 0$$
$$x^2 - 8x + y^2 + 2y = -13$$
$$(x^2 - 8x + 16) + (y^2 + 2y + 1) = -13 + 16 + 1$$
$$(x-4)^2 + (y+1)^2 = 4$$
$$(x-4)^2 + (y+1)^2 = 2^2$$

b. The graph is a circle with center (4, –1) and radius 2.

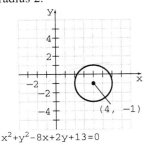

$x^2+y^2-8x+2y+13=0$

113. $x^2 + y^2 = 16$
$x^2 + y^2 = 4^2$
The graph is a circle with its center at the origin and radius 4.

$$\text{Area} = \pi r^2 = \pi(4)^2 = 16\pi \approx 50.3 \text{ sq. units}$$

115. x-intercept:
$x = 0^2 - 6(0) - 7$
$x = -7$
The x-intercept is $(-7, 0)$
y-intercepts:
$0 = y^2 - 6y - 7$
$0 = (y+1)(y-7)$
$y = -1$ or $y = 7$
The y-intercepts are $(0, -1)$ and $(0, 7)$.

117. x-intercept:
$x = 2(0-5)^2 + 6$
$x = 56$
The x-intercept is $(56, 0)$.
Y-intercepts:
$0 = 2(y-5)^2 + 6$
Since $2(y-5)^2 + 6 \geq 6$ for all real values of y, this equation has no real solutions.
There are no y-intercepts.

119. No. For example, the origin is the midpoint of both the segment from (1, 1) to (–1, –1) and the segment from (2, 2) to (–2, –2), but these segments have different lengths.

121. The distance from the midpoint (4, –6) to the endpoint (7, –2) is half the length of the line segment.

$$\frac{d}{2} = \sqrt{(7-4)^2 + [-2-(-6)]^2}$$
$$= \sqrt{3^2 + 4^2}$$
$$= \sqrt{25}$$
$$= 5$$

Since $\frac{d}{2} = 5$, $d = 10$. The length is 10 units.

123. Since (–5, 2) is 2 units above the x-axis, the radius is 2.
$$(x-h)^2 + (y-k)^2 = r^2$$
$$(x+5)^2 + (y-2)^2 = 2^2$$
$$(x+5)^2 + (y-2)^2 = 4$$

125. a. Diameter $= \sqrt{(x_2 - x_1)^2 + (y_2 - y_1)^2}$

$= \sqrt{(9 - 5)^2 + (8 - 4)^2}$

$= \sqrt{4^2 + 4^2}$

$= \sqrt{16 + 16}$

$= \sqrt{32}$

$= 4\sqrt{2}$

Since the diameter is $4\sqrt{2}$ units, the radius is $2\sqrt{2}$ units.

b. Midpoint $= \left(\dfrac{x_1 + x_2}{2}, \dfrac{y_1 + y_2}{2} \right)$

$= \left(\dfrac{5 + 9}{2}, \dfrac{4 + 8}{2} \right)$

$= (7, \ 6)$

The center is $(7, 6)$.

c. $(x - h)^2 + (y - k)^2 = r^2$

$(x - 7)^2 + (y - 6)^2 = \left(2\sqrt{2} \right)^2$

$(x - 7)^2 + (y - 6)^2 = 8$

127. The minimum number is 0 and the maximum number is 4 as shown in the diagrams.

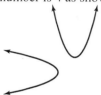

No points of inter

4 points of inter

129. a. Since $150 - 2(68.2) = 13.6$, the clearance is 13.6 feet.

b. Since $150 - 68.2 = 81.8$, the center of the wheel is 81.8 feet above the ground.

c. $(x - h)^2 + (y - k)^2 = r^2$

$(x - 0)^2 + (y - 81.8)^2 = 68.2^2$

$x^2 + (y - 81.8)^2 = 68.2^2$

$x^2 + (y - 81.8)^2 = 4651.24$

131. a. The center of the blue circle is the origin, and the radius is 4.

$x^2 + y^2 = r^2$

$x^2 + y^2 = 4^2$

$x^2 + y^2 = 16$

b. The center of the red circle is $(2, 0)$, and the radius is 2.

$(x - h)^2 + (y - k)^2 = r^2$

$(x - 2)^2 + (y - 0)^2 = 2^2$

$(x - 2)^2 + y^2 = 4$

c. The center of the green circle is $(-2, 0)$, and the radius is 2.

$(x - h)^2 + (y - k)^2 = r^2$

$[x - (-2)]^2 + (y - 0)^2 = 2^2$

$(x + 2)^2 + y^2 = 4$

d. Shaded area $=$ (blue circle area) $-$ (red circle area) $-$ (green circle area)

$= \pi\left(4^2 \right) - \pi\left(2^2 \right) - \pi\left(2^2 \right)$

$= 16\pi - 4\pi - 4\pi$

$= 8\pi$

133. The radii are 4 and 8, respectively. So, the area between the circles is

$\pi(8)^2 - \pi(4)^2 = 64\pi - 16\pi = 48\pi$.

137. $-4 < 3x - 4 < 8$

$-4 + 4 < 3x - 4 + 4 < 8 + 4$

$0 < 3x < 12$

$\dfrac{0}{3} < \dfrac{3x}{3} < \dfrac{12}{3}$

$0 < x < 4$

In interval notation: $(0, 4)$

139. a. area 1: a^2 area 2: ab

area 3: ab area 4: b^2

b. $(a + b)^2$

Exercise Set 10.2

1. An ellipse is a set of points in a plane, the sum of whose distances from two fixed points is constant.

3. $\dfrac{(x-h)^2}{a^2} + \dfrac{(y-k)^2}{b^2} = 1$

5. If $a = b$, the formula for a circle is obtained.

7. First divide both sides by 360.

9. No, the sign in front of the y^2 is negative.

11. $\dfrac{x^2}{4} + \dfrac{y^2}{1} = 1$

Since $a^2 = 4$, $a = 2$.
Since $b^2 = 1$, $b = 1$.

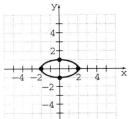

13. $\dfrac{x^2}{4} + \dfrac{y^2}{9} = 1$

Since $a^2 = 4$, $a = 2$.
Since $b^2 = 9$, $b = 3$.

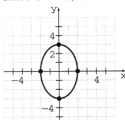

15. $\dfrac{x^2}{25} + \dfrac{y^2}{9} = 1$

Since $a^2 = 25$, $a = 5$.
Since $b^2 = 9$, $b = 3$.

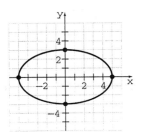

17. $\dfrac{x^2}{16} + \dfrac{y^2}{25} = 1$

Since $a^2 = 16$, $a = 4$.
Since $b^2 = 25$, $b = 5$.

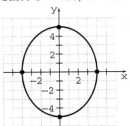

19. $x^2 + 36y^2 = 36$

$\dfrac{x^2}{36} + \dfrac{36y^2}{36} = 1$

$\dfrac{x^2}{36} + \dfrac{y^2}{1} = 1$

Since $a^2 = 36$, $a = 6$.
Since $b^2 = 1$, $b = 1$.

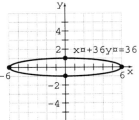

21. $9x^2 + 25y^2 = 225$

$\dfrac{9x^2}{225} + \dfrac{25y^2}{225} = 1$

$\dfrac{x^2}{25} + \dfrac{y^2}{9} = 1$

Since $a^2 = 25$, $a = 5$.
Since $b^2 = 9$, $b = 3$.

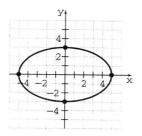

23. $9x^2 + 4y^2 = 36$

$$\frac{9x^2}{36} + \frac{4y^2}{36} = 1$$

$$\frac{x^2}{4} + \frac{y^2}{9} = 1$$

Since $a^2 = 4$, $a = 2$.

Since $b^2 = 9$, $b = 3$.

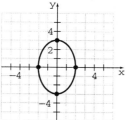

25. $100x^2 + 25y^2 = 400$

$$4x^2 + y^2 = 16$$

$$\frac{4x^2}{16} + \frac{y^2}{16} = 1$$

$$\frac{x^2}{4} + \frac{y^2}{16} = 1$$

Since $a^2 = 4$, $a = 2$.

Since $b^2 = 16$, $b = 4$.

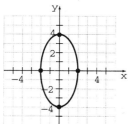

27. $x^2 + 2y^2 = 8$

$$\frac{x^2}{8} + \frac{2y^2}{8} = 1$$

$$\frac{x^2}{8} + \frac{y^2}{4} = 1$$

Since $a^2 = 8$, $a = \sqrt{8} = 2\sqrt{2} \approx 2.83$.

Since $b^2 = 4$, $b = 2$.

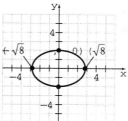

29. $\dfrac{x^2}{16} + \dfrac{(y-2)^2}{9} = 1$

The center is $(0, 2)$.

Since $a^2 = 16$, $a = 4$.

Since $b^2 = 9$, $b = 3$.

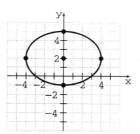

31. $\dfrac{(x-4)^2}{9} + \dfrac{(y+3)^2}{25} = 1$

The center is $(4, -3)$.

Since $a^2 = 9$, $a = 3$.

Since $b^2 = 25$, $b = 5$.

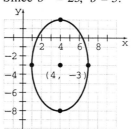

33. $\dfrac{(x+1)^2}{9}+\dfrac{(y-2)^2}{4}=1$

The center is $(-1, 2)$.

Since $a^2=9$, $a=3$.

Since $b^2=4$, $b=2$.

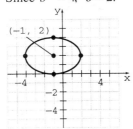

35. $(x+3)^2+9(y+1)^2=81$

$\dfrac{(x+3)^2}{81}+\dfrac{9(y+1)^2}{81}=1$

$\dfrac{(x+3)^2}{81}+\dfrac{(y+1)^2}{9}=1$

The center is $(-3, -1)$.

Since $a^2=81$, $a=9$.

Since $b^2=9$, $b=3$.

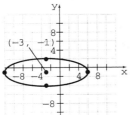

37. $4(x-2)^2+9(y+2)^2=36$

$\dfrac{4(x-2)^2}{36}+\dfrac{9(y+2)^2}{36}=1$

$\dfrac{(x-2)^2}{9}+\dfrac{(y+2)^2}{4}=1$

The center is $(2, -2)$.

Since $a^2=9$, $a=3$.

Since $b^2=4$, $b=2$.

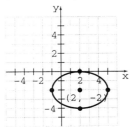

39. $12(x+4)^2+3(y-1)^2=48$

$\dfrac{12(x+4)^2}{48}+\dfrac{3(y-1)^2}{48}=1$

$\dfrac{(x+4)^2}{4}+\dfrac{(y-1)^2}{16}=1$

The center is $(-4, 1)$.

Since $a^2=4$, $a=2$.

Since $b^2=16$, $b=4$.

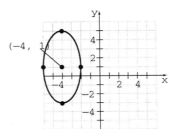

41. $\dfrac{x^2}{4}+\dfrac{y^2}{1}=1$

Since $a^2=4$, $a=2$.

Since $b^2=1$, $b=1$.

Area $=\pi ab$

$=\pi(2)(1)$

$=2\pi$

≈6.3 square units

43. There is only one point, at $(0, 0)$. The only way two non-negative numbers can sum to 0 is if they are both 0.

45. The center is the origin, $a=3$, and $b=5$.

$\dfrac{x^2}{a^2}+\dfrac{y^2}{b^2}=1$

$\dfrac{x^2}{3^2}+\dfrac{y^2}{5^2}=1$

$\dfrac{x^2}{9}+\dfrac{y^2}{25}=1$

47. The center is the origin, $a=2$, and $b=3$.

$\dfrac{x^2}{a^2}+\dfrac{y^2}{b^2}=1$

$\dfrac{x^2}{2^2}+\dfrac{y^2}{3^2}=1$

$\dfrac{x^2}{4}+\dfrac{y^2}{9}=1$

49. There are no points of intersection, because the ellipse with $a = 2$ and $b = 3$ is completely inside the circle of radius 4.

51.
$$x^2 + 4y^2 - 4x - 8y - 92 = 0$$
$$x^2 - 4x + 4y^2 - 8y = 92$$
$$(x^2 - 4x + 4) + 4(y^2 - 2y + 1) = 92 + 4 + 4$$
$$(x - 2)^2 + 4(y - 1)^2 = 100$$
$$\frac{(x - 2)^2}{100} + \frac{(y - 1)^2}{25} = 1$$
The center is (2, 1).

53. Since $90.2 - 20.7 = 69.5$, the distance between the foci is 69.5 feet.

55.
   a. Consider the ellipse to be centered at the origin, (0, 0). Here, $a = 10$ and $b = 24$. The equation is
$$\frac{x^2}{10^2} + \frac{y^2}{24^2} = 1 \implies \frac{x^2}{100} + \frac{y^2}{576} = 1.$$

   b. Area $= \pi ab$
$$= \pi(10)(24)$$
$$= 240\pi \approx 753.98 \text{ square feet}$$

   c. Area of opening is half the area of ellipse
$$= \frac{\pi ab}{2}$$
$$= \frac{\pi(10)(24)}{2}$$
$$= 120\pi \approx 376.99 \text{ square feet}$$

57. Using $a = 3$ and $b = 2$, we may assume that the ellipse has the equation $\frac{x^2}{9} + \frac{y^2}{4} = 0$ and that the foci are located at $(\pm c, \ 0)$. Apply the definition of an ellipse using the points (3, 0) and (0, 2). That is, the distance from (3, 0) to (−c, 0) plus the distance from (3, 0) to (c, 0) is the same as the sum of the distance from (0, 2) to (−c, 0) and the distance from (0, 2) to (c, 0).
$$\sqrt{[3-(-c)]^2 + (0-0)^2} + \sqrt{(3-c)^2 + (0-0)^2}$$
$$= \sqrt{[0-(-c)]^2 + (2-0)^2} + \sqrt{(0-c)^2 + (2-0)^2}$$
$$|3+c| + |3-c| = \sqrt{c^2+4} + \sqrt{(-c)^2+4}$$

Note that the foci are inside the ellipse, so $3 + c > 0$ and $3 - c > 0$. So, $|3 + c| = 3 + c$ and $|3 - c| = 3 - c$.

$$(3 + c) + (3 - c) = 2\sqrt{c^2 + 4}$$
$$6 = 2\sqrt{c^2 + 4}$$
$$3 = \sqrt{c^2 + 4}$$
$$9 = c^2 + 4$$
$$5 = c^2$$
$$c = \pm\sqrt{5}$$
The foci are located at $\left(\pm\sqrt{5}, \ 0\right)$.

That is, the foci are $\sqrt{5} \approx 2.24$ feet, in both directions, from the center of the ellipse, along the major axis.

59. Answers will vary.

61. Answers will vary.

63. The center is (4, 2).
$a = 2, b = 3.$
$$\frac{(x - h)^2}{a^2} + \frac{(y - k)^2}{b^2} = 1$$
$$\frac{(x - 4)^2}{2^2} + \frac{(y - 2)^2}{3^2} = 1$$
$$\frac{(x - 4)^2}{4} + \frac{(y - 2)^2}{9} = 1$$

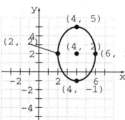

65.
$$S = \frac{n}{2}(f + l), \text{ for } l$$
$$S = \frac{nf}{2} + \frac{nl}{2}$$
$$S - \frac{nf}{2} = \frac{nl}{2}$$
$$2\left(S - \frac{nf}{2}\right) = 2\left(\frac{nl}{2}\right)$$
$$2S - nf = nl$$
$$\frac{2S - nf}{n} = \frac{nl}{n} \implies l = \frac{2S - nf}{n}$$

67. $\sqrt{8b-15} = 10-b$

$8b-15 = (10-b)^2$

$8b-15 = 100-20b+b^2$

$b^2-28b+115 = 0$

$(b-5)(b-23) = 0$

$b-5 = 0$ or $b-23 = 0$

$b = 5$ $b = 23$

Upon checking $b = 23$ is extraneous. The solution is $b = 5$.

69. $\log_6 4000 = \dfrac{\log 4000}{\log 6} \approx 4.6290$

Exercise Set 10.3

1. A hyperbola is the set of points in a plane, the difference of whose distances from two fixed points is a constant.

3. The graph of $\dfrac{x^2}{a^2} - \dfrac{y^2}{b^2} = 1$ is a hyperbola with vertices at $(a, 0)$ and $(-a, 0)$. Its transverse axis lies along the x-axis. The asymptotes are $y = \pm \dfrac{b}{a} x$.

5. No, equations of hyperbolas have one positive square term and one negative square term. This equation has two positive square terms.

7. Yes, equations of hyperbolas have one positive square term and one negative square term. This equation satisfies that condition.

9. The first step is to divide both sides by 81 in order to make the right side equal to 1.

11. a. $\dfrac{x^2}{9} - \dfrac{y^2}{4} = 1$

Since $a^2 = 9$ and $b^2 = 4$, $a = 3$ and $b = 2$. The equations of the asymptotes are $y = \pm \dfrac{b}{a} x$, or $y = \pm \dfrac{2}{3} x$.

    b. .To graph the asymptotes, plot the points $(3, 2)$, $(-3, 2)$, $(3, -2)$, and $(-3, -2)$. The graph intersects the x-axis at $(-3, 0)$ and $(3, 0)$.

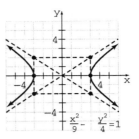

13. a. $\dfrac{x^2}{4} - \dfrac{y^2}{1} = 1$

Since $a^2 = 4$ and $b^2 = 1$, $a = 2$ and $b = 1$. The equations of the asymptotes are $y = \pm \dfrac{b}{a} x$, or $y = \pm \dfrac{1}{2} x$.

    b. To graph the asymptotes, plot the points $(2, 1)$, $(-2, 1)$, $(2, -1)$, and $(-2, -1)$. The graph intersects the x-axis at $(-2, 0)$ and $(2, 0)$.

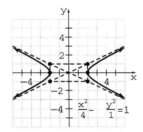

15. a. $\dfrac{x^2}{9} - \dfrac{y^2}{25} = 1$

Since $a^2 = 9$ and $b^2 = 25$, $a = 3$ and $b = 5$. The equations of the asymptotes are $y = \pm \dfrac{b}{a} x$, or $y = \pm \dfrac{5}{3} x$.

    b. To graph the asymptotes, plot the points $(3, 5)$, $(-3, 5)$, $(3, -5)$, and $(-3, -5)$. The graph intersects the x-axis at $(-3, 0)$ and $(3, 0)$.

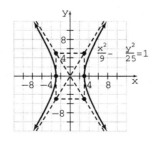

17. **a.** $\dfrac{x^2}{25} - \dfrac{y^2}{16} = 1$

Since $a^2 = 25$ and $b^2 = 16$, $a = 5$ and $b = 4$. The equations of the asymptotes are $y = \pm\dfrac{b}{a}x$, or $y = \pm\dfrac{4}{5}x$.

b. To graph the asymptotes, plot the points $(5, 4)$, $(-5, 4)$, $(5, -4)$, and $(-5, -4)$. The graph intersects the *x*-axis at $(-5, 0)$ and $(5, 0)$.

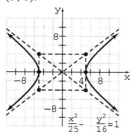

19. **a.** $\dfrac{y^2}{9} - \dfrac{x^2}{16} = 1$

Since $a^2 = 16$ and $b^2 = 9$, $a = 4$ and $b = 3$. The equations of the asymptotes are $y = \pm\dfrac{b}{a}x$, or $= y \pm \dfrac{3}{4}x$.

b. To graph the asymptotes, plot the points $(4, 3)$, $(-4, 3)$, $(4, -3)$ and $(-4, -3)$. The graph intersects the *y*-axis at $(0, -3)$ and $(0, 3)$.

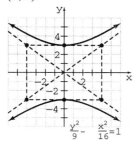

21. **a.** $\dfrac{y^2}{25} - \dfrac{x^2}{36} = 1$

Since $a^2 = 36$ and $b^2 = 25$, $a = 6$ and $b = 5$. The equations of the asymptotes are $y = \pm\dfrac{b}{a}x$, or $y = \pm\dfrac{5}{6}x$.

b. To graph the asymptotes, plot the points $(6, 5)$, $(-6, 5)$, $(6, -5)$, and $(-6, -5)$. The graph intersects the *y*-axis at $(0, -5)$ and $(0, 5)$.

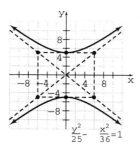

23. **a.** $\dfrac{y^2}{25} - \dfrac{x^2}{4} = 1$

Since $a^2 = 4$ and $b^2 = 25$, $a = 2$ and $b = 5$. The equations of the asymptotes are $y = \pm\dfrac{b}{a}x$ or $y = \pm\dfrac{5}{2}x$.

b. To graph the asymptotes, plot the points $(2, 5)$, $(-2, 5)$, $(2, -5)$ and $(-2, -5)$. The graph intersects the *y*-axis at $(0, -5)$ and $(0, 5)$.

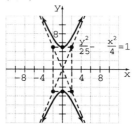

25. **a.** $\dfrac{y^2}{16} - \dfrac{x^2}{81} = 1$

Since $a^2 = 81$ and $b^2 = 16$, $a = 9$ and $b = 4$. The equations of the asymptotes are $y = \pm\dfrac{b}{a}x$, or $y = \pm\dfrac{4}{9}x$.

b. To graph the asymptotes, plot the points $(9, 4)$, $(-9, 4)$, $(9, -4)$, and $(-9, -4)$. The graph intersects the *y*-axis at $(0, -4)$ and $(0, 4)$.

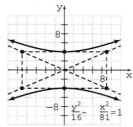

27. a. $x^2 - 25y^2 = 25$

$$\frac{x^2}{25} - \frac{25y^2}{25} = 1$$

$$\frac{x^2}{25} - \frac{y^2}{1} = 1$$

Since $a^2 = 25$ and $b^2 = 1$, $a = 5$ and $b = 1$. The equations of the asymptotes are

$$y = \pm \frac{b}{a}x, \text{ or } y = \pm \frac{1}{5}x.$$

b. To graph the asymptotes, plot the points $(5, 1)$, $(-5, 1)$, $(5, -1)$, and $(-5, -1)$. The graph intersects the x-axis at $(-5, 0)$, and $(5, 0)$.

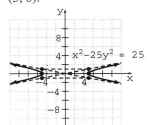

29. a. $16x^2 - 4y^2 = 64$

$$\frac{16x^2}{64} - \frac{4y^2}{64} = 1$$

$$\frac{x^2}{4} - \frac{y^2}{16} = 1$$

Since $a^2 = 4$ and $b^2 = 16$, $a = 2$ and $b = 4$. The equations of the asymptotes are

$$y = \pm \frac{b}{a}x, \text{ or } y = \pm 2x.$$

b. To graph the asymptotes, plot the points $(2, 4)$, $(-2, 4)$, $(2, -4)$, and $(-2, -4)$. The graph intersects the x-axis at $(-2, 0)$ and $(2, 0)$.

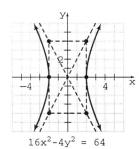

$16x^2 - 4y^2 = 64$

31. a. $9y^2 - x^2 = 9$

$$\frac{9y^2}{9} - \frac{x^2}{9} = 1$$

$$\frac{y^2}{1} - \frac{x^2}{9} = 1$$

Since $a^2 = 9$ and $b^2 = 1$, $a = 3$ and $b = 1$. The equations of the asymptotes are

$$y = \pm \frac{b}{a}x, \text{ or } \pm \frac{1}{3}x.$$

b. To graph the asymptotes, plot the points $(3, 1)$, $(-3, 1)$, $(3, -1)$, and $(-3, -1)$. The graph intersects the y-axis at $(0, -1)$ and $(0, 1)$.

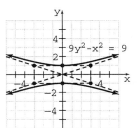

33. a. $25x^2 - 9y^2 = 225$

$$\frac{25x^2}{225} - \frac{9y^2}{225} = 1$$

$$\frac{x^2}{9} - \frac{y^2}{25} = 1$$

Since $a^2 = 9$ and $b^2 = 25$, $a = 3$ and $b = 5$. The equations of the asymptotes are

$$y = \pm \frac{b}{a}x, \text{ or } y = \pm \frac{5}{3}x.$$

b. To graph the asymptotes, plot the points $(3, 5)$, $(-3, 5)$, $(3, -5)$, and $(-3, -5)$. The graph intersects the x-axis at $(-3, 0)$ and $(3, 0)$.

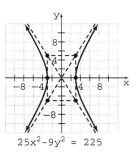

$25x^2 - 9y^2 = 225$

35. **a.** $4y^2 - 36x^2 = 144$

$$\frac{4y^2}{144} - \frac{36x^2}{144} = 1$$

$$\frac{y^2}{36} - \frac{x^2}{4} = 1$$

Since $a^2 = 4$ and $b^2 = 36$, $a = 2$ and $b = 6$. The equations of the asymptotes are $y = \pm\dfrac{b}{a}x$, or $y = \pm 3x$.

b. To graph the asymptotes, plot the points $(2, 6)$, $(-2, 6)$, $(2, -6)$, and $(-2, -6)$. The graph intersects the y-axis at $(0, -6)$ and $(0, 6)$.

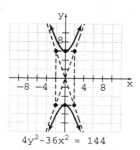

$4y^2 - 36x^2 = 144$

37. $5x^2 + 5y^2 = 125$

$$\frac{5x^2}{5} + \frac{5y^2}{5} = \frac{125}{5}$$

$$x^2 + y^2 = 25$$

The graph is a circle.

39. $x^2 + 5y^2 = 125$

$$\frac{x^2}{125} + \frac{5y^2}{125} = 1$$

$$\frac{x^2}{125} + \frac{y^2}{25} = 1$$

The graph is an ellipse.

41. $4x^2 - 4y^2 = 29$

$$\frac{4x^2}{29} - \frac{4y^2}{29} = 1$$

$$\frac{x^2}{\frac{29}{4}} - \frac{y^2}{\frac{29}{4}} = 1$$

The graph is a hyperbola.

43. $2y = 12x^2 - 8x + 20$

$$y = -6x^2 - 4x + 10$$

The graph is a parabola.

45. $6x^2 + 7y^2 = 42$

$$\frac{6x^2}{42} + \frac{7y^2}{42} = 1$$

$$\frac{x^2}{7} + \frac{y^2}{6} = 1$$

The graph is an ellipse.

47. $3x = -2y^2 + 9y - 15$

$$x = -\frac{2}{3}y^2 + 3y - 5$$

The graph is a parabola.

49. $6x^2 + 6y^2 = 36$

$$\frac{6x^2}{6} + \frac{6y^2}{6} = 36$$

$$x^2 + y^2 = 6$$

The graph is a circle.

51. $5y^2 = 7x^2 + 35$

$$5y^2 - 7x^2 = 35$$

$$\frac{5y^2}{35} - \frac{7x^2}{35} = 1$$

$$\frac{y^2}{7} - \frac{x^2}{5} = 1$$

The graph is a hyperbola.

53. $x + y = 2y^2 + 5$

$$x = 2y^2 - y + 5$$

The graph is a parabola.

55. $3x^2 = 12y^2 + 48$

$$3x^2 - 12y^2 = 48$$

$$\frac{3x^2}{48} - \frac{12y^2}{48} = 1$$

$$\frac{x^2}{16} - \frac{y^2}{4} = 1$$

The graph is a hyperbola.

57. $y - x + 2 = x^2$

$$y = x^2 + x - 2$$

The graph is a parabola.

59.
$$-3x^2 - 3y^2 = -243$$
$$\frac{-3x^2}{-3} + \frac{-3y^2}{-3} = \frac{-243}{-3}$$
$$x^2 + y^2 = 81$$
The graph is a circle.

61. Since the vertices are $(0, \pm 2)$, the hyperbola is of the form $\dfrac{y^2}{b^2} - \dfrac{x^2}{a^2} = 1$ with $b = 2$. Since the asymptotes are $y = \pm\dfrac{1}{2}x$, we have $\dfrac{b}{a} = \dfrac{1}{2}$.

Therefore, $\dfrac{2}{a} = \dfrac{1}{2}$, so $a = 4$. The equation of the hyperbola is $\dfrac{y^2}{2^2} - \dfrac{x^2}{4^2} = 1$, or $\dfrac{y^2}{4} - \dfrac{x^2}{16} = 1$.

63. Since the vertices are $(0, \pm 3)$, the hyperbola is of the form $\dfrac{x^2}{a^2} - \dfrac{y^2}{b^2} = 1$ with $a = 3$. Since the asymptotes are $y = \pm 2x$, we have $\dfrac{b}{a} = 2$.

Therefore, $\dfrac{b}{3} = 2$, so $b = 6$. The equation of the hyperbola is $\dfrac{x^2}{3^2} - \dfrac{y^2}{6^2} = 1$, or $\dfrac{x^2}{9} - \dfrac{y^2}{36} = 1$.

65. Since the transverse axis is along the x-axis, the equation is of the form $\dfrac{x^2}{a^2} - \dfrac{y^2}{b^2} = 1$ Since the asymptotes are $y = \pm\dfrac{5}{3}x$, we require $\dfrac{b}{a} = \dfrac{5}{3}$.
Using $a = 3$ and $b = 5$, the equation of the hyperbola is $\dfrac{x^2}{3^2} - \dfrac{y^2}{5^2} = 1$, or $\dfrac{x^2}{9} - \dfrac{y^2}{25} = 1$.
No, this is not the only possible answer, because a and b are not uniquely determined.
$\dfrac{x^2}{18} - \dfrac{y^2}{50} = 1$ and others will also work.

67. No, for each value of x with $|x| > a$, there are 2 possible values of y.

69. $\dfrac{x^2}{9} - \dfrac{y^2}{4} = 1$. This hyperbola has its transverse axis along the x-axis with vertices at $(\pm 3, 0)$.
Domain: $(-\infty, -3] \cup [3, \infty)$
Range: R

71. The equation is changed from $\dfrac{x^2}{a^2} - \dfrac{y^2}{b^2} = 1$ to $\dfrac{x^2}{b^2} - \dfrac{y^2}{a^2} = 1$. Both graphs have a transverse axis along the x-axis. The vertices of the second graph will be closer to the origin, at $(\pm b, 0)$ instead of $(\pm a, 0)$. The second graph will open wider.

73. Answers will vary.

75. The points are $(-6, 4)$ and $(-2, 2)$.
$$m = \frac{y_2 - y_1}{x_2 - x_1} = \frac{2-4}{-2-(-6)} = \frac{-2}{4} = -\frac{1}{2}$$
Use $y - y_1 = m(x - x_1)$, with $m = -\dfrac{1}{2}, (-2, 2)$
$$y - 2 = -\frac{1}{2}\left(x - (-2)\right)$$
$$y - 2 = -\frac{1}{2}x - 1$$
$$y = -\frac{1}{2}x + 1$$

77.
$$5(-4x + 9y = 7) \implies -20x + 45y = 35$$
$$4(5x + 6y = -3) \implies \underline{20x + 24y = -12}$$
$$69y = 23$$
$$y = \frac{1}{3}$$
$$5x + 6\left(\frac{1}{3}\right) = -3 \implies 5x + 2 = -3 \implies x = -1$$
The solution is $\left(-1, \dfrac{1}{3}\right)$.

79. $E = \dfrac{1}{2}mv^2$, for v
$$2E = mv^2$$
$$\frac{2E}{m} = v^2$$
$$\sqrt{\frac{2E}{m}} = v \quad \text{or} \quad v = \sqrt{\frac{2E}{m}}$$

Exercise Set 10.4

1. A nonlinear system of equations is a system in which at least one equation is nonlinear.

3. Yes

5. Yes

7. $x^2 + y^2 = 8$
$x + y = 0$
Solve $x + y = 0$ for x: $x = -y$.
Substitute $x = -y$ for x in $x^2 + y^2 = 8$.
$$x^2 + y^2 = 8$$
$$(-y)^2 + y^2 = 8$$
$$y^2 + y^2 = 8$$
$$2y^2 = 8$$
$$y^2 = 4$$
$$y = \pm 2$$
$y = 2$ or $y = -2$
$x = -2$ $x = 2$

The solutions are $(2, -2)$ and $(-2, 2)$.

9. $x^2 + y^2 = 9$
$x + 2y = 3$
Solve $x + 2y = 3$ for x: $x = 3 - 2y$.
Substitute $3 - 2y$ for x in $x^2 + y^2 = 9$.
$$x^2 + y^2 = 9$$
$$(3 - 2y)^2 + y^2 = 9$$
$$9 - 12y + 4y^2 + y^2 = 9$$
$$5y^2 - 12y = 0$$
$$y(5y - 12) = 0$$
$y = 0$ or $y = \dfrac{12}{5}$

$x = 3 - 2y$ $x = 3 - 2y$
$x = 3 - 2(0)$ $x = 3 - 2\left(\dfrac{12}{5}\right)$
$x = 3$ $x = -\dfrac{9}{5}$

The solutions are $(3, 0)$ and $\left(-\dfrac{9}{5}, \ \dfrac{12}{5}\right)$.

11. $y = x^2 - 5$
$3x + 2y = 10$
Substitute $x^2 - 5$ for y in $3x + 2y = 10$
$$3x + 2y = 10$$
$$3x + 2(x^2 - 5) = 10$$
$$3x + 2x^2 - 10 = 10$$
$$2x^2 + 3x - 20 = 0$$
$$(x + 4)(2x - 5) = 0$$
$x = -4$ or $x = \dfrac{5}{2}$

$y = x^2 - 5$ $y = x^2 - 5$
$y = (-4)^2 - 5$ $y = \left(\dfrac{5}{2}\right)^2 - 5$
$y = 11$ $y = \dfrac{5}{4}$

The solutions are $(-4, \ 11)$ and $\left(\dfrac{5}{2}, \ \dfrac{5}{4}\right)$.

13. $x + y = 4$
$x^2 - y^2 = 4$
Solve $x + y = 4$ for y: $y = 4 - x$.
Substitute $4 - x$ for y in $x^2 - y^2 = 4$
$$x^2 - y^2 = 4$$
$$x^2 - (4 - x)^2 = 4$$
$$x^2 - (16 - 8x + x^2) = 4$$
$$-16 + 8x = 4$$
$$8x = 20$$
$$x = \dfrac{5}{2}$$
$y = 4 - x$
$y = 4 - \dfrac{5}{2}$
$y = \dfrac{3}{2}$

The solution is $\left(\dfrac{5}{2}, \ \dfrac{3}{2}\right)$.

15. $x + y^2 = 4 \Rightarrow y^2 = -x + 4$

$x^2 + y^2 = 6$

Substitute $-x + 4$ for y^2 in $x^2 + y^2 = 6$.

$x^2 + y^2 = 6$

$x^2 + (-x + 4) = 6$

$x^2 - x - 2 = 0$

$(x - 2)(x + 1) = 0$

$x = 2 \qquad\qquad x = -1$

or

$y^2 = -x + 4$	$y^2 = -x + 4$
$y^2 = -2 + 4$	$y^2 = -(-1) + 4$
$y^2 = 2$	$y^2 = 5$
$y = \pm\sqrt{2}$	$y = \pm\sqrt{5}$

The solutions are $\left(2,\ \sqrt{2}\right)$, $\left(2,\ -\sqrt{2}\right)$,

$\left(-1,\ \sqrt{5}\right)$, and $\left(-1,\ -\sqrt{5}\right)$.

17. $x^2 + y^2 = 4$

$y = x^2 - 12 \Rightarrow x^2 = y + 12$

Substitute $y + 12$ for x^2 in $x^2 + y^2 = 4$.

$x^2 + y^2 = 4$

$(y + 12) + y^2 = 4$

$y^2 + y + 8 = 0$

$$y = \frac{-1 \pm \sqrt{1^2 - 4(1)(8)}}{2(1)}$$

$$= \frac{-1 \pm \sqrt{-31}}{2}$$

$$= \frac{-1 \pm i\sqrt{31}}{2}$$

There is no real solution.

19. $x^2 + y^2 = 9$

$y = x^2 - 3$

Solve $y = x^2 - 3$ for x^2: $x^2 = y + 3$.

Substitute $y + 3$ for x^2 in $x^2 + y^2 = 9$.

$x^2 + y^2 = 9$

$(y + 3) + y^2 = 9$

$y^2 + y - 6 = 0$

$(y - 2)(y + 3) = 0$

$y = 2 \qquad\qquad \text{or} \qquad\qquad y = -3$

$x^2 = y + 3$	$x^2 = y + 3$
$x^2 = 2 + 3$	$x^2 = -3 + 3$
$x^2 = 5$	$x^2 = 0$
$x = \pm\sqrt{5}$	$x = 0$

The solutions are $(0,\ -3)$, $\left(\sqrt{5}, 2\right)$, and

$\left(-\sqrt{5}, 2\right)$.

21. $2x^2 - y^2 = -8$

$x - y = 6$

Solve the second equation for y: $y = x - 6$.

Substitute $x - 6$ for y in $2x^2 - y^2 = -8$.

$2x^2 - y^2 = -8$

$2x^2 - (x - 6)^2 = -8$

$2x^2 - (x^2 - 12x + 36) = -8$

$2x^2 - x^2 + 12x - 36 = -8$

$x^2 + 12x - 28 = 0$

$(x - 2)(x + 14) = 0$

$x = 2 \qquad\qquad \text{or} \qquad\qquad x = -14$

$y = x - 6$	$y = x - 6$
$y = 2 - 6$	$y = -14 - 6$
$y = -4$	$y = -20$

The solutions are $(2, -4)$ and $(-14, -20)$.

23. $x^2 - y^2 = 4$

$\underline{2x^2 + y^2 = 8}$

$3x^2 \qquad = 12$

$x^2 = 4$

$x = 2 \qquad\qquad\qquad\qquad\qquad x = -2$

or

$x^2 - y^2 = 4$	$x^2 - y^2 = 4$
$2^2 - y^2 = 4$	$(-2)^2 - y^2 = 4$
$y^2 = 0$	$y^2 = 0$
$y = 0$	$y = 0$

The solutions are $(2, 0)$ and $(-2, 0)$.

25.

$x^2 + y^2 = 13 \quad (1)$

$2x^2 + 3y^2 = 30 \quad (2)$

$-2x^2 - 2y^2 = -26 \quad (1) \text{ multiplied by } -2$

$\underline{2x^2 + 3y^2 = 30 \quad (2)}$

$y^2 = 4$

$y = 2$ or $y = -2$

$x^2 + y^2 = 13$ $x^2 + y^2 = 13$

$x^2 + 2^2 = 13$ $x^2 + (-2)^2 = 13$

$x^2 = 9$ $x^2 = 9$

$x = \pm 3$ $x = \pm 3$

The solutions are (3, 2), (3, –2), (–3, 2), and (–3, –2).

27.

$x^2 + y^2 = 25$ (1)

$x^2 - 2y^2 = 7$ (2)

$2x^2 + 2y^2 = 50$ (1) Multiplied by 2

$\underline{x^2 - 2y^2 = 7}$ (2)

$3x^2 = 57$

$x^2 = 19$

$x = \sqrt{19}$ or $x = -\sqrt{19}$

$x^2 + y^2 = 25$ $x^2 + y^2 = 25$

$\left(\sqrt{19}\right)^2 + y^2 = 25$ $\left(-\sqrt{19}\right)^2 + y^2 = 25$

$y^2 = 6$ $y^2 = 6$

$y = \pm\sqrt{6}$ $y = \pm\sqrt{6}$

The solutions are $\left(\sqrt{19},\ \sqrt{6}\right), \left(\sqrt{19},\ -\sqrt{6}\right),$ $\left(-\sqrt{19},\ \sqrt{6}\right),$ and $\left(-\sqrt{19},\ -\sqrt{6}\right).$

29.

$4x^2 + 9y^2 = 36$

$\underline{2x^2 - 9y^2 = 18}$

$6x^2 = 54$

$x^2 = 9$

$x = 3$ or $x = -3$

$4x^2 + 9y^2 = 36$ $4x^2 + 9y^2 = 36$

$4(3)^2 + 9y^2 = 36$ $4(-3)^2 + 9y^2 = 36$

$9y^2 = 0$ $9y^2 = 0$

$y^2 = 0$ $y^2 = 0$

$y = 0$ $y = 0$

The solutions are (3, 0) and (–3, 0).

31.

$5x^2 - 2y^2 = -13$ (1)

$3x^2 + 4y^2 = 39$ (2)

$10x^2 - 4y^2 = -26$ (1) multiplied by 2

$\underline{3x^2 + 4y^2 = 39}$ (2)

$13x^2 = 13$

$x^2 = 1$

$x = 1$ or $x = -1$

$3x^2 + 4y^2 = 39$ $3x^2 + 4y^2 = 39$

$3(1)^2 + 4y^2 = 39$ $3(-1)^2 + 4y^2 = 39$

$4y^2 = 36$ $4y^2 = 36$

$y^2 = 9$ $y^2 = 9$

$y = \pm 3$ $y = \pm 3$

The solutions are (1, 3), (1, –3), (–1, 3), and (–1, –3).

33.

$x^2 - 2y^2 = 7$ (1)

$x^2 + y^2 = 34$ (2)

$-x^2 + 2y^2 = -7$ (1) multiplied by – 1

$\underline{x^2 + y^2 = 34}$ (2)

$3y^2 = 27$

$y^2 = 9$

$y = 3$ or $y = -3$

$x^2 + y^2 = 34$ $x^2 + y^2 = 34$

$x^2 + 3^2 = 34$ $x^2 + (-3)^2 = 34$

$x^2 = 25$ $x^2 = 25$

$x = \pm 5$ $x = \pm 5$

The solutions are (5, 3), (5, –3), (–5, 3), and (–5, –3).

35.

$x^2 + y^2 = 9$ (1)

$16x^2 - 4y^2 = 64$ (2)

$4x^2 + 4y^2 = 36$ (1) multiplied by 4

$\underline{16x^2 - 4y^2 = 64}$ (2)

$20x^2 = 100$

$x^2 = 5$

$x = \sqrt{5}$ or $x = -\sqrt{5}$

$x^2 + y^2 = 9$ $x^2 + y^2 = 9$

$\left(\sqrt{5}\right)^2 + y^2 = 9$ $\left(-\sqrt{5}\right)^2 + y^2 = 9$

$y^2 = 4$ $y^2 = 4$

$y = \pm 2$ $y = \pm 2$

The solutions are $\left(\sqrt{5},\ 2\right), \left(\sqrt{5},\ -2\right),$ $\left(-\sqrt{5},\ 2\right),$ and $\left(-\sqrt{5},\ -2\right).$

37. Answers will vary.

39. Let x = length
y = width
$xy = 500$

$2x + 2y = 90$
Solve $2x + 2y = 90$ for y: $y = 45 - x$.
Substitute $45 - x$ for y in $xy = 500$.

$$xy = 500$$
$$x(45 - x) = 500$$
$$45x - x^2 = 500$$
$$x^2 - 45x + 500 = 0$$
$$(x - 20)(x - 25) = 0$$

$x - 20 = 0 \qquad\qquad x - 25 = 0$
$\quad x = 20 \quad$ or $\quad x = 25$

$y = 45 - x \qquad y = 45 - 25$
$y = 45 - 20 \qquad y = 45 - 25$
$y = 25 \qquad\qquad y = 20$

The solutions are (20, 25) and (25, 20).
The dimensions of the dance floor are 20 m by 25 m.

41. $xy = 48$
$2x + y = 20$
Solve $2x + y = 20$ for y: $y = 20 - 2x$.
Substitute $20 - 2x$ for y in $xy = 48$.

$$xy = 48$$
$$x(20 - 2x) = 48$$
$$20x - 2x^2 = 48$$
$$2x^2 - 20x + 48 = 0$$
$$x^2 - 10x + 24 = 0$$
$$(x - 4)(x - 6) = 0$$

$x - 4 = 0 \qquad$ or
$\quad x = 4$

$y = 20 - 2x$
$y = 20 - 2(4)$
$y = 12$
$x - 6 = 0$
$\quad x = 6$

$y = 20 - 2x$
$y = 20 - 2(6)$
$y = 8$

The solutions are (4, 12) and (6, 8).
The dimensions are 6 ft by 8 ft or 4 ft by 12 ft.

43. Let x = length
y = width
$xy = 112$
$x^2 + y^2 = \left(\sqrt{260}\right)^2$
Solve $xy = 112$ for y: $y = \dfrac{112}{x}$.

$$x^2 + y^2 = 260$$
$$x^2 + \left(\frac{112}{x}\right)^2 = 260$$
$$x^2 + \frac{12,544}{x^2} = 260$$
$$x^4 + 12,544 = 260x^2$$
$$x^4 - 260x^2 + 12,544 = 0$$
$$(x^2 - 64)(x^2 - 196) = 0$$

$x^2 - 64 = 0 \qquad\qquad$ or
$\quad x^2 = 64$
$\quad x = \pm 8$
$x^2 - 196 = 0$
$\quad x^2 = 196$
$\quad x = \pm 14$

Since x must be positive, $x = 8$ or $x = 14$.
If $x = 8$, then $y = \dfrac{112}{8} = 14$.
If $x = 14$, then $y = \dfrac{112}{14} = 8$.

The dimensions of the new bill are 8 cm by 14 cm.

45. Let x = length
y = width
$x^2 + y^2 = 17^2$
$x + y + 17 = 40$
Solve $x + y + 17 = 40$ for y: $y = 23 - x$.
Substitute $23 - x$ for y in $x^2 + y^2 = 17^2$.

$$x^2 + y^2 = 17^2$$
$$x^2 + (23 - x)^2 = 17^2$$
$$x^2 + (529 - 46x + x^2) = 289$$
$$2x^2 - 46 + 529 = 289$$
$$2x^2 - 46x + 240 = 0$$
$$x^2 - 23x + 120 = 0$$
$$(x - 8)(x - 15) = 0$$

$x - 8 = 0$ or $x - 15 = 0$
$x = 8$ $x = 15$

$y = 23 - x$ $y = 23 - x$
$y = 23 - 8$ $y = 23 - 15$
$y = 15$ $y = 8$

The solutions are $(8, 15)$ and $(15, 8)$.
The dimensions of the piece of wood are 8 in. by 15 in.

47.
$d = -16t^2 + 64t$
$d = -16t^2 + 16t + 80$
Substitute $-16t^2 + 64t$ for d in
$d = -16t^2 + 16t + 80$.
$$d = -16t^2 + 16t + 80$$
$-16t^2 + 64t = -16t^2 + 16t + 80$
$64t = 16t + 80$
$48t = 80$
$t = \dfrac{80}{48} = \dfrac{5}{3} \approx 1.67$

The balls are the same height above the ground at $t \approx 1.67$ sec.

49. Since $t = 1$ year, we may write the formula as
$i = pr$.
$7.50 = pr$
$7.50 = (p + 25)(r - 0.01)$
Rewrite the second equation by multiplying the binomials. Then substitute 7.50 for pr and solve for r.
$7.50 = (p + 25)(r - 0.01)$
$7.50 = pr - 0.01p + 25r - 0.25$
$7.50 = 7.50 - 0.01p + 25r - 0.25$
$0 = -0.01p + 25r - 0.25$
$0.01p + 0.25 = 25r$
$\dfrac{0.01p}{25} + \dfrac{0.25}{25} = \dfrac{25r}{25}$
$r = 0.0004p + 0.01$
Substitute $0.0004p + 0.01$ for r in $7.50 = pr$.
$7.50 = pr$
$7.50 = p(0.0004p + 0.01)$
$7.50 = 0.0004p^2 + 0.01p$
$0 = 0.0004p^2 + 0.01p - 7.50$
$0 = p^2 + 25p - 18,750$
$0 = (p - 125)(p + 150)$

$p - 125 = 0$ or
$p = 125$
$p + 150 = 0$
$p = -150$
Since the principal must be positive, use $p = 125$.

$r = 0.0004p + 0.01$
$r = 0.0004(125) + 0.01$
$r = 0.06$
The principal is \$125 and the interest rate is 6%.

51. $C = 10x + 300$
$R = 30x - 0.1x^2$
$$C = R$$
$10x + 300 = 30x - 0.1x^2$
$0.1x^2 - 20x + 300 = 0$
$x = \dfrac{-b \pm \sqrt{b^2 - 4ac}}{2a}$
$= \dfrac{-(-20) \pm \sqrt{(-20)^2 - 4(0.1)(300)}}{2(0.1)}$
$= \dfrac{20 \pm \sqrt{280}}{0.2}$
$x = \dfrac{20 + \sqrt{280}}{0.2} \approx 183.7$ or
$x = \dfrac{20 - \sqrt{280}}{0.2} \approx 16.3$
The break-even points are ≈ 16 and ≈ 184.

53. $C = 80x + 900$
$R = 120x - 0.2x^2$
$$C = R$$
$80x + 900 = 120x - 0.2x^2$
$0.2x^2 - 40x + 900 = 0$
$x = \dfrac{-b \pm \sqrt{b^2 - 4ac}}{2a}$
$= \dfrac{-(-40) \pm \sqrt{(-40)^2 - 4(0.2)(900)}}{2(0.2)}$
$= \dfrac{40 \pm \sqrt{880}}{0.4}$
$x = \dfrac{40 + \sqrt{880}}{0.4} \approx 174.2$ or
$x = \dfrac{40 - \sqrt{880}}{0.4} \approx 25.8$
The break-even points are ≈ 26 and ≈ 174.

55. Solve each equation for y.
$3x - 5y = 12$
$-5y = -3x + 12$
$y = \dfrac{3}{5}x - \dfrac{12}{5}$
$x^2 + y^2 = 10$
$y^2 = 10 - x^2$
$y = \pm\sqrt{10 - x^2}$
Use $y_1 = \dfrac{3}{5}x - \dfrac{12}{5}$, $y_2 = \sqrt{10 - x^2}$, and

$y_2 = -\sqrt{10 - x^2}$.

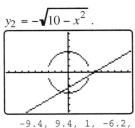

-9.4, 9.4, 1, -6.2,

Approximate solutions: $(-1, -3)$, $(3.12, -0.53)$

57. Let x = length of one leg

y = length of other leg

$x^2 + y^2 = 26^2$

$\dfrac{1}{2} xy = 120$

Solve $\dfrac{1}{2} xy = 120$ for y: $y = \dfrac{240}{x}$.

Substitute $\dfrac{240}{x}$ for y in $x^2 + y^2 = 26^2$

$$x^2 + y^2 = 26^2$$

$$x^2 + \left(\dfrac{240}{x}\right)^2 = 676$$

$$x^2 + \dfrac{57,600}{x^2} = 676$$

$$x^4 + 57,600 = 676x^2$$

$$x^4 - 676x^2 + 57,600 = 0$$

$$\left(x^2 - 100\right)\left(x^2 - 576\right) = 0$$

$x^2 - 100 = 0$ or

$\quad x^2 = 100$

$\qquad x = \pm 10$

$x^2 - 576 = 0$

$\quad x^2 = 576$

$\qquad x = \pm 24$

Since x is a length, x must be positive.

If $x = 10$, then $y = \dfrac{240}{10} = 24$.

If $x = 24$, then $y = \dfrac{240}{24} = 10$.

The legs have lengths 10 yards and 24 yards.

59. The operations are evaluated in the following order: parentheses, exponents, multiplication or division, addition or subtraction.

61. $x = \dfrac{k}{P^2}$

$10 = \dfrac{k}{6^2} \;\Rightarrow\; k = 360 \;\Rightarrow\; x = \dfrac{360}{P^2}$

$x = \dfrac{360}{20^2} = \dfrac{360}{400} = \dfrac{9}{10}$ or   0.9

63. $A = A_0 e^{kt}$, for k

$\dfrac{A}{A_0} = e^{kt}$

$\ln\dfrac{A}{A_0} = \ln e^{kt}$

$\ln A - \ln A_0 = kt$

$\dfrac{\ln A - \ln A_0}{t} = k$

Review Exercises

1.
$$d = \sqrt{(x_2 - x_1)^2 + (y_2 - y_1)^2}$$
$$= \sqrt{(3-0)^2 + (-4-0)^2}$$
$$= \sqrt{3^2 + (-4)^2}$$
$$= \sqrt{9+16}$$
$$= \sqrt{25}$$
$$= 5$$
$$\text{Midpoint} = \left(\frac{x_1 + x_2}{2}, \frac{y_1 + y_2}{2}\right)$$
$$= \left(\frac{0+3}{2}, \frac{0+(-4)}{2}\right)$$
$$= \left(\frac{3}{2}, -2\right)$$

2.
$$d = \sqrt{(x_2 - x_1)^2 + (y_2 - y_1)^2}$$
$$= \sqrt{(-1-(-4))^2 + (5-1)^2}$$
$$= \sqrt{3^2 + 4^2}$$
$$= \sqrt{9+16}$$
$$= \sqrt{25}$$
$$= 5$$
$$\text{Midpoint} = \left(\frac{x_1 + x_2}{2}, \frac{y_1 + y_2}{2}\right)$$
$$= \left(\frac{-4+(-1)}{2}, \frac{1+5}{2}\right)$$
$$= \left(-\frac{5}{2}, 3\right)$$

3.
$$d = \sqrt{(x_2 - x_1)^2 + (y_2 - y_1)^2}$$
$$= \sqrt{[-6-(-1)]^2 + [10-(-2)]^2}$$
$$= \sqrt{(-5)^2 + 12^2}$$
$$= \sqrt{25+144}$$
$$= \sqrt{169}$$
$$= 13$$
$$\text{Midpoint} = \left(\frac{x_1 + x_2}{2}, \frac{y_1 + y_2}{2}\right)$$
$$= \left(\frac{-6+(-1)}{2}, \frac{-2+10}{2}\right)$$
$$= \left(-\frac{7}{2}, 4\right)$$

4.
$$d = \sqrt{(x_2 - x_1)^2 + (y_2 - y_1)^2}$$
$$= \sqrt{[-2-(-4)]^2 + (5-3)^2}$$
$$= \sqrt{2^2 + 2^2}$$
$$= \sqrt{4+4}$$
$$= \sqrt{8}$$
$$\approx 2.83$$
$$\text{Midpoint} = \left(\frac{x_1 + x_2}{2}, \frac{y_1 + y_2}{2}\right)$$
$$= \left(\frac{-4+(-2)}{2}, \frac{3+5}{2}\right)$$
$$= (-3, 4)$$

5. $y = (x-2)^2 + 1$
This is a parabola in the form
$y = a(x-h)^2 + k$ with $a = 1$, $h = 2$, and $k = 1$.
Since $a > 0$, the parabola opens upward. The
vertex is (2, 1). The y-intercept is (0, 5).
There are no x-intercepts.

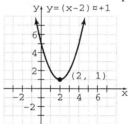

6. $y = (x+3)^2 - 4$
This is a parabola in the form
$y = a(x-h)^2 + k$ with $a = 1$, $h = -3$,
and $k = -4$. Since $a > 0$, the parabola opens
upward. The vertex is (−3, −4). The y-
intercept is (0, 5).
The x-intercepts are about (−5, 0) and
(−1, 0).

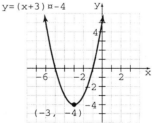

7. $x = (y-1)^2 + 4$
   This is a parabola in the form
   $x = a(y-k)^2 + h$ with $a = 1$, $h = 4$, and
   $k = 1$. Since $a > 0$, the parabola opens to the
   right. The vertex is (4, 1). There are no y-
   intercepts.
   The x-intercept is (5, 0).

   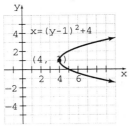

8. $x = -2(y+4)^2 - 3$
   This is a parabola in the form
   $x = a(y-k)^2 + h$ with $a = -2$, $h = -3$, and
   $k = -4$. Since $a < 0$, the parabola opens to
   the left. The vertex is
   (−3, −4). There are no y-intercepts.
   The x-intercept is (−35, 0).

   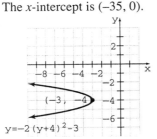

9. a. $y = x^2 - 8x + 22$
   $y = \left(x^2 - 8x + 16\right) + 22 - 16$
   $y = (x-4)^2 + 6$

   b. This is a parabola in the form
   $y = a(x-h)^2 + k$ with $a = 1$, $h = 4$,
   and $k = 6$. Since $a > 0$, the parabola
   opens upward. The vertex is (4, 6). The
   y-intercept is (0, 22). There are no y-
   intercepts.

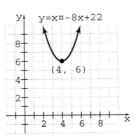

10. a. $x = -y^2 - 2y + 5$
   $x = -(y^2 + 2y) + 5$
   $x = -(y^2 + 2y + 1) + 1 + 5$
   $x = -(y+1)^2 + 6$

   b. This is a parabola in the form
   $x = a(y-k)^2 + h$ with $a = -1$, $h = 6$,
   and $k = -1$. Since $a < 0$, the parabola
   opens to the left. The vertex is (6, −1).
   The y-intercepts are about (0, −3.45) and
   (0, 1.45). The x-intercept is (5, 0).

   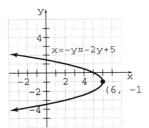

11. a. $x = y^2 + 5y + 4$
   $x = \left(y^2 + 5y + \dfrac{25}{4}\right) - \dfrac{25}{4} + 4$
   $x = \left(y + \dfrac{5}{2}\right)^2 - \dfrac{9}{4}$

   b. This is a parabola in the form
   $x = a(y-k)^2 + h$ with $a = 1$, $h = -\dfrac{9}{4}$,
   and $k = -\dfrac{5}{2}$. Since $a > 0$, the parabola
   opens to the right. The vertex is
   $\left(-\dfrac{9}{4}, -\dfrac{5}{2}\right)$.
   The y-intercepts are (0, −4) and (0, −1).
   The x-intercept is (4, 0).

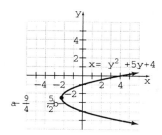

12. **a.** $y = 2x^2 - 8x - 24$

$y = 2(x^2 - 4x) - 24$

$y = 2(x^2 - 4x + 4) - 8 - 24$

$y = 2(x - 2)^2 - 32$

b. This is a parabola in the form
$y = a(x - h)^2 + k$ with $a = 2$, $h = 2$,
and $k = -32$. Since $a > 0$, the parabola
opens upward. The vertex is $(2, -32)$.
The
y-intercept is $(0, -24)$. The x-intercepts
are $(-2, 0)$ and $(6, 0)$.

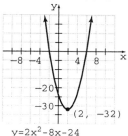

13. **a.** $(x - h)^2 + (y - k)^2 = r^2$

$(x - 0)^2 + (y - 0)^2 = 4^2$

$x^2 + y^2 = 4^2$

b.

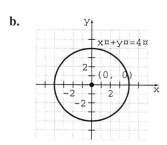

14. **a.** $(x - h)^2 + (y - k)^2 = r^2$

$[x - (-3)]^2 + (y - 4)^2 = 1^2$

$(x + 3)^2 + (y - 4)^2 = 1^2$

b.

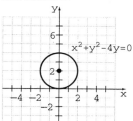

15. **a.** $x^2 + y^2 - 4y = 0$

$x^2 + (y^2 - 4y + 4) = 4$

$x^2 + (y - 2)^2 = 2^2$

b. The graph is a circle with center $(0, 2)$
and radius 2.

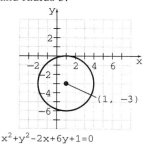

16. **a.** $x^2 + y^2 - 2x + 6y + 1 = 0$

$x^2 - 2x + y^2 + 6y = -1$

$(x^2 - 2x + 1) + (y^2 + 6y + 9) = -1 + 1 + 9$

$(x - 1)^2 + (y + 3)^2 = 9$

$(x - 1)^2 + (y + 3)^2 = 3^2$

b. The graph is a circle with center $(1, -3)$
and radius 3.

17. **a.** $x^2 - 8x + y^2 - 10y + 40 = 0$

$(x^2 - 8x + 16) + (y^2 - 10y + 25) = -40 + 16 + 25$

$(x - 4)^2 + (y - 5)^2 = 1$

$(x - 4)^2 + (y - 5)^2 = 1^2$

b. The graph is a circle with center (4, 5) and radius 1.

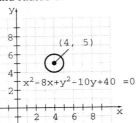

18. **a.**
$$x^2+y^2-4x+10y+17=0$$
$$x^2-4x+y^2+10y=-17$$
$$(x^2-4x+4)+(y^2+10y+25)=-17+4+25$$
$$(x-2)^2+(y+5)^2=12$$
$$(x-2)^2+(y+5)^2=\left(\sqrt{12}\right)^2$$

b. The graph is a circle with center (2, –5) and radius $\sqrt{12} \approx 3.46$.

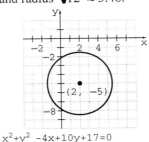

$$x^2+y^2-4x+10y+17=0$$

19.
$$y=\sqrt{9-x^2}$$
If we solve $x^2 + y^2 = 9$ for y, we obtain $y = \pm\sqrt{9-x^2}$. Therefore, the graph of $y = \sqrt{9-x^2}$ is the upper half $(y \geq 0)$ of a circle with its center at the origin and radius 4.

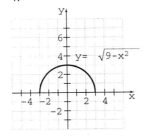

20.
$$y=-\sqrt{25-x^2}$$
If we solve $x^2 + y^2 = 25$ for y, we obtain $y = \pm\sqrt{25-x^2}$. Therefore, the graph of $y = -\sqrt{25-x^2}$ is the lower half $(y \leq 0)$ of a circle with its center at the origin and radius 5.

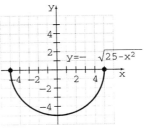

21. The center is (–1, 1) and the radius is 2.
$$(x-h)^2+(y-k)^2=r^2$$
$$[x-(-1)]^2+(y-1)^2=2^2$$
$$(x+1)^2+(y-1)^2=4$$

22. The center is (5, –3) and the radius is 3.
$$(x-h)^2+(y-k)^2=r^2$$
$$(x-5)^2+[y-(-3)]^2=3^2$$
$$(x-5)^2+(y+3)^2=9$$

23.
$$\frac{x^2}{4}+\frac{y^2}{9}=1$$
Since $a^2 = 4$, $a = 2$.
Since $b^2 = 9$, $b = 3$.

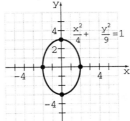

24.

$\dfrac{x^2}{36} + \dfrac{y^2}{64} = 1$

Since $a^2 = 36$, $a = 6$.

Since $b^2 = 64$, $b = 8$.

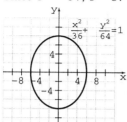

25.

$4x^2 + 9y^2 = 36$

$\dfrac{4x^2}{36} + \dfrac{9y^2}{36} = 1$

$\dfrac{x^2}{9} + \dfrac{y^2}{4} = 1$

Since $a^2 = 9$, $a = 3$.

Since $b^2 = 4$, $b = 2$.

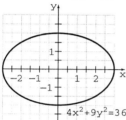

26.

$9x^2 + 16y^2 = 144$

$\dfrac{9x^2}{144} + \dfrac{16y^2}{144} = 1$

$\dfrac{x^2}{16} + \dfrac{y^2}{9} = 1$

Since $a^2 = 16$, $a = 4$.

Since $b^2 = 9$, $b = 3$.

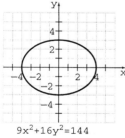

27.

$\dfrac{(x-3)^2}{16} + \dfrac{(y+2)^2}{4} = 1$

The center is $(3, -2)$.

Since $a^2 = 16$, $a = 4$.

Since $b^2 = 4$, $b = 2$.

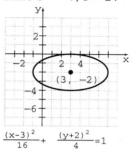

28.

$\dfrac{(x+3)^2}{9} + \dfrac{y^2}{25} = 1$

The center is $(-3, 0)$.

Since $a^2 = 9$, $a = 3$.

Since $b^2 = 25$, $b = 5$.

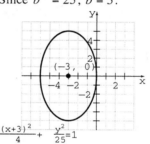

29.

$25(x-2)^2 + 9(y-1)^2 = 225$

$\dfrac{25(x-2)^2}{225} + \dfrac{9(y-1)^2}{225} = 1$

$\dfrac{(x-2)^2}{9} + \dfrac{(y-1)^2}{25} = 1$

The center is $(2, 1)$.

Since $a^2 = 9$, $a = 3$.

Since $b^2 = 25$, $b = 5$.

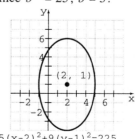

30.

$$\frac{x^2}{4} + \frac{y^2}{9} = 1$$

Since $a^2 = 4$, $a = 2$.

Since $b^2 = 9$, $b = 3$.

Area $= \pi ab = \pi(2)(3) = 6\pi \approx 18.85$ sq. units

31. a.

$$\frac{x^2}{4} - \frac{y^2}{16} = 1$$

Since $a^2 = 4$ and $b^2 = 16$, $a = 2$ and $b = 4$. The equations of the asymptotes are $y = \pm \dfrac{b}{a} x$, or $y = \pm 2x$.

b. To graph the asymptotes, plot the points $(2, 4)$, $(-2, 4)$, $(2, -4)$, and $(-2, -4)$. The graph intersects the x-axis at $(-2, 0)$ and $(2, 0)$.

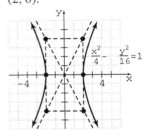

32. a.

$$\frac{x^2}{4} - \frac{y^2}{4} = 1$$

Since $a^2 = 4$ and $b^2 = 4$, $a = 2$ and $b = 2$. The equations of the asymptotes are $y = \pm \dfrac{b}{a} x$, or

$y = \pm \dfrac{2}{2} x = \pm x$.

b. To graph the asymptotes, plot the points $(2, 2)$, $(-2, 2)$, $(2, -2)$, and $(-2, -2)$. The graph intersects the x-axis at $(-2, 0)$ and $(2, 0)$.

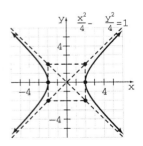

33. a.

$$\frac{y^2}{4} - \frac{x^2}{36} = 1$$

Since $a^2 = 36$ and $b^2 = 4$, $a = 6$ and $b = 2$. The equations of the asymptotes are $y = \pm \dfrac{b}{a} x$, or $y = \pm \dfrac{1}{3}$.

b. To graph the asymptotes, plot the points $(6, 2)$, $(6, -2)$, $(-6, 2)$, and $(-6, -2)$. The graph intersects the y-axis at $(0, -2)$ and $(0, 2)$.

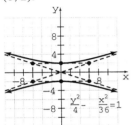

34. a.

$$\frac{y^2}{25} - \frac{x^2}{16} = 1$$

Since $a^2 = 16$ and $b^2 = 25$, $a = 4$ and $b = 5$. The equations of the asymptotes are $y = \pm \dfrac{b}{a} x$, or $y = \pm \dfrac{5}{4} x$.

b. To graph the asymptotes, plot the points $(4, 5)$, $(4, -5)$, $(-4, 5)$, and $(-4, -5)$. The graph intersects the y-axis at $(0, -5)$ and $(0, 5)$.

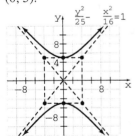

35. a.

$$x^2 - 9y^2 = 9$$

$$\frac{x^2}{9} - \frac{9y^2}{9} = 1$$

$$\frac{x^2}{9} - \frac{y^2}{1} = 1$$

b. Since $a^2 = 9$ and $b^2 = 1$, $a = 3$ and $b = 1$. The equations of the asymptotes are $y = \pm \dfrac{b}{a} x$, or $y = \pm \dfrac{1}{3} x$.

c. To graph the asymptotes, plot the points $(3, 1)$, $(-3, 1)$, $(3, -1)$, and $(-3, -1)$. The graph intersects the *x*-axis at $(-3, 0)$ and $(3, 0)$.

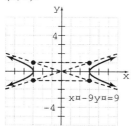

36. a. $25x^2 - 16y^2 = 400$

$$\frac{25x^2}{400} - \frac{16y^2}{400} = 1$$

$$\frac{x^2}{16} - \frac{y^2}{25} = 1$$

b. Since $a^2 = 16$ and $b^2 = 25$, $a = 4$ and $b = 5$. The equations of the asymptotes are $y = \pm \dfrac{b}{a} x$, or $y = \pm \dfrac{5}{4} x$.

c. To graph the asymptotes, plot the points $(4, 5)$, $(-4, 5)$, $(4, -5)$, and $(-4, -5)$. The graph intersects the *x*-axis at $(-4, 0)$ and $(4, 0)$.

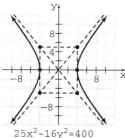

37. a. $4y^2 - 25x^2 = 100$

$$\frac{4y^2}{100} - \frac{25x^2}{100} = 1$$

$$\frac{y^2}{25} - \frac{x^2}{4} = 1$$

b. Since $a^2 = 4$ and $b^2 = 25$, $a = 2$ and $b = 5$. The equations of the asymptotes are $y = \pm \dfrac{b}{a} x$, or $y = \pm \dfrac{5}{2} x$.

c. To graph the asymptotes, plot the points $(2, 5)$, $(2, -5)$, $(-2, 5)$, and $(-2, -5)$. The graph intersects the *y*-axis at $(0, -5)$ and $(0, 5)$.

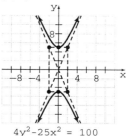

38. a. $49y^2 - 9x^2 = 441$

$$\frac{49y^2}{441} - \frac{9x^2}{441} = 1$$

$$\frac{y^2}{9} - \frac{x^2}{49} = 1$$

b. Since $a^2 = 49$ and $b^2 = 9$, $a = 7$ and $b = 3$. The equations of the asymptotes are $y = \pm \dfrac{b}{a} x$, or $y = \pm \dfrac{3}{7} x$.

c. To graph the asymptotes, plot the points $(7, 3)$, $(-7, 3)$, $(7, -3)$, and $(-7, -3)$. The graph intersects the *y*-axis at $(0, -3)$ and $(0, 3)$.

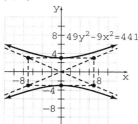

39. $\dfrac{x^2}{64} - \dfrac{y^2}{25} = 1$

The graph is a hyperbola.

40. $3x^2 + 7y^2 = 21$

$$\frac{3x^2}{21} + \frac{7y^2}{21} = 1$$

$$\frac{x^2}{7} + \frac{y^2}{3} = 1$$

The graph is an ellipse.

41. $4x^2 + 4y^2 = 100$

$$\frac{4x^2}{4} + \frac{4y^2}{4} = \frac{100}{4}$$

$$x^2 + y^2 = 25$$

The graph is a circle.

42. $4x^2 - 25y^2 = 25$

$$\frac{4x^2}{25} - \frac{25y^2}{25} = 1$$

$$\frac{x^2}{6.25} - \frac{y^2}{1} = 1$$

The graph is a hyperbola.

43. $\frac{x^2}{7} + \frac{y^2}{9} = 1$

The graph is an ellipse.

44. $y = (x-3)^2 + 1$

The graph is a parabola.

45. $4x^2 + 9y^2 = 36$

$$\frac{4x^2}{36} + \frac{9y^2}{36} = 1$$

$$\frac{x^2}{9} + \frac{y^2}{4} = 1$$

The graph is an ellipse.

46. $x = -y^2 + 6y - 7$

The graph is a parabola.

47. $x^2 + y^2 = 16$

$x^2 - y^2 = 16 \Rightarrow x^2 = y^2 + 16$

Substitute $y^2 + 16$ for x^2 in $x^2 + y^2 = 16$.

$x^2 + y^2 = 16$

$y^2 + 16 + y^2 = 16$

$2y^2 = 0$

$y^2 = 0$

Substitute 0 for y^2 in $x^2 = y^2 + 16$

$x^2 + 0 = 16 \Rightarrow x = \pm 4$

The solution is (4, 0), and (–4, 0).

48. $x^2 = y^2 + 4$

$x + y = 4$

Solve $x + y = 4$ for y: $y = 4 - x$.

Substitute $4 - x$ for y in $x^2 = y^2 + 4$.

$x^2 = y^2 + 4$

$x^2 = (4-x)^2 + 4$

$x^2 = (16 - 8x + x^2) + 4$

$8x - 16 = 4$

$8x = 20$

$x = \frac{5}{2}$

$y = 4 - x$

$y = 4 - \frac{5}{2}$

$y = \frac{3}{2}$

The solution is $\left(\frac{5}{2}, \frac{3}{2}\right)$.

49. 47. $x^2 + y^2 = 9$

$y = 3x + 9$

Substitute $3x + 9$ for y in $x^2 + y^2 = 9$.

$x^2 + y^2 = 9$

$x^2 + (3x+9)^2 = 9$

$x^2 + 9x^2 + 54x + 81 = 9$

$10x^2 + 54x + 72 = 0$

$5x^2 + 27x + 36 = 0$

$(x+3)(5x+12) = 0$

$x + 3 = 0$ or $5x + 12 = 0$

$x = -3$ $\qquad x = -\frac{12}{5}$

$y = 3x + 9$

$y = 3(-3) + 9$ $\qquad y = 3x + 9$

$y = 0$ $\qquad y = 3\left(-\frac{12}{5}\right) + 9$

$\qquad y = \frac{9}{5}$

The solutions are (–3, 0) and $\left(-\frac{12}{5}, \frac{9}{5}\right)$.

50. $x^2 + 2y^2 = 7$

$x^2 - 6y^2 = 29$

Solve $x^2 + 2y^2 = 7$ for x^2: $x^2 = 7 - 2y^2$.

Substitute $7 - 2y^2$ for x^2 in $x^2 - 6y^2 = 29$.

$x^2 - 6y^2 = 29$

$(7 - 2y^2) - 6y^2 = 29$

$7 - 8y^2 = 29$

$-8y^2 = 22$

$y^2 = -\dfrac{22}{8}$ or $-\dfrac{11}{4}$

$y = \pm i \sqrt{\dfrac{11}{4}}$

There is no real solution.

51. $x^2 + y^2 = 49$

$\dfrac{x^2 - y^2 = 49}{2x^2 = 98}$

$x^2 = 49$

$x = 7 \qquad\qquad x = -7$

or

$x^2 + y^2 = 49 \qquad x^2 + y^2 = 49$

$7^2 + y^2 = 49 \qquad (-7)^2 + y^2 = 49$

$y^2 = 0 \qquad\qquad y^2 = 0$

$y = 0 \qquad\qquad y = 0$

The solutions are $(7, 0)$ and $(-7, 0)$.

52. $x^2 + y^2 = 25$ (1)

$x^2 - 2y^2 = -2$ (2)

$2x^2 + 2y^2 = 50$ (1) multiplied by 2

$\dfrac{x^2 - 2y^2 = -2}{3x^2 = 48}$ (2)

$x^2 = 16$

$x = 4 \qquad$ or

$x^2 + y^2 = 25$

$4^2 + y^2 = 25$

$y^2 = 9$

$y = \pm 3$

$x = -4$

$x^2 + y^2 = 25$

$(-4)^2 + y^2 = 25$

$y^2 = 9$

$y = \pm 3$

The solutions are $(4, 3)$, $(4, -3)$, $(-4, 3)$ and $(-4, -3)$.

53. $-4x^2 + y^2 = -12$ (1)

$8x^2 + 2y^2 = -8$ (2)

$-4x^2 + y^2 = -12$ (1)

$\dfrac{4x^2 + y^2 = -4}{2y^2 = -16}$ (2) divided by 2

$y^2 = -8$

$y = \pm i \sqrt{8}$

$= \pm 2i \sqrt{2}$

There is no real solution.

54.
$$-2x^2 - 3y^2 = -6 \quad (1)$$
$$5x^2 + 4y^2 = 15 \quad (2)$$
$$-10x^2 - 15y^2 = -30 \quad (1) \text{ multiplied by } 5$$
$$\underline{10x^2 + 8y^2 = 30} \quad (2) \text{ multiplied by } 2$$
$$-7y^2 = 0$$
$$y^2 = 0$$
$$y = 0$$
$$5x^2 + 4y^2 = 15$$
$$5x^2 + 4(0)^2 = 15$$
$$5x^2 = 15$$
$$x^2 = 3$$
$$x = \pm\sqrt{3}$$

The solutions are $\left(\sqrt{3},\ 0\right)$ and $\left(-\sqrt{3},\ 0\right)$.

55. Let $x =$ length
$y =$ width
$$xy = 36$$
$$2x + 2y = 26$$
Solve $2x + 2y = 26$ for y: $y = 13 - x$.
Substitute $13 - x$ for y in $xy = 36$.
$$xy = 36$$
$$x(13 - x) = 36$$
$$13x - x^2 = 36$$
$$x^2 - 13x + 36 = 0$$
$$(x - 4)(x - 9) = 0$$

$x - 4 = 0$	$x - 9 = 0$
$x = 4$ or	$x = 9$

$y = 13 - x$	$y = 12 - x$
$y = 13 - 4$	$y = 12 - 9$
$y = 9$	$y = 3$

The solutions are (4, 9) and (9, 4).
The dimensions of the pool table are 4 feet by 9 feet.

56.
$$C = 20.3x + 120$$
$$R = 50.2x - 0.2x^2$$
$$C = R$$
$$20.3x + 120 = 50.2x - 0.2x^2$$
$$0.2x^2 - 29.9 + 120 = 0$$
$$x = \frac{29.9 \pm \sqrt{(-29.9)^2 - 4(0.2)(120)}}{2(0.2)}$$
$$x = \frac{29.9 \pm \sqrt{798.01}}{0.4}$$
$$x \approx 145 \text{ or } 4$$
The company must sell either 4 bottles or 145 bottles to break even.

57. Since $t = 1$ year, we may rewrite the formula $i = prt$ as $i = pr$.
$$250 = pr$$
$$250 = (p + 1250)(r - 0.01)$$
Rewrite the second equation by multiplying the binomials. Then substitute 250 for pr and solve for r.
$$250 = pr - 0.01p + 1250r - 12.5$$
$$250 = 250 - 0.01p + 1250r - 12.5$$
$$0 = -0.01p + 1250r - 12.5$$
$$0.01p + 12.5 = 1250r$$
$$\frac{0.01p}{1250} + \frac{12.5}{1250} = r$$
$$r = 0.000008p + 0.01$$
Substitute $0.000008p + 0.01$ for r in
$$250 = pr.$$
$$250 = pr$$
$$250 = p(0.000008p + 0.01)$$
$$250 = 0.000008p^2 + 0.01p$$
$$0 = 0.000008p^2 + 0.01p - 250$$
$$0 = p^2 + 1250p - 31{,}250{,}000$$
$$0 = (p - 5000)(p + 6250)$$
$$p - 5000 = 0 \quad \text{or } p + 6250 = 0$$
$$p = 5000 \qquad p = -6250$$
The principal must be positive, so use $p = 5000$.
$$r = 0.000008p + 0.01$$
$$r = 0.000008(5000) + 0.01$$
$$r = 0.05$$
The principal is $5000 and the rate is 5%.

Practice Test

1. They are formed by cutting a cone or pair of cones.

2. $d = \sqrt{(x_2 - x_1)^2 + (y_2 - y_1)^2}$

   $= \sqrt{[3 - (-4)]^2 + (4 - 5)^2}$

   $= \sqrt{7^2 + (-1)^2}$

   $= \sqrt{49 + 1}$

   $= \sqrt{50}$

   The length is $\sqrt{50} \approx 7.07$ units.

3. $\text{Midpoint} = \left(\dfrac{x_1 + x_2}{2}, \dfrac{y_1 + y_2}{2} \right)$

   $= \left(\dfrac{-3 + 7}{2}, \dfrac{4 + (-1)}{2} \right)$

   $= \left(2, \dfrac{3}{2} \right)$

4. $y = -2(x + 3)^2 + 1$

   This is a parabola in the form
   $y = a(x - h)^2 + k$
   with $a = -2$, $h = -3$, and $k = 1$. Since $a < 0$, the parabola opens downward. The vertex is $(-3, 1)$. The y-intercept is $(0, -17)$. The x-intercepts are about $(-3.71, 0)$ and $(-2.29, 0)$.

   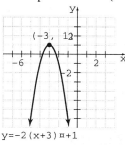

   y=−2(x+3)¤+1

5. $x = y^2 - 2y + 4$

   $x = (y^2 - 2y + 1) - 1 + 4$

   $x = (y - 1)^2 + 3$

   This is a parabola in the form
   $x = a(y - k)^2 + h$
   with $a = 1$, $h = 3$ and $k = 1$. Since $a > 0$, the parabola opens to the right. The vertex is $(3, 1)$.
   There is no y-intercept. The x-intercept is $(4, 0)$.

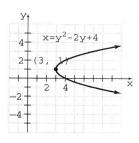

6. $x = -y^2 - 4y - 5$

   $x = -(y^2 + 4y) - 5$

   $x = -(y^2 + 4y + 4) + 4 - 5$

   $x = -(y + 2)^2 - 1$

   This is a parabola in the form
   $x = a(y - k)^2 + h$
   with $a = -1$, $h = -1$, and $k = -2$. Since $a < 0$, the parabola opens to the left. The vertex is $(-1, -2)$. There are no y-intercepts. The x-intercept is $(-5, 0)$.

   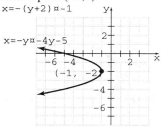

7. $(x - h)^2 + (y - k)^2 = r^2$

   $[x - 2]^2 + [y - 4]^2 = 3^2$

   $(x - 2)^2 + (y - 4)^2 = 9$

8. $(x + 5)^2 + (y - 5)^2 = 9$. The graph of this equation is a circle with center $(-5, 5)$ and radius 3.
   $\text{Area} = \pi r^2$

   $= \pi 3^2 = 9\pi \approx 28.27$ sq. units

9. The center is (3, –1) and the radius is 4.
$$(x-h)^2 + (y-k)^2 = r^2$$
$$(x-3)^2 + [y-(-1)]^2 = 4^2$$
$$(x-3)^2 + (y+1)^2 = 16$$

10.
$$y = -\sqrt{16-x^2}$$
If we solve $x^2 + y^2 = 16$ for y, we obtain $y = \pm\sqrt{16-x^2}$. Therefore, the graph of $y = -\sqrt{16-x^2}$ is the lower half ($y \leq 0$) of a circle with its center at the origin and radius 4.

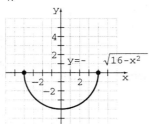

11.
$$x^2 + y^2 + 2x - 6y + 1 = 0$$
$$x^2 + 2x + y^2 - 6y = -1$$
$$(x^2 + 2x + 1) + (y^2 - 6y + 9) = -1 + 1 + 9$$
$$(x+1)^2 + (y-3)^2 = 9$$
The graph is a circle with center (1, 3) and radius 3.

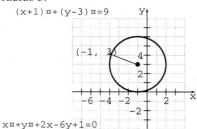

12.
$$4x^2 + 25y^2 = 100$$
$$\frac{4x^2}{100} + \frac{25y^2}{100} = 1$$
$$\frac{x^2}{25} + \frac{y^2}{4} = 1$$
Since $a^2 = 25$, $a = 5$
Since $b^2 = 4$, $b = 2$.

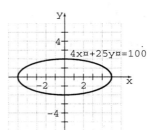

13. The center is (–2, –1), $a = 4$, and $b = 2$.
$$\frac{(x-h)^2}{a^2} + \frac{(y-k)^2}{b^2} = 1$$
$$\frac{[x-(-2)]^2}{4^2} + \frac{[y-(-1)]^2}{2^2} = 1$$
$$\frac{(x+2)^2}{16} + \frac{(y+1)^2}{4} = 1$$
The values of a^2 and b^2 are switched, so this is not the graph of the given equation.

14.
$$4(x-4)^2 + 36(y+2)^2 = 36$$
$$\frac{4(x-4)^2}{36} + \frac{36(y+2)^2}{36} = 1$$
$$\frac{(x-4)^2}{9} + \frac{(y+2)^2}{1} = 1$$
The center is (4, –2). Since $a^2 = 9$, $a = 3$
Since $b^2 = 1$, $b = 1$

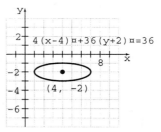

15.
$$3(x-5)^2 + 6(y+3)^2 = 18$$
$$\frac{3(x-5)^2}{18} + \frac{6(y+3)^2}{18} = 1$$
$$\frac{(x-5)^2}{6} + \frac{(y+3)^2}{3} = 1$$
The center is $(5, -3.)$

16. The transverse axis lies along the axis corresponding to the positive term of the equation in standard form.

17. $\dfrac{x^2}{16} - \dfrac{y^2}{36} = 1$

Since $a^2 = 16$ and $b^2 = 36$, $a = 4$ and $b = 6$.
The equations of the asymptotes are
$y = \pm \dfrac{b}{a} x$, or $y = \pm \dfrac{3}{2} x$.

18. $\dfrac{y^2}{25} - \dfrac{x^2}{1} = 1$

Since $a^2 = 1$ and $b^2 = 25$, $a = 1$ and $b = 5$.
The equations of the asymptotes are
$y = \pm \dfrac{b}{a} x$, or $y = \pm 5x$.
To graph the asymptotes, plot the points (1, 5),
(–1, 5), (1, –5), and (–1, –5).
The graph intersects the *y*-axis at (0, –5) and (0, 5).

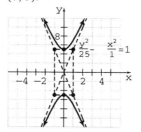

19. $\dfrac{x^2}{4} - \dfrac{y^2}{9} = 1$

Since $a^2 = 4$ and $b^2 = 9$, $a = 2$ and $b = 3$.
The equations of the asymptotes are
$y = \pm \dfrac{b}{a} x$, or $y = \pm \dfrac{3}{2} x$.
To graph the asymptotes, plot the points
(2, 3), (–2, 3), (2, –3), and (–2, –3). The
graph intersects the *x*-axis at (–2, 0) and (2, 0).

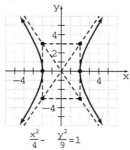

20. $4x^2 - 16y^2 = 48$

$\dfrac{4x^2}{48} - \dfrac{16y^2}{48} = 1$

$\dfrac{x^2}{12} - \dfrac{y^2}{3} = 1$

Since the equation is of the form
$\dfrac{x^2}{a^2} - \dfrac{y^2}{b^2} = 1$, the graph is a hyperbola.

21. $16x^2 + 4y^2 = 64$

$\dfrac{16x^2}{64} + \dfrac{4y^2}{64} = 1$

$\dfrac{x^2}{4} + \dfrac{y^2}{16} = 1$

Since the equation is of the form
$\dfrac{x^2}{a^2} + \dfrac{y^2}{b^2} = 1$, the graph is an ellipse.

22. $x^2 + y^2 = 7 \quad \overset{\times 3}{\Rightarrow} \quad 3x^2 + 3y^2 = 21$

$2x^2 - 3y^2 = -1 \qquad \dfrac{2x^2 - 3y^2 = -1}{5x^2 \quad\;\; = 20}$

$x^2 \quad\;\; = 4$

$\begin{array}{ccc}
x = 2 & \text{or} & x = -2 \\
x^2 + y^2 = 7 & & x^2 + y^2 = 7 \\
(2)^2 + y^2 = 7 & & (-2)^2 + y^2 = 7 \\
4 + y^2 = 7 & & 4 + y^2 = 7 \\
y^2 = 3 & & y^2 = 3 \\
y = \pm\sqrt{3} & & y = \pm\sqrt{3}
\end{array}$

The solutions are $\left(2, \ \sqrt{3}\right)$, $\left(2, -\sqrt{3}\right)$,
$\left(-2, \ \sqrt{3}\right)$, and $\left(-2, -\sqrt{3}\right)$.

23. $x + y = 8$

$x^2 + y^2 = 9$

Solve $x + y = 8$ for *y*: $y = 8 - x$.
Substitute $8 - x$ for *y* in $x^2 + y^2 = 9$.

$x^2 + y^2 = 9$

$x^2 + (8 - x)^2 = 9$

$x^2 + 64 - 16x + x^2 = 9$

$2x^2 - 16x + 55 = 0$

$$x = \frac{-b \pm \sqrt{b^2 - 4ac}}{2a}$$

$$= \frac{-(-16) \pm \sqrt{(-16)^2 - 4(2)(55)}}{2(2)}$$

$$= \frac{16 \pm \sqrt{-184}}{4}$$

$$= \frac{10 \pm 2i\sqrt{46}}{4}$$

$$= \frac{5 \pm i\sqrt{23}}{2}$$

There is no real solution.

24. Let x = length,
y = width.
$$xy = 6000$$
$$2x + 2y = 320$$
Solve $2x + 2y = 320$ for y: $y = 160 - x$.
Substitute $160 - x$ for y in $xy = 6000$.
$$xy = 6000$$
$$x(160 - x) = 6000$$
$$160x - x^2 = 6000$$
$$x^2 - 160x + 6000 = 0$$
$$(x - 60)(x - 100) = 0$$
$$x - 60 = 0 \quad \text{or} \quad x - 100 = 0$$

$$x = 60 \qquad\qquad x = 100$$
$$y = 160 - x \qquad y = 160 - x$$
$$y = 160 - 60 \qquad y = 160 - 100$$
$$y = 100 \qquad\qquad y = 60$$

The solutions are $(60, 100)$ and $(100, 60)$.
The dimensions are 60 m by 100 m.

25. Let x = length
y = width
$$xy = 60$$
$$x^2 + y^2 = 13^2$$
Solve $xy = 60$ for y: $y = \dfrac{60}{x}$.

Substitute $\dfrac{60}{x}$ for y in $x^2 + y^2 = 13^2$.
$$x^2 + y^2 = 13^2$$
$$x^2 + \left(\frac{60}{x}\right)^2 = 169$$
$$x^2 + \frac{3600}{x^2} = 169$$
$$x^4 + 3600 = 169x^2$$
$$x^4 - 169x^2 + 3600 = 0$$
$$(x^2 - 25)(x^2 - 144) = 0$$

$$x^2 - 25 = 0 \quad \text{or} \quad x^2 - 144 = 0$$
$$x^2 = 25 \qquad\qquad x^2 = 144$$
$$x = \pm 5 \qquad\qquad x^2 = \pm 12$$
Since x must be positive, $x = 5$ or $x = 12$.
If $x = 5$, then $y = \dfrac{60}{5} = 12$. If $x = 12$, then

$y = \dfrac{60}{12} = 5$. The dimensions of the bed of the
truck are 5 feet by 12 feet

Cumulative Review Test

1. $\left(7x^2 y^5\right)\left(-3xy^4\right) = (7)(-3)x^{2+1}y^{5+4}$

$$= -21x^3 y^9$$

2. $4x - 2(3x - 7) = 2x - 5$
$$4x - 6x + 14 = 2x - 5$$
$$-2x + 14 = 2x - 5$$
$$-4x = -19$$
$$x = \frac{-19}{-4} \quad \text{or} \quad \frac{19}{4}$$

3. $2(x - 3) + 2x = 4x - 5$
$$2x - 6 + 2x = 4x - 5$$
$$4x - 6 = 4x - 5$$
$$-6 = -5 \quad \text{This is a contradiction.}$$
The solution is $\varnothing$.

4. $\qquad |3x + 1| > 4$
$$3x + 1 > 4 \qquad\quad 3x + 1 < -4$$
$$3x > 3 \qquad\qquad 3x < -5 \qquad \text{The solution is}$$
$$x > 1 \qquad\qquad x < -\frac{5}{3}$$
$$\left\{ x \,\middle|\, x < -\frac{5}{3} \text{ or } x > 1 \right\}$$

5. $y = -2x + 2$
The slope is -2 and the y-intercept
is $(0, 2)$.

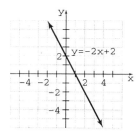

feet.

6. $f(x) = x^2 + 3x + 1$

$f(10) = (10)^2 + 3(10) + 1$

$= 100 + 30 + 1$

$= 131$

7. $\frac{1}{2}x - \frac{1}{3}y = 2 \quad \overset{\times(-6)}{\Rightarrow} \quad -3x + 2y = -12$

$\frac{1}{4}x + \frac{2}{3}y = 6 \quad \overset{\times 12}{\Rightarrow} \quad \underline{3x + 8y = 72}$

$\qquad\qquad\qquad\qquad 10y = 60$

$\qquad\qquad\qquad\qquad\quad y = 6$

Substitute $y = 6$ into $-3x + 2y = -12$

$-3x + 2(6) = -12$

$-3x + 12 = -12$

$-3x = -24 \quad \Rightarrow \quad x = 8$

The solution is $(8, 6)$.

8. $x^4 - x^2 - 6 \qquad$ let $u = x^2$

$u^2 - u - 6$

$(u - 3)(u + 2)$

$(x^2 - 3)(x^2 + 2)$

9. Let x be the base of the sign. Then the height can be expressed as $x - 6$.

Area $= \frac{1}{2}$ (base $\times$ height)

$56 = \frac{1}{2}(x - 6)(x)$

$112 = x^2 - 6x$

$0 = x^2 - 6x - 112$

$0 = (x - 14)(x + 8)$

$x - 14 = 0 \quad$ or $\quad x + 8 = 0$

$x = 14 \qquad\qquad x = -8$

Disregard the negative value. The base of the sign is 14 feet and the height is $14 - 6 = 8$

10. $\frac{3x^2 - x - 4}{4x^2 + 5x + 1} \cdot \frac{2x^2 - 5x - 12}{6x^2 + x - 12}$

$\frac{(3x - 4)(x + 1)}{(4x + 1)(x + 1)} \cdot \frac{(2x + 3)(x - 4)}{(3x - 4)(2x + 3)}$

$\frac{(3x - 4)(x + 1)(2x + 3)(x - 4)}{(4x + 1)(x + 1)(3x - 4)(2x + 3)}$

$\frac{x - 4}{4x + 1}$

11. $\frac{x}{x + 3} - \frac{x + 1}{2x^2 - 2x - 24}$

$= \frac{x}{x + 3} - \frac{x + 1}{2(x + 3)(x - 4)}$

$= \frac{2x(x - 4)}{2(x + 3)(x - 4)} - \frac{x + 1}{2(x + 3)(x - 4)}$

$= \frac{2x^2 - 8x - (x + 1)}{2(x + 3)(x - 4)}$

$= \frac{2x^2 - 9x - 1}{2(x + 3)(x - 4)}$

12. $\frac{3}{x + 3} + \frac{5}{x + 4} = \frac{12x + 19}{x^2 + 7x + 12}$

$\left(\frac{3}{x + 3} + \frac{5}{x + 4} = \frac{12x + 19}{(x + 3)(x + 4)} \right)(x + 3)(x + 4)$

$3(x + 4) + 5(x + 3) = 12x + 19$

$3x + 12 + 5x + 15 = 12x + 19$

$8x + 27 = 12x + 19$

$-4x = -8$

$x = 2$

13. $\left(\frac{81x^{1/2}y^3}{9x^{3/2}} \right)^{1/2} = \left(\frac{81}{9}x^{1/2 - 3/2}y^3 \right)^{1/2}$

$= \left(9x^{-1}y^3 \right)^{1/2}$

$= 9^{1/2}x^{-1/2}y^{3/2}$

$= \sqrt{9} \cdot x^{-1/2}y^{3/2}$

$= \frac{3y^{3/2}}{x^{1/2}}$

14.
$$\frac{4\sqrt{x}}{\sqrt{x}-y} = \frac{4\sqrt{x}}{\sqrt{x}-y} \cdot \frac{\sqrt{x}+y}{\sqrt{x}+y}$$

$$= \frac{4x+4y\sqrt{x}}{x+y\sqrt{x}-y\sqrt{x}-y^2}$$

$$= \frac{4x+4y\sqrt{x}}{x-y^2}$$

15.
$$3\sqrt[3]{2x+2} = \sqrt[3]{80x-24}$$
$$\left(3\sqrt[3]{2x+2}\right)^3 = \left(\sqrt[3]{80x-24}\right)^3$$
$$27(2x+2) = (80x-24)$$
$$54x+54 = 80x-24$$
$$54x = 80x-78$$
$$-26x = -78$$
$$x = 3$$
Check: $3\sqrt[3]{2(3)+2}\ 0\ \sqrt[3]{80(3)-24}$
$$3\sqrt[3]{8}\ 0\ \sqrt[3]{216}$$
$$3\cdot 2 = 6\ \text{True}$$
The solution is 3.

16.
$$3x^2 - 4x + 5 = 0$$
$$x = \frac{-b \pm \sqrt{b^2 - 4ac}}{2a}$$

$$= \frac{-(-4) \pm \sqrt{(-4)^2 - 4(3)(5)}}{2(3)}$$

$$= \frac{4 \pm \sqrt{-44}}{6}$$

$$= \frac{4 \pm 2i\sqrt{11}}{6}$$

$$= \frac{2 \pm i\sqrt{11}}{3}$$

17.
$$\log(3x-4) + \log(4) = \log(x+6)$$
$$\log 4(3x-4) = \log(x+6)$$
$$\log(12x-16) = \log(x+6)$$
$$12x-16 = x+6$$
$$12x = x+22$$
$$11x = 22$$
$$x = 2$$
Check: $\log[3(2)-4] + \log 4\ 0\ \log(2+6)$
$$\log 2 + \log 4\ 0\ \log 8$$
$$\log(2\cdot 4) = \log(8)\ \text{True}$$
The solution is 2.

18.
$$35 = 70e^{-0.3t}$$
$$\frac{1}{2} = e^{-0.3t}$$
$$\ln\frac{1}{2} = \ln e^{-0.3t}$$
$$\ln\frac{1}{2} = -0.3t$$
$$-\frac{1}{0.3}\ln\frac{1}{2} = t$$
$$t = -\frac{1}{0.3}\ln\frac{1}{2} \approx 2.31$$

19.
$$9x^2 + 4y^2 = 36$$
$$\frac{9x^2}{36} + \frac{4y^2}{36} = 1$$
$$\frac{x^2}{4} + \frac{y^2}{9} = 1$$
Since $a^2 = 4$, $a = 2$.
Since $b^2 = 9$, $b = 3$

20.
$$\frac{y^2}{25} - \frac{x^2}{16} = 1$$
Since $a^2 = 25$ and $b^2 = 16$, $a = 5$ and $b = 4$
The equations of the asymptotes are
$y = \pm\frac{b}{a}x$, or $y = \pm\frac{5}{4}x$. To graph the
asymptotes, plot the points (4, 5), (4, –5), (–4, 5), and (–4, –5).
The graph intersects the y-axis at (0, –5) and (0, 5).

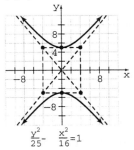

Chapter 11

Exercise Set 11.1

1. A sequence is a list of numbers arranged in a specific order.

3. A finite sequence is a function whose domain includes only the first n natural numbers.

5. In a decreasing sequence, the terms decrease.

7. A series is the sum of the terms of a sequence.

9. $\displaystyle\sum_{n=1}^{5}(n+2)$

The sum as n goes from 1 to 5 of $n+2$.

11. This is an increasing sequence since the coefficient of n is positive.

13. Yes, this is an alternating sequence since $(-2)^n$ alternates between positive and negative values as n alternates from odd to even.

15. $a_n = 3n$
$a_1 = 3(1) = 3$
$a_2 = 3(2) = 6$
$a_3 = 3(3) = 9$
$a_4 = 3(4) = 12$
$a_5 = 3(5) = 15$
The terms are 3, 6, 9, 12, 15.

17. $a_n = 4n-1$
$a_1 = 4(1)-1 = 3$
$a_2 = 4(2)-1 = 7$
$a_3 = 4(3)-1 = 11$
$a_4 = 4(4)-1 = 15$
$a_5 = 4(5)-1 = 19$
The terms are 3, 7, 11, 15, 19.

19. $a_n = \dfrac{2}{n}$
$a_1 = \dfrac{2}{1} = 2$
$a_2 = \dfrac{2}{2} = 1$
$a_3 = \dfrac{2}{3}$
$a_4 = \dfrac{2}{4} = \dfrac{1}{2}$
$a_5 = \dfrac{2}{5}$
The terms are $2,\ 1,\ \dfrac{2}{3},\ \dfrac{1}{2},$ and $\dfrac{2}{5}$.

21. $a_n = \dfrac{n+2}{n+1}$
$a_1 = \dfrac{1+2}{1+1} = \dfrac{3}{2}$
$a_2 = \dfrac{2+2}{2+1} = \dfrac{4}{3}$
$a_3 = \dfrac{3+2}{3+1} = \dfrac{5}{4}$
$a_4 = \dfrac{4+2}{4+1} = \dfrac{6}{5}$
$a_5 = \dfrac{5+2}{5+1} = \dfrac{7}{6}$
The terms are $\dfrac{3}{2}, \dfrac{4}{3}, \dfrac{5}{4}, \dfrac{6}{5}, \dfrac{7}{6}$.

23. $a_n = (-1)^n$
$a_1 = (-1)^1 = -1$
$a_2 = (-1)^2 = 1$
$a_3 = (-1)^3 = -1$
$a_4 = (-1)^4 = 1$
$a_5 = (-1)^5 = -1$
The terms are $-1, 1, -1, 1, -1$.

25. $a_n = (-2)^{n+1}$
$a_1 = (-2)^{1+1} = (-2)^2 = 4$
$a_2 = (-2)^{2+1} = (-2)^3 = -8$
$a_3 = (-2)^{3+1} = (-2)^4 = 16$
$a_4 = (-2)^{4+1} = (-2)^5 = -32$
$a_5 = (-2)^{5+1} = (-2)^6 = 64$
The terms are $4, -8, 16, -32, 64$.

27.
$$a_n = 2n + 7$$
$$a_{12} = 2(12) + 7$$
$$= 24 + 7$$
$$= 31$$

29.
$$a_n = \frac{n}{4} + 5$$
$$a_{16} = \frac{16}{4} + 5$$
$$= 4 + 5$$
$$= 9$$

31.
$$a_n = (-1)^n$$
$$a_8 = (-1)^8$$
$$= 1$$

33.
$$a_n = n(n + 2)$$
$$a_9 = 9(9 + 2)$$
$$= 9(11)$$
$$= 99$$

35.
$$a_n = \frac{n^2}{2n + 1}$$
$$a_9 = \frac{9^2}{2(9) + 1}$$
$$= \frac{81}{18 + 1}$$
$$= \frac{81}{19}$$

37.
$$a_n = 3n - 1$$
$$a_1 = 3(1) - 1 = 3 - 1 = 2$$
$$a_2 = 3(2) - 1 = 6 - 1 = 5$$
$$a_3 = 3(3) - 1 = 9 - 1 = 8$$

$$s_1 = a_1 = 2$$
$$s_3 = a_1 + a_2 + a_3$$
$$= 2 + 5 + 8$$
$$= 15$$

39.
$$a_n = 2^n + 1$$
$$a_1 = 2^1 + 1 = 3$$
$$a_2 = 2^2 + 1 = 4 + 1 = 5$$
$$a_3 = 2^3 + 1 = 8 + 1 = 9$$

$$s_1 = a_1 = 3$$
$$s_3 = a_1 + a_2 + a_3$$
$$= 3 + 5 + 9$$
$$= 17$$

41.
$$a_n = \frac{n - 1}{n + 1}$$
$$a_1 = \frac{1 - 1}{1 + 1} = \frac{0}{2} = 0$$
$$a_2 = \frac{2 - 1}{2 + 1} = \frac{1}{3}$$
$$a_3 = \frac{3 - 1}{3 + 1} = \frac{2}{4} = \frac{1}{2}$$

$$s_1 = a_1 = 0$$
$$s_3 = a_1 + a_2 + a_3$$
$$= 0 + \frac{1}{3} + \frac{1}{2}$$
$$= \frac{5}{6}$$

43.
$$a_n = (-1)^n$$
$$a_1 = (-1)^1 = -1$$
$$a_2 = (-1)^2 = 1$$
$$a_3 = (-1)^3 = -1$$

$$s_1 = a_1 = -1$$
$$s_3 = a_1 + a_2 + a_3$$
$$= -1 + 1 + -1$$
$$= -1$$

45.
$$a_n = \frac{n^2}{2}$$
$$a_1 = \frac{1^2}{2} = \frac{1}{2}$$
$$a_2 = \frac{2^2}{2} = \frac{4}{2} = 2$$
$$a_3 = \frac{3^2}{2} = \frac{9}{2}$$

$$s_1 = a_1 = \frac{1}{2}$$
$$s_3 = a_1 + a_2 + a_3$$
$$= \frac{1}{2} + \frac{4}{2} + \frac{9}{2}$$
$$= \frac{14}{2}$$
$$= 7$$

47. Each term is twice the preceding term. The next three terms are 64, 128, 256.

49. Each term is two more than the preceding term. The next three terms are 15, 17, 19.

51. Each denominator is one more than the preceding one while each numerator is one. The next three terms are $\dfrac{1}{6}, \dfrac{1}{7}, \dfrac{1}{8}$.

53. Each term is -1 times the previous term. The next three terms are $1, -1, 1$.

55. Each denominator is three times the previous one while each numerator is one. The next three terms are $\dfrac{1}{81}, \dfrac{1}{243}, \dfrac{1}{729}$.

57. Each term is $-\dfrac{1}{2}$ times the preceding term. The next three terms are $\dfrac{1}{16}, -\dfrac{1}{32}, \dfrac{1}{64}$.

59. Each term is eight less than the previous term. The next three terms are $-25, -33, -41$.

63.
$$\sum_{k=1}^{6}\left(k^2-1\right)=\left(1^2-1\right)+\left(2^2-1\right)+\left(3^2-1\right)+\left(4^2-1\right)+\left(5^2-1\right)+\left(6^2-1\right)$$
$$=\left(1-1\right)+\left(4-1\right)+\left(9-1\right)+\left(16-1\right)+\left(25-1\right)+\left(36-1\right)$$
$$=0+3+8+15+24+35$$
$$=85$$

65.
$$\sum_{i=1}^{4}\frac{i^2}{2}=\frac{1^2}{2}+\frac{2^2}{2}+\frac{3^2}{2}+\frac{4^2}{2}$$
$$=\frac{1}{2}+\frac{4}{2}+\frac{9}{2}+\frac{16}{2}$$
$$=\frac{30}{2}$$
$$=15$$

67.
$$\sum_{j=2}^{4}\frac{j^2+j}{j+1}=\frac{2^2+2}{2+1}+\frac{3^2+3}{3+1}+\frac{4^2+4}{4+1}$$
$$=\frac{6}{3}+\frac{12}{4}+\frac{20}{5}$$
$$=2+3+4$$
$$=9$$

69. $a_n=n+3$

The fifth partial sum is $\displaystyle\sum_{i=1}^{5}\left(i+3\right)$.

71.
$$a_n=\frac{n^2}{4}$$

The third partial sum is $\displaystyle\sum_{k=1}^{3}\frac{k^2}{4}$.

73.
$$\sum_{i=1}^{5}x_i=x_1+x_2+x_3+x_4+x_5$$
$$=2+3+5+\left(-1\right)+4$$
$$=13$$

75.
$$\left(\sum_{i=1}^{5}x_i\right)^2=\left(x_1+x_2+x_3+x_4+x_5\right)^2$$
$$=\left(2+3+5+\left(-1\right)+4\right)^2$$
$$=13^2$$
$$=169$$

77.
$$\sum_{i=1}^{5} x_i^2 = x_1^2 + x_2^2 + x_3^2 + x_4^2 + x_5^2$$
$$= 2^2 + 3^2 + 5^2 + (-1)^2 + 4^2$$
$$= 55$$

79. $\bar{x} = \dfrac{15+20+25+30+35}{5} = \dfrac{125}{5} = 25$

81. $\bar{x} = \dfrac{72+83+4+60+18+20}{6} = \dfrac{257}{6} \approx 42.83$

83. a. perimeter of rectangle: $p = 2l + 2w$
$$p_1 = 2(1) + 2(2 \cdot 1) = 2 + 4 = 6$$
$$p_2 = 2(2) + 2(2 \cdot 2) = 4 + 8 = 12$$
$$p_3 = 2(3) + 2(2 \cdot 3) = 6 + 12 = 18$$
$$p_4 = 2(4) + 2(2 \cdot 4) = 8 + 16 = 24$$

b. $p_n = 2n + 2(2n)$
$$= 2n + 4n$$
$$= 6n$$

85. Answers will vary.

87. Answers will vary.

89.
$$\bar{x} = \frac{\sum x}{n}$$
$$n\bar{x} = n \cdot \frac{\sum x}{n}$$
$$n\bar{x} = \sum x \text{ or}$$
$$\sum x = n\bar{x}$$

91.
Yes; $\displaystyle\sum_{i=1}^{n} 2x_i = 2\sum_{i=1}^{n} x_i$; Examples will vary.

93. a. $\sum x = x_1 + x_2 + x_3$
$$= 3 + 5 + 2$$
$$= 10$$

b. $\sum y = y_1 + y_2 + y_3$
$$= 4 + 1 + 6$$
$$= 11$$

c. $\sum x \cdot \sum y = 10 \cdot 11$
$$= 110$$

d. $\sum xy = x_1 y_1 + x_2 y_2 + x_3 y_3$
$$= 3(4) + 5(1) + 2(6)$$
$$= 12 + 5 + 12$$
$$= 29$$

e. No, $\displaystyle\sum xy \ne \sum x \cdot \sum y$

95. $8y^3 - 64x^6 = 8\left(y^3 - 8x^6\right)$
$$= 8\left[(y)^3 - \left(2x^2\right)^3\right]$$
$$= 8\left[\left(y - 2x^2\right)\left(y^2 + 2x^2 y + \left(2x^2\right)^2\right)\right]$$
$$= 8\left[\left(y - 2x^2\right)\left(y^2 + 2x^2 y + 4x^4\right)\right]$$

97. $V = \pi r^2 h$, for r
$$\frac{V}{\pi h} = \frac{\pi r^2 h}{\pi h}$$
$$\frac{V}{\pi h} = r^2$$
$$\sqrt{\frac{V}{\pi h}} = r$$

Exercise Set 11.2

1. In an arithmetic sequence, each term differs by a constant amount.

3. It is called the common difference.

5. The common difference, d, must be a positive number.

7. Yes. For example, $-1, -2, -3, -4, \ldots$ is an arithmetic sequence with $a_1 = -1$ and $d = -1$.

9. Yes. For example, $2, 4, 6, 8, \ldots$ is an arithmetic sequence with $a_1 = 2$ and $d = 2$.

11. $a_1 = 4$
$$a_2 = 4 + (2-1)(3) = 4 + 3 = 7$$
$$a_3 = 4 + (3-1)(3) = 4 + 2(3) = 4 + 6 = 10$$
$$a_4 = 4 + (4-1)(3) = 4 + 3(3) = 4 + 9 = 13$$
$$a_5 = 4 + (5-1)(3) = 4 + 4(3) = 4 + 12 = 16$$
The terms are 4, 7, 10, 13, 16.
The general term is $a_n = 4 + (n-1)3$ or
$$a_n = 3n + 1.$$

13. $a_1 = 7$

$a_2 = 7 + (2-1)(-2) = 7 - 2 = 5$

$a_3 = 7 + (3-1)(-2) = 7 + 2(-2) = 7 - 4 = 3$

$a_4 = 7 + (4-1)(-2) = 7 + 3(-2) = 7 - 6 = 1$

$a_5 = 7 + (5-1)(-2) = 7 + 4(-2) = 7 - 8 = -1$

The terms are 7, 5, 3, 1, -1. The general term is $a_n = 7 + (n-1)(-2)$ or $a_n = -2n + 9$.

15. $a_1 = \dfrac{1}{2}$

$a_2 = \dfrac{1}{2} + (2-1)\left(\dfrac{3}{2}\right) = \dfrac{1}{2} + \dfrac{3}{2} = \dfrac{4}{2} = 2$

$a_3 = \dfrac{1}{2} + (3-1)\left(\dfrac{3}{2}\right) = \dfrac{1}{2} + 2\left(\dfrac{3}{2}\right) = \dfrac{1}{2} + \dfrac{6}{2} = \dfrac{7}{2}$

$a_4 = \dfrac{1}{2} + (4-1)\left(\dfrac{3}{2}\right) = \dfrac{1}{2} + 3\left(\dfrac{3}{2}\right) = \dfrac{1}{2} + \dfrac{9}{2} = \dfrac{10}{2} = 5$

$a_5 = \dfrac{1}{2} + (5-1)\left(\dfrac{3}{2}\right) = \dfrac{1}{2} + 4\left(\dfrac{3}{2}\right) = \dfrac{1}{2} + \dfrac{12}{2} = \dfrac{13}{2}$

The terms are $\dfrac{1}{2}$, 2, $\dfrac{7}{2}$, 5, $\dfrac{13}{2}$. The general term is $a_n = \dfrac{1}{2} + (n-1)\dfrac{3}{2}$ or $a_n = \dfrac{3}{2}n - 1$.

17. $a_1 = 100$

$a_2 = 100 + (2-1)(-5) = 100 + (-5) = 100 - 5 = 95$

$a_3 = 100 + (3-1)(-5) = 100 + 2(-5) = 100 - 10 = 90$

$a_4 = 100 + (4-1)(-5) = 100 + 3(-5) = 100 - 15 = 85$

$a_5 = 100 + (5-1)(-5) = 100 + 4(-5) = 100 - 20 = 80$

The terms are 100, 95, 90, 85, 80. The general term is $a_n = 100 + (n-1)(-5)$ or $a_n = -5n + 105$.

19. $a_n = a_1 + (n-1)d$

$a_4 = 8 + (4-1)3$

$\quad = 8 + 3 \cdot 3$

$\quad = 8 + 9$

$\quad = 17$

21. $a_n = a_1 + (n-1)d$

$a_{10} = -9 + (10-1)(4)$

$\quad = -9 + 9 \cdot (4)$

$\quad = -9 + (36)$

$\quad = 27$

23. $a_n = a_1 + (n-1)d$

$a_{13} = -2 + 12\left(\dfrac{5}{3}\right) = -2 + 20 = 18$

25. $a_n = a_1 + (n-1)d$

$21 = 5 + (9-1)d$

$16 = 8d$

$\dfrac{16}{8} = d$ or $d = 2$

27. $a_n = a_1 + (n-1)d$

$28 = 4 + (n-1)(3)$

$28 = 4 + 3n - 3$

$28 = 1 + 3n$

$27 = 3n$

$\dfrac{27}{3} = n$ or $n = 9$

29.
$$a_n = a_1 + (n-1)d$$
$$60 = 100 + (n-1)(-8)$$
$$60 = 100 - 8n + 8$$
$$60 = 108 - 8n$$
$$-48 = -8n$$
$$\frac{-48}{-8} = n \text{ or } n = 6$$

31.
$$s_{10} = \frac{10(a_1 + a_{10})}{2} = \frac{10(1+19)}{2} = 5(20) = 100$$
$$a_{10} = a_1 + (10-1)d$$
$$a_{10} = a_1 + 9d$$
$$19 = 1 + 9d$$
$$18 = 9d$$
$$\frac{18}{9} = d \text{ or } d = 2$$

33.
$$s_8 = \frac{8(a_1 + a_8)}{2} = \frac{8\left(\frac{3}{5}+2\right)}{2} = 4\left(\frac{3}{5}+2\right)$$
$$= 4\left(\frac{3}{5}+\frac{10}{5}\right) = 4\left(\frac{13}{5}\right) = \frac{52}{5}$$
$$a_8 = a_1 + (8-1)d$$
$$a_8 = a_1 + 7d$$
$$2 = \frac{3}{5} + 7d$$
$$\frac{7}{5} = 7d$$
$$\frac{1}{5} = d \text{ or } d = \frac{1}{5}$$

35.
$$s_6 = \frac{6(a_1 + a_6)}{2} = \frac{6(-3+15.5)}{2} = \frac{6(12.5)}{2} = 37.5$$
$$a_6 = a_1 + (6-1)d$$
$$a_6 = a_1 + 5d$$
$$15.5 = -3 + 5d$$
$$18.5 = 5d$$
$$\frac{18.5}{5} = d \text{ or } d = 3.7$$

37.
$$s_{11} = \frac{11(a_1 + a_{11})}{2} = \frac{11(7+67)}{2} = \frac{11(74)}{2} = 407$$
$$a_{11} = a_1(11-1)d$$
$$a_{11} = a_1 + 10d$$
$$67 = 7 + 10d$$
$$60 = 10d$$
$$\frac{60}{10} = d \text{ or } d = 6$$

39.
$$a_1 = 4$$
$$a_2 = 4 + (2-1)(3) = 4 + 3 = 7$$
$$a_3 = 4 + (3-1)(3) = 4 + 2(3) = 4 + 6 = 10$$
$$a_4 = 4 + (4-1)(3) = 4 + 3(3) = 4 + 9 = 13$$
The terms are 4, 7, 10, 13.
$$a_{10} = 4 + (10-1)(3) = 4 + 9(3) = 4 + 27 = 31$$
$$s_{10} = \frac{10(4+31)}{2} = \frac{10(35)}{2} = 175$$

41.
$$a_1 = 5$$
$$a_2 = 5 + (2-1)(-3) = 5 + -3 = 2$$
$$a_3 = 5 + (3-1)(-3) = 5 + 2(-3) = 5 + -6 = -1$$
$$a_4 = 5 + (4-1)(-3) = 5 + 3(-3) = 5 + -9 = -4$$
The terms are 5, 2, –1, –4.
$$a_{10} = 5 + (10-1)(-3) = 5 + 9(-3) = 5 - 27 = -22$$
$$s_{10} = \frac{10(5+(-22))}{2} = \frac{10(-17)}{2} = -85$$

43.
$$a_1 = -8$$
$$a_2 = -8 + (2-1)(-5)$$
$$= -8 - 5$$
$$= -13$$
$$a_3 = -8 + (3-1)(-5)$$
$$= -8 + 2(-5)$$
$$= -8 - 10$$
$$= -18$$
$$a_4 = -8 + (4-1)(-5)$$
$$= -8 + 3(-5)$$
$$= -8 - 15$$
$$= -23$$
The terms are –8, –13, –18, –23.
$$a_{10} = -8 + (10-1)(-5)$$
$$= -8 + 9(-5)$$
$$= -8 - 45$$
$$= -53$$
$$s_{10} = \frac{10\left[-8+(-53)\right]}{2} = 5(-61) = -305$$

45. $a_1 = 100$

$$a_2 = 100 + (2-1)(-7)$$
$$= 100 - 7$$
$$= 93$$
$$a_3 = 100 + (3-1)(-7)$$
$$= 100 + 2(-7)$$
$$= 100 - 14$$
$$= 86$$
$$a_4 = 100 + (4-1)(-7)$$
$$= 100 + 3(-7)$$
$$= 100 - 21$$
$$= 79$$

The terms are 100, 93, 86, 79.

$$a_{10} = 100 + (10-1)(-7)$$
$$= 100 + 9(-7)$$
$$= 100 - 63$$
$$= 37$$
$$s_{10} = \frac{10(100+37)}{2} = 5(137) = 685$$

47. $a_1 = \dfrac{9}{5}$

$$a_2 = \frac{9}{5} + (2-1)\left(\frac{3}{5}\right) = \frac{9}{5} + \frac{3}{5} = \frac{12}{5}$$

$$a_3 = \frac{9}{5} + (3-1)\left(\frac{3}{5}\right) = \frac{9}{5} + 2\left(\frac{3}{5}\right) = \frac{9}{5} + \frac{6}{5} = \frac{15}{5} = 3$$

$$a_4 = \frac{9}{5} + (4-1)\left(\frac{3}{5}\right) = \frac{9}{5} + 3\left(\frac{3}{5}\right) = \frac{9}{5} + \frac{9}{5} = \frac{18}{5}$$

The terms are $\dfrac{9}{5}, \dfrac{12}{5}, 3, \dfrac{18}{5}$.

$$a_{10} = \frac{9}{5} + (10-1)\left(\frac{3}{5}\right)$$

$$= \frac{9}{5} + 9\left(\frac{3}{5}\right) = \frac{9}{5} + \frac{27}{5} = \frac{36}{5}$$

$$s_{10} = \frac{10\left(\frac{9}{5} + \frac{36}{5}\right)}{2} = 5\left(\frac{45}{5}\right) = 45$$

49. $d = 4 - 1 = 3$

$$a_n = a_1 + (n-1)(d)$$
$$= 1 + (n-1)(3)$$
$$= 1 + 3n - 3$$
$$= -2 + 3n$$
$$43 = -2 + 3n$$
$$45 = 3n$$
$$\frac{45}{3} = n \text{ or } n = 15$$

$$s_{15} = \frac{15(a_1 + a_{15})}{2}$$

$$= \frac{15(1+43)}{2} = \frac{15(44)}{2} = 330$$

51. $d = -5 - (-9) = -5 + 9 = 4$

$$a_n = a_1 + (n-1)d$$
$$= -9 + (n-1)(4)$$
$$= -9 + 4n - 4$$
$$= -13 + 4n$$
$$27 = -13 + 4n$$
$$40 = 4n$$
$$\frac{40}{4} = n \text{ or } n = 10$$

$$s_{10} = \frac{10(a_1 + a_{10})}{2} = \frac{10(-9+27)}{2} = 5(18) = 90$$

53. $d = \dfrac{2}{2} - \dfrac{1}{2} = \dfrac{1}{2}$

$$a_n = \frac{1}{2} + (n-1)\left(\frac{1}{2}\right) = \frac{1}{2} + \frac{1}{2}n - \frac{1}{2} = \frac{1}{2}n$$

$$\frac{17}{2} = \frac{1}{2}n \text{ or } n = 17$$

$$s_{17} = \frac{17\left(\frac{1}{2} + \frac{17}{2}\right)}{2} = \frac{17\left(\frac{18}{2}\right)}{2} = \frac{17(9)}{2} = \frac{153}{2}$$

55. $d = 12 - 9 = 3$

$$a_n = a_1 + (n-1)d$$
$$= 9 + (n-1)(3)$$
$$= 9 + 3n - 3$$
$$= 6 + 3n$$
$$93 = 6 + 3n$$
$$87 = 3n$$
$$\frac{87}{3} = n \text{ or } n = 29$$

$$s_{29} = \frac{29(9+93)}{2} = \frac{29(102)}{2} = 1479$$

57.
$$s_n = \frac{n(a_1 + a_n)}{2}$$

$$s_{50} = \frac{50(1+50)}{2}$$

$$s_{50} = 1275$$

59.
$$s_n = \frac{n(a_1 + a_n)}{2}$$

$$s_{50} = \frac{50(1+99)}{2}$$

$$s_{50} = 2500$$

61.
$$s_n = \frac{n(a_1 + a_n)}{2}$$

$$s_{20} = \frac{20(3+60)}{2}$$

$$s_{20} = 630$$

63. The smallest number greater than 7 that is divisible by 6 is 12. The largest number less than 1610 that is divisible by 6 is 1608. Now find n in the equation $a_n = a_1 + (n-1)d$.

$$1608 = 12 + (n-1)6$$
$$1596 = 6(n-1)$$
$$266 = n-1$$
$$267 = n$$

There are 267 numbers between 7 and 1610 that are divisible by 6.

65. $a_1 = 18, d = 2, n = 12$

$$a_n = a_1 + (n-1)d$$
$$a_{12} = 18 + (12-1)(2) = 18 + 22 = 40$$
$$s_n = \frac{n(a_1 + a_n)}{2}$$
$$s_{12} = \frac{12(18+40)}{2} = \frac{12(58)}{2} = \frac{696}{2} = 348$$

There are 40 seats in the twelfth row and 348 seats in the first twelve rows.

67. $20 + 19 + 18 + \cdots + 1$ or $1 + 2 + 3 + \cdots + 20$

$$s_n = \frac{n(a_1 + a_n)}{2}$$
$$s_{20} = \frac{20(1+20)}{2} = 10(21) = 210$$

There are 210 logs in the pile.

69. $a_1 = 1, d = 2, n = 13$

$$a_n = a_1 + (n-1)d$$
$$a_{12} = 1 + (13-1)(2) = 1 + 24 = 25$$
$$s_n = \frac{n(a_1 + a_n)}{2}$$
$$s_{12} = \frac{13(1+25)}{2} = \frac{13(26)}{2} = 169$$

There are 25 glasses in the 13th row and 169 glasses in all.

71. $1 + 2 + 3 + \cdots + 100$
$$= (1+100) + (2+99) + \cdots + (50+51)$$
$$= 101 + 101 + \cdots + 101$$
$$= 50(101)$$
$$= 5050$$

73.
$$s_n = \frac{n(a_1 + a_n)}{2}$$
$$s_n = \frac{n(1 + 2n - 1)}{2}$$
$$s_n = \frac{2n^2}{2}$$
$$s_n = n^2$$

75. a. $a_1 = 22, d = -\dfrac{1}{2}, n = 7$

$$a_n = a_1 + (n-1)d$$
$$a_7 = 22 + (7-1)\left(-\frac{1}{2}\right) = 22 - 3 = 19$$

Her seventh swing is 19 feet.

b.
$$s_n = \frac{n(a_1 + a_n)}{2}$$
$$s_7 = \frac{7(22+19)}{2} = 143.5$$

She travels 143.5 feet during the seven swings.

77. $d = -6$ in. $= -\dfrac{1}{2}$ ft, $a_1 = 6$

$$a_n = a_1 + (n-1)d$$
$$a_{11} = 6 + (11-1)\left(-\frac{1}{2}\right) = 6 - 5 = 1$$

The ball bounces 1 foot on the eleventh bounce.

79. a. Note that if March 17th is day 1, then March 21st is day 5.

$$a_1 = 105, d = 10, n = 5$$
$$a_n = a_1 + (n-1)d$$
$$a_5 = 105 + (5-1)(10) = 105 + 40 = 145$$

He can prepare 145 packages for shipment on March 21st.

b.
$$s_n = \frac{n(a_1 + a_n)}{2}$$
$$s_5 = \frac{5(105+145)}{2} = \frac{5(250)}{2} = \frac{1250}{2} = 625$$

He can prepare 625 packages for shipment from March 17th through March 21st.

81.

$$s_n = \frac{n(a_1 + a_n)}{2}$$

$$s_{31} = \frac{31(1 + 31)}{2} = \frac{31(32)}{2} = 496$$

On day 31, Craig will have saved $496.

83. **a.** $a_{10} = 32,000 + (10 - 1)(400) = 35,600$

She will receive $35,600 in her tenth year of retirement.

b.

$$s_{10} = \frac{10(32,000 + 35,600)}{2}$$

$$= 5(67,600)$$

$$= 338,000$$

In her first 10 years, she will receive a total of $338,000.

85. $360 - 180 = 180$

$540 - 360 = 180$

$720 - 540 = 180$

The terms form an arithmetic sequence with $d = 180$ and $a_3 = 180$.

$$a_n = a_1 + (n - 1)d$$

$$180 = a_1 + (3 - 1)180$$

$$180 = a_1 + 360$$

$$-180 = a_1$$

$$a_n = a_1 + (n - 1)d$$

$$a_n = -180 + (n - 1)(180)$$

$$= -180 + 180n - 180$$

$$= 180n - 360$$

$$= 180(n - 2)$$

93. $A = P + \Pr t$, for r.

$$A - P = \Pr t$$

$$\frac{A - P}{Pt} = r \text{ or } r = \frac{A - P}{Pt}$$

95. $8n^2 - 4n - 20n + 10$

$$2\left(4n^2 - 2n - 10n + 5\right)$$

$$2\left[\left(4n^2 - 2n\right) - (10n - 5)\right]$$

$$2\left[2n(2n - 1) - 5(2n - 1)\right]$$

$$2\left[(2n - 1)(2n - 5)\right]$$

Exercise Set 11.3

1. A geometric sequence is a sequence in which each term after the first is the same multiple of the preceding term.

3. To find the common ratio, take any term except the first and divide by the term that precedes it.

5. r^n approaches 0 as n gets larger and larger when $|r| < 1$.

7. Yes

9. Yes, s_∞ exists.

$$s_\infty = \frac{a_1}{1 - r} = \frac{6}{1 - \frac{1}{4}} = \frac{6}{\frac{3}{4}} = 6 \cdot \frac{4}{3} = 8$$

This is true since $|r| < 1$.

11. $a_1 = 2$

$$a_2 = 2(3)^{2-1} = 2(3) = 6$$

$$a_3 = 2(3)^{3-1} = 2(3)^2 = 2(9) = 18$$

$$a_4 = 2(3)^{4-1} = 2(3)^3 = 2(27) = 54$$

$$a_5 = 2(3)^{5-1} = 2(3)^4 = 2(81) = 162$$

The terms are 2, 6, 18, 54, 162.

13. $a_1 = 6$

$$a_2 = 6\left(\frac{1}{2}\right)^{2-1} = 6\left(\frac{1}{2}\right) = 3$$

$$a_3 = 6\left(\frac{1}{2}\right)^{3-1} = 6\left(\frac{1}{2}\right)^2 = 6\left(\frac{1}{4}\right) = \frac{3}{2}$$

$$a_4 = 6\left(\frac{1}{2}\right)^{4-1} = 6\left(\frac{1}{2}\right)^3 = 6\left(\frac{1}{8}\right) = \frac{3}{4}$$

$$a_5 = 6\left(\frac{1}{2}\right)^{5-1} = 6\left(\frac{1}{2}\right)^4 = 6\left(\frac{1}{16}\right) = \frac{3}{8}$$

The terms are 6, 3, $\frac{3}{2}$, $\frac{3}{4}$, $\frac{3}{8}$.

15. $a_1 = 80$

$$a_2 = 80\left(\frac{1}{4}\right)^{2-1} = 80\left(\frac{1}{4}\right) = 20$$

$$a_3 = 80\left(\frac{1}{4}\right)^{3-1} = 80\left(\frac{1}{4}\right)^2 = 80\left(\frac{1}{16}\right) = 5$$

$$a_4 = 80\left(\frac{1}{4}\right)^{4-1} = 80\left(\frac{1}{4}\right)^3 = 80\left(\frac{1}{64}\right) = \frac{5}{4}$$

$$a_5 = 80\left(\frac{1}{4}\right)^{5-1} = 80\left(\frac{1}{4}\right)^4 = 80\left(\frac{1}{256}\right) = \frac{5}{16}$$

The terms are $80, 20, 5, \frac{5}{4}, \frac{5}{16}$.

17. $a_1 = 90$

$$a_2 = 90\left(-\frac{1}{3}\right)^{2-1} = 90\left(-\frac{1}{3}\right) = -30$$

$$a_3 = 90\left(-\frac{1}{3}\right)^{3-1} = 90\left(-\frac{1}{3}\right)^2 = 90\left(\frac{1}{9}\right) = 10$$

$$a_4 = 90\left(-\frac{1}{3}\right)^{4-1} = 90\left(-\frac{1}{3}\right)^3 = 90\left(-\frac{1}{27}\right) = -\frac{10}{3}$$

$$a_5 = 90\left(-\frac{1}{3}\right)^{5-1} = 90\left(-\frac{1}{3}\right)^4 = 90\left(\frac{1}{81}\right) = \frac{10}{9}$$

The terms are $90, -30, 10, -\frac{10}{3}, \frac{10}{9}$.

19. $a_1 = -1$

$$a_2 = -1(3)^{2-1} = -1(3) = -3$$

$$a_3 = -1(3)^{3-1} = -1(3)^2 = -1(9) = -9$$

$$a_4 = -1(3)^{4-1} = -1(3)^3 = -1(27) = -27$$

$$a_5 = -1(3)^{5-1} = -1(3)^4 = -1(81) = -81$$

The terms are $-1, -3, -9, -27, -81$.

21. $a_1 = 6$

$$a_2 = 6(-2)^{2-1} = 6(-2)^1 = 6(-2) = -12$$

$$a_3 = 6(-2)^{3-1} = 6(-2)^2 = 6(4) = 24$$

$$a_4 = 6(-2)^{4-1} = 6(-2)^3 = 6(-8) = -48$$

$$a_5 = 6(-2)^{5-1} = 6(-2)^4 = 6(16) = 96$$

The terms are $6, -12, 24, -48, 96$.

23. $a_1 = \frac{1}{3}$

$$a_2 = \frac{1}{3}\left(\frac{1}{2}\right)^{2-1} = \frac{1}{3}\left(\frac{1}{2}\right) = \frac{1}{6}$$

$$a_3 = \frac{1}{3}\left(\frac{1}{2}\right)^{3-1} = \frac{1}{3}\left(\frac{1}{2}\right)^2 = \frac{1}{3}\left(\frac{1}{4}\right) = \frac{1}{12}$$

$$a_4 = \frac{1}{3}\left(\frac{1}{2}\right)^{4-1} = \frac{1}{3}\left(\frac{1}{2}\right)^3 = \frac{1}{3}\left(\frac{1}{8}\right) = \frac{1}{24}$$

$$a_5 = \frac{1}{3}\left(\frac{1}{2}\right)^{5-1} = \frac{1}{3}\left(\frac{1}{2}\right)^4 = \frac{1}{3}\left(\frac{1}{16}\right) = \frac{1}{48}$$

The terms are $\frac{1}{3}, \frac{1}{6}, \frac{1}{12}, \frac{1}{24}, \frac{1}{48}$.

25. $a_1 = 3$

$$a_2 = 3\left(\frac{3}{2}\right)^{2-1} = 3\left(\frac{3}{2}\right) = \frac{9}{2}$$

$$a_3 = 3\left(\frac{3}{2}\right)^{3-1} = 3\left(\frac{3}{2}\right)^2 = 3\left(\frac{9}{4}\right) = \frac{27}{4}$$

$$a_4 = 3\left(\frac{3}{2}\right)^{4-1} = 3\left(\frac{3}{2}\right)^3 = 3\left(\frac{27}{8}\right) = \frac{81}{8}$$

$$a_5 = 3\left(\frac{3}{2}\right)^{5-1} = 3\left(\frac{3}{2}\right)^4 = 3\left(\frac{81}{16}\right) = \frac{243}{16}$$

The terms are $3, \frac{9}{2}, \frac{27}{4}, \frac{81}{8}, \frac{243}{16}$.

27. $a_6 = a_1 r^{6-1}$

$$a_6 = 4(2)^{6-1} = 4(2)^5 = 4(32) = 128$$

29. $a_{10} = a_1 r^{10-1}$

$$a_{10} = \frac{1}{8}(2)^{10-1} = \frac{1}{8}(2)^9 = \frac{1}{8}(512) = 64$$

31. $a_9 = a_1 r^{9-1}$

$$a_9 = -12\left(\frac{1}{2}\right)^{9-1} = -12\left(\frac{1}{2}\right)^8 = -12\left(\frac{1}{256}\right) = -\frac{3}{64}$$

33. $a_{12} = a_1 r^{12-1}$

$$a_{12} = -3(-2)^{12-1}$$
$$= -3(-2)^{11}$$
$$= -3(-2048)$$
$$= 6144$$

35. $a_8 = a_1 r^{8-1}$

$$a_8 = 2\left(\frac{1}{2}\right)^{8-1} = 2\left(\frac{1}{2}\right)^7 = 2\left(\frac{1}{128}\right) = \frac{1}{64}$$

37.

$$a_{10} = a_1 r^{10-1}$$

$$a_{10} = 50\left(\frac{1}{3}\right)^{10-1}$$

$$= 50\left(\frac{1}{3}\right)^{9}$$

$$= 50\left(\frac{1}{19,683}\right)$$

$$= \frac{50}{19,683}$$

39.

$$s_5 = \frac{a_1(1-r^5)}{1-r}$$

$$s_5 = \frac{3(1-2^5)}{1-2}$$

$$= \frac{3(1-32)}{-1}$$

$$= \frac{3(-31)}{-1}$$

$$= \frac{-93}{-1}$$

$$= 193$$

41.

$$s_6 = \frac{a_1(1-r^6)}{1-r}$$

$$s_6 = \frac{4(1-5^6)}{1-5}$$

$$= \frac{4(1-15,625)}{-4}$$

$$= \frac{4(-15,624)}{-4}$$

$$= \frac{-15,624}{-1}$$

$$= 15,624$$

43.

$$s_7 = \frac{a_1(1-r^7)}{1-r}$$

$$s_7 = \frac{80(1-2^7)}{1-2}$$

$$= \frac{80(1-128)}{-1}$$

$$= \frac{80(-127)}{-1}$$

$$= \frac{-10,160}{-1}$$

$$= 10,160$$

45.

$$s_9 = \frac{a_1(1-r^9)}{1-r}$$

$$s_9 = \frac{-30\left[1-\left(-\frac{1}{2}\right)^9\right]}{1-\left(-\frac{1}{2}\right)}$$

$$= \frac{-30\left[1-\left(-\frac{1}{512}\right)\right]}{\frac{3}{2}}$$

$$= \frac{-30\left(1+\frac{1}{512}\right)}{\frac{3}{2}}$$

$$= \frac{-30\left(\frac{513}{512}\right)}{\frac{3}{2}}$$

$$= -30\left(\frac{513}{512}\right)\left(\frac{2}{3}\right)$$

$$= -\frac{2565}{128}$$

47.

$$s_5 = \frac{a_1(1-r^5)}{1-r}$$

$$s_5 = \frac{-9\left[1-\left(\frac{2}{5}\right)^5\right]}{1-\frac{2}{5}}$$

$$= \frac{-9\left(1-\frac{32}{3125}\right)}{\frac{3}{5}}$$

$$= \frac{-9\left(\frac{3093}{3125}\right)}{\frac{3}{5}}$$

$$= -9\left(\frac{3093}{3125}\right)\left(\frac{5}{3}\right)$$

$$= -\frac{9279}{625}$$

49.

$$r = \frac{3}{2} \div 3 = \frac{3}{2} \cdot \frac{1}{3} = \frac{1}{2}$$

$$a_n = 3\left(\frac{1}{2}\right)^{n-1}$$

51.

$$r = 14 \div 7 = 2$$

$$a_n = 7(2)^{n-1}$$

53.

$$r = -6 \div 2 = -3$$

$$a_n = 2(-3)^{n-1}$$

55.

$$r = -3 \div -1 = 3$$

$$a_n = -1(3)^{n-1}$$

57. $r = \dfrac{1}{2} \div 1 = \dfrac{1}{2}$

$S_\infty = \dfrac{1}{1 - \frac{1}{2}} = \dfrac{1}{\frac{1}{2}} = 1\left(\dfrac{2}{1}\right) = 2$

59. $r = \dfrac{1}{5} \div 1 = \dfrac{1}{5}$

$S_\infty = \dfrac{1}{1 - \frac{1}{5}} = \dfrac{1}{\frac{4}{5}} = 1\left(\dfrac{5}{4}\right) = \dfrac{5}{4}$

61. $r = 3 \div 6 = \dfrac{1}{2}$

$S_\infty = \dfrac{6}{1 - \frac{1}{2}} = \dfrac{6}{\frac{1}{2}} = 6\left(\dfrac{2}{1}\right) = 12$

63 $r = 2 \div 5 = \dfrac{2}{5}$

$S_\infty = \dfrac{5}{1 - \frac{2}{5}} = \dfrac{5}{\frac{3}{5}} = 5\left(\dfrac{5}{3}\right) = \dfrac{25}{3}$

65. $r = \dfrac{4}{15} \div \dfrac{1}{3} = \dfrac{4}{15}\left(\dfrac{3}{1}\right) = \dfrac{4}{5}$

$S_\infty = \dfrac{\frac{1}{3}}{1 - \frac{4}{5}} = \dfrac{\frac{1}{3}}{\frac{1}{5}} = \dfrac{1}{3}\left(\dfrac{5}{1}\right) = \dfrac{5}{3}$

67. $r = -1 \div 9 = -\dfrac{1}{9}$

$S_\infty = \dfrac{9}{1 - \left(-\frac{1}{9}\right)}$

$= \dfrac{9}{1 + \frac{1}{9}}$

$= \dfrac{9}{\frac{10}{9}}$

$= 9\left(\dfrac{9}{10}\right)$

$= \dfrac{81}{10}$

69. $r = 1 \div 2 = \dfrac{1}{2}$

$S_\infty = \dfrac{2}{1 - \frac{1}{2}} = \dfrac{2}{\frac{1}{2}} = 2\left(\dfrac{2}{1}\right) = 4$

71. $r = \dfrac{16}{3} \div 8 = \dfrac{16}{3}\left(\dfrac{1}{8}\right) = \dfrac{2}{3}$

$S_\infty = \dfrac{8}{1 - \frac{2}{3}} = \dfrac{8}{\frac{1}{3}} = 8\left(\dfrac{3}{1}\right) = 24$

73. $r = 20 \div -60 = \dfrac{20}{-60} = -\dfrac{1}{3}$

$S_\infty = \dfrac{-60}{1 - \left(-\frac{1}{3}\right)} = \dfrac{-60}{1 + \frac{1}{3}} = \dfrac{-60}{\frac{4}{3}} = -60\left(\dfrac{3}{4}\right) = -45$

75. $r = -\dfrac{12}{5} \div -12 = -\dfrac{12}{5}\left(-\dfrac{1}{12}\right) = \dfrac{1}{5}$

$S_\infty = \dfrac{-12}{1 - \frac{1}{5}} = \dfrac{-12}{\frac{4}{5}} = -12\left(\dfrac{5}{4}\right) = -15$

77. $0.2727\cdots = 0.27 + 0.0027 + 0.000027 + \cdots$

$\quad = 0.27 + 0.27(0.01) + 0.27(0.01)^2 + \cdots$

$r = 0.01$ and $a_1 = 0.27$

$S_\infty = \dfrac{0.27}{1 - 0.01} = \dfrac{0.27}{0.99} = \dfrac{27}{99} = \dfrac{3}{11}$

79. $0.7777\ldots = 0.7 + 0.07 + 0.007 + \cdots$

$\quad = 0.7 + 0.7(0.1) + 0.7(0.1)^2 + \cdots$

$r = 0.1$ and $a_1 = 0.7$

$S_\infty = \dfrac{0.7}{1 - 0.1} = \dfrac{0.7}{0.9} = \dfrac{7}{9}$

81. $0.515151\cdots = 0.51 + 0.0051 + 0.000051 + \cdots$

$\quad = 0.51 + 0.51(0.01) + 0.51(0.01)^2 + \cdots$

$r = 0.01$ and $a_1 = 0.51$

$S_\infty = \dfrac{0.51}{1 - 0.01} = \dfrac{0.51}{0.99} = \dfrac{51}{99} = \dfrac{17}{33}$

83. Consider a new series b_1, b_2, b_3, ... where
$b_1 = 28$

$\dfrac{112}{28} = r^2$

$4 = r^2$

so that $r = 2$ or $r = -2$. From the original series

$a_1 = \dfrac{a_3}{r^2} = \dfrac{28}{4} = 7$. and $b_3 = 112$. Now

$b_3 = b_1 r^{3-1}$ becomes

$112 = 28r^2$

85. Consider a new series b_1, b_2, b_3, ... where
$b_1 = 15$ and $b_4 = 405$. Now $b_4 = b_1 r^{4-1}$
becomes

$405 = 15r^3$

$\dfrac{405}{15} = r^3$

$27 = r^3$

$\sqrt[3]{27} = r$

$3 = r$

From the original series, $a_1 = \dfrac{a_2}{r} = \dfrac{15}{3} = 5$.

87. $a_1 = 1.40$, $n = 9$, $r = 1.03$

$a_n = a_1 r^{n-1}$

$a_8 = 1.4(1.03)^{9-1} \approx 1.77$

In 8 years, a loaf of bread would cost $1.77.

89. $r = \dfrac{1}{2}$. Let a_n be the amount left after the nth

day. After 1 day there are $300\left(\dfrac{1}{2}\right) = 150$

grams left, so $a_1 = 150$.

a.

$37.5 = 150\left(\dfrac{1}{2}\right)^{n-1}$

$\left(\dfrac{1}{2}\right)^{n-1} = \dfrac{37.5}{150} = \dfrac{1}{4} = \left(\dfrac{1}{2}\right)^2$

$n - 1 = 2$

$n = 3$

37.5 grams are left after 3 days.

b.

$a_8 = 150\left(\dfrac{1}{2}\right)^{8-1} = 150\left(\dfrac{1}{128}\right) \approx 1.172$

After 8 days, about 1.172 grams of the substance remain.

91. Each year the population is 1.022 times the population in the previous year, so $r = 1.022$. Let a_n be the population after the nth year. After the first year, the population is $a_1 = 281(1.022) = 287.182$ million

a. $a_{10} = a_1 r^{10-1}$

$= 287.182(1.022)^9$

$= 341.31$ million

In ten years, the population is about 341.31 million people.

b. $a_n = 2(281) = 562$

Now, use $a_n = a_1 r^{n-1}$

$562 = 287.182(1.022)^{n-1}$

$\dfrac{562}{287.182} = (1.022)^{n-1}$

Now, use logarithms.

$\log \dfrac{562}{287.182} = \log(1.022)^{n-1}$

$\log \dfrac{562}{287.182} = (n-1)\log 1.022$

$\dfrac{\log \frac{562}{287.182}}{\log 1.022} = n - 1$

$30.9 \approx n - 1$

$31.9 \approx n$

The population will double after about 31.9 years.

93. a. After 1 meter there is $\dfrac{1}{2}$ of the original

light remaining, so $a_1 = \dfrac{1}{2}$.

$a_1 = \dfrac{1}{2}$

$a_2 = \dfrac{1}{2}\left(\dfrac{1}{2}\right)^{2-1} = \left(\dfrac{1}{2}\right)\left(\dfrac{1}{2}\right) = \dfrac{1}{4}$

$a_3 = \dfrac{1}{2}\left(\dfrac{1}{2}\right)^{3-1} = \left(\dfrac{1}{2}\right)\left(\dfrac{1}{4}\right) = \dfrac{1}{8}$

$a_4 = \dfrac{1}{2}\left(\dfrac{1}{2}\right)^{4-1} = \left(\dfrac{1}{2}\right)\left(\dfrac{1}{8}\right) = \dfrac{1}{16}$

$a_5 = \dfrac{1}{2}\left(\dfrac{1}{2}\right)^{5-1} = \left(\dfrac{1}{2}\right)\left(\dfrac{1}{16}\right) = \dfrac{1}{32}$

b. $a_n = \dfrac{1}{2}\left(\dfrac{1}{2}\right)^{n-1} = \left(\dfrac{1}{2}\right)^n$

c. $a_7 = \left(\dfrac{1}{2}\right)^7 = \dfrac{1}{128} \approx 0.0078$ or 0.78%

95. After 1 hour there is $\dfrac{2}{3}$ of the original dye

left, so $a_1 = \dfrac{2}{3}$. Also, $r = \dfrac{2}{3}$ and $n = 10$.

$$a_{10} = \dfrac{2}{3}\left(\dfrac{2}{3}\right)^{10-1}$$

$$= \dfrac{2}{3}\left(\dfrac{2}{3}\right)^{9}$$

$$= \left(\dfrac{2}{3}\right)^{10}$$

$$\approx 0.017$$

0.017 or 1.7% of the dye remains after 10 hours.

97.   **a.** $a_1 = 0.6(220) = 132$, $r = 0.6$

$a_n = a_1 r^{n-1}$

$a_3 = 132(0.6)^{3-1}$

$a_3 = 47.52$

The height of the third bounce is 47.52 feet.

     b $s_\infty = \dfrac{a_1}{1-r}$

$$s_\infty = \dfrac{220}{1-0.6} = 550$$

She travels a total of 550 feet in the downward direction.

99.   **a.** $a_1 = 30(0.7) = 21$, $r = 0.7$

$a_n = a_1 r^{n-1}$

$a_4 = 21(0.7)^{4-1}$

$a_4 = 7.203$

The ball will bounce 7.203 inches on the fourth bounce.

     b. $s_\infty = \dfrac{a_1}{1-r}$

$$s_\infty = \dfrac{30}{1-0.7}$$

$$s_\infty = 100$$

The ball travels a total of 100 inches in the downward direction.

101. Blue: $a_1 = 1$, $r = 2$

Red: $a_1 = 1$, $r = 3$

$a_6 = a_1 r^{6-1}$

Blue: $a_6 = 1(2)^5 = 32$

Red: $a_6 = 1(3)^5 = 243$

$243 - 32 = 211$

There are 211 more chips in the sixth stack of red chips.

103. Let a_n = value left after the nth year. After

the first year there is $15000\left(\dfrac{4}{5}\right) = 12000$ of

the value left, so $a_1 = 12000$, $r = \dfrac{4}{5}$.

$$a_2 = 12000\left(\dfrac{4}{5}\right)^{2-1} = 12000\left(\dfrac{4}{5}\right) = 9600$$

$$a_3 = 12000\left(\dfrac{4}{5}\right)^{3-1} = 12000\left(\dfrac{16}{25}\right) = 7680$$

$$a_4 = 12000\left(\dfrac{4}{5}\right)^{4-1} = 12000\left(\dfrac{64}{125}\right) = 6144$$

     a. $12{,}000$, $9{,}600$, $7{,}680$, $6{,}144$

     b.

$$a_n = 12000\left(\dfrac{4}{5}\right)^{n-1}$$

     c.

$$a_5 = 12000\left(\dfrac{4}{5}\right)^{5-1} = 12000\left(\dfrac{256}{625}\right) = 4915.20$$

After 5 years, the value of the car is $4,915.20.

105. Each time the ball bounces it goes up and then comes down the same distance. Therefore, the total vertical distance will be twice the height it rises after each bounce plus the initial 10 feet. The heights after each bounce form an infinite geometric sequence with $r = 0.9$ and $a_1 = 9$.

$$s_\infty = \dfrac{9}{1-0.9} = \dfrac{9}{0.1} = 90$$

Total distance: 6

$$2(s_\infty) + 10 = 2(90) + 10 = 190$$

The total vertical distance is 190 feet.

107. a. y_2 goes up more steeply.

b.

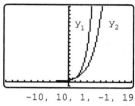

-10, 10, 1, -1, 19

y_2 goes up more steeply.

109.

This is a geometric sequence with $r = \dfrac{2}{1} = 2$.

Also, $a_n = 1,048,576 = 2^{20}$. Using

$a_n = a_1 r^{n-1}$ gives

$2^{20} = 1(2)^{n-1}$

$2^{20} = 2^{n-1}$

$20 = n - 1$

$21 = n$

Thus, there are 21 terms in the sequence.

$S_{21} = \dfrac{a_1\left(1 - r^{21}\right)}{1 - r}$

$= \dfrac{1\left(1 - 2^{21}\right)}{1 - 2}$

$= \dfrac{1 - 2,097,152}{-1}$

$= \dfrac{-2,097,151}{-1}$

$= 2,097,151$

111.

$$
\begin{array}{r}
3x^2 + 4xy - 2y^2 \\
\times \quad\quad\quad 2x - 3y \\
\hline
-9x^2 y - 12xy^2 + 6y^3 \\
6x^3 + 8x^2 y - 4xy^2 \quad\quad\quad \\
\hline
6x^3 - x^2 y - 16xy^2 + 6y^3
\end{array}
$$

113. $g(x) = x^3 + 6 \;\Rightarrow\; y = x^3 + 6$

$x = y^3 + 6$

$x - 6 = y^3 \;\Rightarrow\; y = \sqrt[3]{x - 6}$

$g^{-1}(x) = \sqrt[3]{x - 6}$

115.   Let x and y be the lengths of the legs. Then

$x^2 + y^2 = 15^2$

$x + y + 15 = 36 \;\Rightarrow\; y = 21 - x$

$x^2 + (21 - x)^2 = 225$

$x^2 + 441 - 42x + x^2 = 225$

$2x^2 - 42x + 216 = 0$

$2\left(x^2 - 21x + 108\right) = 0$

$2(x - 9)(x - 12) = 0$

$x - 9 = 0 \quad$ or $\quad x - 12 = 0$

$\quad\quad x = 9 \quad\quad\quad\quad\quad x = 12$

$\quad\quad y = 12 \quad\quad\quad\quad\quad y = 9$

The solutions are (9, 12) and (12, 9). The legs are 9 meters and 12 meters.

Exercise Set 11.4

1. The first and last numbers in each row are 1 and the inner numbers are obtained by adding the two numbers in the row above (to the right and left).

```
            1
         1     1
      1     2     1
   1     3     3     1
1     4     6     4     1
```

3. $1! = 1$

5. No. Factorials are only defined for nonnegative integers.

7. The expansion of $(a + b)^{12}$ has 13 terms, one more than the power to which the binomial is raised.

9. $\dbinom{5}{2} = \dfrac{5!}{2! \cdot (5 - 2)!}$

$= \dfrac{5!}{2! \cdot 3!}$

$= \dfrac{5 \cdot 4 \cdot 3 \cdot 2 \cdot 1}{(2 \cdot 1)(3 \cdot 2 \cdot 1)}$

$= \dfrac{20}{2}$

$= 10$

11. $\dbinom{5}{5} = \dfrac{5!}{5!(5 - 5)!} = \dfrac{1}{0!} = 1$

13. $\dbinom{7}{0} = \dfrac{7!}{0!(7-0)!} = \dfrac{7!}{7!} = 1$

17. $\dbinom{8}{2} = \dfrac{8!}{2!\cdot(8-2)!}$

$= \dfrac{8!}{2!\cdot 6!}$

$= \dfrac{8\cdot 7\cdot 6\cdot 5\cdot 4\cdot 3\cdot 2\cdot 1}{(2\cdot 1)\cdot(6\cdot 5\cdot 4\cdot 3\cdot 2\cdot 1)}$

$= \dfrac{56}{2}$

$= 28$

15. $\dbinom{8}{4} = \dfrac{8!}{4!\cdot(8-4)!}$

$= \dfrac{8!}{4!\cdot 4!}$

$= \dfrac{8\cdot 7\cdot 6\cdot 5\cdot 4\cdot 3\cdot 2\cdot 1}{(4\cdot 3\cdot 2\cdot 1)(4\cdot 3\cdot 2\cdot 1)}$

$= \dfrac{1680}{24}$

$= 70$

19. $(x+4)^3 = \dbinom{3}{0}x^3 4^0 + \dbinom{3}{1}x^2 4^1 + \dbinom{3}{2}x^1 4^2 + \dbinom{3}{3}x^0 4^3$

$= 1x^3(1) + 3x^2(4) + 3x(16) + 1(1)64$

$= x^3 + 12x^2 + 48x + 64$

21. $(2x+3)^3 = \dbinom{3}{0}(2x)^3(3)^0 + \dbinom{3}{1}(2x)^2(3)^1 + \dbinom{3}{2}(2x)^1(3)^2 + \dbinom{3}{3}(2x)^0(3)^3$

$= 1(8x^3)(1) + 3(4x^2)(3) + 3(2x)(9) + 1(1)(27)$

$= 8x^3 + 36x^2 + 54x + 27$

23. $(a-b)^4 = \dbinom{4}{0}a^4(-b)^0 + \dbinom{4}{1}a^3(-b)^1 + \dbinom{4}{2}a^2(-b)^2 + \dbinom{4}{3}a^1(-b)^3 + \dbinom{4}{4}a^0(-b)^4$

$= 1a^4(1) + 4a^3(-b) + 6a^2 b^2 + 4a(-b^3) + 1(1)b^4$

$= a^4 - 4a^3 b + 6a^2 b^2 - 4ab^3 + b^4$

25. $(3a-b)^5 = \dbinom{5}{0}(3a)^5(-b)^0 + \dbinom{5}{1}(3a)^4(-b)^1 + \dbinom{5}{2}(3a)^3(-b)^2 + \dbinom{5}{3}(3a)^2(-b)^3 + \dbinom{5}{4}(3a)^1(-b)^4 + \dbinom{5}{5}(3a)^0(-b)^5$

$= 1(243a^5)(1) + 5(81a^4)(-b) + 10(27a^3)b^2 + 10(9a^2)(-b^3) + 5(3a)b^4 + 1(1)(-b^5)$

$= 243a^5 - 405a^4 b + 270a^3 b^2 - 90a^2 b^3 + 15ab^4 - b^5$

27. $\left(2x+\dfrac{1}{2}\right)^4 = \dbinom{4}{0}(2x)^4\left(\dfrac{1}{2}\right)^0 + \dbinom{4}{1}(2x)^3\left(\dfrac{1}{2}\right)^1 + \dbinom{4}{2}(2x)^2\left(\dfrac{1}{2}\right)^2 + \dbinom{4}{3}(2x)^1\left(\dfrac{1}{2}\right)^3 + \dbinom{4}{4}(2x)^0\left(\dfrac{1}{2}\right)^4$

$= 1(16x^4)(1) + 4(8x^3)\left(\dfrac{1}{2}\right) + 6(4x^2)\left(\dfrac{1}{4}\right) + 4(2x)\left(\dfrac{1}{8}\right) + 1(1)\left(\dfrac{1}{16}\right)$

$= 16x^4 + 16x^3 + 6x^2 + x + \dfrac{1}{16}$

29. $\left(\dfrac{x}{2}-3\right)^4 = \dbinom{4}{0}\left(\dfrac{x}{2}\right)^4(-3)^0 + \dbinom{4}{1}\left(\dfrac{x}{2}\right)^3(-3)^1 + \dbinom{4}{2}\left(\dfrac{x}{2}\right)^2(-3)^2 + \dbinom{4}{3}\left(\dfrac{x}{2}\right)^1(-3)^3 + \dbinom{4}{4}\left(\dfrac{x}{2}\right)^0(-3)^4$

$= 1\left(\dfrac{x^4}{16}\right)(1) + 4\left(\dfrac{x^3}{8}\right)(-3) + 6\left(\dfrac{x^2}{4}\right)(9) + 4\left(\dfrac{x}{2}\right)(-27) + 1(1)(81)$

$= \dfrac{x^4}{16} - \dfrac{3x^3}{2} + \dfrac{27x^2}{2} - 54x + 81$

31.
$$(x+10)^{10} = \binom{10}{0}x^{10}(10)^0 + \binom{10}{1}x^9(10)^1 + \binom{10}{2}x^8(10)^2 + \binom{10}{3}x^7(10)^3 + \cdots$$
$$= 1x^{10}(1) + \frac{10}{1}x^9(10) + \frac{10\cdot9}{2\cdot1}x^8(100) + \frac{10\cdot9\cdot8}{3\cdot2\cdot1}x^7(1000) + \cdots$$
$$= x^{10} + 100x^9 + 4{,}500x^8 + 120{,}000x^7 + \cdots$$

33.
$$(3x - y)^7 = \binom{7}{0}(3x)^7(-y)^0 + \binom{7}{1}(3x)^6(-y)^1 + \binom{7}{2}(3x)^5(-y)^2 + \binom{7}{3}(3x)^4(-y)^3 + \cdots$$
$$= 1(2187x^7)(1) + \frac{7}{1}(729x^6)(-y) + \frac{7\cdot6}{2\cdot1}(243x^5)(y^2) + \frac{7\cdot6\cdot5}{3\cdot2\cdot1}(81x^4)(-y^3) + \cdots$$
$$= 2187x^7 + 7(729x^6)(-y) + 21(243x^5)(y^2) + 35(81x^4)(-y^3) + \cdots$$
$$= 2187x^7 - 5103x^6y + 5103x^5y^2 - 2835x^4y^3 + \cdots$$

35.
$$(x^2 - 3y)^8 = \binom{8}{0}(x^2)^8(-3y)^0 + \binom{8}{1}(x^2)^7(-3y)^1 + \binom{8}{2}(x^2)^6(-3y)^2 + \binom{8}{3}(x^2)^5(-3y)^3 + \cdots$$
$$= 1(x^{16})(1) + \frac{8}{1}(x^{14})(-3y) + \frac{8\cdot7}{2\cdot1}(x^{12})(9y^2) + \frac{8\cdot7\cdot6}{3\cdot2\cdot1}(x^{10})(-27y^3) + \cdots$$
$$= x^{16} + 8(x^{14})(-3y) + 28(x^{12})(9y^2) + 56(x^{10})(-27y^3) + \cdots$$
$$= x^{16} - 24x^{14}y + 252x^{12}y^2 - 1512x^{10}y^3 + \cdots$$

37. Yes, $n! = n\cdot(n-1)!$
$$4! = 4\cdot3\cdot2\cdot1 = 4\cdot(3\cdot2\cdot1) = 4\cdot(3)! = 4\cdot(4-1)!$$

39. Yes, $(n-3)! = (n-3)(n-4)(n-5)!$ for $n \ge 5$.
Let $n = 7$:
$$(7-3)! = (7-3)(7-4)(7-5)! \text{ or}$$
$$4! = 4\cdot3\cdot2! = 4\cdot3\cdot2\cdot1 = 4!$$

41. $\binom{n}{m} = 1$ when $n = m$ or $m = 0$.

43. $(x+3)^8$

First term is $\binom{8}{0}(x)^8(3)^0 = 1(x^8)(1) = x^8$.

Second term is
$$\binom{8}{1}(x)^7(3)^1 = 8(x^7)(3) = 24x^7.$$

Next to last term is
$$\binom{8}{7}(x)^1(3)^7 = 8(x)(2187) = 17{,}496x$$

Last term is $\binom{8}{8}(x)^0(3)^8 = 1(1)(6561) = 6561$.

45.
$$(a + b)^n = \sum_{i=0}^{n}\binom{n}{i}a^{n-i}b^i$$

47. Let $x = 0$
$$2x + y = 6$$
$$2(0) + y = 6 \implies y = 6$$
The y-intercept is $(0, 6)$.

49.
$$x(x-12) = 20$$
$$x^2 - 12x - 20 = 0$$
$$(x-10)(x-2) = 0$$
$$x - 10 = 0 \quad \text{or} \quad x - 2 = 0$$
$$x = 10 \qquad\qquad x = 2$$

51. $f(x) = 2x + 8 \implies y = 2x + 8$
$$x = 2y + 8 \implies 2y = x - 8 \implies y = \frac{x-8}{2}$$
$$f^{-1}(x) = \frac{x-8}{2}$$

Review Exercises

1. $a_1 = 1 + 2 = 3$
   $a_2 = 2 + 2 = 4$
   $a_3 = 3 + 2 = 5$
   $a_4 = 4 + 2 = 6$
   $a_5 = 5 + 2 = 7$
   The terms are 3, 4, 5, 6, 7.

2. $a_1 = 1^2 + 1 - 3 = -1$
   $a_2 = 2^2 + 2 - 3 = 3$
   $a_3 = 3^2 + 3 - 3 = 9$
   $a_4 = 4^2 + 4 - 3 = 17$
   $a_5 = 5^2 + 5 - 3 = 27$

   The terms are -1, 3, 9, 17, 27.

3. $a_1 = \dfrac{4}{1} = 4$

   $a_2 = \dfrac{4}{2} = 2$

   $a_3 = \dfrac{4}{3}$

   $a_4 = \dfrac{4}{4} = 1$

   $a_5 = \dfrac{4}{5}$

   The terms are 4, 2, $\dfrac{4}{3}$, 1, $\dfrac{4}{5}$.

4. $a_1 = \dfrac{1^2}{1+4} = \dfrac{1}{5}$

   $a_2 = \dfrac{2^2}{2+4} = \dfrac{4}{6} = \dfrac{2}{3}$

   $a_3 = \dfrac{3^2}{3+4} = \dfrac{9}{7}$

   $a_4 = \dfrac{4^2}{4+4} = \dfrac{16}{8} = 2$

   $a_5 = \dfrac{5^2}{5+4} = \dfrac{25}{9}$

   The terms are $\dfrac{1}{5}, \dfrac{2}{3}, \dfrac{9}{7}, 2, \dfrac{25}{9}$.

5. $a_7 = 3(7) - 11 = 21 - 11 = 10$

6. $a_7 = (-1)^7 + 3 = -1 + 3 = 2$

7. $a_9 = \dfrac{9+7}{9^2} = \dfrac{16}{81}$

8. $a_{11} = 11(11 - 3) = 11(8) = 88$

9. $a_1 = 2(1) + 7 = 2 + 7 = 9$
   $a_2 = 2(2) + 7 = 4 + 7 = 11$
   $a_3 = 2(3) + 7 = 6 + 7 = 13$
   $s_1 = a_1 = 9$
   $s_3 = a_1 + a_2 + a_3 = 9 + 11 + 13 = 33$

10. $a_1 = (1)^2 + 5 = 1 + 5 = 6$
    $a_2 = (2)^2 + 5 = 4 + 5 = 9$
    $a_3 = (3)^2 + 5 = 9 + 5 = 14$
    $s_1 = a_1 = 6$
    $s_3 = a_1 + a_2 + a_3 = 6 + 9 + 14 = 29$

11. $a_1 = \dfrac{1+3}{1+2} = \dfrac{4}{3}$

    $a_2 = \dfrac{2+3}{2+2} = \dfrac{5}{4}$

    $a_3 = \dfrac{3+3}{3+2} = \dfrac{6}{5}$

    $s_1 = a_1 = \dfrac{4}{3}$

    $s_3 = a_1 + a_2 + a_3$

    $= \dfrac{4}{3} + \dfrac{5}{4} + \dfrac{6}{5}$

    $= \dfrac{80}{60} + \dfrac{75}{60} + \dfrac{72}{60}$

    $= \dfrac{227}{60}$

12. $a_1 = (-1)^1(1+8) = (-1)(9) = -9$
    $a_2 = (-1)^2(2+8) = 1(10) = 10$
    $a_3 = (-1)^3(3+8) = -1(11) = -11$
    $s_1 = a_1 = -9$
    $s_3 = a_1 + a_2 + a_3 = -9 + 10 - 11 = -10$

13. This is a geometric sequence. $r = 4 \div 2 = 2$
    $$a_5 = 2(2)^{5-1} = 2 \cdot 2^4 = 32$$
    $a_1 = 2$ $a_6 = 2(2)^{6-1} = 2 \cdot 2^5 = 64$
    $$a_7 = 2(2)^{7-1} = 2 \cdot 2^6 = 128$$
    The terms are 32, 64, 128.

14. This is a geometric sequence.
    $$r = 9 \div (-27) = \dfrac{9}{-27} = -\dfrac{1}{3}$$
    $a_1 = -27$

$$a_5 = -27\left(-\frac{1}{3}\right)^4 = -27\left(\frac{1}{81}\right) = -\frac{1}{3}$$

$$a_6 = -27\left(-\frac{1}{3}\right)^5 = -27\left(-\frac{1}{243}\right) = \frac{1}{9}$$

$$a_5 = -27\left(-\frac{1}{3}\right)^6 = -27\left(\frac{1}{729}\right) = -\frac{1}{27}$$

The terms are $-\frac{1}{3}, \frac{1}{9}, -\frac{1}{27}$.

$$a_n = -27\left(-\frac{1}{3}\right)^{n-1} \quad \text{or} \quad a_n = (-1)^n\left(3^{4-n}\right)$$

15. This is a geometric sequence.

$$r = \frac{2}{5} \div \frac{1}{5} = \frac{2}{5}\left(\frac{5}{1}\right) = 2$$

$$a_1 = \frac{1}{5}$$

$$a_5 = \frac{1}{5}(2)^{5-1} = \frac{2^4}{5} = \frac{16}{5}$$

$$a_6 = \frac{1}{5}(2)^{6-1} = \frac{2^5}{5} = \frac{32}{5}$$

$$a_7 = \frac{1}{5}(2)^{7-1} = \frac{2^6}{5} = \frac{64}{5}$$

The terms are $\frac{16}{5}, \frac{32}{5}, \frac{64}{5}$.

$$a_n = \frac{1}{5}(2)^{n-1} = \frac{2^{n-1}}{5}$$

16. This is an arithmetic sequence.

$$d = 8 - 12 = -4$$

$$a_1 = 12$$

$$a_5 = 12 + (5-1)(-4) = 12 - 16 = -4$$

$$a_6 = 12 + (6-1)(-4) = 12 - 20 = -8$$

$$a_7 = 12 + (7-1)(-4) = 12 - 24 = -12$$

The terms are $-4, -8, -12$.

$$a_n = a_1 + (n-1)d$$

$$= 12 + (n-1)(-4)$$

$$= 12 - 4n + 4$$

$$= 16 - 4n$$

17.

$$\sum_{j=1}^{3}(j^2 + 4) = (1^2 + 4) + (2^2 + 4) + (3^2 + 4)$$

$$= 5 + 8 + 13$$

$$= 26$$

18.

$$\sum_{k=1}^{4} k(k + 2)$$

$$= 1(1 + 2) + 2(2 + 2) + 3(3 + 2) + 4(4 + 2)$$

$$= 1(3) + 2(4) + 3(5) + 4(6)$$

$$= 3 + 8 + 15 + 24$$

$$= 50$$

19.

$$\sum_{k=1}^{5}\frac{k^2}{6} = \frac{1^2}{6} + \frac{2^2}{6} + \frac{3^2}{6} + \frac{4^2}{6} + \frac{5^2}{6}$$

$$= \frac{1}{6} + \frac{4}{6} + \frac{9}{6} + \frac{16}{6} + \frac{25}{6}$$

$$= \frac{55}{6}$$

20.

$$\sum_{i=1}^{4}\frac{i}{i+1} = \frac{1}{1+1} + \frac{2}{2+1} + \frac{3}{3+1} + \frac{4}{4+1}$$

$$= \frac{1}{2} + \frac{2}{3} + \frac{3}{4} + \frac{4}{5}$$

$$= \frac{163}{60}$$

21.

$$\sum_{i=1}^{4} x_i = x_1 + x_2 + x_3 + x_4$$

$$= 3 + 9 + 5 + 10$$

$$= 27$$

22.

$$\sum_{i=1}^{4}(x_i)^2 = x_1^2 + x_2^2 + x_3^2 + x_4^2$$

$$= 3^2 + 9^2 + 5^2 + 10^2$$

$$= 9 + 81 + 25 + 100$$

$$= 215$$

23.

$$\sum_{i=2}^{3}(x_i^2 + 1) = (x_2^2 + 1) + (x_3^2 + 1)$$

$$= (9^2 + 1) + (5^2 + 1)$$

$$= (81 + 1) + (25 + 1)$$

$$= 82 + 26$$

$$= 108$$

24.

$$\left(\sum_{i=1}^{4} x_i\right)^2 = (x_1 + x_2 + x_3 + x_4)^2$$

$$= (3 + 9 + 5 + 10)^2$$

$$= 27^2$$

$$= 729$$

25. a. perimeter of rectangle: $p = 2l + 2w$
$p_1 = 2(1) + 2(1+3) = 2 + 8 = 10$
$p_2 = 2(2) + 2(2+3) = 4 + 10 = 14$
$p_3 = 2(3) + 2(3+3) = 6 + 12 = 18$
$p_4 = 2(4) + 2(4+3) = 8 + 14 = 22$

b. $p_n = 2n + 2(n+3)$
$= 2n + 2n + 6$
$= 4n + 6$

26. a. area of rectangle: $a = l \cdot w$
$a_1 = (1)(1+3) = 4$
$a_2 = (2)(2+3) = 10$
$a_3 = (3)(3+3) = 18$
$a_4 = (4)(4+3) = 28$

b. $a_n = (n)(n+3)$
$= n^2 + 3n$

27. $a_1 = 5$
$a_2 = 5 + (2-1)(2) = 5 + 2 = 7$
$a_3 = 5 + (3-1)(2) = 5 + 2(2) = 9$
$a_4 = 5 + (4-1)(2) = 5 + 3(2) = 11$
$a_5 = 5 + (5-1)(2) = 5 + 4(2) = 13$
The terms are 5, 7, 9, 11, 13.

28. $a_1 = -12$
$a_2 = -12 + (2-1)\left(-\frac{1}{2}\right) = -12 - \frac{1}{2} = -\frac{25}{2}$
$a_3 = -12 + (3-1)\left(-\frac{1}{2}\right)$
$= -12 + 2\left(-\frac{1}{2}\right)$
$= -12 - 1$
$= -13$
$a_4 = -12 + (4-1)\left(-\frac{1}{2}\right)$
$= -12 + 3\left(-\frac{1}{2}\right)$
$= -12 - \frac{3}{2}$
$= -\frac{27}{2}$
$a_5 = -12 + (5-1)\left(-\frac{1}{2}\right)$
$= -12 + 4\left(-\frac{1}{2}\right)$
$= -12 - 2$
$= -14$
The terms are -12, $-\frac{25}{2}$, -13, $-\frac{27}{2}$, -14.

29. $a_1 = \frac{1}{2}$
$a_2 = \frac{1}{2} + (2-1)(-2) = \frac{1}{2} - 2 = -\frac{3}{2}$
$a_3 = \frac{1}{2} + (3-1)(-2) = \frac{1}{2} - 4 = -\frac{7}{2}$
$a_4 = \frac{1}{2} + (4-1)(-2) = \frac{1}{2} - 6 = -\frac{11}{2}$
$a_5 = \frac{1}{2} + (5-1)(-2) = \frac{1}{2} - 8 = -\frac{15}{2}$
The terms are $\frac{1}{2}$, $-\frac{3}{2}$, $-\frac{7}{2}$, $-\frac{11}{2}$, $-\frac{15}{2}$.

30. $a_1 = -100$
$a_2 = -100 + (2-1)\left(\frac{1}{5}\right) = -100 + \frac{1}{5} = -\frac{499}{5}$
$a_3 = -100 + (3-1)\left(\frac{1}{5}\right) = -100 + \frac{2}{5} = -\frac{498}{5}$
$a_4 = -100 + (4-1)\left(\frac{1}{5}\right) = -100 + \frac{3}{5} = -\frac{497}{5}$
$a_5 = -100 + (5-1)\left(\frac{1}{5}\right) = -100 + \frac{4}{5} = -\frac{496}{5}$
The terms are -100, $-\frac{499}{5}$, $-\frac{498}{5}$, $-\frac{497}{5}$, $-\frac{496}{5}$.

31. $a_8 = a_1 + (8-1)d$
$a_8 = 6 + (8-1)(3) = 6 + 7(3) = 27$

32.
$$a_7 = a_1 + (7-1)d$$
$$-14 = 10 + 6d$$
$$-24 = 6d$$
$$-\frac{24}{6} = d \text{ or } d = -4$$

33.
$$a_9 = a_1 + (9-1)d$$
$$1 = -3 + 8d$$
$$4 = 8d$$
$$\frac{4}{8} = d$$
$$\frac{1}{2} = d$$

34.
$$a_n = a_1 + (n-1)d$$
$$-3 = 22 + (n-1)(-5)$$
$$-3 = 22 - 5n + 5$$
$$-3 = 27 - 05n$$
$$-30 = -5n$$
$$\frac{-30}{-5} = n \text{ or } n = 6$$

35.
$$a_8 = a_1 + (8-1)d$$
$$21 = 7 + 7d$$
$$14 = 7d$$
$$2 = d \text{ or } d = 2$$
$$s_8 = \frac{8(a_1 + a_8)}{2}$$
$$= \frac{8(7+21)}{2}$$
$$= \frac{8(28)}{2}$$
$$= 4(28)$$
$$= 112$$

36.
$$a_7 = a_1 + (7-1)d$$
$$-48 = -12 + 6d$$
$$-36 = 6d$$
$$\frac{-36}{6} = d$$
$$-6 = d \text{ or } d = -6$$
$$s_7 = \frac{7(a_1 + a_7)}{2}$$
$$= \frac{7(-12-48)}{2} = \frac{7(-60)}{2} = -210$$

37.
$$a_7 = a_1 + (7-1)d$$
$$3 = \frac{3}{5} + 6d$$
$$3 - \frac{3}{5} = 6d$$
$$\frac{12}{5} = 6d$$
$$\frac{1}{6}\left(\frac{12}{5}\right) = \frac{1}{6}(6d)$$
$$\frac{2}{5} = d \text{ or } d = \frac{2}{5}$$
$$s_7 = \frac{7(a_1 + a_7)}{2}$$
$$= \frac{7\left(\frac{3}{5} + 3\right)}{2}$$
$$= \frac{7\left(\frac{18}{5}\right)}{2}$$
$$= 7\left(\frac{18}{5}\right)\left(\frac{1}{2}\right)$$
$$= \frac{63}{5}$$

38.
$$a_9 = a_1 + (9-1)d$$
$$-6 = -\frac{10}{3} + 8d$$
$$-6 + \frac{10}{3} = 8d$$
$$-\frac{8}{3} = 8d$$
$$\frac{1}{8}\left(-\frac{8}{3}\right) = \frac{1}{8}(8d)$$
$$-\frac{1}{3} = d \text{ or } d = -\frac{1}{3}$$
$$s_9 = \frac{9(a_1 + a_n)}{2}$$
$$= \frac{9\left(-\frac{10}{3} - 6\right)}{2}$$
$$= \frac{9\left(-\frac{28}{3}\right)}{2}$$
$$= 9\left(-\frac{28}{3}\right)\left(\frac{1}{2}\right)$$
$$= -42$$

39. $a_1 = -8$

$a_2 = -8 + (2-1)(4) = -8 + 4 = -4$

$a_3 = -8 + (3-1)(4) = -8 + 8 = 0$

$a_4 = -8 + (4-1)(4) = -8 + 12 = 4$

The terms are $-8, -4, 0, 4$.

$a_{10} = -8 + (10-1)(4) = -8 + 9(4) = -8 + 36 = 28$

$s_{10} = \dfrac{10(-8 + 28)}{2} = 5(20) = 100$

40. $a_1 = 5$

$a_2 = 5 + (2-1)(-3) = 5 - 3 = 2$

$a_3 = 5 + (3-1)(-3) = 5 - 6 = -1$

$a_4 = 5 + (4-1)(-3) = 5 - 9 = -4$

The terms are $5, 2, -1, -4$.

$a_{10} = 5 + (10-1)(-3) = 5 - 27 = -22$

$s_{10} = \dfrac{10(5 - 22)}{2} = 5(-17) = -85$

41. $a_1 = \dfrac{5}{6}$

$a_2 = \dfrac{5}{6} + (2-1)\left(\dfrac{2}{3}\right) = \dfrac{5}{6} + \dfrac{2}{3} = \dfrac{9}{6} = \dfrac{3}{2}$

$a_3 = \dfrac{5}{6} + (3-1)\left(\dfrac{2}{3}\right) = \dfrac{5}{6} + 2\left(\dfrac{2}{3}\right) = \dfrac{5}{6} + \dfrac{4}{3} = \dfrac{13}{6}$

$a_4 = \dfrac{5}{6} + (4-1)\left(\dfrac{2}{3}\right) = \dfrac{5}{6} + 3\left(\dfrac{2}{3}\right) = \dfrac{5}{6} + \dfrac{6}{3} = \dfrac{17}{6}$

The terms are $\dfrac{5}{6}, \dfrac{3}{2}, \dfrac{13}{6}, \dfrac{17}{6}$.

$a_{10} = \dfrac{5}{6} + (10-1)\left(\dfrac{2}{3}\right)$

$= \dfrac{5}{6} + 9\left(\dfrac{2}{3}\right) = \dfrac{5}{6} + \dfrac{18}{3} = \dfrac{41}{6}$

$s_{10} = \dfrac{10\left(\dfrac{5}{6} + \dfrac{41}{6}\right)}{2}$

$= \dfrac{10\left(\dfrac{46}{6}\right)}{2}$

$= 5\left(\dfrac{46}{6}\right)$

$= 5\left(\dfrac{23}{3}\right)$

$= \dfrac{115}{3}$

42. $a_1 = -60$

$a_2 = -60 + (2-1)(5) = -60 + 5 = -55$

$a_3 = -60 + (3-1)(5) = -60 + 10 = -50$

$a_4 = -60 + (4-1)(5) = -60 + 15 = -45$

The terms are $-60, -55, -50, -45$.

$a_{10} = -60 + (10-1)(5) = -60 + 45 = -15$

$s_{10} = \dfrac{10(-60 - 15)}{2} = 5(-75) = -375$

43. $d = 9 - 4 = 5$

$a_n = a_1 + (n-1)d$

$59 = 4 + (n-1)5$

$55 = 5n - 5$

$60 = 5n \implies n = 12$

$s_{12} = \dfrac{12(a_1 + a_{12})}{2}$

$= \dfrac{12(4 + 59)}{2}$

$= \dfrac{12(63)}{2}$

$= 6(63)$

$= 378$

44. $d = -4 - (-7) = 3$

$a_n = a_1 + (n-1)d$

$14 = -7 + (n-1)3$

$21 = 3n - 3$

$24 = 3n \implies n = 8$

$s_8 = \dfrac{8(a_1 + a_9)}{2} = \dfrac{8(-7 + 14)}{2} = \dfrac{8(7)}{2} = 28$

45. $d = \dfrac{9}{10} - \dfrac{6}{10} = \dfrac{3}{10}$

$a_n = a_1 + (n-1)d$

$\dfrac{36}{10} = \dfrac{6}{10} + (n-1)\dfrac{3}{10}$

$\dfrac{36}{10} = \dfrac{6}{10} + \dfrac{3}{10}n - \dfrac{3}{10}$

$\dfrac{36}{10} = \dfrac{3}{10} + \dfrac{3}{10}n$

$\dfrac{33}{10} = \dfrac{3}{10}n$

$\dfrac{10}{3}\left(\dfrac{33}{10}\right) = \dfrac{10}{3}\left(\dfrac{3}{10}n\right)$

$11 = n$ or $n = 11$

$s_{11} = \dfrac{11(a_1 + a_{11})}{2}$

$= \dfrac{11\left(\dfrac{6}{10} + \dfrac{36}{10}\right)}{2}$

$= \dfrac{11\left(\dfrac{42}{10}\right)}{2}$

$= 11\left(\dfrac{42}{10}\right)\left(\dfrac{1}{2}\right)$

$= \dfrac{231}{10}$

46. $d = -3 - (-9) = 6$

$a_n = a_1 + (n-1)d$

$69 = -9 + (n-1)6$

$69 = -9 + 6n - 6$

$69 = -15 + 6n$

$84 = 6n$

$14 = n$ or $n = 14$

$s_{14} = \dfrac{14(a_1 + a_{19})}{2}$

$= \dfrac{14(-9 + 69)}{2}$

$= \dfrac{14(60)}{2}$

$= 7(60)$

$= 420$

47. $a_1 = 5$

$a_2 = 5(2)^{2-1} = 5(2) = 10$

$a_3 = 5(2)^{3-1} = 5(2)^2 = 5(4) = 20$

$a_4 = 5(2)^{4-1} = 5(2)^3 = 5(8) = 40$

$a_5 = 5(2)^{5-1} = 5(2)^4 = 5(16) = 80$

The terms are 5, 10, 20, 40, 80.

48. $a_1 = -12$

$a_2 = -12\left(\dfrac{1}{2}\right)^{2-1} = -12\left(\dfrac{1}{2}\right) = -6$

$a_3 = -12\left(\dfrac{1}{2}\right)^{3-1} = -12\left(\dfrac{1}{4}\right) = -3$

$a_4 = -12\left(\dfrac{1}{2}\right)^{4-1} = -12\left(\dfrac{1}{8}\right) = -\dfrac{3}{2}$

$a_5 = -12\left(\dfrac{1}{2}\right)^{5-1} = -12\left(\dfrac{1}{16}\right) = -\dfrac{3}{4}$

The terms are $-12, -6, -3,$

49. $a_1 = 20$

$a_2 = 20\left(-\dfrac{2}{3}\right)^{2-1}$

$= 20\left(-\dfrac{2}{3}\right) = -\dfrac{40}{3}$

$a_3 = 20\left(-\dfrac{2}{3}\right)^{3-1}$

$= 20\left(-\dfrac{2}{3}\right)^2 = 20\left(\dfrac{4}{9}\right) = \dfrac{80}{9}$

$a_4 = 20\left(-\dfrac{2}{3}\right)^{4-1} =$

$20\left(-\dfrac{2}{3}\right)^3 = 20\left(-\dfrac{8}{27}\right) = -\dfrac{160}{27}$

$a_5 = 20\left(-\dfrac{2}{3}\right)^{5-1}$

$= 20\left(-\dfrac{2}{3}\right)^4 = 20\left(\dfrac{16}{81}\right) = \dfrac{320}{81}$

The terms are $20, \ -\dfrac{40}{3}, \ \dfrac{80}{9}, \ -\dfrac{160}{27}, \ \dfrac{320}{81}$.

50. $a_1 = -100$

$a_2 = -100\left(\dfrac{1}{5}\right)^{2-1} = -100\left(\dfrac{1}{5}\right) = -20$

$a_3 = -100\left(\dfrac{1}{5}\right)^{3-1} = -100\left(\dfrac{1}{25}\right) = -4$

$a_4 = -100\left(\dfrac{1}{5}\right)^{4-1} = -100\left(\dfrac{1}{125}\right) = -\dfrac{4}{5}$

$a_5 = -100\left(\dfrac{1}{5}\right)^{5-1} = -100\left(\dfrac{1}{625}\right) = -\dfrac{4}{25}$

The terms are $-100, -20, -4, -\dfrac{4}{5}, -\dfrac{4}{25}$.

51. $a_5 = 6\left(\dfrac{1}{3}\right)^{5-1} = 6\left(\dfrac{1}{81}\right) = \dfrac{2}{27}$

52. $a_7 = 15(2)^{7-1} = 15(64) = 960$

53. $a_6 = -8(-3)^{6-1} = -8(-243) = 1944$

54. $a_5 = \frac{1}{12}\left(\frac{2}{3}\right)^{5-1} = \frac{1}{12}\left(\frac{16}{81}\right) = \frac{4}{243}$

55. $\begin{aligned} s_7 &= \frac{7(1-2^7)}{1-2} \\ &= \frac{7(1-128)}{-1} \\ &= \frac{7(-127)}{-1} \\ &= 889 \end{aligned}$

56. $\begin{aligned} s_5 &= \frac{-84\left[1-\left(-\frac{1}{4}\right)^5\right]}{1-\left(-\frac{1}{4}\right)} \\ &= \frac{-84\left[1-\left(-\frac{1}{1024}\right)\right]}{1+\frac{1}{4}} \\ &= \frac{-84\left(1+\frac{1}{1024}\right)}{\frac{5}{4}} \\ &= -84 \cdot \left(\frac{1025}{1024}\right) \cdot \frac{4}{5} \\ &= -\frac{4305}{64} \end{aligned}$

57. $\begin{aligned} s_4 &= \frac{9\left[1-\left(\frac{3}{2}\right)^4\right]}{1-\frac{3}{2}} \\ &= \frac{9\left(1-\frac{81}{16}\right)}{-\frac{1}{2}} \\ &= 9\left(-\frac{65}{16}\right)\left(-\frac{2}{1}\right) \\ &= \frac{585}{8} \end{aligned}$

58. $\begin{aligned} s_7 &= \frac{\frac{3}{5}\left[1-\left(\frac{5}{3}\right)^7\right]}{1-\frac{5}{3}} \\ &= \frac{\frac{3}{5}\left(1-\frac{78,125}{2187}\right)}{-\frac{2}{3}} \\ &= \frac{3}{5}\left(-\frac{75,938}{2187}\right)\left(-\frac{3}{2}\right) \\ &= \frac{37,969}{1215} \end{aligned}$

59. $r = 12 \div 6 = 2$
$a_n = 6(2)^{n-1}$

60. $r = -20 \div -4 = \frac{-20}{-4} = 5$
$a_n = -4(5)^{n-1}$

61. $r = \frac{7}{3} \div 7 = \frac{7}{3} \cdot \frac{1}{7} = \frac{1}{3}$
$a_n = 7\left(\frac{1}{3}\right)^{n-1}$

62. $r = \frac{18}{15} \div \frac{9}{5} = \frac{18}{15} \cdot \frac{5}{9} = \frac{2}{3}$
$a_n = \frac{9}{5}\left(\frac{2}{3}\right)^{n-1}$

63. $r = \frac{3}{2} \div 3 = \frac{3}{2} \cdot \frac{1}{3} = \frac{1}{2}$
$s_\infty = \frac{3}{1-\frac{1}{2}} = \frac{3}{\frac{1}{2}} = 3\left(\frac{2}{1}\right) = 6$

64. $r = 1 \div \frac{5}{2} = 1\left(\frac{2}{5}\right) = \frac{2}{5}$
$s_\infty = \frac{\frac{5}{2}}{1-\frac{2}{5}} = \frac{\frac{5}{2}}{\frac{3}{5}} = \frac{5}{2}\left(\frac{5}{3}\right) = \frac{25}{6}$

65. $r = \frac{8}{3} \div (-8) = \frac{8}{3}\left(-\frac{1}{8}\right) = -\frac{1}{3}$
$s_\infty = \frac{-8}{1-\left(-\frac{1}{3}\right)} = \frac{-8}{\frac{4}{3}} = -8\left(\frac{3}{4}\right) = -6$

66. $r = -4 \div -6 = \frac{-4}{-6} = \frac{2}{3}$
$s_\infty = \frac{-6}{1-\frac{2}{3}} = \frac{-6}{\frac{1}{3}} = -6\left(\frac{3}{1}\right) = -18$

67. $r = 4 \div 8 = \frac{1}{2}$
$s_\infty = \frac{8}{1-\frac{1}{2}} = \frac{8}{\frac{1}{2}} = 8\left(\frac{2}{1}\right) = 16$

68. $r = \frac{7}{3} \div 7 = \frac{7}{3} \cdot \frac{1}{7} = \frac{1}{3}$
$s_\infty = \frac{7}{1-\frac{1}{3}} = \frac{7}{\frac{2}{3}} = 7\left(\frac{3}{2}\right) = \frac{21}{2}$

69. $r = -1 \div 5 = -\frac{1}{5}$
$s_\infty = \frac{5}{1-\left(-\frac{1}{5}\right)} = \frac{5}{\frac{6}{5}} = 5\left(\frac{5}{6}\right) = \frac{25}{6}$

70.
$$r = -\frac{8}{3} \div -4 = -\frac{8}{3}\left(-\frac{1}{4}\right) = \frac{2}{3}$$
$$s_\infty = \frac{-4}{1-\frac{2}{3}} = \frac{-4}{\frac{1}{3}} = -4\left(\frac{3}{1}\right) = -12$$

71. $0.2626 \cdots = 0.26 + 0.0026 + 0.000026 + \cdots = 0.26 + 0.26(0.01) + 0.26(0.01)^2 + \cdots$

$a_1 = 0.26$ and $r = 0.01$

$$s_\infty = \frac{0.26}{1-0.01} = \frac{0.26}{0.99} = \frac{26}{99}$$

72. $0.621621\ldots = 0.621 + 0.000621 + 0.000000621 + \cdots = 0.621 + 0.621(0.001) + 0.621(0.001)^2 + \cdots$

$a_1 = 0.621$ and $r = 0.001$

$$s_\infty = \frac{0.621}{1-0.001} = \frac{0.621}{0.999} = \frac{621}{999} = \frac{23}{37}$$

73. $(3x + y)^4 = \binom{4}{0}(3x)^4(y)^0 + \binom{4}{1}(3x)^3(y)^1 + \binom{4}{2}(3x)^2(y)^2 + \binom{4}{3}(3x)^1(y)^3 + \binom{4}{4}(3x)^0(y)^4$

$\qquad = 1(81x^4)(1) + 4(27x^3)(y) + 6(9x^2)(y^2) + 4(3x)(y^3) + 1(1)(y^4)$

$\qquad = 81x^4 + 108x^3y + 54x^2y^2 + 12xy^3 + y^4$

74. $(2x - 3y^2)^3 = \binom{3}{0}(2x)^3(-3y^2)^0 + \binom{3}{1}(2x)^2(-3y^2)^1 + \binom{3}{2}(2x)^1(-3y^2)^2 + \binom{3}{3}(2x)^0(-3y^2)^3$

$\qquad = 1(8x^3)(1) + 3(4x^2)(-3y^2) + 3(2x)(9y^4) + 1(1)(-27y^6)$

$\qquad = 8x^3 - 36x^2y^2 + 54xy^4 - 27y^6$

75. $(x - 2y)^9 = \binom{9}{0}(x)^9(-2y)^0 + \binom{9}{1}(x)^8(-2y)^1 + \binom{9}{2}(x)^7(-2y)^2 + \binom{9}{3}(x)^6(-2y)^3 + \cdots$

$\qquad = 1(x^9)(1) + 9(x^8)(-2y) + 36(x^7)(4y^2) + 84(x^6)(-8y^3) + \cdots$

$\qquad = x^9 - 18x^8y + 144x^7y^2 - 672x^6y^3 + \cdots$

76. $(2a^2 + 3b)^8 = \binom{8}{0}(2a^2)^8(3b)^0 + \binom{8}{1}(2a^2)^7(3b)^1 + \binom{8}{2}(2a^2)^6(3b)^2 + \binom{8}{3}(2a^2)^5(3b)^3 + \cdots$

$\qquad = 1(256a^{16})(1) + 8(128a^{14})(3b) + 28(64a^{12})(9b^2) + 56(32a^{10})(27b^3) + \cdots$

$\qquad = 256a^{16} + 3072a^{14}b + 16{,}128a^{12}b^2 + 48{,}384a^{10}b^3 + \cdots$

77. This is an arithmetic series with $d = 1$, $a_1 = 100$, and $a_n = 200$.

$a_n = a_1 + (n-1)d$

$200 = 100 + (n-1)(1)$

$200 = 99 + n$

$101 = n$

The sum is

$s_{101} = \dfrac{101(100 + 200)}{2}$

$\qquad = \dfrac{101(300)}{2}$

$\qquad = 101(150)$

$\qquad = 15{,}150$

78. $a_1 = 20, d = -1, n = ?$

The top row has only one barrel, so $a_n = 1$

$a_n = a_1 + (n-1)d$

$1 = 20 + (n-1)(-1)$

$-19 = -n+1 \implies n = 20$

$S_n = \dfrac{n(a_1 + a_n)}{2}$

$S_{20} = \dfrac{20(20+1)}{2} = \dfrac{20(21)}{2} = \dfrac{420}{2} = 210$

210 barrels are stacked in the pyramid.

79. This is an arithmetic sequence with $d = 1000$

a. $a_1 = 30,000$

$a_2 = 30,000 + (2-1)(1000)$

$= 30,000 + 1000$

$= 31,000$

$a_3 = 30,000 + (3-1)(1000)$

$= 30,000 + 2000$

$= 32,000$

$a_4 = 30,000 + (4-1)(1000)$

$= 30,000 + 3000$

$= 33,000$

His salaries for the first four years are $30,000, $31,000, $32,000, and $33,000.

b. $a_n = 30,000 + (n-1)(1000)$

$= 30,000 + 1000(n-1)$

$= 29,000 + 1000n$

c.   After 6 years is the 7th year.

$a_7 = 29,000 + 1000(7)$

$= 29,000 + 7,000$

$= 36,000$

His salary would be $36,000.

d. $a_{11} = 30,000 + (11-1)1000 = 40,000$

$S_n = \dfrac{n(a_1 + a_n)}{2}$

$S_{11} = \dfrac{11(30,000 + 40,000)}{2}$

$= \dfrac{11(70,000)}{2}$

$= 385,000$

He will make $385,000 in the next 11 years.

80. This is a geometric series with $r = 2$, $a_1 = 100$ and $n = 11$.

(There are 11 terms here since 200 represents the first doubling.)

$a_{11} = a_1 r^{10} = 100(2)^{10} = 100(1024) = 102,400$

You would have $102,400.

81. $a_1 = 1600$, $r = 1.04$, $a_n = a_1 r^{n-1}$

a.   July $\implies n = 7$

$a_7 = 1600(1.04)^{7-1} \approx 2024.51$

Her salary is expected to be $2,024.51 in July.

b.   December $\implies n = 12$

$a_{12} = 1600(1.04)^{12-1} \approx 2463.13$

Her salary is expected to be $2,463.13 in December.

c. $S_n = \dfrac{a_1(1-r^n)}{1-r}, n = 11$

$S_{12} = \dfrac{1600\left(1-(1.04)^{12}\right)}{1-1.04} \approx 24,041.29$

She is expected to make $24,041.29 during the entire year.

82. Each year, the cost of the object will be 1.08 times greater than the previous year. After 12 years will be the 13th year. Therefore,

$a_{13} = 200(1.08)^{13-1}$

$= 200(1.08)^{12}$

$\approx 200(2.51817)$

≈ 503.63

The item would cost $503.63.

83. This is an infinite geometric series with $r = 0.92$ and $a_1 = 8$.

$S_\infty = \dfrac{8}{1-0.92} = \dfrac{8}{0.08} = 100$

The pendulum travels a total distance of 100 feet.

Practice Test

1. A series is the sum of the terms of a sequence

2. a. An arithmetic sequence is one whose terms differ by a constant amount.

   b. A geometric sequence is one whose terms differ by a common multiple.

3. $a_n = \dfrac{n-1}{3n}$

$a_1 = \dfrac{1-1}{3(1)} = \dfrac{0}{3} = 0$

$a_2 = \dfrac{2-1}{3(2)} = \dfrac{1}{6}$

$a_3 = \dfrac{3-1}{3(3)} = \dfrac{2}{9}$

$a_4 = \dfrac{4-1}{3(4)} = \dfrac{3}{12} = \dfrac{1}{4}$

$a_5 = \dfrac{5-1}{3(5)} = \dfrac{4}{15}$

The terms are $0,\ \dfrac{1}{6},\ \dfrac{2}{9},\ \dfrac{1}{4},\ \dfrac{4}{15}$.

4. $a_n = \dfrac{2n+1}{n^2}$

$a_1 = \dfrac{2(1)+1}{1^2} = \dfrac{2+1}{1} = 3$

$a_2 = \dfrac{2(2)+1}{2^2} = \dfrac{4+1}{4} = \dfrac{5}{4}$

$a_3 = \dfrac{2(3)+1}{3^2} = \dfrac{6+1}{9} = \dfrac{7}{9}$

$s_1 = a_1 = 3$

$s_3 = a_1 + a_2 + a_3$

$\quad = 3 + \dfrac{5}{4} + \dfrac{7}{9}$

$\quad = \dfrac{181}{36}$

5. $\displaystyle\sum_{i=1}^{5}(2i^2 + 3) = [2(1^2)+3] + [\,2(2^2)+3\,] + [2(3^2)+3] + [2(4^2)+3] + [2(5^2)+3]$

$\quad = (2+3) + (8+3) + (18+3) + (32+3) + (50+3)$

$\quad = 5 + 11 + 21 + 35 + 53$

$\quad = 125$

6. $\displaystyle\sum_{i=1}^{4}(x_i)^2 = x_1^2 + x_2^2 + x_3^2 + x_4^2$

$\quad = 4^2 + 2^2 + 8^2 + 12^2$

$\quad = 16 + 4 + 64 + 144$

$\quad = 228$

7. $d = \dfrac{2}{3} - \dfrac{1}{3} = \dfrac{1}{3}$

$a_n = a_1 + (n-1)d$

$\quad = \dfrac{1}{3} + (n-1)\left(\dfrac{1}{3}\right)$

$\quad = \dfrac{1}{3} + \dfrac{1}{3}n - \dfrac{1}{3}$

$\quad = \dfrac{1}{3}n$

8. $r = 10 \div 5 = \dfrac{10}{5} = 2$

$a_n = a_1 r^{n-1} = 5(2)^{n-1}$

9. $a_1 = 15$

$a_2 = 15 + (2-1)(-4) = 15 + 1(-4) = 15 - 4 = 11$

$a_3 = 15 + (3-1)(-4) = 15 + 2(-4) = 15 - 8 = 7$

$a_4 = 15 + (4-1)(-4) = 15 + 3(-4) = 15 - 12 = 3$

The terms are 15, 11, 7, 3.

10. $a_1 = \dfrac{5}{12}$

$a_2 = a_1 r^1 = \dfrac{5}{12}\left(\dfrac{2}{3}\right) = \dfrac{5}{18}$

$a_3 = a_1 r^2 = \dfrac{5}{12}\left(\dfrac{4}{9}\right) = \dfrac{5}{27}$

$a_4 = a_1 r^3 = \dfrac{5}{12}\left(\dfrac{8}{27}\right) = \dfrac{10}{81}$

The terms are $\dfrac{5}{12},\ \dfrac{5}{18},\ \dfrac{5}{27},\ \dfrac{10}{81}$.

11. $a_{10} = a_1 + (10-1)d$

$\quad = 40 + (9)(-8)$

$\quad = 40 - 72$

$\quad = -32$

12. $s_8 = \dfrac{8(a_1 + a_8)}{2} = \dfrac{8[7 + (-12)]}{2} = \dfrac{8(-5)}{2} = -20$

13. $d = -16 - (-4) = -16 + 4 = -12$

$a_n = a_1 + (n-1)d$

$-148 = -4 + (n-1)(-12)$

$-148 = -4 - 12n + 12$

$-148 = 8 - 12n$

$-156 = -12n$

$\dfrac{-156}{-12} = n$

$13 = n$

14. $a_7 = a_1 r^6 = 8\left(\dfrac{2}{3}\right)^6 = 8\left(\dfrac{64}{729}\right) = \dfrac{512}{729}$

15.

$s_7 = \dfrac{a_1(1 - r^7)}{1 - r}$

$= \dfrac{\frac{3}{5}\left[1 - (-5)^7\right]}{1 - (-5)}$

$= \dfrac{\frac{3}{5}\left[1 - (-78,125)\right]}{1 - (-5)}$

$= \dfrac{\frac{3}{5}(1 + 78,125)}{1 + 5}$

$= \dfrac{\frac{3}{5}(78,126)}{6}$

$= \dfrac{3(78,126)}{5 \cdot 6}$

$= \dfrac{78,126}{5 \cdot 2}$

$= \dfrac{39,063}{5}$

16. $r = 5 \div 15 = \dfrac{5}{15} = \dfrac{1}{3}$

$a_n = a_1 r^{n-1} = 15\left(\dfrac{1}{3}\right)^{n-1}$

17. $r = \dfrac{4}{3} \div 2 = \dfrac{4}{3} \cdot \dfrac{1}{2} = \dfrac{2}{3}$

$s_\infty = \dfrac{2}{1 - \frac{2}{3}} = \dfrac{2}{\frac{1}{3}} = 2 \cdot \dfrac{3}{1} = 6$

18. $0.4141\cdots = 0.41 + 0.0041 + 0.000041 + \cdots$

$= 0.41 + 0.41(0.01) + 0.41(0.01)^2 + \cdots$

$r = 0.01$ and $a_1 = 0.41$

$s_\infty = \dfrac{0.41}{1 - 0.01} = \dfrac{0.41}{0.99} = \dfrac{41}{99}$

19. $\dbinom{8}{2} = \dfrac{8!}{2!(8-2)!}$

$= \dfrac{8!}{2!\,6!}$

$= \dfrac{8 \cdot 7 \cdot 6 \cdot 5 \cdot 4 \cdot 3 \cdot 2 \cdot 1}{(2 \cdot 1)(6 \cdot 5 \cdot 4 \cdot 3 \cdot 2 \cdot 1)}$

$= \dfrac{56}{2}$

$= 28$

20. $(x + 2y)^4 = \dbinom{4}{0}(x)^4(2y)^0 + \dbinom{4}{1}(x)^3(2y)^1 + \dbinom{4}{2}(x)^2(2y)^2 + \dbinom{4}{3}(x)^1(2y)^3 + \dbinom{4}{4}(x)^0(2y)^4$

$= 1(x^4)(1) + 4(x^3)(2y) + 6(x^2)(4y^2) + 4(x)(8y^3) + 1(1)(16y^4)$

$= x^4 + 8x^3 y + 24x^2 y^2 + 32xy^3 + 16y^4$

21. $\bar{x} = \dfrac{\sum x}{n} = \dfrac{74 + 93 + 83 + 87 + 68}{5} = \dfrac{405}{5} = 81$

22. $a_1 = 12, d = -1, n = 21$

$$s_n = \frac{n(a_1 + a_n)}{2}$$

$$s_{12} = \frac{12(12+1)}{2} = \frac{12(13)}{2} = \frac{156}{2} = 78$$

78 logs are stacked in the pyramid.

23. $a_1 = 1000$, $n = 20$

$a_n = a_1 + (n-1)d$

$a_{20} = 1000 + (20-1)(1000) = 20,000$

$$s_{20} = \frac{20(1000 + 20,000)}{2} = 210,000$$

After 20 years, she will have saved $210,000.

24. $a_1 = 700$, $r = 1.04$, $a_n = a_1 r^{n-1}$

$a_6 = 700(1.04)^{6-1} \approx 851.66$

She will be making about $851.66 in the sixth week.

25. $r = 3$, $a_1 = 500(3) = 1500$

$a_8 = a_1 r^7 = 1500(3)^7 = 1500(2187) = 3,280,500$

Cumulative Review Test

1. $A = \dfrac{1}{2}bh$, for b

$2A = bh$

$\dfrac{2A}{h} = \dfrac{bh}{h}$

$\dfrac{2A}{h} = b$

2. $m = \dfrac{y_2 - y_1}{x_2 - x_1} = \dfrac{9 - (-2)}{1 - 4} = \dfrac{11}{-3} = -\dfrac{11}{3}$

Use point-slope with $m = -\dfrac{11}{3}$ and $(4, -2)$.

$y - y_1 = m(x - x_1)$

$y - (-2) = -\dfrac{11}{3}(x - 4)$

$y + 2 = -\dfrac{11}{3}x + \dfrac{44}{3}$

$y = -\dfrac{11}{3}x + \dfrac{44}{3} - 2$

$y = -\dfrac{11}{3}x + \dfrac{38}{3}$

3.
$x + y + z = 1$ (1)
$2x + 2y + 2z = 2$ (2)
$3x + 3y + 3z = 3$ (3)
Notice that if you multiply equation (1) by 2, the result is exactly the same as equation (2). This implies that this is a dependent system and therefore has infinitely many solutions.

4.
$$5x^3 + 4x^2 - 6x + 2$$
$$\underline{ \quad x + 5}$$
$$5x^4 + 4x^3 - 6x^2 + 2x$$
$$\underline{25x^3 + 20x^2 - 30x + 10}$$
$$5x^4 + 29x^3 + 14x^2 - 28x + 10$$

5. $x^3 + 2x - 5x^2 - 10$

$(x^3 + 2x) - (5x^2 + 10)$

$x(x^2 + 2) - 5(x^2 + 2)$

$(x - 5)(x^2 + 2)$

6. $(a+b)^2 + 6(a+b) + 9$ let $u = a + b$

$u^2 + 6u + 9$

$(u + 3)(u + 3)$

$(u + 3)^2$ replace u with $a + b$

$(a + b + 3)^2$

7. $5 - \dfrac{x - 1}{x^2 + 3x - 10}$

$= \dfrac{5(x^2 + 3x - 10)}{x^2 + 3x - 10} - \dfrac{x - 1}{x^2 + 3x - 10}$

$= \dfrac{5x^2 + 15x - 50}{x^2 + 3x - 10} - \dfrac{x - 1}{x^2 + 3x - 10}$

$= \dfrac{5x^2 + 15x - 50 - (x - 1)}{x^2 + 3x - 10}$

$= \dfrac{5x^2 + 14x - 49}{x^2 + 3x - 10}$

8. $y = kz^2$

$80 = k(20)^2 \Rightarrow k = \dfrac{80}{400} = 0.2$

$y = 0.2z^2$

$y = 0.2(90)^2 = 1620$

9. $f(x) = 3\sqrt[3]{x-2}$, $g(x) = \sqrt[3]{7x-14}$

$$f(x) = g(x)$$
$$3\sqrt[3]{x-2} = \sqrt[3]{7x-14}$$
$$\left(3\sqrt[3]{x-2}\right)^3 = \left(\sqrt[3]{7x-14}\right)^3$$
$$27(x-2) = 7x-14$$
$$27x-54 = 7x-14$$
$$20x = 40$$
$$x = 2$$

10. $\sqrt{6x-5} - \sqrt{2x+6} - 1 = 0$

$$\sqrt{6x-5} = 1 + \sqrt{2x+6}$$
$$\left(\sqrt{6x-5}\right)^2 = \left(1 + \sqrt{2x+6}\right)^2$$
$$6x-5 = 1 + 2\sqrt{2x+6} + 2x+6$$
$$4x-12 = 2\sqrt{2x+6}$$
$$2x-6 = \sqrt{2x+6}$$
$$(2x-6)^2 = \left(\sqrt{2x+6}\right)^2$$
$$4x^2 - 24x + 36 = 2x+6$$
$$4x^2 - 26x + 30 = 0$$
$$2\left(2x^2 - 13x + 15\right) = 0$$
$$2(2x-3)(x-5) = 0$$
$$2x-3 = 0 \quad \text{or} \quad x-5 = 0$$
$$x = \frac{3}{2} \qquad\qquad x = 5$$

Upon checking, $x = \frac{3}{2}$ is an extraneous solution. The solution is $x = 5$.

11. $x^2 + 2x + 12 = 0$

$$x^2 + 2x + 1 = -12 + 1$$
$$(x+1)^2 = -11$$
$$x+1 = \pm\sqrt{-11}$$
$$x = -1 \pm \sqrt{-11}$$

12. $x^2 - \dfrac{x}{5} - \dfrac{1}{3} = 0 \overset{\times 15}{\Rightarrow} 15x^2 - 3x - 5 = 0$

$$x = \frac{-b \pm \sqrt{b^2 - 4ac}}{2a}$$
$$= \frac{-(-3) \pm \sqrt{(-3)^2 - 4(15)(-5)}}{2(15)}$$
$$= \frac{3 \pm \sqrt{9 + 300}}{30}$$
$$= \frac{3 \pm \sqrt{309}}{30}$$

13. Let x be the number. Then
$$2x^2 - 3x = 20$$
$$2x^2 - 3x - 20 = 0$$
$$(2x+5)(x-4) = 0$$
$$2x+5 = 0 \quad \text{or} \quad x-4 = 0$$
$$x = -\frac{5}{2} \qquad\qquad x = 4$$

Since the number must be positive, disregard $x = -\frac{5}{2}$. The number is 4.

14. $y = x^2 - 4x$
$$y = \left(x^2 - 4x + 4\right) - 4$$
$$y = (x-2)^2 - 4$$
The vertex is $(2, -4)$.

15. $\log_a \dfrac{1}{64} = 3$

$$a^3 = \frac{1}{64} = \left(\frac{1}{4}\right)^3 \Rightarrow a = \frac{1}{4}$$

16. $y = 2^x - 1$

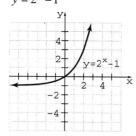

17. $(h, k) = (-6, 2)$, $r = 4$

$(x - h)^2 + (y - k)^2 = r^2$

$(x - (-6))^2 + (y - 2)^2 = 4^2$

$(x + 6)^2 + (y - 2)^2 = 16$

18. $(x + 3)^2 + (y + 1)^2 = 16$

center: $(-3, -1)$ radius: 4

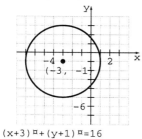

$(x+3)^2 + (y+1)^2 = 16$

19. $9x^2 + 16y^2 = 144$

$\dfrac{9x^2}{144} + \dfrac{16y^2}{144} = 1$

$\dfrac{x^2}{16} + \dfrac{y^2}{9} = 1 \;\Rightarrow\; a = 4 \text{ and } b = 3$

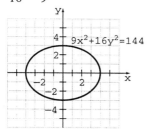

20.

$r = \dfrac{16}{3} \div 8 = \dfrac{16}{3} \cdot \dfrac{1}{8} = \dfrac{2}{3}$

$s_\infty = \dfrac{a_1}{1 - r}$

$= \dfrac{8}{1 - \dfrac{2}{3}} = \dfrac{8}{\dfrac{1}{3}} = 8 \cdot \dfrac{3}{1} = 24$